PEARSON CUSTOM LIBRARY

ENGINEERING

Select Chapters from Electrical Engineering
Principles and Applications by A.R. Hambley

PEARSON

Cover Art: "Abstract Sphere Garden," courtesy of iStockphoto; "Abstract Scheme," courtesy of Andrey Prokhorov/iStockphoto; "Confederation Bridge," courtesy of Shaun Lowe Photographic/iStockphoto; "Rebar Reinforcements 5," courtesy of Bailey Digital Images/iStockphoto; "Airliner in Storm," courtesy of iStockphoto; "Train Passing Next to High-rise Building," courtesy of Terry Husebye/Getty Images; "Highway Intersection," courtesy of Maciej Noskowski/Getty Images; "Golden Gate Bridge Roadway and Cables," courtesy of David Sanger/Getty Images; "Geodesic Dome," courtesy of Russell Hart/Getty Images; "Bridge Architecture," courtesy of Tetra images/Getty Images. Additional images courtesy of Photodisc/Getty Images.

V092

Please visit our website at *www.pearsonlearningsolutions.com*.

Attention bookstores: For permission to return any unsold stock, contact us at *pe-uscustomreturns@pearson.com*.

Pearson Learning Solutions, 501 Boylston Street, Suite 900, Boston, MA 02116
A Pearson Education Company
www.pearsoned.com

PEARSON

ISBN 10: 1-269-10979-0
ISBN 13: 978-1-269-10979-6

Table of Contents

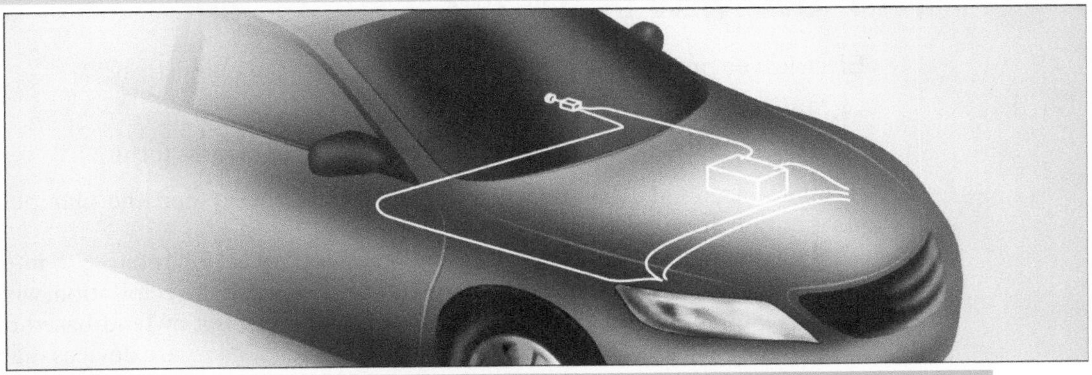

Introduction

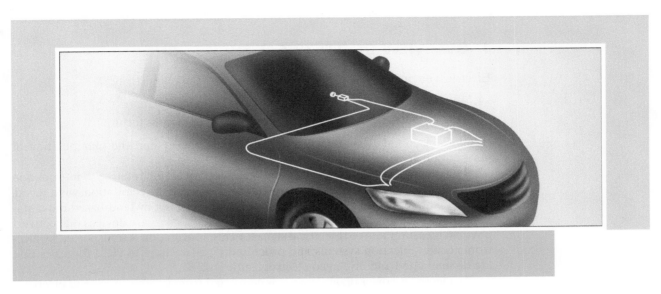

Study of this chapter will enable you to:

- Recognize interrelationships between electrical engineering and other fields of science and engineering.
- List the major subfields of electrical engineering.
- List several important reasons for studying electrical engineering.
- Define current, voltage, and power, including their units.
- Calculate power and energy and determine whether energy is supplied or absorbed by a circuit element.
- State and apply Kirchhoff's current and voltage laws.
- Recognize series and parallel connections.
- Identify and describe the characteristics of voltage and current sources.
- State and apply Ohm's law.
- Solve for currents, voltages, and powers in simple circuits.

Introduction to this chapter:

In this chapter, we introduce electrical engineering, define circuit variables (current, voltage, power, and energy), study the laws that these circuit variables obey, and meet several circuit elements (current sources, voltage sources, and resistors).

From Chapter 1 of *Electrical Engineering: Principles and Applications*, Sixth Edition. Allan R. Hambley.

1 OVERVIEW OF ELECTRICAL ENGINEERING

Electrical engineers design systems that have two main objectives:

1. To gather, store, process, transport, and present *information.*
2. To distribute, store, and convert *energy* between various forms.

In many electrical systems, the manipulation of energy and the manipulation of information are interdependent.

For example, numerous aspects of electrical engineering relating to information are applied in weather prediction. Data about cloud cover, precipitation, wind speed, and so on are gathered electronically by weather satellites, by land-based radar stations, and by sensors at numerous weather stations. (Sensors are devices that convert physical measurements to electrical signals.) This information is transported by electronic communication systems and processed by computers to yield forecasts that are disseminated and displayed electronically.

In electrical power plants, energy is converted from various sources to electrical form. Electrical distribution systems transport the energy to virtually every factory, home, and business in the world, where it is converted to a multitude of useful forms, such as mechanical energy, heat, and light.

No doubt you can list scores of electrical engineering applications in your daily life. Increasingly, electrical and electronic features are integrated into new products. Automobiles and trucks provide just one example of this trend. The electronic content of the average automobile is growing rapidly in value. Auto designers realize that electronic technology is a good way to provide increased functionality at lower cost. Table 1 shows some of the applications of electrical engineering in automobiles.

You may find it interesting to search the web for sites related to "mechatronics."

As another example, we note that many common household appliances contain keypads for operator control, sensors, electronic displays, and computer chips, as well as more conventional switches, heating elements, and motors. Electronics have become so intimately integrated with mechanical systems that the name **mechatronics** is used for the combination.

Subdivisions of Electrical Engineering

Next, we give you an overall picture of electrical engineering by listing and briefly discussing eight of its major areas.

1. Communication systems transport information in electrical form. Cellular phone, radio, satellite television, and the Internet are examples of communication systems. It is possible for virtually any two people (or computers) on the globe to communicate almost instantaneously. A climber on a mountaintop in Nepal can call or send e-mail to friends whether they are hiking in Alaska or sitting in a New York City office. This kind of connectivity affects the way we live, the way we conduct business, and the design of everything we use. For example, communication systems will change the design of highways because traffic and road-condition information collected by roadside sensors can be transmitted to central locations and used to route traffic. When an accident occurs, an electrical signal can be emitted automatically when the airbags deploy, giving the exact location of the vehicle, summoning help, and notifying traffic-control computers.

Computers that are part of products such as appliances and automobiles are called *embedded computers.*

2. Computer systems process and store information in digital form. No doubt you have already encountered computer applications in your own field. Besides the computers of which you are aware, there are many in unobvious places, such as household appliances and automobiles. A typical modern automobile contains several

Table 1. Current and Emerging Electronic/Electrical Applications in Automobiles and Trucks

Safety
- Antiskid brakes
- Inflatable restraints
- Collision warning and avoidance
- Blind-zone vehicle detection (especially for large trucks)
- Infrared night vision systems
- Heads-up displays
- Automatic accident notification
- Rear-view cameras

Communications and entertainment
- AM/FM radio
- Digital audio broadcasting
- CD/DVD player
- Cellular phone
- Computer/e-mail
- Satellite radio

Convenience
- Electronic GPS navigation
- Personalized seat/mirror/radio settings
- Electronic door locks

Emissions, performance, and fuel economy
- Vehicle instrumentation
- Electronic ignition
- Tire inflation sensors
- Computerized performance evaluation and maintenance scheduling
- Adaptable suspension systems

Alternative propulsion systems
- Electric vehicles
- Advanced batteries
- Hybrid vehicles

dozen special-purpose computers. Chemical processes and railroad switching yards are routinely controlled through computers.

3. Control systems gather information with sensors and use electrical energy to control a physical process. A relatively simple control system is the heating/cooling system in a residence. A sensor (thermostat) compares the temperature with the desired value. Control circuits operate the furnace or air conditioner to achieve the desired temperature. In rolling sheet steel, an electrical control system is used to obtain the desired sheet thickness. If the sheet is too thick (or thin), more (or less) force is applied to the rollers. The temperatures and flow rates in chemical processes are controlled in a similar manner. Control systems have even been installed in tall buildings to reduce their movement due to wind.

4. Electromagnetics is the study and application of electric and magnetic fields. The device (known as a magnetron) used to produce microwave energy in an oven is one application. Similar devices, but with much higher power levels, are employed in manufacturing sheets of plywood. Electromagnetic fields heat the glue between layers of wood so that it will set quickly. Cellular phone and television antennas are also examples of electromagnetic devices.

5. Electronics is the study and application of materials, devices, and circuits used in amplifying and switching electrical signals. The most important electronic devices are transistors of various kinds. They are used in nearly all places where electrical information or energy is employed. For example, the cardiac pacemaker is an electronic circuit that senses heart beats, and if a beat does not occur when it should, applies a minute electrical stimulus to the heart, forcing a beat. Electronic instrumentation and electrical sensors are found in every field of science and engineering. Many of the aspects of electronic amplifiers have direct application to the instrumentation used in your field of engineering.

Electronic devices are based on controlling electrons. Photonic devices perform similar functions by controlling photons.

6. Photonics is an exciting new field of science and engineering that promises to replace conventional computing, signal-processing, sensing, and communication devices based on manipulating electrons with greatly improved products based on manipulating photons. Photonics includes light generation by lasers and light-emitting diodes, transmission of light through optical components, as well as switching, modulation, amplification, detection, and steering light by electrical, acoustical, and photon-based devices. Current applications include readers for DVD disks, holograms, optical signal processors, and fiber-optic communication systems. Future applications include optical computers, holographic memories, and medical devices. Photonics offers tremendous opportunities for nearly all scientists and engineers.

7. Power systems convert energy to and from electrical form and transmit energy over long distances. These systems are composed of generators, transformers, distribution lines, motors, and other elements. Mechanical engineers often utilize electrical motors to empower their designs. The selection of a motor having the proper torque–speed characteristic for a given mechanical application is another example of how you can apply the information given.

8. Signal processing is concerned with information-bearing electrical signals. Often, the objective is to extract useful information from electrical signals derived from sensors. An application is machine vision for robots in manufacturing. Another application of signal processing is in controlling ignition systems of internal combustion engines. The timing of the ignition spark is critical in achieving good performance and low levels of pollutants. The optimum ignition point relative to crankshaft rotation depends on fuel quality, air temperature, throttle setting, engine speed, and other factors.

If the ignition point is advanced slightly beyond the point of best performance, *engine knock* occurs. Knock can be heard as a sharp metallic noise that is caused by rapid pressure fluctuations during the spontaneous release of chemical energy in the combustion chamber. A combustion-chamber pressure pulse displaying knock is shown in Figure 1. At high levels, knock will destroy an engine in a very short time. Prior to the advent of practical signal-processing electronics for this application, engine timing needed to be adjusted for distinctly suboptimum performance to avoid knock under varying combinations of operating conditions.

By connecting a sensor through a tube to the combustion chamber, an electrical signal proportional to pressure is obtained. Electronic circuits process this signal to determine whether the rapid pressure fluctuations characteristic of knock are present. Then electronic circuits continuously adjust ignition timing for optimum performance while avoiding knock.

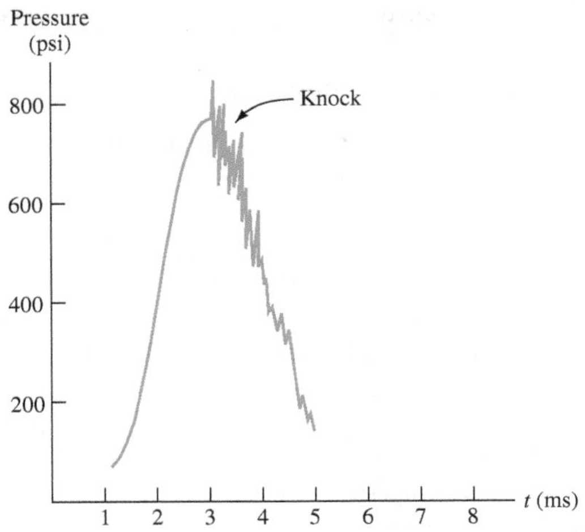

Figure 1 Pressure versus time for an internal combustion engine experiencing knock. Sensors convert pressure to an electrical signal that is processed to adjust ignition timing for minimum pollution and good performance.

Why You Need to Study Electrical Engineering

You may be majoring in a field of engineering or science and taking a required course in electrical engineering. Your immediate objective is probably to meet the course requirements for a degree in your chosen field. However, there are several other good reasons to learn and retain some basic knowledge of electrical engineering:

1. *To pass the Fundamentals of Engineering (FE) Examination as a first step in becoming a Registered Professional Engineer.* In the United States, before performing engineering services for the public, you will need to become registered as a Professional Engineer (PE). This chapter gives you the knowledge to answer questions relating to electrical engineering on the registration examinations. (See Appendix "The Fundamentals of Engineering Examination" for more on the FE exam.)

2. *To have a broad enough knowledge base so that you can lead design projects in your own field.* Increasingly, electrical engineering is interwoven with nearly all scientific experiments and design projects in other fields of engineering. Industry has repeatedly called for engineers who can see the big picture and work effectively in teams. Engineers or scientists who narrow their focus strictly to their own field are destined to be directed by others. (Electrical engineers are somewhat fortunate in this respect because the basics of structures, mechanisms, and chemical processes are familiar from everyday life. On the other hand, electrical engineering concepts are somewhat more abstract and hidden from the casual observer.)

3. *To be able to operate and maintain electrical systems, such as those found in control systems for manufacturing processes.* The vast majority of electrical-circuit malfunctions can be readily solved by the application of basic electrical-engineering principles. You will be a much more versatile and valuable engineer or scientist if you can apply electrical-engineering principles in practical situations.

4. *To be able to communicate with electrical-engineering consultants.* Very likely, you will often need to work closely with electrical engineers in your career.

2 CIRCUITS, CURRENTS, AND VOLTAGES

Overview of an Electrical Circuit

Before we carefully define the terminology of electrical circuits, let us gain some basic understanding by considering a simple example: the headlight circuit of an automobile. This circuit consists of a battery, a switch, the headlamps, and wires connecting them in a closed path, as illustrated in Figure 2.

The battery voltage is a measure of the energy gained by a unit of charge as it moves through the battery.

Chemical forces in the battery cause electrical charge (electrons) to flow through the circuit. The charge gains energy from the chemicals in the battery and delivers energy to the headlamps. The battery voltage (nominally, 12 volts) is a measure of the energy gained by a unit of charge as it moves through the battery.

Electrons readily move through copper but not through plastic insulation.

The wires are made of an excellent electrical conductor (copper) and are insulated from one another (and from the metal auto body) by electrical insulation (plastic) coating the wires. Electrons readily move through copper but not through the plastic insulation. Thus, the charge flow (electrical current) is confined to the wires until it reaches the headlamps. Air is also an insulator.

The switch is used to control the flow of current. When the conducting metallic parts of the switch make contact, we say that the switch is **closed** and current flows through the circuit. On the other hand, when the conducting parts of the switch do not make contact, we say that the switch is **open** and current does not flow.

Electrons experience collisions with the atoms of the tungsten wires, resulting in heating of the tungsten.

Energy is transferred by the chemical action in the battery to the electrons and then to the tungsten.

The headlamps contain special tungsten wires that can withstand high temperatures. Tungsten is not as good an electrical conductor as copper, and the electrons experience collisions with the atoms of the tungsten wires, resulting in heating of the tungsten. We say that the tungsten wires have electrical resistance. Thus, energy is transferred by the chemical action in the battery to the electrons and then to the tungsten, where it appears as heat. The tungsten becomes hot enough so that copious light is emitted. We will see that the power transferred is equal to the product of current (rate of flow of charge) and the voltage (also called electrical potential) applied by the battery.

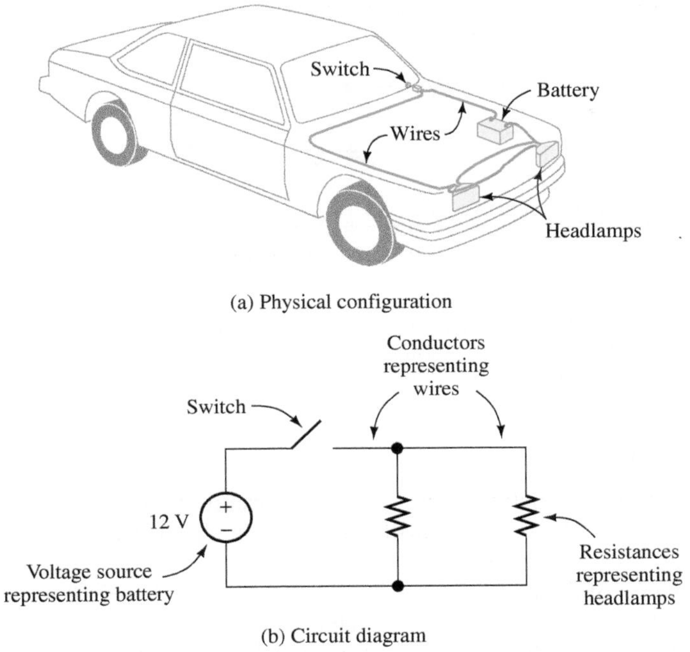

Figure 2 The headlight circuit. (a) The actual physical layout of the circuit. (b) The circuit diagram.

(Actually, the simple description of the headlight circuit we have given is most appropriate for older cars. In more modern automobiles, sensors provide information to an embedded computer about the ambient light level, whether or not the ignition is energized, and whether the transmission is in park or drive. The dashboard switch merely inputs a logic level to the computer, indicating the intention of the operator with regard to the headlights. Depending on these inputs, the computer controls the state of an electronic switch in the headlight circuit. When the ignition is turned off and if it is dark, the computer keeps the lights on for a few minutes so the passengers can see to exit and then turns them off to conserve energy in the battery. This is typical of the trend to use highly sophisticated electronic and computer technology to enhance the capabilities of new designs in all fields of engineering.)

Fluid-Flow Analogy

Electrical circuits are analogous to fluid-flow systems. The battery is analogous to a pump, and charge is analogous to the fluid. Conductors (usually copper wires) correspond to frictionless pipes through which the fluid flows. Electrical current is the counterpart of the flow rate of the fluid. Voltage corresponds to the pressure differential between points in the fluid circuit. Switches are analogous to valves. Finally, the electrical resistance of a tungsten headlamp is analogous to a constriction in a fluid system that results in turbulence and conversion of energy to heat. Notice that current is a measure of the flow of charge *through* the cross section of a circuit element, whereas voltage is measured *across* the ends of a circuit element or *between* any other two points in a circuit.

The fluid-flow analogy can be very helpful initially in understanding electrical circuits.

Now that we have gained a basic understanding of a simple electrical circuit, we will define the concepts and terminology more carefully.

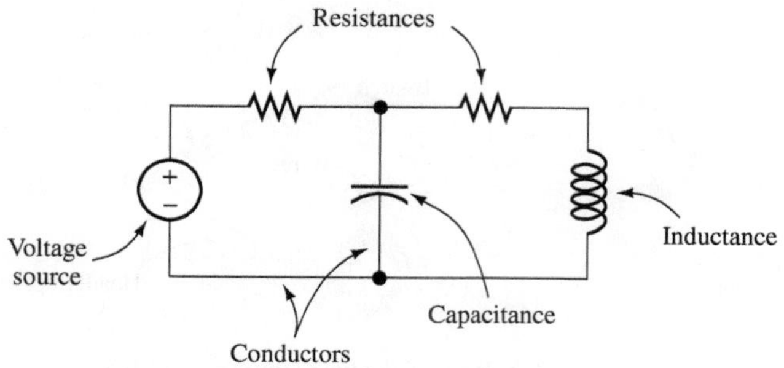

Figure 3 An electrical circuit consists of circuit elements, such as voltage sources, resistances, inductances, and capacitances, connected in closed paths by conductors.

Electrical Circuits

An electrical circuit consists of various types of circuit elements connected in closed paths by conductors.

An **electrical circuit** consists of various types of circuit elements connected in closed paths by conductors. An example is illustrated in Figure 3. The circuit elements can be resistances, inductances, capacitances, and voltage sources, among others. The symbols for some of these elements are illustrated in the figure. Eventually, we will carefully discuss the characteristics of each type of element.

Charge flows easily through conductors.

Charge flows easily through conductors, which are represented by lines connecting circuit elements. Conductors correspond to connecting wires in physical circuits. Voltage sources create forces that cause charge to flow through the conductors and other circuit elements. As a result, energy is transferred between the circuit elements, resulting in a useful function.

Electrical Current

Current is the time rate of flow of electrical charge. Its units are amperes (A), which are equivalent to coulombs per second (C/s).

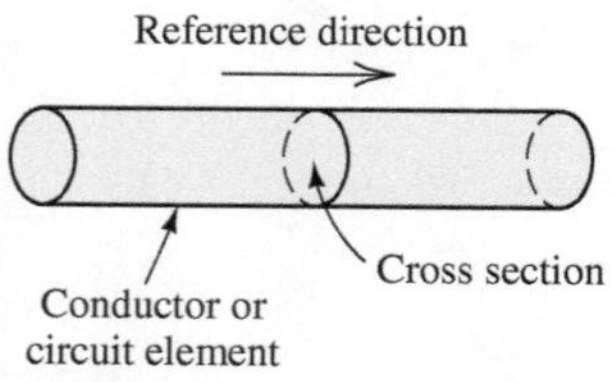

Figure 4 Current is the time rate of charge flow through a cross section of a conductor or circuit element.

Electrical current is the time rate of flow of electrical charge through a conductor or circuit element. The units are amperes (A), which are equivalent to coulombs per second (C/s). (The charge on an electron is -1.602×10^{-19} C.)

Conceptually, to find the current for a given circuit element, we first select a cross section of the circuit element roughly perpendicular to the flow of current. Then, we select a **reference direction** along the direction of flow. Thus, the reference direction points from one side of the cross section to the other. This is illustrated in Figure 4.

Next, suppose that we keep a record of the net charge flow through the cross section. Positive charge crossing in the reference direction is counted as a positive contribution to net charge. Positive charge crossing opposite to the reference is counted as a negative contribution. Furthermore, negative charge crossing in the reference direction is counted as a negative contribution, and negative charge against the reference direction is a positive contribution to charge.

Thus, in concept, we obtain a record of the net charge in coulombs as a function of time in seconds denoted as $q(t)$. The electrical current flowing through the element in the reference direction is given by

Colored shading is used to indicate key equations throughout this chapter.

$$i(t) = \frac{dq(t)}{dt} \tag{1}$$

A constant current of one ampere means that one coulomb of charge passes through the cross section each second.

To find charge given current, we must integrate. Thus, we have

$$q(t) = \int_{t_0}^{t} i(t)\,dt + q(t_0) \tag{2}$$

in which t_0 is some initial time at which the charge is known. (Throughout this chapter, we assume that time t is in seconds unless stated otherwise.)

Current flow is the same for all cross sections of a circuit element. The current that enters one end flows through the element and exits through the other end.

Example 1 Determining Current Given Charge

Suppose that charge versus time for a given circuit element is given by

$$q(t) = 0 \qquad \text{for } t < 0$$

and

$$q(t) = 2 - 2e^{-100t}\,\text{C} \qquad \text{for } t > 0$$

Sketch $q(t)$ and $i(t)$ to scale versus time.

Solution First we use Equation 1 to find an expression for the current:

$$\begin{aligned} i(t) &= \frac{dq(t)}{dt} \\ &= 0 \qquad \text{for } t < 0 \\ &= 200e^{-100t}\,\text{A} \qquad \text{for } t > 0 \end{aligned}$$

Plots of $q(t)$ and $i(t)$ are shown in Figure 5. ■

Reference Directions

In analyzing electrical circuits, we may not initially know the *actual direction* of current flow in a particular circuit element. Therefore, we start by assigning current

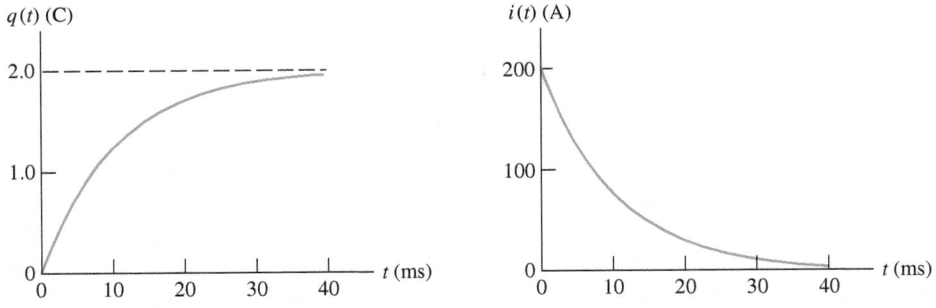

Figure 5 Plots of charge and current versus time for Example 1. *Note*: The time scale is in milliseconds (ms). One millisecond is equivalent to 10^{-3} seconds.

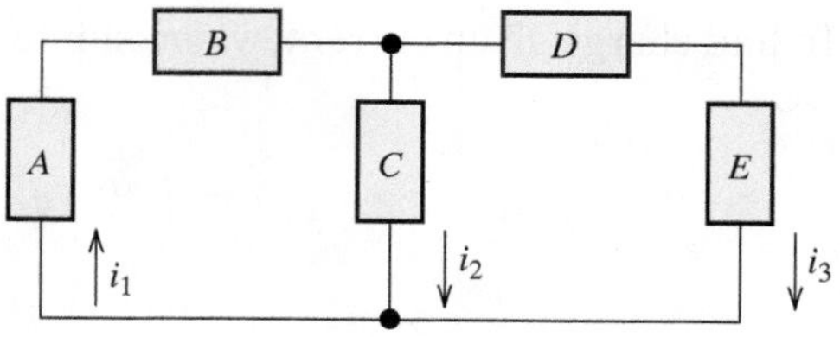

Figure 6 In analyzing circuits, we frequently start by assigning current variables i_1, i_2, i_3, and so forth.

variables and arbitrarily selecting a *reference direction* for each current of interest. It is customary to use the letter i for currents and subscripts to distinguish different currents. This is illustrated by the example in Figure 6, in which the boxes labeled A, B, and so on represent circuit elements. After we solve for the current values, we may find that some currents have negative values. For example, suppose that $i_1 = -2$ A in the circuit of Figure 6. Because i_1 has a negative value, we know that current actually flows in the direction opposite to the reference initially selected for i_1. Thus, the actual current is 2 A flowing downward through element A.

Direct Current and Alternating Current

Dc currents are constant with respect to time, whereas ac currents vary with time.

When a current is constant with time, we say that we have **direct current**, abbreviated as dc. On the other hand, a current that varies with time, reversing direction periodically, is called **alternating current**, abbreviated as ac. Figure 7 shows the values of a dc current and a sinusoidal ac current versus time. When $i_b(t)$ takes a negative value, the actual current direction is opposite to the reference direction for $i_b(t)$. The designation ac is used for other types of time-varying currents, such as the triangular and square waveforms shown in Figure 8.

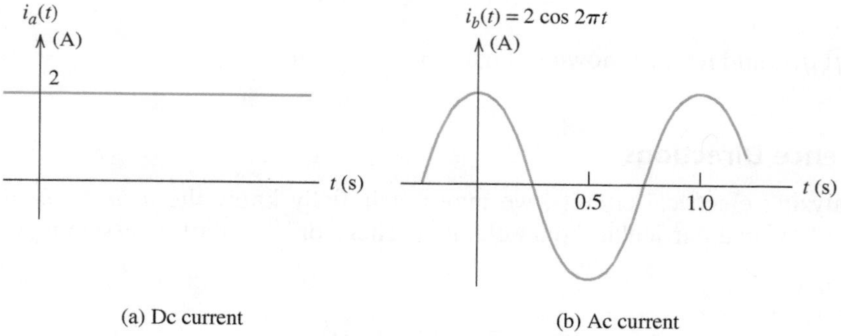

Figure 7 Examples of dc and ac currents versus time.

Double-Subscript Notation for Currents

So far we have used arrows alongside circuit elements or conductors to indicate reference directions for currents. Another way to indicate the current and reference direction for a circuit element is to label the ends of the element and use double subscripts to define the reference direction for the current. For example, consider the resistance of Figure 9. The current denoted by i_{ab} is the current through the element with its reference direction pointing from a to b. Similarly, i_{ba} is the current with its reference directed from b to a. Of course, i_{ab} and i_{ba} are the same in magnitude and

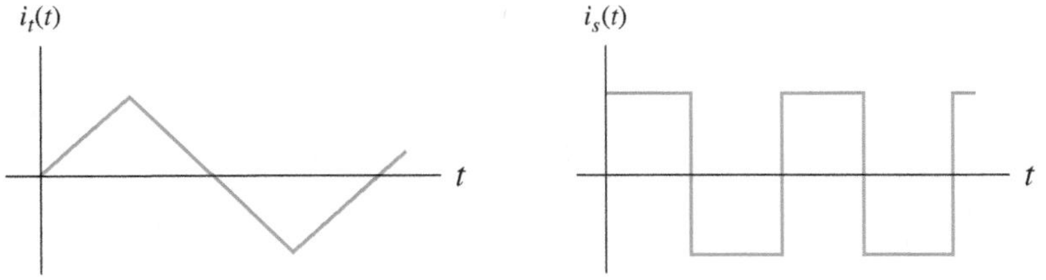

(a) Triangular waveform (b) Square waveform

Figure 8 Ac currents can have various waveforms.

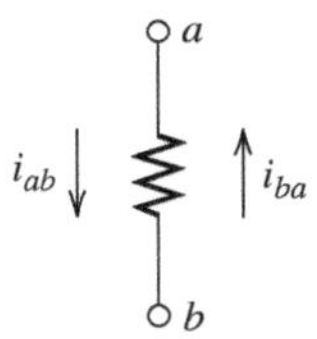

Figure 9 Reference directions can be indicated by labeling the ends of circuit elements and using double subscripts on current variables. The reference direction for i_{ab} points from a to b. On the other hand, the reference direction for i_{ba} points from b to a.

opposite in sign, because they denote the same current but with opposite reference directions. Thus, we have

$$i_{ab} = -i_{ba}$$

Exercise 1 A constant current of 2 A flows through a circuit element. In 10 seconds (s), how much net charge passes through the element?
Answer 20 C. □

Exercise 2 The charge that passes through a circuit element is given by $q(t) = 0.01\sin(200t)$ C, in which the angle is in radians. Find the current as a function of time.
Answer $i(t) = 2\cos(200t)$ A. □

Exercise 3 In Figure 6, suppose that $i_2 = 1$ A and $i_3 = -3$ A. Assuming that the current consists of positive charge, in which direction (upward or downward) is charge moving in element C? In element E?
Answer Downward in element C and upward in element E. □

Voltages

When charge moves through circuit elements, energy can be transferred. In the case of automobile headlights, stored chemical energy is supplied by the battery and absorbed by the headlights where it appears as heat and light. The **voltage** associated with a circuit element is the energy transferred per unit of charge that flows through the element. The units of voltage are volts (V), which are equivalent to joules per coulomb (J/C).

Voltage is a measure of the energy transferred per unit of charge when charge moves from one point in an electrical circuit to a second point.

For example, consider the storage battery in an automobile. The voltage across its terminals is (nominally) 12 V. This means that 12 J are transferred to or from the battery for each coulomb that flows through it. When charge flows in one direction, energy is supplied by the battery, appearing elsewhere in the circuit as heat or light or perhaps as mechanical energy at the starter motor. If charge moves through the battery in the opposite direction, energy is absorbed by the battery, where it appears as stored chemical energy.

Notice that voltage is measured across the ends of a circuit element, whereas current is a measure of charge flow through the element.

Voltages are assigned polarities that indicate the direction of energy flow. If positive charge moves from the positive polarity through the element toward the negative polarity, the element absorbs energy that appears as heat, mechanical energy, stored chemical energy, or as some other form. On the other hand, if positive charge moves from the negative polarity toward the positive polarity, the element supplies energy. This is illustrated in Figure 10. For negative charge, the direction of energy transfer is reversed.

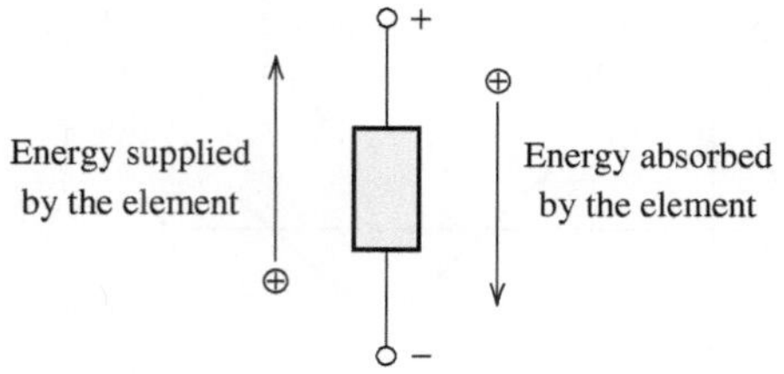

Figure 10 Energy is transferred when charge flows through an element having a voltage across it.

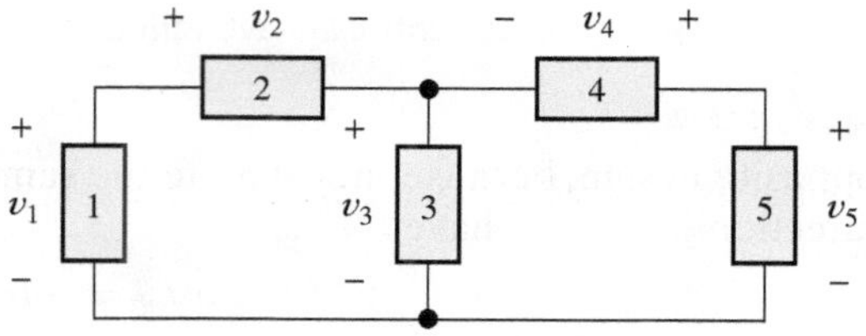

Figure 11 If we do not know the voltage values and polarities in a circuit, we can start by assigning voltage variables choosing the reference polarities arbitrarily. (The boxes represent unspecified circuit elements.)

Reference Polarities

When we begin to analyze a circuit, we often do not know the actual polarities of some of the voltages of interest in the circuit. Then, we simply assign voltage variables choosing *reference* polarities arbitrarily. (Of course, the *actual* polarities are not arbitrary.) This is illustrated in Figure 11. Next, we apply circuit principles (discussed later), obtaining equations that are solved for the voltages. If a given voltage has an actual polarity opposite to our arbitrary choice for the reference polarity, we obtain a negative value for the voltage. For example, if we find that $v_3 = -5\,\text{V}$ in Figure 11, we know that the voltage across element 3 is 5 V in magnitude and its actual polarity is opposite to that shown in the figure (i.e., the actual polarity is positive at the bottom end of element 3 and negative at the top).

In circuit analysis, we frequently assign reference polarities for voltages arbitrarily. If we find at the end of the analysis that the value of a voltage is negative, then we know that the true polarity is opposite of the polarity selected initially.

We usually do not put much effort into trying to assign "correct" references for current directions or voltage polarities. If we have doubt about them, we make arbitrary choices and use circuit analysis to determine true directions and polarities (as well as the magnitudes of the currents and voltages).

Voltages can be constant with time or they can vary. Constant voltages are called **dc voltages**. On the other hand, voltages that change in magnitude and alternate in polarity with time are said to be **ac voltages**. For example,

$$v_1(t) = 10\text{ V}$$

is a dc voltage. It has the same magnitude and polarity for all time. On the other hand,

$$v_2(t) = 10\cos(200\pi t)\text{V}$$

is an ac voltage that varies in magnitude and polarity. When $v_2(t)$ assumes a negative value, the actual polarity is opposite the reference polarity.

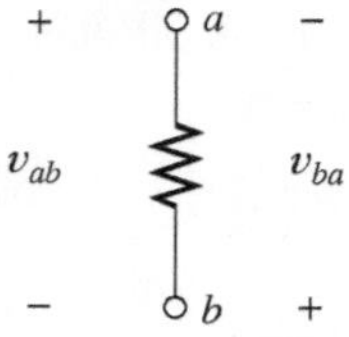

Figure 12 The voltage v_{ab} has a reference polarity that is positive at point *a* and negative at point *b*.

Double-Subscript Notation for Voltages

Another way to indicate the reference polarity of a voltage is to use double subscripts on the voltage variable. We use letters or numbers to label the terminals between which the voltage appears, as illustrated in Figure 12. For the resistance shown in the figure, v_{ab} represents the voltage between points *a* and *b* with the positive reference at point a. The two subscripts identify the points between which the voltage appears, and the first subscript is the positive reference. Similarly, v_{ba} is the voltage between a and b with the positive reference at point b. Thus, we can write

$$v_{ab} = -v_{ba} \tag{3}$$

because v_{ba} has the same magnitude as v_{ab} but has opposite polarity.

Still another way to indicate a voltage and its reference polarity is to use an arrow, as shown in Figure 13. The positive reference corresponds to the head of the arrow.

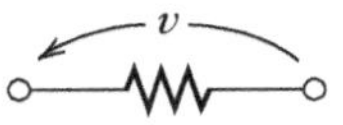

Figure 13 The positive reference for v is at the head of the arrow.

Switches

Switches control the currents in circuits. When an ideal switch is open, the current through it is zero and the voltage across it is determined by the remainder of the circuit. When an ideal switch is closed, the voltage across it is zero and the current through it is determined by the remainder of the circuit.

Exercise 4 The voltage across a given circuit element is $v_{ab} = 20$ V. A positive charge of 2 C moves through the circuit element from terminal b to terminal a. How much energy is transferred? Is the energy supplied by the circuit element or absorbed by it?

Answer 40 J are supplied by the circuit element. □

3 POWER AND ENERGY

Consider the circuit element shown in Figure 14. Because the current i is the rate of flow of charge and the voltage v is a measure of the energy transferred per unit of charge, the product of the current and the voltage is the rate of energy transfer. In other words, the product of current and voltage is power:

$$p = vi \tag{4}$$

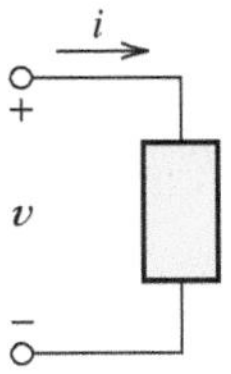

Figure 14 When current flows through an element and voltage appears across the element, energy is transferred. The rate of energy transfer is $p = vi$.

The physical units of the quantities on the right-hand side of this equation are

$$\begin{aligned} \text{volts} \times \text{amperes} &= \\ (\text{joules/coulomb}) \times (\text{coulombs/second}) &= \\ \text{joules/second} &= \\ \text{watts} & \end{aligned}$$

Passive Reference Configuration

Now we may ask whether the power calculated by Equation 4 represents energy supplied by or absorbed by the element. Refer to Figure 14 and notice that the current reference enters the positive polarity of the voltage. We call this arrangement the **passive reference configuration**. Provided that the references are picked in this manner, a positive result for the power calculation implies that energy is being absorbed by the element. On the other hand, a negative result means that the element is supplying energy to other parts of the circuit.

If the current reference enters the negative end of the reference polarity, we compute the power as

$$p = -vi \tag{5}$$

Then, as before, a positive value for p indicates that energy is absorbed by the element, and a negative value shows that energy is supplied by the element.

If the circuit element happens to be an electrochemical battery, positive power means that the battery is being charged. In other words, the energy absorbed by the battery is being stored as chemical energy. On the other hand, negative power indicates that the battery is being discharged. Then the energy supplied by the battery is delivered to some other element in the circuit.

Sometimes currents, voltages, and powers are functions of time. To emphasize this fact, we can write Equation 4 as

$$p(t) = v(t)i(t) \tag{6}$$

Example 2 Power Calculations

Consider the circuit elements shown in Figure 15. Calculate the power for each element. If each element is a battery, is it being charged or discharged?

Solution In element A, the current reference enters the positive reference polarity. This is the passive reference configuration. Thus, power is computed as

$$p_a = v_a i_a = 12 \text{ V} \times 2 \text{ A} = 24 \text{ W}$$

Because the power is positive, energy is absorbed by the device. If it is a battery, it is being charged.

In element B, the current reference enters the negative reference polarity. (Recall that the current that enters one end of a circuit element must exit from the other end, and vice versa.) This is opposite to the passive reference configuration. Hence, power is computed as

$$p_b = -v_b i_b = -(12 \text{ V}) \times 1 \text{ A} = -12 \text{ W}$$

Since the power is negative, energy is supplied by the device. If it is a battery, it is being discharged.

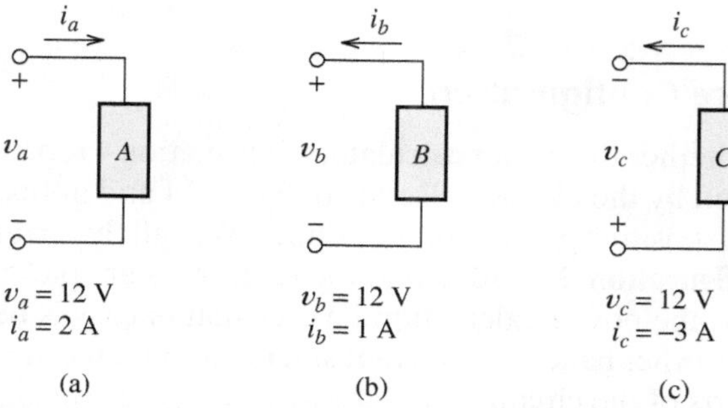

Figure 15 Circuit elements for Example 2.

In element C, the current reference enters the positive reference polarity. This is the passive reference configuration. Thus, we compute power as

$$p_c = v_c i_c = 12 \text{ V} \times (-3 \text{ A}) = -36 \text{ W}$$

Since the result is negative, energy is supplied by the element. If it is a battery, it is being discharged. (Notice that since i_c takes a negative value, current actually flows downward through element C.) ■

Energy Calculations

To calculate the energy w delivered to a circuit element between time instants t_1 and t_2, we integrate power:

$$w = \int_{t_1}^{t_2} p(t)\, dt \tag{7}$$

Here we have explicitly indicated that power can be a function of time by using the notation $p(t)$.

Example 3 Energy Calculation

Find an expression for the power for the voltage source shown in Figure 16. Compute the energy for the interval from $t_1 = 0$ to $t_2 = \infty$.

Solution The current reference enters the positive reference polarity. Thus, we compute power as

$$\begin{aligned} p(t) &= v(t)i(t) \\ &= 12 \times 2e^{-t} \\ &= 24e^{-t} \text{ W} \end{aligned}$$

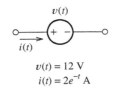

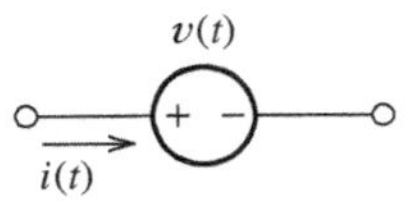

$v(t) = 12$ V
$i(t) = 2e^{-t}$ A

Figure 16 Circuit element for Example 3.

Subsequently, the energy transferred is given by

$$\begin{aligned} w &= \int_0^{\infty} p(t)\, dt \\ &= \int_0^{\infty} 24e^{-t}\, dt \\ &= \left[-24e^{-t}\right]_0^{\infty} = -24e^{-\infty} - (-24e^{0}) = 24 \text{ J} \end{aligned}$$

Because the energy is positive, it is absorbed by the source. ■

Prefixes

In electrical engineering, we encounter a tremendous range of values for currents, voltages, powers, and other quantities. We use the prefixes shown in Table 2 when working with very large or small quantities. For example, 1 milliampere (1 mA) is equivalent to 10^{-3} A, 1 kilovolt (1 kV) is equivalent to 1000 V, and so on.

Table 2. Prefixes Used for Large or Small Physical Quantities

Prefix	Abbreviation	Scale Factor
giga-	G	10^9
meg- or mega-	M	10^6
kilo-	k	10^3
milli-	m	10^{-3}
micro-	μ	10^{-6}
nano-	n	10^{-9}
pico-	p	10^{-12}
femto-	f	10^{-15}

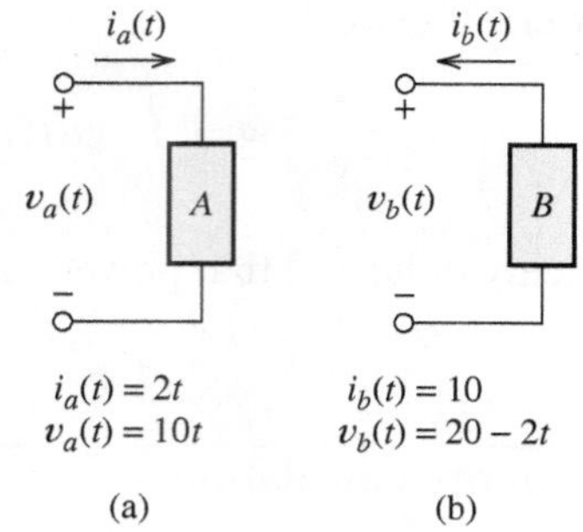

Figure 17 See Exercise 6.

Exercise 5 The ends of a circuit element are labeled a and b, respectively. Are the references for i_{ab} and v_{ab} related by the passive reference configuration? Explain.
Answer The reference direction for i_{ab} enters terminal a, which is also the positive reference for v_{ab}. Therefore, the current reference direction enters the positive reference polarity, so we have the passive reference configuration. □

Exercise 6 Compute the power as a function of time for each of the elements shown in Figure 17. Find the energy transferred between $t_1 = 0$ and $t_2 = 10$ s. In each case is energy supplied or absorbed by the element?
Answer **a.** $p_a(t) = 20t^2$ W, $w_a = 6667$ J; since w_a is positive, energy is absorbed by element A. **b.** $p_b(t) = 20t - 200$ W, $w_b = -1000$ J; since w_b is negative, energy is supplied by element B. □

4 KIRCHHOFF'S CURRENT LAW

Kirchhoff's current law states that the net current entering a node is zero.

A **node** in an electrical circuit is a point at which two or more circuit elements are joined together. Examples of nodes are shown in Figure 18.

An important principle of electrical circuits is **Kirchhoff's current law**: *The net current entering a node is zero.* To compute the *net* current entering a node, we add the currents entering and subtract the currents leaving. For illustration, consider the nodes of Figure 18. Then, we can write:

$$\text{Node } a: \quad i_1 + i_2 - i_3 = 0$$
$$\text{Node } b: \quad i_3 - i_4 = 0$$
$$\text{Node } c: \quad i_5 + i_6 + i_7 = 0$$

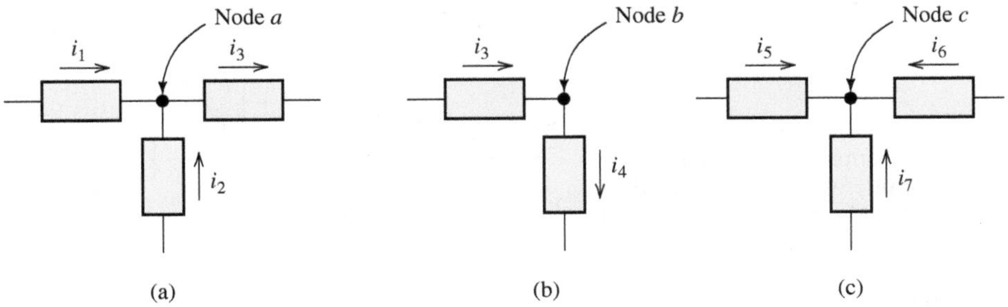

Figure 18 Partial circuits showing one node each to illustrate Kirchhoff's current law.

Notice that for node b, Kirchhoff's current law requires that $i_3 = i_4$. In general, if only two circuit elements are connected at a node, their currents must be equal. The current flows into the node through one element and out through the other. Usually, we will recognize this fact and assign a single current variable for both circuit elements.

For node c, either all of the currents are zero or some are positive while others are negative.

We abbreviate Kirchhoff's current law as KCL. There are two other equivalent ways to state KCL. One way is: *The net current leaving a node is zero.* To compute the net current leaving a node, we add the currents leaving and subtract the currents entering. For the nodes of Figure 18, this yields the following:

$$\text{Node } a: \quad -i_1 - i_2 + i_3 = 0$$
$$\text{Node } b: \quad -i_3 + i_4 = 0$$
$$\text{Node } c: \quad -i_5 - i_6 - i_7 = 0$$

Of course, these equations are equivalent to those obtained earlier.

Another way to state KCL is: *The sum of the currents entering a node equals the sum of the currents leaving a node.* Applying this statement to Figure 18, we obtain the following set of equations:

An alternative way to state Kirchhoff's current law is that the sum of the currents entering a node is equal to the sum of the currents leaving a node.

$$\text{Node } a: \quad i_1 + i_2 = i_3$$
$$\text{Node } b: \quad i_3 = i_4$$
$$\text{Node } c: \quad i_5 + i_6 + i_7 = 0$$

Again, these equations are equivalent to those obtained earlier.

Physical Basis for Kirchhoff's Current Law

An appreciation of why KCL is true can be obtained by considering what would happen if it were violated. Suppose that we could have the situation shown in Figure 18(a), with $i_1 = 3$ A, $i_2 = 2$ A, and $i_3 = 4$ A. Then, the net current entering the node would be

$$i_1 + i_2 - i_3 = 1 \text{ A} = 1 \text{ C/s}$$

In this case, 1 C of charge would accumulate at the node during each second. After 1 s, we would have +1 C of charge at the node, and −1 C of charge somewhere else in the circuit.

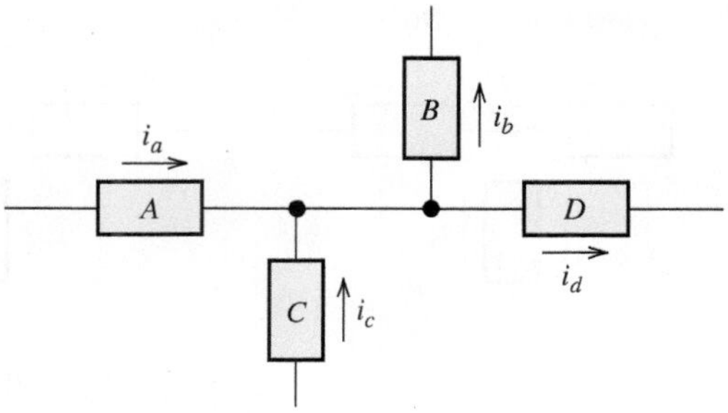

Figure 19 Elements A, B, C, and D can be considered to be connected to a common node, because all points in a circuit that are connected directly by conductors are electrically equivalent to a single point.

Suppose that these charges are separated by a distance of one meter (m). Recall that unlike charges experience a force of attraction. The resulting force turns out to be approximately 8.99×10^9 newtons (N) (equivalent to 2.02×10^9 pounds). Very large forces are generated when charges of this magnitude are separated by moderate distances. In effect, KCL states that such forces prevent charge from accumulating at the nodes of a circuit.

All points in a circuit that are connected directly by conductors can be considered to be a single node.

All points in a circuit that are connected directly by conductors can be considered to be a single node. For example, in Figure 19, elements A, B, C, and D are connected to a common node. Applying KCL, we can write

$$i_a + i_c = i_b + i_d$$

Series Circuits

We make frequent use of KCL in analyzing circuits. For example, consider the elements A, B, and C shown in Figure 20. When elements are connected end to end, we say that they are connected in **series**. *In order for elements A and B to be in series, no other path for current can be connected to the node joining A and B. Thus, all elements in a series circuit have identical currents.* For example, writing Kirchhoff's current law at node 1 for the circuit of Figure 20, we have

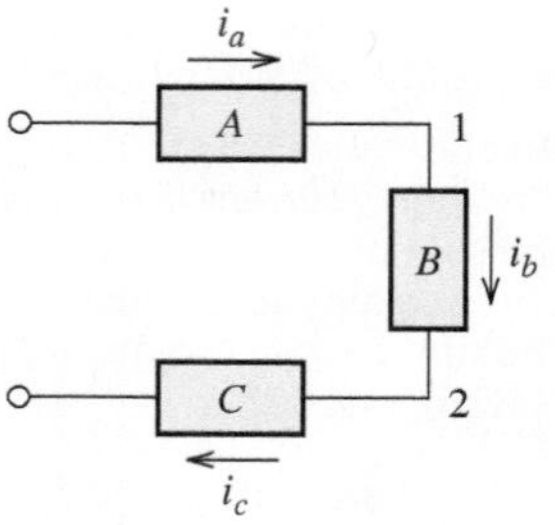

Figure 20 Elements A, B, and C are connected in series.

$$i_a = i_b$$

At node 2, we have

$$i_b = i_c$$

Thus, we have

$$i_a = i_b = i_c$$

The current that enters a series circuit must flow through each element in the circuit.

Exercise 7 Use KCL to determine the values of the unknown currents shown in Figure 21.

Answer $i_a = 4$ A, $i_b = -2$ A, $i_c = -8$ A. □

Exercise 8 Consider the circuit of Figure 22. Identify the groups of circuit elements that are connected in series.

Answer Elements A and B are in series; elements E, F, and G form another series combination. □

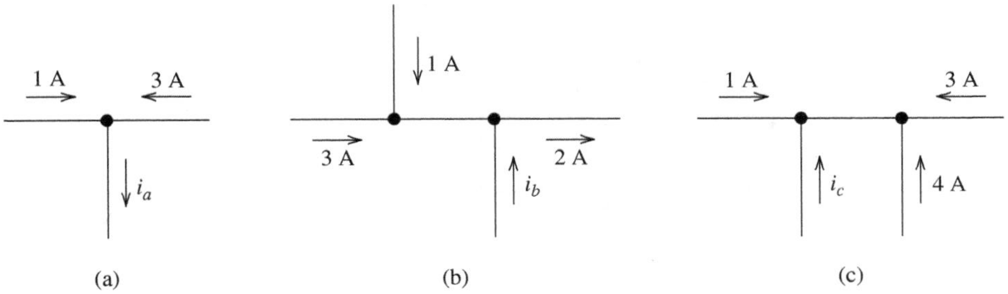

Figure 21 See Exercise 7.

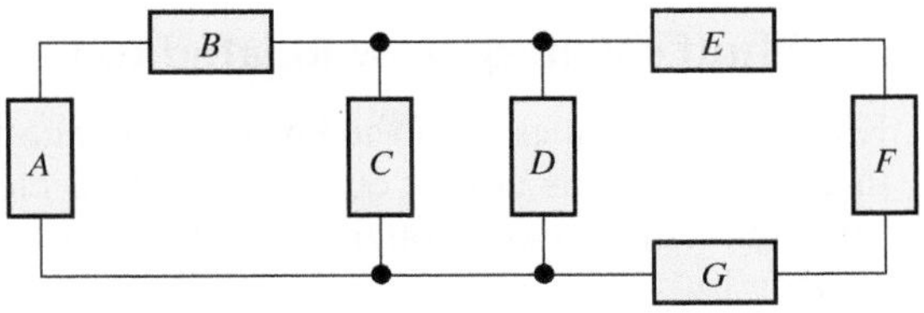

Figure 22 Circuit for Exercise 8.

5 KIRCHHOFF'S VOLTAGE LAW

Kirchhoff's voltage law (KVL) states that the algebraic sum of the voltages equals zero for any closed path (loop) in an electrical circuit.

A **loop** in an electrical circuit is a closed path starting at a node and proceeding through circuit elements, eventually returning to the starting node. Frequently, several loops can be identified for a given circuit. For example, in Figure 22, one loop consists of the path starting at the top end of element A and proceeding clockwise through elements B and C, returning through A to the starting point. Another loop starts at the top of element D and proceeds clockwise through E, F, and G, returning to the start through D. Still another loop exists through elements A, B, E, F, and G around the periphery of the circuit.

Kirchhoff's voltage law (KVL) states: *The algebraic sum of the voltages equals zero for any closed path (loop) in an electrical circuit.* In traveling around a loop, we encounter various voltages, some of which carry a positive sign while others carry a negative sign in the algebraic sum. A convenient convention is to use the first polarity mark encountered for each voltage to decide if it should be added or subtracted in the algebraic sum. If we go through the voltage from the positive polarity reference to the negative reference, it carries a plus sign. If the polarity marks are encountered in the opposite direction (minus to plus), the voltage carries a negative sign. This is illustrated in Figure 23.

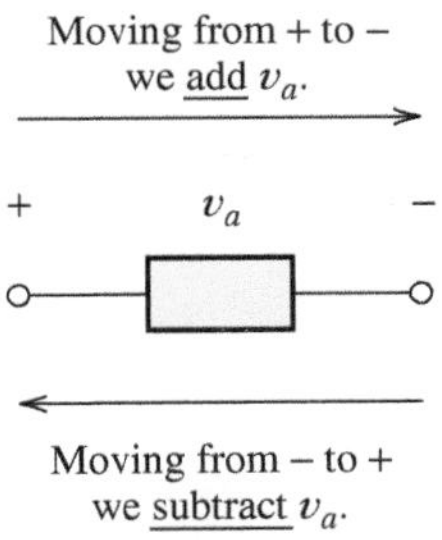

Figure 23 In applying KVL to a loop, voltages are added or subtracted depending on their reference polarities relative to the direction of travel around the loop.

For the circuit of Figure 24, we obtain the following equations:

$$\text{Loop 1:}\quad -v_a + v_b + v_c = 0$$

$$\text{Loop 2:}\quad -v_c - v_d + v_e = 0$$

$$\text{Loop 3:}\quad v_a - v_b + v_d - v_e = 0$$

Notice that v_a is subtracted for loop 1, but it is added for loop 3, because the direction of travel is different for the two loops. Similarly, v_c is added for loop 1 and subtracted for loop 2.

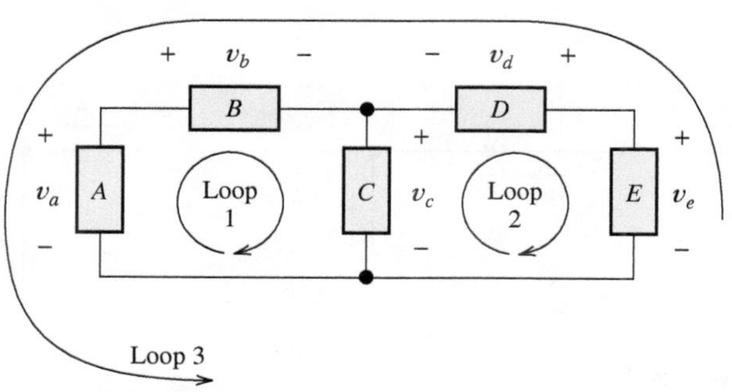

Figure 24 Circuit used for illustration of Kirchhoff's voltage law.

Kirchhoff's Voltage Law Related to Conservation of Energy

KVL is a consequence of the law of energy conservation. Consider the circuit shown in Figure 25. This circuit consists of three elements connected in series. Thus, the same current i flows through all three elements. The power for each of the elements is given by

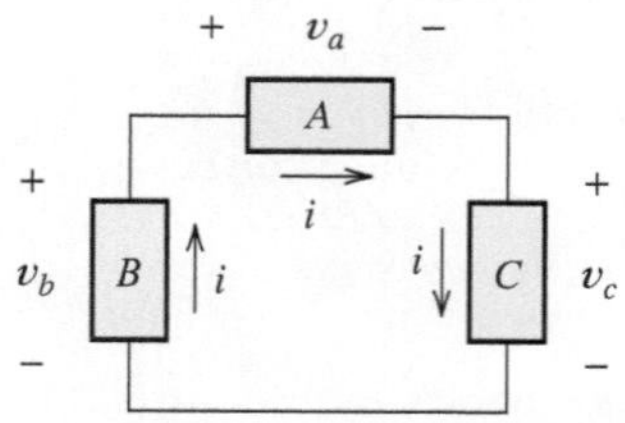

Figure 25 In this circuit, conservation of energy requires that $v_b = v_a + v_c$.

$$\text{Element } A: \quad p_a = v_a i$$
$$\text{Element } B: \quad p_b = -v_b i$$
$$\text{Element } C: \quad p_c = v_c i$$

Notice that the current and voltage references have the passive configuration (the current reference enters the plus polarity mark) for elements A and C. For element B, the relationship is opposite to the passive reference configuration. That is why we have a negative sign in the calculation of p_b.

At a given instant, the sum of the powers for all of the elements in a circuit must be zero. Otherwise, for an increment of time taken at that instant, more energy would be absorbed than is supplied by the circuit elements (or vice versa):

$$p_a + p_b + p_c = 0$$

Substituting for the powers, we have

$$v_a i - v_b i + v_c i = 0$$

Canceling the current i, we obtain

$$v_a - v_b + v_c = 0$$

This is exactly the same equation that is obtained by adding the voltages around the loop and setting the sum to zero for a clockwise loop in the circuit of Figure 25.

One way to check our results after solving for the currents and voltages in a circuit is the check to see that the power adds to zero for all of the elements.

Two circuit elements are connected in parallel if both ends of one element are connected directly (i.e., by conductors) to corresponding ends of the other.

Parallel Circuits

We say that two circuit elements are connected in **parallel** if both ends of one element are connected directly (i.e., by conductors) to corresponding ends of the other. For

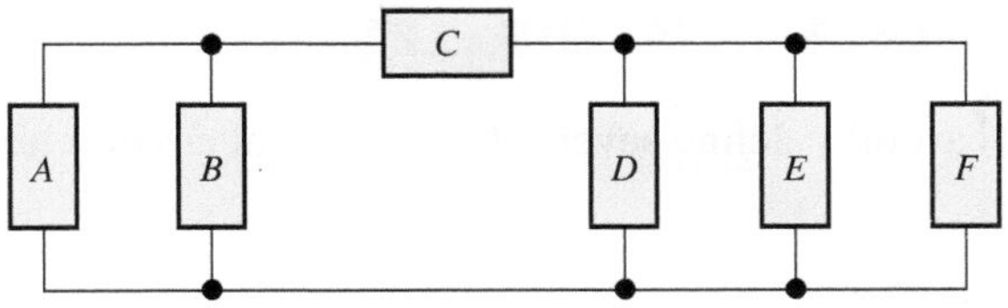

Figure 26 In this circuit, elements A and B are in parallel. Elements D, E, and F form another parallel combination.

example, in Figure 26, elements A and B are in parallel. Similarly, we say that the three circuit elements D, E, and F are in parallel. Element B is *not* in parallel with D because the top end of B is not *directly* connected to the top end of D.

The voltages across parallel elements are equal in magnitude and have the same polarity. For illustration, consider the partial circuit shown in Figure 27. Here elements A, B, and C are connected in parallel. Consider a loop from the bottom end of A upward and then down through element B back to the bottom of A. For this clockwise loop, we have $-v_a + v_b = 0$. Thus, KVL requires that

$$v_a = v_b$$

Next, consider a clockwise loop through elements A and C. For this loop, KVL requires that

$$-v_a - v_c = 0$$

This implies that $v_a = -v_c$. In other words, v_a and v_c have opposite algebraic signs. Furthermore, one or the other of the two voltages must be negative (unless both are zero). Therefore, one of the voltages has an actual polarity opposite to the reference polarity shown in the figure. Thus, the actual polarities of the voltages are the same (either both are positive at the top of the circuit or both are positive at the bottom).

Usually, when we have a parallel circuit, we simply use the same voltage variable for all of the elements as illustrated in Figure 28.

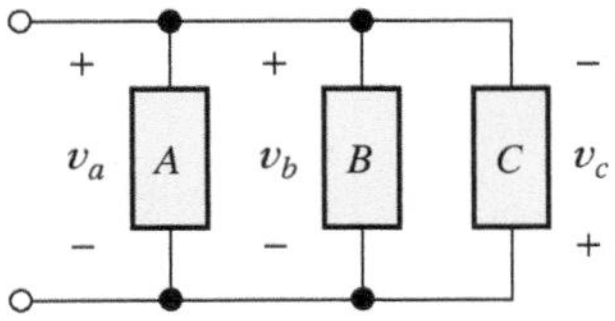

Figure 27 For this circuit, we can show that $v_a = v_b = -v_c$. Thus, the magnitudes and *actual* polarities of all three voltages are the same.

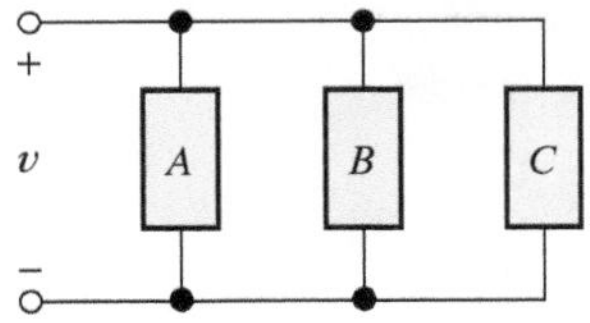

Figure 28 Analysis is simplified by using the same voltage variable and reference polarity for elements that are in parallel.

Exercise 9 Use repeated application of KVL to find the values of v_c and v_e for the circuit of Figure 29.

Answer $v_c = 8$ V, $v_e = -2$ V. □

Exercise 10 Identify elements that are in parallel in Figure 29. Identify elements in series.

Answer Elements E and F are in parallel; elements A and B are in series. □

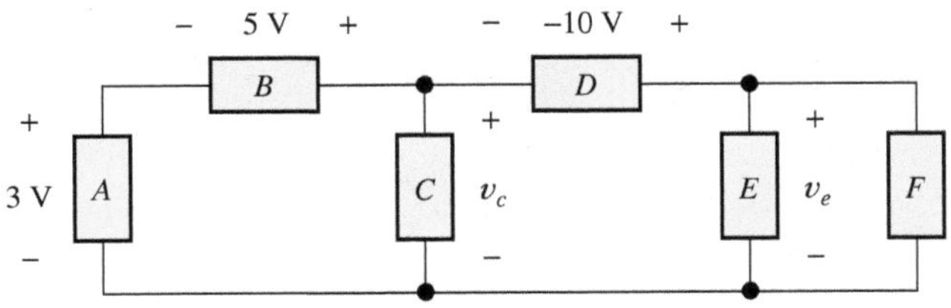

Figure 29 Circuit for Exercises 9 and 10.

6 INTRODUCTION TO CIRCUIT ELEMENTS

In this section, we carefully define several types of ideal circuit elements:

Conductors
Voltage sources
Current sources
Resistors

We will encounter additional elements, including inductors and capacitors. Eventually, we will be able to use these idealized circuit elements to describe (model) complex real-world electrical devices.

Conductors

We have already encountered conductors. Ideal conductors are represented in circuit diagrams by unbroken lines between the ends of other circuit elements. We define ideal circuit elements in terms of the relationship between the voltage across the element and the current through it.

The voltage between the ends of an ideal conductor is zero regardless of the current flowing through the conductor.

The voltage between the ends of an ideal conductor is zero regardless of the current flowing through the conductor. When two points in a circuit are connected together by an ideal conductor, we say that the points are **shorted** together. Another term for an ideal conductor is **short circuit**. All points in a circuit that are connected by ideal conductors can be considered as a single node.

All points in a circuit that are connected by ideal conductors can be considered as a single node.

If no conductors or other circuit elements are connected between two parts of a circuit, we say that an **open circuit** exists between the two parts of the circuit. No current can flow through an ideal open circuit.

Independent Voltage Sources

An ideal independent voltage source maintains a specified voltage across its terminals.

An **ideal independent voltage source** maintains a specified voltage across its terminals. The voltage across the source is independent of other elements that are connected to it and of the current flowing through it. We use a circle enclosing the reference polarity marks to represent independent voltage sources. The value of the voltage is indicated alongside the symbol. The voltage can be constant or it can be a function of time. Several voltage sources are shown in Figure 30.

In Figure 30(a), the voltage across the source is constant. Thus, we have a dc voltage source. On the other hand, the source shown in Figure 30(b) is an ac voltage source having a sinusoidal variation with time. We say that these are *independent* sources because the voltages across their terminals are independent of all other voltages and currents in the circuit.

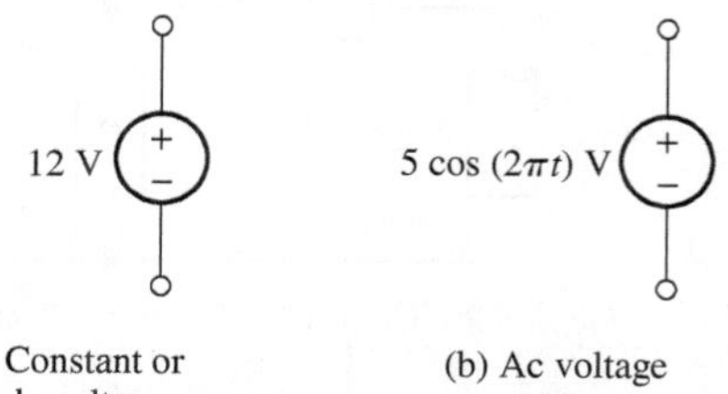

Figure 30 Independent voltage sources.

(a) Constant or dc voltage source

(b) Ac voltage source

Ideal Circuit Elements versus Reality

Here we are giving definitions of *ideal* circuit elements. It is possible to draw ideal circuits in which the definitions of various circuit elements conflict. For example, Figure 31 shows a 12-V voltage source with a conductor connected across its terminals. In this case, the definition of the voltage source requires that $v_x = 12$ V. On the other hand, the definition of an ideal conductor requires that $v_x = 0$. In our study of ideal circuits, we avoid such conflicts.

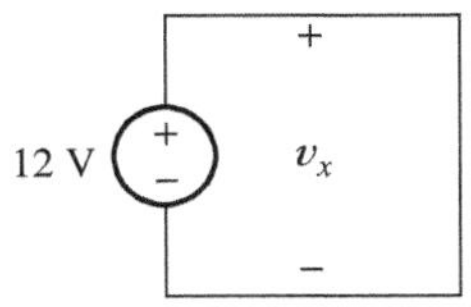

Figure 31 We avoid self-contradictory circuit diagrams such as this one.

In the real world, an automobile battery is nearly an ideal 12-V voltage source, and a short piece of heavy-gauge copper wire is nearly an ideal conductor. If we place the wire across the terminals of the battery, a very large current flows through the wire, stored chemical energy is converted to heat in the wire at a very high rate, and the wire will probably melt or the battery be destroyed.

When we encounter a contradictory idealized circuit model, we often have an undesirable situation (such as a fire or destroyed components) in the real-world counterpart to the model. In any case, a contradictory circuit model implies that we have not been sufficiently careful in choosing circuit models for the real circuit elements. For example, an automobile battery is not exactly modeled as an ideal voltage source. We will see that a better model (particularly if the currents are very large) is an ideal voltage source in series with a resistance. (We will discuss resistance very soon.) A short piece of copper wire is not modeled well as an ideal conductor, in this case. Instead, we will see that it is modeled better as a small resistance. If we have done a good job at picking circuit models for real-world circuits, we will not encounter contradictory circuits, and the results we calculate using the model will match reality very well.

Dependent Voltage Sources

A **dependent** or **controlled voltage source** is similar to an independent source except that the voltage across the source terminals is a function of other voltages or currents in the circuit. Instead of a circle, it is customary to use a diamond to represent controlled sources in circuit diagrams. Two examples of dependent sources are shown in Figure 32.

A **voltage-controlled voltage source** is a voltage source having a voltage equal to a constant times the voltage across a pair of terminals elsewhere in the network.

A voltage-controlled voltage source maintains a voltage across its terminals equal to a constant times a voltage elsewhere in the circuit.

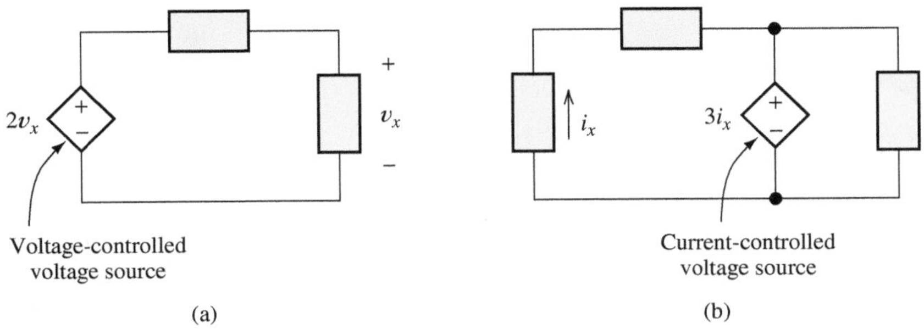

Figure 32 Dependent voltage sources (also known as controlled voltage sources) are represented by diamond-shaped symbols. The voltage across a controlled voltage source depends on a current or voltage that appears elsewhere in the circuit.

An example is shown in Figure 32(a). The dependent voltage source is the diamond symbol. The reference polarity of the source is indicated by the marks inside the diamond. The voltage v_x determines the value of the voltage produced by the source. For example, if it should turn out that $v_x = 3$ V, the source voltage is $2v_x = 6$ V. If v_x should equal -7 V, the source produces $2v_x = -14$ V (in which case, the actual positive polarity of the source is at the bottom end).

A current-controlled voltage source maintains a voltage across its terminals equal to a constant times a current flowing through some other element in the circuit.

A **current-controlled voltage source** is a voltage source having a voltage equal to a constant times the current through some other element in the circuit. An example is shown in Figure 32(b). In this case, the source voltage is three times the value of the current i_x. The factor multiplying the current is called the **gain parameter**. We assume that the voltage has units of volts and the current is in amperes. Thus, the gain parameter [which is 3 in Figure 32(b)] has units of volts per ampere (V/A). (Shortly, we will see that the units V/A are the units of resistance and are called ohms.)

Returning our attention to the voltage-controlled voltage source in Figure 32(a), we note that the gain parameter is 2 and is unitless (or we could say that the units are V/V).

We will see that controlled sources are very useful in modeling transistors, amplifiers, and electrical generators, among other things.

Independent Current Sources

An ideal independent current source forces a specified current to flow through itself.

An ideal **independent current source** forces a specified current to flow through itself. The symbol for an independent current source is a circle enclosing an arrow that gives the reference direction for the current. The current through an independent current source is independent of the elements connected to it and of the voltage across it. Figure 33 shows the symbols for a dc current source and for an ac current source.

If an open circuit exists across the terminals of a current source, we have a contradictory circuit. For example, consider the 2-A dc current source shown in Figure 33(a). This current source is shown with an open circuit across its terminals. By definition, the current flowing into the top node of the source is 2 A. Also by definition, no current can flow through the open circuit. Thus, KCL is not satisfied at this node. In good models for actual circuits, this situation does not occur. Thus, we will avoid current sources with open-circuited terminals in our discussion of ideal networks.

A battery is a good example of a voltage source, but an equally familiar example does not exist for a current source. However, current sources are useful in constructing theoretical models. Later, we will see that a good approximation to an ideal current source can be achieved with electronic amplifiers.

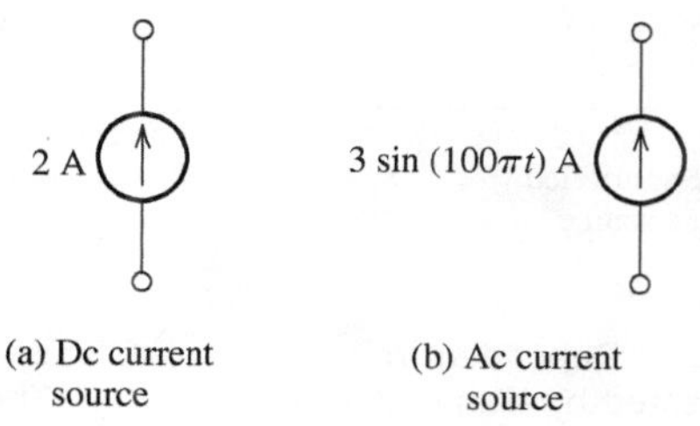

Figure 33 Independent current sources.

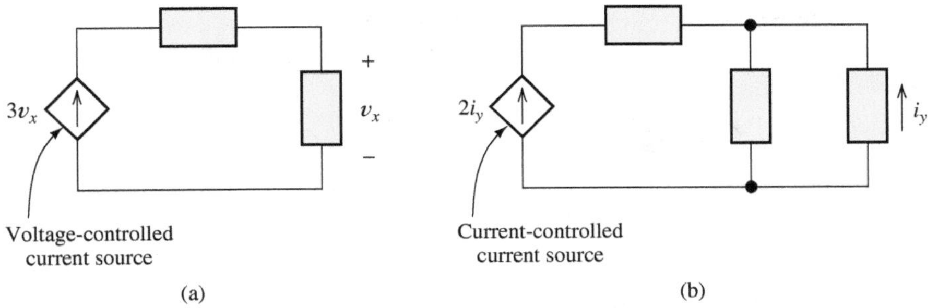

Figure 34 Dependent current sources. The current through a dependent current source depends on a current or voltage that appears elsewhere in the circuit.

Dependent Current Sources

The current flowing through a dependent current source is determined by a current or voltage elsewhere in the circuit.

The current flowing through a **dependent current source** is determined by a current or voltage elsewhere in the circuit. The symbol is a diamond enclosing an arrow that indicates the reference direction. Two types of controlled current sources are shown in Figure 34.

In Figure 34(a), we have a **voltage-controlled current source**. The current through the source is three times the voltage v_x. The gain parameter of the source (3 in this case) has units of A/V (which we will soon see are equivalent to siemens or inverse ohms). If it turns out that v_x has a value of 5 V, the current through the controlled current source is $3v_x = 15$ A.

Figure 34(b) illustrates a **current-controlled current source**. In this case, the current through the source is twice the value of i_y. The gain parameter, which has a value of 2 in this case, has units of A/A (i.e., it is unitless).

Like controlled voltage sources, controlled current sources are useful in constructing circuit models for many types of real-world devices, such as electronic amplifiers, transistors, transformers, and electrical machines. If a controlled source is needed for some application, it can be implemented by using electronic amplifiers. In sum, these are the four kinds of controlled sources:

1. Voltage-controlled voltage sources
2. Current-controlled voltage sources
3. Voltage-controlled current sources
4. Current-controlled current sources

Resistors and Ohm's Law

The voltage v across an ideal **resistor** is proportional to the current i through the resistor. The constant of proportionality is the resistance R. The symbol used for a resistor is shown in Figure 35(a). Notice that the current reference and voltage polarity reference conform to the passive reference configuration. In other words, the reference direction for the current is into the positive polarity mark and out of the negative polarity mark. In equation form, the voltage and current are related by **Ohm's law**:

$$v = iR$$

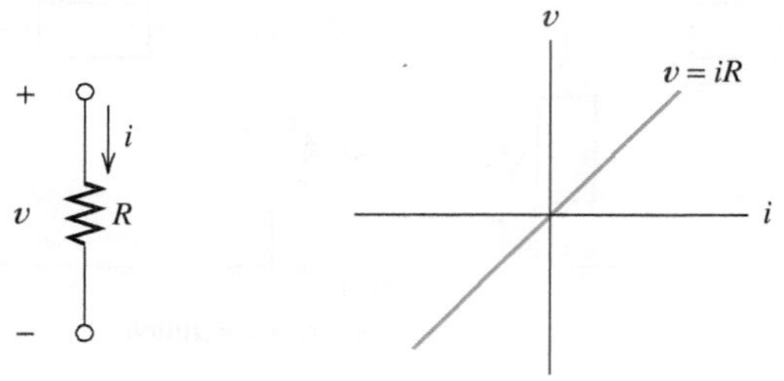

(a) Resistance symbol (b) Ohm's law

Figure 35 Voltage is proportional to current in an ideal resistor. Notice that the references for v and i conform to the passive reference configuration.

The units of resistance are V/A, which are called ohms. The uppercase Greek letter omega (Ω) represents ohms. In practical circuits, we encounter resistances ranging from milliohms (mΩ) to megohms (MΩ).

Except for rather unusual situations, the resistance R assumes positive values. (In certain types of electronic circuits, we can encounter negative resistance, but for now we assume that R is positive.) In situations for which the current reference direction enters the *negative* reference of the voltage, Ohm's law becomes

$$v = -iR$$

This is illustrated in Figure 36.

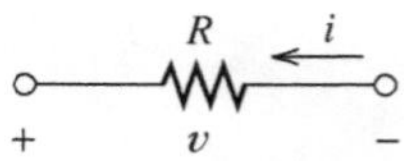

Figure 36 If the references for v and i are opposite to the passive configuration, we have $v = -Ri$.

The relationship between current direction and voltage polarity can be neatly included in the equation for Ohm's law if double-subscript notation is used. (Recall that to use double subscripts, we label the ends of the element under consideration, which is a resistance in this case.) If the order of the subscripts is the same for the current as for the voltage (i_{ab} and v_{ab}, for example), the current reference direction enters the first terminal and the positive voltage reference is at the first terminal. Thus, we can write

$$v_{ab} = i_{ab}R$$

On the other hand, if the order of the subscripts is not the same, we have

$$v_{ab} = -i_{ba}R$$

Conductance

Solving Ohm's law for current, we have

$$i = \frac{1}{R}v$$

We call the quantity $1/R$ a **conductance**. It is customary to denote conductances with the letter G:

$$G = \frac{1}{R} \qquad (8)$$

Conductances have the units of inverse ohms (Ω^{-1}), which are called siemens (abbreviated S). Thus, we can write Ohm's law as

$$i = Gv \tag{9}$$

Resistors

It turns out that we can construct nearly ideal resistors by attaching terminals to many types of conductive materials. This is illustrated in Figure 37. Conductive materials that can be used to construct resistors include most metals, their alloys, and carbon.

On a microscopic level, current in metals consists of electrons moving through the material. (On the other hand, in solutions of ionic compounds, current is carried partly by positive ions.) The applied voltage creates an electric field that accelerates the electrons. The electrons repeatedly collide with the atoms of the material and lose their forward momentum. Then they are accelerated again. The net effect is a constant average velocity for the electrons. At the macroscopic level, we observe a current that is proportional to the applied voltage.

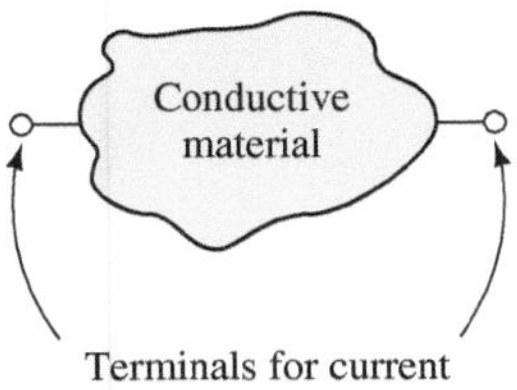

Figure 37 We construct resistors by attaching terminals to a piece of conductive material.

Resistance Related to Physical Parameters

The dimensions and geometry of the resistor as well as the particular material used to construct a resistor influence its resistance. We consider only resistors that take the form of a long cylinder or bar with terminals attached at the ends, as illustrated in Figure 38. The cross-sectional area A is constant along the length of the cylinder or bar. If the length L of the resistor is much greater than the dimensions of its cross section, the resistance is approximately given by

$$R = \frac{\rho L}{A} \tag{10}$$

in which ρ is the *resistivity* of the material used to construct the resistor. The units of resistivity are ohm meters (Ωm).

Materials can be classified as conductors, semiconductors, or insulators, depending on their resistivity. **Conductors** have the lowest resistivity and easily conduct electrical current. **Insulators** have very high resistivity and conduct very little current (at least for moderate voltages). **Semiconductors** fall between conductors and insulators. Certain semiconductors are very useful in constructing electronic devices. Table 3 gives approximate values of resistivity for several materials.

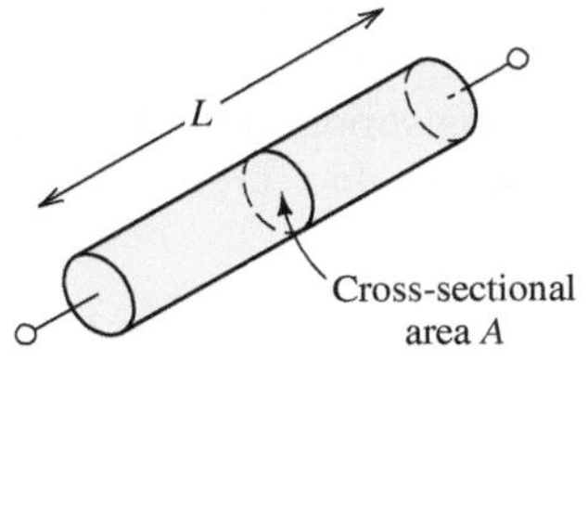

Figure 38 Resistors often take the form of a long cylinder (or bar) in which current enters one end and flows along the length.

Table 3. Resistivity Values (Ωm) for Selected Materials at 300 K

Conductors	
Aluminum	2.73×10^{-8}
Carbon (amorphous)	3.5×10^{-5}
Copper	1.72×10^{-8}
Gold	2.27×10^{-8}
Nichrome	1.12×10^{-6}
Silver	1.63×10^{-8}
Tungsten	5.44×10^{-8}
Semiconductors	
Silicon (device grade) depends on impurity concentration	10^{-5} to 1
Insulators	
Fused quartz	$> 10^{21}$
Glass (typical)	1×10^{12}
Teflon	1×10^{19}

Example 4 Resistance Calculation

Compute the resistance of a copper wire having a diameter of 2.05 mm and a length of 10 m.

Solution First, we compute the cross-sectional area of the wire:

$$A = \frac{\pi d^2}{4} = \frac{\pi(2.05 \times 10^{-3})^2}{4} = 3.3 \times 10^{-6}\ \text{m}^2$$

Then, the resistance is given by

$$R = \frac{\rho L}{A} = \frac{1.72 \times 10^{-8} \times 10}{3.3 \times 10^{-6}} = 0.052\ \Omega$$

These are the approximate dimensions of a piece of 12-gauge copper wire that we might find connecting an electrical outlet to the distribution box in a residence. Of course, two wires are needed for a complete circuit. ■

Power Calculations for Resistances

Recall that we compute power for a circuit element as the product of the current and voltage:

$$p = vi \tag{11}$$

If v and i have the passive reference configuration, a positive sign for power means that energy is being absorbed by the device. Furthermore, a negative sign means that energy is being supplied by the device.

If we use Ohm's law to substitute for v in Equation 11, we obtain

$$p = Ri^2 \tag{12}$$

On the other hand, if we solve Ohm's law for i and substitute into Equation 11, we obtain

$$p = \frac{v^2}{R} \tag{13}$$

Notice that power for a resistance is positive regardless of the sign of v or i (assuming that R is positive, which is ordinarily the case). Thus, power is absorbed by resistances. If the resistance results from collisions of electrons with the atoms of the material composing a resistor, this power shows up as heat.

Some applications for conversion of electrical power into heat are heating elements for ovens, water heaters, cooktops, and space heaters. In a typical space heater, the heating element consists of a nichrome wire that becomes red hot in operation. (Nichrome is an alloy of nickel, chromium, and iron.) To fit the required length of wire in a small space, it is coiled rather like a spring.

PRACTICAL APPLICATION 1

Using Resistance to Measure Strain

Civil and mechanical engineers routinely employ the dependence of resistance on physical dimensions of a conductor to measure strain. These measurements are important in experimental stress–strain analysis of mechanisms and structures. (Strain is defined as fractional change in length, given by $\epsilon = \Delta L/L$.)

A typical resistive strain gauge consists of nickel–copper alloy foil that is photoetched to obtain multiple conductors aligned with the direction of the strain to be measured. This is illustrated in Figure PA1. Typically, the conductors are bonded to a thin polyimide (a tough flexible plastic) backing, which in turn is attached to the structure under test by a suitable adhesive, such as cyanoacrylate cement.

The resistance of a conductor is given by

$$R = \frac{\rho L}{A}$$

As strain is applied, the length and area change, resulting in changes in resistance. The strain and the change in resistance are related by the gauge factor:

$$G = \frac{\Delta R/R_0}{\epsilon}$$

in which R_0 is the resistance of the gauge before strain. A typical gauge has $R_0 = 350\ \Omega$ and $G = 2.0$. Thus, for a strain of 1%, the change in resistance is $\Delta R = 7\ \Omega$. Usually, a Wheatstone bridge is used to measure the small changes in resistance associated with accurate strain determination.

Sensors for force, torque, and pressure are constructed by using resistive strain gauges.

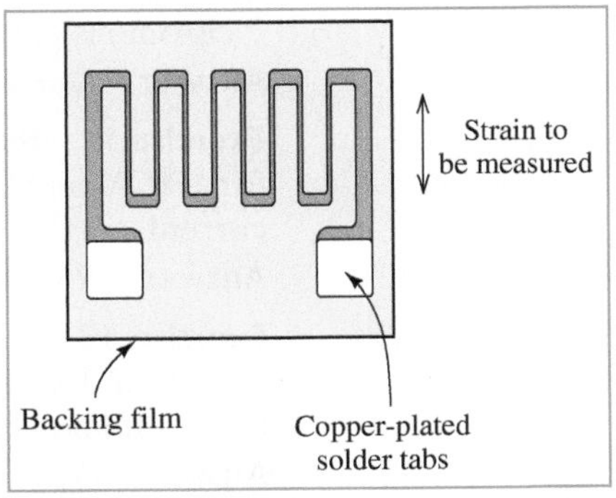

Figure PA1

Resistors versus Resistances

As an aside, we mention that resistance is often useful in modeling devices in which electrical power is converted into forms other than heat. For example, a loudspeaker appears to have a resistance of 8 Ω. Part of the power delivered to the loudspeaker is converted to acoustic power. Another example is a transmitting antenna having a resistance of 50 Ω. The power delivered to an antenna is radiated, traveling away as an electromagnetic wave.

There is a slight distinction between the terms *resistor* and *resistance*. A resistor is a two-terminal device composed of a conductive material. Resistance is a circuit property for which voltage is proportional to current. Thus, resistors have the property of resistance. However, resistance is also useful in modeling antennas and loudspeakers, which are quite different from resistors. Often, we are not careful about this distinction in using these terms.

Example 5 **Determining Resistance for Given Power and Voltage Ratings**

A certain electrical heater is rated for 1500 W when operated from 120 V. Find the resistance of the heater element and the operating current. (Resistance depends on temperature, and we will find the resistance at the operating temperature of the heater.)

Solution Solving Equation 13 for resistance, we obtain

$$R = \frac{v^2}{p} = \frac{120^2}{1500} = 9.6\ \Omega$$

Then, we use Ohm's law to find the current:

$$i = \frac{v}{R} = \frac{120}{9.6} = 12.5\ \text{A}$$

■

Exercise 11 The 9.6-Ω resistance of Example 5 is in the form of a nichrome wire having a diameter of 1.6 mm. Find the length of the wire. (*Hint:* The resistivity of nichrome is given in Table 3.)

Answer $L = 17.2$ m. □

Exercise 12 Suppose we have a typical incandescent electric light bulb that is rated for 100 W and 120 V. Find its resistance (at operating temperature) and operating current.

Answer $R = 144\ \Omega, i = 0.833$ A. □

Exercise 13 A 1-kΩ resistor used in a television receiver is rated for a maximum power of 1/4 W. Find the current and voltage when the resistor is operated at maximum power.

Answer $v_{max} = 15.8$ V, $i_{max} = 15.8$ mA. □

7 INTRODUCTION TO CIRCUITS

In this chapter, we have defined electrical current and voltage, discussed Kirchhoff's laws, and introduced several ideal circuit elements: voltage sources, current sources, and resistances. Now we illustrate these concepts by considering a few relatively simple circuits.

Consider the circuit shown in Figure 39(a). Suppose that we want to know the current, voltage, and power for each element. To obtain these results, we apply

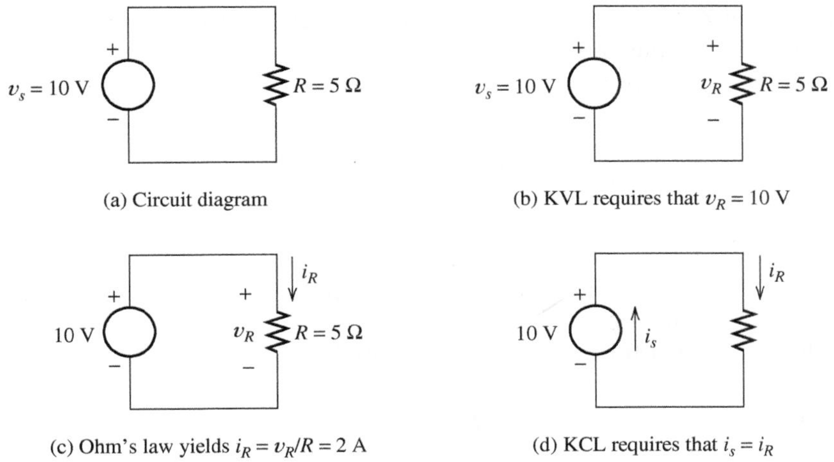

Figure 39 A circuit consisting of a voltage source and a resistance.

the basic principles introduced in this chapter. At first, we proceed in small, methodical steps. Furthermore, for ease of understanding, we initially select reference polarities and directions that agree with the actual polarities and current directions.

KVL requires that the sum of the voltages around the circuit shown in Figure 39 must equal zero. Thus, traveling around the circuit clockwise, we have $v_R - v_s = 0$. Consequently, $v_R = v_s$, and the voltage across the resistor v_R must have an actual polarity that is positive at the top end and a magnitude of 10 V.

An alternative way of looking at the voltages in this circuit is to notice that the voltage source and the resistance are in parallel. (The top ends of the voltage source and the resistance are connected, and the bottom ends are also connected.) Recall that when elements are in parallel, the voltage magnitude and polarity are the same for all elements.

Now consider Ohm's law. Because 10 V appears across the 5-Ω resistance, the current is $i_R = 10/5 = 2$ A. This current flows through the resistance from the positive polarity to the negative polarity. Thus, $i_R = 2$ A flows downward through the resistance, as shown in Figure 39(c).

According to KCL, the sum of the currents entering a given node must equal the sum of the currents leaving. There are two nodes for the circuit of Figure 39: one at the top and one at the bottom. The current i_R leaves the top node through the resistance. Thus, an equal current must enter the top node through the voltage source. The actual direction of current flow is upward through the voltage source, as shown in Figure 39(d).

Another way to see that the currents i_s and i_R are equal is to notice that the voltage source and the resistance are in series. In a series circuit, the current that flows in one element must continue through the other element. (Notice that for this circuit the voltage source and the resistance are in parallel and they are also in series. A two-element circuit is the only case for which this occurs. If more than two elements are interconnected, a pair of elements that are in parallel cannot also be in series, and vice versa.)

Notice that in Figure 39, the current in the voltage source flows from the negative polarity toward the positive polarity. It is only for resistances that the current is required to flow from plus to minus. For a voltage source, the current can flow in either direction, depending on the circuit to which the source is connected.

It is only for resistances that the current is required to flow from plus to minus. Current may flow in either direction for a voltage source depending on the other elements in the circuit.

Now let us calculate the power for each element. For the resistance, we have several ways to compute power:

$$p_R = v_R i_R = 10 \times 2 = 20 \text{ W}$$
$$p_R = i_R^2 R = 2^2 \times 5 = 20 \text{ W}$$
$$p_R = \frac{v_R^2}{R} = \frac{10^2}{5} = 20 \text{ W}$$

Of course, all the calculations yield the same result. Energy is delivered to the resistance at the rate of 20 J/s.

To find the power for the voltage source, we have

$$p_s = -v_s i_s$$

where the minus sign is used because the reference direction for the current enters the negative voltage reference (opposite to the passive reference configuration). Substituting values, we obtain

$$p_s = -v_s i_s = -10 \times 2 = -20 \text{ W}$$

Because p_s is negative, we understand that energy is being delivered by the voltage source.

As a check, if we add the powers for all the elements in the circuit, the result should be zero, because energy is neither created nor destroyed in an electrical circuit. Instead, it is transported and changed in form. Thus, we can write

$$p_s + p_R = -20 + 20 = 0$$

Using Arbitrary References

In the previous discussion, we selected references that agree with actual polarities and current directions. This is not always possible at the start of the analysis of more complex circuits. Fortunately, it is not necessary. We can pick the references in an arbitrary manner. Application of circuit laws will tell us not only the magnitudes of the currents and voltages but the true polarities and current directions as well.

Example 6 Circuit Analysis Using Arbitrary References

Analyze the circuit of Figure 39 using the current and voltage references shown in Figure 40. Verify that the results are in agreement with those found earlier.

Solution Traveling clockwise and applying KVL, we have

$$-v_s - v_x = 0$$

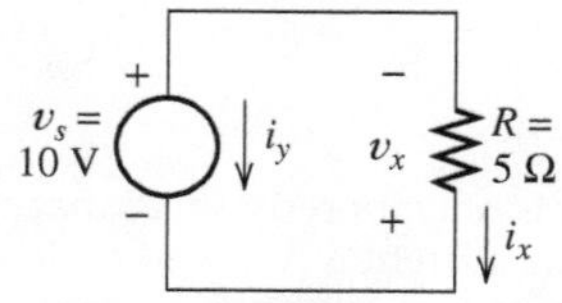

Figure 40 Circuit for Example 6.

This yields $v_x = -v_s = -10$ V. Since v_x assumes a negative value, the actual polarity is opposite to the reference. Thus, as before, we conclude that the voltage across the resistance is actually positive at the top end.

According to Ohm's law,

$$i_x = -\frac{v_x}{R}$$

where the minus sign appears because v_x and i_x have references opposite to the passive reference configuration. Substituting values, we get

$$i_x = -\frac{-10}{5} = 2 \text{ A}$$

Since i_x assumes a positive value, the actual current direction is downward through the resistance.

Next, applying KCL at the bottom node of the circuit, we have

$$\text{total current entering} = \text{total current leaving}$$
$$i_y + i_x = 0$$

Thus, $i_y = -i_x = -2$ A, and we conclude that a current of 2 A actually flows upward through the voltage source.

The power for the voltage source is

$$p_s = v_s i_y = 10 \times (-2) = -20 \text{ W}$$

Finally, the power for the resistance is given by

$$p_R = -v_x i_x$$

where the minus sign appears because the references for v_x and i_x are opposite to the passive reference configuration. Substituting, we find that $p_R = -(-10) \times (2) = 20$ W. Because p_R has a positive value, we conclude that energy is delivered to the resistance. ■

Sometimes circuits can be solved by repeated application of Kirchhoff's laws and Ohm's law. We illustrate with an example.

Example 7 Using KVL, KCL, and Ohm's Law to Solve a Circuit

Solve for the source voltage in the circuit of Figure 41 in which we have a current-controlled current source and we are given that the voltage across the 5-Ω resistance is 15 V.

Solution First, we use Ohm's Law to determine the value of i_y:

$$i_y = \frac{15 \text{ V}}{5 \text{ Ω}} = 3 \text{ A}$$

Next, we apply KCL at the top end of the controlled source:

$$i_x + 0.5 i_x = i_y$$

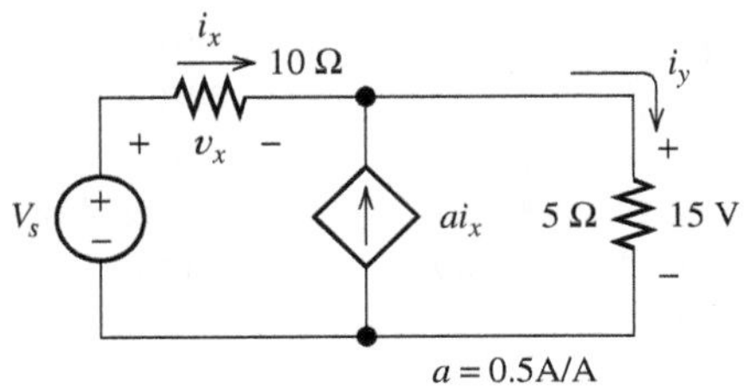

Figure 41 Circuit for Example 7.

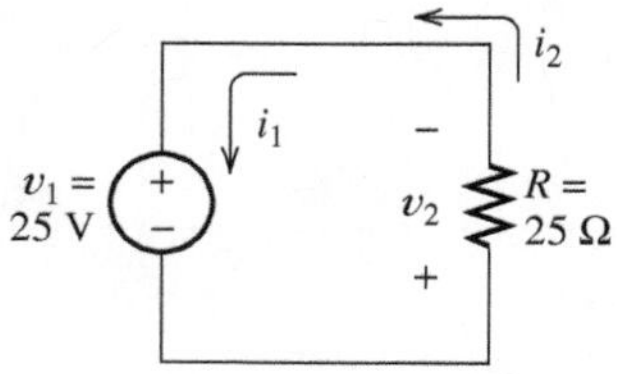

Figure 42 Circuit for Exercise 14.

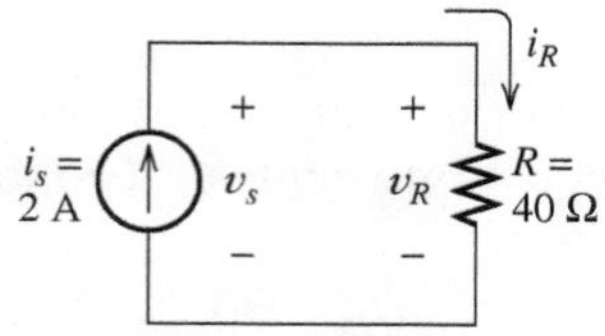

Figure 43 Circuit for Exercise 15.

Substituting the value found for i_y and solving, we determine that $i_x = 2$ A. Then Ohm's law yields $v_x = 10i_x = 20$ V. Applying KCL around the periphery of the circuit gives

$$V_s = v_x + 15$$

Finally, substituting the value found for v_x yields $V_s = 35$ V. ■

Exercise 14 Analyze the circuit shown in Figure 42 to find the values of i_1, i_2, and v_2. Use the values found to compute the power for each element.

Answer $i_1 = i_2 = -1$ A, $v_2 = -25$ V, $p_R = 25$ W, $p_s = -25$ W. □

Exercise 15 Figure 43 shows an independent current source connected across a resistance. Analyze to find the values of i_R, v_R, v_s, and the power for each element.

Answer $i_R = 2$ A, $v_s = v_R = 80$ V, $p_s = -160$ W, $p_R = 160$ W. □

Summary

1. Electrical and electronic features are increasingly integrated into the products and systems designed by engineers in other fields. Furthermore, instrumentation in all fields of engineering and science is based on the use of electrical sensors, electronics, and computers.
2. Some of the main areas of electrical engineering are communication systems, computer systems, control systems, electromagnetics, photonics, electronics, power systems, and signal processing.
3. Some important reasons to learn basic electrical engineering principles are to pass the Fundamentals of Engineering Examination, to have a broad enough knowledge base to lead design projects in your own field, to be able to identify and correct simple malfunctions in electrical systems, and to be able to communicate efficiently with electrical engineering consultants.
4. Current is the time rate of flow of electrical charge. Its units are amperes (A), which are equivalent to coulombs per second (C/s).
5. The voltage associated with a circuit element is the energy transferred per unit of charge that flows through the element. The units of voltages are volts (V), which are equivalent to joules per coulomb (J/C). If positive charge moves from the positive reference to the negative reference, energy is absorbed by the circuit element. If the charge moves in the opposite direction, energy is delivered by the element.
6. In the passive reference configuration, the current reference direction enters the positive reference polarity.
7. If the references have the passive configuration, power for a circuit element is computed as the product of the current through the element and the voltage across it:

$$p = vi$$

If the references are opposite to the passive configuration, we have

$$p = -vi$$

In either case, if p is positive, energy is being absorbed by the element.

8. A node in an electrical circuit is a point at which two or more circuit elements are joined together. All points joined by ideal conductors are electrically equivalent and constitute a single node.
9. Kirchhoff's current law (KCL) states that the sum of the currents entering a node equals the sum of the currents leaving.
10. Elements connected end to end are said to be in series. For two elements to be in series, no other current path can be connected to their common node. The current is identical for all elements in a series connection.

11. A loop in an electrical circuit is a closed path starting at a node and proceeding through circuit elements eventually returning to the starting point.
12. Kirchhoff's voltage law (KVL) states that the algebraic sum of the voltages in a loop must equal zero. If the positive polarity of a voltage is encountered first in going around the loop, the voltage carries a plus sign in the sum. On the other hand, if the negative polarity is encountered first, the voltage carries a minus sign.
13. Two elements are in parallel if both ends of one element are directly connected to corresponding ends of the other element. The voltages of parallel elements are identical.
14. The voltage between the ends of an ideal conductor is zero regardless of the current flowing through the conductor. All points in a circuit that are connected by ideal conductors can be considered as a single point.
15. An ideal independent voltage source maintains a specified voltage across its terminals independent of other elements that are connected to it and of the current flowing through it.
16. For a controlled voltage source, the voltage across the source terminals depends on other voltages or currents in the circuit. A voltage-controlled voltage source is a voltage source having a voltage equal to a constant times the voltage across a pair of terminals elsewhere in the network. A current-controlled voltage source is a voltage source having a voltage equal to a constant times the current through some other element in the circuit.
17. An ideal independent current source forces a specified current to flow through itself, independent of other elements that are connected to it and of the voltage across it.
18. For a controlled current source, the current depends on other voltages or currents in the circuit. A voltage-controlled current source produces a current equal to a constant times the voltage across a pair of terminals elsewhere in the network. A current-controlled current source produces a current equal to a constant times the current through some other element in the circuit.
19. For constant resistances, voltage is proportional to current. If the current and voltage references have the passive configuration, Ohm's law states that $v = Ri$. For references opposite to the passive configuration, $v = -Ri$.

Problems

Section 1: Overview of Electrical Engineering

P1. Broadly speaking, what are the two main objectives of electrical systems?

P2. Name eight subdivisions of electrical engineering.

P3. Briefly describe four important reasons that other engineering students need to learn the fundamentals of electrical engineering.

P4. Write a few paragraphs describing an interesting application of electrical engineering in your field. Consult engineering journals and trade magazines such as the *IEEE Spectrum, Automotive Engineering, Chemical Engineering*, or *Civil Engineering* for ideas.

Section 2: Circuits, Currents, and Voltages

P5. Carefully define or explain each of the following terms in your own words giving units where appropriate: **a.** Electrical current; **b.** Voltage; **c.** An open switch; **d.** A closed switch; **e.** Direct current; **f.** Alternating current.

P6. In the fluid-flow analogy for electrical circuits, what is analogous to: **a.** a conductor; **b.** an open switch; **c.** a resistance; **d.** a battery?

***P7.** The ends of a length of wire are labeled a and b. If the current in the wire is $i_{ab} = -3$ A, are electrons moving toward a or b? How much charge passes through a cross section of the wire in 3 seconds?

* Denotes that answers are contained in the Student Solutions files. See Appendix "On-Line Student Resources" for more information about accessing the Student Solutions.

***P8.** The net charge through a cross section of a circuit element is given by $q(t) = 2t + t^2$ C. As usual, t is in seconds. Find the current through the element in amperes.

***P9.** The current through a given circuit element is given by $i(t) = 2e^{-t}$ A. As usual, time t is in seconds. Find the net charge that passes through the element in the interval from $t = 0$ to $t = \infty$. (*Hint:* Current is the rate of flow of charge. Thus, to find charge, we must integrate current with respect to time.)

***P10.** A certain lead-acid storage battery has a mass of 30 kg. Starting from a fully charged state, it can supply 5 A for 24 hours with a terminal voltage of 12 V before it is totally discharged. **a.** If the energy stored in the fully charged battery is used to lift the battery with 100-percent efficiency, what height is attained? Assume that the acceleration due to gravity is 9.8 m/s^2 and is constant with height. **b.** If the stored energy is used to accelerate the battery with 100 percent efficiency, what velocity is attained? **c.** Gasoline contains about 4.5×10^7 J/kg. Compare this with the energy content per unit mass for the fully charged battery.

***P11.** A typical "deep-cycle" battery (used for electric trolling motors for fishing boats) is capable of delivering 12.6 V and 10 A for a period of 10 hours. How much charge flows through the battery in this interval? How much energy does the battery deliver?

P12. An ac current given by $i\,(t) = 5\sin(200\pi t)$ A, in which t is in seconds and the angle is in radians, flows through an element of an electrical circuit. **a.** Sketch $i(t)$ to scale versus time for t ranging from 0 to 15 ms. **b.** Determine the net charge that passes through the element between $t = 0$ and $t = 10$ ms. **c.** Repeat for the interval from $t = 0$ to $t = 15$ ms.

P13. Consider the headlight circuit of Figure 2. For current to flow through the headlight, should the switch be open or closed? In the fluid-flow analogy for the circuit, would the valve corresponding to the switch be open or closed? What state for a valve, open or closed, is analogous to an open switch?

P14. What is the net number of electrons per second that pass through the cross-section of a wire carrying 5 A of dc current? The current flow is due to electrons, and the magnitude of the charge of each electron is 1.60×10^{-19} C.

P15. The circuit element shown in Figure P15 has $v = 15$ V and $i = -3$ A. What are the values of v_{ba} and i_{ba}? Be sure to give the correct algebraic signs. Is energy being delivered to the element or taken from it?

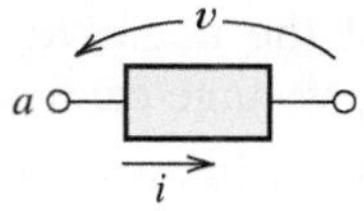

Figure P15

P16. Suppose that the net charge passing through the cross section of a certain circuit element is given by $q(t) = 2t + 3t^2$ C, with time t in seconds. Determine the current through the element as a function of time.

P17. In typical residential wiring, the copper wire has a diameter of 2.05 mm and carries a maximum current of $15\sqrt{2}$ A due solely to electrons, each of which has a charge of 1.60×10^{-19} C. Given that the free electron (these are the electrons capable of moving through the copper) concentration in copper is 10^{29} electrons/m^3, find the average velocity of the electrons in the wire when the maximum current is flowing.

P18. The charge carried by an electron is -1.60×10^{-19} C. Suppose that an electron moves through a voltage of 120 V from the negative polarity to the positive polarity. How much energy is transferred? Does the electron gain or lose energy?

P19. Consider a circuit element, with terminals a and b, that has $v_{ab} = -12$ V and $i_{ab} = 3$ A. Over a period of 2 seconds, how much charge moves through the element? If electrons carry the charge, which terminal do they enter? How much energy is transferred? Is it delivered to the element or taken from it?

Section 3: Power and Energy

P20. What does the term *passive reference configuration* imply? When do we have this configuration if we are using double subscript notation for an element having terminals a and b?

***P21.** Compute the power for each element shown in Figure P21. For each element, state whether energy is being absorbed by the element or supplied by it.

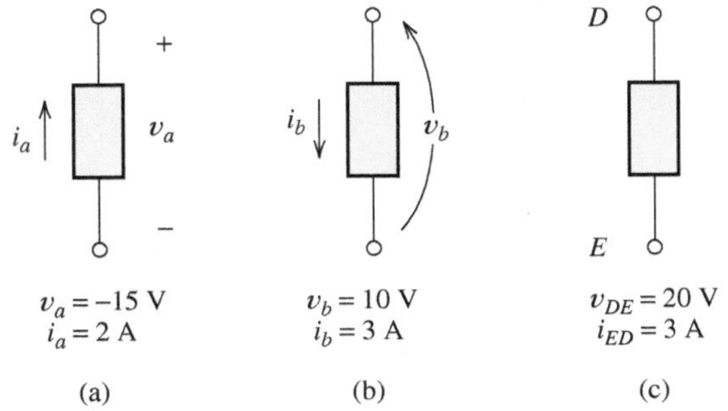

Figure P21

***P22.** A certain battery has terminals labeled a and b. The battery voltage is $v_{ab} = 12$ V. To increase the chemical energy stored in the battery by 600 J, how much charge must move through the battery? Should electrons move from a to b or from b to a?

P23. The terminals of an electrical device are labeled a and b. If $v_{ab} = 25$ V, how much energy is exchanged when a positive charge of 4 C moves through the device from a to b? Is the energy delivered to the device or taken from it?

P24. Consider the element shown in Figure P24 which has $v(t) = -15$ V and $i(t) = 3e^{-2t}$ A. Compute the power for the circuit element. Find the energy transferred between $t = 0$ and $t = \infty$. Is this energy absorbed by the element or supplied by it?

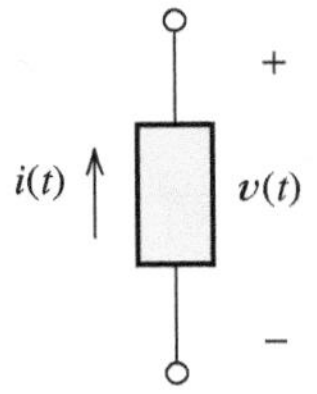

Figure P24

P25. Suppose that the cost of electrical energy is \$0.12 per kilowatt hour and that your electrical bill for 30 days is \$60. Assume that the power delivered is constant over the entire 30 days. What is the power in watts? If a voltage of 120 V supplies this power, what current flows? Part of your electrical load is a 60-W light that is on continuously. By what percentage can your energy consumption be reduced by turning this light off?

P26. An electrical device has $i_{ab}(t) = 2$ A and $v_{ab}(t) = 10\sin(100\pi t)$ V, in which the angle is in radians. **a.** Find the power delivered to the device and sketch it to scale versus time for t ranging from 0 to 30 ms. **b.** Determine the energy delivered to the device for the interval from $t = 0$ to $t = 10$ ms. **c.** Repeat for the interval from $t = 0$ to $t = 20$ ms.

P27. A fully charged deep-cycle lead–acid storage battery is rated for 12.6 V and 100 ampere hours. (The ampere-hour rating of the battery is the operating time to discharge the battery multiplied by the current.) This battery is used aboard a sailboat to power the electronics which consume 30 W. Assume that the battery voltage is constant during the discharge. For how many hours can the electronics be operated from the battery without recharging? How much energy in kilowatt hours is initially stored in the battery? If the battery costs \$95 and has a life of 250 charge–discharge cycles, what is the cost of the energy in dollars per kilowatt hour? Neglect the cost of recharging the battery.

***P28.** Figure P28 shows an ammeter (AM) and voltmeter (VM) connected to measure the current and voltage, respectively, for circuit element A. When current actually enters the + terminal of the ammeter the reading is positive, and when current leaves the + terminal the reading is negative. If the actual voltage polarity is positive at the + terminal of the VM, the reading is positive; otherwise, it is negative. (Actually, for the connection shown, the ammeter reads the sum of the current in element A and the very small current taken by the voltmeter. For purposes of this problem, assume that the current taken by the voltmeter is negligible.) Find the power for element A and state whether energy is being delivered to element A or taken from it if: **a.** the ammeter reading is +2 A and the voltmeter reading is −25 V; **b.** the ammeter reading is −2 A and the voltmeter reading is +25 V; **c.** the ammeter reading is −2 A and the voltmeter reading is −25 V.

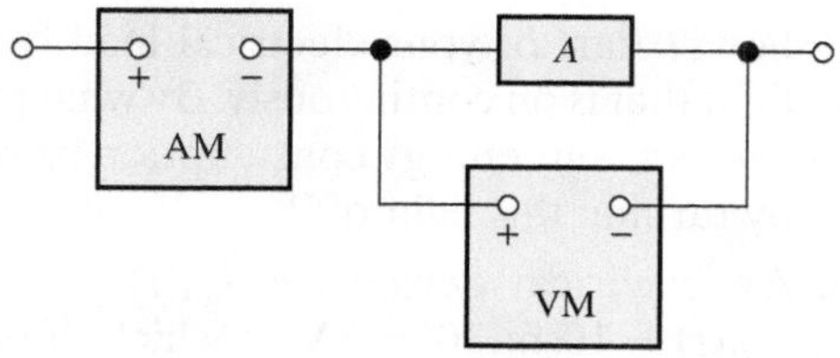

Figure P28

P29. Repeat Problem P28 with the meters connected as shown in Figure P29.

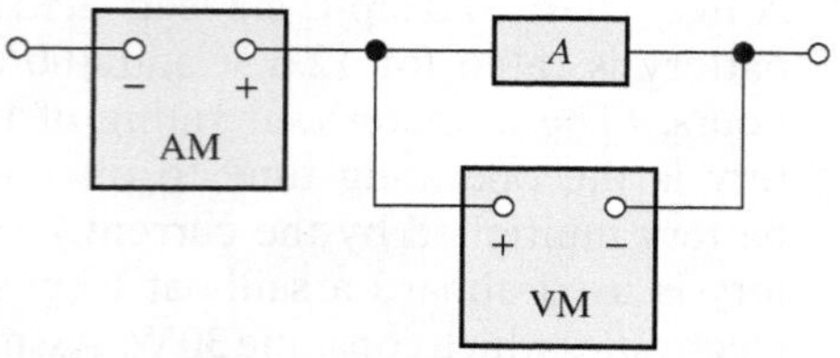

Figure P29

P30. Determine the cost per kilowatt hour for the energy delivered by a typical alkaline 9-V "transistor" battery that costs \$1.95 and is capable of delivering a current of 50 mA for a period of 10 hours. (For comparison, the approximate cost of energy purchased from electric utilities in the United States is \$0.12 per kilowatt hour.)

Section 4: Kirchhoff's Current Law

P31. Define the term *node* as it applies in electrical circuits. Identify the nodes in the circuit of Figure P31. Keep in mind that all points connected by ideal conductors are considered to be a single node in electrical circuits.

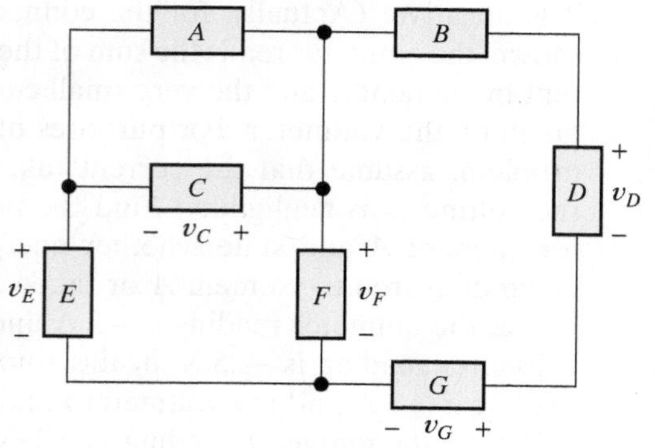

Figure P31

***P32.** Use KCL to find the values of i_a, i_c, and i_d for the circuit of Figure P32. Which elements are connected in series in this circuit?

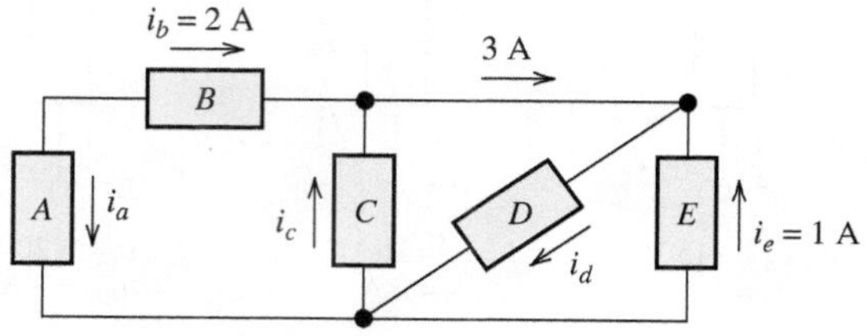

Figure P32

P33. What can you say about the currents through series-connected elements in an electrical circuit?

P34. State Kirchhoff's current law in your own words. Why is it true?

***P35.** Identify elements that are in series in the circuit of Figure P31.

P36. In the fluid-flow analogy for an electrical circuit, the analog of electrical current is volumetric flow rate with units of cm^3/s. For a proper analogy to electrical circuits, must the fluid be compressible or incompressible? Must the walls of the pipes be elastic or inelastic? Explain your answers.

***P37.** Given that $i_a = 2$ A, $i_b = 3$ A, $i_d = -5$ A, and $i_h = 4$ A, determine the values of the other currents in Figure P37.

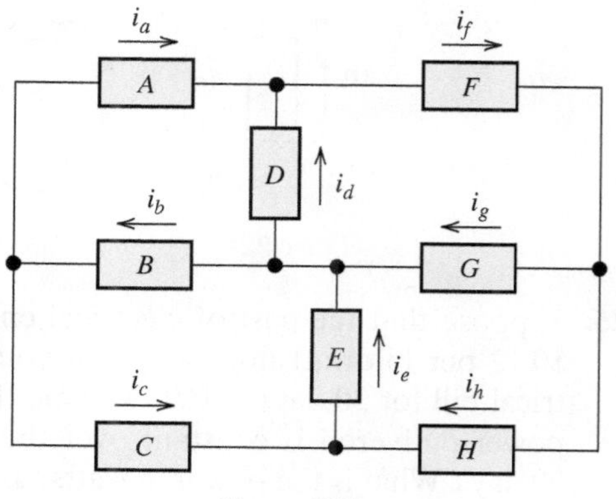

Figure P37

P38. Determine the values of the other currents in Figure P37, given that $i_a = 2$ A, $i_c = -3$ A, $i_g = 6$ A, and $i_h = 1$ A.

P39. **a.** Which elements are in series in Figure P39? **b.** What is the relationship between i_d and i_c? **c.** Given that $i_a = 6$ A and $i_c = -2$ A, determine the values of i_b and i_d.

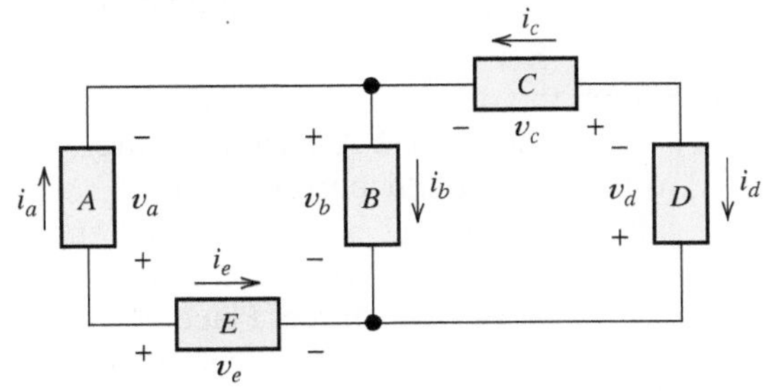

Figure P39

Section 5: Kirchhoff's Voltage Law

P40. Explain Kirchhoff's voltage law in your own words. Why is it true?

***P41.** Use KVL and KCL to solve for the labeled currents and voltages in Figure P41. Compute the power for each element and show that power is conserved (i.e., the algebraic sum of the powers is zero).

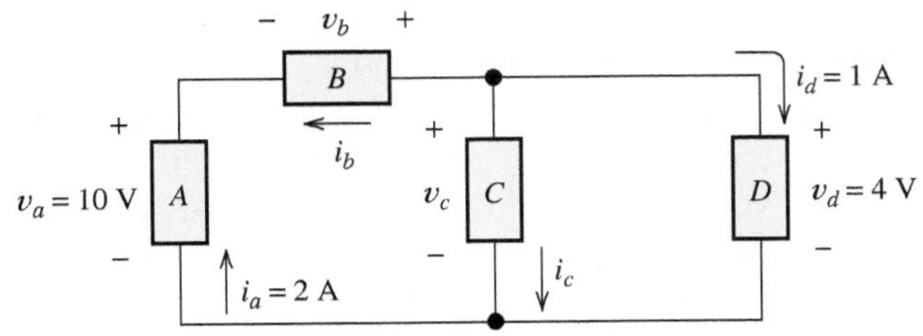

Figure P41

***P42.** Use KVL to solve for the voltages v_a, v_b, and v_c in Figure P42.

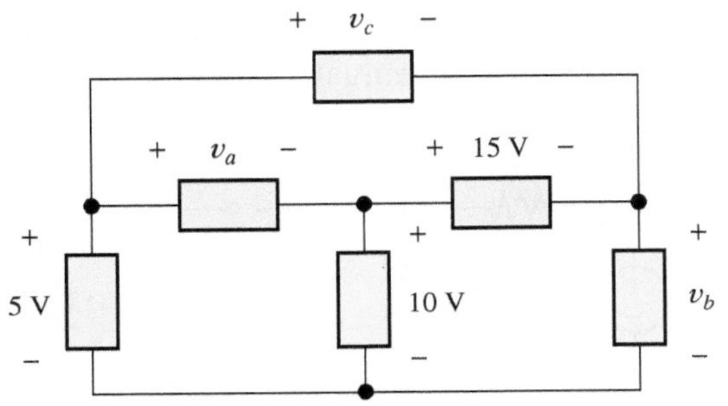

Figure P42

P43. We know that $v_a = 10$ V, $v_b = -3$ V, $v_f = 12$ V, and $v_h = 5$ V, solve for the other voltages shown in Figure P43.

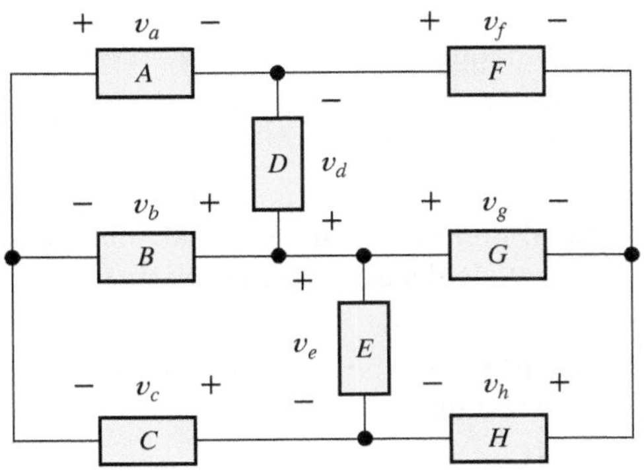

Figure P43

P44. Consider the circuit shown in Figure P31. **a.** Which elements are in parallel? **b.** What is the relationship between v_A and v_C? **c.** Given that $v_A = 8$ V and $v_E = 4$ V, determine the values of v_C and v_F.

P45. Identify the elements that are in parallel: **a.** in Figure P32, **b.** in Figure P43.

P46. Identify the nodes in Figure P46. Which elements are in series? Which are in parallel?

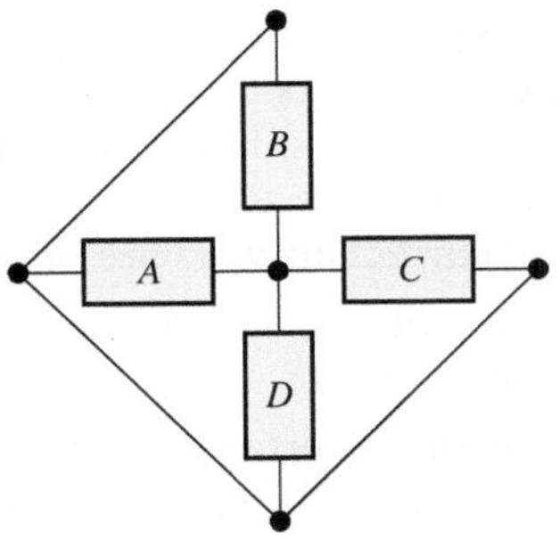

Figure P46

P47. Consider a circuit containing four nodes labeled a, b, c, and d. Also, we know that $v_{ab} = 12$ V, $v_{cb} = -4$ V, and $v_{da} = 8$ V. Determine the values of v_{ac} and v_{cd}. (*Hint:* Draw a picture showing the nodes and the known voltages.)

P48. A typical golf cart uses a number of 6-V batteries (which, for the purposes of this problem, can be modeled as ideal 6-V voltage sources). If the motor requires 36 V, what is the minimum number of batteries needed? How should they be connected? Sketch a diagram for the battery connections showing the polarity of each battery.

Section 6: Introduction to Circuit Elements

P49. Explain Ohm's law in your own words, including references.

P50. Define these terms in your own words: **a.** an ideal conductor; **b.** an ideal voltage source; **c.** an ideal current source; **d.** short circuit; **e.** open circuit.

P51. Name four types of dependent sources and give the units for the gain parameter of each type.

P52. **a.** Show that for wires of identical dimensions but made of different materials, such as copper and aluminum, the resistance is proportional to the resistivity of the material. (See Table 3 for resistivity values of some materials used in electrical wiring.) **b.** We know that the resistance of a certain copper wire is 1.5 Ω. Determine the resistance of an aluminum wire having the same dimensions as the copper wire.

***P53.** Draw a circuit that contains a 5-Ω resistance, a 10-V independent voltage source, and a 2-A independent current source. Connect all three elements in series. (Because the polarity of the voltage source and reference direction for the current source are not specified, several correct answers are possible.)

P54. Repeat Problem P53, placing all three elements in parallel.

P55. Suppose that a certain wire has a resistance of 10 Ω. Find the new resistance: **a.** if the length of the wire is doubled; **b.** if the diameter of the wire is doubled.

P56. Suppose we have a copper wire with a resistance of 2 Ω. We want to replace the copper wire with an aluminum wire of the same length and resistance. By what factor must the diameter of the wire be increased?

***P57.** A power of 100 W is delivered to a certain resistor when the applied voltage is 100 V. Find the resistance. Suppose that the voltage is reduced by 10 percent (to 90 V). By what percentage is the power reduced? Assume that the resistance remains constant.

P58. Sketch the diagram of a circuit that contains a 3-Ω resistor, a 10-V voltage source, and a current-controlled current source having a gain constant of 0.4 A/A. Assume that the current through the resistor is the control current for the controlled source. Place all three elements in parallel. Several answers are possible, depending on the polarities and reference directions chosen.

P59. Sketch the diagram of a circuit that contains a 3-Ω resistor, a 2-A current source, and a voltage-controlled current source having a gain constant of 2 S. Assume that the voltage across the resistor is the control voltage for the controlled source. Place all three elements in parallel. Several answers are possible, depending on the polarities and reference directions chosen.

P60. The current through a 10-Ω resistor is given by $i(t) = 10\exp(-2t)$ A. Determine the energy delivered to the resistor between $t = 0$ and $t = \infty$.

P61. The voltage across a 12-Ω resistor is given by $v(t) = 24\cos(2\pi t)$ V. Calculate the energy delivered to the resistor between $t = 0$ and $t = 2$ s. The argument of the cosine function, $2\pi t$, is in radians.

Section 7: Introduction to Circuits

***P62.** Which of the following are self-contradictory combinations of circuit elements? **a.** A 12-V voltage source in parallel with a 2-A current source. **b.** A 2-A current source in series with a 3-A current source. **c.** A 2-A current source in parallel with a short circuit. **d.** A 2-A current source in series with an open circuit. **e.** A 5-V voltage source in parallel with a short circuit.

***P63.** Consider the circuit shown in Figure P63. Use repeated applications of Ohm's law, KVL, and KCL to eventually find V_x.

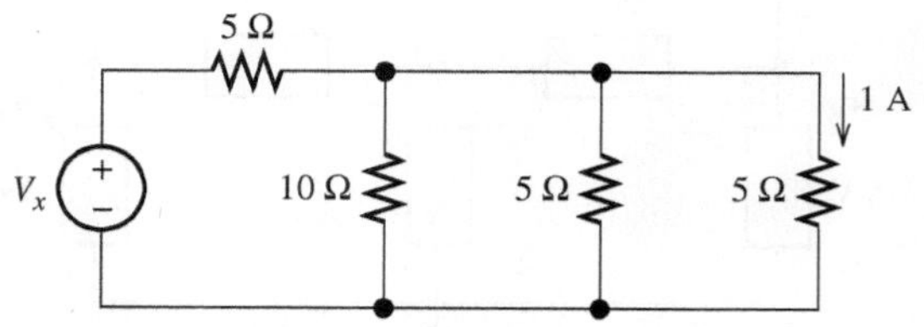

Figure P63

***P64.** Consider the circuit shown in Figure P64. Find the current i_R flowing through the resistor. Find the power for each element in the circuit. Which elements are absorbing power?

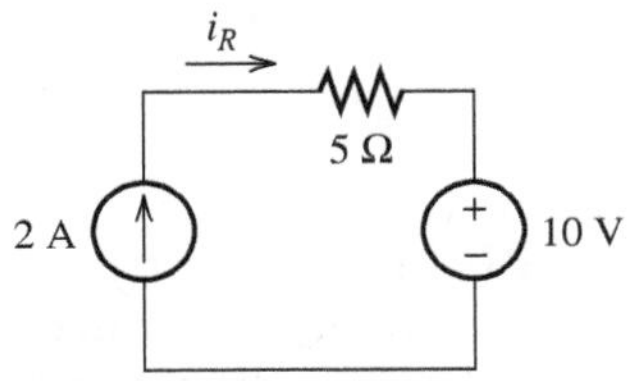

Figure P64

P65. Plot, to scale, i_{ab} versus v_{ab} for each of the parts of Figure P65.

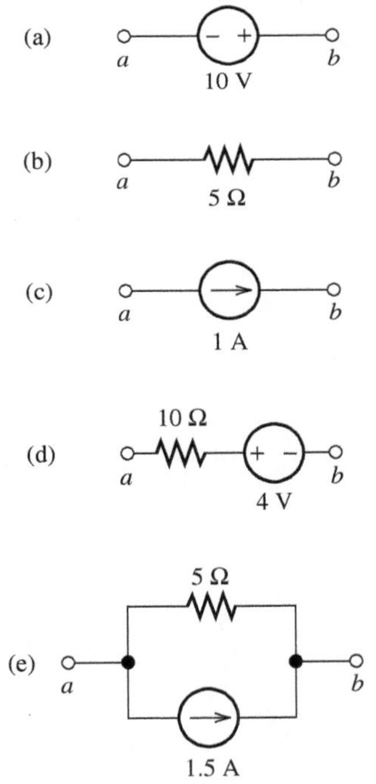

Figure P65

P66. Consider the circuit shown in Figure P66. **a.** Which elements are in series? **b.** Which elements are in parallel? **c.** Apply Ohm's and Kirchhoff's laws to solve for v_x.

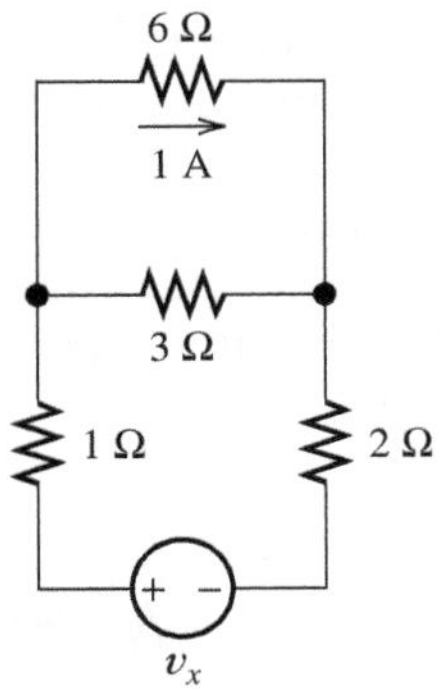

Figure P66

P67. Given the circuit shown in Figure P67, find the power for each source. Which source is absorbing power? Which is delivering power?

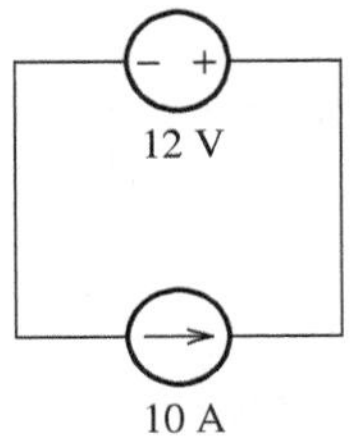

Figure P67

P68. Consider the circuit shown in Figure P68. Find the current i_R flowing through the resistor. Find the power for each element in the circuit. Which elements are absorbing energy?

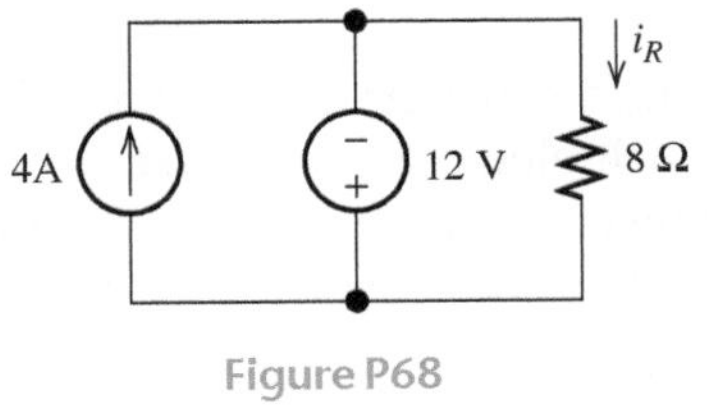

Figure P68

P69. Use repeated applications of Ohm's law, KVL, and KCL to eventually find the value of I_x in the circuit of Figure P69.

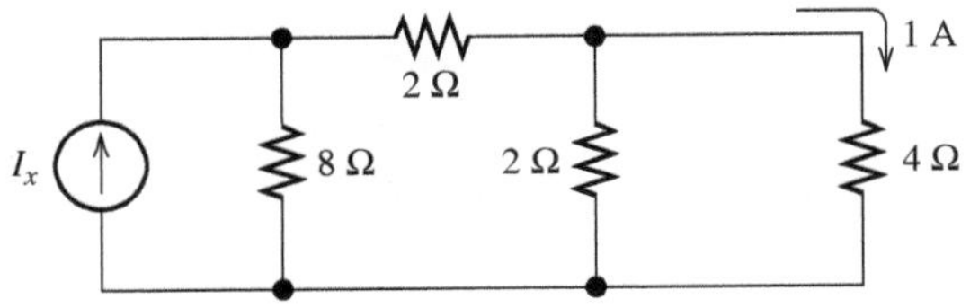

Figure P69

***P70.** The circuit shown in Figure P70 contains a voltage-controlled voltage source. **a.** Use KVL to write an equation relating the voltages and solve for v_x. **b.** Use Ohm's law to find the current i_x. **c.** Find the power for each element in the circuit and verify that power is conserved.

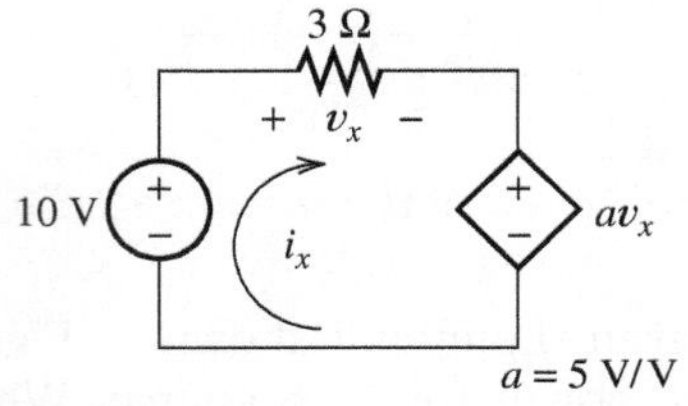

Figure P70

***P71.** What type of controlled source is shown in the circuit of Figure P71? Solve for v_s.

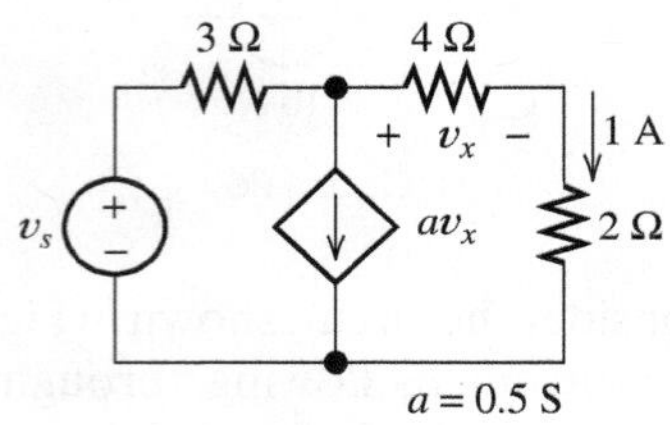

Figure P71

P72. Consider the circuit shown in Figure P72. **a.** Which elements are in series? **b.** Which elements are in parallel? **c.** Apply Ohm's and Kirchhoff's laws to solve for R_x.

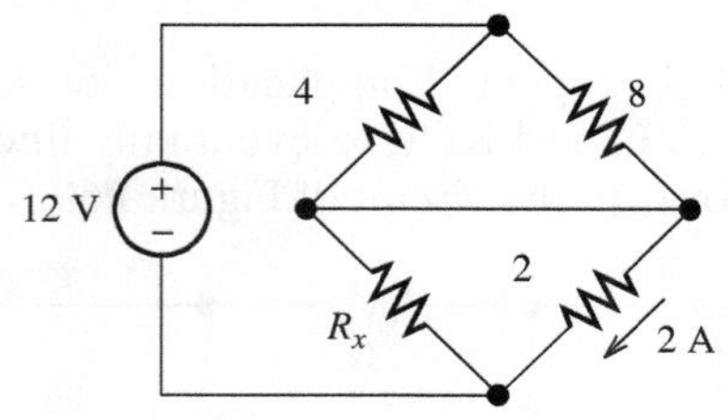

Figure P72

P73. Solve for the currents shown in Figure P73.

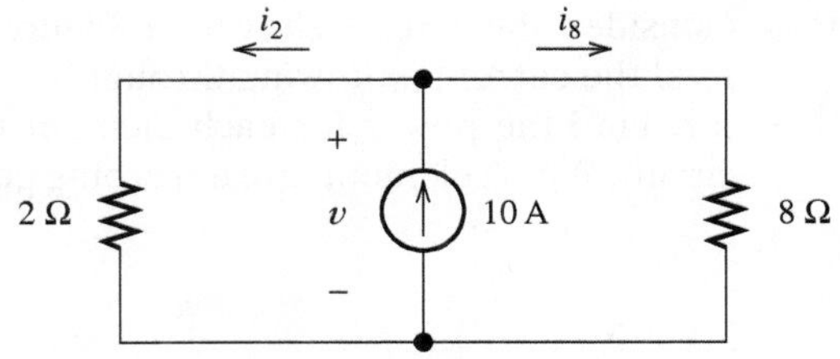

Figure P73

P74. Figure P74 is the electrical model for an electronic megaphone, in which the 16-Ω resistance models a loudspeaker, the source I_x and the 5-Ω resistance represent a microphone, and the remaining elements model an amplifier. What is the name of the type of controlled source shown? Given that the power delivered to the 16-Ω resistance is 16 W, determine the current flowing in the controlled source. Also, determine the value of the microphone current I_x.

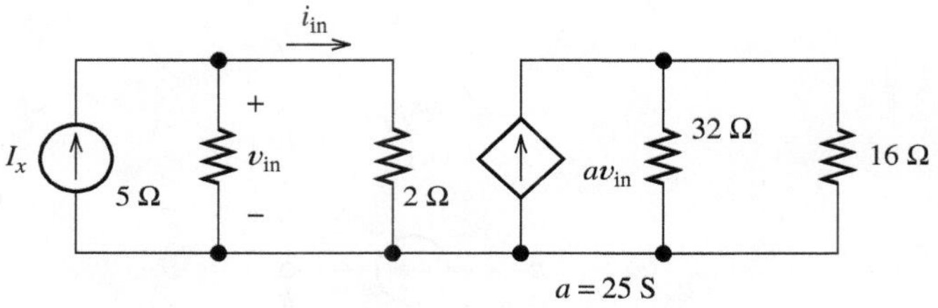

Figure P74

P75. What type of controlled source appears in the circuit of Figure P75? Determine the values of v_x and i_y.

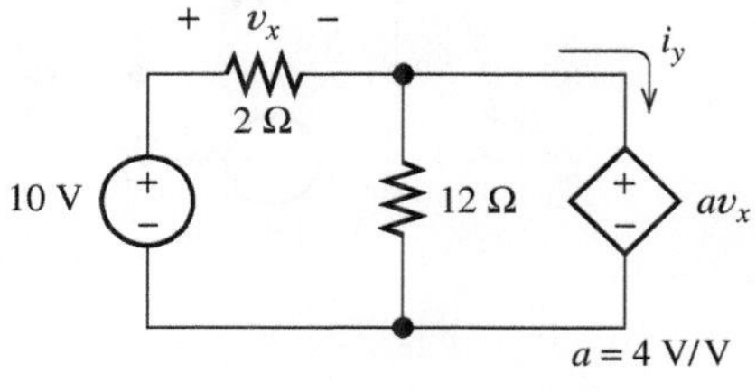

Figure P75

P76. A 10-A independent current source is connected in series with a 2-Ω resistance between terminals a and b. What can you say about

i_{ab} and v_{ab}? What single circuit element is equivalent to this series combination?

P77. A 10-V independent voltage source is connected in parallel with a 2-Ω resistance between terminals a and b. What can you say about i_{ab} and v_{ab}? What single circuit element is equivalent to this parallel combination?

P78. Consider the circuit shown in Figure P78, given $R_1 = 15\ \Omega$, $R_2 = 10\ \Omega$, and $I_s = 4$ A. **a.** Use KCL to write an equation relating the currents. **b.** Use Ohm's law to write equations relating i_1 and i_2 to the voltage v. **c.** Substitute the equations from part (b) into the equation from part (a) and solve for v. **d.** Find the power for each element in the circuit and verify that power is conserved.

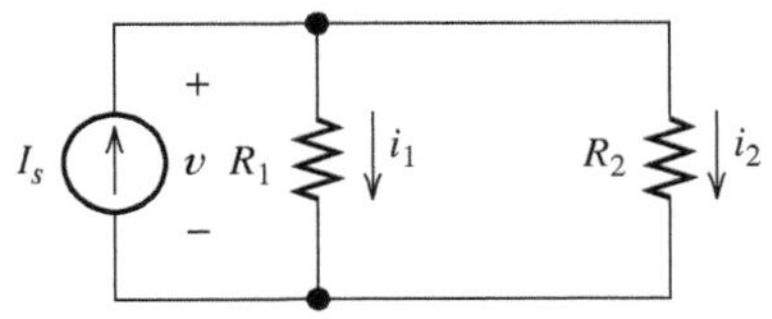

Figure P78

P79. Consider the circuit shown in Figure P79, given $R_1 = 3\ \Omega$, $R_2 = 4\ \Omega$, and $I_s = 2$ A. **a.** Use KVL to write an equation relating the voltages. **b.** Use Ohm's law to write equations relating v_1 and v_2 to the current I_s. **c.** Substitute the equations from part (b) into the equation from part (a) and solve for v. **d.** Find the power for each element in the circuit and verify that power is conserved.

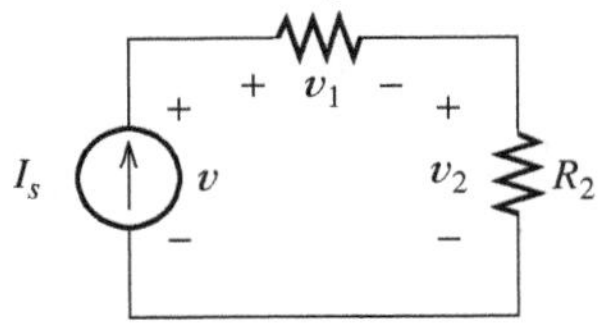

Figure P79

P80. What types of sources are present in the circuit shown in Figure P80? Solve for I_s and the voltage v.

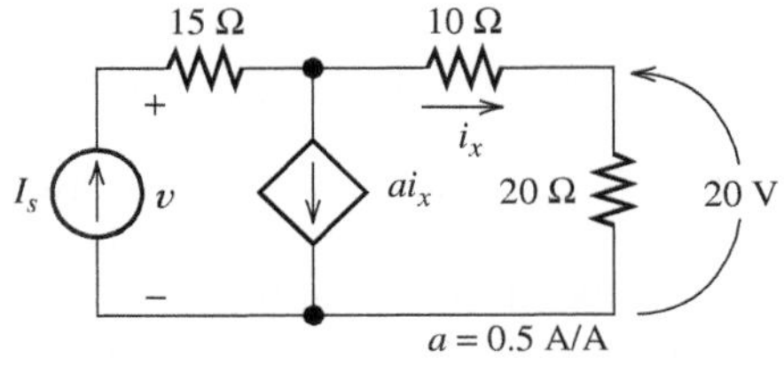

Figure P80

P81. KVL is a consequence of KCL and conservation of power in electrical circuits. This problem illustrates this fact for the circuit of Figure P81. **a.** Write the KCL equation for the circuit. **b.** Apply conservation of power to the circuit, summing the powers for the elements (observing the proper algebraic signs) and setting the sum to zero. **c.** Use the KCL equation to substitute for i_3 in the equation of part (b) and put the result into the form $Ai_1 + Bi_2 = 0$, in which A and B are algebraic sums of the voltages. **d.** Now, suppose that we have control of the current sources. For any values we select for i_1 and i_2, the equation of part (c) must be satisfied. This can only happen if we have $A = 0$ and $B = 0$. Show that this gives the KVL equations for the circuit.

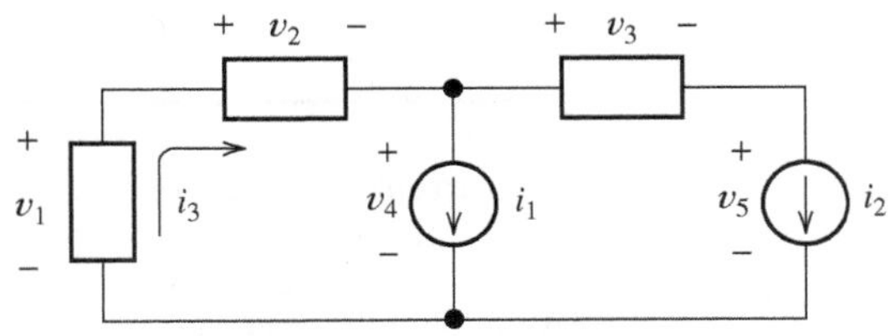

Figure P81

P82. What types of sources are present in the circuit of Figure P82? Solve for the current i_x.

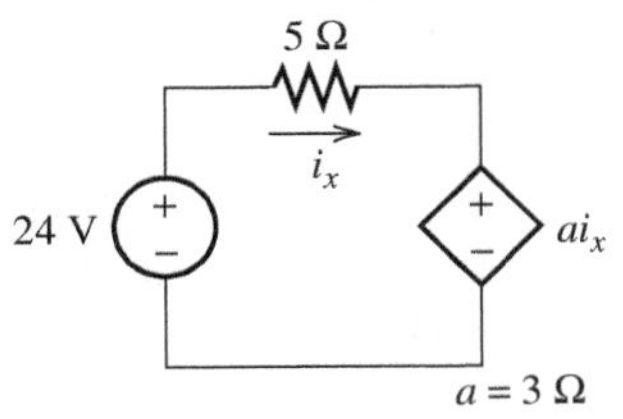

Figure P82

Practice Test

Here is a practice test you can use to check your comprehension of the most important concepts in this chapter. Answers can be found in Appendix "Answers for the Practice Tests" and complete solutions are included in the Student Solutions files. See Appendix "On-Line Student Resources" for more information about the Student Solutions.

T1. Match each entry in Table T1(a) with the best choice from the list given in Table T1(b).

Table T1

Item	Best Match
(a)	
a. Node	
b. Loop	
c. KVL	
d. KCL	
e. Ohm's law	
f. Passive reference configuration	
g. Ideal conductor	
h. Open circuit	
i. Current source	
j. Parallel connected elements	
k. Controlled source	
l. Units for voltage	
m. Units for current	
n. Units for resistance	
o. Series connected elements	

(b)

1. $v_{ab} = Ri_{ab}$
2. The current reference for an element enters the positive voltage reference
3. A path through which no current can flow
4. Points connected by ideal conductors
5. An element that carries a specified current
6. An element whose current or voltage depends on a current or voltage elsewhere in the circuit
7. A path starting at a node and proceeding from node to node back to the starting node
8. An element for which the voltage is zero
9. A/V
10. V/A
11. J/C
12. C/V
13. C/s
14. Elements connected so their currents must be equal
15. Elements connected so their voltages must be equal
16. The algebraic sum of voltages for a closed loop is zero
17. The algebraic sum of the voltages for elements connected to a node is zero
18. The sum of the currents entering a node equals the sum of those leaving

[Items in Table T1(b) may be used more than once or not at all.]

T2. Consider the circuit of Figure T2 with $I_s = 3\,\text{A}$, $R = 2\ \Omega$, and $V_s = 10\,\text{V}$. **a.** Determine the value of v_R. **b.** Determine the magnitude of the power for the voltage source and state whether the voltage source is absorbing energy or delivering it. **c.** How many nodes does this circuit have? **d.** Determine the magnitude of the power for the current source and state whether the current source is absorbing energy or delivering it.

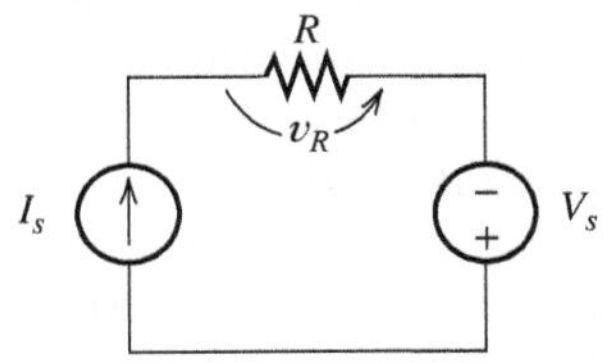

Figure T2

T3. The circuit of Figure T3 has $I_1 = 3\,\text{A}$, $I_2 = 1\,\text{A}$, $R_1 = 12\ \Omega$, and $R_2 = 6\ \Omega$. **a.** Determine the value of v_{ab}. **b.** Determine the power for each current source and state whether it is absorbing energy or delivering it. **c.** Compute the power absorbed by R_1 and by R_2.

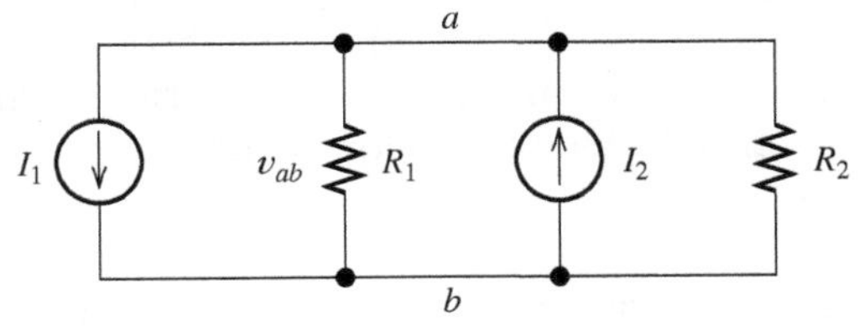

Figure T3

T4. The circuit shown in Figure T4 has $V_s = 12\,\text{V}$, $v_2 = 4\,\text{V}$, and $R_1 = 4\ \Omega$. **a.** Find the values of: **a.** v_1; **b.** i; **c.** R_2.

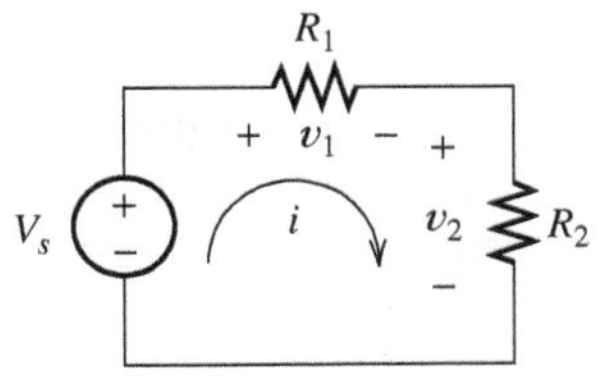

Figure T4

T5. We are given $V_s = 15\,\text{V}$, $R = 10\ \Omega$, and $a = 0.3\,\text{S}$ for the circuit of Figure T5. Find the value of the current i_{sc} flowing through the short circuit.

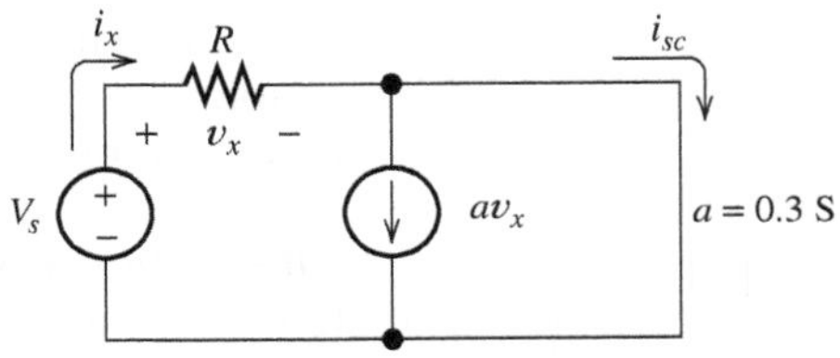

Figure T5

THE FUNDAMENTALS OF ENGINEERING EXAMINATION

Becoming licensed as a Professional Engineer (PE) is a very important step toward success in your engineering career. In the United States, a PE license is required by all 50 states for engineers whose work may affect life, health, or property, or who offer their services to the public. Thus, a license is an absolute requirement for many types of work. Furthermore, licensed engineers have more opportunities and earn higher salaries (from 15 percent to 25 percent) than other engineers.

Licensure requirements are set by the various states, but are similar from state to state. Furthermore, by reciprocal agreements, many states recognize licenses granted in other states. Generally, a degree from an ABET-accredited engineering program, four years of relevant work experience, and successful completion of two state examinations are required. A master's degree or equivalent may become a requirement for professional registration in 2020. The National Council of Examiners for Engineering and Surveying (NCEES) prepares and scores the examinations. The examinations are the Fundamentals of Engineering (FE) Examination, which can be taken any time, and the Principles and Practice of Engineering (PE) Examination, which must be taken after at least four years of experience.

Up-to-date information about the PE license can be found at the following URL: `http://www.ncees.org/`

You should plan on taking the FE Examination before or shortly after you graduate, rather than later, because it contains questions on a wide variety of subjects. To pass the FE Examination, many engineers struggle to relearn topics that they were familiar with at graduation. Most likely, if you are a mechanical, civil, or chemical engineer, you will not routinely work with electrical circuits. After 10 or more years, you may not be able to answer questions regarding electrical circuits that you could have easily answered when you finished the courses for which you used this text. Thus, taking the examination in your senior year is best. Keep this text to refresh your knowledge of electrical circuits just before taking the FE Examination.

Starting in January 2014, NCEES will make many changes to the FE exam, some of which have not been finalized at the time of this writing. Among other changes, the exam will become computer based instead of pencil and paper, there will be completely separate exams for the various engineering fields rather than a common morning session, and the exam will be administered on many dates throughout the year at Pearson VUE test centers. **If you are taking the exam in 2014 or later, you should consult the NCEES website for up-to-date information. The following description applies only for exams to be given in 2013.**

In 2013, the examination will be offered in April and October. The 2013 FE Examinations will consist of a morning session (120 questions) that is common to all disciplines and an afternoon session (60 questions) that is separate for each discipline. The morning sessions will contain 120 questions on mathematics, engineering probability and statistics, chemistry, computers, ethics and business practices, engineering economics, engineering mechanics (statics and dynamics), strength of materials, material properties, fluid mechanics, electricity and magnetism, and thermodynamics. The questions on electricity and magnetism include the following topics:

- Charge, energy, current, voltage, power
- Work done in moving a charge in an electric field (relationship between voltage and work)
- Force between charges
- Current and voltage laws (Kirchhoff, Ohm)
- Equivalent circuits (series, parallel)
- Capacitance and inductance
- Reactance and impedance, susceptance and admittance
- AC circuits
- Basic complex algebra

Next, we present electrical-circuit questions typical of those found in the morning session of the examination. The correct answers are listed at the end of this Appendix and the solutions are included in the Student Solutions files.

P1. A dc current of 3 A flows through an initially uncharged capacitor. After two microseconds, the magnitude of the net electric charge on one plate of the capacitor is most nearly:

a. 3 μC
b. 6 μC
c. 0 μC
d. 0.667 μC

P2. For the circuit of Figure P2, the power dissipated in the 10-Ω resistor is most nearly:

a. 22.5 W
b. 8.27 W
c. 1.84 W
d. 7.35 W

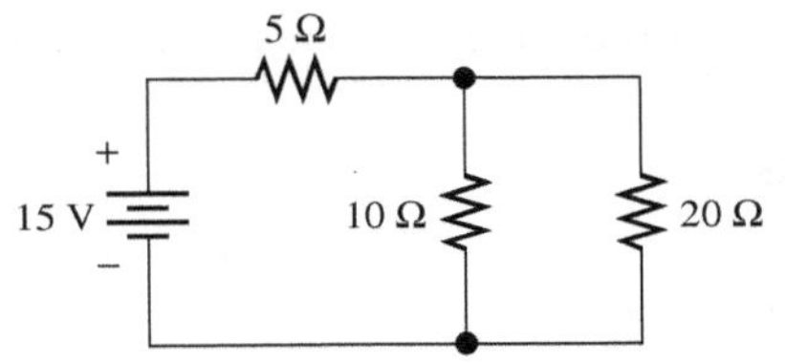

Figure P2

P3. Two initially uncharged capacitors have values of 6 μF and 12 μF. The capacitors are connected in series, and a 200-V dc source is applied to the combination. The charge taken from the source is most nearly:

a. 800 μC
b. 3600 μC
c. 600 μC
d. 1200 μC

P4. A 2-hp 220-V-rms single-phase induction motor operates at full load with 80 percent efficiency and 0.75 lagging power factor. The magnitude of the rms motor current is most nearly:

a. 4.07 A
b. 11.3 A
c. 6.35 A
d. 8.78 A

P5. A 30-Ω resistor, a pure capacitance having a reactance magnitude of 80 Ω, and a pure inductance having a reactance magnitude of 40 Ω are in series. The impedance magnitude of the series combination is most nearly:

a. 150 Ω
b. 50 Ω

c. 14.1 Ω
d. 17.1 Ω

P6. The apparent power supplied to a load in an ac circuit is 2000 volt-amperes with a power factor of 0.6 lagging. The reactive power is most nearly:

a. 1200 VAR
b. 3333 VAR
c. 1600 VAR
d. 2500 VAR

P7. A 150-microfarad capacitor has been charged to a potential of 100 V. A 50-Ω resistor is placed across the capacitor. After 20 time constants, the total energy delivered to the resistor is most nearly:

a. 1.5 J
b. 0 J
c. 0.75 J
d. 15×10^{-3} J

P8. The current through the 50-Ω resistor for the circuit shown in Figure P8 is most nearly:

a. 1.56 A rms
b. 1.10 A rms
c. 2.20 A rms
d. 0.52 A rms

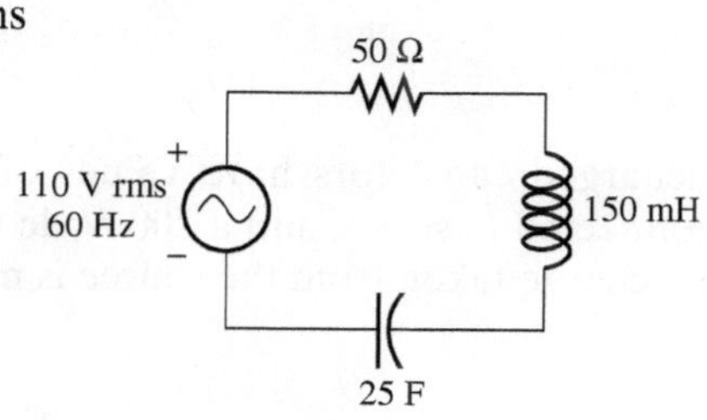

Figure P8

P9. For time t greater than zero, the mathematical expression of the current through the 25-Ω resistance of Figure P9 is:

a. $1 - \exp(-2t)$ A
b. $1 - \exp(-t/2)$ A
c. $\exp(-2t)$ A
d. $\exp(-t/2)$ A

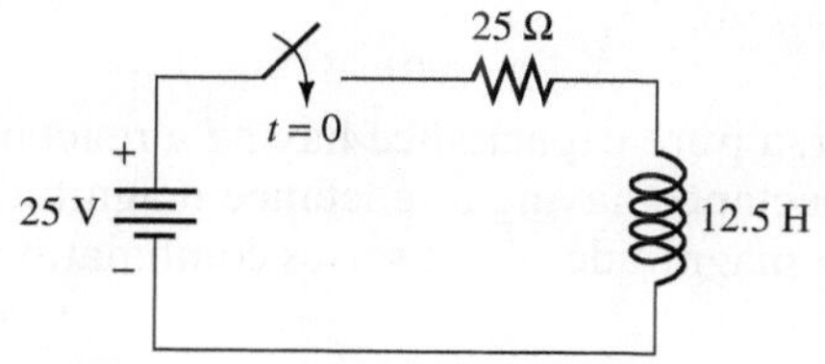

Figure P9

P10. We have three points A, B, and C in an electrical circuit and voltages $V_{AC} = 200$ V and $V_{CB} = 50$ V. The energy needed to move a charge of 0.2 C from point B to point A is most nearly:

a. 30 J

b. 40 J

c. 10 J

d. 50 J

Answers:

P1. b	P6. c
P2. d	P7. c
P3. a	P8. a
P4. b	P9. a
P5. b	P10. d

ANSWERS FOR THE PRACTICE TESTS

Complete solutions for the practice tests are included in the Student Solutions files. See Appendix "On-Line Student Resources" for information on how to access these files.

T1. **a.** 4; **b.** 7; **c.** 16; **d.** 18; **e.** 1; **f.** 2; **g.** 8; **h.** 3; **i.** 5; **j.** 15; **k.** 6; **l.** 11; **m.** 13; **n.** 9; **o.** 14.

T2. **a.** $v_R = -6$ V. **b.** The voltage source is delivering 30 W. **c.** There are 3 nodes. **d.** The current source is absorbing 12 W.

T3. **a.** $v_{ab} = -8$ V. **b.** Source I_1 is supplying 24 W. Source I_2 is absorbing 8 W. **c.** $P_{R1} = 5.33$ W and $P_{R2} = 10.67$ W.

T4. **a.** $v_1 = 8$ V; **b.** $i = 2$ A; **c.** $R_2 = 2\ \Omega$.

T5. $i_{sc} = -3$ A.

ON-LINE STUDENT RESOURCES

Users of the text can access the Student Solutions Manual (and other folders mentioned below) in electronic form by following links starting from the website:

`www.pearsonhighered.com/hambley`

The MATLAB folder contains m-files. Except for the examples that use the Symbolic Toolbox, these files work equally well with MathScript, which is sometimes included with the LabVIEW program. The Hambley MathScript folder contains the m-files that work with MathScript.

The Virtual Instruments folder contains LabVIEW programs.

Resistive Circuits

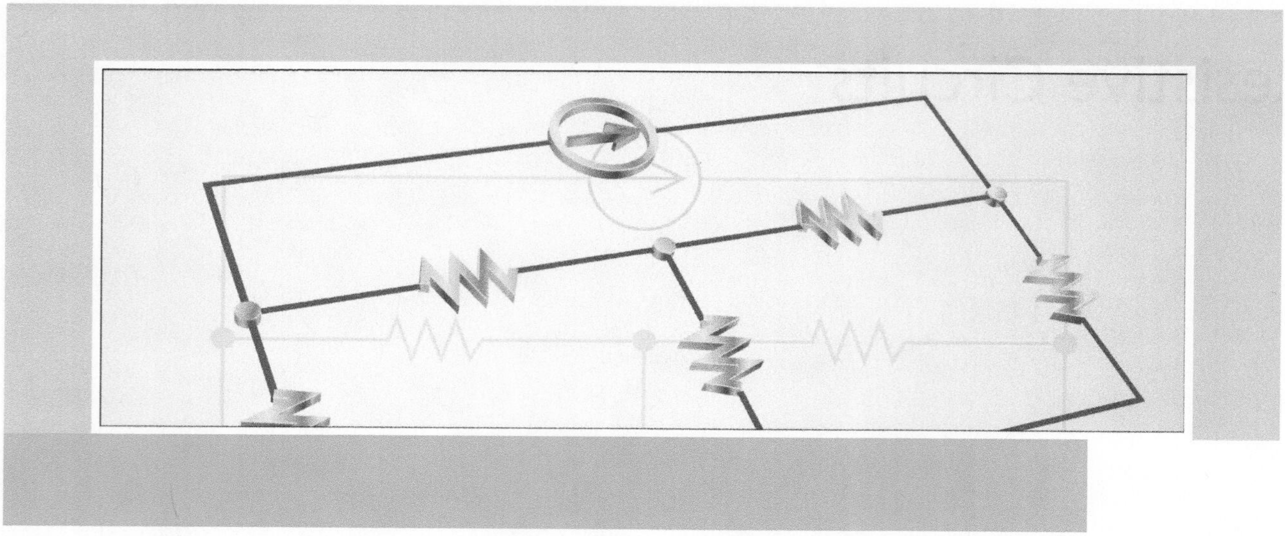

Resistive Circuits

Study of this chapter will enable you to:

- Solve circuits (i.e., find currents and voltages of interest) by combining resistances in series and parallel.
- Apply the voltage-division and current-division principles.
- Solve circuits by the node-voltage technique.
- Solve circuits by the mesh-current technique.
- Find Thévenin and Norton equivalents and apply source transformations.
- Use MATLAB® to solve circuit equations numerically and symbolically.
- Understand and apply the superposition principle.
- Draw the circuit diagram and state the principles of operation for the Wheatstone bridge.

Introduction to this chapter:

In applications of electrical engineering, we often face circuit-analysis problems for which the structure of a circuit, including element values, is known and the currents, voltages, and powers need to be found. In this chapter, we examine techniques for analyzing circuits composed of resistances, voltage sources, and current sources.

Over the years, you will meet many applications of electrical engineering in your field of engineering or science. This chapter will give you the skills needed to work effectively with the electronic instrumentation and other circuits that you will encounter. The material in this chapter will help you to answer questions on the Fundamentals of Engineering Examination and become a Registered Professional Engineer.

1 RESISTANCES IN SERIES AND PARALLEL

In this section, we show how to replace series or parallel combinations of resistances by equivalent resistances. Then, we demonstrate how to use this knowledge in solving circuits.

Series Resistances

Consider the series combination of three resistances shown in Figure 1(a). Recall that in a series circuit the elements are connected end to end and that the same current flows through all of the elements. By Ohm's law, we can write

$$v_1 = R_1 i \tag{1}$$

$$v_2 = R_2 i \tag{2}$$

and

$$v_3 = R_3 i \tag{3}$$

Using KVL, we can write

$$v = v_1 + v_2 + v_3 \tag{4}$$

Substituting Equations 1, 2, and 3 into Equation 4, we obtain

$$v = R_1 i + R_2 i + R_3 i \tag{5}$$

Factoring out the current i, we have

$$v = (R_1 + R_2 + R_3)i \tag{6}$$

Now, we define the equivalent resistance R_{eq} to be the sum of the resistances in series:

$$R_{eq} = R_1 + R_2 + R_3 \tag{7}$$

Using this to substitute into Equation 6, we have

$$v = R_{eq} i \tag{8}$$

Thus, we conclude that the three resistances in series can be replaced by the equivalent resistance R_{eq} shown in Figure 1(b) with no change in the relationship between

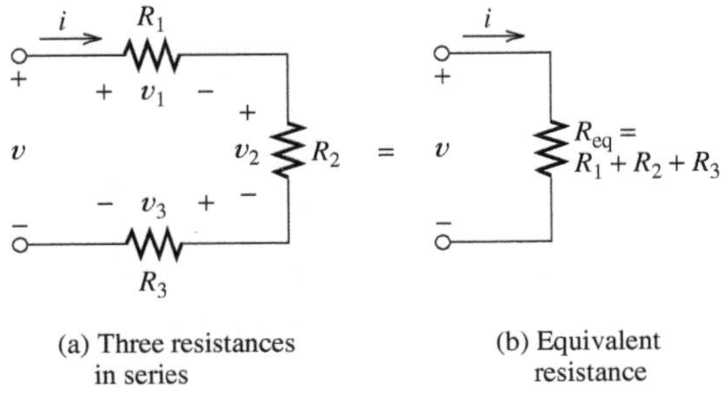

Figure 1 Series resistances can be combined into an equivalent resistance.

the voltage v and current i. If the three resistances are part of a larger circuit, replacing them by a single equivalent resistance would make no changes in the currents or voltages in other parts of the circuit.

A series combination of resistances has an equivalent resistance equal to the sum of the original resistances.

This analysis can be applied to any number of resistances. For example, two resistances in series can be replaced by a single resistance equal to the sum of the original two. To summarize, *a series combination of resistances has an equivalent resistance equal to the sum of the original resistances.*

Parallel Resistances

Figure 2(a) shows three resistances in parallel. In a parallel circuit, the voltage across each element is the same. Applying Ohm's law in Figure 2(a), we can write

$$i_1 = \frac{v}{R_1} \quad (9)$$

$$i_2 = \frac{v}{R_2} \quad (10)$$

$$i_3 = \frac{v}{R_3} \quad (11)$$

The top ends of the resistors in Figure 2(a) are connected to a single node. (Recall that all points in a circuit that are connected by conductors constitute a node.) Thus, we can apply KCL to the top node of the circuit and obtain

$$i = i_1 + i_2 + i_3 \quad (12)$$

Now using Equations 9, 10, and 11 to substitute into Equation 12, we have

$$i = \frac{v}{R_1} + \frac{v}{R_2} + \frac{v}{R_3} \quad (13)$$

Factoring out the voltage, we obtain

$$i = \left(\frac{1}{R_1} + \frac{1}{R_2} + \frac{1}{R_3}\right) v \quad (14)$$

Now, we define the equivalent resistance as

$$R_{eq} = \frac{1}{1/R_1 + 1/R_2 + 1/R_3} \quad (15)$$

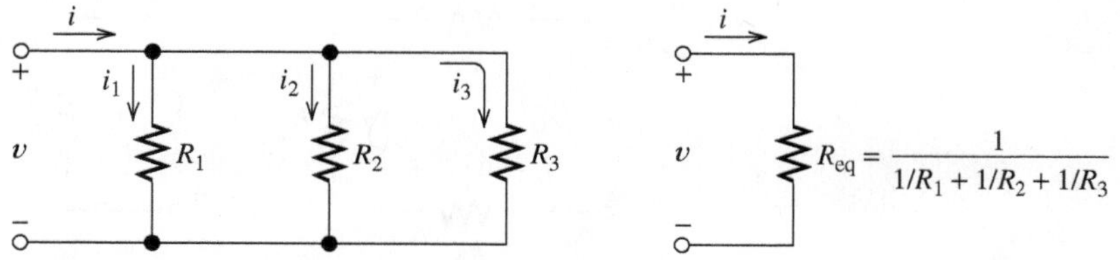

(a) Three resistances in parallel (b) Equivalent resistance

Figure 2 Parallel resistances can be combined into an equivalent resistance.

In terms of the equivalent resistance, Equation 14 becomes

$$i = \frac{1}{R_{\text{eq}}} v \tag{16}$$

Comparing Equations 14 and 16, we see that i and v are related in the same way by both equations provided that R_{eq} is given by Equation 15. Therefore, a parallel combination of resistances can be replaced by its equivalent resistance without changing the currents and voltages in other parts of the circuit. The equivalence is illustrated in Figure 2(b).

A parallel combination of resistances can be replaced by its equivalent resistance without changing the currents and voltages in other parts of the circuit.

This analysis can be applied to any number of resistances in parallel. For example, if four resistances are in parallel, the equivalent resistance is

$$R_{\text{eq}} = \frac{1}{1/R_1 + 1/R_2 + 1/R_3 + 1/R_4} \tag{17}$$

Similarly, for two resistances, we have

$$R_{\text{eq}} = \frac{1}{1/R_1 + 1/R_2} \tag{18}$$

This can be put into the form

$$R_{\text{eq}} = \frac{R_1 R_2}{R_1 + R_2} \tag{19}$$

(Notice that Equation 19 applies only for two resistances. The product over the sum does not apply for more than two resistances.)

The product over the sum does not apply for more than two resistances.

Sometimes, resistive circuits can be reduced to a single equivalent resistance by repeatedly combining resistances that are in series or parallel.

Example 1 Combining Resistances in Series and Parallel

Find a single equivalent resistance for the network shown in Figure 3(a).

Solution First, we look for a combination of resistances that is in series or in parallel. In Figure 3(a), R_3 and R_4 are in series. (In fact, as it stands, no other two resistances in this network are either in series or in parallel.) Thus, our first step is to combine R_3 and R_4, replacing them by their equivalent resistance. Recall that for a series combination, the equivalent resistance is the sum of the resistances in series:

1. Find a series or parallel combination of resistances.
2. Combine them.
3. Repeat until the network is reduced to a single resistance (if possible).

$$R_{\text{eq1}} = R_3 + R_4 = 5 + 15 = 20\ \Omega$$

Figure 3(b) shows the network after replacing R_3 and R_4 by their equivalent resistance. Now we see that R_2 and R_{eq1} are in parallel. The equivalent resistance for this combination is

$$R_{\text{eq2}} = \frac{1}{1/R_{\text{eq1}} + 1/R_2} = \frac{1}{1/20 + 1/20} = 10\ \Omega$$

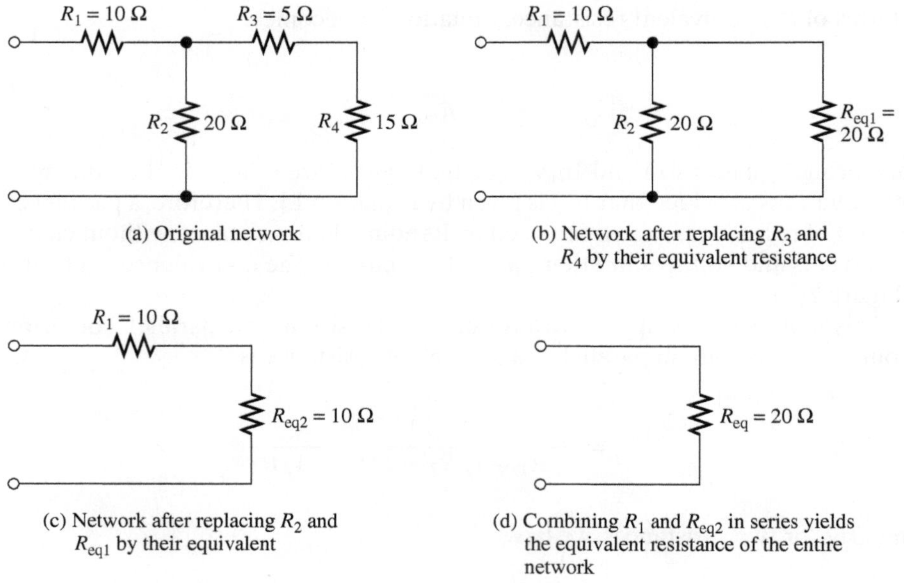

Figure 3 Resistive network for Example 1.

Making this replacement gives the equivalent network shown in Figure 3(c).

Finally, we see that R_1 and R_{eq2} are in series. Thus, the equivalent resistance for the entire network is

$$R_{eq} = R_1 + R_{eq2} = 10 + 10 = 20\ \Omega$$ ■

Exercise 1 Find the equivalent resistance for each of the networks shown in Figure 4. [*Hint for part (b):* R_3 and R_4 are in parallel.]

Answer **a.** 3 Ω; **b.** 5 Ω; **c.** 52.1 Ω; **d.** 1.5 kΩ. □

Conductances in Series and Parallel

Recall that conductance is the reciprocal of resistance. Using this fact to change resistances to conductances for a series combination of n elements, we readily obtain:

Combine conductances in series as you would resistances in parallel. Combine conductances in parallel as you would resistances in series.

$$G_{eq} = \frac{1}{1/G_1 + 1/G_2 + \cdots + 1/G_n} \quad (20)$$

Thus, we see that conductances in series combine as do resistances in parallel. For two conductances in series, we have:

$$G_{eq} = \frac{G_1 G_2}{G_1 + G_2}$$

For n conductances in parallel, we can show that

$$G_{eq} = G_1 + G_2 + \cdots + G_n \quad (21)$$

Conductances in parallel combine as do resistances in series.

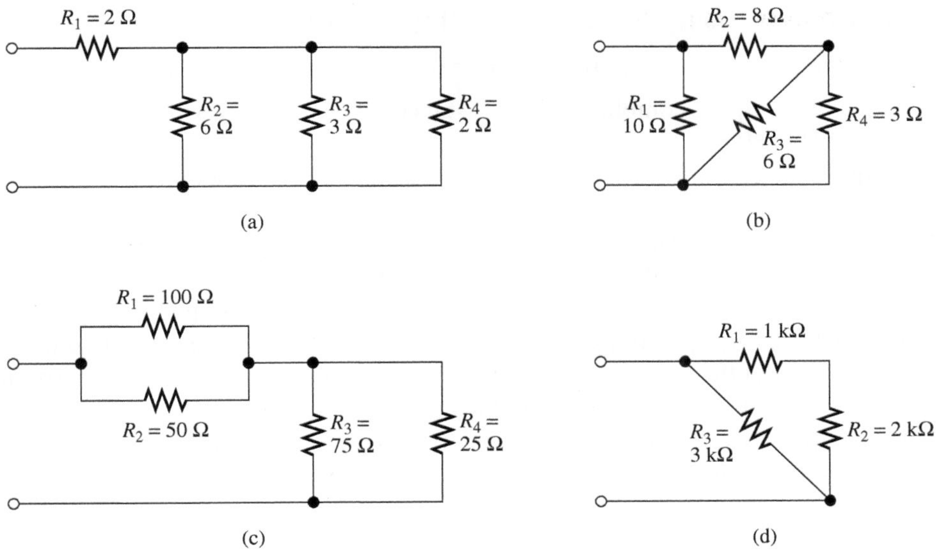

Figure 4 Resistive networks for Exercise 1.

Series versus Parallel Circuits

An element such as a toaster or light bulb that absorbs power is called a **load**. When we want to distribute power from a single voltage source to various loads, we usually place the loads in parallel. A switch in series with each load can break the flow of current to that load without affecting the voltage supplied to the other loads.

When we want to distribute power from a single voltage source to various loads, we usually place the loads in parallel.

Sometimes, to save wire, strings of Christmas lights consist of bulbs connected in series. The bulbs tend to fail or "burn out" by becoming open circuits. Then the entire string is dark and the defective bulb can be found only by trying each in turn. If several bulbs are burned out, it can be very tedious to locate the failed units. In a parallel connection, only the failed bulbs are dark.

2 NETWORK ANALYSIS BY USING SERIES AND PARALLEL EQUIVALENTS

An electrical **network** (or electrical circuit) consists of circuit elements, such as resistances, voltage sources, and current sources, connected together to form closed paths. **Network analysis** is the process of determining the current, voltage, and power for each element, given the circuit diagram and the element values. In this and the sections that follow, we study several useful techniques for network analysis.

An electrical network consists of circuit elements such as resistances, voltage sources, and current sources, connected together to form closed paths.

Sometimes, we can determine the currents and voltages for each element in a resistive circuit by repeatedly replacing series and parallel combinations of resistances by their equivalent resistances. Eventually, this may reduce the circuit sufficiently that the equivalent circuit can be solved easily. The information gained from the simplified circuit is transferred to the previous steps in the chain of equivalent circuits. In the end, we gain enough information about the original circuit to determine all the currents and voltages.

Circuit Analysis Using Series/Parallel Equivalents

Here are the steps in solving circuits using series/parallel equivalents:

Some good advice for beginners: Don't try to combine steps. Be very methodical and do one step at a time. Take the time to redraw each equivalent carefully and label unknown currents and voltages consistently in the various circuits. The slow methodical approach will be faster and more accurate when you are learning. Walk now—later you will be able to run.

1. Begin by locating a combination of resistances that are in series or parallel. Often the place to start is farthest from the source.
2. Redraw the circuit with the equivalent resistance for the combination found in step 1.
3. Repeat steps 1 and 2 until the circuit is reduced as far as possible. Often (but not always) we end up with a single source and a single resistance.
4. Solve for the currents and voltages in the final equivalent circuit. Then, transfer results back one step and solve for additional unknown currents and voltages. Again transfer the results back one step and solve. Repeat until all of the currents and voltages are known in the original circuit.
5. Check your results to make sure that KCL is satisfied at each node, KVL is satisfied for each loop, and the powers add to zero.

Example 2 Circuit Analysis Using Series/Parallel Equivalents

Find the current, voltage, and power for each element of the circuit shown in Figure 5(a).

Steps 1, 2, and 3.

Solution First, we combine resistances in series and parallel. For example, in the original circuit, R_2 and R_3 are in parallel. Replacing R_2 and R_3 by their parallel equivalent, we obtain the circuit shown in Figure 5(b). Next, we see that R_1 and R_{eq1} are in series. Replacing these resistances by their sum, we obtain the circuit shown in Figure 5(c).

After we have reduced a network to an equivalent resistance connected across the source, we solve the simplified network. Then, we transfer results back through the chain of equivalent circuits. We illustrate this process in Figure 6. (Figure 6 is identical to Figure 5, except for the currents and voltages shown in Figure 6.

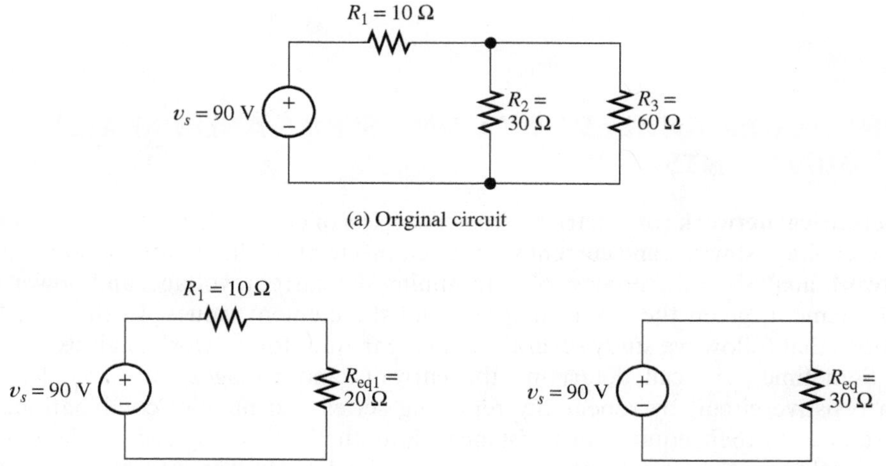

(b) Circuit after replacing R_2 and R_3 by their equivalent

(c) Circuit after replacing R_1 and R_{eq1} by their equivalent

Figure 5 A circuit and its simplified versions. See Example 2.

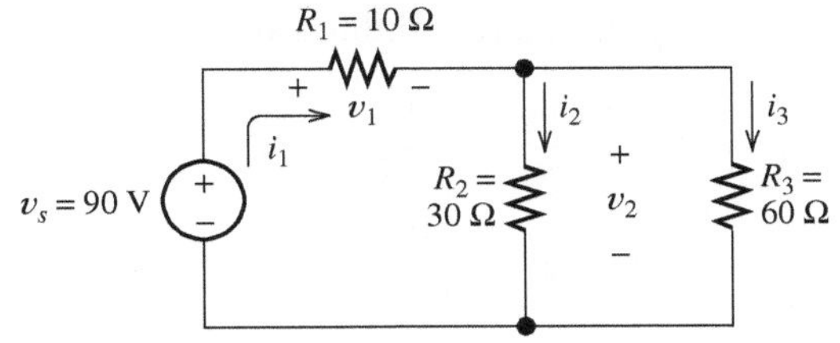

(a) Third, we use known values of i_1 and v_2 to solve for the remaining currents and voltages

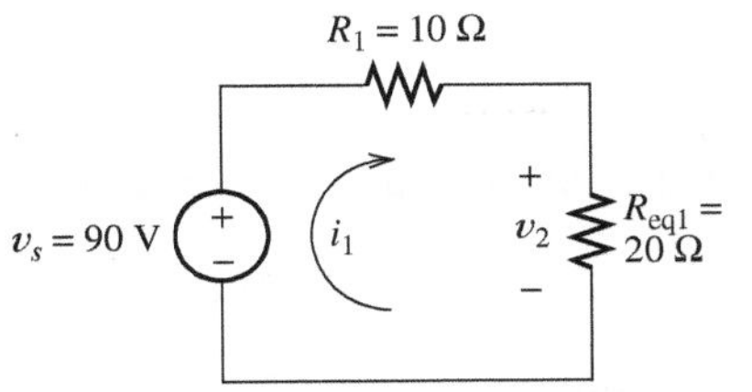

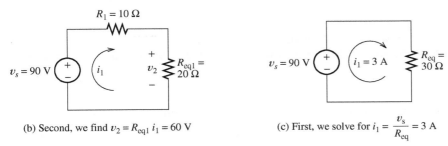

(b) Second, we find $v_2 = R_{eq1}\, i_1 = 60$ V

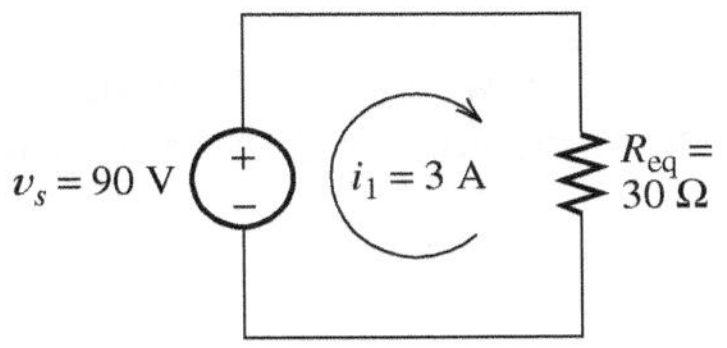

(c) First, we solve for $i_1 = \dfrac{v_s}{R_{eq}} = 3$ A

Figure 6 After reducing the circuit to a source and an equivalent resistance, we solve the simplified circuit. Then, we transfer results back to the original circuit. Notice that the logical flow in solving for currents and voltages starts from the simplified circuit in (c).

Usually, in solving a network by this technique, we first draw the chain of equivalent networks and then write results on the same drawings. However, this might be confusing in our first example.)

Step 4.

First, we solve the simplified network shown in Figure 6(c). Because R_{eq} is in parallel with the 90-V voltage source, the voltage across R_{eq} must be 90 V, with its positive polarity at the top end. Thus, the current flowing through R_{eq} is given by

$$i_1 = \frac{v_s}{R_{eq}} = \frac{90\ \text{V}}{30\ \Omega} = 3\ \text{A}$$

We know that this current flows downward (from plus to minus) through R_{eq}. Since v_s and R_{eq} are in series in Figure 6(c), the current must also flow upward through v_s. Thus, $i_1 = 3$ A flows clockwise around the circuit, as shown in Figure 6(c).

Because R_{eq} is the equivalent resistance seen by the source in all three parts of Figure 6, the current through v_s must be $i_1 = 3$ A, flowing upward in all three equivalent circuits. In Figure 6(b), we see that i_1 flows clockwise through v_s, R_1, and R_{eq1}. The voltage across R_{eq1} is given by

$$v_2 = R_{eq1} i_1 = 20\ \Omega \times 3\ \text{A} = 60\ \text{V}$$

Because R_{eq1} is the equivalent resistance for the parallel combination of R_2 and R_3, the voltage v_2 also appears across R_2 and R_3 in the original network.

At this point, we have found that the current through v_s and R_1 is $i_1 = 3$ A. Furthermore, the voltage across R_2 and R_3 is 60 V. This information is shown in

Figure 6(a). Now, we can compute the remaining values desired:

$$i_2 = \frac{v_2}{R_2} = \frac{60 \text{ V}}{30 \ \Omega} = 2 \text{ A}$$

$$i_3 = \frac{v_2}{R_3} = \frac{60 \text{ V}}{60 \ \Omega} = 1 \text{ A}$$

(As a check, we can use KCL to verify that $i_1 = i_2 + i_3$.)

Next, we can use Ohm's law to compute the value of v_1:

$$v_1 = R_1 i_1 = 10 \ \Omega \times 3 \text{ A} = 30 \text{ V}$$

Step 5. (As a check, we use KVL to verify that $v_s = v_1 + v_2$.)

Now, we compute the power for each element. For the voltage source, we have

$$p_s = -v_s i_1$$

We have included the minus sign because the references for v_s and i_1 are opposite to the passive configuration. Substituting values, we have

$$p_s = -(90 \text{ V}) \times 3 \text{ A} = -270 \text{ W}$$

Because the power for the source is negative, we know that the source is supplying energy to the other elements in the circuit.

The powers for the resistances are

$$p_1 = R_1 i_1^2 = 10 \ \Omega \times (3 \text{ A})^2 = 90 \text{ W}$$

$$p_2 = \frac{v_2^2}{R_2} = \frac{(60 \text{ V})^2}{30 \ \Omega} = 120 \text{ W}$$

$$p_3 = \frac{v_2^2}{R_3} = \frac{(60 \text{ V})^2}{60 \ \Omega} = 60 \text{ W}$$

(As a check, we verify that $p_s + p_1 + p_2 + p_3 = 0$, showing that power is conserved.) ■

Power Control by Using Heating Elements in Series or Parallel

Resistances are commonly used as heating elements for the reaction chamber of chemical processes. For example, the catalytic converter of an automobile is not effective until its operating temperature is achieved. Thus, during engine warm-up, large amounts of pollutants are emitted. Automotive engineers have proposed and studied the use of electrical heating elements to heat the converter more quickly, thereby reducing pollution. By using several heating elements that can be operated individually, in series, or in parallel, several power levels can be achieved. This is useful in controlling the temperature of a chemical process.

Exercise 2 Find the currents labeled in Figure 7 by combining resistances in series and parallel.

Answer **a.** $i_1 = 1.04$ A, $i_2 = 0.480$ A, $i_3 = 0.320$ A, $i_4 = 0.240$ A; **b.** $i_1 = 1$ A, $i_2 = 1$ A; **c.** $i_1 = 1$ A, $i_2 = 0.5$ A, $i_3 = 0.5$ A. □

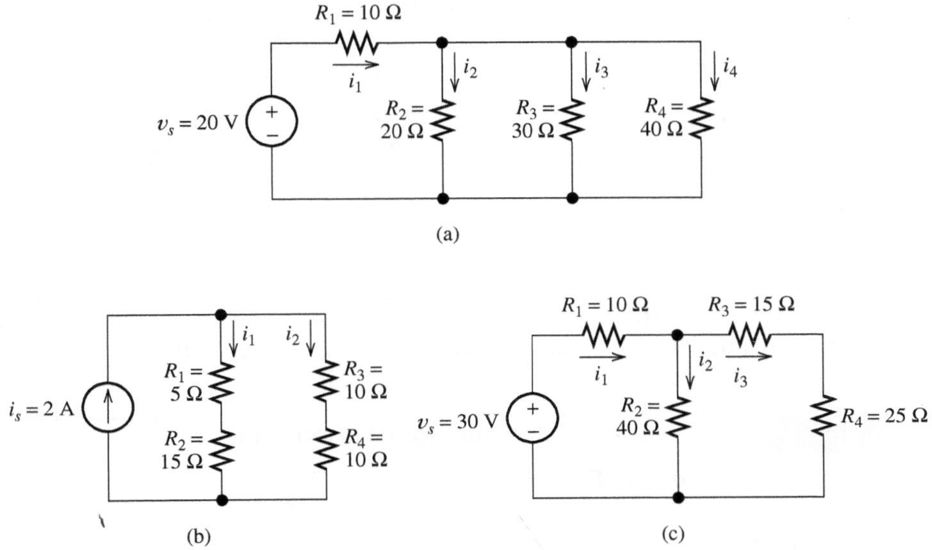

Figure 7 Circuits for Exercise 2.

3 VOLTAGE-DIVIDER AND CURRENT-DIVIDER CIRCUITS

Voltage Division

When a voltage is applied to a series combination of resistances, a fraction of the voltage appears across each of the resistances. Consider the circuit shown in Figure 8. The equivalent resistance seen by the voltage source is

$$R_{eq} = R_1 + R_2 + R_3 \tag{22}$$

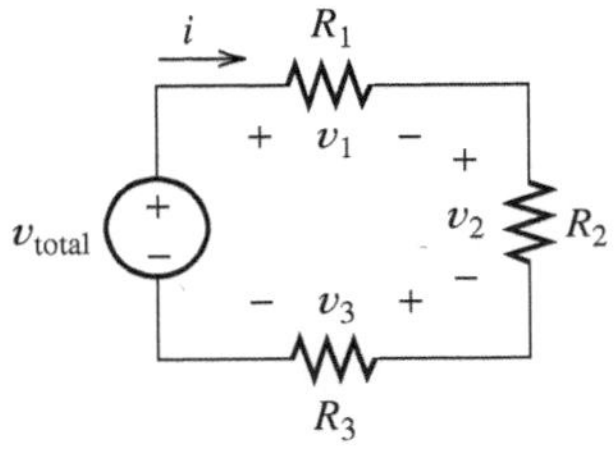

Figure 8 Circuit used to derive the voltage-division principle.

The current is the total voltage divided by the equivalent resistance:

$$i = \frac{v_{total}}{R_{eq}} = \frac{v_{total}}{R_1 + R_2 + R_3} \tag{23}$$

Furthermore, the voltage across R_1 is

$$v_1 = R_1 i = \frac{R_1}{R_1 + R_2 + R_3} v_{total} \tag{24}$$

Similarly, we have

$$v_2 = R_2 i = \frac{R_2}{R_1 + R_2 + R_3} v_{total} \tag{25}$$

and

$$v_3 = R_3 i = \frac{R_3}{R_1 + R_2 + R_3} v_{total} \tag{26}$$

Of the total voltage, the fraction that appears across a given resistance in a series circuit is the ratio of the given resistance to the total series resistance.

We can summarize these results by the statement: *Of the total voltage, the fraction that appears across a given resistance in a series circuit is the ratio of the given resistance to the total series resistance.* This is known as the **voltage-division principle**.

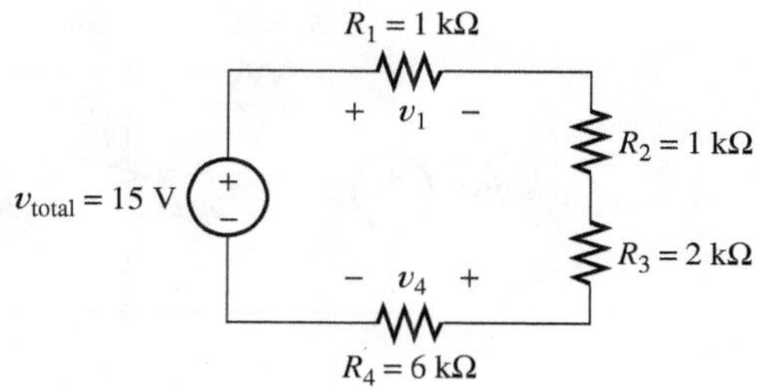

Figure 9 Circuit for Example 3.

We have derived the voltage-division principle for three resistances in series, but it applies for any number of resistances as long as they are connected in series.

Example 3 Application of the Voltage-Division Principle

Find the voltages v_1 and v_4 in Figure 9.

Solution Using the voltage-division principle, we find that v_1 is the total voltage times the ratio of R_1 to the total resistance:

$$v_1 = \frac{R_1}{R_1 + R_2 + R_3 + R_4} v_{total}$$
$$= \frac{1000}{1000 + 1000 + 2000 + 6000} \times 15 = 1.5 \text{ V}$$

Similarly,

$$v_4 = \frac{R_4}{R_1 + R_2 + R_3 + R_4} v_{total}$$
$$= \frac{6000}{1000 + 1000 + 2000 + 6000} \times 15 = 9 \text{ V}$$

Notice that the largest voltage appears across the largest resistance in a series circuit. ■

Current Division

The total current flowing into a parallel combination of resistances divides, and a fraction of the total current flows through each resistance. Consider the circuit shown in Figure 10. The equivalent resistance is given by

$$R_{eq} = \frac{R_1 R_2}{R_1 + R_2} \quad (27)$$

The voltage across the resistances is given by

$$v = R_{eq} i_{total} = \frac{R_1 R_2}{R_1 + R_2} i_{total} \quad (28)$$

Now, we can find the current in each resistance:

$$i_1 = \frac{v}{R_1} = \frac{R_2}{R_1 + R_2} i_{total} \quad (29)$$

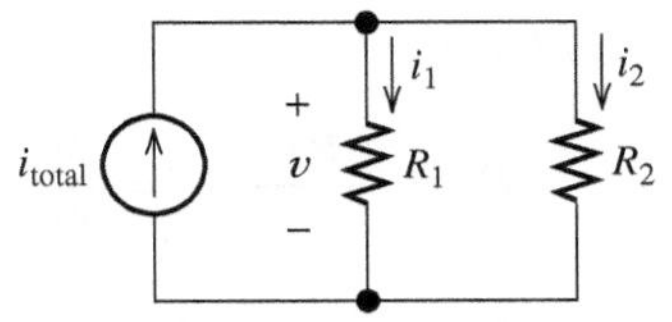

Figure 10 Circuit used to derive the current-division principle.

and

$$i_2 = \frac{v}{R_2} = \frac{R_1}{R_1 + R_2} i_{total} \tag{30}$$

We can summarize these results by stating the **current-division principle**: *For two resistances in parallel, the fraction of the total current flowing in a resistance is the ratio of the other resistance to the sum of the two resistances.* Notice that this principle applies only for two resistances. If we have more than two resistances in parallel, we should combine resistances so we only have two before applying the current-division principle.

For two resistances in parallel, the fraction of the total current flowing in a resistance is the ratio of the other resistance to the sum of the two resistances.

An alternative approach is to work with conductances. For n conductances in parallel, it can be shown that

Current division using conductances uses a formula with the same form as the formula for voltage division using resistances.

$$i_1 = \frac{G_1}{G_1 + G_2 + \cdots + G_n} i_{total}$$

$$i_2 = \frac{G_2}{G_1 + G_2 + \cdots + G_n} i_{total}$$

and so forth. In other words, current division using conductances uses a formula with the same form as the formula for voltage division using resistances.

Example 4 Applying the Current- and Voltage-Division Principles

Use the voltage-division principle to find the voltage v_x in Figure 11(a). Then find the source current i_s and use the current-division principle to compute the current i_3.

Solution The voltage-division principle applies only for resistances in series. Therefore, we first must combine R_2 and R_3. The equivalent resistance for the parallel

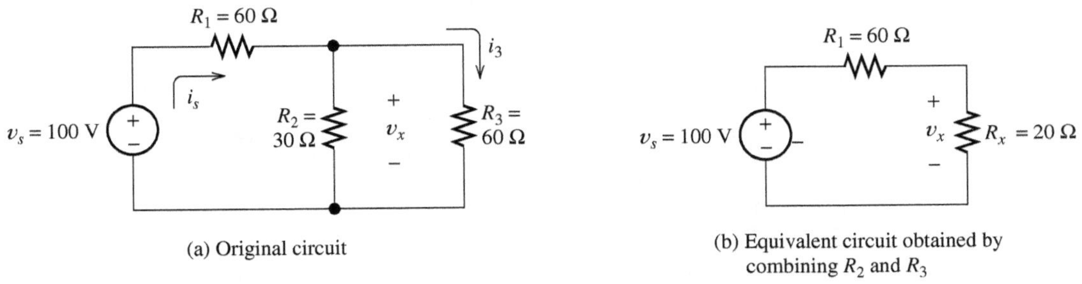

Figure 11 Circuit for Example 4.

combination of R_2 and R_3 is

$$R_x = \frac{R_2 R_3}{R_2 + R_3} = \frac{30 \times 60}{30 + 60} = 20\ \Omega$$

The equivalent network is shown in Figure 11(b).

Now, we can apply the voltage-division principle to find v_x. The voltage v_x is equal to the total voltage times R_x divided by the total series resistance:

$$v_x = \frac{R_x}{R_1 + R_x} v_s = \frac{20}{60 + 20} \times 100 = 25\ \text{V}$$

The source current i_s is given by

$$i_s = \frac{v_s}{R_1 + R_x} = \frac{100}{60 + 20} = 1.25\ \text{A}$$

Now, we can use the current-division principle to find i_3. The fraction of the source current i_s that flows through R_3 is $R_2/(R_2 + R_3)$. Thus, we have

$$i_3 = \frac{R_2}{R_2 + R_3} i_s = \frac{30}{30 + 60} \times 1.25 = 0.417\ \text{A}$$

As a check, we can also compute i_3 another way:

$$i_3 = \frac{v_x}{R_3} = \frac{25}{60} = 0.417\ \text{A}$$ ■

Example 5 Application of the Current-Division Principle

The current-division principle applies for *two* resistances in parallel. Therefore, our first step is to combine R_2 and R_3.

Use the current-division principle to find the current i_1 in Figure 12(a).

Solution The current-division principle applies for two resistances in parallel. Therefore, our first step is to combine R_2 and R_3:

$$R_{eq} = \frac{R_2 R_3}{R_2 + R_3} = \frac{30 \times 60}{30 + 60} = 20\ \Omega$$

The resulting equivalent circuit is shown in Figure 12(b). Applying the current-division principle, we have

$$i_1 = \frac{R_{eq}}{R_1 + R_{eq}} i_s = \frac{20}{10 + 20} 15 = 10\ \text{A}$$

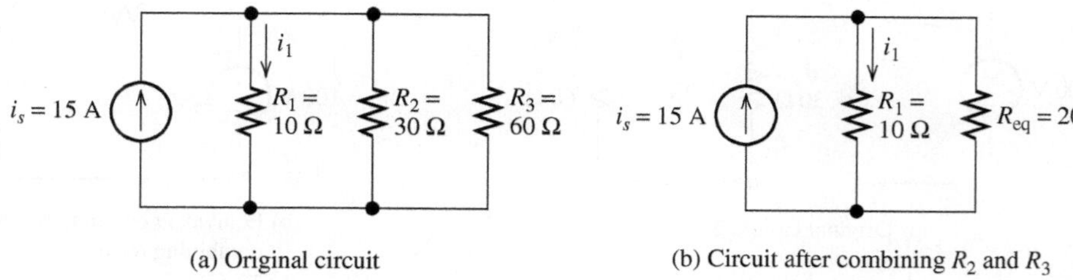

Figure 12 Circuit for Example 5.

Reworking the calculations using conductances, we have

$$G_1 = \frac{1}{R_1} = 100\,\text{mS}, \quad G_2 = \frac{1}{R_2} = 33.33\,\text{mS}, \quad \text{and} \quad G_3 = \frac{1}{R_3} = 16.67\,\text{mS}$$

Then, we compute the current

$$i_1 = \frac{G_1}{G_1 + G_2 + G_3} i_s = \frac{100}{100 + 33.33 + 16.67} 15 = 10\,\text{A}$$

which is the same value that we obtained working with resistances. ■

Position Transducers Based on the Voltage-Division Principle

Transducers are used to produce a voltage (or sometimes a current) that is proportional to a physical quantity of interest, such as distance, pressure, or temperature. For example, Figure 13 shows how a voltage that is proportional to the rudder angle of a boat or aircraft can be obtained. As the rudder turns, a sliding contact moves along a resistance such that R_2 is proportional to the rudder angle θ. The total resistance $R_1 + R_2$ is fixed. Thus, the output voltage is

$$v_o = v_s \frac{R_2}{R_1 + R_2} = K\theta$$

where K is a constant of proportionality that depends on the source voltage v_s and the construction details of the transducer. Many examples of transducers such as this are employed in all areas of science and engineering.

Exercise 3 Use the voltage-division principle to find the voltages labeled in Figure 14.

Answer **a.** $v_1 = 10$ V, $v_2 = 20$ V, $v_3 = 30$ V, $v_4 = 60$ V; **b.** $v_1 = 6.05$ V, $v_2 = 5.88$ V, $v_4 = 8.07$ V. □

Exercise 4 Use the current-division principle to find the currents labeled in Figure 15.

Answer **a.** $i_1 = 1$ A, $i_3 = 2$ A; **b.** $i_1 = i_2 = i_3 = 1$ A. □

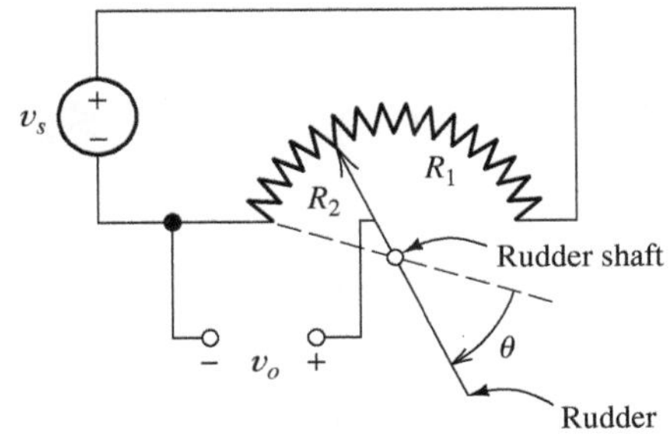

Figure 13 The voltage-division principle forms the basis for some position sensors. This figure shows a transducer that produces an output voltage v_o proportional to the rudder angle θ.

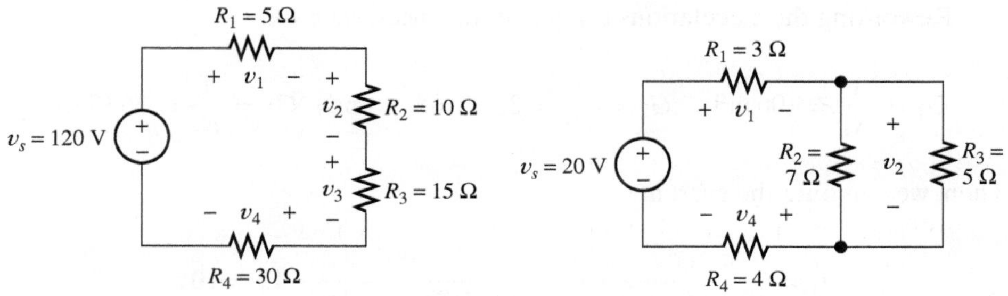

(a) (b)

Figure 14 Circuits for Exercise 3.

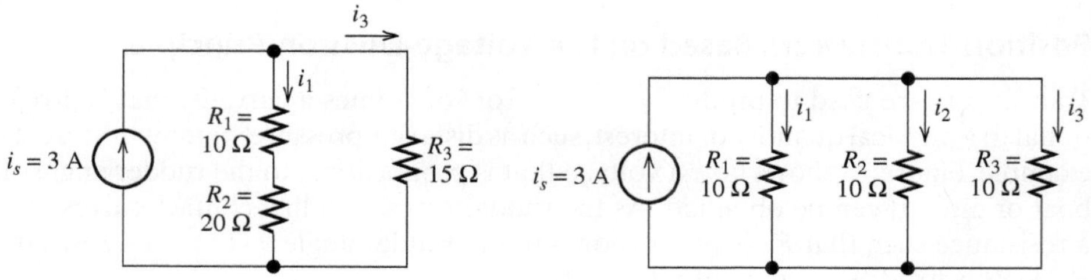

(a) (b)

Figure 15 Circuits for Exercise 4.

4 NODE-VOLTAGE ANALYSIS

Although they are very important concepts, series/parallel equivalents and the current/voltage division principles are not sufficient to solve all circuits.

The network analysis methods that we have studied so far are useful, but they do not apply to all networks. For example, consider the circuit shown in Figure 16. We cannot solve this circuit by combining resistances in series and parallel because no series or parallel combination of resistances exists in the circuit. Furthermore, the voltage-division and current-division principles cannot be applied to this circuit. In this section, we learn **node-voltage analysis**, which is a general technique that can be applied to any circuit.

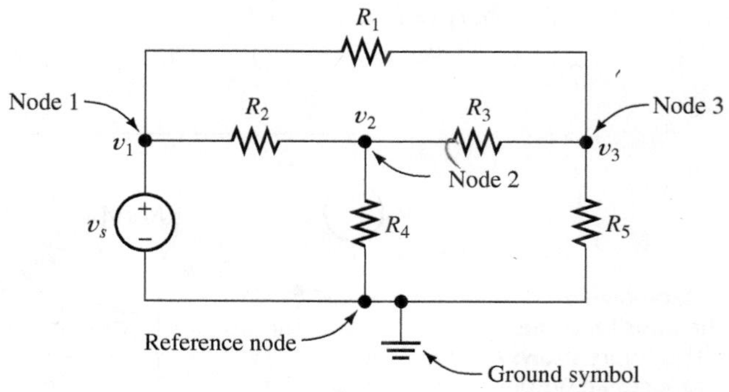

Figure 16 The first step in node analysis is to select a reference node and label the voltages at each of the other nodes.

Selecting the Reference Node

A **node** is a point at which two or more circuit elements are joined together. In node-voltage analysis, we first select one of the nodes as the **reference node**. In principle, any node can be picked to be the reference node. However, the solution is usually facilitated by selecting one end of a voltage source as the reference node. We will see why this is true as we proceed.

For example, the circuit shown in Figure 16 has four nodes. Let us select the bottom node as the reference node. We mark the reference node by the **ground symbol**, as shown in the figure.

Assigning Node Voltages

Next, we label the voltages at each of the other nodes. For example, the voltages at the three nodes are labeled v_1, v_2, and v_3 in Figure 16. The voltage v_1 is the voltage between node 1 and the reference node. The reference polarity for v_1 is positive at node 1 and negative at the reference node. Similarly, v_2 is the voltage between node 2 and the reference node. The reference polarity for v_2 is positive at node 2 and negative at the reference node. *In fact, the negative reference polarity for each of the node voltages is at the reference node.* We say that v_1 is the voltage at node 1 with respect to the reference node.

The negative reference polarity for each of the node voltages is at the reference node.

Finding Element Voltages in Terms of the Node Voltages

In node-voltage analysis, we write equations and eventually solve for the node voltages. Once the node voltages have been found, it is relatively easy to find the current, voltage, and power for each element in the circuit.

For example, suppose that we know the values of the node voltages and we want to find the voltage across R_3 with its positive reference on the left-hand side. To avoid additional labels in Figure 16, we have made a second drawing of the circuit, which is shown in Figure 17. The node voltages and the voltage v_x across R_3 are shown in Figure 17, where we have used arrows to indicate reference polarities. (Recall that the positive reference is at the head of the arrow.) Notice that v_2, v_x, and v_3 are the voltages encountered in traveling around the closed path through R_4, R_3, and R_5. Thus, these voltages must obey Kirchhoff's voltage law. Traveling around the loop

Once the node voltages have been determined, it is relatively easy to determine other voltages and currents in the circuit.

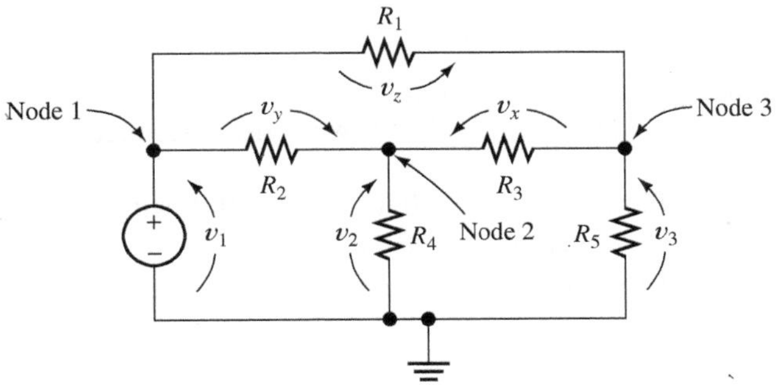

Figure 17 Assuming that we can determine the node voltages v_1, v_2, and v_3, we can use KVL to determine v_x, v_y, and v_z. Then using Ohm's law, we can find the current in each of the resistances. Thus, the key problem is in determining the node voltages.

This is the same circuit shown in Figure 16. We have redrawn it simply to avoid cluttering the original diagram with the voltages v_x, v_y, and v_z that are not involved in the final node equations.

clockwise and summing voltages, we have

$$-v_2 + v_x + v_3 = 0$$

Solving for v_x, we obtain

$$v_x = v_2 - v_3$$

Thus, we can find the voltage across any element in the network as the difference between node voltages. (If one end of an element is connected to the reference node, the voltage across the element is a node voltage.)

After the voltages are found, Ohm's law and KCL can be used to find the current in each element. Then, power can be computed by taking the product of the voltage and current for each element.

Exercise 5 In the circuit of Figure 17, find expressions for v_y and v_z in terms of the node voltages v_1, v_2, and v_3.

Answer $v_y = v_2 - v_1$, $v_z = v_3 - v_1$. □

Writing KCL Equations in Terms of the Node Voltages

After choosing the reference node and assigning the voltage variables, we write equations that can be solved for the node voltages.

After choosing the reference node and assigning the voltage variables, we write equations that can be solved for the node voltages. We demonstrate by continuing with the circuit of Figure 16.

In Figure 16, the voltage v_1 is the same as the source voltage v_s:

$$v_1 = v_s$$

(In this case, one of the node voltages is known without any effort. This is the advantage in selecting the reference node at one end of an independent voltage source.)

Therefore, we need to determine the values of v_2 and v_3, and we must write two independent equations. We usually start by trying to write current equations at each of the nodes corresponding to an unknown node voltage. For example, at node 2 in Figure 16, the current leaving through R_4 is given by

$$\frac{v_2}{R_4}$$

This is true because v_2 is the voltage across R_4 with its positive reference at node 2. Thus, the current v_2/R_4 flows from node 2 toward the reference node, which is away from node 2.

Next, referring to Figure 17, we see that the current flowing out of node 2 through R_3 is given by v_x/R_3. However, we found earlier that $v_x = v_2 - v_3$. Thus, the current flowing out of node 2 through R_3 is given by

$$\frac{v_2 - v_3}{R_3}$$

To find the current flowing out of node n through a resistance toward node k, we subtract the voltage at node k from the voltage at node n and divide the difference by the resistance.

At this point, we pause in our analysis to make a useful observation. *To find the current flowing out of node n through a resistance toward node k, we subtract the voltage at node k from the voltage at node n and divide the difference by the resistance.*

Thus, if v_n and v_k are the node voltages and R is the resistance connected between the nodes, the current flowing from node n toward node k is given by

$$\frac{v_n - v_k}{R}$$

Applying this observation in Figure 16 to find the current flowing out of node 2 through R_2, we have

$$\frac{v_2 - v_1}{R_2}$$

[In Exercise 5, we found that $v_y = v_2 - v_1$ (see Figure 17). The current flowing to the left through R_2 is v_y/R_2. Substitution yields the aforementioned expression.]

Of course, if the resistance is connected between node n and the reference node, the current away from node n toward the reference node is simply the node voltage v_n divided by the resistance. For example, as we noted previously, the current leaving node 2 through R_4 is given by v_2/R_4.

Now we apply KCL, adding all of the expressions for the currents leaving node 2 and setting the sum to zero. Thus, we obtain

$$\frac{v_2 - v_1}{R_2} + \frac{v_2}{R_4} + \frac{v_2 - v_3}{R_3} = 0$$

Writing the current equation at node 3 is similar. We try to follow the same pattern in writing each equation. Then, the equations take a familiar form, and mistakes are less frequent. We usually write expressions for the currents leaving the node under consideration and set the sum to zero. Applying this approach at node 3 of Figure 16, we have

$$\frac{v_3 - v_1}{R_1} + \frac{v_3}{R_5} + \frac{v_3 - v_2}{R_3} = 0$$

In many networks, we can obtain all of the equations needed to solve for the node voltages by applying KCL to the nodes at which the unknown voltages appear.

Example 6 Node-Voltage Analysis

Write equations that can be solved for the node voltages v_1, v_2, and v_3 shown in Figure 18.

Solution We use KCL to write an equation at node 1:

$$\frac{v_1}{R_1} + \frac{v_1 - v_2}{R_2} + i_s = 0$$

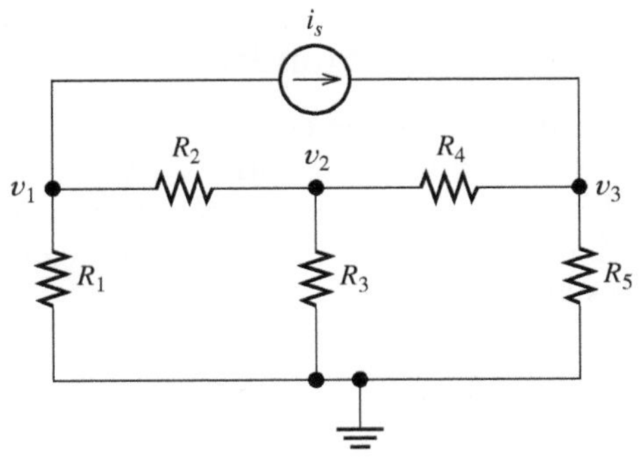

Figure 18 Circuit for Example 6.

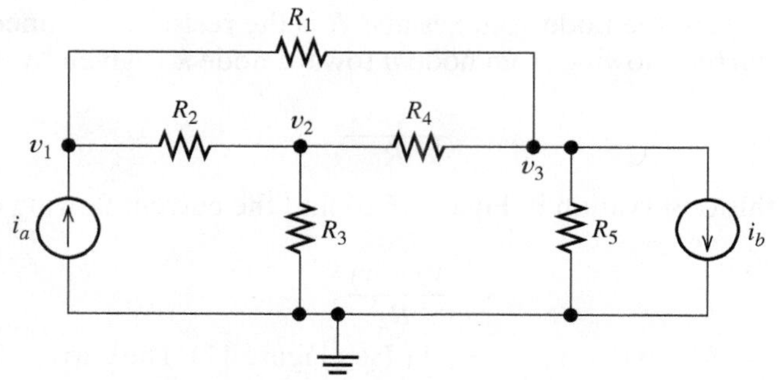

Figure 19 Circuit for Exercise 6.

Each term on the left-hand side of this equation represents a current leaving node 1. Summing the currents leaving node 2, we have

$$\frac{v_2 - v_1}{R_2} + \frac{v_2}{R_3} + \frac{v_2 - v_3}{R_4} = 0$$

Similarly, at node 3, we get

$$\frac{v_3}{R_5} + \frac{v_3 - v_2}{R_4} = i_s$$

Here, the currents leaving node 3 are on the left-hand side and the current entering is on the right-hand side. ■

Exercise 6 Use KCL to write equations at each node (except the reference node) for the circuit shown in Figure 19.

Answer

$$\text{Node 1:} \quad \frac{v_1 - v_3}{R_1} + \frac{v_1 - v_2}{R_2} = i_a$$

$$\text{Node 2:} \quad \frac{v_2 - v_1}{R_2} + \frac{v_2}{R_3} + \frac{v_2 - v_3}{R_4} = 0$$

$$\text{Node 3:} \quad \frac{v_3}{R_5} + \frac{v_3 - v_2}{R_4} + \frac{v_3 - v_1}{R_1} + i_b = 0$$ □

Circuit Equations in Standard Form

Once we have written the equations needed to solve for the node voltages, we put the equations into standard form. We group the node-voltage variables on the left-hand sides of the equations and place terms that do not involve the node voltages on the right-hand sides. For two node voltages, this eventually puts the node-voltage equations into the following form:

$$g_{11}v_1 + g_{12}v_2 = i_1 \quad (31)$$

$$g_{21}v_1 + g_{22}v_2 = i_2 \quad (32)$$

If we have three unknown node voltages, the equations can be put into the form

$$g_{11}v_1 + g_{12}v_2 + g_{13}v_3 = i_1 \quad (33)$$

$$g_{21}v_1 + g_{22}v_2 + g_{23}v_3 = i_2 \quad (34)$$

$$g_{31}v_1 + g_{32}v_2 + g_{33}v_3 = i_3 \quad (35)$$

We have chosen the letter g for the node-voltage coefficients because they are often (but not always) conductances with units of siemens. Similarly, we have used i for the terms on the right-hand sides of the equations because they are often currents.

In matrix form, the equations can be written as

$$\mathbf{GV} = \mathbf{I}$$

in which we have

$$\mathbf{G} = \begin{bmatrix} g_{11} & g_{12} \\ g_{21} & g_{22} \end{bmatrix} \quad \text{or} \quad \mathbf{G} = \begin{bmatrix} g_{11} & g_{12} & g_{13} \\ g_{21} & g_{22} & g_{23} \\ g_{31} & g_{32} & g_{33} \end{bmatrix}$$

depending on whether we have two or three unknown node voltages. Also, $\mathbf{V}$ and $\mathbf{I}$ are column vectors:

$$\mathbf{V} = \begin{bmatrix} v_1 \\ v_2 \end{bmatrix} \quad \text{or} \quad \mathbf{V} = \begin{bmatrix} v_1 \\ v_2 \\ v_3 \end{bmatrix} \quad \text{and} \quad \mathbf{I} = \begin{bmatrix} i_1 \\ i_2 \end{bmatrix} \quad \text{or} \quad \mathbf{I} = \begin{bmatrix} i_1 \\ i_2 \\ i_3 \end{bmatrix}$$

As the number of nodes and node voltages increases, the dimensions of the matrices increase.

One way to solve for the node voltages is to find the inverse of $\mathbf{G}$ and then compute the solution vector as:

$$\mathbf{V} = \mathbf{G}^{-1}\mathbf{I}$$

A Shortcut to Writing the Matrix Equations

If we put the node equations for the circuit of Exercise 6 (Figure 19) into matrix form, we obtain

$$\begin{bmatrix} \frac{1}{R_1} + \frac{1}{R_2} & -\frac{1}{R_2} & -\frac{1}{R_1} \\ -\frac{1}{R_2} & \frac{1}{R_2} + \frac{1}{R_3} + \frac{1}{R_4} & -\frac{1}{R_4} \\ -\frac{1}{R_1} & -\frac{1}{R_4} & \frac{1}{R_1} + \frac{1}{R_4} + \frac{1}{R_5} \end{bmatrix} \begin{bmatrix} v_1 \\ v_2 \\ v_3 \end{bmatrix} = \begin{bmatrix} i_a \\ 0 \\ -i_b \end{bmatrix}$$

Let us take a moment to compare the circuit in Figure 19 with the elements in this equation. First, look at the elements on the diagonal of the $\mathbf{G}$ matrix, which are

$$g_{11} = \frac{1}{R_1} + \frac{1}{R_2} \quad g_{22} = \frac{1}{R_2} + \frac{1}{R_3} + \frac{1}{R_4} \quad \text{and} \quad g_{33} = \frac{1}{R_1} + \frac{1}{R_4} + \frac{1}{R_5}$$

We see that the diagonal elements of $\mathbf{G}$ are equal to the sums of the conductances connected to the corresponding nodes. Next, notice the off diagonal terms:

$$g_{12} = -\frac{1}{R_2} \quad g_{13} = -\frac{1}{R_1} \quad g_{21} = -\frac{1}{R_2} \quad g_{23} = -\frac{1}{R_4} \quad g_{31} = -\frac{1}{R_1} \quad g_{32} = -\frac{1}{R_4}$$

In each case, g_{jk} is equal to the negative of the conductance connected between node j and k. The terms in the **I** matrix are the currents pushed into the corresponding nodes by the current sources. These observations hold whenever the network consists of resistances and independent current sources, assuming that we follow our usual pattern in writing the equations.

Thus, if a circuit consists of resistances and independent current sources, we can use the following steps to rapidly write the node equations directly in matrix form.

This is a shortcut way to write the node equations in matrix form, *provided that the circuit contains only resistances and independent current sources.*

1. Make sure that the circuit contains only resistances and independent current sources.
2. The diagonal terms of **G** are the sums of the conductances connected to the corresponding nodes.
3. The off diagonal terms of **G** are the negatives of the conductances connected between the corresponding nodes.
4. The elements of **I** are the currents pushed into the corresponding nodes by the current sources.

Keep in mind that if the network contains voltage sources or controlled sources this pattern does not hold.

Exercise 7 Working directly from Figure 18, write its node-voltage equations in matrix form.

Answer

$$\begin{bmatrix} \frac{1}{R_1}+\frac{1}{R_2} & -\frac{1}{R_2} & 0 \\ -\frac{1}{R_2} & \frac{1}{R_2}+\frac{1}{R_3}+\frac{1}{R_4} & -\frac{1}{R_4} \\ 0 & -\frac{1}{R_4} & \frac{1}{R_4}+\frac{1}{R_5} \end{bmatrix} \begin{bmatrix} v_1 \\ v_2 \\ v_3 \end{bmatrix} = \begin{bmatrix} -i_s \\ 0 \\ i_s \end{bmatrix}$$ □

Example 7 Node-Voltage Analysis

Write the node-voltage equations in matrix form for the circuit of Figure 20.

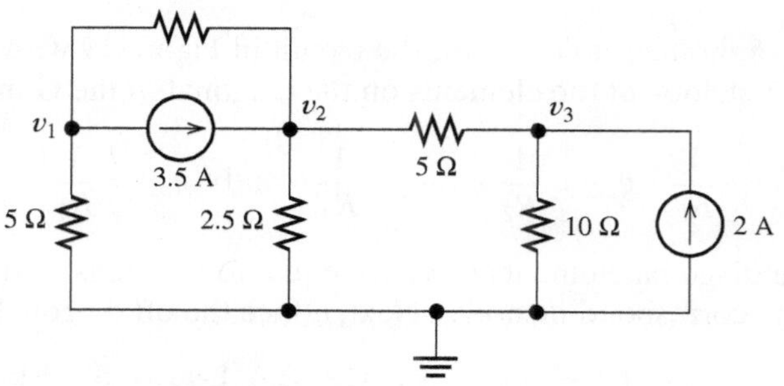

Figure 20 Circuit for Example 7.

Solution Writing KCL at each node, we have

$$\frac{v_1}{5} + \frac{v_1 - v_2}{4} + 3.5 = 0$$

$$\frac{v_2 - v_1}{4} + \frac{v_2}{2.5} + \frac{v_2 - v_3}{5} = 3.5$$

$$\frac{v_3 - v_2}{5} + \frac{v_3}{10} = 2$$

Manipulating the equations into standard form, we have

$$0.45v_1 - 0.25v_2 = -3.5$$

$$-\,0.25v_1 + 0.85v_2 - 0.2v_3 = 3.5$$

$$-\,0.2v_2 + 0.35v_3 = 2$$

Then, in matrix form, we obtain

$$\begin{bmatrix} 0.45 & -0.25 & 0 \\ -0.25 & 0.85 & -0.20 \\ 0 & -0.20 & 0.30 \end{bmatrix} \begin{bmatrix} v_1 \\ v_2 \\ v_3 \end{bmatrix} = \begin{bmatrix} -3.5 \\ 3.5 \\ 2 \end{bmatrix} \tag{36}$$

Because the circuit contains no voltage sources or controlled sources, we could have used the shortcut method to write the matrix form directly. For example, $g_{11} = 0.45$ is the sum of the conductances connected to node 1, $g_{12} = -0.25$ is the negative of the conductance connected between nodes 1 and 2, $i_3 = 2$ is the current pushed into node 3 by the 2-A current source, and so forth. ■

Solving the Network Equations

After we have obtained the equations in standard form, we can solve them by a variety of methods, including substitution, Gaussian elimination, and determinants. As an engineering student, you may own a powerful calculator such as the TI-84 or TI-89 that has the ability to solve systems of linear equations. You should learn to do this by practicing on the exercises and the problems at the end of this chapter.

In some situations, you may not be allowed to use one of the more advanced calculators or a notebook computer. For example, only fairly simple scientific calculators are allowed on the Fundamentals of Engineering (FE) Examination, which is the first step in becoming a registered professional engineer in the United States. The calculator policy for the professional engineering examinations can be found at `http://ncees.org/`. Thus, even if you own an advanced calculator, you may wish to practice with one of those allowed in the FE Examination.

Exercise 8 Use your calculator to solve Equation 36.
Answer $v_1 = -5\,\text{V}$, $v_2 = 5\,\text{V}$, $v_3 = 10\,\text{V}$. □

Using MATLAB to Solve Network Equations

When you have access to a computer and MATLAB software, you have a very powerful system for engineering and scientific calculations. This software is available to students at many engineering schools and is very likely to be encountered in some of your other courses.

In this chapter, we illustrate the application of MATLAB to various aspects of circuit analysis, but we cannot possibly cover all of its many useful features. If you are new to MATLAB, and it is available to you, use the video and/or getting started documentation that appear at the top of the command screen and/or in the Help menu to gain some initial familiarity with the software. Furthermore, you can gain access to a variety of online interactive tutorials at `http://www.mathworks.com/academia/student_center/tutorials/register.html`. If you have already used the program, the MATLAB commands we present may be familiar to you. In either case, you should be able to easily modify the examples we present to work out similar circuit problems.

Next, we illustrate the solution for Equation 36 using MATLAB. Instead of using $\mathbf{V} = \mathbf{G}^{-1}\mathbf{I}$ to compute node voltages, MATLAB documentation recommends using the command V = G\I which invokes a more accurate algorithm for computing solutions to systems of linear equations.

The comments following the % sign are ignored by MATLAB. For improved clarity, we use a **bold** font for the input commands, a regular font for comments, and a color font for the responses from MATLAB, otherwise the following has the appearance of the MATLAB command screen for this problem. (>> is the MATLAB command prompt.)

```
>> clear  % First we clear the work space.
>> % Then, we enter the coefficient matrix of Equation 36 with
>> % spaces between elements in each row and semicolons between rows.
>> G = [0.45 -0.25 0; -0.25 0.85 -0.2; 0 -0.2 0.30]
G =
    0.4500   -0.2500         0
   -0.2500    0.8500   -0.2000
         0   -0.2000    0.3000
>> % Next, we enter the column vector for the right-hand side.
>> I = [-3.5; 3.5; 2]
I =
   -3.5000
    3.5000
    2.0000
>>  % The MATLAB documentation recommends computing the node
>>  % voltages using V = G\I instead of using V = inv(G)*I.
>> V = G\I
V =
   -5.0000
    5.0000
   10.0000
```

Thus, we have $v_1 = -5\,\text{V}$, $v_2 = 5\,\text{V}$, and $v_3 = 10\,\text{V}$, as you found when working Exercise 8 with your calculator.

LabVIEW MathScript

If you have access to LabVIEW software including the RT (Real Time) Module, you can use its "On-Line Student Resources" MathScript option to solve equations. To do this, first start a Blank VI in LabVIEW. This will bring up two windows: a Block Diagram window and a Front Panel window. Left click on **Tools** in the menu bar of either window and then left click on **MathScript Window**..., which will open a window in which you can use many commands identical to those of MATLAB. At this point, you can close the Block Diagram and Front Panel windows. Enter the commands in the Command Window, and the results will appear in the Output Window. If you wish to try this software alternative, start by trying to duplicate the solution to the example of the previous several pages. Simply enter the commands

```
clear
G = [0.45 -0.25 0; -0.25 0.85 -0.2; 0 -0.2 0.30]
I = [-3.5; 3.5; 2]
V = G\I
```

in the Command Window and the results will appear in the Output Window.

Example 8 Node-Voltage Analysis

Solve for the node voltages shown in Figure 21 and determine the value of the current i_x.

Solution Our first step in solving a circuit is to select the reference node and assign the node voltages. This has already been done, as shown in Figure 21.

Next, we write equations. In this case, we can write a current equation at each node. This yields

$$\text{Node 1:} \quad \frac{v_1}{10} + \frac{v_1 - v_2}{5} + \frac{v_1 - v_3}{20} = 0$$

$$\text{Node 2:} \quad \frac{v_2 - v_1}{5} + \frac{v_2 - v_3}{10} = 10$$

$$\text{Node 3:} \quad \frac{v_3}{5} + \frac{v_3 - v_2}{10} + \frac{v_3 - v_1}{20} = 0$$

Next, we place these equations into standard form:

$$\begin{aligned} 0.35v_1 - 0.2v_2 - 0.05v_3 &= 0 \\ -0.2v_1 + 0.3v_2 - 0.10v_3 &= 10 \\ -0.05v_1 - 0.10v_2 + 0.35v_3 &= 0 \end{aligned}$$

In matrix form, the equations are

$$\begin{bmatrix} 0.35 & -0.2 & -0.05 \\ -0.2 & 0.3 & -0.1 \\ -0.05 & -0.1 & 0.35 \end{bmatrix} \begin{bmatrix} v_1 \\ v_2 \\ v_3 \end{bmatrix} = \begin{bmatrix} 0 \\ 10 \\ 0 \end{bmatrix}$$

or $\mathbf{GV} = \mathbf{I}$

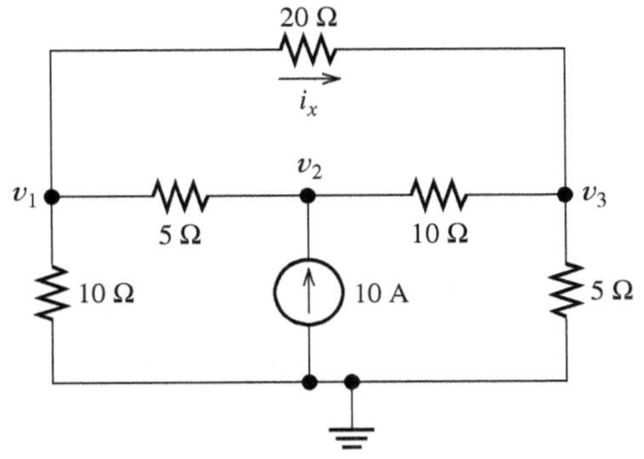

Figure 21 Circuit for Example 8.

in which **G** represents the coefficient matrix of conductances, **V** is the column vector of node voltages, and **I** is the column vector of currents on the right-hand side.

Here again, we could write the equations directly in standard or matrix form using the short cut method because the circuit contains only resistances and independent current sources.

The MATLAB solution is:

```
>> clear
>> G = [0.35 -0.2 -0.05; -0.2 0.3 -0.1; -0.05 -0.1 0.35];
>> % A semicolon at the end of a command suppresses the
>> % MATLAB response.
>> I = [0; 10; 0];
>> V = G\I
V =
    45.4545
    72.7273
    27.2727
>> % Finally, we calculate the current.
>> Ix = (V(1) - V(3))/20
Ix =
     0.9091
```

Alternatively, you can use the same commands with LabVIEW MathScript to obtain the answers. ■

Exercise 9 Repeat the analysis of the circuit of Example 8, using the reference node and node voltages shown in Figure 22. **a.** First write the network equations. **b.** Put the network equations into standard form. **c.** Solve for v_1, v_2, and v_3. (The values will be different than those we found in Example 8 because v_1, v_2, and v_3 are not the same voltages in the two figures.) **d.** Find i_x. (Of course, i_x is the same in both figures, so it should have the same value.)

Answer

a.

$$\frac{v_1 - v_3}{20} + \frac{v_1}{5} + \frac{v_1 - v_2}{10} = 0$$

$$\frac{v_2 - v_1}{10} + 10 + \frac{v_2 - v_3}{5} = 0$$

$$\frac{v_3 - v_1}{20} + \frac{v_3}{10} + \frac{v_3 - v_2}{5} = 0$$

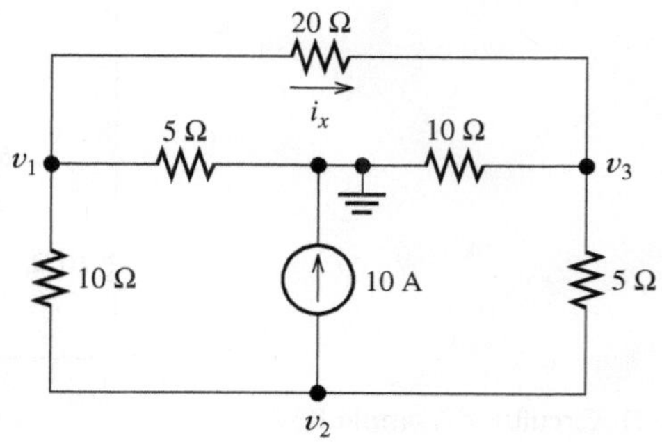

Figure 22 Circuit of Example 8 with a different choice for the reference node. See Exercise 9.

b.

$$
\begin{aligned}
0.35v_1 - 0.10v_2 - 0.05v_3 &= 0 \\
-0.10v_1 + 0.30v_2 - 0.20v_3 &= -10 \\
-0.05v_1 - 0.20v_2 + 0.35v_3 &= 0
\end{aligned}
$$

c. $v_1 = -27.27, v_2 = -72.73, v_3 = -45.45$

d. $i_x = 0.909$ A

□

Circuits with Voltage Sources

When a circuit contains a single voltage source, we can often pick the reference node at one end of the source, and then we have one less unknown node voltage for which to solve.

Example 9 Node-Voltage Analysis

Write the equations for the network shown in Figure 23 and put them into standard form.

Solution Notice that we have selected the reference node at the bottom end of the voltage source. Thus, the voltage at node 3 is known to be 10 V, and we do not need to assign a variable for that node.

Writing current equations at nodes 1 and 2, we obtain

$$\frac{v_1 - v_2}{5} + \frac{v_1 - 10}{2} = 1$$

$$\frac{v_2}{5} + \frac{v_2 - 10}{10} + \frac{v_2 - v_1}{5} = 0$$

Now if we group terms and place the constants on the right-hand sides of the equations, we have

$$0.7v_1 - 0.2v_2 = 6$$

$$-0.2v_1 + 0.5v_2 = 1$$

Thus, we have obtained the equations needed to solve for v_1 and v_2 in standard form. ■

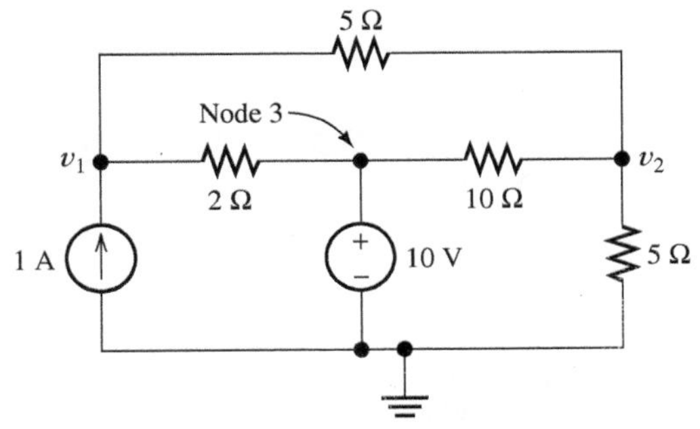

Figure 23 Circuit for Example 9.

Exercise 10 Solve the equations of Example 9 for v_1 and v_2.
Answer $v_1 = 10.32$ V, $v_2 = 6.129$ V. □

Exercise 11 Solve for the node voltages v_1 and v_2 in the circuit of Figure 24.
Answer $v_1 = 6.77$ V, $v_2 = 4.19$ V. □

Sometimes, the pattern for writing node-voltage equations that we have illustrated so far must be modified. For example, consider the network and node voltages shown in Figure 25. Notice that $v_3 = -15$ V because of the 15-V source connected between node 3 and the reference node. Therefore, we need two equations relating the unknowns v_1 and v_2.

If we try to write a current equation at node 1, we must include a term for the current through the 10-V source. We could assign an unknown for this current, but then we would have a higher-order system of equations to solve. Especially if we are solving the equations manually, we want to minimize the number of unknowns. For this circuit, it is not possible to write a current equation in terms of the node voltages for any single node (even the reference node) because a voltage source is connected to each node.

Another way to obtain a current equation is to form a **supernode**. This is done by drawing a dashed line around several nodes, including the elements connected between them. This is shown in Figure 25. Two supernodes are indicated, one enclosing each of the voltage sources.

Another way to state Kirchhoff's current law is that the net current flowing through any closed surface must equal zero.

We can state Kirchhoff's current law in a slightly more general form than we have previously: *The net current flowing through any closed surface must equal zero.* Thus, we can apply KCL to a supernode. For example, for the supernode enclosing

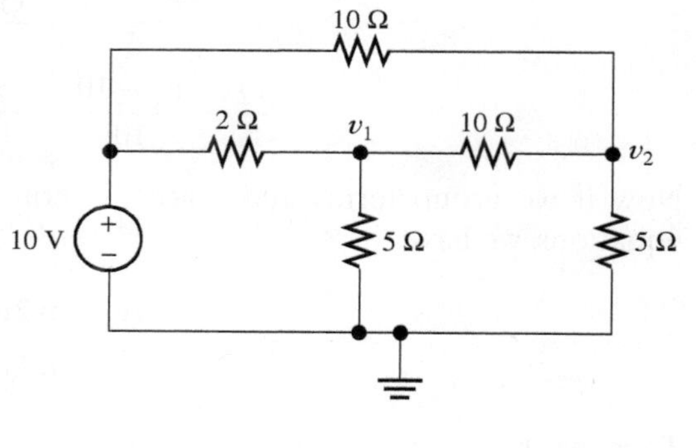

Figure 24 Circuit for Exercise 11.

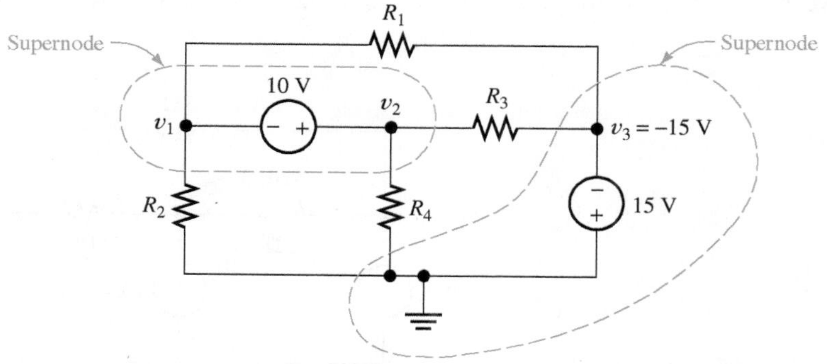

Figure 25 A supernode is formed by drawing a dashed line enclosing several nodes and any elements connected between them.

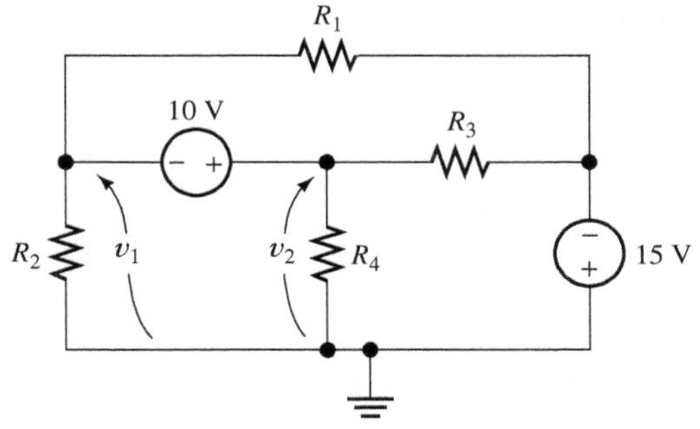

Figure 26 Node voltages v_1 and v_2 and the 10-V source form a closed loop to which KVL can be applied. (This is the same circuit as that of Figure 25.)

the 10-V source, we sum currents leaving and obtain

$$\frac{v_1}{R_2} + \frac{v_1 - (-15)}{R_1} + \frac{v_2}{R_4} + \frac{v_2 - (-15)}{R_3} = 0 \quad (37)$$

Each term on the left-hand side of this equation represents a current leaving the supernode through one of the resistors. Thus, by enclosing the 10-V source within the supernode, we have obtained a current equation without introducing a new variable for the current in the source.

Next, we might be tempted to write another current equation for the other supernode. However, we would find that the equation is equivalent to the one already written. *In general, we obtain dependent equations if we use all of the nodes in writing current equations.* Nodes 1 and 2 were part of the first supernode, while node 3 and the reference node are part of the second supernode. Thus, in writing equations for both supernodes, we would have used all four nodes in the network.

We obtain dependent equations if we use all of the nodes in a network to write KCL equations.

If we tried to solve for the node voltages by using substitution, at some point all of the terms would drop out of the equations and we would not be able to solve for those voltages. In MATLAB, you will receive a warning that the G matrix is singular, in other words, its determinant is zero. If this happens, we know that we should return to writing equations and find another equation to use in the solution. This will not happen if we avoid using all of the nodes in writing current equations.

There is a way to obtain an independent equation for the network under consideration. We can use KVL because v_1, the 10-V source, and v_2 form a closed loop. This is illustrated in Figure 26, where we have used arrows to indicate the polarities of v_1 and v_2. Traveling clockwise and summing the voltages around the loop, we obtain

$$-v_1 - 10 + v_2 = 0 \quad (38)$$

Equations 37 and 38 form an independent set that can be used to solve for v_1 and v_2 (assuming that the resistance values are known).

When a voltage source is connected between nodes so that current equations cannot be written at the individual nodes, first write a KVL equation, including the voltage source, and then enclose the voltage source in a supernode and write a KCL equation for the supernode.

Exercise 12 Write the current equation for the supernode that encloses the 15-V source in Figure 25. Show that your equation is equivalent to Equation 37. □

Exercise 13 Write a set of independent equations for the node voltages shown in Figure 27.

Answer

KVL:

$$-v_1 + 10 + v_2 = 0$$

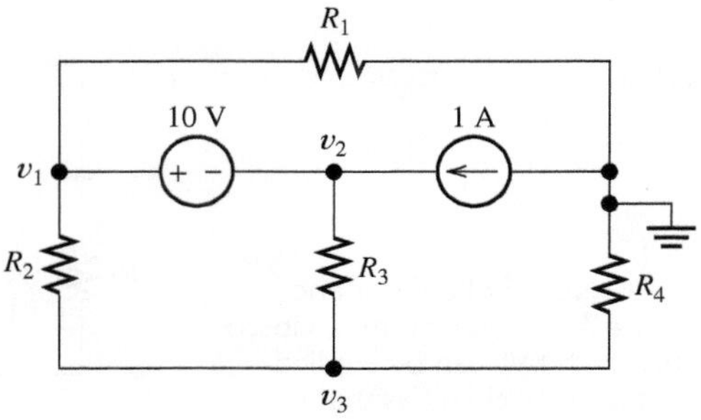

Figure 27 Circuit for Exercise 13.

KCL for the supernode enclosing the 10-V source:

$$\frac{v_1}{R_1} + \frac{v_1 - v_3}{R_2} + \frac{v_2 - v_3}{R_3} = 1$$

KCL for node 3:

$$\frac{v_3 - v_1}{R_2} + \frac{v_3 - v_2}{R_3} + \frac{v_3}{R_4} = 0$$

KCL at the reference node:

$$\frac{v_1}{R_1} + \frac{v_3}{R_4} = 1$$

For independence, the set must include the KVL equation. Any two of the three KCL equations can be used to complete the three-equation set. (The three KCL equations use all of the network nodes and, therefore, do not form an independent set.) □

Circuits with Controlled Sources

Controlled sources present a slight additional complication of the node-voltage technique. (Recall that the value of a controlled source depends on a current or voltage elsewhere in the network.) In applying node-voltage analysis, first we write equations exactly as we have done for networks with independent sources. Then, we express the controlling variable in terms of the node-voltage variables and substitute into the network equations. We illustrate with two examples.

Example 10 Node-Voltage Analysis with a Dependent Source

Write an independent set of equations for the node voltages shown in Figure 28.

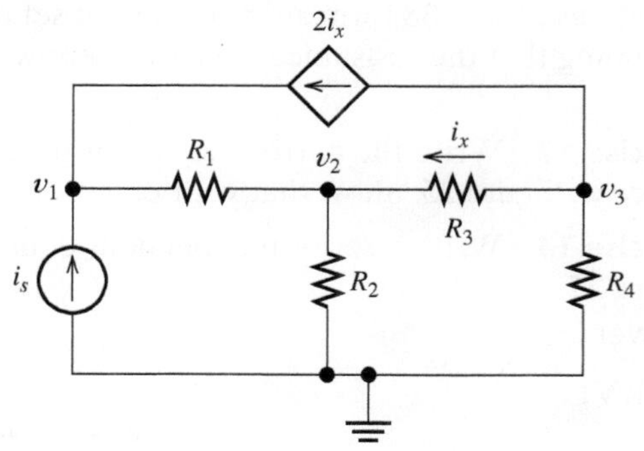

Figure 28 Circuit containing a current-controlled current source. See Example 10.

Solution First, we write KCL equations at each node, including the current of the controlled source just as if it were an ordinary current source:

$$\frac{v_1 - v_2}{R_1} = i_s + 2i_x \tag{39}$$

$$\frac{v_2 - v_1}{R_1} + \frac{v_2}{R_2} + \frac{v_2 - v_3}{R_3} = 0 \tag{40}$$

$$\frac{v_3 - v_2}{R_3} + \frac{v_3}{R_4} + 2i_x = 0 \tag{41}$$

Next, we find an expression for the controlling variable i_x in terms of the node voltages. Notice that i_x is the current flowing away from node 3 through R_3. Thus, we can write

$$i_x = \frac{v_3 - v_2}{R_3} \tag{42}$$

Finally, we use Equation 42 to substitute into Equations 39, 40, and 41. Thus, we obtain the required equation set:

$$\frac{v_1 - v_2}{R_1} = i_s + 2\frac{v_3 - v_2}{R_3} \tag{43}$$

$$\frac{v_2 - v_1}{R_1} + \frac{v_2}{R_2} + \frac{v_2 - v_3}{R_3} = 0 \tag{44}$$

$$\frac{v_3 - v_2}{R_3} + \frac{v_3}{R_4} + 2\frac{v_3 - v_2}{R_3} = 0 \tag{45}$$

Assuming that the value of i_s and the resistances are known, we could put this set of equations into standard form and solve for v_1, v_2, and v_3. ■

Example 11 Node-Voltage Analysis with a Dependent Source

Write an independent set of equations for the node voltages shown in Figure 29.

Solution First, we ignore the fact that the voltage source is a dependent source and write equations just as we would for a circuit with independent sources. We cannot write a current equation at either node 1 or node 2, because of the voltage source connected between them. However, we can write a KVL equation:

$$-v_1 + 0.5v_x + v_2 = 0 \tag{46}$$

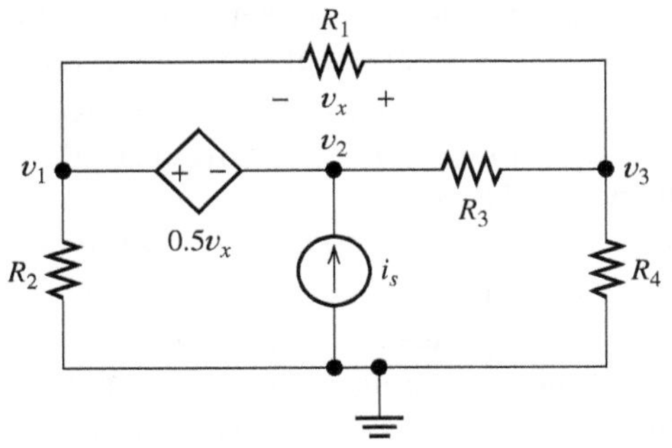

Figure 29 Circuit containing a voltage-controlled voltage source. See Example 11.

Then, we use KCL to write current equations. For a supernode enclosing the controlled voltage source,

$$\frac{v_1}{R_2} + \frac{v_1 - v_3}{R_1} + \frac{v_2 - v_3}{R_3} = i_s$$

For node 3,

$$\frac{v_3}{R_4} + \frac{v_3 - v_2}{R_3} + \frac{v_3 - v_1}{R_1} = 0 \qquad (47)$$

For the reference node,

$$\frac{v_1}{R_2} + \frac{v_3}{R_4} = i_s \qquad (48)$$

Of course, these current equations are dependent because we have used all four nodes in writing them. We must use Equation 46 and two of the KCL equations to form an independent set. However, Equation 46 contains the controlling variable v_x, which must be eliminated before we have equations in terms of the node voltages.

Thus, our next step is to write an expression for the controlling variable v_x in terms of the node voltages. Notice that v_1, v_x, and v_3 form a closed loop. Traveling clockwise and summing voltages, we have

$$-v_1 - v_x + v_3 = 0$$

Solving for v_x, we obtain

$$v_x = v_3 - v_1$$

Now if we substitute into Equation 46, we get

$$v_1 = 0.5(v_3 - v_1) + v_2 \qquad (49)$$

Equation 49 along with any two of the KCL equations forms an independent set that can be solved for the node voltages. ■

Using the principles we have discussed in this section, we can write node-voltage equations for any network consisting of sources and resistances. Thus, given a computer or calculator to help in solving the equations, we can compute the currents and voltages for any network.

Next, we summarize the steps in analyzing circuits by the node-voltage technique:

Here is a convenient step-by-step guide to node-voltage analysis.

1. Select a reference node and assign variables for the unknown node voltages. If the reference node is chosen at one end of an independent voltage source, one node voltage is known at the start, and fewer need to be computed.
2. Write network equations. First, use KCL to write current equations for nodes and supernodes. Write as many current equations as you can without using all of the nodes. Then if you do not have enough equations because of voltage sources connected between nodes, use KVL to write additional equations.
3. If the circuit contains dependent sources, find expressions for the controlling variables in terms of the node voltages. Substitute into the network equations, and obtain equations having only the node voltages as unknowns.
4. Put the equations into standard form and solve for the node voltages.

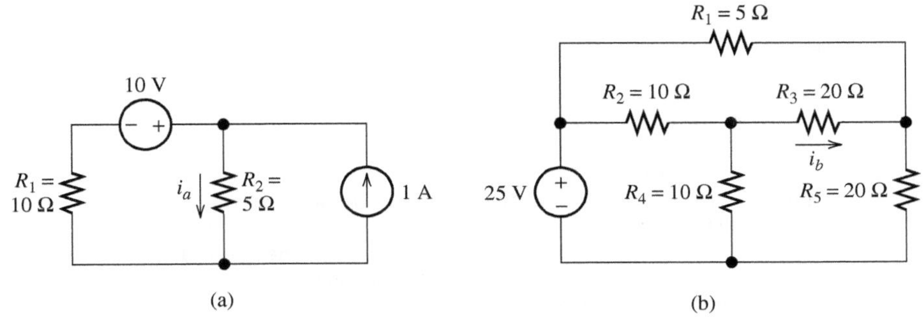

Figure 30 Circuits for Exercise 14.

5. Use the values found for the node voltages to calculate any other currents or voltages of interest.

Exercise 14 Use the node-voltage technique to solve for the currents labeled in the circuits shown in Figure 30.

Answer **a.** $i_a = 1.33$ A; **b.** $i_b = -0.259$ A. □

Exercise 15 Use the node-voltage technique to solve for the values of i_x and i_y in Figure 31.

Answer $i_x = 0.5$ A, $i_y = 2.31$ A. □

Using the MATLAB Symbolic Toolbox to Obtain Symbolic Solutions

If the Symbolic Toolbox is included with your version of MATLAB, you can use it to solve node voltage and other equations symbolically. (LabVIEW MathScript does not have symbolic mathematics capabilities.) We illustrate by solving Equations 43, 44, and 45 from Example 10.

For help with a command such as "solve" simply type "help solve" at the command prompt.

```
>> clear
>> % First we clear the workspace, then we enter the equations into
>> % the solve command followed by the variables for which we want
>> % to solve.
>> [V1, V2, V3] = solve('(V1 - V2)/R1 = Is + 2*(V3 - V2)/R3', ...
                  '(V2 - V1)/R1 + V2/R2 + (V2 - V3)/R3 = 0', ...
                  '(V3 - V2)/R3 + V3/R4 + 2*(V3 - V2)/R3 = 0',...
                  'V1','V2','V3')
```

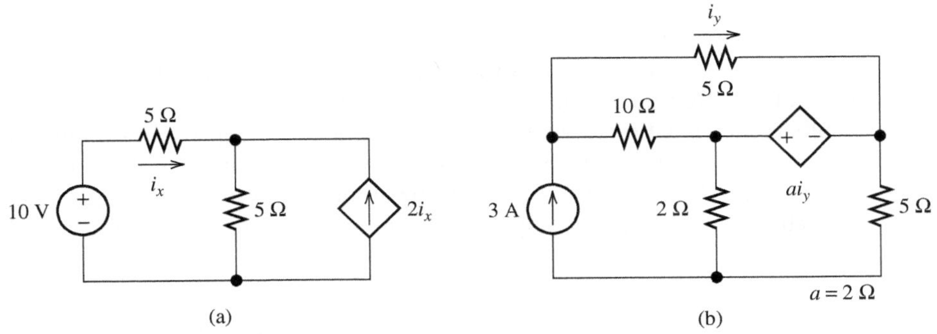

Figure 31 Circuits for Exercise 15.

```
V1 =
(Is*R1*R2 + Is*R1*R3 + 3*Is*R1*R4 + Is*R2*R3 + 3*Is*R2*R4)/(3*R2 + R3 +
3*R4)
V2 =
(Is*R2*R3 + 3*Is*R2*R4)/(3*R2 + R3 + 3*R4)
V3 =
(3*Is*R2*R4)/(3*R2 + R3 + 3*R4)
>> % The solve command gives the answers, but in a form that is
>> % somewhat difficult to read.
>> % A more readable version of the answers is obtained using the
>> % pretty command. We combine the three commands on one line
>> % by placing commas between them.
>> pretty(V1), pretty(V2), pretty(V3)
   Is R1 R2 + Is R1 R3 + 3 Is R1 R4 + Is R2 R3 + 3 Is R2 R4
   --------------------------------------------------------
                     3 R2 + R3 + 3 R4

   Is R2 R3 + 3 Is R2 R4
   ---------------------
     3 R2 + R3 + 3 R4

     3 Is R2 R4
   ----------------
   3 R2 + R3 + 3 R4
```

(Here we have shown the results obtained using MATLAB version R2008b; other versions may give results different in appearance but equivalent mathematically.) In more standard mathematical format, the results are:

$$v_1 = \frac{i_s R_1 R_2 + i_s R_1 R_3 + 3 i_s R_1 R_4 + i_s R_2 R_3 + 3 i_s R_2 R_4}{3R_2 + R_3 + 3R_4}$$

$$v_2 = \frac{i_s R_2 R_3 + 3 i_s R_2 R_4}{3R_2 + R_3 + 3R_4}$$

$$\text{and } v_3 = \frac{3 i_s R_2 R_4}{3R_2 + R_3 + 3R_4}$$

Checking Answers

As usual, it is a good idea to apply some checks to the answers. First of all, make sure that the answers have proper units, which are volts in this case. If the units don't check, look to see if any of the numerical values entered in the equations have units. Referring to the circuit (Figure 28), we see that the only numerical parameter entered into the equations was the gain of the current-controlled current source, which has no units.

Again referring to the circuit diagram, we can see that we should have $v_2 = v_3$ for $R_3 = 0$, and we check the results to see that this is the case. Another check is obtained by observing that we should have $v_3 = 0$ for $R_4 = 0$. Still another check of the results comes from observing that, in the limit as R_3 approaches infinity, we should have $i_x = 0$, (so the controlled current source becomes an open circuit), $v_3 = 0$, $v_1 = i_s(R_1 + R_2)$, and $v_2 = i_s R_2$. Various other checks of a similar nature can be applied. This type of checking may not guarantee correct results, but it can find a lot of errors.

Exercise 16 Use the symbolic math features of MATLAB to solve Equations 47, 48, and 49 for the node voltages in symbolic form.

Answer

$$v_1 = \frac{2i_s R_1 R_2 R_3 + 3i_s R_1 R_2 R_4 + 2i_s R_2 R_3 R_4}{3R_1R_2 + 2R_1R_3 + 3R_1R_4 + 2R_2R_3 + 2R_3R_4}$$

$$v_2 = \frac{3i_s R_1 R_2 R_3 + 3i_s R_1 R_2 R_4 + 2i_s R_2 R_3 R_4}{3R_1R_2 + 2R_1R_3 + 3R_1R_4 + 2R_2R_3 + 2R_3R_4}$$

$$v_3 = \frac{3i_s R_1 R_2 R_4 + 2i_s R_2 R_3 R_4}{3R_1R_2 + 2R_1R_3 + 3R_1R_4 + 2R_2R_3 + 2R_3R_4}$$

Depending on the version of MATLAB and the Symbolic Toolbox that you use, your answers may have a different appearance but should be algebraically equivalent to these. □

5 MESH-CURRENT ANALYSIS

In this section, we show how to analyze networks by using another general technique, known as mesh-current analysis. Networks that can be drawn on a plane without having one element (or conductor) crossing over another are called **planar networks**. On the other hand, circuits that must be drawn with one or more elements crossing others are said to be **nonplanar**. We consider only planar networks.

Let us start by considering the planar network shown in Figure 32(a). Suppose that the source voltages and resistances are known and that we wish to solve for the currents. We first write equations for the currents shown in Figure 32(a), which are called branch currents because a separate current is defined in each branch of the network. However, we will eventually see that using the mesh currents illustrated in Figure 32(b) makes the solution easier.

Three independent equations are needed to solve for the three branch currents shown in Figure 32(a). In general, the number of independent KVL equations that can be written for a planar network is equal to the number of open areas defined by the network layout. For example, the circuit of Figure 32(a) has two open areas: one defined by v_A, R_1, and R_3, while the other is defined by R_3, R_2, and v_B. Thus, for this network, we can write only two independent KVL equations. We must employ KCL to obtain the third equation.

Application of KVL to the loop consisting of v_A, R_1, and R_3 yields

$$R_1 i_1 + R_3 i_3 = v_A \tag{50}$$

Similarly, for the loop consisting of R_3, R_2, and v_B, we get

$$-R_3 i_3 + R_2 i_2 = -v_B \tag{51}$$

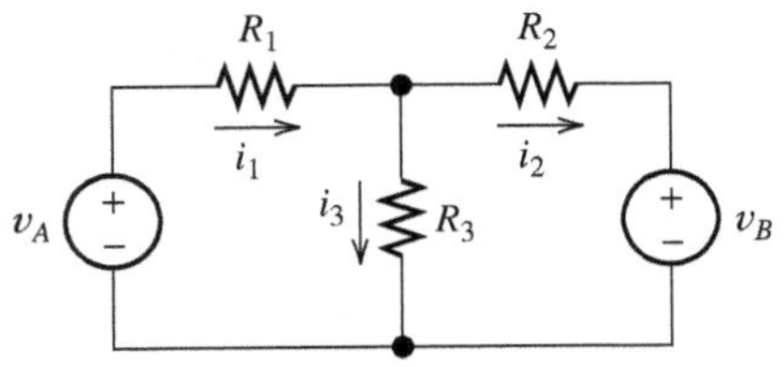

(a) Circuit with branch currents

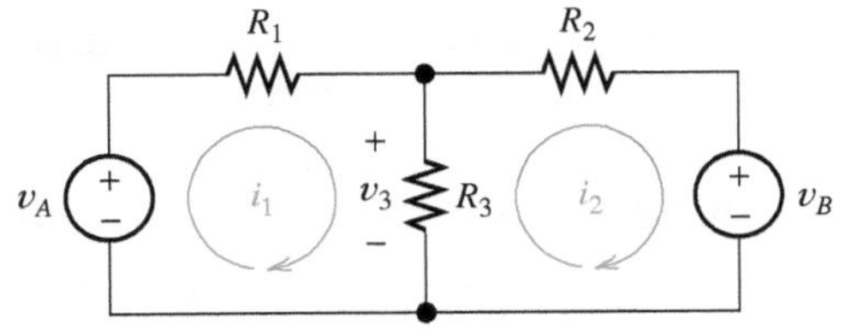

(b) Circuit with mesh currents

Figure 32 Circuit for illustrating the mesh-current method of circuit analysis.

Applying KCL to the node at the top end of R_3, we have

$$i_1 = i_2 + i_3 \tag{52}$$

Next, we solve Equation 52 for i_3 and substitute into Equations 50 and 51. This yields the following two equations:

$$R_1 i_1 + R_3(i_1 - i_2) = v_A \tag{53}$$

$$-R_3(i_1 - i_2) + R_2 i_2 = -v_B \tag{54}$$

Thus, we have used the KCL equation to reduce the KVL equations to two equations in two unknowns.

When several mesh currents flow through one element, we consider the current in that element to be the algebraic sum of the mesh currents.

Now, consider the mesh currents i_1 and i_2 shown in Figure 32(b). As indicated in the figure, mesh currents are considered to flow around closed paths. Hence, mesh currents automatically satisfy KCL. *When several mesh currents flow through one element, we consider the current in that element to be the algebraic sum of the mesh currents.* Thus, assuming a reference direction pointing downward, the current in R_3 is $(i_1 - i_2)$. Thus, $v_3 = R_3(i_1 - i_2)$. Now if we follow i_1 around its loop and apply KVL, we get Equation 53 directly. Similarly, following i_2, we obtain Equation 54 directly.

Because mesh currents automatically satisfy KCL, some work is saved in writing and solving the network equations. The circuit of Figure 32 is fairly simple, and the advantage of mesh currents is not great. However, for more complex networks, the advantage can be quite significant.

Choosing the Mesh Currents

For a planar circuit, we can choose the current variables to flow through the elements around the periphery of each of the open areas of the circuit diagram. For consistency, we usually define the mesh currents to flow clockwise.

We usually choose the current variables to flow clockwise around the periphery of each of the open areas of the circuit diagram.

Two networks and suitable choices for the mesh currents are shown in Figure 33. When a network is drawn with no crossing elements, it resembles a window, with each open area corresponding to a pane of glass. Sometimes it is said that the mesh currents are defined by "soaping the window panes."

Keep in mind that, if two mesh currents flow through a circuit element, we consider the current in that element to be the algebraic sum of the mesh currents. For example, in Figure 33(a), the current in R_2 referenced to the left is $i_3 - i_1$. Furthermore, the current referenced upward in R_3 is $i_2 - i_1$.

Exercise 17 Consider the circuit shown in Figure 33(b). In terms of the mesh currents, find the current in **a.** R_2 referenced upward; **b.** R_4 referenced to the right; **c.** R_8 referenced downward; **d.** R_8 referenced upward.

Answer **a.** $i_4 - i_1$; **b.** $i_2 - i_1$; **c.** $i_3 - i_4$; **d.** $i_4 - i_3$. [Notice that the answer for part (d) is the negative of the answer for part (c).] □

Writing Equations to Solve for Mesh Currents

If a network contains only resistances and independent voltage sources, we can write the required equations by following each current around its mesh and applying KVL. (We do not need to apply KCL because the mesh currents flow out of each node that they flow into.)

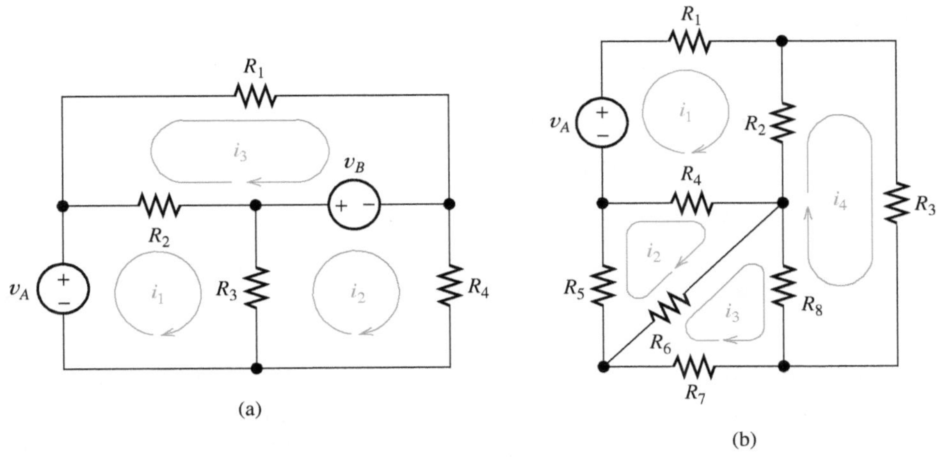

Figure 33 Two circuits and their mesh-current variables.

Example 12 Mesh-Current Analysis

Write the equations needed to solve for the mesh currents in Figure 33(a).

Solution Using a pattern in solving networks by the mesh-current method helps to avoid errors. Part of the pattern that we use is to select the mesh currents to flow clockwise. Then, we write a KVL equation for each mesh, going around the meshes clockwise. As usual, we add a voltage if its positive reference is encountered first in traveling around the mesh, and we subtract the voltage if the negative reference is encountered first. Our pattern is always to take the first end of each resistor encountered as the positive reference for its voltage. Thus, we are always adding the resistor voltages.

If a network contains only resistances and independent voltage sources, we can write the required equations by following each current around its mesh and applying KVL.

For example, in mesh 1 of Figure 33(a), we first encounter the left-hand end of R_2. The voltage across R_2 referenced positive on its left-hand end is $R_2(i_1 - i_3)$. Similarly, we encounter the top end of R_3 first, and the voltage across R_3 referenced positive at the top end is $R_3(i_1 - i_2)$. By using this pattern, we add a term for each resistor in the KVL equation, consisting of the resistance times the current in the mesh under consideration minus the current in the adjacent mesh (if any). Using this pattern for mesh 1 of Figure 33(a), we have

$$R_2(i_1 - i_3) + R_3(i_1 - i_2) - v_A = 0$$

Similarly, for mesh 2, we obtain

$$R_3(i_2 - i_1) + R_4 i_2 + v_B = 0$$

Finally, for mesh 3, we have

$$R_2(i_3 - i_1) + R_1 i_3 - v_B = 0$$

Notice that we have taken the positive reference for the voltage across R_3 at the top in writing the equation for mesh 1 and at the bottom for mesh 3. This is not an error because the terms for R_3 in the two equations are opposite in sign.

In standard form, the equations become:

$$(R_2 + R_3)i_1 - R_3 i_2 - R_2 i_3 = v_A$$
$$- R_3 i_1 + (R_3 + R_4) i_2 = -v_B$$
$$- R_2 i_1 + (R_1 + R_2) i_3 = v_B$$

In matrix form, we have

$$\begin{bmatrix} (R_2 + R_3) & -R_3 & -R_2 \\ -R_3 & (R_3 + R_4) & 0 \\ -R_2 & 0 & (R_1 + R_2) \end{bmatrix} \begin{bmatrix} i_1 \\ i_2 \\ i_3 \end{bmatrix} = \begin{bmatrix} v_A \\ -v_B \\ v_B \end{bmatrix}$$

Often, we use **R** to represent the coefficient matrix, **I** to represent the column vector of mesh currents, and **V** to represent the column vector of the terms on the right-hand sides of the equations in standard form. Then, the mesh-current equations are represented as:

$$\mathbf{RI} = \mathbf{V}$$

We refer to the element of the ith row and jth column of **R** as r_{ij}. ■

Exercise 18 Write the equations for the mesh currents in Figure 32(b) and put them into matrix form.

Answer Following each mesh current in turn, we obtain

$$R_1 i_1 + R_2(i_1 - i_4) + R_4(i_1 - i_2) - v_A = 0$$
$$R_5 i_2 + R_4(i_2 - i_1) + R_6(i_2 - i_3) = 0$$
$$R_7 i_3 + R_6(i_3 - i_2) + R_8(i_3 - i_4) = 0$$
$$R_3 i_4 + R_2(i_4 - i_1) + R_8(i_4 - i_3) = 0$$

$$\begin{bmatrix} (R_1 + R_2 + R_4) & -R_4 & 0 & -R_2 \\ -R_4 & (R_4 + R_5 + R_6) & -R_6 & 0 \\ 0 & -R_6 & (R_6 + R_7 + R_8) & -R_8 \\ -R_2 & 0 & -R_8 & (R_2 + R_3 + R_8) \end{bmatrix} \begin{bmatrix} i_1 \\ i_2 \\ i_3 \\ i_4 \end{bmatrix} = \begin{bmatrix} v_A \\ 0 \\ 0 \\ 0 \end{bmatrix} \quad (55)$$

□

Solving Mesh Equations

After we write the mesh-current equations, we can solve them by using the methods that we discussed in Section 4 for the node-voltage approach. We illustrate with a simple example.

Example 13 Mesh-Current Analysis

Solve for the current in each element of the circuit shown in Figure 34.

Solution First, we select the mesh currents. Following our standard pattern, we define the mesh currents to flow clockwise around each mesh of the circuit. Then, we write a KVL equation around mesh 1:

$$20(i_1 - i_3) + 10(i_1 - i_2) - 70 = 0 \quad (56)$$

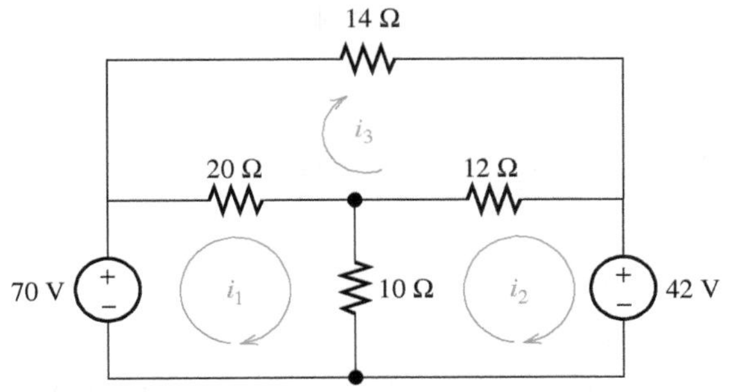

Figure 34 Circuit of Example 13.

For meshes 2 and 3, we have:

$$10(i_2 - i_1) + 12(i_2 - i_3) + 42 = 0 \quad (57)$$

$$20(i_3 - i_1) + 14i_3 + 12(i_3 - i_2) = 0 \quad (58)$$

Putting the equations into standard form, we have:

$$30i_1 - 10i_2 - 20i_3 = 70 \quad (59)$$

$$-10i_1 + 22i_2 - 12i_3 = -42 \quad (60)$$

$$-20i_1 - 12i_2 + 46i_3 = 0 \quad (61)$$

In matrix form, the equations become:

$$\begin{bmatrix} 30 & -10 & -20 \\ -10 & 22 & -12 \\ -20 & -12 & 46 \end{bmatrix} \begin{bmatrix} i_1 \\ i_2 \\ i_3 \end{bmatrix} = \begin{bmatrix} 70 \\ -42 \\ 0 \end{bmatrix}$$

These equations can be solved in a variety of ways. We will demonstrate using MATLAB. (The same results can be obtained by using these same commands in LabVIEW MathScript.) We use **R** for the coefficient matrix, because the coefficients often are resistances. Similarly, we use **V** for the column vector for the right-hand side of the equations and **I** for the column vector of the mesh currents. The commands and results are:

```
>> R = [30 -10 -20; -10 22 -12; -20 -12 46];
>> V = [70; -42; 0];
>> I = R\V % Try to avoid using i, which represents the square root of
>> % -1 in MATLAB.
I =
    4.0000
    1.0000
    2.0000
```

Thus, the values of the mesh currents are $i_1 = 4\,\text{A}$, $i_2 = 1\,\text{A}$, and $i_3 = 2\,\text{A}$. Next, we can find the current in any element. For example, the current flowing downward in the 10-Ω resistance is $i_1 - i_2 = 3\,\text{A}$. ■

Exercise 19 Use mesh currents to solve for the current flowing through the 10-Ω resistance in Figure 35. Check your answer by combining resistances in series and parallel to solve the circuit. Check a second time by using node voltages.

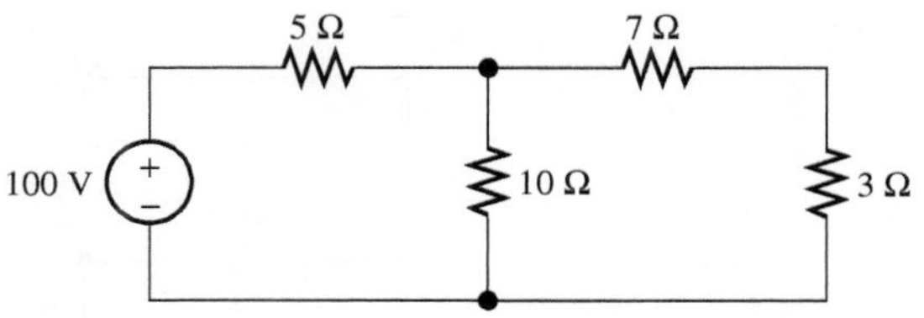

Figure 35 Circuit of Exercise 19.

Answer The current through the 10-Ω resistance is 5 A. □

Exercise 20 Use mesh currents to solve for the current flowing through the 2-Ω resistance in Figure 24.

Answer The current is 1.613 A directed toward the right. □

Writing Mesh Equations Directly in Matrix Form

If a circuit contains only resistances and independent voltage sources, and if we select the mesh currents flowing clockwise, the mesh equations can be obtained directly in matrix form using these steps:

This is a shortcut way to write the mesh equations in matrix form, *provided that the circuit contains only resistances and independent voltage sources.*

1. Make sure that the circuit contains only resistances and independent voltage sources. Select all of the mesh currents to flow in the clockwise direction.

2. Write the sum of the resistances contained in each mesh as the corresponding element on the main diagonal of **R**. In other words, r_{jj} equals the sum of the resistances encountered in going around mesh j.

3. Insert the negatives of the resistances common to the corresponding meshes as the off diagonal terms of **R**. Thus, for $i \neq j$, the elements r_{ij} and r_{ji} are the same and are equal to negative of the sum of the resistances common to meshes i and j.

4. For each element of the **V** matrix, go around the corresponding mesh clockwise, *subtracting* the values of voltage sources for which we encounter the positive reference first and *adding* the values of voltage sources for which we encounter the negative reference first. (We have reversed the rules for adding or subtracting the voltage source values from what we used when writing KVL equations because the elements of **V** correspond to terms on the opposite side of the KVL equations.)

Keep in mind that this procedure does not apply to circuits having current sources or controlled sources.

Example 14 Writing Mesh Equations Directly in Matrix Form

Write the mesh equations directly in matrix form for the circuit of Figure 36.

Solution The matrix equation is:

$$\begin{bmatrix} (R_2 + R_4 + R_5) & -R_2 & -R_5 \\ -R_2 & (R_1 + R_2 + R_3) & -R_3 \\ -R_5 & -R_3 & (R_3 + R_5 + R_6) \end{bmatrix} \begin{bmatrix} i_1 \\ i_2 \\ i_3 \end{bmatrix} = \begin{bmatrix} -v_A + v_B \\ v_A \\ -v_B \end{bmatrix}$$

Notice that mesh 1 includes R_2, R_4, and R_5, so the r_{11} element of **R** is the sum of these resistances. Similarly, mesh 2 contains R_1, R_2, and R_3, so r_{22} is the sum of these resistances. Because R_2 is common to meshes 1 and 2, we have $r_{12} = r_{21} = -R_2$. Similar observations can be made for the other elements of **R**.

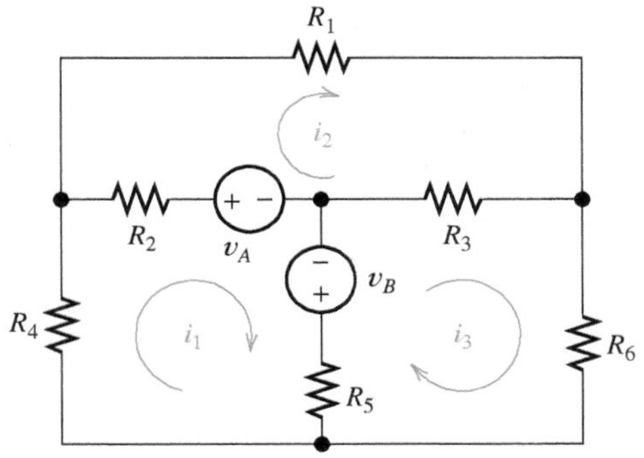

Figure 36 Circuit of Example 14.

As we go around mesh 1 clockwise, we encounter the positive reference for v_A first and the negative reference for v_B first, so we have $v_1 = -v_A + v_B$, and so forth. ■

Exercise 21 Examine the circuit of Figure 33(a), and write its mesh equations directly in matrix form.

Answer

$$\begin{bmatrix} (R_2 + R_3) & -R_3 & -R_2 \\ -R_3 & (R_3 + R_4) & 0 \\ -R_2 & 0 & (R_1 + R_2) \end{bmatrix} \begin{bmatrix} i_1 \\ i_2 \\ i_3 \end{bmatrix} = \begin{bmatrix} v_A \\ -v_B \\ v_B \end{bmatrix}$$ □

Mesh Currents in Circuits Containing Current Sources

Recall that a current source forces a specified current to flow through its terminals, but the voltage across its terminals is not predetermined. Instead, the voltage across a current source depends on the circuit to which the source is connected. Often, it is not easy to write an expression for the voltage across a current source. *A common mistake made by beginning students is to assume that the voltages across current sources are zero.*

A common mistake made by beginning students is to assume that the voltages across current sources are zero.

Consequently, when a circuit contains a current source, we must depart from the pattern that we use for circuits consisting of voltage sources and resistances. First, consider the circuit of Figure 37. As usual, we have defined the mesh currents flowing clockwise. If we were to try to write a KVL equation for mesh 1, we would need to include an unknown for the voltage across the current source. Because we do not wish to increase the number of unknowns in our equations, we avoid writing KVL equations for loops that include current sources. In the circuit in Figure 37, we have defined the current in the current source as i_1. However, we know that this

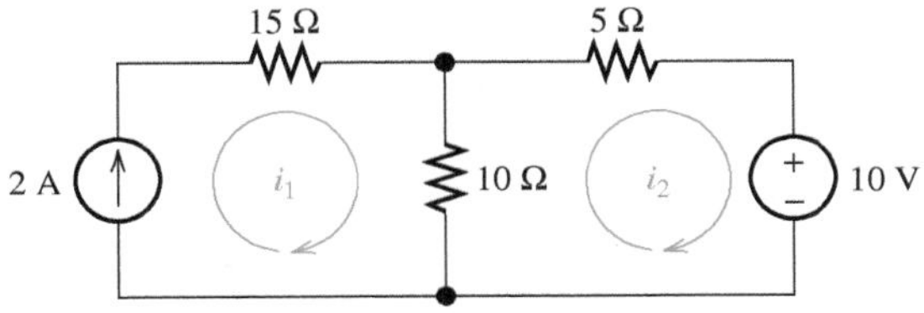

Figure 37 In this circuit, we have $i_1 = 2$ A.

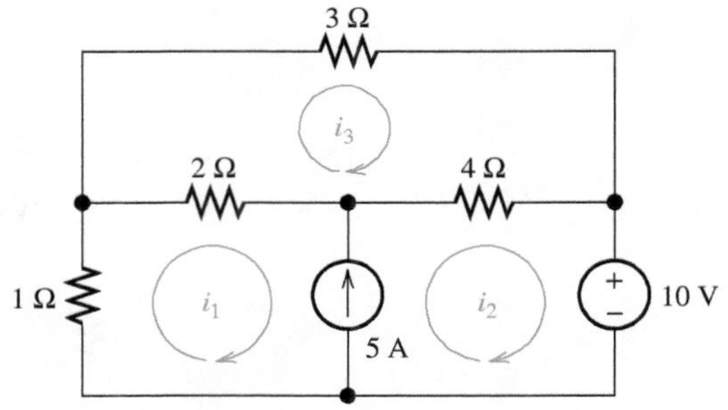

Figure 38 A circuit with a current source common to two meshes.

current is 2 A. Thus, we can write

$$i_1 = 2 \text{ A} \tag{62}$$

The second equation needed can be obtained by applying KVL to mesh 2, which yields

$$10(i_2 - i_1) + 5i_2 + 10 = 0 \tag{63}$$

Equations 62 and 63 can readily be solved for i_2. Notice that in this case the presence of a current source facilitates the solution.

Now let us consider the somewhat more complex situation shown in Figure 38. As usual, we have defined the mesh currents flowing clockwise. We cannot write a KVL equation around mesh 1 because the voltage across the 5-A current source is unknown (and we do not want to increase the number of unknowns in our equations). A solution is to combine meshes 1 and 2 into a **supermesh**. In other words, we write a KVL equation around the periphery of meshes 1 and 2 combined. This yields

$$i_1 + 2(i_1 - i_3) + 4(i_2 - i_3) + 10 = 0 \tag{64}$$

Next, we can write a KVL equation for mesh 3:

$$3i_3 + 4(i_3 - i_2) + 2(i_3 - i_1) = 0 \tag{65}$$

Finally, we recognize that we have defined the current in the current source referenced upward as $i_2 - i_1$. However, we know that the current flowing upward through the current source is 5 A. Thus, we have

$$i_2 - i_1 = 5 \tag{66}$$

It is important to realize that Equation 66 is not a KCL equation.

It is important to realize that Equation 66 is not a KCL equation. Instead, it simply states that we have defined the current referenced upward through the current source in terms of the mesh currents as $i_2 - i_1$, but this current is known to be 5 A. Equations 64, 65, and 66 can be solved for the mesh currents.

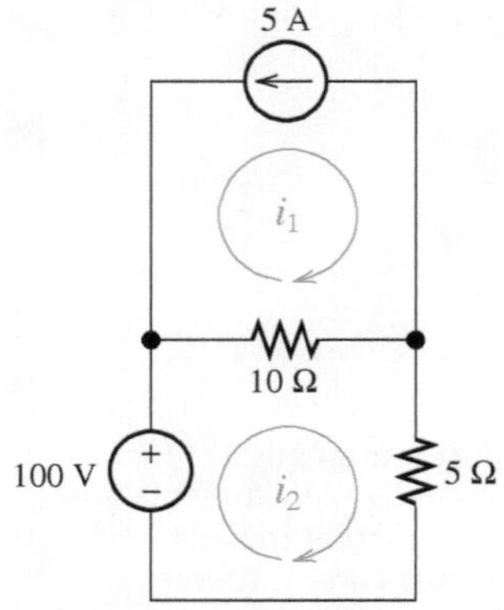

Figure 39 The circuit for Exercise 22.

Exercise 22 Write the equations needed to solve for the mesh currents in Figure 39.
Answer

$$i_1 = -5 \text{ A}$$
$$10(i_2 - i_1) + 5i_2 - 100 = 0$$

□

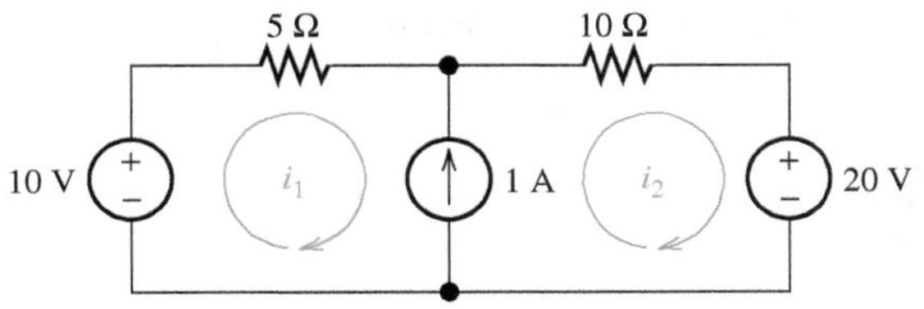

Figure 40 The circuit for Exercise 23.

Exercise 23 Write the equations needed to solve for the mesh currents in Figure 40. Then solve for the currents.

Answer The equations are $i_2 - i_1 = 1$ and $5i_1 + 10i_2 + 20 - 10 = 0$. Solving, we have $i_1 = -4/3$ A and $i_2 = -1/3$ A. □

Circuits with Controlled Sources

Controlled sources present a slight additional complication to the mesh-current technique. First, we write equations exactly as we have done for networks with independent sources. Then, we express the controlling variables in terms of the mesh-current variables and substitute into the network equations. We illustrate with an example.

Example 15 Mesh-Current Analysis with Controlled Sources

Solve for the currents in the circuit of Figure 41(a), which contains a voltage-controlled current source common to the two meshes.

Solution First, we write equations for the mesh currents as we have done for independent sources. Since there is a current source common to mesh 1 and mesh 2, we start by combining the meshes to form a supermesh and write a voltage equation:

$$-20 + 4i_1 + 6i_2 + 2i_2 = 0 \tag{67}$$

Then, we write an expression for the source current in terms of the mesh currents:

$$av_x = 0.25v_x = i_2 - i_1 \tag{68}$$

Next, we see that the controlling voltage is

$$v_x = 2i_2 \tag{69}$$

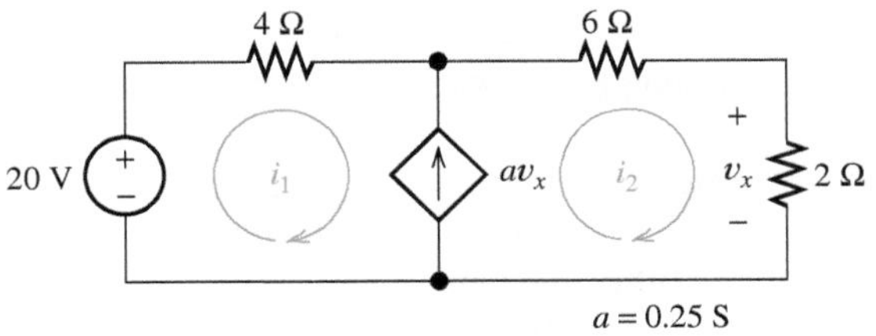

Figure 41 A circuit with a voltage-controlled current source. See Example 15.

Using Equation 58 to substitute for v_x in Equation 57, we have

$$\frac{i_2}{2} = i_2 - i_1 \tag{70}$$

Finally, we put Equations 67 and 70 into standard form, resulting in

$$4i_1 + 8i_2 = 20 \tag{71}$$

$$i_1 - \frac{i_2}{2} = 0 \tag{72}$$

Solving these equations yields $i_1 = 1$ A and $i_2 = 2$ A. ■

Using the principles we have discussed in this section, we can write mesh-current equations for any planar network consisting of sources and resistances.

Next, we summarize the steps in analyzing planar circuits by the mesh-current technique:

Here is a convenient step-by-step guide to mesh-current analysis.

1. If necessary, redraw the network without crossing conductors or elements. Then, define the mesh currents flowing around each of the open areas defined by the network. For consistency, we usually select a clockwise direction for each of the mesh currents, but this is not a requirement.
2. Write network equations, stopping after the number of equations is equal to the number of mesh currents. First, use KVL to write voltage equations for meshes that do not contain current sources. Next, if any current sources are present, write expressions for their currents in terms of the mesh currents. Finally, if a current source is common to two meshes, write a KVL equation for the supermesh.
3. If the circuit contains dependent sources, find expressions for the controlling variables in terms of the mesh currents. Substitute into the network equations, and obtain equations having only the mesh currents as unknowns.
4. Put the equations into standard form. Solve for the mesh currents by use of determinants or other means.
5. Use the values found for the mesh currents to calculate any other currents or voltages of interest.

Exercise 24 Use the mesh-current technique to solve for the currents labeled in the circuits shown in Figure 30.

Answer **a.** $i_a = 1.33$ A; **b.** $i_b = -0.259$ A. □

Exercise 25 Use the mesh-current technique to solve for the values of i_x and i_y in Figure 31.

Answer $i_x = 0.5$ A, $i_y = 2.31$ A. □

6 THÉVENIN AND NORTON EQUIVALENT CIRCUITS

In this section, we learn how to replace two-terminal circuits containing resistances and sources by simple equivalent circuits. By a two-terminal circuit, we mean that the original circuit has only two points that can be connected to other circuits. The original circuit can be any complex interconnection of resistances and sources. However, a restriction is that the controlling variables for any controlled sources must appear inside the original circuit.

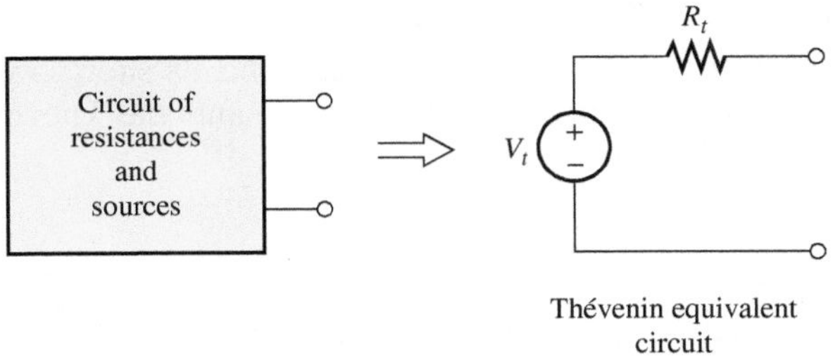

Figure 42 A two-terminal circuit consisting of resistances and sources can be replaced by a Thévenin equivalent circuit.

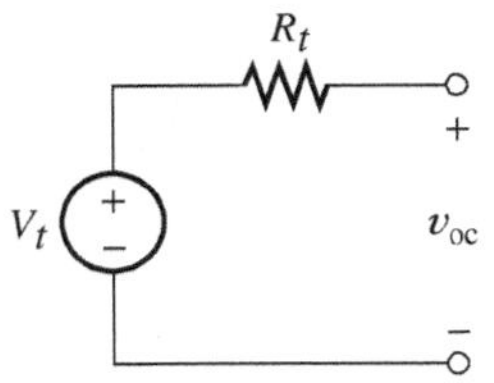

Figure 43 Thévenin equivalent circuit with open-circuited terminals. The open-circuit voltage v_{oc} is equal to the Thévenin voltage V_t.

Thévenin Equivalent Circuits

The Thévenin equivalent circuit consists of an independent voltage source in series with a resistance.

One type of equivalent circuit is the **Thévenin equivalent**, which consists of an independent voltage source in series with a resistance. This is illustrated in Figure 42.

Consider the Thévenin equivalent with open-circuited terminals as shown in Figure 43. By definition, no current can flow through an open circuit. Therefore, no current flows through the Thévenin resistance, and the voltage across the resistance is zero. Applying KVL, we conclude that

$$V_t = v_{oc}$$

Both the original circuit and the equivalent circuit are required to have the same open-circuit voltage. *Thus, the Thévenin source voltage V_t is equal to the open-circuit voltage of the original network.*

Now, consider the Thévenin equivalent with a short circuit connected across its terminals as shown in Figure 44. The current flowing in this circuit is

The Thévenin voltage v_t is equal to the open-circuit voltage of the original network.

$$i_{sc} = \frac{V_t}{R_t}$$

The short-circuit current i_{sc} is the same for the original circuit as for the Thévenin equivalent. Solving for the Thévenin resistance, we have

$$R_t = \frac{V_t}{i_{sc}} \tag{73}$$

Using the fact that the Thévenin voltage is equal to the open-circuit voltage of the network, we have

$$R_t = \frac{v_{oc}}{i_{sc}} \tag{74}$$

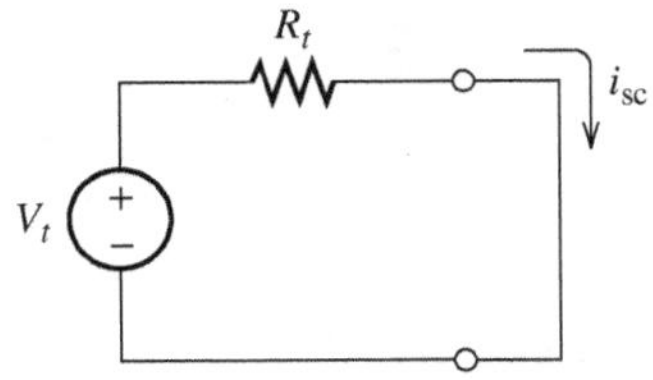

Figure 44 Thévenin equivalent circuit with short-circuited terminals. The short-circuit current is $i_{sc} = V_t/R_t$.

The Thévenin resistance is equal to the open-circuit voltage divided by the short-circuit current.

Thus, to determine the Thévenin equivalent circuit, we can start by analyzing the original network for its open-circuit voltage and its short-circuit current. The Thévenin voltage equals the open-circuit voltage, and the Thévenin resistance is given by Equation 74.

Example 16 Determining the Thévenin Equivalent Circuit

Find the Thévenin equivalent for the circuit shown in Figure 45(a).

Solution First, we analyze the circuit with open-circuited terminals. This is shown in Figure 45(b). The resistances R_1 and R_2 are in series and have an equivalent resistance of $R_1 + R_2$. Therefore, the current circulating is

$$i_1 = \frac{v_s}{R_1 + R_2} = \frac{15}{100 + 50} = 0.10 \text{ A}$$

The open-circuit voltage is the voltage across R_2:

$$v_{oc} = R_2 i_1 = 50 \times 0.10 = 5 \text{ V}$$

Thus, the Thévenin voltage is $V_t = 5$ V.

Now, we consider the circuit with a short circuit connected across its terminals as shown in Figure 45(c). By definition, the voltage across a short circuit is zero. Hence, the voltage across R_2 is zero, and the current through it is zero, as shown in the figure. Therefore, the short-circuit current i_{sc} flows through R_1. The source voltage v_s appears across R_1, so we can write

$$i_{sc} = \frac{v_s}{R_1} = \frac{15}{100} = 0.15 \text{ A}$$

Now, we can use Equation 74 to determine the Thévenin resistance:

$$R_t = \frac{v_{oc}}{i_{sc}} = \frac{5 \text{ V}}{0.15 \text{ A}} = 33.3 \ \Omega$$

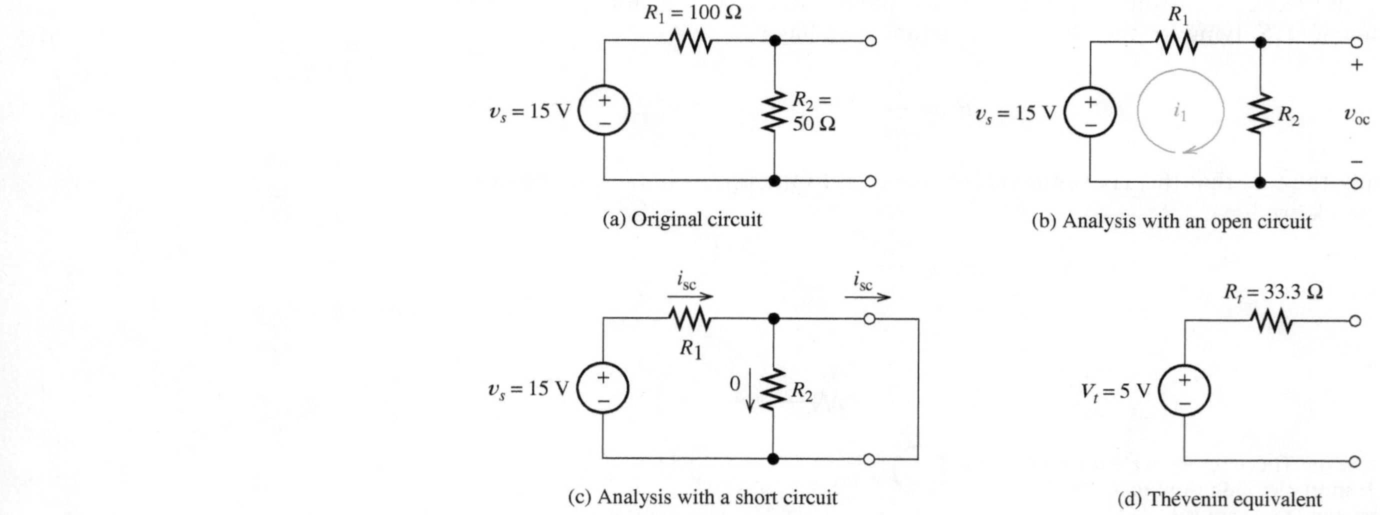

Figure 45 Circuit for Example 16.

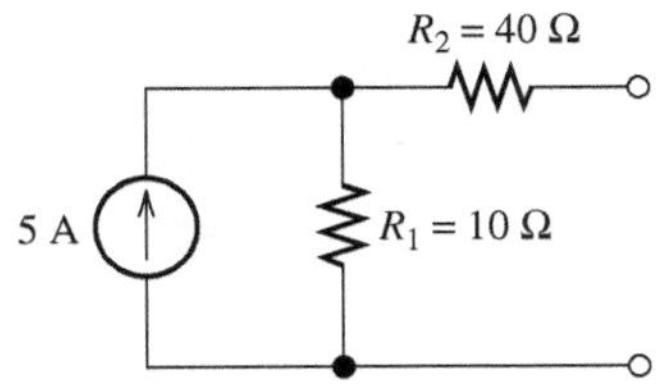

Figure 46 Circuit for Exercise 26.

The Thévenin equivalent circuit is shown in Figure 45(d). ■

Exercise 26 Find the Thévenin equivalent circuit for the circuit shown in Figure 46.
Answer $V_t = 50$ V, $R_t = 50\ \Omega$. □

Finding the Thévenin Resistance Directly. If a network contains no dependent sources, there is an alternative way to find the Thévenin resistance. First, we *zero* the sources in the network. In zeroing a voltage source, we reduce its voltage to zero. A voltage source with zero voltage is equivalent to a short circuit.

In zeroing a current source, we reduce its current to zero. By definition, an element that always carries zero current is an open circuit. *Thus, to zero the independent sources, we replace voltage sources with short circuits and replace current sources with open circuits.*

When zeroing a current source, it becomes an open circuit. When zeroing a voltage source, it becomes a short circuit.

Figure 47 shows a Thévenin equivalent before and after zeroing its voltage source. Looking back into the terminals after the source is zeroed, we see the Thévenin resistance. *Thus, we can find the Thévenin resistance by zeroing the sources in the original network and then computing the resistance between the terminals.*

We can find the Thévenin resistance by zeroing the sources in the original network and then computing the resistance between the terminals.

Example 17 Zeroing Sources to Find Thévenin Resistance

Find the Thévenin resistance for the circuit shown in Figure 48(a) by zeroing the sources. Then, find the short-circuit current and the Thévenin equivalent circuit.

Solution To zero the sources, we replace the voltage source by a short circuit and replace the current source by an open circuit. The resulting circuit is shown in Figure 48(b).

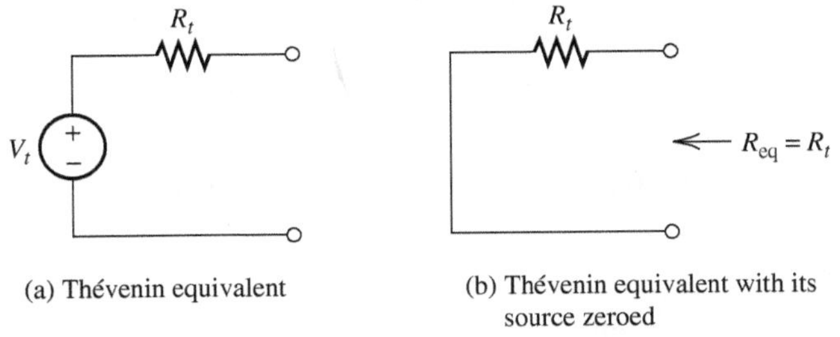

Figure 47 When the source is zeroed, the resistance seen from the circuit terminals is equal to the Thévenin resistance.

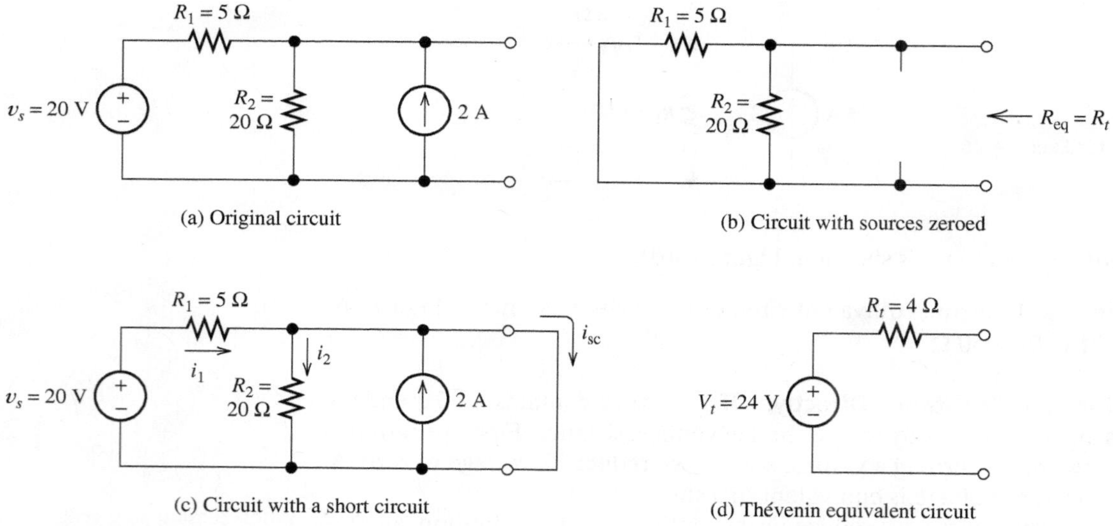

Figure 48 Circuit for Example 17.

The Thévenin resistance is the equivalent resistance between the terminals. This is the parallel combination of R_1 and R_2, which is given by

$$R_t = R_{eq} = \frac{1}{1/R_1 + 1/R_2} = \frac{1}{1/5 + 1/20} = 4\ \Omega$$

Next, we find the short-circuit current for the circuit. The circuit is shown in Figure 48(c). In this circuit, the voltage across R_2 is zero because of the short circuit. Thus, the current through R_2 is zero:

$$i_2 = 0$$

Furthermore, the voltage across R_1 is equal to 20 V. Thus, the current is

$$i_1 = \frac{v_s}{R_1} = \frac{20}{5} = 4\ \text{A}$$

Finally, we write a current equation for the node joining the top ends of R_2 and the 2-A source. Setting the sum of the currents entering equal to the sum of the currents leaving, we have

$$i_1 + 2 = i_2 + i_{sc}$$

This yields $i_{sc} = 6$ A.

Now, the Thévenin voltage can be found. Applying Equation 74, we get

$$V_t = R_t i_{sc} = 4 \times 6 = 24\ \text{V}$$

The Thévenin equivalent circuit is shown in Figure 48(d). ■

Exercise 27 Use node-voltage analysis of the circuit shown in Figure 48(a) to show that the open-circuit voltage is equal to the Thévenin voltage found in Example 17. □

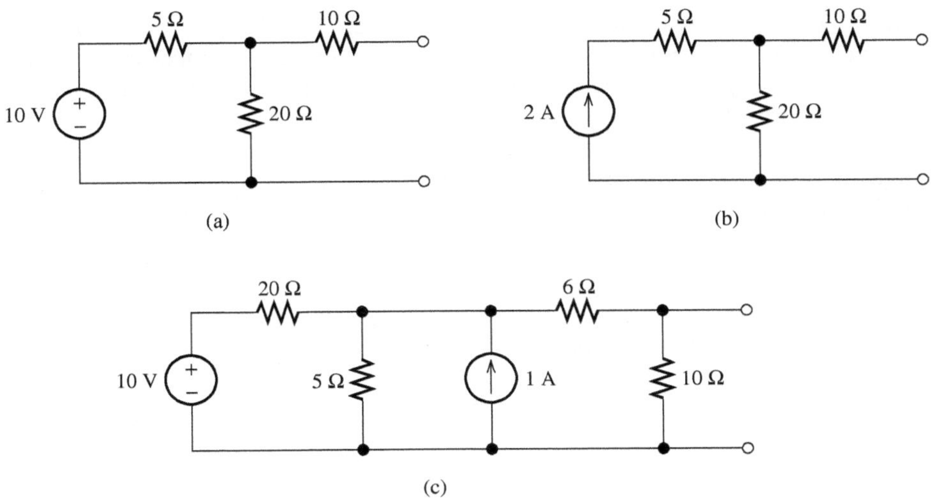

Figure 49 Circuits for Exercise 28.

Exercise 28 Find the Thévenin resistance for each of the circuits shown in Figure 49 by zeroing the sources.

Answer **a.** $R_t = 14\ \Omega$; **b.** $R_t = 30\ \Omega$; **c.** $R_t = 5\ \Omega$. □

We complete our discussion of Thévenin equivalent circuits with one more example.

Example 18 Thévenin Equivalent of a Circuit with a Dependent Source

Find the Thévenin equivalent for the circuit shown in Figure 50(a).

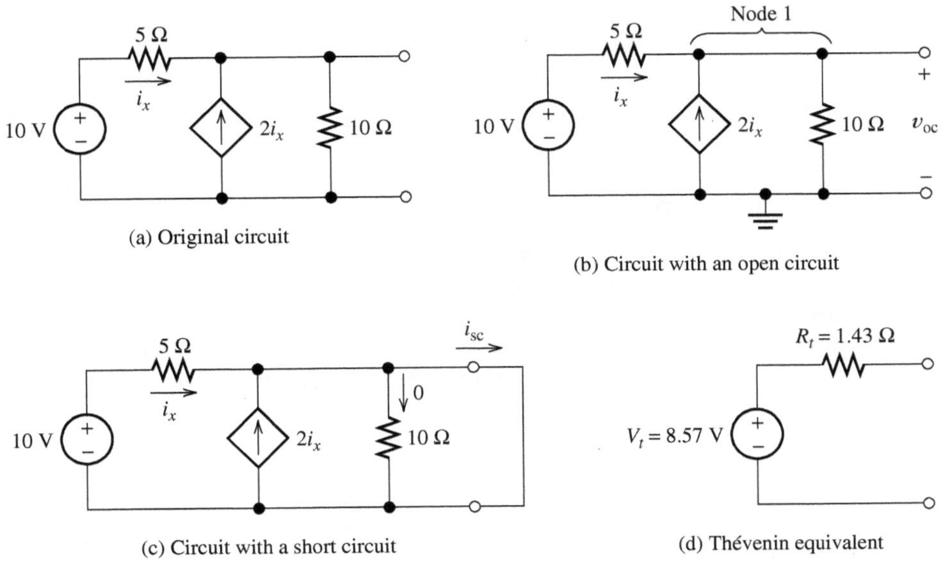

Figure 50 Circuit for Example 18.

Because this circuit contains a dependent source, we cannot find the Thévenin resistance by zeroing the sources and combining resistances in series and parallel.

Solution Because this circuit contains a dependent source, we cannot find the Thévenin resistance by zeroing the sources and combining resistances in series and parallel. Thus, we must analyze the circuit to find the open-circuit voltage and the short-circuit current.

We start with the open-circuit voltage. Consider Figure 50(b). We use node-voltage analysis, picking the reference node at the bottom of the circuit. Then, v_{oc} is the unknown node-voltage variable. First, we write a current equation at node 1.

$$i_x + 2i_x = \frac{v_{oc}}{10} \tag{75}$$

Next, we write an expression for the controlling variable i_x in terms of the node voltage v_{oc}:

$$i_x = \frac{10 - v_{oc}}{5}$$

Substituting this into Equation 75, we have

$$3\frac{10 - v_{oc}}{5} = \frac{v_{oc}}{10}$$

Solving, we find that $v_{oc} = 8.57$ V.

Now, we consider short-circuit conditions as shown in Figure 50(c). In this case, the current through the 10-Ω resistance is zero. Furthermore, we get

$$i_x = \frac{10\text{ V}}{5\ \Omega} = 2\text{ A}$$

and

$$i_{sc} = 3i_x = 6\text{ A}$$

Next, we use Equation 74 to compute the Thévenin resistance:

$$R_t = \frac{v_{oc}}{i_{sc}} = \frac{8.57\text{ V}}{6\text{ A}} = 1.43\ \Omega$$

Finally, the Thévenin equivalent circuit is shown in Figure 50(d). ■

Norton Equivalent Circuit

Another type of equivalent, known as the **Norton equivalent circuit**, is shown in Figure 51. It consists of an independent current source I_n in parallel with the Thévenin resistance. Notice that if we zero the Norton current source, replacing it by an open circuit, the Norton equivalent becomes a resistance of R_t. This also happens if we zero the voltage source in the Thévenin equivalent by replacing the

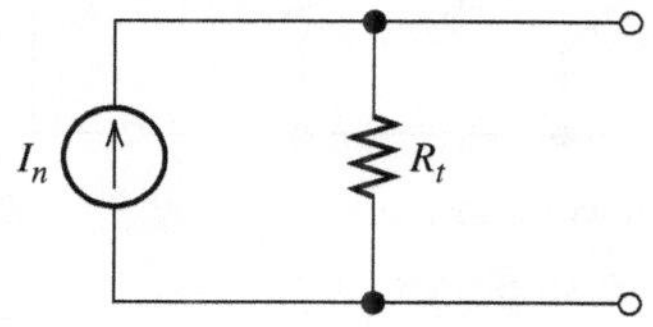

Figure 51 The Norton equivalent circuit consists of an independent current source I_n in parallel with the Thévenin resistance R_t.

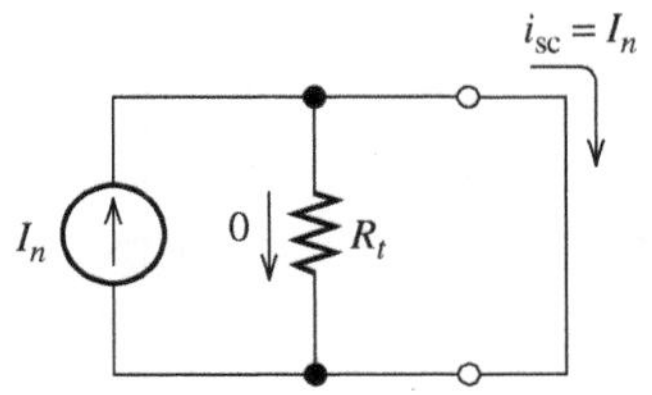

Figure 52 The Norton equivalent circuit with a short circuit across its terminals.

voltage source by a short circuit. Thus, the resistance in the Norton equivalent is the same as the Thévenin resistance.

Consider placing a short circuit across the Norton equivalent as shown in Figure 52. In this case, the current through R_t is zero. *Therefore, the Norton current is equal to the short-circuit current:*

$$I_n = i_{sc}$$

We can find the Norton equivalent by using the same techniques as we used for the Thévenin equivalent.

Step-by-Step Thévenin/Norton-Equivalent-Circuit Analysis

1. Perform two of these:
   - **a.** Determine the open-circuit voltage $V_t = v_{oc}$.
   - **b.** Determine the short-circuit current $I_n = i_{sc}$.
   - **c.** Zero the independent sources and find the Thévenin resistance R_t looking back into the terminals. Do not zero dependent sources.
2. Use the equation $V_t = R_t I_n$ to compute the remaining value.
3. The Thévenin equivalent consists of a voltage source V_t in series with R_t.
4. The Norton equivalent consists of a current source I_n in parallel with R_t.

Example 19 Norton Equivalent Circuit

Find the Norton equivalent for the circuit shown in Figure 53(a).

Solution Because the circuit contains a controlled source, we cannot zero the sources and combine resistances to find the Thévenin resistance. First, we consider the circuit with an open circuit as shown in Figure 53(a). We treat v_{oc} as a node-voltage variable. Writing a current equation at the top of the circuit, we have

$$\frac{v_x}{4} + \frac{v_{oc} - 15}{R_1} + \frac{v_{oc}}{R_2 + R_3} = 0 \qquad (76)$$

Next, we use the voltage-divider principle to write an expression for v_x in terms of resistances and v_{oc}:

$$v_x = \frac{R_3}{R_2 + R_3} v_{oc} = 0.25 v_{oc}$$

Substituting into Equation 76, we find that

$$\frac{0.25 v_{oc}}{4} + \frac{v_{oc} - 15}{R_1} + \frac{v_{oc}}{R_2 + R_3} = 0$$

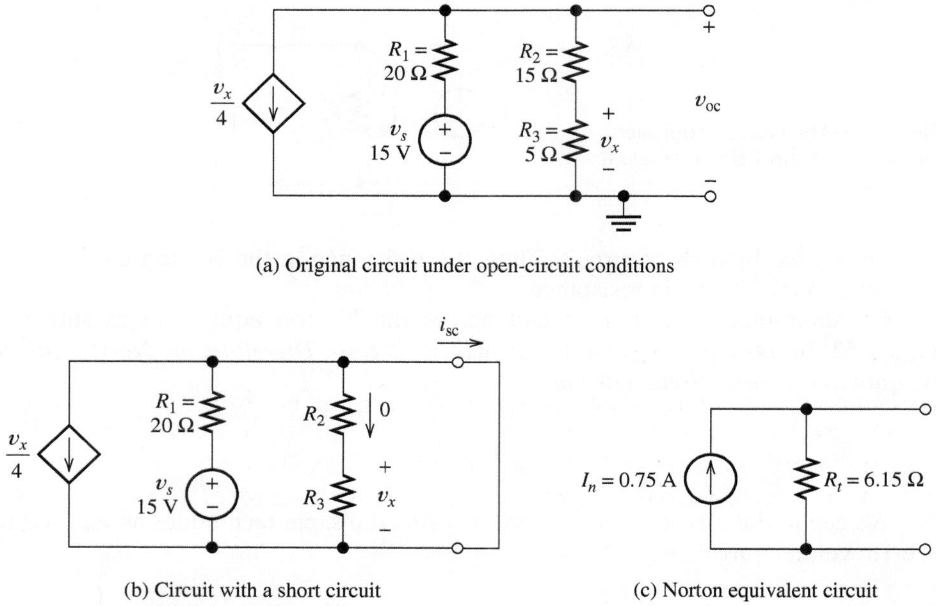

Figure 53 Circuit of Example 19.

Substituting resistance values and solving, we observe that $v_{oc} = 4.62$ V.

Next, we consider short-circuit conditions as shown in Figure 53(b). In this case, the current through R_2 and R_3 is zero. Thus, $v_x = 0$, and the controlled current source appears as an open circuit. The short-circuit current is given by

$$i_{sc} = \frac{v_s}{R_1} = \frac{15\text{ V}}{20\ \Omega} = 0.75\text{ A}$$

Now, we can find the Thévenin resistance:

$$R_t = \frac{v_{oc}}{i_{sc}} = \frac{4.62}{0.75} = 6.15\ \Omega$$

The Norton equivalent circuit is shown in Figure 53(c). ■

Exercise 29 Find the Norton equivalent for each of the circuits shown in Figure 54.
Answer **a.** $I_n = 1.67$ A, $R_t = 9.375\ \Omega$; **b.** $I_n = 2$ A, $R_t = 15\ \Omega$. □

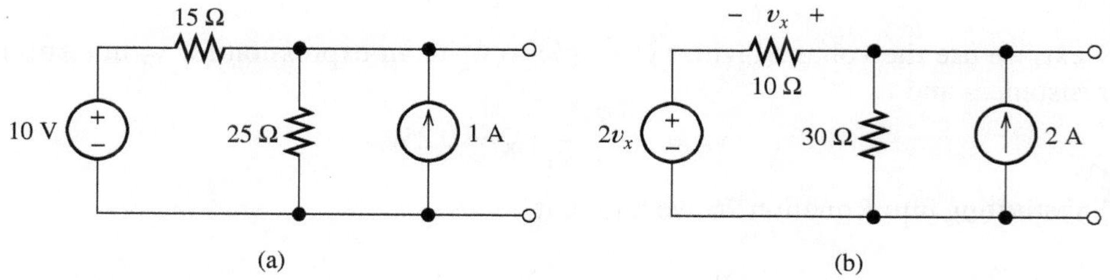

Figure 54 Circuits for Exercise 29.

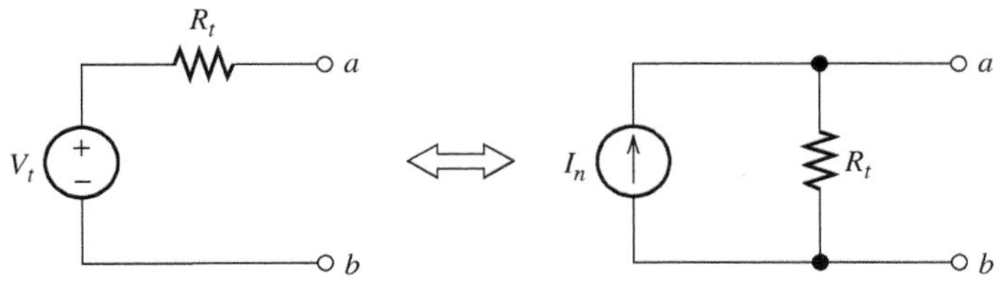

Figure 55 A voltage source in series with a resistance is externally equivalent to a current source in parallel with the resistance, provided that $I_n = V_t/R_t$.

Source Transformations

We can replace a voltage source in series with a resistance by a Norton equivalent circuit, which consists of a current source in parallel with the resistance. This is called a **source transformation** and is illustrated in Figure 55. The two circuits are identical in terms of their external behavior. In other words, the voltages and currents at terminals a and b remain the same after the transformation is made. However, in general, the current flowing through R_t is different for the two circuits. For example, suppose that the two circuits shown in Figure 55 are open circuited. Then no current flows through the resistor in series with the voltage source, but the current I_n flows through the resistance in parallel with the current source.

In making source transformations it is very important to maintain the proper relationship between the reference direction for the current source and the polarity of the voltage source. If the positive polarity is closest to terminal a, the current reference must point toward terminal a, as shown in Figure 55.

Sometimes, we can simplify the solution of a circuit by source transformations. This is similar to solving circuits by combining resistances in series or parallel. We illustrate with an example.

Here is a "trick" question that you might have some fun with: Suppose that the circuits of Figure 55 are placed in identical black boxes with the terminals accessible from outside the box. How could you determine which box contains the Norton equivalent? An answer can be found at the end of the chapter summary.

Example 20 Using Source Transformations

Use source transformations to aid in solving for the currents i_1 and i_2 shown in Figure 56(a).

Solution Several approaches are possible. One is to transform the 1-A current source and R_2 into a voltage source in series with R_2. This is shown in Figure 56(b). Notice that the positive polarity of the 10-V source is at the top, because the 1-A source reference points upward. The single-loop circuit of Figure 56(b) can be solved by writing a KVL equation. Traveling clockwise and summing voltages, we have

$$R_1 i_1 + R_2 i_1 + 10 - 20 = 0$$

Solving and substituting values, we get

$$i_1 = \frac{10}{R_1 + R_2} = 0.667 \text{ A}$$

Then in the original circuit, we can write a current equation at the top node and solve for i_2:

$$i_2 = i_1 + 1 = 1.667 \text{ A}$$

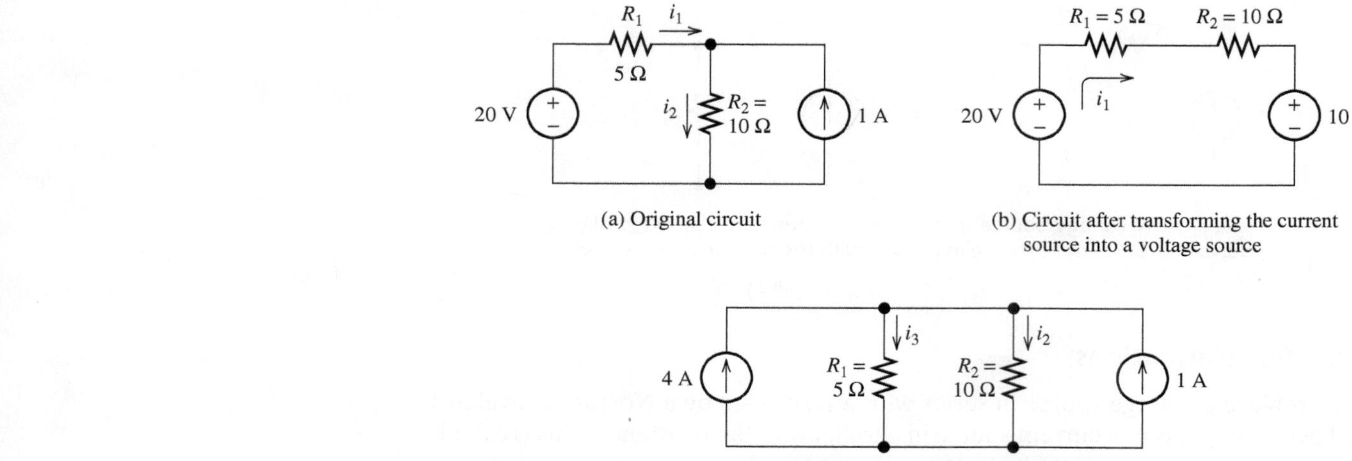

(a) Original circuit

(b) Circuit after transforming the current source into a voltage source

(c) Circuit after transforming the voltage source into a current source

Figure 56 Circuit for Example 20.

Another approach is to transform the voltage source and R_1 into a current source in parallel with R_1. Making this change to the original circuit yields the circuit shown in Figure 56(c). Notice that we have labeled the current through R_1 as i_3 rather than i_1. This is because the current in the resistance of the transformed source is not the same as in the original circuit. Now, in Figure 56(c), we see that a total current of 5 A flows into the parallel combination of R_1 and R_2. Using the current-division principle, we find the current through R_2:

$$i_2 = \frac{R_1}{R_1 + R_2} i_{\text{total}} = \frac{5}{5 + 10}(5) = 1.667 \text{ A}$$

This agrees with our previous result. ■

Exercise 30 Use source transformations to solve for the values of i_1 and i_2 in Figure 57. First, transform the current source and R_1 into a voltage source in series with R_1. (Make sure in making the transformation that the polarity of the voltage source bears the correct relationship to the current reference direction.) Solve the circuit by a second approach. Starting with the original circuit, transform the 10-V source and R_2 into a current source in parallel with R_2. Of course, the answers should be the same for both approaches.

Answer $i_1 = -0.667$ A, $i_2 = 1.333$ A. □

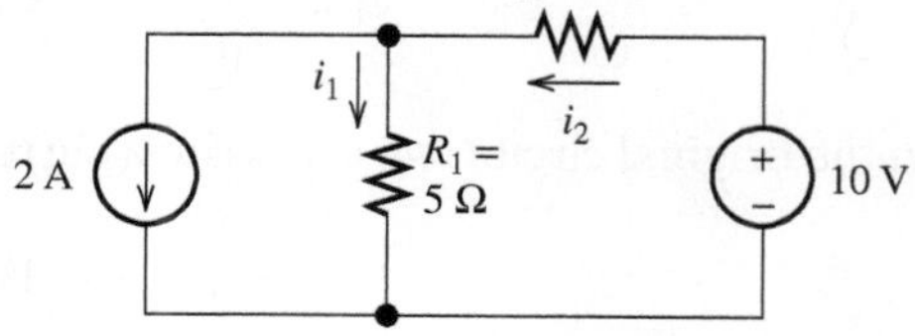

Figure 57 Circuit for Exercise 30.

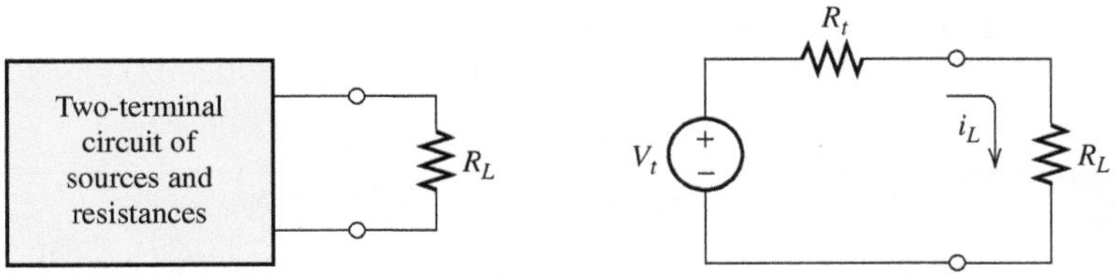

(a) Original circuit with load

(b) Thévenin equivalent circuit with load

Figure 58 Circuits for analysis of maximum power transfer.

Maximum Power Transfer

Suppose that we have a two-terminal circuit and we want to connect a load resistance R_L such that the maximum possible power is delivered to the load. This is illustrated in Figure 58(a). To analyze this problem, we replace the original circuit by its Thévenin equivalent as shown in Figure 58(b). The current flowing through the load resistance is given by

$$i_L = \frac{V_t}{R_t + R_L}$$

The power delivered to the load is

$$p_L = i_L^2 R_L$$

Substituting for the current, we have

$$p_L = \frac{V_t^2 R_L}{(R_t + R_L)^2} \qquad (77)$$

To find the value of the load resistance that maximizes the power delivered to the load, we set the derivative of p_L with respect to R_L equal to zero:

$$\frac{dp_L}{dR_L} = \frac{V_t^2(R_t + R_L)^2 - 2V_t^2 R_L(R_t + R_L)}{(R_t + R_L)^4} = 0$$

Solving for the load resistance, we have

$$R_L = R_t$$

Thus, the load resistance that absorbs the maximum power from a two-terminal circuit is equal to the Thévenin resistance. The maximum power is found by substituting $R_L = R_t$ into Equation 77. The result is

The load resistance that absorbs the maximum power from a two-terminal circuit is equal to the Thévenin resistance.

$$P_{L\max} = \frac{V_t^2}{4R_t} \qquad (78)$$

An All-Too-Common Example. You may have had difficulty in starting your car on a frigid morning. The battery in your car can be represented by a Thévenin equivalent circuit. It turns out that the Thévenin voltage of the battery does not change greatly with temperature. However, when the battery is very cold, the chemical reactions occur much more slowly and its Thévenin resistance is much higher. Thus, the power that the battery can deliver to the starter motor is greatly reduced.

Example 21 Determining Maximum Power Transfer

Find the load resistance for maximum power transfer from the circuit shown in Figure 59. Also, find the maximum power.

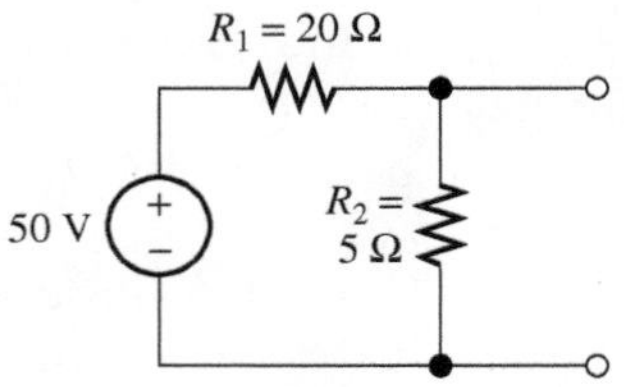

Figure 59 Circuit for Example 21.

Solution First, we must find the Thévenin equivalent circuit. Zeroing the voltage source, we find that the resistances R_1 and R_2 are in parallel. Thus, the Thévenin resistance is

$$R_t = \frac{1}{1/R_1 + 1/R_2} = \frac{1}{1/20 + 1/5} = 4\ \Omega$$

The Thévenin voltage is equal to the open-circuit voltage. Using the voltage-division principle, we find that

$$V_t = v_{oc} = \frac{R_2}{R_1 + R_2}(50) = \frac{5}{5 + 20}(50) = 10\ \text{V}$$

Hence, the load resistance that receives maximum power is

$$R_L = R_t = 4\ \Omega$$

and the maximum power is given by Equation 78:

$$P_{L\,\max} = \frac{V_t^2}{4R_t} = \frac{10^2}{4 \times 4} = 6.25\ \text{W}$$

■

PRACTICAL APPLICATION 1

An Important Engineering Problem: Energy-Storage Systems for Electric Vehicles

Imagine pollution-free electric vehicles with exciting performance and 500-mile range. They do not exist, but they are the target of an ongoing large-scale engineering effort to which you may contribute. Such electric vehicles (EVs) are a worthwhile goal because they can be very efficient in their use of energy, particularly in stop-and-go traffic. Kinetic energy can be recovered during braking and saved for later use during acceleration. Furthermore, EVs emit little pollution into crowded urban environments.

So far, EV range and performance remains less than ideal. The availability of suitable energy-storage devices is the key stumbling block in achieving better EVs (and a multitude of other highly desirable devices, such as laptop computers that do not need recharging for a week).

Capacitors and inductors are capable of storing electrical energy. However, it turns out that their energy content per unit volume is too small to make them a practical solution for EVs. The energy content of modern rechargeable batteries is better but still not on a par with the energy content of gasoline, which is approximately 10,000 watt-hours/liter (Wh/L). In contrast, the energy content of nickel-metal hydride batteries used in current EVs is about 175 Wh/L. Lithium-ion batteries under current development are expected to increase this to about 300 Wh/L. Thus, even allowing for the relative inefficiency of the internal combustion engine in converting chemical energy to mechanical energy, much more usable energy can be obtained from gasoline than from current batteries of comparable volume.

Although EVs do not emit pollutants at the point of use, the mining, refining, and disposal of metals pose grave environmental dangers. We must always consider the entire environmental (as well as economic) impact of the systems we design. As an engineer, you can do a great service to humanity by accepting the challenge to develop safe, clean systems for storing energy in forms that are readily converted to and from electrical form.

Naturally, one possibility currently under intense development is improved electrochemical batteries based on nontoxic chemicals. Another option is a mechanical flywheel system that would be coupled through an electrical generator to electric drive motors. Still another solution is a hybrid vehicle that uses a small internal combustion engine, an electrical generator, an energy-storage system, and electrical drive motors. The engine achieves low pollution levels by being optimized to run at a constant load while charging a relatively small energy-storage system. When the storage capacity becomes full, the engine shuts down automatically and the vehicle runs on stored energy. The engine is just large enough to keep up with energy demands under high-speed highway conditions.

Whatever form the ultimate solution to vehicle pollution may take, we can anticipate that it will include elements from mechanical, chemical, manufacturing, and civil engineering in close combination with electrical-engineering principles.

Application of Maximum Power Transfer. When a load resistance equals the internal Thévenin resistance of the source, half of the power is dissipated in the source resistance and half is delivered to the load. In higher power applications for which efficiency is important, we do not usually design for maximum power transfer. For example, in designing an electric vehicle, we would want to deliver the energy stored in the batteries mainly to the drive motors and minimize the power loss in the resistance of the battery and wiring. This system would approach maximum power transfer rarely when maximum acceleration is needed.

On the other hand, when small amounts of power are involved, we would design for maximum power transfer. For example, we would design a radio receiver to extract the maximum signal power from the receiving antenna. In this application, the power is very small, typically much less than one microwatt, and efficiency is not a consideration.

7 SUPERPOSITION PRINCIPLE

Suppose that we have a circuit composed of resistances, linear dependent sources, and n independent sources. (We will explain the term *linear* dependent source shortly.) The current flowing through a given element (or the voltage across it) is called a **response**, because the currents and voltages appear in response to the independent sources.

Recall that we zeroed the independent sources as a method for finding the Thévenin resistance of a two-terminal circuit. To zero a source, we reduce its value to zero. Then, current sources become open circuits, and voltage sources become short circuits.

The superposition principle states that any response in a linear circuit is the sum of the responses for each independent source acting alone with the other independent sources zeroed. When zeroed, current sources become open circuits and voltage sources become short circuits.

Now, consider zeroing all of the independent sources except the first, observe a particular response (a current or voltage), and denote the value of that response as r_1. (We use the symbol r rather than i or v because the response could be either a current or a voltage.) Similarly, with only source 2 activated, the response is denoted as r_2, and so on. The response with all the sources activated is called the total response, denoted as r_T. The **superposition principle** states that the total response is the sum of the responses to each of the independent sources acting individually. In equation

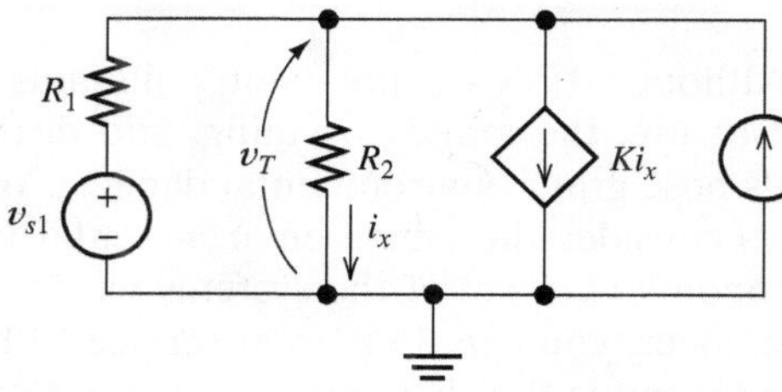

Figure 60 Circuit used to illustrate the superposition principle.

form, this is

$$r_T = r_1 + r_2 + \cdots + r_n \tag{79}$$

Next, we illustrate the validity of superposition for the example circuit shown in Figure 60. In this circuit, there are two independent sources: the first, the voltage source v_{s1}, and the second, the current source i_{s2}. Suppose that the response of interest is the voltage across the resistance R_2.

First, we solve for the total response v_T by solving the circuit with both sources in place. Writing a current equation at the top node, we obtain

$$\frac{v_T - v_{s1}}{R_1} + \frac{v_T}{R_2} + Ki_x = i_{s2} \tag{80}$$

The control variable i_x is given by

$$i_x = \frac{v_T}{R_2} \tag{81}$$

Substituting Equation 81 into Equation 80 and solving for the total response, we get

$$v_T = \frac{R_2}{R_1 + R_2 + KR_1} v_{s1} + \frac{R_1 R_2}{R_1 + R_2 + KR_1} i_{s2} \tag{82}$$

If we set i_{s2} to zero, we obtain the response to v_{s1} acting alone:

$$v_1 = \frac{R_2}{R_1 + R_2 + KR_1} v_{s1} \tag{83}$$

Similarly, if we set v_{s1} equal to zero in Equation 82, the response due to i_{s2} is givenby

$$v_2 = \frac{R_1 R_2}{R_1 + R_2 + KR_1} i_{s2} \tag{84}$$

Comparing Equations 82, 83, and 84, we see that

$$v_T = v_1 + v_2$$

Thus, as expected from the superposition principle, the total response is equal to the sum of the responses for each of the independent sources acting individually.

Notice that if we zero both of the independent sources ($v_{s1} = 0$ and $i_{s2} = 0$), the response becomes zero. Hence, the dependent source does not contribute to the total response. However, the dependent source affects the contributions of the two independent sources. This is evident because the gain parameter K of the dependent source appears in the expressions for both v_1 and v_2. *In general, dependent sources do not contribute a separate term to the total response, and we must not zero dependent sources in applying superposition.*

Dependent sources do not contribute a separate term to the total response, and we must not zero dependent sources in applying superposition.

Linearity

If we plot voltage versus current for a resistance, we have a straight line. This is illustrated in Figure 61. Thus, we say that Ohm's law is a **linear equation**. Similarly, the current in the controlled source shown in Figure 60 is given by $i_{cs} = Ki_x$, which is also a linear equation. In this chapter, the term **linear controlled source** means a source whose value is a constant times a control variable that is a current or a voltage appearing in the network.

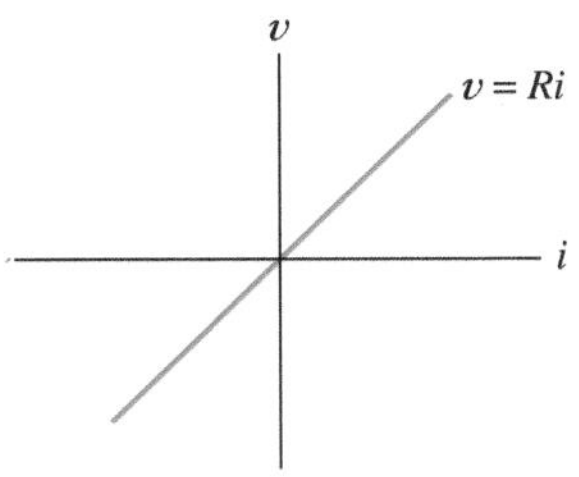

Figure 61 A resistance that obeys Ohm's law is linear.

Some examples of nonlinear equations are

$$v = 10i^2$$

$$i_{cs} = K\cos(i_x)$$

and

$$i = e^v$$

The superposition principle does not apply to any circuit that has element(s) described by nonlinear equation(s). We will encounter nonlinear elements later in our study of electronic circuits.

The superposition principle does not apply to any circuit that has element(s) described by nonlinear equation(s).

Furthermore, superposition does not apply for power in resistances, because $P = v^2/R$ and $P = i^2R$ are nonlinear equations.

Using Superposition to Solve Circuits

We can apply superposition in circuit analysis by analyzing the circuit for each source separately. Then, we add the individual responses to find the total response. Sometimes, the analysis of a circuit is simplified by considering each independent source separately. We illustrate with an example.

Example 22 Circuit Analysis Using Superposition

Use superposition in solving the circuit shown in Figure 62(a) for the voltage v_T.

Solution We analyze the circuit with only one source activated at a time and add the responses. Figure 62(b) shows the circuit with only the voltage source active. The response can be found by applying the voltage-division principle:

$$v_1 = \frac{R_2}{R_1 + R_2} v_s = \frac{5}{5 + 10}(15) = 5 \text{ V}$$

Next, we analyze the circuit with only the current source active. The circuit is shown in Figure 62(c). In this case, the resistances R_1 and R_2 are in parallel, and the equivalent resistance is

$$R_{eq} = \frac{1}{1/R_1 + 1/R_2} = \frac{1}{1/10 + 1/5} = 3.33\ \Omega$$

The voltage due to the current source is given by

$$v_2 = i_s R_{eq} = 2 \times 3.33 = 6.66 \text{ V}$$

Finally, we obtain the total response by adding the individual responses:

$$v_T = v_1 + v_2 = 5 + 6.66 = 11.66$$ ■

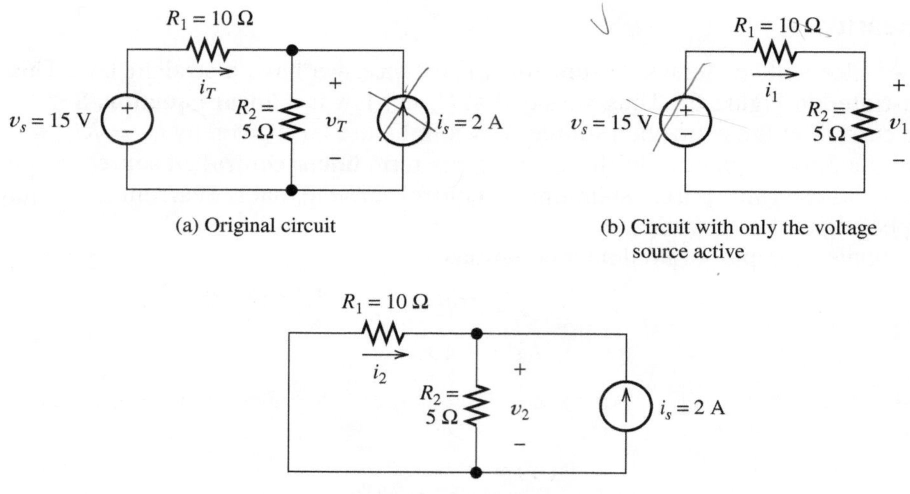

(a) Original circuit

(b) Circuit with only the voltage source active

(c) Circuit with only the current source active

Figure 62 Circuit for Example 22 and Exercise 31.

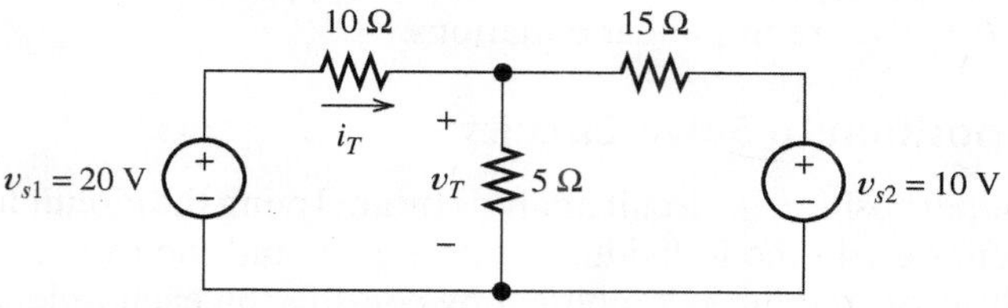

Figure 63 Circuit for Exercise 32.

Exercise 31 Find the responses $i_1, i_2,$ and i_T for the circuit of Figure 62.
Answer $i_1 = 1$ A, $i_2 = -0.667$ A, $i_T = 0.333$ A. □

Exercise 32 Use superposition to find the responses v_T and i_T for the circuit shown in Figure 63.
Answer $v_1 = 5.45$ V, $v_2 = 1.82$ V, $v_T = 7.27$ V, $i_1 = 1.45$ A, $i_2 = -0.181$ A, $i_T = 1.27$ A. □

8 WHEATSTONE BRIDGE

The Wheatstone bridge is used by mechanical and civil engineers to measure the resistances of strain gauges in experimental stress studies of machines and buildings.

The **Wheatstone bridge** is a circuit used to measure unknown resistances. For example, it is used by mechanical and civil engineers to measure the resistances of strain gauges in experimental stress studies of machines and buildings. The circuit is shown in Figure 64. The circuit consists of a dc voltage source v_s, a detector, the unknown resistance to be measured R_x, and three precision resistors, R_1, R_2, and R_3. Usually, R_2 and R_3 are adjustable resistances, which is indicated in the figure by the arrow drawn through the resistance symbols.

The detector is capable of responding to very small currents (less than one microampere). However, it is not necessary for the detector to be calibrated. It is only necessary for the detector to indicate whether or not current is flowing through

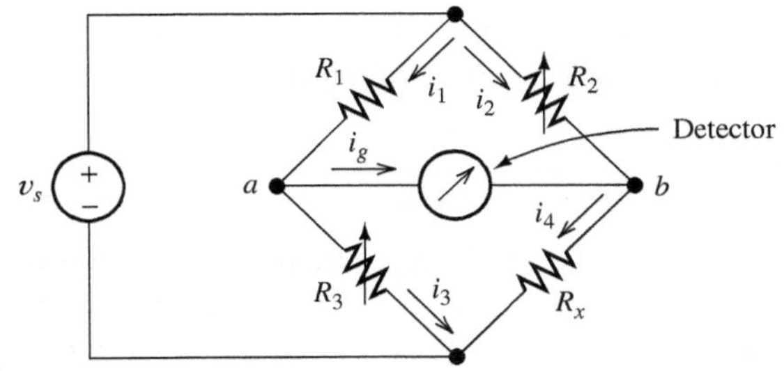

Figure 64 The Wheatstone bridge. When the Wheatstone bridge is balanced, $i_g = 0$ and $v_{ab} = 0$.

it. Often, the detector is a d'Arsonval galvanometer, which has a pointer that deflects one way or the other, depending on the direction of the current through it.

In operation, the resistors R_2 and R_3 are adjusted in value until the detector indicates zero current. In this condition, we say that the bridge is **balanced**. Then, the current i_g and the voltage across the detector v_{ab} are zero.

Applying KCL at node a (Figure 64) and using the fact that $i_g = 0$, we have

$$i_1 = i_3 \tag{85}$$

Similarly, at node b, we get

$$i_2 = i_4 \tag{86}$$

Writing a KVL equation around the loop formed by R_1, R_2, and the detector, we obtain

$$R_1 i_1 + v_{ab} = R_2 i_2 \tag{87}$$

However, when the bridge is balanced, $v_{ab} = 0$, so that

$$R_1 i_1 = R_2 i_2 \tag{88}$$

Similarly, for the loop consisting of R_3, R_4, and the detector, we have

$$R_3 i_3 = R_x i_4 \tag{89}$$

Using Equations 85 and 86 to substitute into Equation 89, we obtain

$$R_3 i_1 = R_x i_2 \tag{90}$$

Dividing each side of Equation 90 by the respective sides of Equation 88, we find that

$$\frac{R_3}{R_1} = \frac{R_x}{R_2}$$

Finally, solving for the unknown resistance, we have

$$R_x = \frac{R_2}{R_1} R_3 \tag{91}$$

Often, in commercial bridges, a multiposition switch selects an order-of-magnitude scale factor R_2/R_1 by changing the value of R_2. Then, R_3 is adjusted by means of calibrated switches until balance is achieved. Finally, the unknown resistance R_x is the scale factor times the value of R_3.

Example 23 Using a Wheatstone Bridge to Measure Resistance

In a certain commercial Wheatstone bridge, R_1 is a fixed 1-kΩ resistor, R_3 can be adjusted in 1-Ω steps from 0 to 1100 Ω, and R_2 can be selected to be 1 kΩ, 10 kΩ, 100 kΩ, or 1 MΩ. **a.** Suppose that the bridge is balanced with $R_3 = 732\ \Omega$ and $R_2 = 10\ \text{k}\Omega$. What is the value of R_x? **b.** What is the largest value of R_x for which the bridge can be balanced? **c.** Suppose that $R_2 = 1\ \text{M}\Omega$. What is the increment between values of R_x for which the bridge can be precisely balanced?

Solution

1. From Equation 91, we have

$$R_x = \frac{R_2}{R_1} R_3 = \frac{10\ \text{k}\Omega}{1\ \text{k}\Omega} \times 732\ \Omega = 7320\ \Omega$$

Notice that R_2/R_1 is a scale factor that can be set at 1, 10, 100, or 1000, depending on the value selected for R_2. The unknown resistance is the scale factor times the value of R_3 needed to balance the bridge.

2. The maximum resistance for which the bridge can be balanced is determined by the largest values available for R_2 and R_3. Thus,

$$R_{x\,\text{max}} = \frac{R_{2\,\text{max}}}{R_1} R_{3\,\text{max}} = \frac{1\ \text{M}\Omega}{1\ \text{k}\Omega} \times 1100\ \Omega = 1.1\ \text{M}\Omega$$

3. The increment between values of R_x for which the bridge can be precisely balanced is the scale factor times the increment in R_3:

$$R_{x\text{inc}} = \frac{R_2}{R_1} R_{3\text{inc}} = \frac{1\ \text{M}\Omega}{1\ \text{k}\Omega} \times 1\ \Omega = 1\ \text{k}\Omega$$

■

Strain Measurements

The Wheatstone bridge circuit configuration is often employed with strain gauges in measuring strains of beams and other mechanical structures. (See the Practical Application information about strain gauges.)

For example, consider the cantilevered beam subject to a downward load force at its outer end as shown in Figure 65(a). Two strain gauges are attached to the top of the beam where they are stretched, increasing their resistance by ΔR when the load is applied. The change in resistance is given by

$$\Delta R = R_0 G \frac{\Delta L}{L} \qquad (92)$$

in which $\Delta L/L$ is the strain for the surface of the beam to which the gauge is attached, R_0 is the gauge resistance before strain is applied, and G is the **gauge factor** which is typically about 2. Similarly, two gauges on the bottom of the beam are compressed, reducing their resistance by ΔR with load. (For simplicity, we have assumed that the strain magnitude is the same for all four gauges.)

The four gauges are connected in a Wheatstone bridge as shown in Figure 65(b).

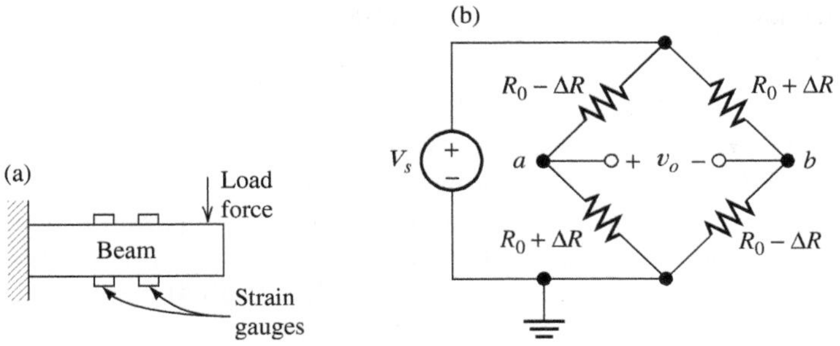

Figure 65 Strain measurements using the Wheatstone bridge.

The resistances labeled $R_0 + \Delta R$ are the gauges on the top of the beam and are being stretched, and those labeled $R_0 - \Delta R$ are those on the bottom and are being compressed. Before the load is applied, all four resistances have a value of R_0, the Wheatstone bridge is balanced, and the output voltage v_o is zero.

It can be shown that the output voltage v_o from the bridge is given by

$$v_o = V_s \frac{\Delta R}{R_0} = V_s G \frac{\Delta L}{L} \qquad (93)$$

Thus, the output voltage is proportional to the strain of the beam.

In principle, the resistance of one of the gauges could be measured and the strain determined from the resistance measurements. However, the changes in resistance are very small, and the measurements would need to be very precise. Furthermore, gauge resistance changes slightly with temperature. In the bridge arrangement with the gauges attached to the beam, the temperature changes tend to track very closely and have very little effect on v_o.

Usually, v_o is amplified by an instrumentation-quality differential amplifier. The amplified voltage can be converted to digital form and input to a computer or relayed wirelessly to a remote location for monitoring.

Summary

1. Series resistances have an equivalent resistance equal to their sum. For n resistances in series, we have

$$R_{\text{eq}} = R_1 + R_2 + \cdots + R_n$$

2. Parallel resistances have an equivalent resistance equal to the reciprocal of the sum of their reciprocals. For n resistances in parallel, we get

$$R_{\text{eq}} = \frac{1}{1/R_1 + 1/R_2 + \cdots + 1/R_n}$$

3. Some resistive networks can be solved by repeatedly combining resistances in series or parallel. The simplified network is solved, and results are transferred back through the chain of equivalent circuits. Eventually, the currents and voltages of interest in the original circuit are found.

4. The voltage-division principle applies when a voltage is applied to several resistances in series. A fraction of the total voltage appears across each resistance. The fraction that appears across a given resistance is the ratio of the given resistance to the total series resistance.

5. The current-division principle applies when current flows through two resistances in parallel. A fraction of the total current flows through each resistance. The fraction of the total current flowing through R_1 is equal to $R_2/(R_1 + R_2)$.
6. The node-voltage method can be used to solve for the voltages in any resistive network.
7. A step-by-step procedure to write the node-voltage equations directly in matrix form for circuits consisting of resistances and independent current sources is given.
8. The mesh-current method can be used to solve for the currents in any planar resistive network. A step-by-step summary of the method is given.
9. A step-by-step procedure to write the mesh-current equations directly in matrix form for circuits consisting of resistances and independent voltage sources is given. For this method to apply, all of the mesh currents must flow in the clockwise direction.
10. A two-terminal network of resistances and sources has a Thévenin equivalent that consists of a voltage source in series with a resistance. The Thévenin voltage is equal to the open-circuit voltage of the original network. The Thévenin resistance is the open-circuit voltage divided by the short-circuit current of the original network. Sometimes, the Thévenin resistance can be found by zeroing the independent sources in the original network and combining resistances in series and parallel. When independent voltage sources are zeroed, they are replaced by short circuits. Independent current sources are replaced by open circuits. Dependent sources must not be zeroed.
11. A two-terminal network of resistances and sources has a Norton equivalent that consists of a current source in parallel with a resistance. The Norton current is equal to the short-circuit current of the original network. The Norton resistance is the same as the Thévenin resistance. A step-by-step procedure for determining Thévenin and Norton equivalent circuits is given.
12. Sometimes source transformations (i.e., replacing a Thévenin equivalent with a Norton equivalent or vice versa) are useful in solving networks.
13. For maximum power from a two-terminal network, the load resistance should equal the Thévenin resistance.
14. The superposition principle states that the total response in a resistive circuit is the sum of the responses to each of the independent sources acting individually. The superposition principle does not apply to any circuit that has element(s) described by nonlinear equation(s).
15. The Wheatstone bridge is a circuit used to measure unknown resistances. The circuit consists of a voltage source, a detector, three precision calibrated resistors, of which two are adjustable, and the unknown resistance. The resistors are adjusted until the bridge is balanced, and then the unknown resistance is given in terms of the three known resistances.

Here's the answer to the trick question: Suppose that we open circuit the terminals. Then, no current flows through the Thévenin equivalent, but a current I_n circulates in the Norton equivalent. Thus, the box containing the Norton equivalent will become warm because of power dissipation in the resistance. The point of this question is that the circuits are equivalent in terms of their terminal voltage and current, not in terms of their internal behavior.

***Note:* You can check the answers to many of the problems in this chapter by using a computer-aided circuit-analysis program such as Multisim from National Instruments or OrCAD Capture from Cadence Inc.**

Problems

Section 1: Resistances in Series and Parallel

***P1.** Reduce each of the networks shown in Figure P1 to a single equivalent resistance by combining resistances in series and parallel.

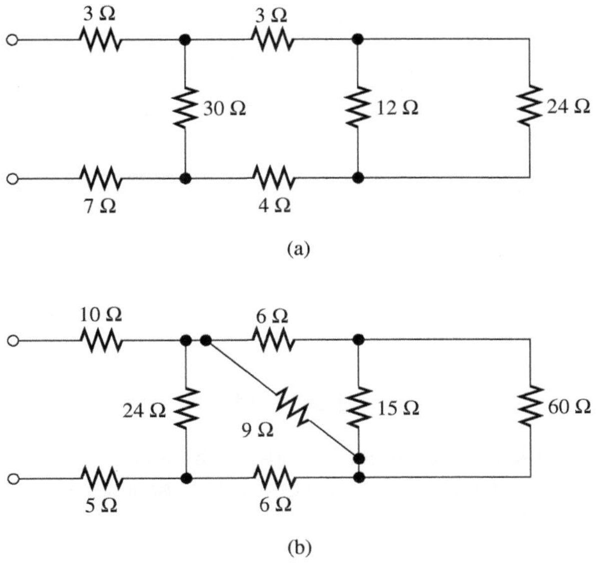

Figure P1

***P2.** A 4-Ω resistance is in series with the parallel combination of a 20-Ω resistance and an unknown resistance R_x. The equivalent resistance for the network is 8 Ω. Determine the value of R_x.

***P3.** Find the equivalent resistance between terminals a and b in Figure P3.

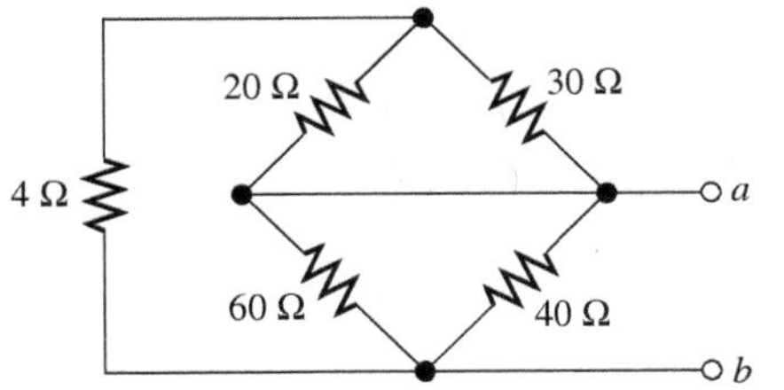

Figure P3

***P4.** Find the equivalent resistance looking into terminals a and b in Figure P4.

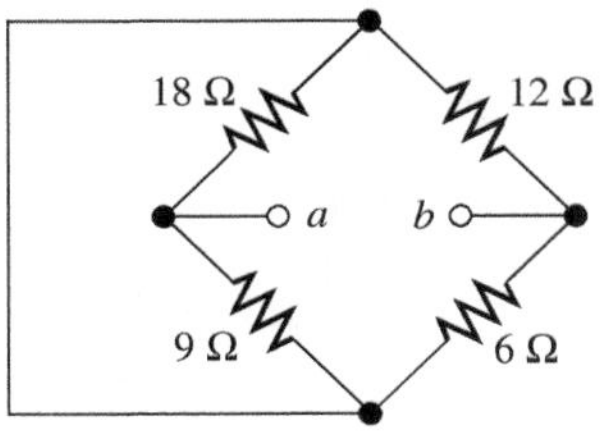

Figure P4

***P5.** Suppose that we need a resistance of 1.5 kΩ and you have a box of 1-kΩ resistors. Devise a network of 1-kΩ resistors so the equivalent resistance is 1.5 kΩ. Repeat for an equivalent resistance of 2.2 kΩ.

P6. **a.** Determine the resistance between terminals c and d for the network shown in Figure P6. **b.** Repeat after removing the short circuit between terminals a and b.

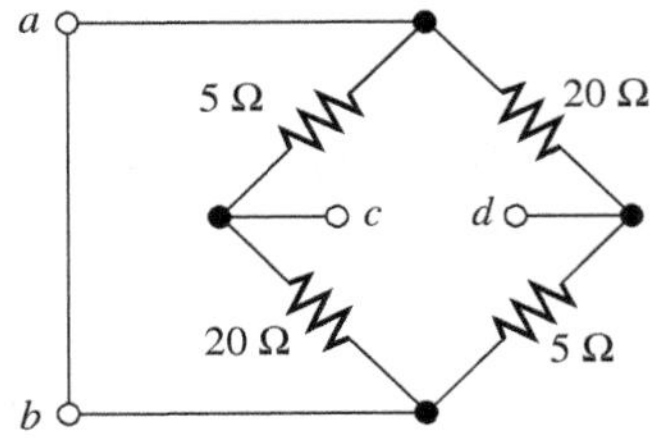

Figure P6

P7. Two resistances R_1 and R_2 are connected in series. We know that $R_1 = 60\ \Omega$ and that the voltage across R_2 is three times the value of the voltage across R_1. Determine the value of R_2.

P8. Find the equivalent resistance between terminals a and b for each of the networks shown in Figure P8.

P9. What resistance in parallel with 70 Ω results in an equivalent resistance of 20 Ω?

P10. Two resistances having values of $2R$ and $3R$ are in parallel. R and the equivalent resistance are both integers. What are the possible values for R?

P11. A network connected between terminals a and b consists of two parallel combinations that are in series. The first parallel

* Denotes that answers are contained in the Student Solutions files. See Appendix "On-Line Student Resources" for more information about accessing the Student Solutions.

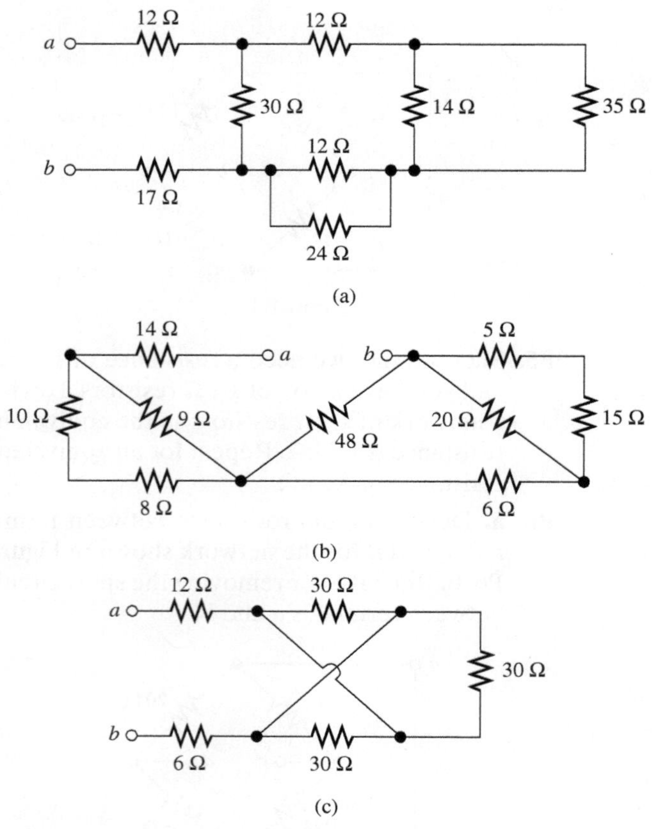

Figure P8

combination is composed of a 10-Ω resistor and a 15-Ω resistor. The second parallel combination is composed of a 14-Ω resistor and a 35-Ω resistor. Draw the network and determine its equivalent resistance.

P12. The heating element of an electric cook top has two resistive elements, $R_1 = 40\ \Omega$ and $R_2 = 100\ \Omega$, which can be operated separately, in series, or in parallel from voltages of either 120 V or 240 V. For the lowest power, R_1 is in series with R_2, and the combination is operated from 120 V. What is the lowest power? For the highest power, how should the elements be operated? What power results? List three more modes of operation and the resulting power for each.

P13. Find the equivalent resistance for the infinite network shown in Figure P13(a). Because of its form, this network is called a semi-infinite ladder. (*Hint:* If another section is added to the ladder as shown in Figure P13(b), the equivalent resistance is the same. Thus, working from Figure P13(b), we can write an expression for R_{eq} in terms of R_{eq}. Then, we can solve for R_{eq}.)

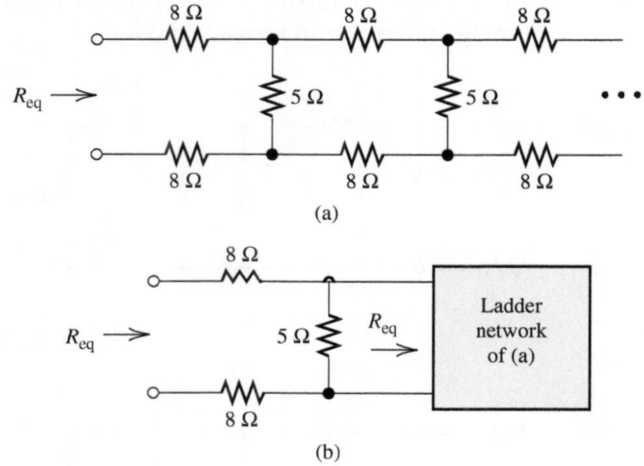

Figure P13

P14. If we connect n 1000-Ω resistances in parallel, what value is the equivalent resistance?

P15. We are designing an electric space heater to operate from 120 V. Two heating elements with resistances R_1 and R_2 are to be used that can be operated in parallel, separately, or in series. The highest power is to be 960 watts, and the lowest power is to be 180 watts. What values are needed for R_1 and R_2? What intermediate power settings are available?

P16. The equivalent resistance between terminals a and b in Figure P16 is $R_{ab} = 40\ \Omega$. Determine the value of R.

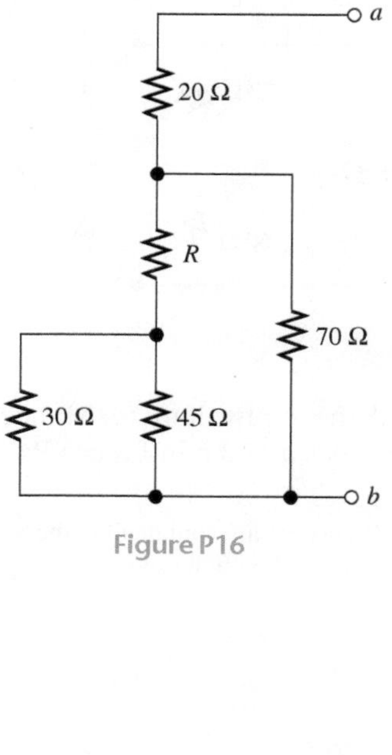

Figure P16

P17. Sometimes, we can use symmetry considerations to find the resistance of a circuit that cannot be reduced by series or parallel combinations. A classic problem of this type is illustrated in Figure P17. Twelve 1-Ω resistors are arranged on the edges of a cube, and terminals a and b are connected to diagonally opposite corners of the cube. The problem is to find the resistance between the terminals. Approach the problem this way: Assume that 1 A of current enters terminal a and exits through terminal b. Then, the voltage between terminals a and b is equal to the unknown resistance. By symmetry considerations, we can find the current in each resistor. Then, using KVL, we can find the voltage between a and b.

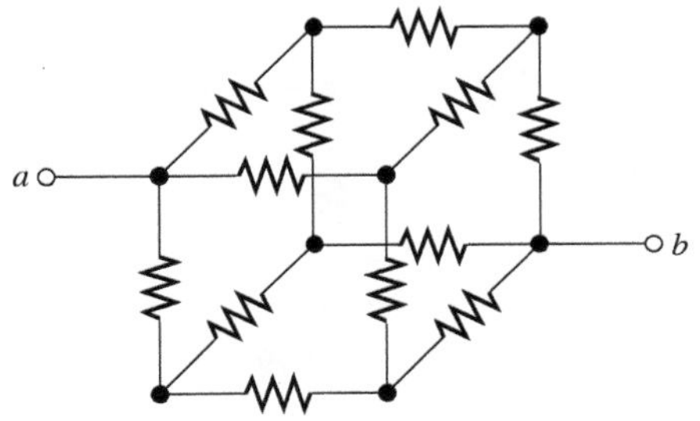

Figure P17

P18. **a.** Three conductances G_1, G_2, and G_3 are in series. Write an expression for the equivalent conductance $G_{eq} = 1/R_{eq}$ in terms of G_1, G_2, and G_3. **b.** Repeat part (a) with the conductances in parallel.

P19. Most sources of electrical power behave as (approximately) ideal voltage sources. In this case, if we have several loads that we want to operate independently, we place the loads in parallel with a switch in series with each load. Thereupon, we can switch each load on or off without affecting the power delivered to the other loads.

How would we connect the loads and switches if the source were an ideal independent current source? Draw the diagram of the current source and three loads with on–off switches such that each load can be switched on or off without affecting the power supplied to the other loads. To turn a load off, should the corresponding switch be opened or closed? Explain.

P20. Often, we encounter delta-connected loads, such as that illustrated in Figure P20, in three-phase power distribution systems. If we only have access to the three terminals, a method for determining the resistances is to repeatedly short two terminals together and measure the resistance between the shorted terminals and the third terminal. Then, the resistances can be calculated from the three measurements. Suppose that the measurements are $R_{as} = 24\ \Omega$, $R_{bs} = 30\ \Omega$, and $R_{cs} = 40\ \Omega$, where R_{as} is the resistance between terminal a and the short between b and c, etc. Determine the values of R_a, R_b, and R_c. (*Hint*: You may find the equations easier to deal with if you work in terms of conductances rather than resistances. Once the conductances are known, you can easily invert their values to find the resistances.)

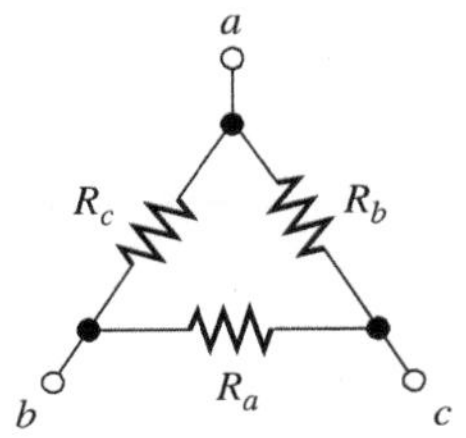

Figure P20

P21. The resistance between terminals a and b with c open circuited for the network shown in Figure P21 is $R_{ab} = 30\ \Omega$. Similarly, the resistance between terminals b and c with a open is $R_{bc} = 50\ \Omega$, and between c and a with b open, the resistance is $R_{ca} = 40\ \Omega$. Now, suppose that a short circuit is connected from terminal b to terminal c, and determine the resistance between terminal a and the shorted terminals b–c.

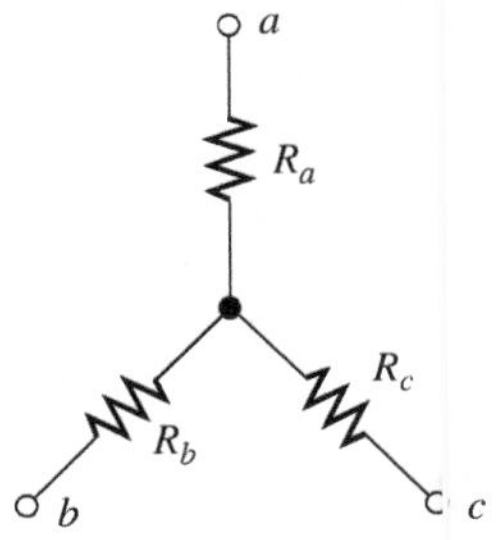

Figure P21

Section 2: Network Analysis by Using Series and Parallel Equivalents

P22. From memory, list the steps in solving a circuit by network reduction (series/parallel combinations). Does this method always provide the solution? Explain.

***P23.** Find the values of i_1 and i_2 in Figure P23.

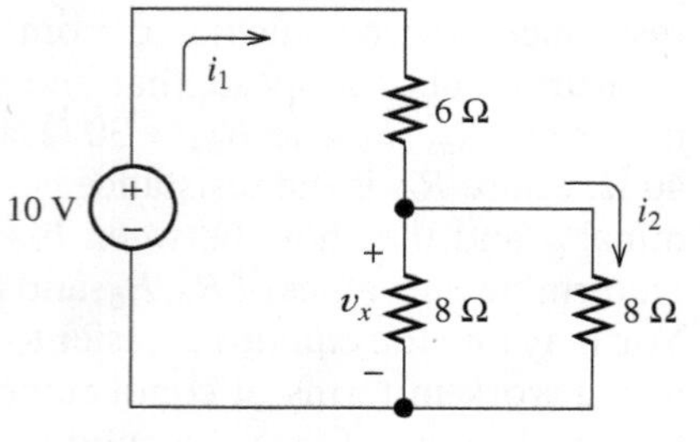

Figure P23

***P24.** Find the values of i_1 and i_2 in Figure P24. Find the power for each element in the circuit, and state whether each is absorbing or delivering energy. Verify that the total power absorbed equals the total power delivered.

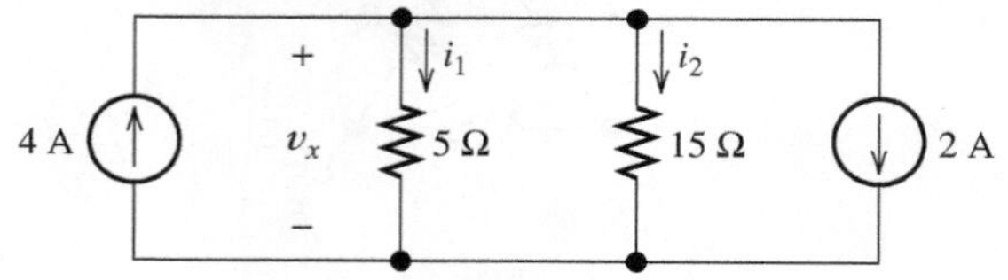

Figure P24

***P25.** Find the values of v and i in Figure P25.

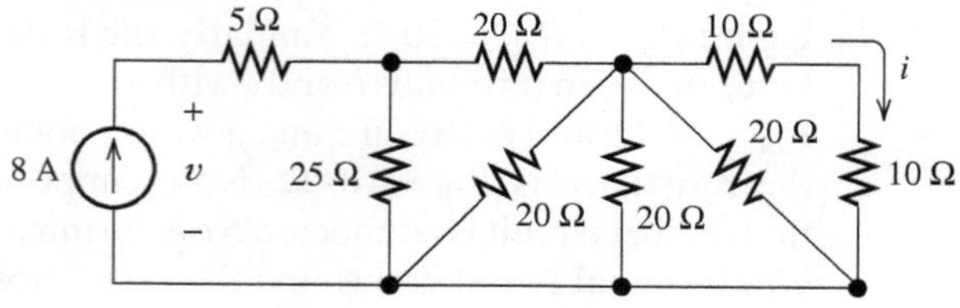

Figure P25

***P26.** Find the voltages v_1 and v_2 for the circuit shown in Figure P26 by combining resistances in series and parallel.

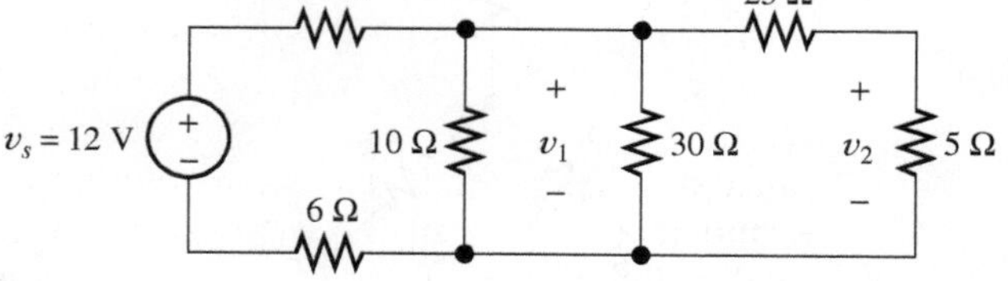

Figure P26

P27. Consider the circuit shown in Figure P26. Suppose that the value of v_s is adjusted until $v_1 = 10$ V. Determine the new values for v_2 and v_s. (*Hint*: Start at the location of v_2 and compute currents and voltages, moving to the right and left.)

P28. Find the values of v_s, v_1, and i_2 in Figure P28.

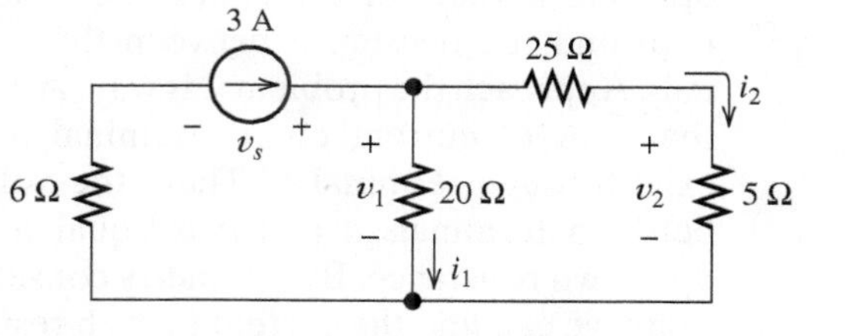

Figure P28

P29. Determine the values of i_1 and i_2 in Figure P29.

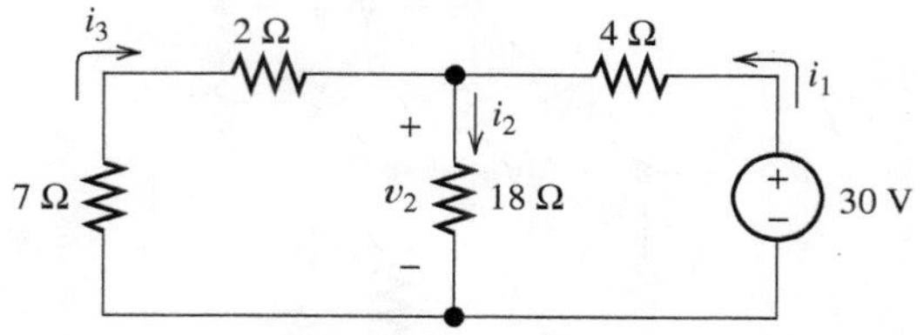

Figure P29

P30. Find the voltage v and the currents i_1 and i_2 for the circuit shown in Figure P30.

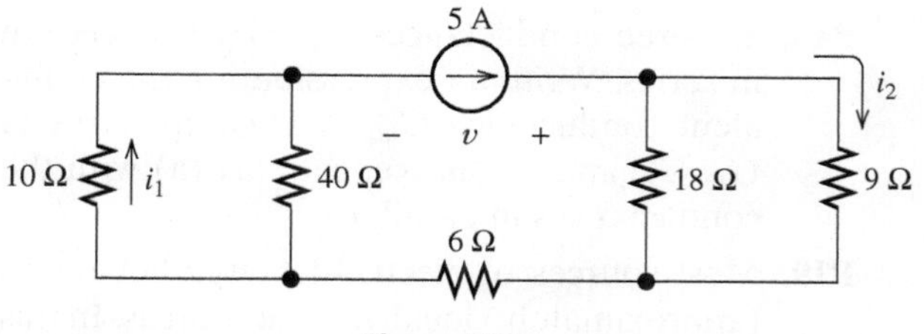

Figure P30

P31. Solve for the values of i_1, i_2, and the powers for the sources in Figure P31. Is the current source absorbing energy or delivering it? Is the voltage source absorbing energy or delivering it? Check to see that power is conserved in the circuit.

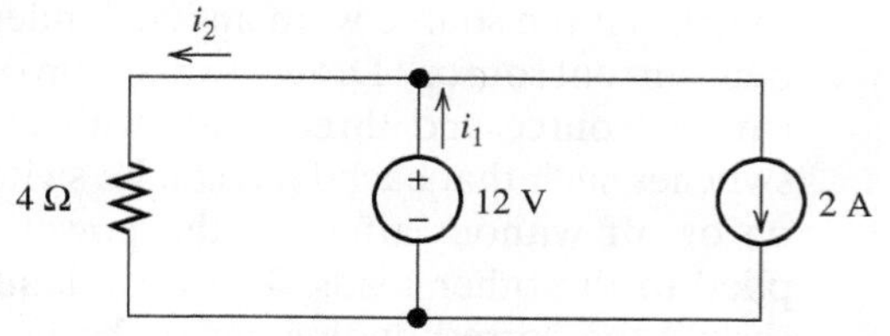

Figure P31

P32. Consider the circuit shown in Figure P32. With the switch open, we have $v_2 = 10$ V. On the other hand, with the switch closed, we have $v_2 = 8$ V. Determine the values of R_2 and R_L.

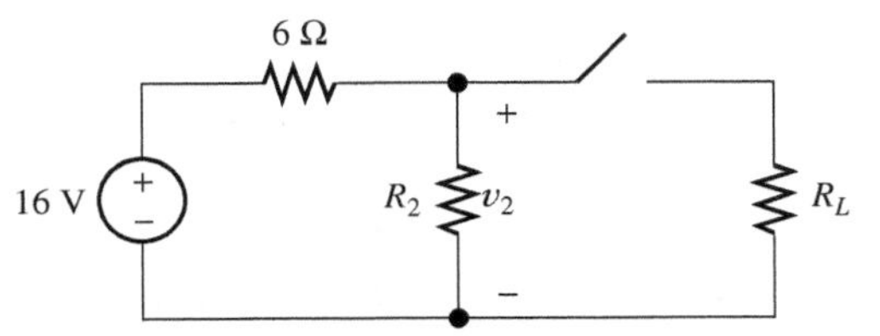

Figure P32

P33. Consider the circuit shown in Figure P33. Find the values of v_1, v_2, v_{ab}, v_{bc}, and v_{ca}.

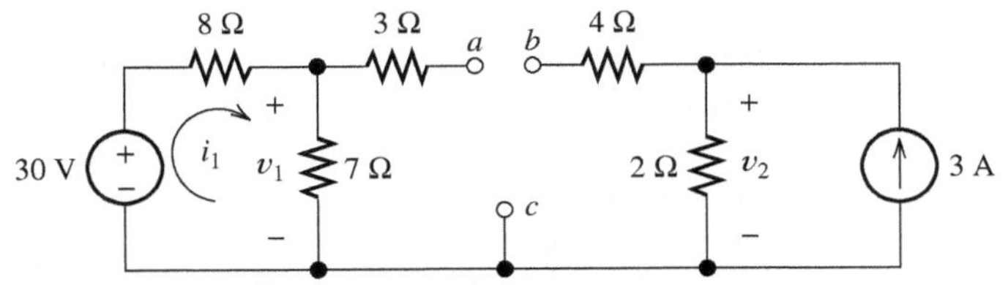

Figure P33

P34. We know that the 10-V source in Figure P34 is delivering 4 W of power. All four resistors have the same value R. Find the value of R.

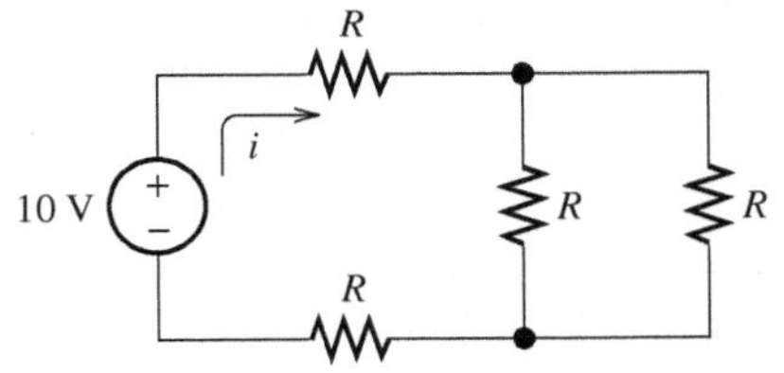

Figure P34

***P35.** Find the values of i_1 and i_2 in Figure P35.

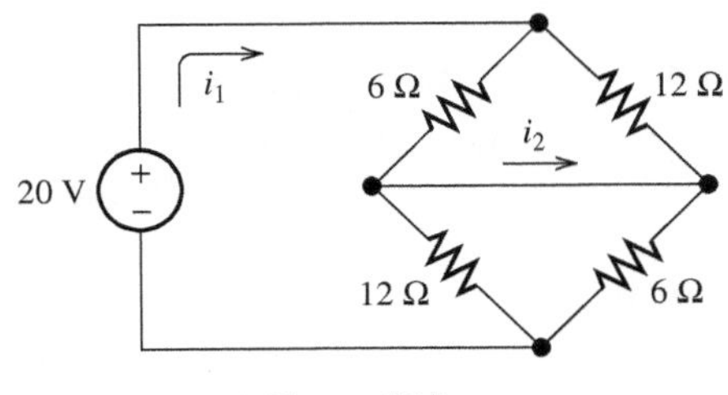

Figure P35

Section 3: Voltage-Divider and Current-Divider Circuits

***P36.** Use the voltage-division principle to calculate v_1, v_2, and v_3 in Figure P36.

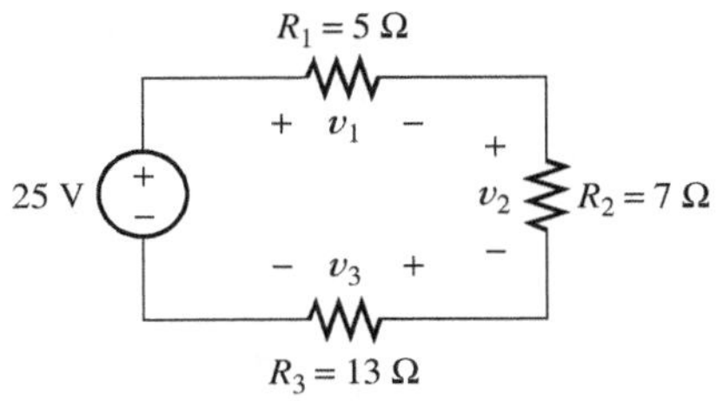

Figure P36

***P37.** Use the current-division principle to calculate i_1 and i_2 in Figure P37.

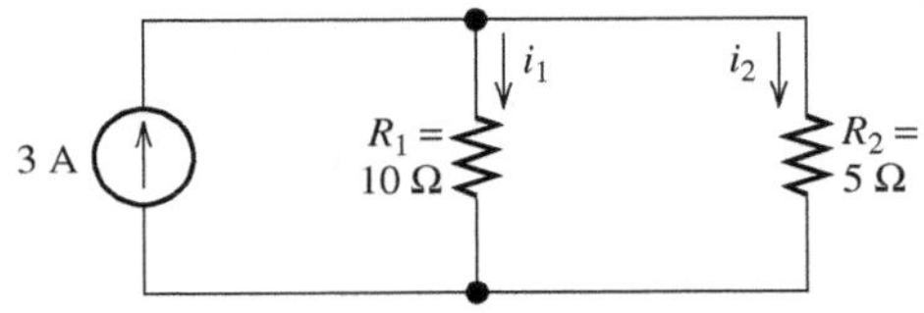

Figure P37

***P38.** Use the voltage-division principle to calculate v in Figure P38.

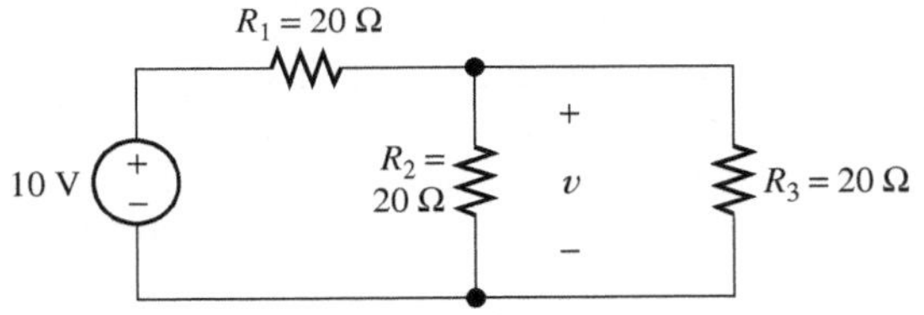

Figure P38

P39. Use the current-division principle to calculate the value of i_3 in Figure P39.

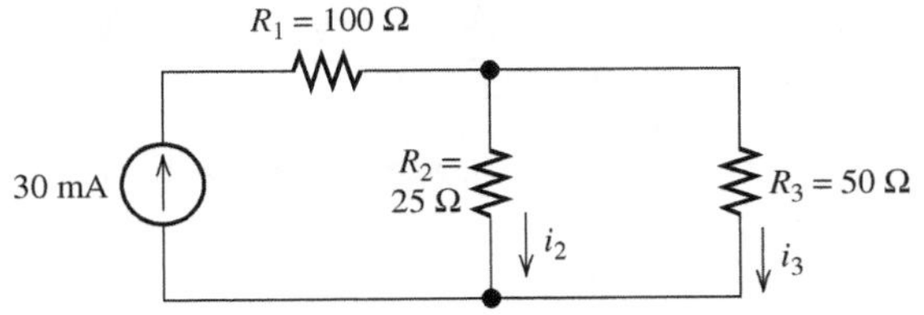

Figure P39

P40. We want to design a voltage-divider circuit to provide an output voltage $v_o = 5$ V from a 9-V battery as shown in Figure P40. The current taken from the 9-V source with no load connected is to be 10 mA. **a.** Find the values of R_1 and R_2. **b.** Now suppose that a load resistance of 1 kΩ is connected across the output terminals (i.e., in parallel with R_2). Find the loaded value of v_o. **c.** How could we change the design so the voltage remains closer to 5 V when the load is connected? How would this affect the life of the battery?

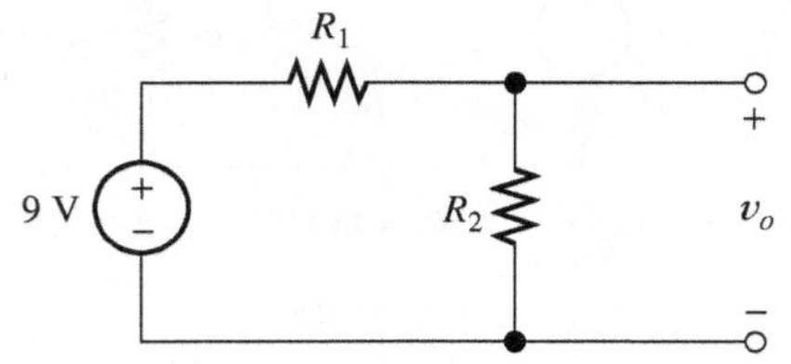

Figure P40

P41. A series-connected circuit has a 240-V voltage source, a 10-Ω resistance, a 5-Ω resistance, and an unknown resistance R_x. The voltage across the 5-Ω resistance is 30 V. Determine the value of the unknown resistance.

P42. A parallel circuit (i.e., all elements are in parallel with one another) has a 60-Ω resistance, a 20-Ω resistance, an unknown resistance R_x, and 30 mA current source. The current through the unknown resistance is 10 mA. Determine the value of R_x.

P43. The circuit of Figure P43 is similar to networks used in some digital-to-analog converters. For this problem, assume that the circuit continues indefinitely to the right. Find the values of i_1, i_2, i_3, and i_4. How is i_{n+2} related to i_n? What is the value of i_{18}? (*Hint:* See Problem P13 for hints on how to handle semi-infinite networks.)

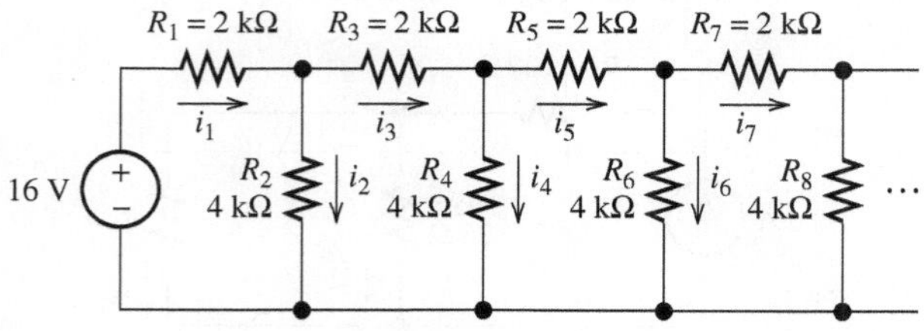

Figure P43

***P44.** A worker is standing on a wet concrete floor, holding an electric drill having a metallic case. The metallic case is connected through the ground wire of a three-terminal power outlet to power-system ground. The resistance of the ground wire is R_g. The resistance of the worker's body is $R_w = 500$ Ω. Due to faulty insulation in the drill, a current of 2 A flows into its metallic case. The circuit diagram for this situation is shown in Figure P44. Find the maximum value of R_g so that the current through the worker does not exceed 0.1 mA.

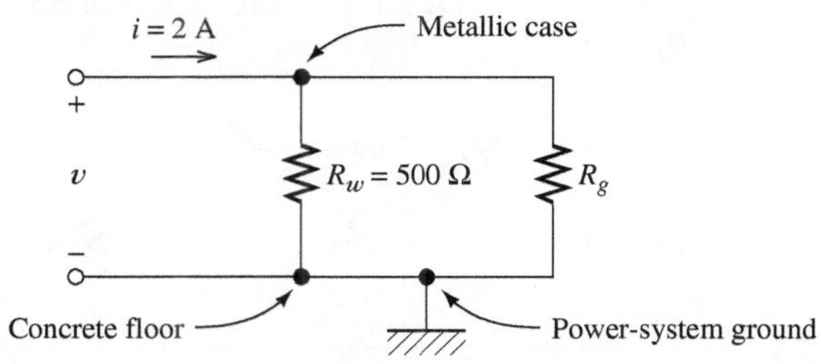

Figure P44

P45. We have a 15-V source and a load that absorbs power and requires a current varying between 0 and 100 mA. The voltage across the load must remain between 4.7 and 5.0 V for all values of load current. Design a voltage-divider network to supply the load. You may assume that resistors of any value desired are available. Also, give the minimum power rating for each resistor.

P46. A load resistance of 150 Ω needs to be supplied with 5 V. A 12.6-V voltage source and resistors of any value needed are available. Draw a suitable circuit consisting of the voltage source, the load, and one additional resistor. Specify the value of the resistor.

P47. Suppose that we wish to supply 500 mW to a 200-Ω load resistance R_L. A 100-mA current source and resistors of any value needed are available. Draw a suitable circuit consisting of the current source, the load, and one additional resistor. Specify the value of the resistor.

Section 4: Node-Voltage Analysis

P48. On your own, using analytical thinking and memory, list the steps to follow in analyzing a general circuit with the node-voltage technique.

***P49.** Write equations and solve for the node voltages shown in Figure P49. Then, find the value of i_1.

P50. Solve for the node voltages shown in Figure P50. What are the new values of the node voltages after the direction of the current source is reversed? How are the values related?

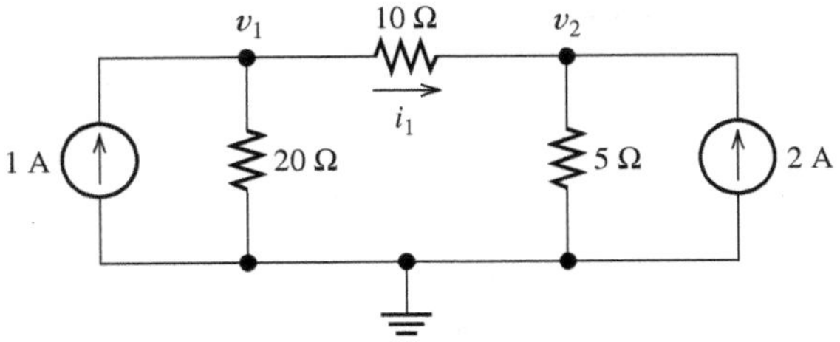

Figure P49

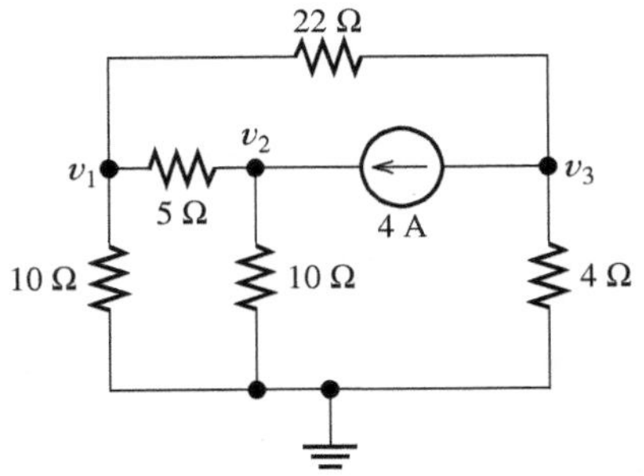

Figure P50

P51. Given $R_1 = 4\ \Omega$, $R_2 = 5\ \Omega$, $R_3 = 8\ \Omega$, $R_4 = 6\ \Omega$, $R_5 = 8\ \Omega$, and $I_s = 4$ A, solve for the node voltages shown in Figure P51.

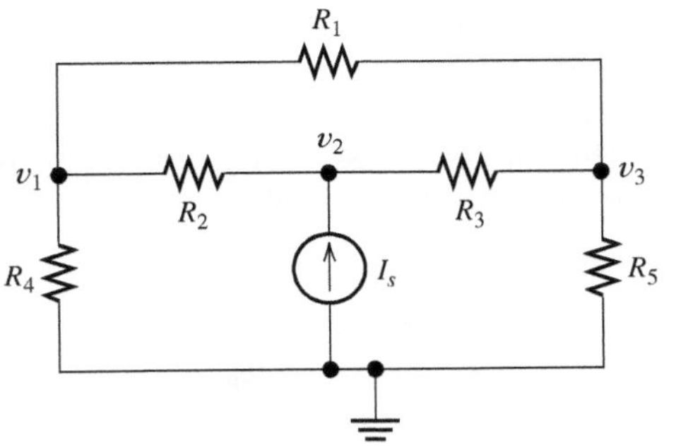

Figure P51

P52. Given $R_1 = 15\ \Omega$, $R_2 = 5\ \Omega$, $R_3 = 20\ \Omega$, $R_4 = 10\ \Omega$, $R_5 = 8\ \Omega$, $R_6 = 4\ \Omega$, and $I_s = 2$ A, solve for the node voltages shown in Figure P52.

***P53.** Solve for the node voltages shown in Figure P53. Then, find the value of i_s.

P54. Determine the value of i_1 in Figure P54 using node voltages to solve the circuit. Select the location of the reference node to minimize the number of unknown node voltages. What effect does the 17-Ω resistance have on the answer? Explain.

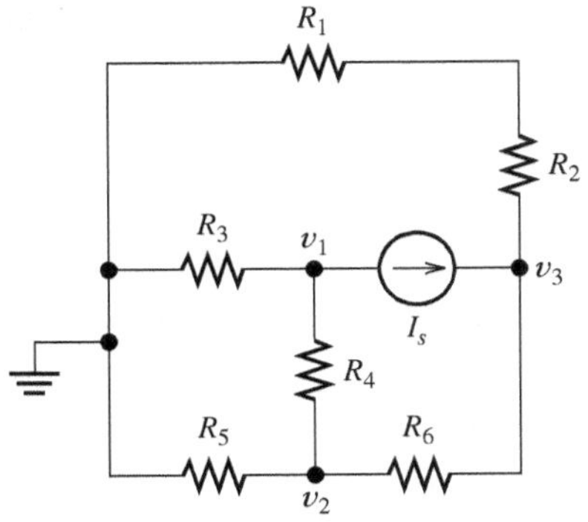

Figure P52

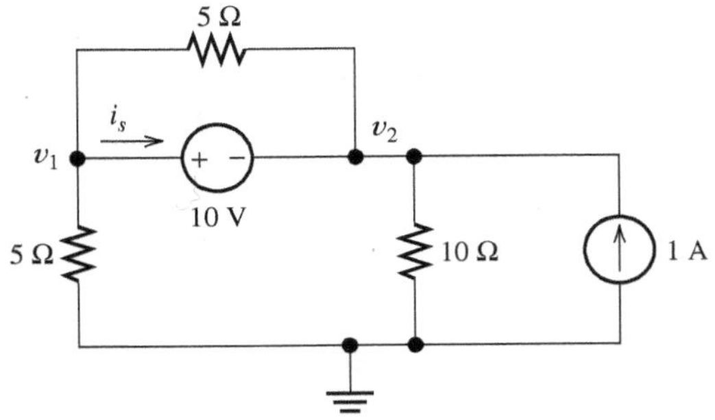

Figure P53

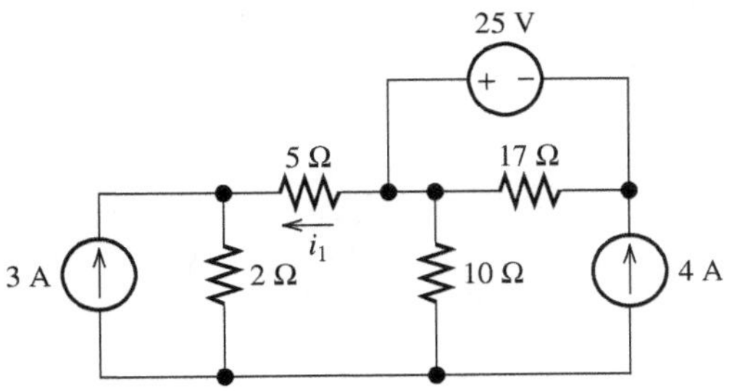

Figure P54

P55. In solving a network, what rule must you observe when writing KCL equations? Why?

P56. Use the symbolic features of MATLAB to find an expression for the equivalent resistance for the network shown in Figure P56. (*Hint:* First, connect a 1-A current source across terminals a and b. Then, solve the network by the node-voltage technique. The voltage across the current source is equal in value to the equivalent resistance.) Finally, use the subs command to evaluate for $R_1 = 15\ \Omega$, $R_2 = 15\ \Omega$, $R_3 = 15\ \Omega$, $R_4 = 10\ \Omega$, and $R_5 = 10\ \Omega$.

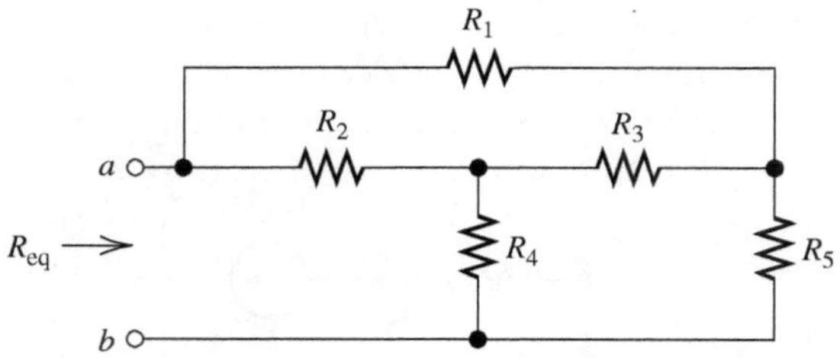

Figure P56

***P57.** Solve for the values of the node voltages shown in Figure P57. Then, find the value of i_x.

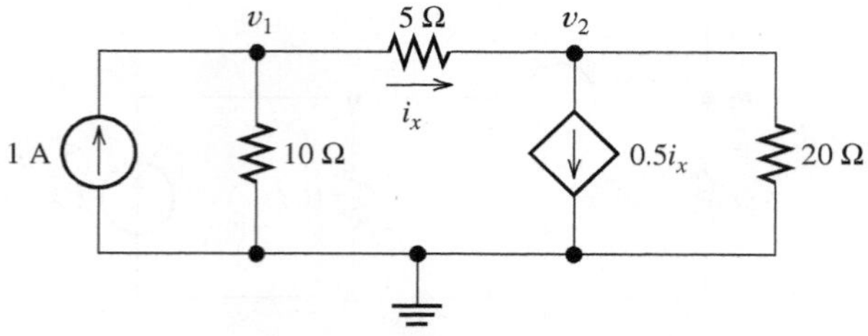

Figure P57

***P58.** Solve for the node voltages shown in Figure P58.

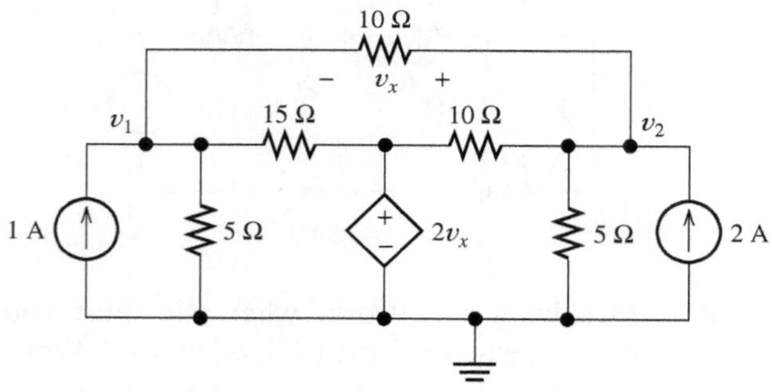

Figure P58

P59. Solve for the node voltages shown in Figure P59.

P60. Solve for the power delivered to the 8-Ω resistance and solve for the node voltages shown in Figure P60.

P61. Find the equivalent resistance looking into terminals a–b for the network shown in Figure P61. (*Hint:* First, connect a 1-A current source across terminals a and b. Then, solve the network by the node-voltage technique. The voltage across the current source is equal in value to the equivalent resistance.)

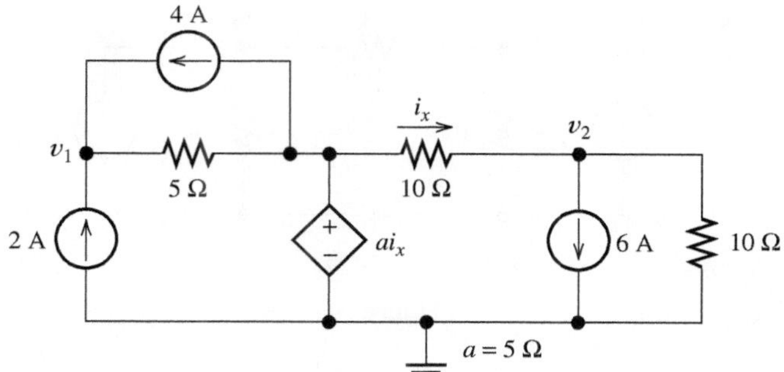

Figure P59

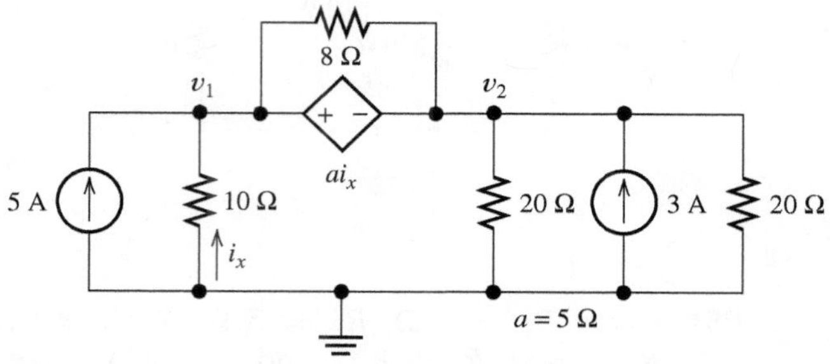

Figure P60

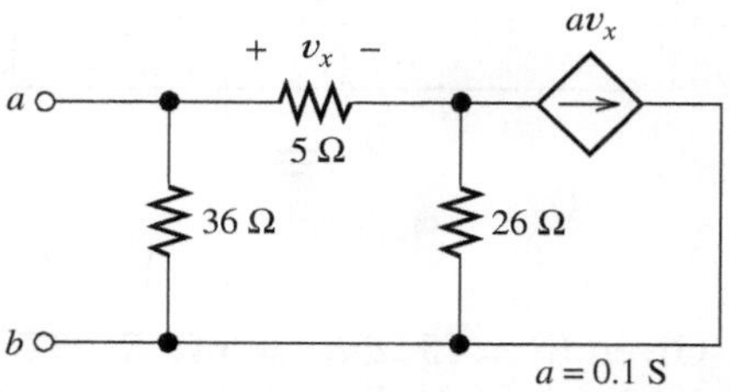

Figure P61

P62. Find the equivalent resistance looking into terminals a–b for the network shown in Figure P62. (*Hint:* First, connect a 1-A current source across terminals a and b. Then, solve the network by the node-voltage technique. The voltage across the current source is equal in value to the equivalent resistance.)

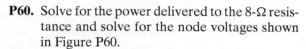

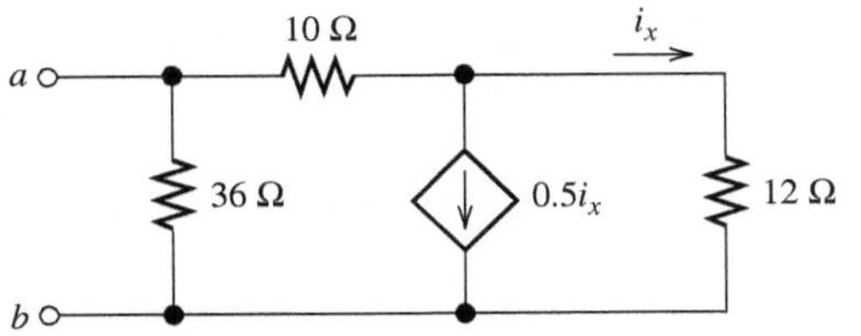

Figure P62

P63. We have a cube with 1-Ω resistances along each edge as illustrated in Figure P63, in which we are looking into the front face which has corners at nodes 1, 2, 7, and the reference node. Nodes 3, 4, 5, and 6 are the corners on the rear face of the cube. (Alternatively, you can consider it to be a planar network.) We want to find the resistance between adjacent nodes, such as node 1 and the reference node. We do this by connecting a 1-A current source as shown and solving for v_1, which by symmetry is equal in value to the resistance between any two adjacent nodes. **a.** Use MATLAB to solve the matrix equation $\mathbf{GV} = \mathbf{I}$ for the node voltages and determine the resistance. **b.** Modify your work to determine the resistance between nodes at the ends of a diagonal across a face, such as node 2 and the reference node. **c.** Finally, find the resistance between opposite corners of the cube. (*Comment*: Part (c) is the same as Problem 17 in which we suggested using symmetry to solve for the resistance. Parts (a) and (b) can also be solved by use of symmetry and the fact that nodes having the same value of voltage can be connected by short circuits without changing the currents and voltages. With the shorts in place, the resistances can be combined in series and parallel to obtain the answers. Of course, if the resistors have arbitrary values, the MATLAB approach will still work, but considerations of symmetry will not.)

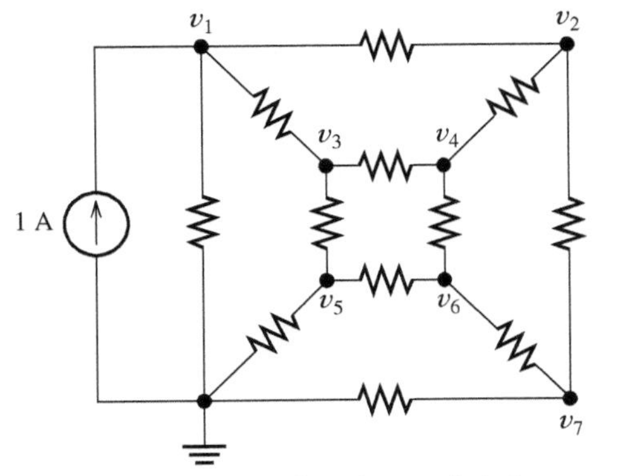

Figure P63 Each resistance is 1 Ω.

P64. Figure P64 shows an unusual voltage-divider circuit. Use node-voltage analysis and the symbolic math commands in MATLAB to solve for the voltage-division ratio V_{out}/V_{in} in terms of the resistances. Notice that the node voltage variables are V_1, V_2, and V_{out}.

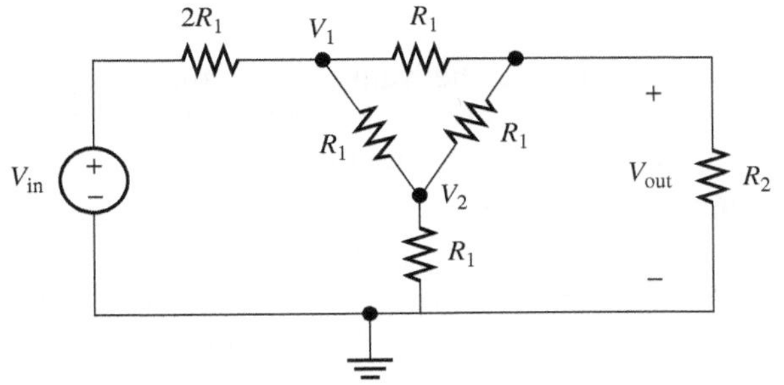

Figure P64

P65. Solve for the node voltages in the circuit of Figure P65. (Disregard the mesh currents, i_1, i_2, i_3, and i_4 when working with the node voltages.)

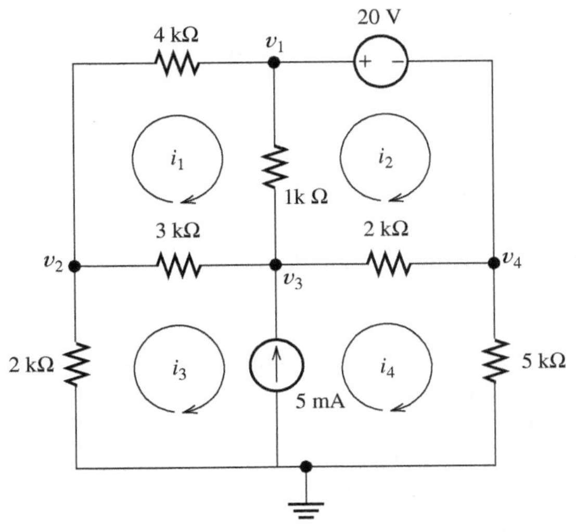

Figure P65

Section 5: Mesh-Current Analysis

P66. List the steps in analyzing a planar network using the mesh-current method. Attempt this as a "closed-book" exam problem.

***P67.** Solve for the power delivered to the 15-Ω resistor and for the mesh currents shown in Figure P67.

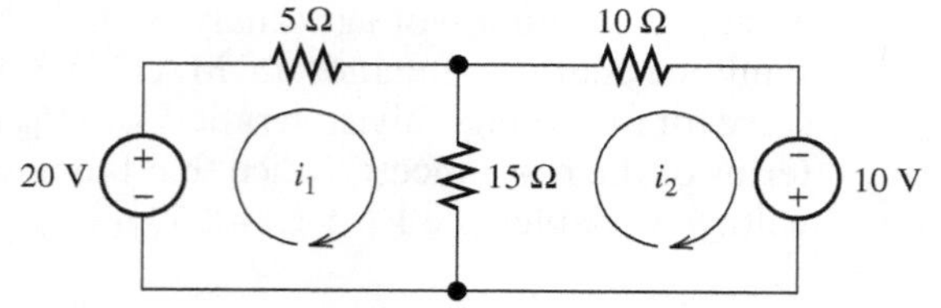

Figure P67

***P68.** Determine the value of v_2 and the power delivered by the source in the circuit of Figure P26 by using mesh-current analysis.

***P69.** Use mesh-current analysis to find the value of i_1 in the circuit of Figure P49.

P70. Solve for the power delivered by the voltage source in Figure P70, using the mesh-current method.

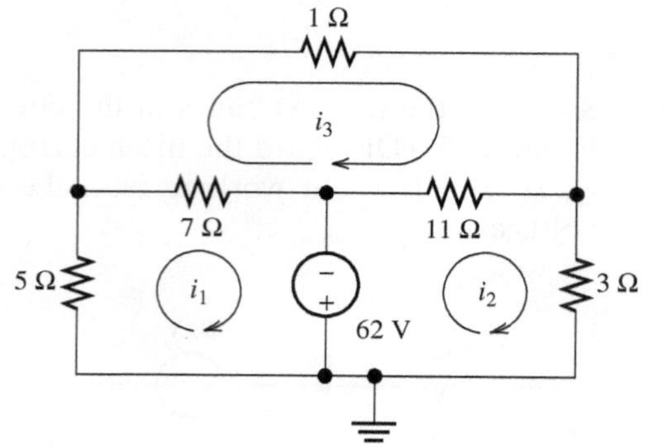

Figure P70

P71. Use mesh-current analysis to find the value of v in the circuit of Figure P38.

P72. Use mesh-current analysis to find the value of i_3 in the circuit of Figure P39. (Choose your mesh-current variables as i_A and i_B to avoid confusion with the current labels on the circuit diagram.)

P73. Use mesh-current analysis to find the values of i_1 and i_2 in Figure P30. Select i_1 clockwise around the left-hand mesh, i_2 clockwise around the right-hand mesh, and i_3 clockwise around the center mesh.

P74. Find the power delivered by the source and the values of i_1 and i_2 in the circuit of Figure P23, using mesh-current analysis.

P75. Use mesh-current analysis to find the values of i_1 and i_2 in Figure P29. First, select i_A clockwise around the left-hand mesh and i_B clockwise around the right-hand mesh. After solving for the mesh currents, i_A and i_B, determine the values of i_1 and i_2.

P76. Use mesh-current analysis to find the values of i_1 and i_2 in Figure P28. First, select i_A clockwise around the left-hand mesh and i_B clockwise around the right-hand mesh. After solving for the mesh currents, i_A and i_B, determine the values of i_1 and i_2.

P77. The circuit shown in Figure P77 is the dc equivalent of a simple residential power distribution system. Each of the resistances labeled R_1 and R_2 represents various parallel-connected loads, such as lights or devices plugged into outlets that nominally operate at 120 V, while R_3 represents a load, such as the heating element in an oven that nominally operates at 240 V. The resistances labeled R_w represent the resistances of wires. R_n represents the "neutral" wire. **a.** Use mesh-current analysis to determine the voltage magnitude for each load and the current in the neutral wire. **b.** Now, suppose that due to a fault in the wiring at the distribution panel, the neutral wire becomes an open circuit. Again, compute the voltages across the loads and comment on the probable outcome for a sensitive device such as a computer or plasma television that is part of the 20-Ω load.

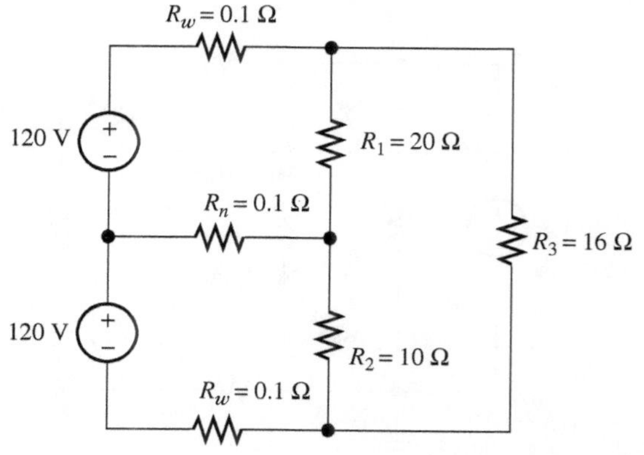

Figure P77

P78. Use MATLAB and mesh-current analysis to determine the value of v_2 in the circuit of Figure P51. The component values are $R_1 = 4\ \Omega, R_2 = 5\ \Omega, R_3 = 8\ \Omega, R_4 = 6\ \Omega, R_5 = 8\ \Omega$, and $I_s = 4$ A.

P79. Connect a 1-V voltage source across terminals a and b of the network shown in Figure P56. Then, solve the network by the mesh-current technique to find the current through the source. Finally, divide the source voltage by the current to determine the equivalent resistance looking into terminals a and b. The resistance values are $R_1 = 15\ \Omega$, $R_2 = 15\ \Omega$, $R_3 = 15\ \Omega$, $R_4 = 10\ \Omega$, and $R_5 = 10\ \Omega$.

P80. Connect a 1-V voltage source across the terminals of the network shown in Figure P1(a). Then, solve the network by the mesh-current technique to find the current through the source. Finally, divide the source voltage by the current to determine the equivalent resistance looking into the terminals. Check your answer by combining resistances in series and parallel.

P81. Use MATLAB to solve for the mesh currents in Figure P65.

Section 6: Thévenin and Norton Equivalent Circuits

P82. List the steps in determining the Thévenin and Norton equivalent circuits for a general two-terminal circuit. Try this as if it were a "closed-book" exam question.

***P83.** Find the Thévenin and Norton equivalent circuits for the two-terminal circuit shown in Figure P83.

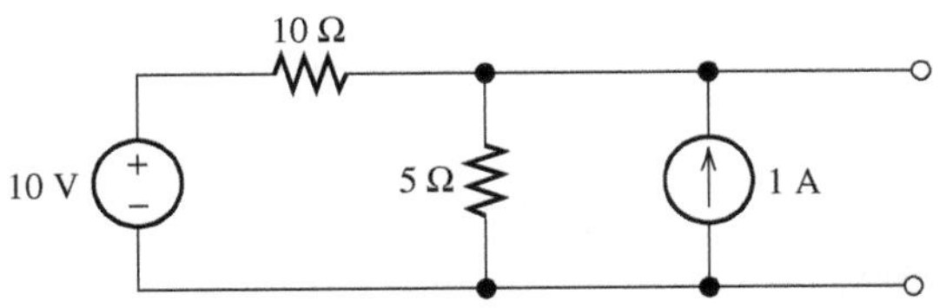

Figure P83

***P84.** We can model a certain battery as a voltage source in series with a resistance. The open-circuit voltage of the battery is 9 V. When a 100-Ω resistor is placed across the terminals of the battery, the voltage drops to 6 V. Determine the internal resistance (Thévenin resistance) of the battery.

P85. Find the Thévenin and Norton equivalent circuits for the circuit shown in Figure P85. Take care that you orient the polarity of the voltage source and the direction of the current source correctly relative to terminals a and b. What effect does the 9-Ω resistor have on the equivalent circuits? Explain your answer.

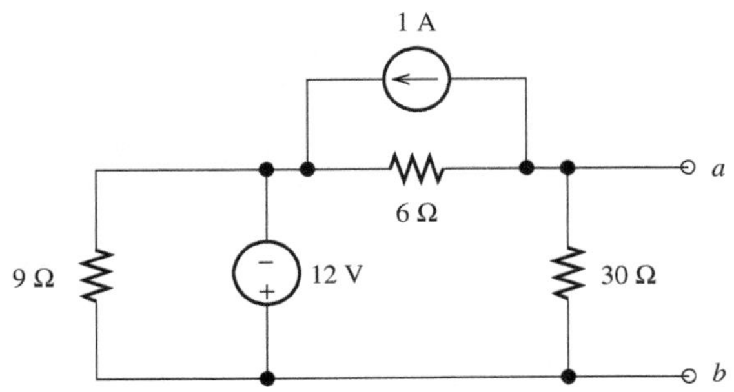

Figure P85

P86. Find the Thévenin and Norton equivalent circuits for the circuit shown in Figure P86.

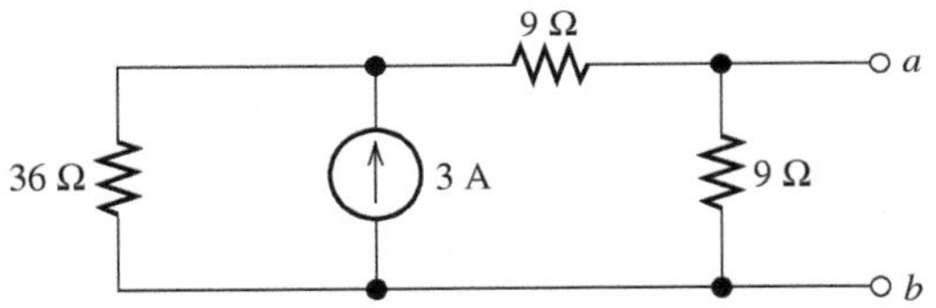

Figure P86

P87. Find the Thévenin and Norton equivalent circuits for the two-terminal circuit shown in Figure P87.

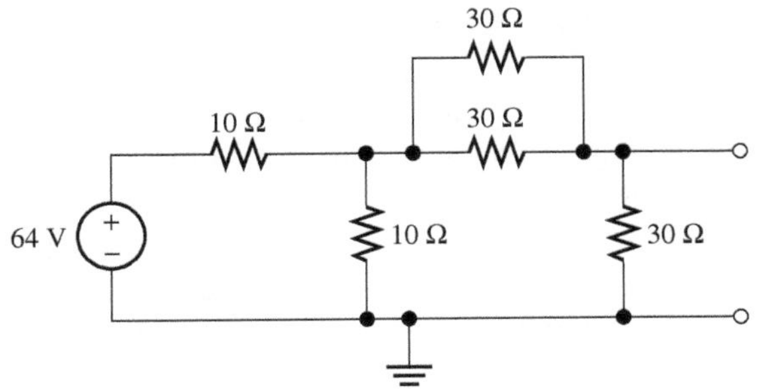

Figure P87

P88. A somewhat discharged automotive battery has an open-circuit voltage of 12.5 V and supplies 50 A when a 0.1-Ω resistance is connected across the battery terminals. Draw the Thévenin and Norton equivalent circuits, including values for the circuit parameters.

What current can this battery deliver to a short circuit? Considering that the energy stored in the battery remains constant under open-circuit conditions, which of these equivalent circuits seems more realistic? Explain.

P89. A certain two-terminal circuit has an open-circuit voltage of 9 V. When a 200-Ω load is attached, the voltage across the load is 7 V. Determine the Thévenin resistance for the circuit.

P90. If we measure the voltage at the terminals of a two-terminal network with two known (and different) resistive loads attached, we can determine the Thévenin and Norton equivalent circuits. When a 1-kΩ load is attached to a two-terminal circuit, the load voltage is 8 V. When the load is increased to 2 kΩ, the load voltage becomes 10 V. Find the Thévenin voltage and resistance for the circuit.

P91. Find the Thévenin and Norton equivalent circuits for the circuit shown in Figure P91.

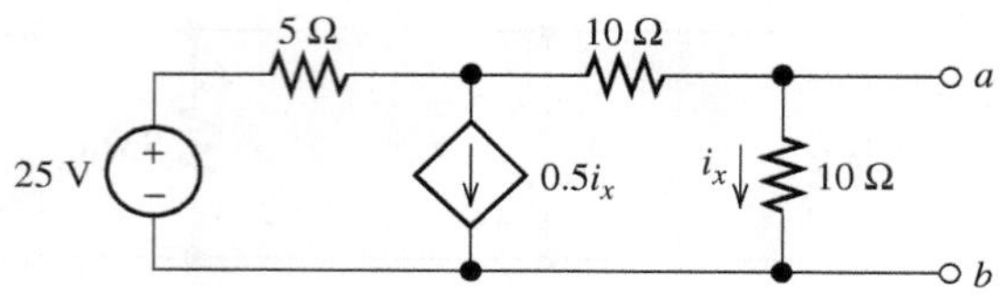

Figure P91

P92. Find the maximum power that can be delivered to a resistive load by the circuit shown in Figure P83. For what value of load resistance is the power maximum?

P93. Find the maximum power that can be delivered to a resistive load by the circuit shown in Figure P86. For what value of load resistance is the power maximum?

P94. A battery can be modeled by a voltage source V_t in series with a resistance R_t. Assuming that the load resistance is selected to maximize the power delivered, what percentage of the power taken from the voltage source V_t is actually delivered to the load? Suppose that $R_L = 9R_t$; what percentage of the power taken from V_t is delivered to the load? Usually, we want to design battery-operated systems so that nearly all of the energy stored in the battery is delivered to the load. Should we design for maximum power transfer?

***P95.** Figure P95 shows a resistive load R_L connected to a Thévenin equivalent circuit. For what value of Thévenin resistance is the power delivered to the load maximized? Find the maximum power delivered to the load. (*Hint:* Be careful; this is a tricky question if you don't stop to think about it.)

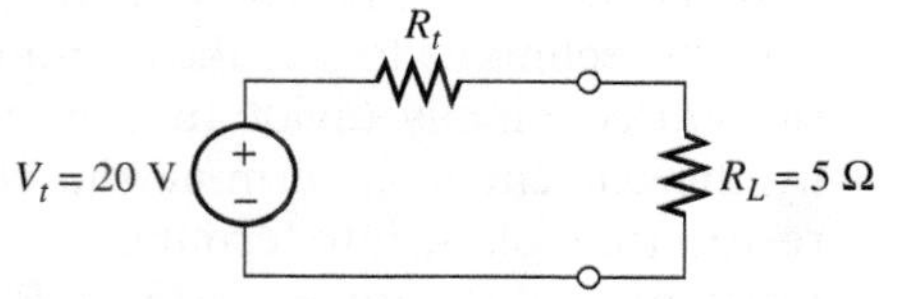

Figure P95

P96. Starting from the Norton equivalent circuit with a resistive load R_L attached, find an expression for the power delivered to the load in terms of I_n, R_t, and R_L. Assuming that I_n and R_t are fixed values and that R_L is a variable, show that maximum power is delivered for $R_L = R_t$. Find an expression for maximum power delivered to the load in terms of I_n and R_t.

Section 7: Superposition Principle

***P97.** Use superposition to find the current i in Figure P97. First, zero the current source and find the value i_v caused by the voltage source alone. Then, zero the voltage source and find the value i_c caused by the current source alone. Finally, add the results algebraically.

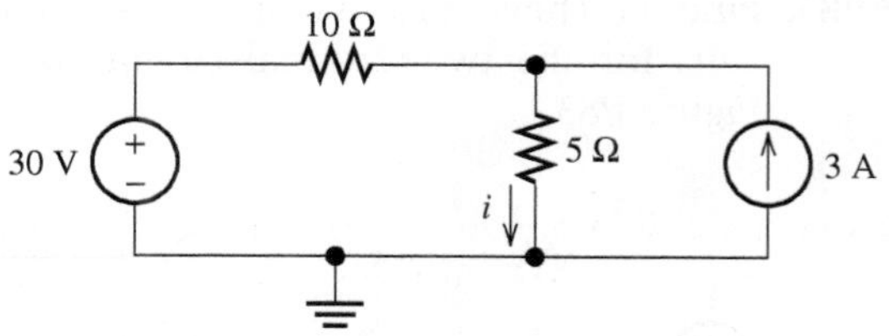

Figure P97

***P98.** Solve for i_s in Figure P53 by using superposition.

P99. Solve the circuit shown in Figure P49 by using superposition. First, zero the 1-A source and find the value of i_1 with only the 2-A source activated. Then, zero the 2-A source and find the value of i_1 with only the 1-A source activated. Finally, find the total value of i_1, with both sources activated, by algebraically adding the previous results.

P100. Solve for i_1 in Figure P24 by using superposition.

P101. Another method of solving the circuit of Figure P26 is to start by assuming that $v_2 = 1$ V. Accordingly, we work backward toward the source, using Ohm's law, KCL, and KVL to find the value of v_s. Since we know that v_2 is proportional to the value of v_s, and since we have found the value of v_s that produces $v_2 = 1$ V, we can calculate the value of v_2 that results when $v_s = 12$ V. Solve for v_2 by using this method.

P102. Use the method of Problem P101 for the circuit of Figure P23, starting with the assumption that $i_2 = 1$ A.

P103. Solve for the actual value of i_6 for the circuit of Figure P103 with $V_s = 10$ V, starting with the assumption that $i_6 = 1$ A. Work back through the circuit to find the value of V_s that results in $i_6 = 1$ A. Then, use proportionality to determine the value of i_6 that results for $V_s = 10$ V.

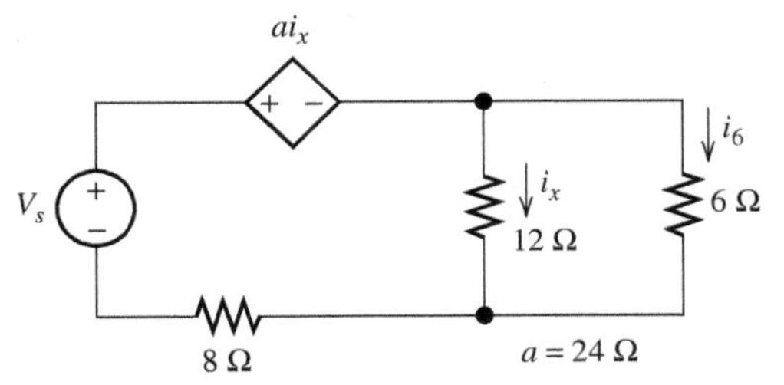

Figure P103

P104. Device A shown in Figure P104 has $v = 2i^3$. **a.** Solve for v with the 2-A source active and the 1-A source zeroed. **b.** Solve for v with the 1-A source active and the 2-A source zeroed. **c.** Solve for v with both sources active. Why doesn't superposition apply?

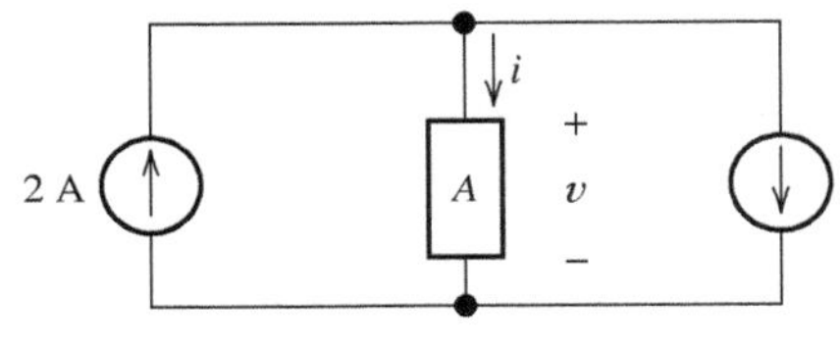

Figure P104

Section 8: Wheatstone Bridge

P105. **a.** The Wheatstone bridge shown in Figure 64 is balanced with $R_1 = 1$ kΩ, $R_3 = 3419$ Ω, and $R_2 = 1$ kΩ. Find R_x. **b.** Repeat if R_2 is 100 kΩ and the other values are unchanged.

***P106.** The Wheatstone bridge shown in Figure 64 has $v_s = 10$ V, $R_1 = 10$ kΩ, $R_2 = 10$ kΩ, and $R_x = 5932$ Ω. The detector can be modeled as a 5-kΩ resistance. **a.** What value of R_3 is required to balance the bridge? **b.** Suppose that R_3 is 1 Ω higher than the value found in part (a). Find the current through the detector. (*Hint:* Find the Thévenin equivalent for the circuit with the detector removed. Then, place the detector across the Thévenin equivalent and solve for the current.) Comment.

P107. In theory, any values can be used for R_1 and R_3 in the Wheatstone bridge of Figure 64. For the bridge to balance, it is only the *ratio* R_3/R_1 that is important. What practical problems might occur if the values are very small? What practical problems might occur if the values are very large?

P108. Derive expressions for the Thévenin voltage and resistance "seen" by the detector in the Wheatstone bridge in Figure 64. (In other words, remove the detector from the circuit and determine the Thévenin resistance for the remaining two-terminal circuit.) What is the value of the Thévenin voltage when the bridge is balanced?

P109. Derive Equation 93 for the bridge circuit of Figure 65.

P110. Consider a strain gauge in the form of a long thin wire having a length L and a cross-sectional area A before strain is applied. After the strain is applied, the length increases slightly to $L + \Delta L$ and the area is reduced so the volume occupied by the wire is constant. Assume that $\Delta L/L << 1$ and that the resistivity ρ of the wire material is constant. Determine the gauge factor

$$G = \frac{\Delta R/R_0}{\Delta L/L}$$

P111. Explain what would happen if, in wiring the bridge circuit of Figure 65, the gauges in tension (i.e., those labeled $R + \Delta R$) were both placed on the top of the bridge circuit diagram, shown in part (b) of the figure, and those in compression were both placed at the bottom of the bridge circuit diagram.

Practice Test

Here is a practice test you can use to check your comprehension of the most important concepts in this chapter. Answers can be found in Appendix "Answers for the Practice Tests" and complete solutions are included in the Student Solutions files. See Appendix "On-Line Student Resources" for more information about the Student Solutions.

T1. Match each entry in Table T1(a) with the best choice from the list given in Table T1(b)

Table T1

Item	Best Match
(a)	
a. The equivalent resistance of parallel-connected resistances...	
b. Resistances in parallel combine as do...	
c. Loads in power distribution systems are most often connected...	
d. Solving a circuit by series/parallel combinations applies to...	
e. The voltage-division principle applies to...	
f. The current-division principle applies to...	
g. The superposition principle applies to...	
h. Node-voltage analysis can be applied to...	
i. In this chapter, mesh-current analysis is applied to...	
j. The Thévenin resistance of a two-terminal circuit equals...	
k. The Norton current source value of a two-terminal circuit equals...	
l. A voltage source in parallel with a resistance is equivalent to...	
(b)	
1. conductances in parallel	
2. in parallel	
3. all circuits	
4. resistances or conductances in parallel	
5. is obtained by summing the resistances	
6. is the reciprocal of the sum of the reciprocals of the resistances	
7. some circuits	
8. planar circuits	
9. a current source in series with a resistance	
10. conductances in series	
11. circuits composed of linear elements	
12. in series	
13. resistances or conductances in series	
14. a voltage source	
15. the open-circuit voltage divided by the short-circuit current	
16. a current source	
17. the short-circuit current	

for circuits composed of sources and resistances. [Items in Table T1(b) may be used more than once or not at all.]

T2. Consider the circuit of Figure T2 with $v_s = 96\,\text{V}$, $R_1 = 6\,\Omega$, $R_2 = 48\,\Omega$, $R_3 = 16\,\Omega$, and $R_4 = 60\,\Omega$. Determine the values of i_s and i_4.

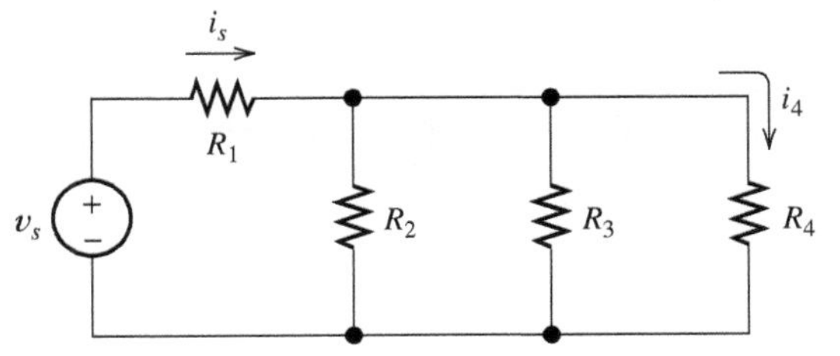

Figure T2

T3. Write MATLAB code to solve for the node voltages for the circuit of Figure T3.

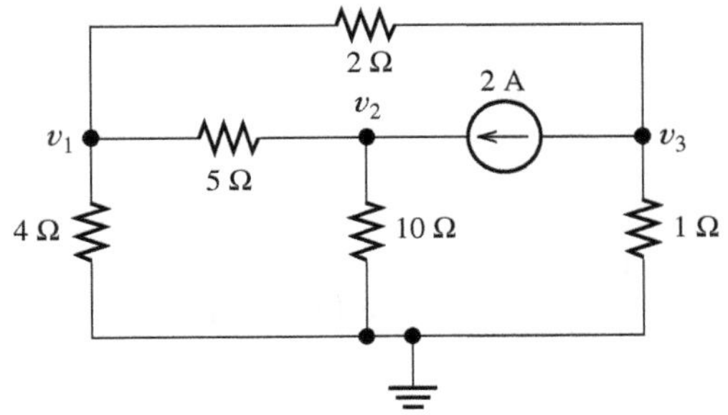

Figure T3

T4. Write a set of equations that can be used to solve for the mesh currents of Figure T4. Be sure to indicate which of the equations you write form the set.

T5. Determine the Thévenin and Norton equivalent circuits for the circuit of Figure T5. Draw the equivalent circuits labeling the terminals to correspond with the original circuit.

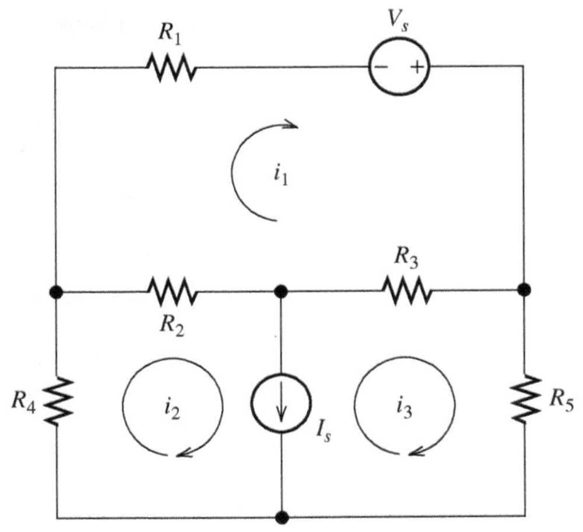

Figure T4

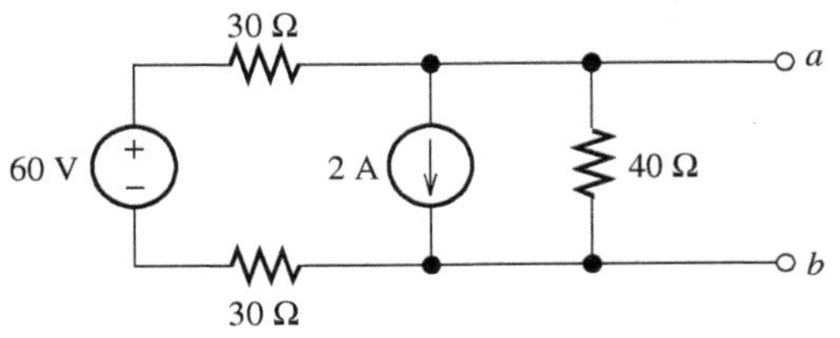

Figure T5

T6. According to the superposition principle, what percentage of the total current flowing through the 5-Ω resistance in the circuit of Figure T6 results from the 5-V source? What percentage of the power supplied to the 5-Ω resistance is supplied by the 5-V source? Assume that both sources are active when answering both questions.

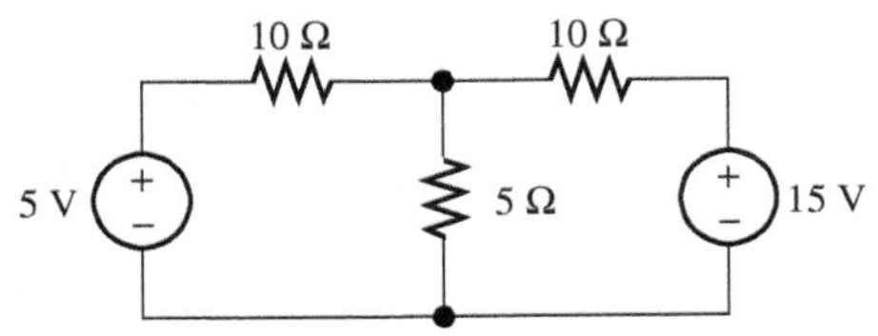

Figure T6

ANSWERS FOR THE PRACTICE TESTS

Complete solutions for the practice tests are included in the Student Solutions files. See Appendix "On-line Student Resources" for information on how to access these files.

T1. **a.** 6; **b.** 10; **c.** 2; **d.** 7; **e.** 10 or 13; **f.** 1 or 4; **g.** 11; **h.** 3; **i.** 8; **j.** 15; **k.** 17; **l.** 14.

T2. $i_s = 6\,\text{A}$; $i_4 = 1\,\text{A}$.

T3.
```
G = [0.95 -0.20 -0.50; -0.20 0.30 0; -0.50 0 1.50] I =
[0; 2; -2] V = G\ I % As an alternative, we
could use V = inv(G)*I
```

T4. A proper set of equations consists of any two of the following three

1. KVL mesh 1:

$$R_1 i_1 - V_s + R_3(i_1 - i_3) + R_2(i_1 - i_2) = 0$$

2. KVL for the supermesh obtained by combining meshes 2 and 3:

$$R_4 i_2 + R_2\,(i_2 - i_1) + R_3\,(i_3 - i_1) + R_5 i_3 = 0$$

3. KVL around the periphery of the circuit:

$$R_1 i_1 - V_s + R_4 i_2 + R_5 i_3 = 0$$

in combination with this equation for the current source:

$$i_2 - i_3 = I_s$$

T5. $V_t = 24\,\text{V}$, $R_t = 24\,\Omega$, and $I_n = 1\,\text{A}$. The reference direction for I_n should point toward terminal b. The positive reference for V_t should be on the side of the b terminal.

T6. By superposition, 25 percent of the current through the 5-Ω resistance is due to the 5-V source. Superposition does not apply for power, but we can see from analysis of the complete circuit that all of the power is supplied by the 15-V source. Thus, 0 percent of the power in the 5-Ω resistance is due to the 5-V source.

ON-LINE STUDENT RESOURCES

Users of the text can access the Student Solutions Manual (and other folders mentioned below) in electronic form by following links starting from the website:

www.pearsonhighered.com/hambley

The MATLAB folder contains m-files. Except for the examples that use the Symbolic Toolbox, these files work equally well with MathScript, which is sometimes included with the LabVIEW program. The Hambley MathScript folder contains the m-files that work with MathScript.

The Virtual Instruments folder contains LabVIEW programs.

Inductance and Capacitance

From Chapter 3 of *Electrical Engineering: Principles and Applications*, Sixth Edition. Allan R. Hambley.

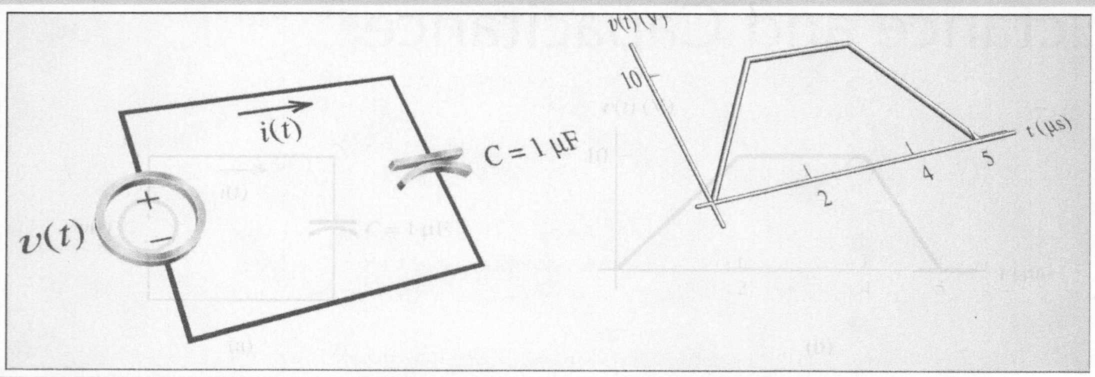

Inductance and Capacitance

Study of this chapter will enable you to:

- Find the current (voltage) for a capacitance or inductance given the voltage (current) as a function of time.
- Compute the capacitances of parallel-plate capacitors.
- Compute the energies stored in capacitances or inductances.
- Describe typical physical construction of capacitors and inductors and identify parasitic effects.
- Find the voltages across mutually coupled inductances in terms of the currents.
- Apply the MATLAB Symbolic Toolbox to the current–voltage relationships for capacitances and inductances.

Introduction to this chapter:

Previously, we studied circuits composed of resistances and sources. In this chapter, we discuss two additional circuit elements: inductors and capacitors. Whereas resistors convert electrical energy into heat, inductors and capacitors are **energy-storage elements**. They can store energy and later return it to the circuit. Capacitors and inductors do not generate energy—only the energy that has been put into these elements can be extracted. Thus, like resistors, they are said to be **passive** elements.

Electromagnetic field theory is the basic approach to the study of the effects of electrical charge. However, circuit theory is a simplification of field theory that is much easier to apply. Capacitance is the circuit property that accounts for energy stored in electric fields. Inductance accounts for energy stored in magnetic fields.

We will learn that the voltage across an ideal inductor is proportional to the time derivative of the current. On the other hand, the voltage across an ideal capacitor is proportional to the time integral of the current.

We will also study mutual inductance, a circuit property that accounts for magnetic fields that are mutual to several inductors. Mutual inductance forms the basis for transformers, which are critical to the transmission of electrical power over long distances.

Several types of transducers are based on inductance and capacitance. For example, one type of microphone is basically a capacitor in which the capacitance changes with sound pressure. An application of mutual inductance is the linear variable differential transformer in which position of a moving iron core is converted into a voltage.

Sometimes an electrical signal that represents a physical variable such as displacement is noisy. For example, in an active (electronically controlled) suspension for an automobile, the position sensors are affected by road roughness as well as by the loading of the vehicle. To obtain an electrical signal representing the displacement of each wheel, the rapid fluctuations due to road roughness must be eliminated. Later, we will see that this can be accomplished using inductance and capacitance in circuits known as filters.

1 CAPACITANCE

Capacitors are constructed by separating two sheets of conductor, which is usually metallic, by a thin layer of insulating material. In a parallel-plate capacitor, the sheets are flat and parallel as shown in Figure 1. The insulating material between the plates, called a **dielectric**, can be air, Mylar®, polyester, polypropylene, mica, or a variety of other materials.

Capacitors are constructed by separating two conducting plates, which are usually metallic, by a thin layer of insulating material.

Let us consider what happens as current flows through a capacitor. Suppose that current flows downward, as shown in Figure 2(a). In most metals, current consists of electrons moving, and conventional current flowing downward represents electrons actually moving upward. As electrons move upward, they collect on the lower plate of the capacitor. Thus, the lower plate accumulates a net negative charge that produces an electric field in the dielectric. This electric field forces electrons to leave the upper plate at the same rate that they accumulate on the lower plate. Therefore, current appears to flow through the capacitor. As the charge builds up, voltage appears across the capacitor.

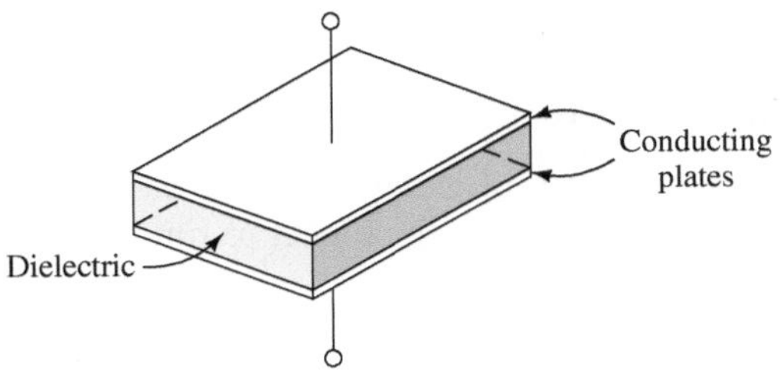

Figure 1 A parallel-plate capacitor consists of two conductive plates separated by a dielectric layer.

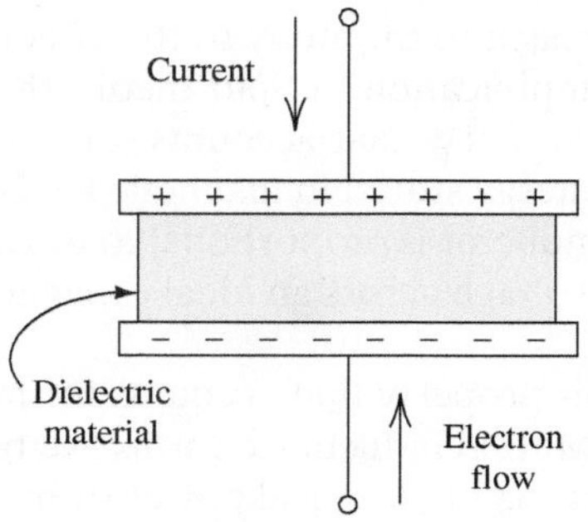

(a) As current flows through a capacitor, charges of opposite signs collect on the respective plates

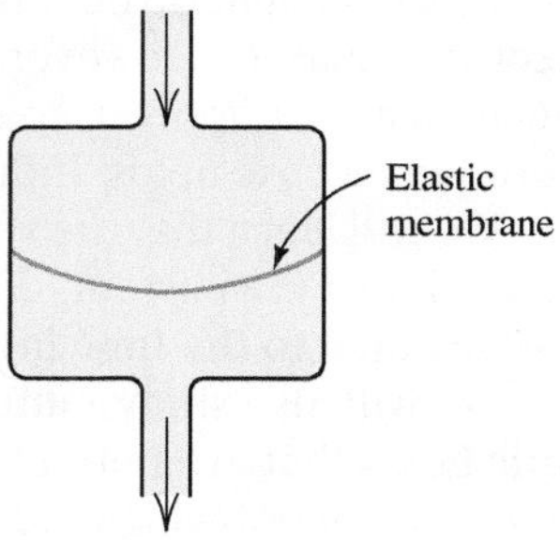

(b) Fluid-flow analogy for capacitance

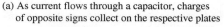

Figure 2 A capacitor and its fluid-flow analogy.

Positive charge on one plate is balanced by negative charge of equal magnitude on the other plate.

We say that the charge accumulated on one plate is stored in the capacitor. However, the total charge on both plates is always zero, because positive charge on one plate is balanced by negative charge of equal magnitude on the other plate.

Fluid-Flow Analogy

In terms of the fluid-flow analogy, a capacitor represents a reservoir with an elastic membrane separating the inlet and outlet.

In terms of the fluid-flow analogy, a capacitor represents a reservoir with an elastic membrane separating the inlet and outlet as shown in Figure 2(b). As the fluid flows into the inlet, the membrane is stretched, creating a force (analogous to capacitor voltage) that opposes further flow. The displaced fluid volume starting from the unstretched membrane position is analogous to the charge stored on one plate of the capacitor.

Stored Charge in Terms of Voltage

In an ideal capacitor, the stored charge q is proportional to the voltage between the plates.

In an ideal capacitor, the stored charge q is proportional to the voltage between the plates:

$$q = Cv \tag{1}$$

The constant of proportionality is the capacitance C, which has units of farads (F). Farads are equivalent to coulombs per volt.

To be more precise, the charge q is the net charge on the plate corresponding to the positive reference for v. Thus, if v is positive, there is positive charge on the plate corresponding to the positive reference for v. On the other hand, if v is negative, there is negative charge on the plate corresponding to the positive reference.

In most applications, we deal with capacitances in the range from a few picofarads up to perhaps 0.01 F.

A farad is a very large amount of capacitance. In most applications, we deal with capacitances in the range from a few picofarads (1 pF $= 10^{-12}$ F) up to perhaps 0.01 F. Capacitances in the femtofarad (1 fF $= 10^{-15}$ F) range are responsible for limiting the performance of computer chips.

Current in Terms of Voltage

Recall that current is the time rate of flow of charge. Taking the derivative of each side of Equation 1 with respect to time, we have

$$i = \frac{dq}{dt} = \frac{d}{dt}(Cv) \tag{2}$$

Ordinarily, capacitance is not a function of time. (An exception is the capacitor microphone mentioned earlier.) Thus, the relationship between current and voltage becomes

$$i = C\frac{dv}{dt} \quad (3)$$

Equations 1 and 3 show that as voltage increases, current flows through the capacitance and charge accumulates on each plate. If the voltage remains constant, the charge is constant and the current is zero. Thus, a capacitor appears to be an open circuit for a steady dc voltage.

Capacitors act as open circuits for steady dc voltages.

The circuit symbol for capacitance and the references for v and i are shown in Figure 3. Notice that the references for the voltage and current have the passive configuration. In other words, the current reference direction points into the positive reference polarity. If the references were opposite to the passive configuration, Equation 3 would have a minus sign:

$$i = -C\frac{dv}{dt} \quad (4)$$

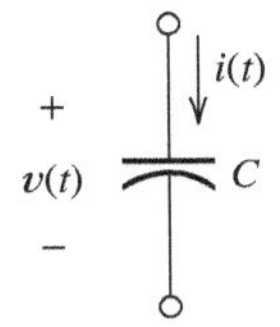

Figure 3 The circuit symbol for capacitance, including references for the current $i(t)$ and voltage $v(t)$.

Sometimes, we emphasize the fact that in general the voltage and current are functions of time by denoting them as $v(t)$ and $i(t)$.

Example 1 Determining Current for a Capacitance Given Voltage

Suppose that the voltage $v(t)$ shown in Figure 4(b) is applied to a 1-μF capacitance. Plot the stored charge and the current through the capacitance versus time.

Solution The charge stored on the top plate of the capacitor is given by Equation 1. [We know that $q(t)$ represents the charge on the top plate because that is the plate corresponding to the positive reference for $v(t)$.] Thus,

$$q(t) = Cv(t) = 10^{-6}v(t)$$

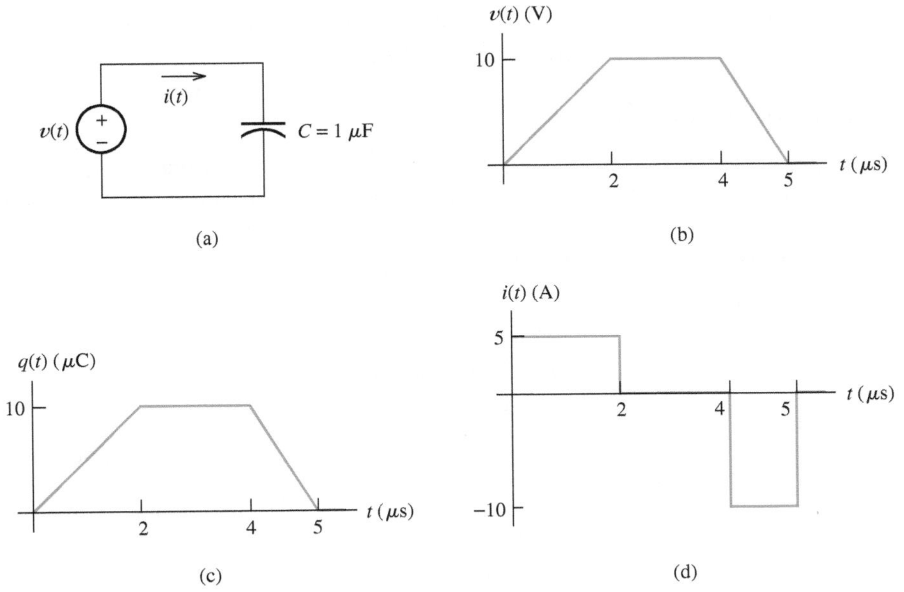

Figure 4 Circuit and waveforms for Example 1.

This is shown in Figure 4(c).

The current flowing through the capacitor is given by Equation 3:

$$i(t) = C\frac{dv(t)}{dt} = 10^{-6}\frac{dv(t)}{dt}$$

Of course, the derivative of the voltage is the slope of the voltage versus time plot. Hence, for t between 0 and 2 μs, we have

$$\frac{dv(t)}{dt} = \frac{10\text{ V}}{2 \times 10^{-6}\text{ s}} = 5 \times 10^{6}\text{ V/s}$$

and

$$i(t) = C\frac{dv(t)}{dt} = 10^{-6} \times 5 \times 10^{6} = 5\text{ A}$$

Between $t = 2$ and 4 μs, the voltage is constant ($dv/dt = 0$) and the current is zero. Finally, between $t = 4$ and 5 μs, we get

$$\frac{dv(t)}{dt} = \frac{-10\text{ V}}{10^{-6}\text{ s}} = -10^{7}\text{ V/s}$$

and

$$i(t) = C\frac{dv(t)}{dt} = 10^{-6} \times (-10^{7}) = -10\text{ A}$$

A plot of $i(t)$ is shown in Figure 4(d).

Notice that as the voltage increases, current flows through the capacitor and charges accumulate on the plates. For constant voltage, the current is zero and the charge is constant. When the voltage decreases, the direction of the current reverses, and the stored charge is removed from the capacitor. ■

Exercise 1 The charge on a 2-μF capacitor is given by

$$q(t) = 10^{-6}\sin(10^{5}t)\text{ C}$$

Find expressions for the voltage and for the current. (The angle is in radians.)
Answer $v(t) = 0.5\sin(10^{5}t)$ V, $i(t) = 0.1\cos(10^{5}t)$ A. □

Voltage in Terms of Current

Suppose that we know the current $i(t)$ flowing through a capacitance C and we want to compute the charge and voltage. Since current is the time rate of charge flow, we must integrate the current to compute charge. Often in circuit analysis problems, action starts at some initial time t_0, and the initial charge $q(t_0)$ is known. Then, charge as a function of time is given by

$$q(t) = \int_{t_0}^{t} i(t)\,dt + q(t_0) \qquad (5)$$

Setting the right-hand sides of Equations 1 and 5 equal to each other and solving for the voltage $v(t)$, we have

$$v(t) = \frac{1}{C}\int_{t_0}^{t} i(t)\,dt + \frac{q(t_0)}{C} \qquad (6)$$

However, the initial voltage across the capacitance is given by

$$v(t_0) = \frac{q(t_0)}{C} \tag{7}$$

Substituting this into Equation 6, we have

$$v(t) = \frac{1}{C}\int_{t_0}^{t} i(t)\,dt + v(t_0) \tag{8}$$

Usually, we take the initial time to be $t_0 = 0$.

Example 2 **Determining Voltage for a Capacitance Given Current**

After $t_0 = 0$, the current in a 0.1-μF capacitor is given by

$$i(t) = 0.5\sin(10^4 t)$$

(The argument of the sin function is in radians.) The initial charge on the capacitor is $q(0) = 0$. Plot $i(t)$, $q(t)$, and $v(t)$ to scale versus time.

Solution First, we use Equation 5 to find an expression for the charge:

$$\begin{aligned} q(t) &= \int_0^t i(t)\,dt + q(0) \\ &= \int_0^t 0.5\sin(10^4 t)\,dt \\ &= -0.5\times 10^{-4}\cos(10^4 t)\Big|_0^t \\ &= 0.5\times 10^{-4}[1-\cos(10^4 t)] \end{aligned}$$

Solving Equation 1 for voltage, we have

$$\begin{aligned} v(t) &= \frac{q(t)}{C} = \frac{q(t)}{10^{-7}} \\ &= 500[1-\cos(10^4 t)] \end{aligned}$$

Plots of $i(t)$, $q(t)$, and $v(t)$ are shown in Figure 5. Immediately after $t = 0$, the current is positive and $q(t)$ increases. After the first half-cycle, $i(t)$ becomes negative and $q(t)$ decreases. At the completion of one cycle, the charge and voltage have returned to zero. ■

Stored Energy

The power delivered to a circuit element is the product of the current and the voltage (provided that the references have the passive configuration):

$$p(t) = v(t)i(t) \tag{9}$$

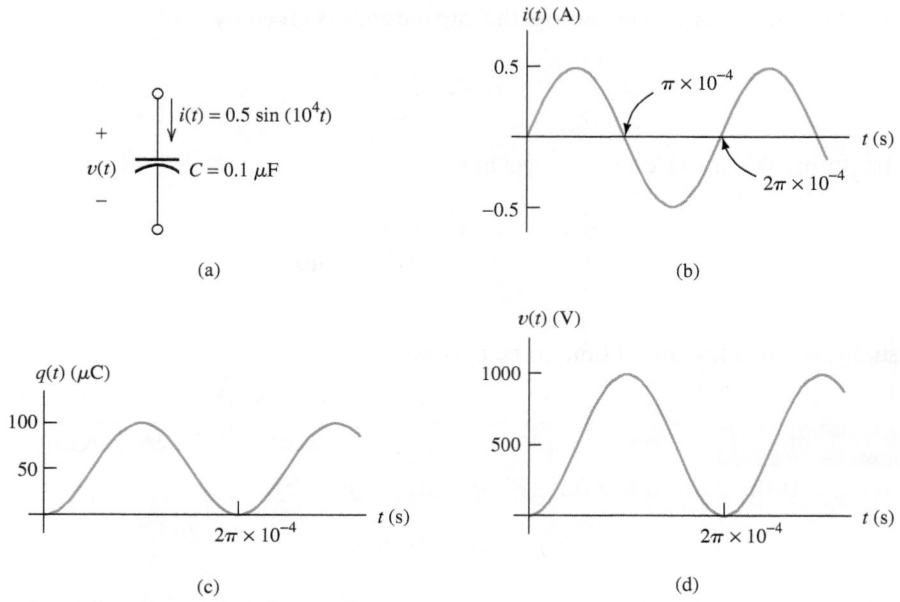

Figure 5 Waveforms for Example 2.

Using Equation 3 to substitute for the current, we have

$$p(t) = Cv\frac{dv}{dt} \tag{10}$$

Suppose we have a capacitor that initially has $v(t_0) = 0$. Then the initial stored electrical energy is zero, and we say that the capacitor is uncharged. Furthermore, suppose that between time t_0 and some later time t the voltage changes from 0 to $v(t)$ volts. As the voltage magnitude increases, energy is delivered to the capacitor, where it is stored in the electric field between the plates.

If we integrate the power delivered from t_0 to t, we find the energy delivered:

$$w(t) = \int_{t_0}^{t} p(t)\,dt \tag{11}$$

Using Equation 10 to substitute for power, we find that

$$w(t) = \int_{t_0}^{t} Cv\frac{dv}{dt}\,dt \tag{12}$$

Canceling differential time and changing the limits to the corresponding voltages, we have

$$w(t) = \int_{0}^{v(t)} Cv\,dv \tag{13}$$

Integrating and evaluating, we get

$$w(t) = \frac{1}{2}Cv^2(t) \tag{14}$$

This represents energy stored in the capacitance that can be returned to the circuit.

Solving Equation 1 for $v(t)$ and substituting into Equation 14, we can obtain two alternative expressions for the stored energy:

$$w(t) = \frac{1}{2}v(t)q(t) \tag{15}$$

$$w(t) = \frac{q^2(t)}{2C} \tag{16}$$

Example 3 Current, Power, and Energy for a Capacitance

Suppose that the voltage waveform shown in Figure 6(a) is applied to a 10-μF capacitance. Find and plot the current, the power delivered, and the energy stored for time between 0 and 5 s.

Solution First, we write expressions for the voltage as a function of time:

$$v(t) = \begin{cases} 1000t \text{ V} & \text{for } 0 < t < 1 \\ 1000 \text{ V} & \text{for } 1 < t < 3 \\ 500(5 - t) \text{ V} & \text{for } 3 < t < 5 \end{cases}$$

Using Equation 3, we obtain expressions for the current:

$$i(t) = C\frac{dv(t)}{dt}$$

$$i(t) = \begin{cases} 10 \times 10^{-3} \text{ A} & \text{for } 0 < t < 1 \\ 0 \text{ A} & \text{for } 1 < t < 3 \\ -5 \times 10^{-3} \text{ A} & \text{for } 3 < t < 5 \end{cases}$$

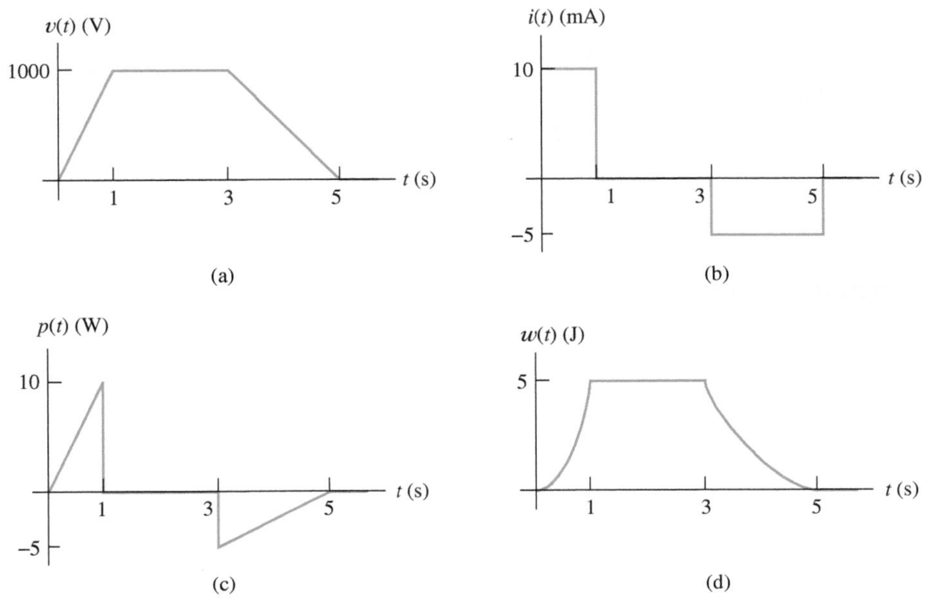

Figure 6 Waveforms for Example 3.

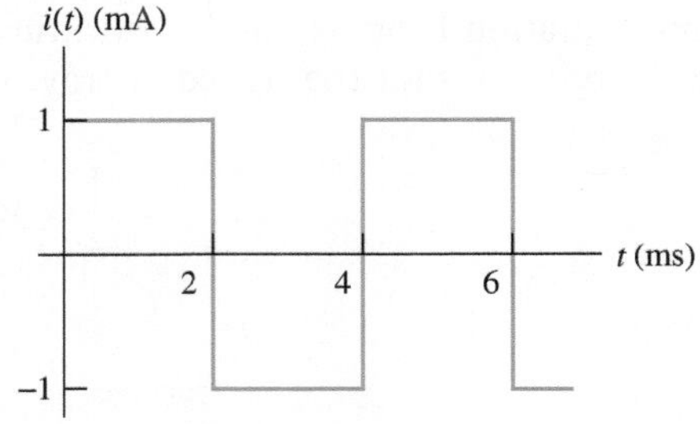

Figure 7 Square-wave current for Exercise 2.

The plot of $i(t)$ is shown in Figure 6(b).

Next, we find expressions for power by multiplying the voltage by the current:

$$p(t) = v(t)i(t)$$

$$p(t) = \begin{cases} 10t \text{ W} & \text{for } 0 < t < 1 \\ 0 \text{ W} & \text{for } 1 < t < 3 \\ 2.5(t-5) \text{ W} & \text{for } 3 < t < 5 \end{cases}$$

The plot of $p(t)$ is shown in Figure 6(c). Notice that between $t = 0$ and $t = 1$ power is positive, showing that energy is being delivered to the capacitance. Between $t = 3$ and $t = 5$, energy flows out of the capacitance back into the rest of the circuit.

Next, we use Equation 14 to find expressions for the stored energy:

$$w(t) = \frac{1}{2}Cv^2(t)$$

$$w(t) = \begin{cases} 5t^2 \text{ J} & \text{for } 0 < t < 1 \\ 5 \text{ J} & \text{for } 1 < t < 3 \\ 1.25(5-t)^2 \text{ J} & \text{for } 3 < t < 5 \end{cases}$$

The plot of $w(t)$ is shown in Figure 6(d). ■

Exercise 2 The current through a 0.1-μF capacitor is shown in Figure 7. At $t_0 = 0$, the voltage across the capacitor is zero. Find the charge, voltage, power, and stored energy as functions of time and plot them to scale versus time.

Answer The plots are shown in Figure 8. □

2 CAPACITANCES IN SERIES AND PARALLEL

Capacitances in Parallel

Suppose that we have three capacitances in parallel as shown in Figure 9. Of course, the same voltage appears across each of the elements in a parallel circuit. The currents are related to the voltage by Equation 3. Thus, we can write

$$i_1 = C_1\frac{dv}{dt} \tag{17}$$

$$i_2 = C_2\frac{dv}{dt} \tag{18}$$

$$i_3 = C_3\frac{dv}{dt} \tag{19}$$

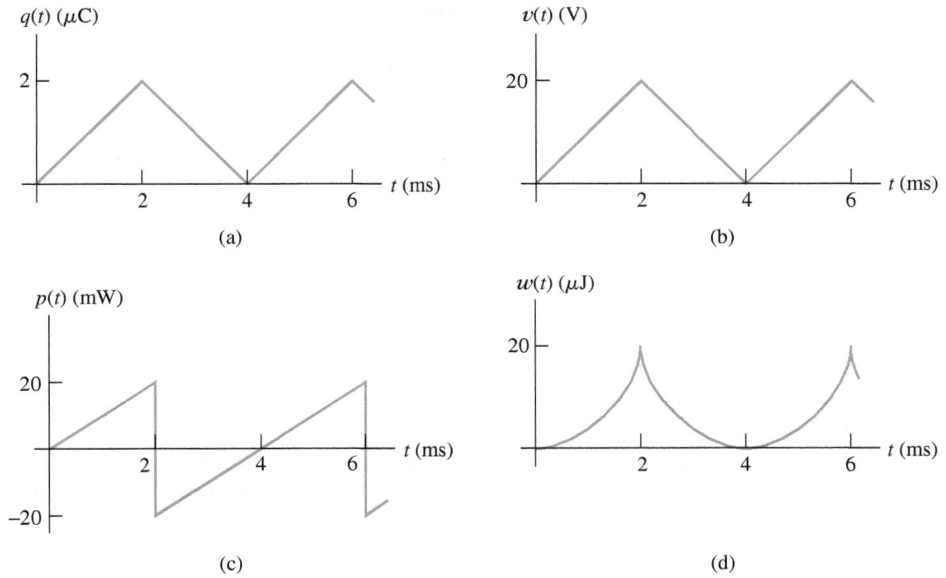

Figure 8 Answers for Exercise 2.

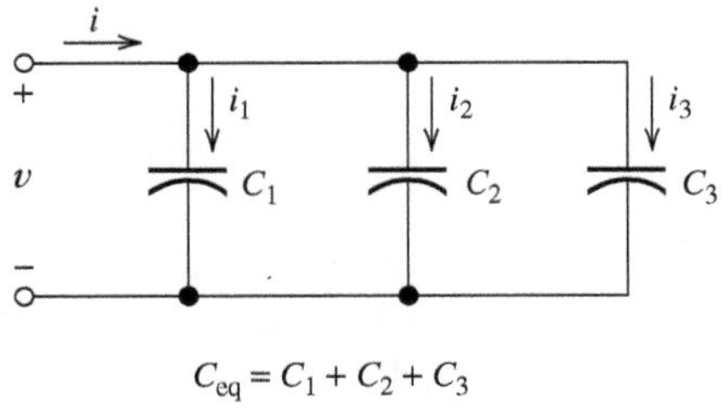

Figure 9 Three capacitances in parallel.

Applying KCL at the top node of the circuit, we have

$$i = i_1 + i_2 + i_3 \tag{20}$$

Using Equations 17, 18, and 19 to substitute into Equation 20, we obtain

$$i = C_1\frac{dv}{dt} + C_2\frac{dv}{dt} + C_3\frac{dv}{dt} \tag{21}$$

This can be written as

$$i = (C_1 + C_2 + C_3)\frac{dv}{dt} \tag{22}$$

Now, we define the equivalent capacitance as the sum of the capacitances in parallel:

$$C_{eq} = C_1 + C_2 + C_3 \tag{23}$$

We add parallel capacitances to find the equivalent capacitance.

Using this definition in Equation 22, we find that

$$i = C_{eq}\frac{dv}{dt} \tag{24}$$

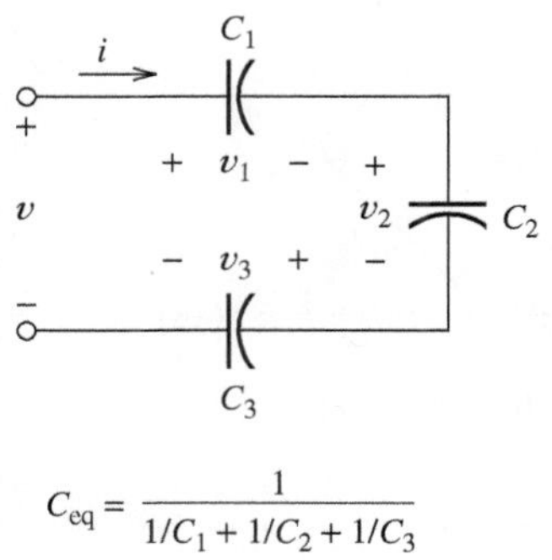

Figure 10 Three capacitances in series.

Thus, the current in the equivalent capacitance is the same as the total current flowing through the parallel circuit.

In sum, we add parallel capacitances to find the equivalent capacitance. Recall that for resistances, the resistances are added if they are in *series* rather than parallel. Thus, we say that capacitances in parallel are combined like resistances in series.

Capacitances in parallel are combined like resistances in series.

Capacitances in Series

By a similar development, it can be shown that the equivalent capacitance for three series capacitances is

Capacitances in series are combined like resistances in parallel.

$$C_{eq} = \frac{1}{1/C_1 + 1/C_2 + 1/C_3} \tag{25}$$

We conclude that capacitances in series are combined like resistances in parallel.

A technique for obtaining high voltages from low-voltage sources is to charge n capacitors in parallel with the source, and then to switch them to a series combination. The resulting voltage across the series combination is n times the source voltage. For example, in some cardiac pacemakers, a 2.5-V battery is used, but 5 V need to be applied to the heart muscle to initiate a beat. This is accomplished by charging two capacitors from the 2.5-V battery. The capacitors are then connected in series to deliver a brief 5-V pulse to the heart.

Exercise 3 Derive Equation 25 for the three capacitances shown in Figure 10. □

Exercise 4 **a.** Two capacitances of 2 μF and 1 μF are in series. Find the equivalent capacitance. **b.** Repeat if the capacitances are in parallel.

Answer **a.** 2/3 μF; **b.** 3 μF. □

3 PHYSICAL CHARACTERISTICS OF CAPACITORS

Capacitance of the Parallel-Plate Capacitor

A parallel-plate capacitor is shown in Figure 11, including dimensions. The area of each plate is denoted as A. (Actually, A is the area of one side of the plate.) The rectangular plate shown has a width W, length L, and area $A = W \times L$. The plates are parallel, and the distance between them is denoted as d.

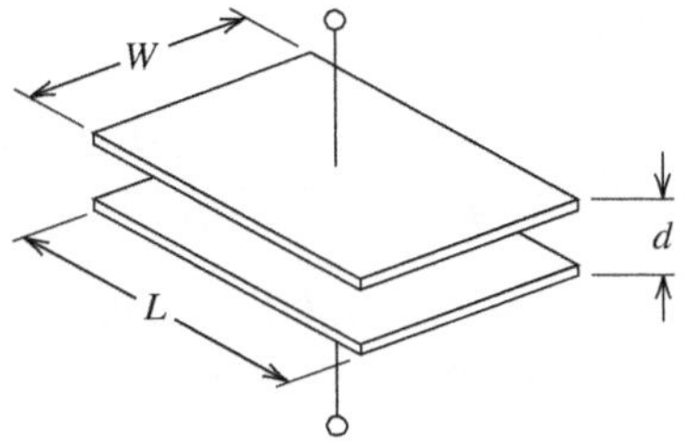

Figure 11 A parallel-plate capacitor, including dimensions.

Table 1. Relative Dielectric Constants for Selected Materials

Air	1.0
Diamond	5.5
Mica	7.0
Polyester	3.4
Quartz	4.3
Silicon dioxide	3.9
Water	78.5

If the distance d between the plates is much smaller than both the width and the length of the plates, the capacitance is approximately given by

$$C = \frac{\epsilon A}{d} \tag{26}$$

in which ϵ is the **dielectric constant** of the material between the plates. For vacuum, the dielectric constant is

$$\epsilon = \epsilon_0 \cong 8.85 \times 10^{-12} \text{ F/m}$$

Dielectric constant of vacuum.

For other materials, the dielectric constant is

$$\epsilon = \epsilon_r \epsilon_0 \tag{27}$$

where ϵ_r is the **relative dielectric constant**. Values of the relative dielectric constant for selected materials are given in Table 1.

Example 4 Calculating Capacitance Given Physical Parameters

Compute the capacitance of a parallel-plate capacitor having rectangular plates 10 cm by 20 cm separated by a distance of 0.1 mm. The dielectric is air. Repeat if the dielectric is mica.

Solution First, we compute the area of a plate:

$$A = L \times W = (10 \times 10^{-2}) \times (20 \times 10^{-2}) = 0.02 \text{ m}^2$$

From Table 1, we see that the relative dielectric constant of air is 1.00. Thus, the dielectric constant is

$$\epsilon = \epsilon_r \epsilon_0 = 1.00 \times 8.85 \times 10^{-12} \text{ F/m}$$

Then, the capacitance is

$$C = \frac{\epsilon A}{d} = \frac{8.85 \times 10^{-12} \times 0.02}{10^{-4}} = 1770 \times 10^{-12}\ \text{F}$$

For a mica dielectric, the relative dielectric constant is 7.0. Thus, the capacitance is seven times larger than for air or vacuum:

$$C = 12{,}390 \times 10^{-12}\ \text{F}$$

■

Exercise 5 We want to design a 1-μF capacitor. Compute the length required for rectangular plates of 2-cm width if the dielectric is polyester of 15-μm thickness.
Answer $L = 24.93$ m. □

Practical Capacitors

To achieve capacitances on the order of a microfarad, the dimensions of parallel-plate capacitors are too large for compact electronic circuits such as portable computers or cellular telephones. Frequently, capacitors are constructed by alternating the plates with two layers of dielectric, which are then rolled to fit in a smaller area. By staggering the plates before rolling, electrical contact can be made with the plates from the ends of the roll. This type of construction is illustrated in Figure 12.

Real capacitors have maximum voltage ratings.

An engineering trade-off exists between compact size and high voltage rating.

To achieve small-volume capacitors, a very thin dielectric having a high dielectric constant is desirable. However, dielectric materials break down and become conductors when the electric field intensity (volts per meter) is too high. Thus, real capacitors have maximum voltage ratings. For a given voltage, the electric field intensity becomes higher as the dielectric layer becomes thinner. Clearly, an engineering trade-off exists between compact size and voltage rating.

Electrolytic Capacitors

In **electrolytic capacitors**, one of the plates is metallic aluminum or tantalum, the dielectric is an oxide layer on the surface of the metal, and the other "plate" is an electrolytic solution. The oxide-coated metallic plate is immersed in the electrolytic solution.

Only voltages of the proper polarity should be applied to electrolytic capacitors.

This type of construction results in high capacitance per unit volume. However, only one polarity of voltage should be applied to electrolytic capacitors. For the opposite polarity, the dielectric layer is chemically attacked, and a conductive path appears between the plates. (Usually, the allowed polarity is marked on the outer case.) On the other hand, capacitors constructed with polyethylene, Mylar®, and so on can be used in applications where the voltage polarity reverses. When the application results in voltages of only one polarity and a large-value capacitance is required, designers frequently use electrolytic capacitors.

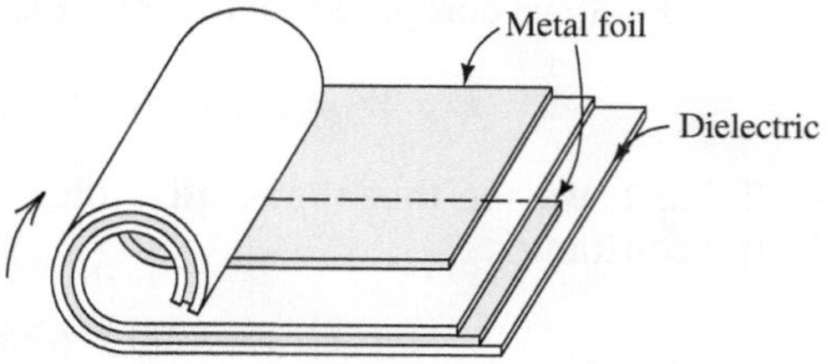

Figure 12 Practical capacitors can be constructed by interleaving the plates with two dielectric layers and rolling them up. By staggering the plates, connection can be made to one plate at each end of the roll.

Parasitic Effects

Real capacitors are not always well modeled simply as a capacitance. A more complete circuit model for a capacitor is shown in Figure 13. In addition to the capacitance C, series resistance R_s appears because of the resistivity of the material composing the plates. A series inductance L_s (we discuss inductance later in this chapter) occurs because the current flowing through the capacitor creates a magnetic field. Finally, no practical material is a perfect insulator, and the resistance R_p represents conduction through the dielectric.

We call R_s, L_s, and R_p **parasitic elements**. We design capacitors to minimize the effects of parasitic circuit elements consistent with other requirements such as physical size and voltage rating. However, parasitics are always present to some degree. In designing circuits, care must be used to select components for which the parasitic effects do not prevent proper operation of the circuit.

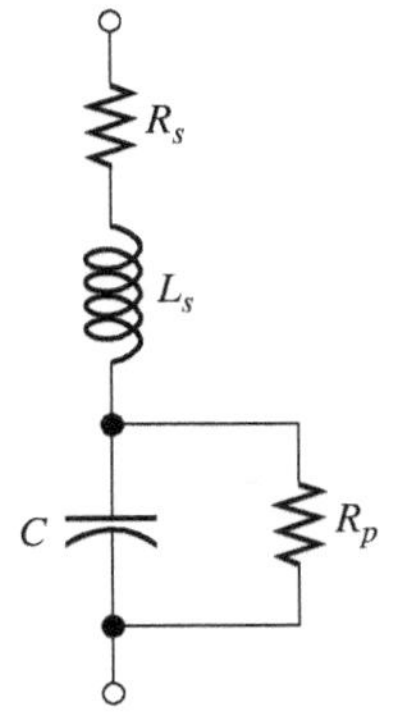

Figure 13 The circuit model for a capacitor, including the parasitic elements R_s, L_s, and R_p.

Example 5 What Happened to the Missing Energy?

Consider the situation shown in Figure 14. Prior to $t = 0$, the capacitor C_1 is charged to a voltage of $v_1 = 100$ V and the other capacitor has no charge (i.e., $v_2 = 0$). At $t = 0$, the switch closes. Compute the total energy stored by both capacitors before and after the switch closes.

Solution The initial stored energy for each capacitor is

$$w_1 = \frac{1}{2}C_1 v_1^2 = \frac{1}{2}(10^{-6})(100)^2 = 5 \text{ mJ}$$

$$w_2 = 0$$

and the total energy is

$$w_{\text{total}} = w_1 + w_2 = 5 \text{ mJ}$$

To find the voltage and stored energy after the switch closes, we make use of the fact that the total charge on the top plates cannot change when the switch closes. This is true because there is no path for electrons to enter or leave the upper part of the circuit.

The charge stored on the top plate of C_1 prior to $t = 0$ is given by

$$q_1 = C_1 v_1 = 1 \times 10^{-6} \times 100 = 100\ \mu\text{C}$$

Furthermore, the initial charge on C_2 is zero:

$$q_2 = 0$$

Thus, after the switch closes, the charge on the equivalent capacitance is

$$q_{\text{eq}} = q_1 + q_2 = 100\ \mu\text{C}$$

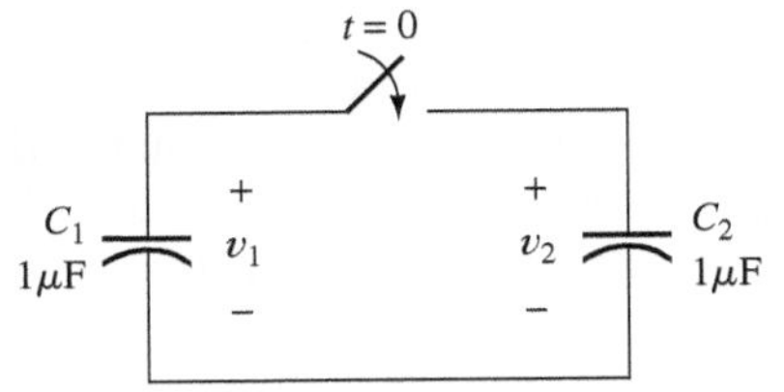

Figure 14 See Example 5.

Also, notice that after the switch is closed, the capacitors are in parallel and have an equivalent capacitance of

$$C_{eq} = C_1 + C_2 = 2\ \mu\text{F}$$

The voltage across the equivalent capacitance is

$$v_{eq} = \frac{q_{eq}}{C_{eq}} = \frac{100\ \mu\text{C}}{2\ \mu\text{F}} = 50\ \text{V}$$

Of course, after the switch is closed, $v_1 = v_2 = v_{eq}$.

Now, we compute the stored energy with the switch closed:

$$w_1 = \frac{1}{2}C_1 v_{eq}^2 = \frac{1}{2}(10^{-6})(50)^2 = 1.25\ \text{mJ}$$

$$w_2 = \frac{1}{2}C_2 v_{eq}^2 = \frac{1}{2}(10^{-6})(50)^2 = 1.25\ \text{mJ}$$

The total stored energy with the switch closed is

$$w_{total} = w_1 + w_2 = 2.5\ \text{mJ}$$

Thus, we see that the stored energy after the switch is closed is half of the value before the switch is closed. What happened to the missing energy?

Usually, the missing energy is absorbed in the parasitic resistances.

Usually, the answer to this question is that it is absorbed in the parasitic resistances. It is impossible to construct capacitors that do not have some parasitic effects. Even if we use superconductors for the wires and capacitor plates, there would be parasitic inductance. If we included the parasitic inductance in the circuit model, we would not have missing energy.

A physical circuit that is modeled exactly by Figure 14 does not exist.

To put it another way, a physical circuit that is modeled exactly by Figure 14 does not exist. Invariably, if we use a realistic model for an actual circuit, we can account for all of the energy. ■

4 INDUCTANCE

Inductors are usually constructed by coiling wire around a form.

An inductor is usually constructed by coiling a wire around some type of form. Several examples of practical construction are illustrated in Figure 15. Current flowing through the coil creates a magnetic field or flux that links the coil. Frequently, the coil form is composed of a magnetic material such as iron or iron oxides that increases the magnetic flux for a given current. (Iron cores are often composed of thin sheets called **laminations**.

When the current changes in value, the resulting magnetic flux changes. According to Faraday's law of electromagnetic induction, time-varying magnetic flux linking a coil induces voltage across the coil. For an ideal inductor, the voltage is proportional to the time rate of change of the current. Furthermore, the polarity of the voltage is such as to oppose the change in current. The constant of proportionality is called inductance, usually denoted by the letter L.

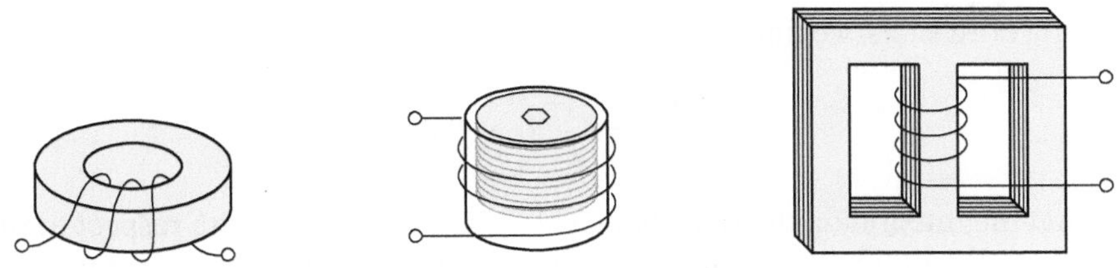

(a) Toroidal inductor

(b) Coil with an iron-oxide slug that can be screwed in or out to adjust the inductance

(c) Inductor with a laminated iron core

Figure 15 An inductor is constructed by coiling a wire around some type of form.

The circuit symbol for inductance is shown in Figure 16. In equation form, the voltage and current are related by

$$v(t) = L\frac{di}{dt} \tag{28}$$

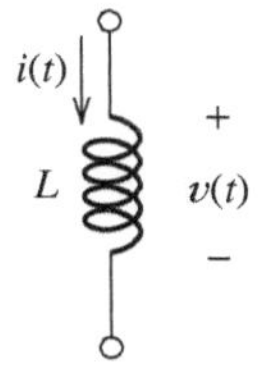

$v(t) = L\dfrac{di}{dt}$

Figure 16 Circuit symbol and the $v - i$ relationship for inductance.

As usual, we have assumed the passive reference configuration. In case the references are opposite to the passive configuration, Equation 28 becomes

$$v(t) = -L\frac{di}{dt} \tag{29}$$

Inductance has units of henries (H), which are equivalent to volt seconds per ampere. Typically, we deal with inductances ranging from a fraction of a microhenry (μH) to several tens of henries.

Inductance has units of henries (H), which are equivalent to volt seconds per ampere.

Fluid-Flow Analogy

The fluid-flow analogy for inductance is the inertia of the fluid flowing through a *frictionless* pipe of constant diameter. The pressure differential between the ends of the pipe is analogous to voltage, and the flow rate or velocity is analogous to current. Thus, the acceleration of the fluid is analogous to rate of change of current. A pressure differential exists between the ends of the pipe only when the flow rate is increasing or decreasing.

The fluid-flow analogy for inductance is the inertia of the fluid flowing through a frictionless pipe of constant diameter.

One place where the inertia of flowing fluid is encountered is when a valve (typically operated by an electrical solenoid) closes suddenly, cutting off the flow. For example, in a washing machine, the sudden change in velocity of the water flow can cause high pressure, resulting in a bang and vibration of the plumbing. This is similar to electrical effects that occur when current in an inductor is suddenly interrupted. An application for the high voltage that appears when current is suddenly interrupted is in the ignition system for a gasoline-powered internal combustion engine.

Current in Terms of Voltage

Suppose that we know the initial current $i(t_0)$ and the voltage $v(t)$ across an inductance. Furthermore, suppose that we need to compute the current for $t > t_0$. Rearranging Equation 28, we have

$$di = \frac{1}{L}v(t)\,dt \tag{30}$$

Integrating both sides, we find that

$$\int_{i(t_0)}^{i(t)} di = \frac{1}{L}\int_{t_0}^{t} v(t)\, dt \tag{31}$$

Notice that the integral on the right-hand side of Equation 31 is with respect to time. Furthermore, the limits are the initial time t_0 and the time variable t. The integral on the left-hand side is with respect to current with limits that correspond to the time limits on the right-hand side. Integrating, evaluating, and rearranging, we have

$$i(t) = \frac{1}{L}\int_{t_0}^{t} v(t)\, dt + i(t_0) \tag{32}$$

Notice that as long as $v(t)$ is finite, $i(t)$ can change only by an incremental amount in a time increment. Thus, $i(t)$ must be continuous with no instantaneous jumps in value (i.e., discontinuities). (Later, we encounter idealized circuits in which infinite voltages appear briefly, and then the current in an inductance can change instantaneously.)

Stored Energy

Assuming that the references have the passive configuration, we compute the power delivered to a circuit element by taking the product of the current and the voltage:

$$p(t) = v(t)i(t) \tag{33}$$

Using Equation 28 to substitute for the voltage, we obtain

$$p(t) = Li(t)\frac{di}{dt} \tag{34}$$

Consider an inductor having an initial current $i(t_0) = 0$. Then, the initial electrical energy stored is zero. Furthermore, assume that between time t_0 and some later time t, the current changes from 0 to $i(t)$. As the current magnitude increases, energy is delivered to the inductor, where it is stored in the magnetic field.

Integrating the power from t_0 to t, we find the energy delivered:

$$w(t) = \int_{t_0}^{t} p(t)\, dt \tag{35}$$

Using Equation 34 to substitute for power, we have

$$w(t) = \int_{t_0}^{t} Li\frac{di}{dt}\, dt \tag{36}$$

Canceling differential time and changing the limits to the corresponding currents, we get

$$w(t) = \int_{0}^{i(t)} Li\, di \tag{37}$$

Integrating and evaluating, we obtain

$$w(t) = \frac{1}{2}Li^2(t) \tag{38}$$

This represents energy stored in the inductance that is returned to the circuit if the current changes back to zero.

Example 6 Voltage, Power, and Energy for an Inductance

The current through a 5-H inductance is shown in Figure 17(a). Plot the voltage, power, and stored energy to scale versus time for t between 0 and 5 s.

Solution We use Equation 28 to compute voltages:

$$v(t) = L\frac{di}{dt}$$

The time derivative of the current is the slope (rise over run) of the current versus time plot. For t between 0 and 2 s, we have $di/dt = 1.5$ A/s and thus, $v = 7.5$ V. For t between 2 and 4 s, $di/dt = 0$, and therefore, $v = 0$. Finally, between 4 and 5 s, $di/dt = -3$ A/s and $v = -15$ V. A plot of the voltage versus time is shown in Figure 17(b).

Next, we obtain power by taking the product of current and voltage at each point in time. The resulting plot is shown in Figure 17(c).

Finally, we use Equation 38 to compute the stored energy as a function of time:

$$w(t) = \frac{1}{2}Li^2(t)$$

The resulting plot is shown in Figure 17(d).

Notice in Figure 17 that as current magnitude increases, power is positive and stored energy accumulates. When the current is constant, the voltage is zero, the

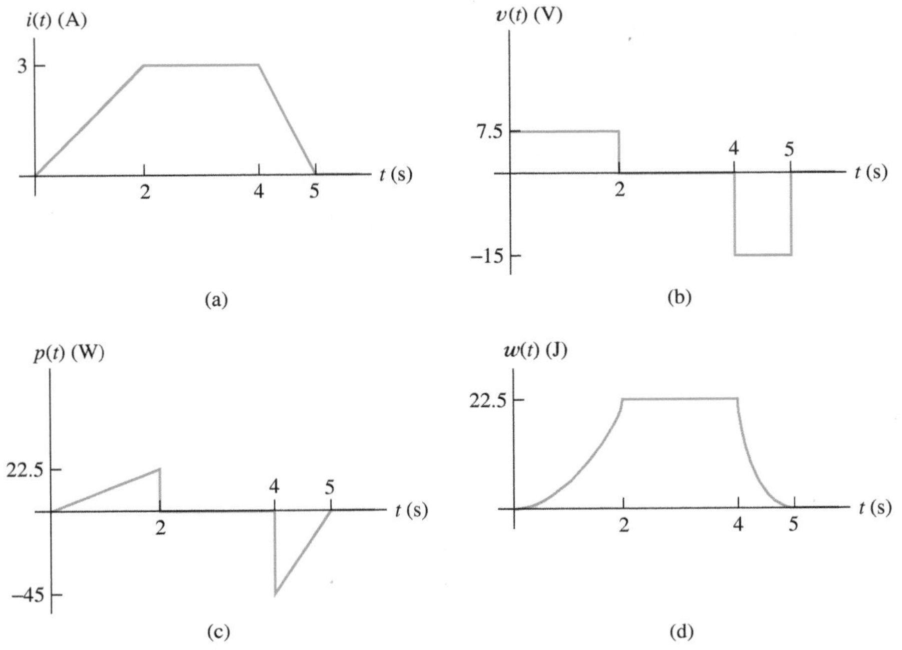

Figure 17 Waveforms for Example 6.

power is zero, and the stored energy is constant. When the current magnitude falls toward zero, the power is negative, showing that energy is being returned to the other parts of the circuit. ■

Example 7 Inductor Current with Constant Applied Voltage

Consider the circuit shown in Figure 18(a). In this circuit, we have a switch that closes at $t = 0$, connecting a 10-V source to a 2-H inductance. Find the current as a function of time.

Solution Notice that because the voltage applied to the inductance is finite, the current must be continuous. Prior to $t = 0$, the current must be zero. (Current cannot flow through an open switch.) Thus, the current must also be zero immediately after $t = 0$.

The voltage across the inductance is shown in Figure 18(b). To find the current, we employ Equation 32:

$$i(t) = \frac{1}{L}\int_{t_0}^{t} v(t)\,dt + i(t_0)$$

In this case, we take $t_0 = 0$, and we have $i(t_0) = i(0) = 0$. Substituting values, we get

$$i(t) = \frac{1}{2}\int_{0}^{t} 10\,dt$$

where we have assumed that t is greater than zero. Integrating and evaluating, we obtain

$$i(t) = 5t \text{ A} \qquad \text{for } t > 0$$

A plot of the current is shown in Figure 18(c).

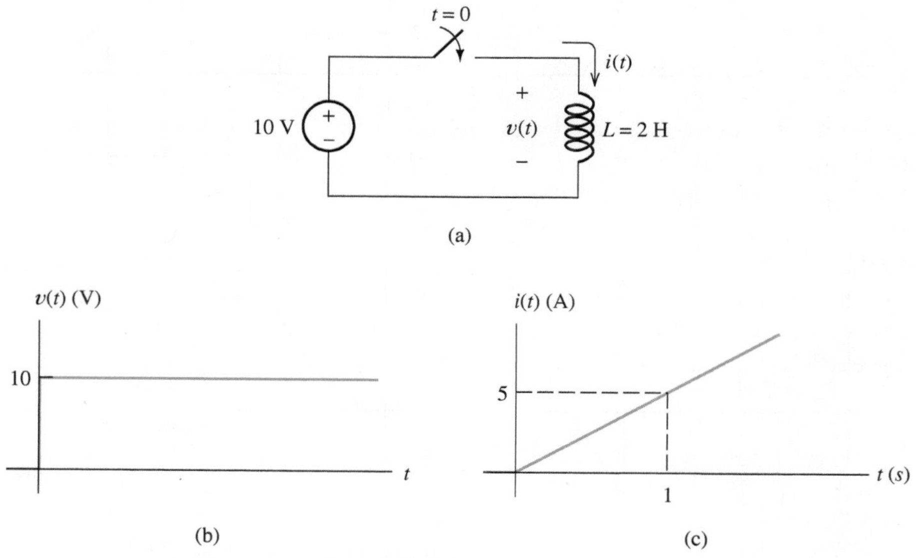

Figure 18 Circuit and waveforms for Example 7.

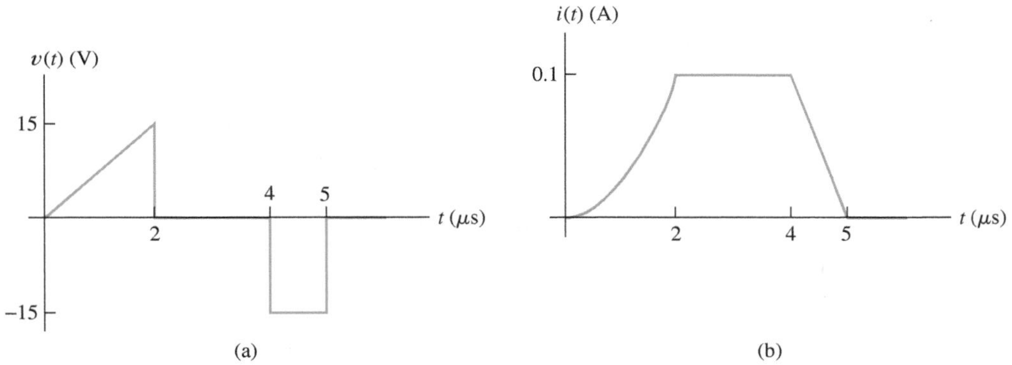

Figure 19 See Exercise 7.

Notice that the current in the inductor gradually increases after the switch is closed. Because a constant voltage is applied after $t = 0$, the current increases at a steady rate as predicted by Equation 28, which is repeated here for convenience:

$$v(t) = L\frac{di}{dt}$$

If $v(t)$ is constant, the rate of change of the current di/dt is constant. ■

Suppose that at $t = 1$ s, we open the switch in the circuit of Figure 18. Ideally, current cannot flow through an open switch. Hence, we expect the current to fall abruptly to zero at $t = 1$ s. However, the voltage across the inductor is proportional to the time rate of change of the current. For an abrupt change in current, this principle predicts infinite voltage across the inductor. This infinite voltage would last for only the instant at which the current falls. Later, we introduce the concept of an impulse function to describe this situation (and similar ones). For now, we simply point out that very large voltages can appear when we switch circuits that contain inductances.

If we set up a real circuit corresponding to Figure 18(a) and open the switch at $t = 1$ s, we will probably find that the high voltage causes an arc across the switch contacts. The arc persists until the energy in the inductor is used up. If this is repeated, the switch will soon be destroyed.

Exercise 6 The current through a 10-mH inductance is $i(t) = 0.1\cos(10^4 t)$ A. Find the voltage and stored energy as functions of time. Assume that the references for $v(t)$ and $i(t)$ have the passive configuration. (The angle is in radians.)
Answer $v(t) = -10\sin(10^4 t)$ V, $w(t) = 50\cos^2(10^4 t)$ μJ. □

Exercise 7 The voltage across a 150-μH inductance is shown in Figure 19(a). The initial current is $i(0) = 0$. Find and plot the current $i(t)$ to scale versus time. Assume that the references for $v(t)$ and $i(t)$ have the passive configuration.
Answer The current is shown in Figure 19(b). □

5 INDUCTANCES IN SERIES AND PARALLEL

It can be shown that the equivalent inductance for a series circuit is equal to the sum of the inductances connected in series. On the other hand, for inductances in parallel, we find the equivalent inductance by taking the reciprocal of the sum of the

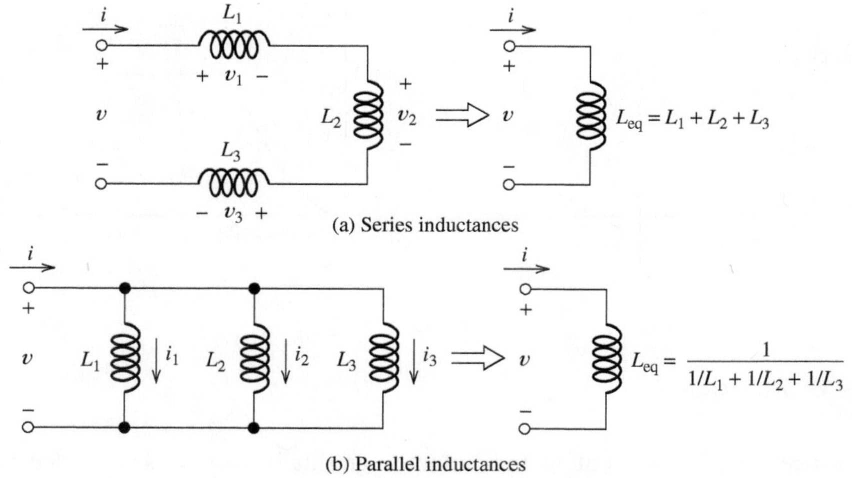

Figure 20 Inductances in series and parallel are combined in the same manner as resistances.

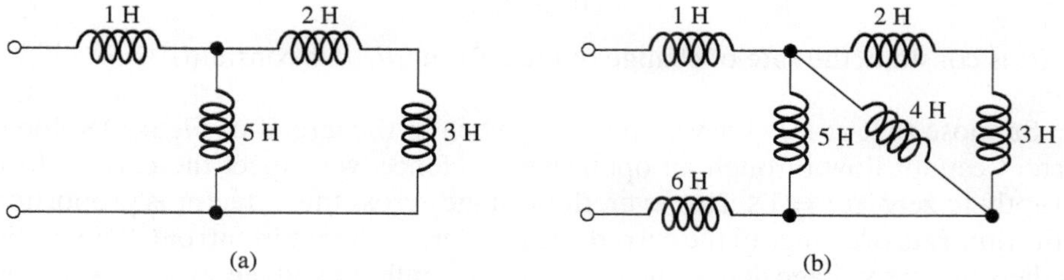

Figure 21 See Exercise 10.

Inductances in series and parallel are combined by using the same rules as for resistances: series inductances are added; parallel inductances are combined by taking the reciprocal of the sum of the reciprocals of the individual inductances.

reciprocals of the parallel inductances. Series and parallel equivalents for inductances are illustrated in Figure 20. Notice that inductances are combined in exactly the same way as are resistances. These facts can be proven by following the pattern used earlier in this chapter to derive the equivalents for series capacitances.

Exercise 8 Prove that inductances in series are added to find the equivalent inductance. □

Exercise 9 Prove that inductances in parallel are combined according to the formula given in Figure 20(b). □

Exercise 10 Find the equivalent inductance for each of the circuits shown in Figure 21.

Answer **a.** 3.5 H; **b.** 8.54 H. □

6 PRACTICAL INDUCTORS

Real inductors take a variety of appearances, depending on their inductance and the application. (Some examples were shown earlier in Figure 15.) For example, a 1-μH inductor could consist of 25 turns of fine (say, number 28) wire wound on an iron oxide toroidal (doughnut-shaped) core having an outside diameter of 1/2 cm.

On the other hand, a typical 5-H inductor consists of several hundred turns of number 18 wire on an iron form having a mass of 1 kg.

Usually, metallic iron forms, also called *cores*, are made of thin sheets called *laminations*. [See Figure 15(c) for an example.] This is necessary because voltages are induced in the core by the changing magnetic field. These voltages cause **eddy currents** to flow in the core, dissipating energy. Usually, this **core loss** is undesirable. Using laminations that are insulated from one another helps to reduce eddy-current loss. The laminations are arranged perpendicular to the expected current direction.

Another way to defeat eddy currents is to use a core composed of **ferrites**, which are oxides of iron that are electrical insulators. Still another approach is to combine powdered iron with an insulating binder.

PRACTICAL APPLICATION 1

Electronic Photo Flash

Figure PA1 shows the electrical circuit of an electronic photo flash such as you may have seen on a camera. The objective of the unit is to produce a bright flash of light by passing a high current through the flash tube while the camera shutter is open. As much as 1000 W is supplied to the flash tube during the flash, which lasts for less than a millisecond. Although the power level is quite high, the total energy delivered is not great because of the short duration of the flash. (The energy is on the order of a joule.)

It is not possible to deliver the power directly from the battery to the flash tube for several reasons. First, practical batteries supply a few tens of volts at most, while several hundred volts are needed to operate the flash tube. Second, applying the principle of maximum power transfer, the maximum power available from the battery is limited to 1 W by its internal Thévenin resistance. This does not nearly meet the needs of the flash tube. Instead, energy is delivered by the battery over a period of several seconds and stored in the capacitor. The stored energy can be quickly extracted from the capacitor because the parasitic resistance in series with the capacitor is very low.

The electronic switch alternates between open and closed approximately 10,000 times per second. (In some units, you can hear a high-pitched whistle resulting from incidental conversion of some of the energy to acoustic form.) While the electronic switch is closed, the battery causes the current in the inductor to build up. Then when the switch opens, the inductor forces current to flow through the diode, charging the capacitor. (Recall that the current in an inductor cannot change instantaneously.)

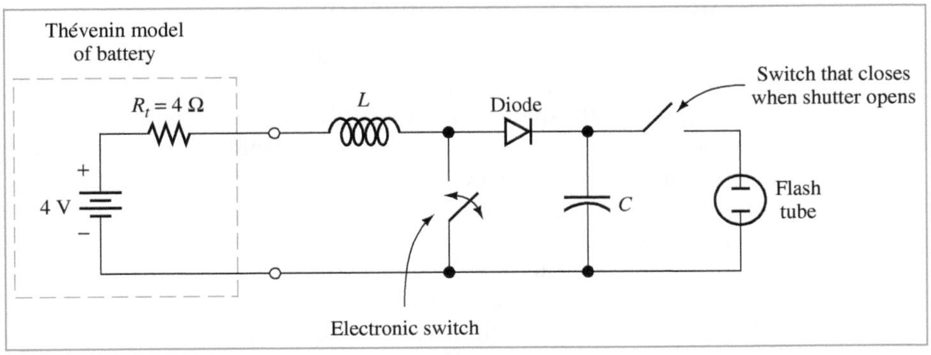

Figure PA1

Current can flow through the diode only in the direction of the arrow. Thus, the diode allows charge to flow into the capacitor when the electronic switch is open and prevents charge from flowing off the capacitor when the electronic switch is closed. Thus, the charge stored on the capacitor increases each time the electronic switch opens. Eventually, the voltage on the capacitor reaches several hundred volts. When the camera shutter is opened, another switch is closed, allowing the capacitor to discharge through the flash tube.

A friend of the author has a remote cabin on the north shore of Lake Superior that has an unusual water system (illustrated in Figure PA2) analogous to the electronic flash circuit. Water flows through a large pipe immersed in the river. Periodically, a valve on the bottom end of the pipe suddenly closes, stopping the flow. The inertia of the flowing water creates a pulse of high pressure when the valve closes. This high pressure forces water through a one-way ball valve into a storage tank. Air trapped in the storage tank is compressed and forces water to flow to the cabin as needed.

Can you identify the features in Figure PA2 that are analogous to each of the circuit elements in Figure PA1?

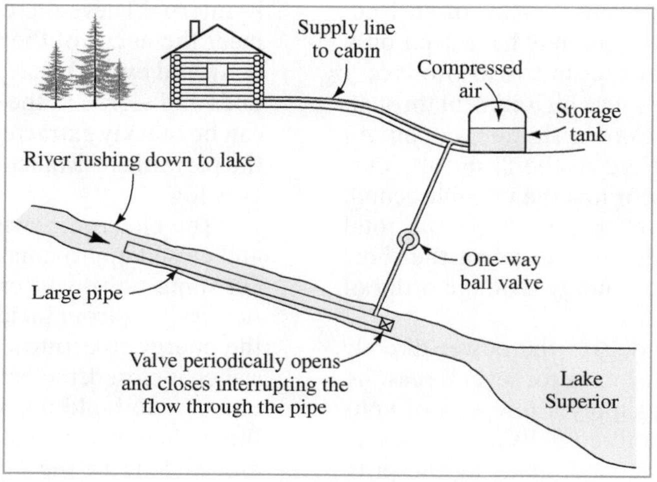

Figure PA2

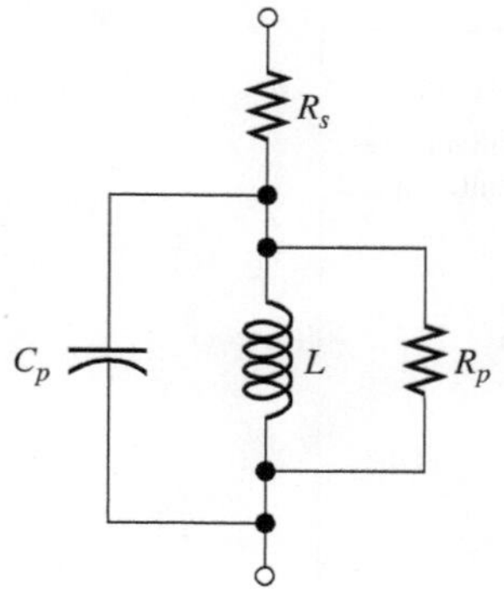

Figure 22 Circuit model for real inductors including several parasitic elements.

Parasitic Effects for Real Inductors

Real inductors have parasitic effects in addition to the desired inductance. A circuit model for a real inductor is shown in Figure 22. The series resistance R_s is caused by the resistivity of the material composing the wire. (This parasitic effect can be avoided by using wire composed of a superconducting material, which has zero resistivity.) The parallel capacitance is associated with the electric field in the dielectric (insulation) between the coils of wire. It is called **interwinding capacitance**. The parallel resistance R_p represents core loss due, in part, to eddy currents in the core.

Actually, the circuit model for a real inductor shown in Figure 22 is an approximation. The series resistance is distributed along the length of the wire, as is the interwinding capacitance. A more accurate model for a real inductor would break each of the parasitic effects into many segments (possibly, an infinite number). Ultimately, we could abandon circuit models altogether and use electromagnetic field theory directly.

Rarely is this degree of detail necessary. Usually, modeling a real inductor as an inductance, including at most a few parasitic effects, is sufficiently accurate. Of course, computer-aided circuit analysis allows us to use more complex models and achieve more accurate results than traditional mathematical analysis.

7 MUTUAL INDUCTANCE

Sometimes, several coils are wound on the same form so that magnetic flux produced by one coil links the others. Then a time-varying current flowing through one coil induces voltages in the other coils. The circuit symbols for two mutually coupled inductances are shown in Figure 23. The **self inductances** of the two coils are denoted as L_1 and L_2, respectively. The **mutual inductance** is denoted as M, which also has units of henries. Notice that we have selected the passive reference configuration for each coil in Figure 23.

The equations relating the voltages to the currents are also shown in Figure 23. The mutual terms, $M\, di_1/dt$ and $M\, di_2/dt$, appear because of the mutual coupling of the coils. The self terms, $L_1\, di_1/dt$ and $L_2\, di_2/dt$, are the voltages induced in each coil due to its own current.

The magnetic flux produced by one coil can either aid or oppose the flux produced by the other coil. The dots on the ends of the coils indicate whether the fields are aiding or opposing. If one current enters a dotted terminal and the other leaves, the fields oppose one another. For example, if both i_1 and i_2 have positive values in Figure 23(b), the fields are opposing. If both currents enter the respective dots (or if both leave), the fields aid. Thus, if both i_1 and i_2 have positive values in Figure 23(a), the fields are aiding.

The magnetic flux produced by one coil can either aid or oppose the flux produced by the other coil.

The signs of the mutual terms in the equations for the voltages depend on how the currents are referenced with respect to the dots. If both currents are referenced into (or if both are referenced out of) the dotted terminals, as in Figure 23(a), the mutual term is positive. If one current is referenced into a dot and the other out, as in Figure 23(b), the mutual term carries a negative sign.

Linear Variable Differential Transformer

An application of mutual inductance can be found in a position transducer known as the linear variable differential transformer (LVDT), illustrated in Figure 24. An ac source connected to the center coil sets up a magnetic field that links both halves of

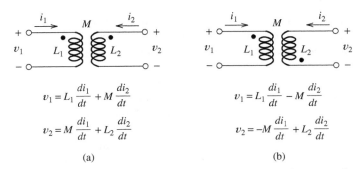

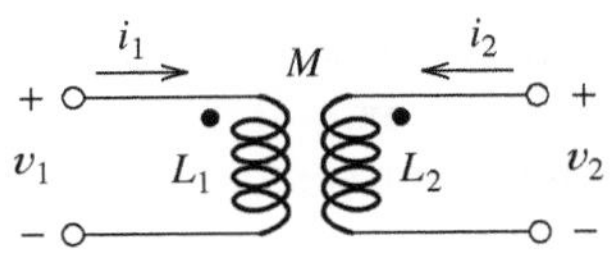

$$v_1 = L_1 \frac{di_1}{dt} + M \frac{di_2}{dt}$$

$$v_2 = M \frac{di_1}{dt} + L_2 \frac{di_2}{dt}$$

(a)

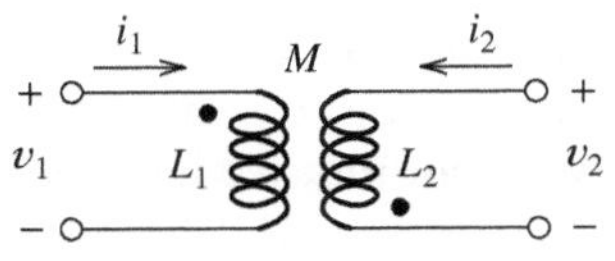

$$v_1 = L_1 \frac{di_1}{dt} - M \frac{di_2}{dt}$$

$$v_2 = -M \frac{di_1}{dt} + L_2 \frac{di_2}{dt}$$

(b)

Figure 23 Circuit symbols and $v - i$ relationships for mutually coupled inductances.

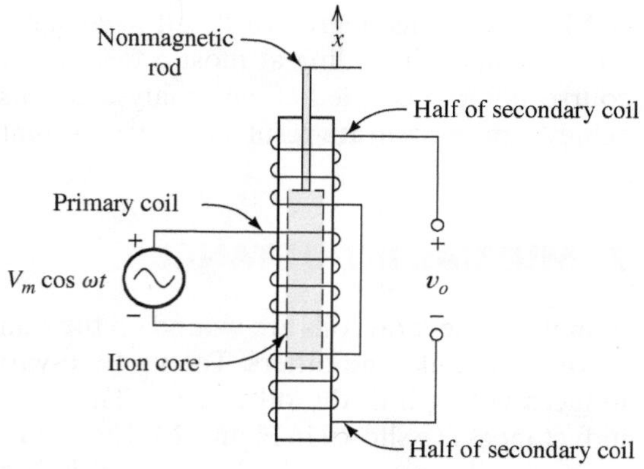

Figure 24 A linear variable differential transformer used as a position transducer.

the secondary coil. When the iron core is centered in the coils, the voltages induced in the two halves of the secondary cancel so that $v_o(t) = 0$. (Notice that the two halves of the secondary winding are wound in opposite directions.) As the core moves up or down, the couplings between the primary and the halves of the secondary change. The voltage across one half of the coil becomes smaller, and the voltage across the other half becomes greater. Ideally, the output voltage is given by

$$v_o(t) = Kx\cos(\omega t)$$

where x is the displacement of the core. LVDTs are used in applications such as automated manufacturing operations to measure displacements.

8 SYMBOLIC INTEGRATION AND DIFFERENTIATION USING MATLAB

As we have seen, finding the current given the voltage (or vice versa) for an energy storage element involves integration or differentiation. Thus, we may sometimes need to find symbolic answers for integrals or derivatives of complex functions, which can be very difficult by traditional methods. Then, we can resort to using symbolic mathematics software. Several programs are available including Maple™ from Maplesoft Corporation, Mathematica™ from Wolfram Research, and the Symbolic Toolbox which is an optional part of MATLAB from Mathsoft. Each of these programs has its strengths and weaknesses, and when a difficult problem warrants the effort, all of them should be tried. Because MATLAB is widely used in Electrical Engineering, we confine our brief discussion to the Symbolic Toolbox.

One note of caution: We have developed the examples, exercises, and problems using MATLAB version R2011b. Keep in mind that if you use versions other than R2011b, you may not be able to reproduce our results. Try running our example m-files before sinking a lot of time into solving the problems. Hopefully, your instructor can give you some guidance on what to expect with the MATLAB versions available to you.

In the following, we assume that you have some familiarity with MATLAB. A variety of online interactive tutorials are available at `https://www.mathworks.com/`. However, you should find it easy to write MATLAB instructions for the exercises and problems in this chapter by modeling your solutions after the code in our examples.

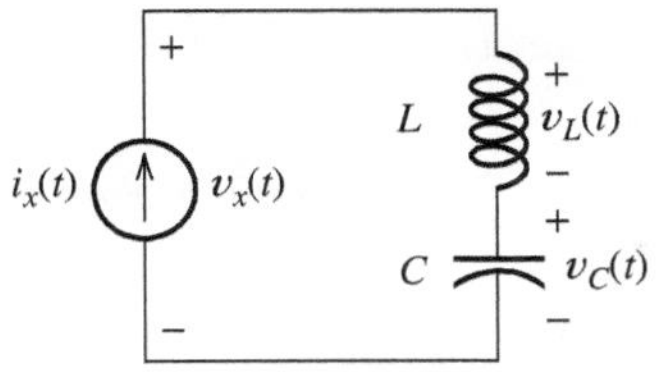

Figure 25 Circuit of Example 8.

Example 8 Integration and Differentiation Using the MATLAB Symbolic Toolbox

Use MATLAB to find expressions for the three voltages shown in Figure 25 given $v_C(0) = 0$ and

$$\begin{aligned} i_x(t) &= kt^2 \exp(-at)\sin(\omega t) \text{ for } t \geq 0 \\ &= 0 \text{ for } t < 0 \end{aligned} \quad (39)$$

Also, plot the current and the voltages for $k = 3, a = 2, \omega = 1, L = 0.5$ H, $C = 1$ F, and $t \geq 0$. (These values have been chosen mainly to facilitate the demonstration of MATLAB capabilities.) The currents are in amperes, voltages are in volts, ωt is in radians, and time t is in seconds.

Solution At first, we use symbols to represent the various parameters (k, a, ω, L, and C), denoting the current and the voltages as ix, vx, vL, and vC. Then, we substitute the numerical values for the symbols and denote the results as ixn, vxn, vLn, and vCn. (The letter "n" is selected to suggest that the "numerical" values of the parameters have been substituted into the expressions.)

We show the commands in **boldface**, comments in regular font, and MATLAB responses in color. Comments (starting with the % sign) are ignored by MATLAB. We present the work as if we were entering the commands and comments one at a time in the MATLAB command window, however, it is usually more convenient to place all of the commands in an m-file and execute them as a group.

To start, we define the various symbols as symbolic objects in MATLAB, define the current ix, and substitute the numerical values of the parameters to obtain ixn.

```
>> clear all % Clear work area of previous work.
>> syms vx ix vC vL vxn ixn vCn vLn k a w t L C
>> % Names for symbolic objects must start with a letter and
>> % contain only alpha-numeric characters.
>> % Next, we define ix.
>> ix=k*t^2*exp(-a*t)*sin(w*t)
     ix =
     (k*t^2*sin(w*t))/exp(a*t)
>> % Next, we substitute k=3, a=2, and w=1
>> % into ix and denote the result as ixn.
>> ixn = subs(ix,[k a w],[3 2 1])
     ixn =
     (3*t^2*sin(t))/exp(a*t)
```

Next, we want to plot the current versus time. We need to consider what range of t should be used for the plot. In standard mathematical typesetting, the expression we need to plot is

$$\begin{aligned} i_x(t) &= 3t^2 \exp(-2t)\sin(t) \text{ for } t \geq 0 \\ &= 0 \text{ for } t < 0 \end{aligned}$$

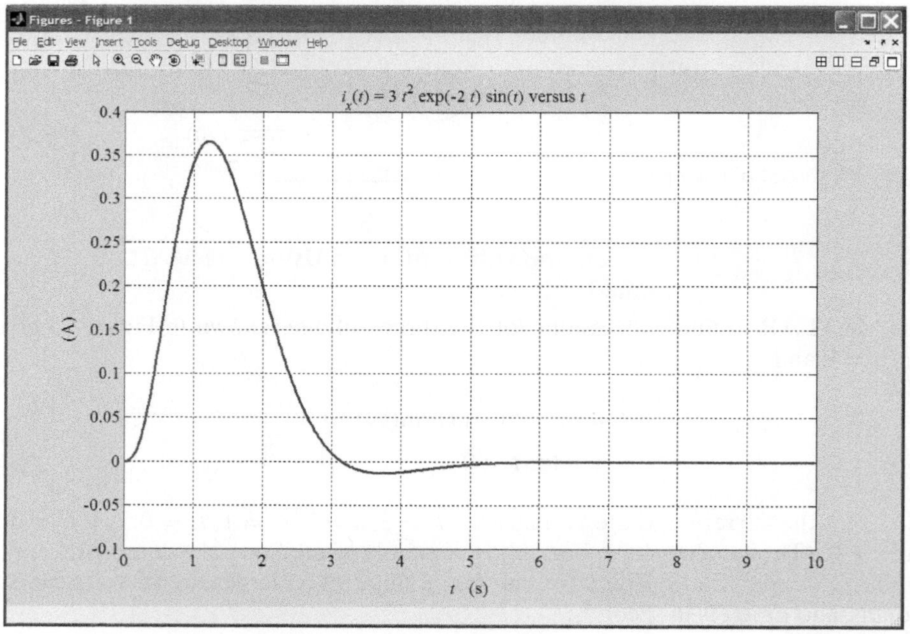

Figure 26 Plot of $i_x(t)$ produced by MATLAB.

Thoughtful examination of this expression (perhaps supplemented with a little work with a calculator) reveals that the current is zero at $t = 0$, builds up quickly after $t = 0$ because of the t^2 term, and decays to relatively small values after about $t = 10$ s because of the exponential term. Thus, we select the range from $t = 0$ to $t = 10$ s for the plot. Continuing in MATLAB, we have

```
>> % Next, we plot ixn for t ranging from 0 to 10s.
>> ezplot(ixn,[0,10])
```

This opens a window with a plot of the current versus time as shown in Figure 26. As expected, the current increases rapidly after $t = 0$ and decays to insignificant values by $t = 10$ s. (We have used various Edit menu commands to improve the appearance of the plot for inclusion in this chapter.)

Next, we determine the inductance voltage, which is given by

$$v_L(t) = L\frac{di_x(t)}{dt}$$

in which the parameters, a, k, and ω are treated as constants. The corresponding MATLAB command and the result are:

```
>> vL=L*diff(ix,t) % L times the derivative of ix with respect to t.
   vL =
   L*((2*k*t*sin(t*w))/exp(a*t) - (a*k*t^2*sin(t*w))/exp(a*t) +
   (k*t^2*w*cos(t*w))/exp(a*t))
>> % A nicer display for vL is produced with the commands:
>> vL = simple(vL);
>> pretty(vL)
   L k t (2 sin(t w) - a t sin(t w) + t w cos(t w))
   ------------------------------------------------
                     exp(a t)
```

In more standard mathematical typesetting, this becomes

$$v_L(t) = Lkt\exp(-at)[2\sin(\omega t) - at\sin(\omega t) + \omega t\cos(\omega t)]$$

which we can verify by manually differentiating the right-hand side of Equation 39 and multiplying by L. Next, we determine the voltage across the capacitance.

$$v_C(t) = \frac{1}{C}\int_0^t i_x(t)dt + v_C(0) \text{ for } t \geq 0$$

Substituting the expressions for the current and initial voltage we obtain,

$$v_C(t) = \frac{1}{C}\int_0^t kt^2\exp(-at)\sin(\omega t)dt \text{ for } t \geq 0$$

This is not a simple integration to perform by hand, but we can accomplish it easily with MATLAB:

```
>> % Integrate ix with respect to t with limits from 0 to t.
>> vC=(1/C)*int(ix,t,0,t);
>> % We included the semicolon to suppress the output, which is
>> % much too complex for easy interpretation.
>> % Next, we find the total voltage vx.
>> vx = vC + vL;
>> % Now we substitute numerical values for the parameters.
>> vLn=subs(vL,[k a w L C],[3 2 1 0.5 1]);
>> vCn=subs(vC,[k a w L C],[3 2 1 0.5 1]);
>> vxn=subs(vx,[k a w L C],[3 2 1 0.5 1]);
>> % Finally, we plot all three voltages in the same window.
>> figure % Open a new figure for this plot.
>> ezplot(vLn,[0,10])
>> hold on % Hold so the following two plots are on the same axes.
>> ezplot(vCn,[0,10])
>> ezplot(vxn,[0,10])
```

The resulting plot is shown in Figure 27. (Here again, we have used various items on the Edit menu to change the scale of the vertical axis and dress up the plot for inclusion in this chapter.)

The commands for this example are included as an m-file named Example_8 in the MATLAB files. (See Appendix "On-Line Student Resources" for information about accessing these MATLAB files.) If you copy the file and place it in a folder in the MATLAB path for your computer, you can run the file and experiment with it. For example, after running the m-file, if you enter the command

```
>> simple(vC)
```

you will see the rather complicated symbolic mathematical expression for the voltage across the capacitance. ■

Exercise 11 Use MATLAB to work Example 2 resulting in plots like those in Figure 5.

Answer The MATLAB commands including some explanatory comments are:

```
clear % Clear the work area.
% We avoid using i alone as a symbol for current because
% we reserve i for the square root of -1 in MATLAB. Thus, we
```

```
% will use iC for the capacitor current.
syms t iC qC vC % Define t, iC, qC and vC as symbolic objects.
iC = 0.5*sin((1e4)*t);
ezplot(iC, [0 3*pi*1e-4])
qC=int(iC,t,0,t); % qC equals the integral of iC.
figure % Plot the charge in a new window.
ezplot(qC, [0 3*pi*1e-4])
vC = 1e7*qC;
figure % Plot the voltage in a new window.
ezplot(vC, [0 3*pi*1e-4])
```

The plots are very similar to those of Figure 5. An m-file (named Exercise_11) can be found in the MATLAB folder. □

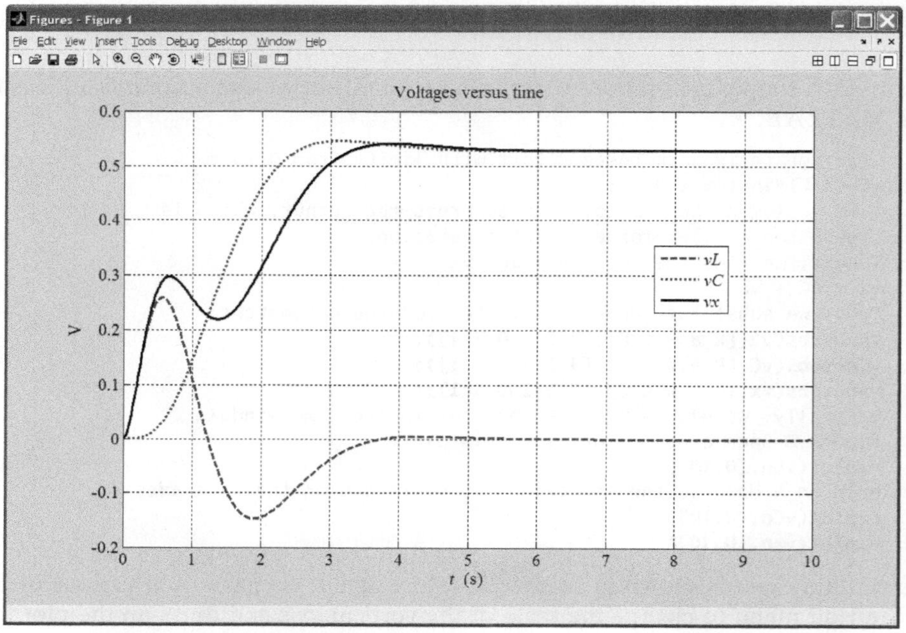

Figure 27 Plots of the voltages for Example 8.

Summary

1. Capacitance is the circuit property that accounts for electric-field effects. The units of capacitance are farads (F), which are equivalent to coulombs per volt.
2. The charge stored by a capacitance is given by $q = Cv$.
3. The relationships between current and voltage for a capacitance are

$$i = C\frac{dv}{dt}$$

and

$$v(t) = \frac{1}{C}\int_{t_0}^{t} i(t)\,dt + v(t_0)$$

4. The energy stored by a capacitance is given by

$$w(t) = \frac{1}{2}Cv^2(t)$$

5. Capacitances in series are combined in the same manner as resistances in parallel.

6. Capacitances in parallel are combined in the same manner as resistances in series.
7. The capacitance of a parallel-plate capacitor is given by
$$C = \frac{\epsilon A}{d}$$
For vacuum, the dielectric constant is $\epsilon = \epsilon_0 \cong 8.85 \times 10^{-12}$ F/m. For other materials, the dielectric constant is $\epsilon = \epsilon_r \epsilon_0$, where ϵ_r is the relative dielectric constant.
8. Real capacitors have several parasitic effects.
9. Inductance accounts for magnetic-field effects. The units of inductance are henries (H).
10. The relationships between current and voltage for an inductance are
$$v(t) = L\frac{di}{dt}$$
and
$$i(t) = \frac{1}{L}\int_{t_0}^{t} v(t)\,dt + i(t_0)$$
11. The energy stored in an inductance is given by
$$w(t) = \frac{1}{2}Li^2(t)$$
12. Inductances in series or parallel are combined in the same manner as resistances.
13. Real inductors have several parasitic effects.
14. Mutual inductance accounts for mutual coupling of magnetic fields between coils.
15. MATLAB is a powerful tool for symbolic integration, differentiation, and plotting of functions.

Problems

Section 1: Capacitance

P1. Describe the internal construction of capacitors.

P2. What current flows through an ideal capacitor if the voltage across the capacitor is constant with time? To what circuit element is an ideal capacitor equivalent in circuits for which the currents and voltages are constant with time?

P3. Explain what a dielectric material is and give two examples.

P4. How can electrical current flow "through" a capacitor even though a nonconducting layer separates the metallic parts?

***P5.** The voltage across a 10-μF capacitor is given by $v(t) = 100\sin(1000t)$. Assume that the argument of the sin function is in radians. Find expressions for the current, power, and stored energy. Sketch the waveforms to scale versus time for time ranging from 0 to 2π ms.

***P6.** A 2000-μF capacitor, initially charged to 100 V, is discharged by a steady current of 100 μA. How long does it take to discharge the capacitor to 0 V?

***P7.** A constant (dc) current $i(t) = 3$ mA flows into a 50-μF capacitor. The voltage at $t = 0$ is $v(0) = -20$ V. The references for $v(t)$ and $i(t)$ have the passive configuration. Find the power at $t = 0$ and state whether the power flow is into or out of the capacitor. Repeat for $t = 1$ s.

***P8.** We want to store sufficient energy in a 0.01-F capacitor to supply 5 horsepower (hp) for 1 hour. To what voltage must the capacitor be charged? (*Note:* One horsepower is equivalent to 745.7 watts.) Does this seem to be a practical method for storing this amount of energy? Do you think that an electric automobile design based on capacitive energy storage is feasible?

P9. Suppose that we have a 5-μF capacitor with 100 V between its terminals. Determine the magnitude of the net charge stored on each plate and the total net charge on both the plates.

P10. Suppose that a current given by $i(t) = I_m\cos(\omega t)$ flows through a capacitance C and the voltage is zero at $t = 0$. Assume that ωt has units of radians. Furthermore, ω is very large, ideally approaching infinity. For this current, does the capacitance approximate either an open or a short circuit? Explain.

* Denotes that answers are contained in the Student Solutions files. See Appendix "On-Line Student Resources" for more information about accessing the Student Solutions.

P11. The voltage across a 1-μF capacitor is given by $v(t) = 100e^{-100t}$. Find expressions for the current, power, and stored energy. Sketch the waveforms to scale versus time.

P12. We are given a 5-μF capacitor that is charged to 200 V. Determine the initial stored charge and energy. If this capacitor is discharged to 0 V in a time interval of 1 μs, find the average power delivered by the capacitor during the discharge interval.

P13. Prior to $t = 0$, a 100-μF capacitance is uncharged. Starting at $t = 0$, the voltage across the capacitor is increased linearly with time to 100 V in 2 s. Then, the voltage remains constant at 100 V. Sketch the voltage, current, power, and stored energy to scale versus time.

P14. The current through a 0.5-μF capacitor is shown in Figure P14. At $t = 0$, the voltage is zero. Sketch the voltage, power, and stored energy to scale versus time.

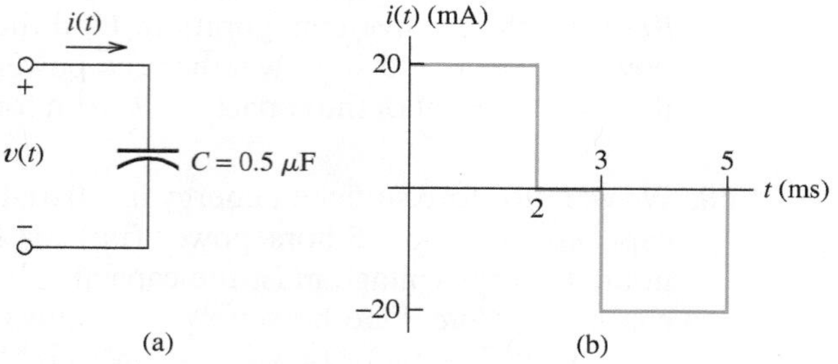

Figure P14

P15. Find the voltage, power, and stored energy at $t = 10$ ms for the capacitance in the circuit of Figure P15.

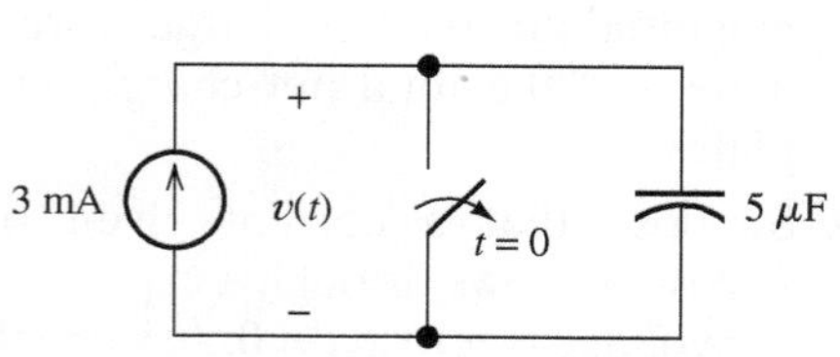

Figure P15

P16. A capacitance and the current through it are shown in Figure P16. At $t = 0$, the voltage is $v_C(0) = 10$ V. Sketch the voltage, power, and stored energy to scale versus time.

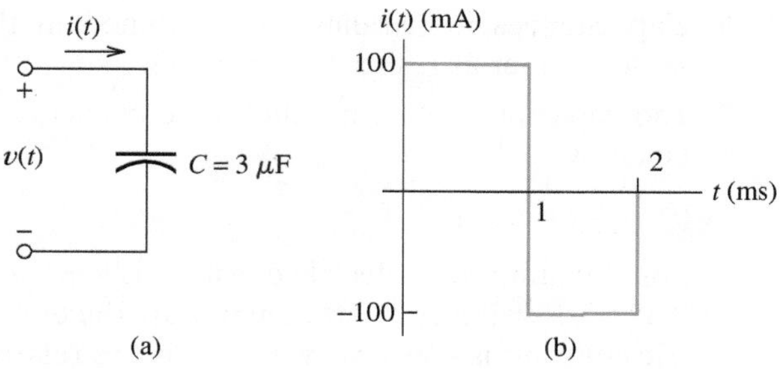

Figure P16

P17. At $t = 5$ s, the energy stored in a 10-μF capacitor is 200 J and is decreasing at 500 J/s. Determine the voltage magnitude and current magnitude at $t = 5$ s. Does the current enter or leave the positive terminal of the capacitor?

P18. Consider a very large capacitance (ideally, infinite) charged to 10 V. What other circuit element has the same current–voltage relationship? Explain your answer.

P19. A certain parallel-plate capacitor, which has one plate rotating so the overlap of the plates is a function of time, has a capacitance given by

$$C = 2 + \sin(200t)\ \mu\text{F}$$

in which the argument of the sine function is in radians. A constant voltage of 100 V is applied to this capacitor. Determine the current as a function of time.

P20. At $t = t_0$ the voltage across a certain capacitance C is zero. A pulse of current flows through the capacitance between t_0 and $t_0 + \Delta t$, and the voltage across the capacitance increases to V_f. What can you say about the peak amplitude I_m and area under the pulse waveform (i.e., current versus time)? What are the units and physical significance of the area under the pulse? What must happen to the peak amplitude and area under the pulse as Δt approaches zero, assuming that V_f remains the same?

P21. First, consider a resistor. What resistance corresponds to a short circuit? Next, consider an uncharged capacitor. What value of capacitance corresponds to a short circuit? Explain your answers. Repeat for an open circuit.

P22. A 20-μF capacitor has a voltage given by

$$v(t) = 3\cos(10^5 t) + 2\sin(10^5 t)$$

Assume that the arguments of the sine and cosine functions are in radians. Find the power at $t = 0$ and state whether the power flow is into or out of the capacitor. Repeat for $t_2 = (\pi/2) \times 10^{-5}$ s.

Section 2: Capacitances in Series and Parallel

P23. Describe how capacitances are combined in series and in parallel. Compare with how resistances are combined.

***P24.** Find the equivalent capacitance for each of the circuits shown in Figure P24.

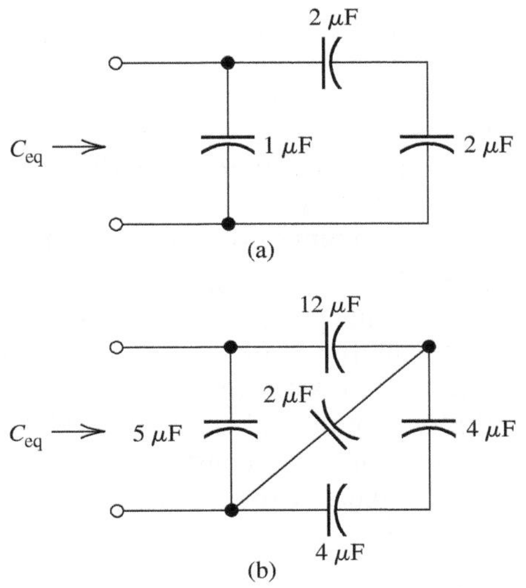

Figure P24

***P25.** Suppose that we are designing a cardiac pacemaker circuit. The circuit is required to deliver pulses of 1-ms duration to the heart, which can be modeled as a 500-Ω resistance. The peak amplitude of the pulses is required to be 5 V. However, the battery delivers only 2.5 V. Therefore, we decide to charge two equal-value capacitors in parallel from the 2.5-V battery and then switch the capacitors in series with the heart during the 1-ms pulse. What is the minimum value of the capacitances required so the output pulse amplitude remains between 4.9 V and 5.0 V throughout its 1-ms duration? If the pulses occur once every second, what is the average current drain from the battery? Use approximate calculations, assuming constant current during the output pulse. Find the ampere-hour rating of the battery so it lasts for five years.

P26. Find the equivalent capacitance between terminals x and y for each of the circuits shown in Figure P26.

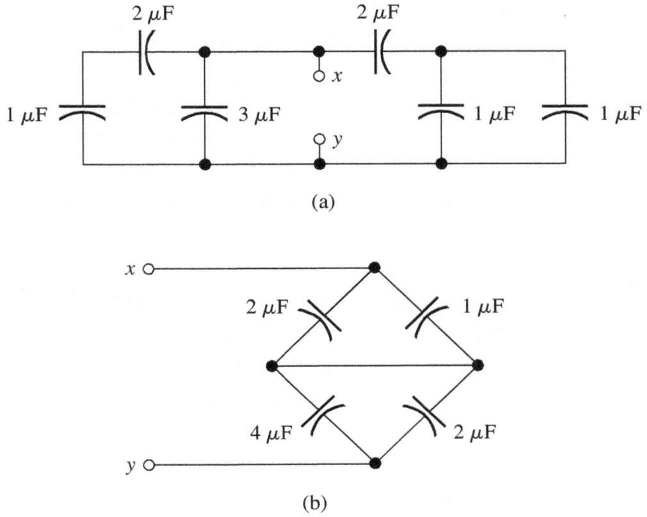

Figure P26

P27. What are the minimum and maximum values of capacitance that can be obtained by connecting two 1-μF capacitors in series and/or parallel? How should the capacitors be connected in each case?

P28. Consider two initially uncharged capacitors $C_1 = 15\ \mu$F and $C_2 = 10\ \mu$F connected in series. Then, a 50-V source is connected to the series combination, as shown in Figure P28. Find the voltages v_1 and v_2 after the source is applied. (*Hint:* The charges stored on the two capacitors must be equal, because the current is the same for both the capacitors.)

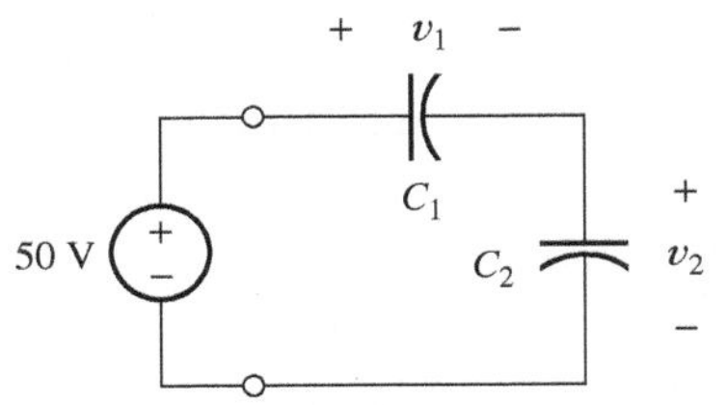

Figure P28

P29. We have capacitor $C_1 = 200\ \mu F$, which is charged to an initial voltage of 50 V, and capacitor $C_2 = 200\ \mu F$, which is charged to 100V. If they are placed in series with the positive terminal of the first connected to the negative terminal of the second, determine the equivalent capacitance and its initial voltage. Now, compute the total energy stored in the two capacitors. Compute the energy stored in the equivalent capacitance. Why is it less than the total energy stored in the original capacitors?

P30. Suppose we have a 2-μF capacitance in parallel with the series combination of a 6-μF capacitance and a 3-μF capacitance. Sketch the circuit diagram and determine the equivalent capacitance of the combination.

Section 3: Physical Characteristics of Capacitors

***P31.** Determine the capacitance of a parallel-plate capacitor having plates 10 cm by 30 cm separated by 0.01 mm. The dielectric has $\epsilon_r = 15$.

P32. We have a 100-pF parallel-plate capacitor, with each plate having a width W and a length L. The plates are separated by air with a distance d. Assume that L and W are both much larger than d. What is the new capacitance if: **a.** both L and W are doubled and the other parameters are unchanged? **b.** the separation d is halved and the other parameters are unchanged from their initial values? **c.** the air dielectric is replaced with oil having a relative dielectric constant of 35 and the other parameters are unchanged from their initial values?

***P33.** Suppose that we have a 1000-pF parallel-plate capacitor with air dielectric charged to 1000 V. The capacitor terminals are open circuited. Find the stored energy. If the plates are moved farther apart so that d is doubled, determine the new voltage on the capacitor and the new stored energy. Where did the extra energy come from?

P34. We have a parallel-plate capacitor, with each plate having a width W and a length L. The plates are separated by air with a distance d. Assume that L and W are both much larger than d. The maximum voltage that can be applied is limited to $V_{\max} = Kd$, in which K is called the breakdown strength of the dielectric. Derive an expression for the maximum energy that can be stored in the capacitor in terms of K and the volume of the dielectric. If we want to store the maximum energy per unit volume, does it matter what values are chosen for L, W, and d? What parameters are important?

P35. One type of microphone is formed from a parallel-plate capacitor arranged so the acoustic pressure of the sound wave affects the distance between the plates. Suppose we have such a microphone in which the plates have an area of 10 cm^2, the dielectric is air and the distance between the plates is a function of time given by

$$d(t) = 100 + 0.3\cos(1000t)\ \mu\text{m}$$

A constant voltage of 200 V is applied to the plates. Determine the current through the capacitance as a function of time by using the approximation $1/(1+x) \cong 1-x$ for $x << 1$. (The argument of the sinusoid is in radians.)

P36. Consider a liquid-level sensor that consists of two parallel plates of conductor immersed in an insulating liquid, as illustrated in Figure P36. When the tank is empty (i.e., $x = 0$), the capacitance of the plates is 200 pF. The relative dielectric constant of the liquid is 15. Determine an expression for the capacitance C as a function of the height x of the liquid.

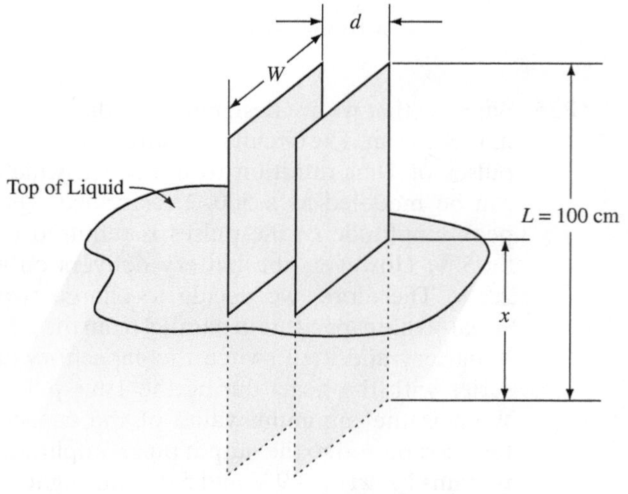

Figure P36

P37. A parallel-plate capacitor like that shown in Figure P36 has a capacitance of 2500 pF when the tank is full so the plates are totally immersed in the insulating liquid. (The dielectric constant of the fluid and the plate dimensions are different for this problem than for Problem P36.) The capacitance is 100 pF when the tank is empty and the space between the plates is filled with air. Suppose that the tank is full and the capacitance is charged to 1000 V. Then, the capacitance is open circuited so the charge on the plates cannot change, and the tank is drained. Compute the voltage after the tank is drained and the electrical energy stored in the capacitor before and after the tank is drained. With the plates open circuited, there is no electrical source for the extra energy. Where could it have come from?

P38. A 0.1-μF capacitor has a parasitic series resistance of 10 Ω as shown in Figure P38. Suppose that the voltage across the capacitance is $v_C(t) = 10\cos(100t)$; find the voltage across the resistance. In this situation, to find the total voltage $v(t) = v_r(t) + v_C(t)$ to within 1% accuracy, is it necessary to include the parasitic resistance? Repeat if $v_C(t) = 0.1\cos(10^7 t)$. The argument of the cosine function is in radians.

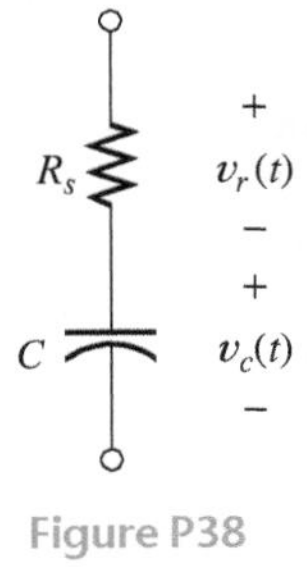

Figure P38

P39. Suppose that a parallel-plate capacitor has a dielectric that breaks down if the electric field exceeds K V/m. Thus, the maximum voltage rating of the capacitor is $V_{\max} = Kd$, where d is the thickness of the dielectric. In working Problem P34, we find that the maximum energy that can be stored before breakdown is $w_{\max} = 1/2\epsilon_r\epsilon_0 K^2(\text{Vol})$, in which Vol is the volume of the dielectric. Air has approximately $K = 32 \times 10^5$ V/m and $\epsilon_r = 1$. Find the minimum volume of air (as a dielectric in a parallel-plate capacitor) needed to store the energy content of one U.S. gallon of gasoline, which is approximately 132 MJ. What thickness should the air dielectric have if we want the voltage for maximum energy storage to be 1000 V?

P40. As shown in Figure P40, two 10-μF capacitors have an initial voltage of 100 V before the switch is closed. Find the total stored energy before the switch is closed. Find the voltage across each capacitor and the total stored energy after the switch is closed. What could have happened to the energy?

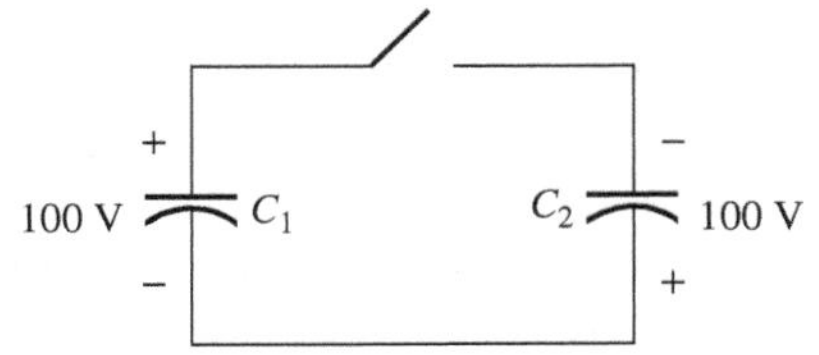

Figure P40

Section 4: Inductance

P41. Explain, in a few sentences, the fluid-flow analogy for an inductor.

P42. How are inductors constructed?

***P43.** The current flowing through a 2-H inductance is shown in Figure P43. Sketch the voltage, power, and stored energy versus time.

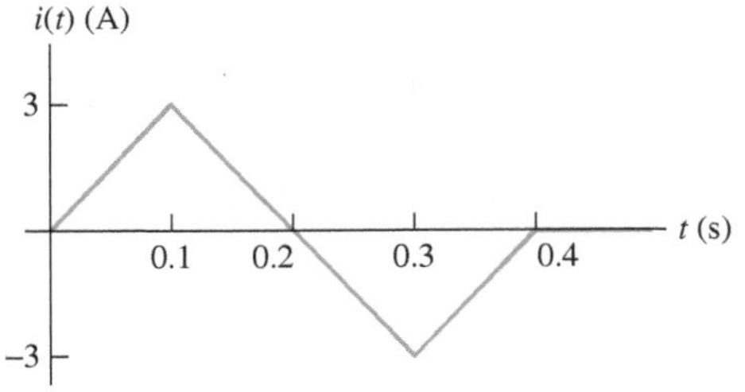

Figure P43

***P44.** At $t = 0$, the current flowing in a 0.5-H inductance is 4 A. What constant voltage must be applied to reduce the current to 0 at $t = 0.2$ s?

***P45.** A constant voltage of 10 V is applied to a 50-μH inductance, as shown in Figure P45. The current in the inductance at $t = 0$ is −100 mA. At what time t_x does the current reach +100 mA?

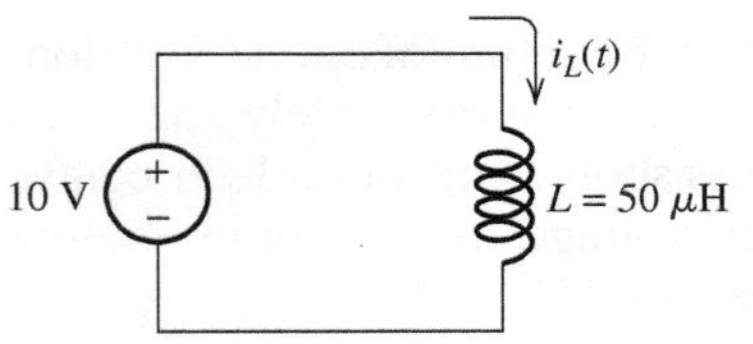

Figure P45

P46. A dc voltage of 10 V is applied to a 3-H inductor at $t = 0$, starting with an initial current of zero. Determine the current, power, and stored energy at $t_1 = 6$ s.

P47. The current flowing through an inductor is decreasing in magnitude. Is energy flowing into or out of the inductor? What if the current is constant with time?

P48. What is the value of the voltage across an ideal inductor if the current through it is constant with time? Comment. To what circuit element is an ideal inductor equivalent for circuits with constant currents and voltages?

P49. The current in a 100-mH inductance is given by 0.5 sin(1000t) A. Find expressions and sketch the waveforms to scale for the voltage, power, and stored energy, allowing t to range from 0 to 3π ms. The argument of the sine function is in radians.

P50. The current flowing through a 300-mH inductance is given by $5\exp(-200t)$ A. Find expressions for the voltage, power, and stored energy. Sketch the waveforms to scale for $0 < t < 20$ ms.

P51. The voltage across a 2-H inductance is shown in Figure P51. The initial current in the inductance is $i(0) = 0$. Sketch the current, power, and stored energy to scale versus time.

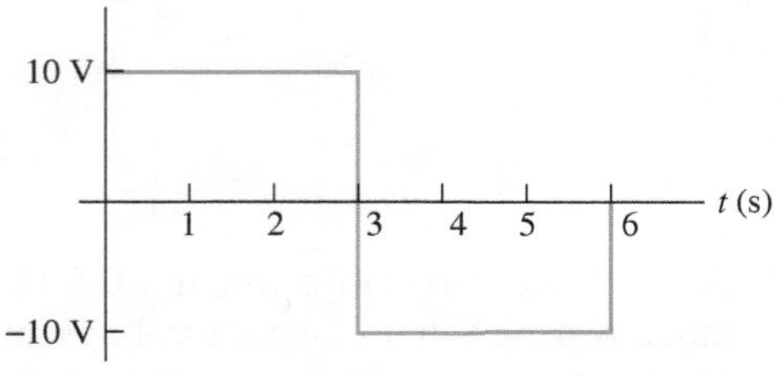

Figure P51

P52. The voltage across a 10-μH inductance is given by $v_L(t) = 5\sin(10^6 t)$ V. The argument of the sine function is in radians. The initial current is $i_L(0) = -0.5$ A. Find expressions for the current, power, and stored energy for $t > 0$. Sketch the waveforms to scale for time ranging from zero to $2\pi\ \mu$s.

P53. What is the equivalent circuit element for a very large (ideally, infinite) inductance having an initial current of 10 A. Explain your answer.

P54. The energy stored in a 2-H inductor is 100 J and is increasing at 200 J/s at $t = 4$ s. Determine the voltage magnitude and current magnitude at $t = 4$ s. Does the current enter or leave the positive terminal of the inductor?

P55. What value of inductance corresponds to an open circuit, assuming zero initial current? Explain your answer. Repeat for a short circuit.

P56. Before $t = 0$, the current in a 2-H inductance is zero. Starting at $t = 0$, the current is increased linearly with time to 5 A in 1 s. Then, the current remains constant at 5 A. Sketch the voltage, current, power, and stored energy to scale versus time.

P57. The voltage across an inductance is given by $v(t) = V_m\cos(\omega t)$ and the initial current in the inductor is zero. Suppose that ω is very large—ideally, approaching infinity. For this voltage, does the inductance approximate either an open or a short circuit? Explain.

P58. Suppose that at $t = t_0$ the current through a certain inductance is zero. A voltage pulse is applied to the inductance between t_0 and $t_0 + \Delta t$, and the current through the inductance increases to I_f. What can you say about the peak amplitude V_m and the area under the pulse waveform (i.e., voltage versus time)? What are the units of the area under the pulse? What must happen to the peak amplitude and the area under the pulse as Δt approaches zero, assuming that I_f remains the same?

Section 5: Inductances in Series and Parallel

P59. Describe how inductances are combined in series and in parallel. Compare with how resistances are combined.

***P60.** Determine the equivalent inductance for each of the series and parallel combinations shown in Figure P60.

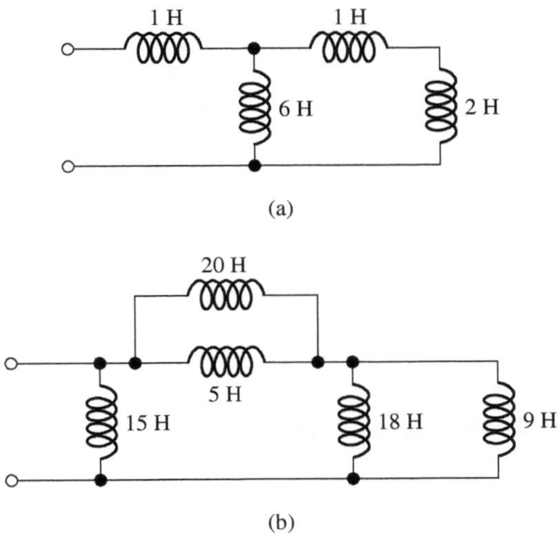

Figure P60

P61. Find the equivalent inductance for each of the series and parallel combinations shown in Figure P61.

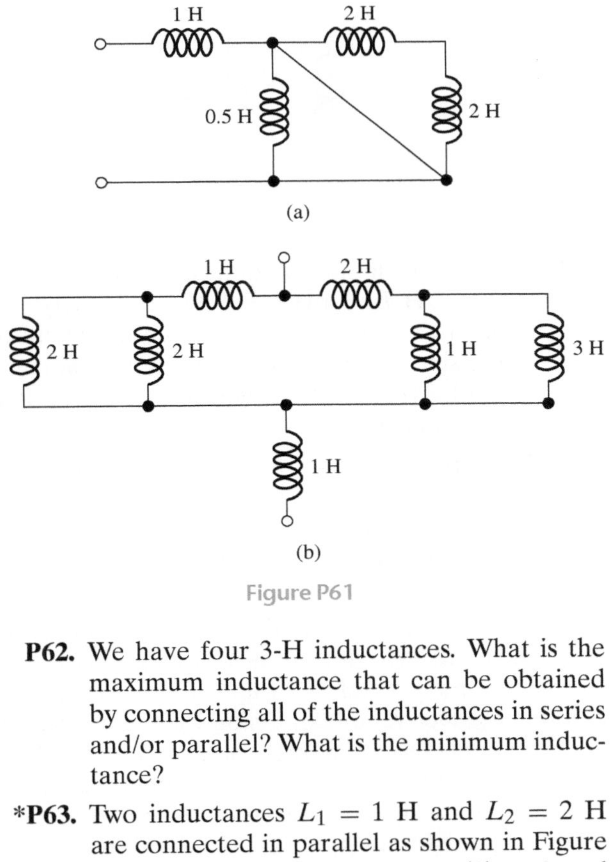

Figure P61

P62. We have four 3-H inductances. What is the maximum inductance that can be obtained by connecting all of the inductances in series and/or parallel? What is the minimum inductance?

***P63.** Two inductances $L_1 = 1$ H and $L_2 = 2$ H are connected in parallel as shown in Figure P63. The initial currents are $i_1(0) = 0$ and $i_2(0) = 0$. Find an expression for $i_1(t)$ in terms of $i(t)$, L_1, and L_2. Repeat for $i_2(t)$. Comment.

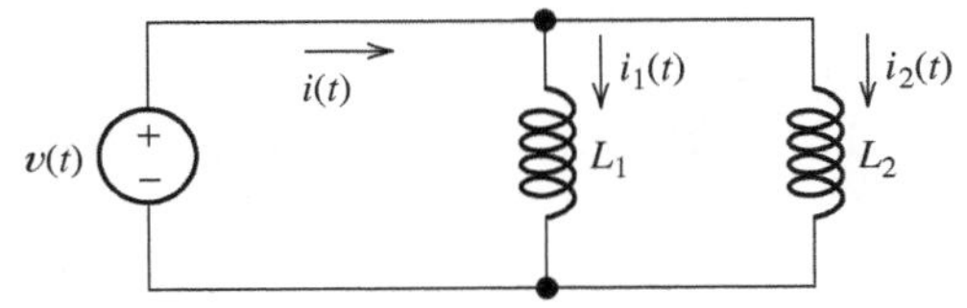

Figure P63

P64. We need to combine (in series or in parallel) an unknown inductance L with a second inductance of 4 H to attain an equivalent inductance of 3 H. Should L be placed in series or in parallel with the original inductance? What value is required for L?

P65. We need to combine (in series or in parallel) an unknown inductance L with a second inductance of 10 H to attain an equivalent inductance of 6 H. Should L be placed in series or in parallel with the original inductance? What value is required for L?

Section 6: Practical Inductors

P66. Draw the equivalent circuit for a real inductor, including three parasitic effects.

P67. A 10-mH inductor has a parasitic series resistance of $R_s = 1\ \Omega$ as shown in Figure P67. **a.** The current is given by $i(t) = 0.1\cos(10^5 t)$. The argument of the cosine function is in radians. Find $v_R(t)$, $v_L(t)$, and $v(t)$. In this case, for 1% accuracy in computing $v(t)$, could the resistance be neglected? **b.** Repeat if $i(t) = 0.1\cos(10t)$.

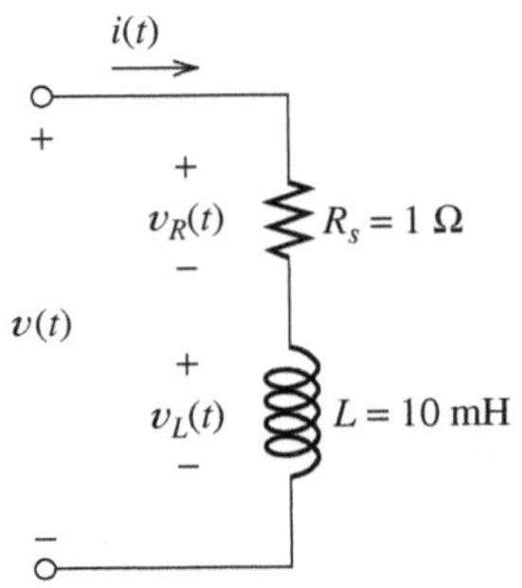

Figure P67

P68. A constant (dc) current of 100 mA flows through a real inductor and the voltage across its external terminals is 400 mV. Which of the circuit parameters of Figure 22 can be deduced from this information and what is its value? Explain how you arrived at your answer.

P69. Find $v(t)$, $i_C(t)$, $i(t)$, the energy stored in the capacitance, the energy stored in the inductance, and the total stored energy for the circuit of Figure P69, given that $i_L(t) = \sin(10^4 t)$ A. (The argument of the sine function is in radians.) Show that the total stored energy is constant with time. Comment on the results.

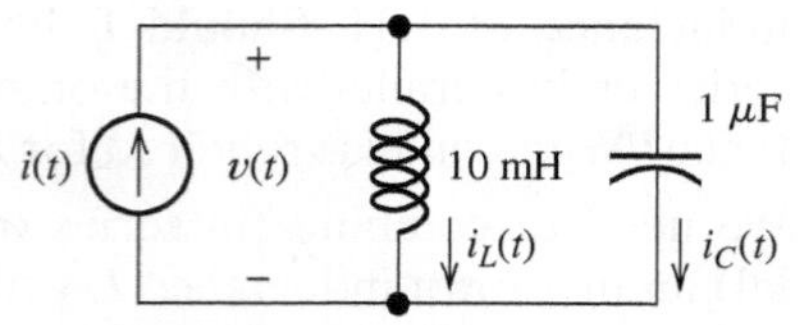

Figure P69

P70. For the circuit of Figure P70, determine $i(t)$, $v_L(t)$, $v(t)$, the energy stored in the capacitance, the energy stored in the inductance, and the total stored energy, given that $v_C(t) = 40\cos(1000t)$ V. (The argument of the cosine function is in radians.) Show that the total stored energy is constant with time. Comment on the results.

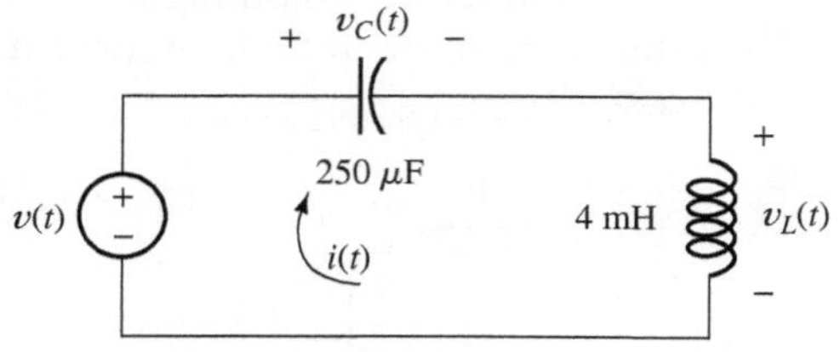

Figure P70

Section 7: Mutual Inductance

P71. Describe briefly the physical basis for mutual inductance.

***P72. a.** Derive an expression for the equivalent inductance for the circuit shown in Figure P72. **b.** Repeat if the dot for L_2 is moved to the bottom end.

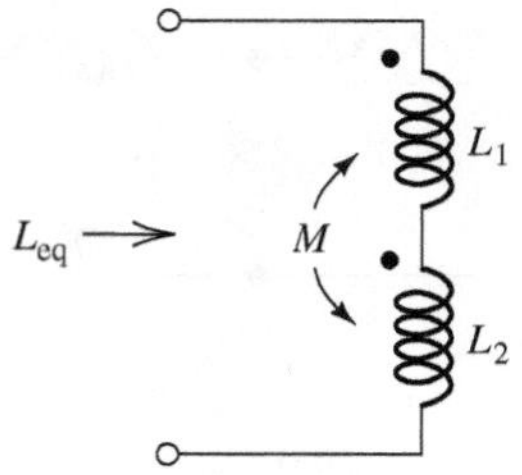

Figure P72

P73. The mutually coupled inductances in Figure P73 have $L_1 = 2$ H, $L_2 = 3$ H, and $M = 1$ H. Furthermore, $i_1(t) = \sin(20t)$ A and $i_2(t) = 0.5\cos(30t)$ A. (The arguments of the sine and cosine functions are in radians.) **a.** Find expressions for $v_1(t)$ and $v_2(t)$. **b.** Repeat with the dot placed at the bottom of L_2.

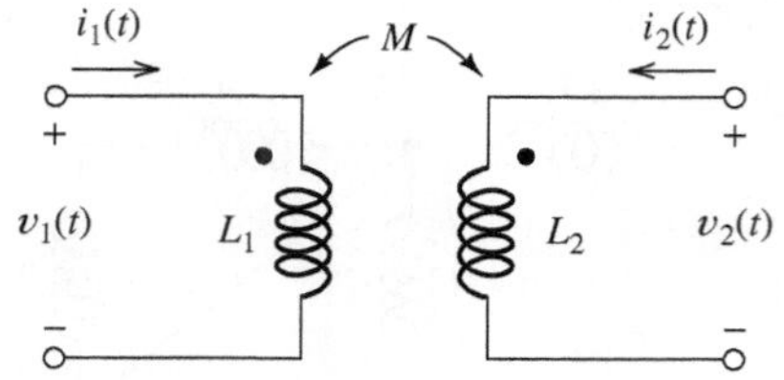

Figure P73

P74. A pair of mutually coupled inductances has $L_1 = 2$ H, $L_2 = 1$ H, $i_1 = 2\cos(1000t)$ A, $i_2 = 0$, and $v_2 = 2000\sin(1000t)$ V. (The arguments of the sine and cosine functions are in radians.) Find $v_1(t)$ and the magnitude of the mutual inductance.

P75. Suppose we place a short circuit across the terminals of L_2 in the mutually coupled inductors shown in Figure 23(a). Derive an expression for the equivalent inductance seen looking into the terminals of L_1.

P76. Consider the parallel inductors shown in Figure P63, with mutual coupling and the dots at the top end of L_1 and the bottom end of L_2. Derive an expression for the equivalent inductance seen by the source in terms of L_1, L_2, and M. [*Hint*: Write the circuit equations and manipulate them to obtain an expression of the form $v(t) = L_{eq} di(t)/dt$ in which L_{eq} is a function of L_1, L_2, and M.]

Section 8: Symbolic Integration and Differentiation using MATLAB

P77. The current through a 200-mH inductance is given by $i_L(t) = \exp(-2t)\sin(4\pi t)$ A in which the angle is in radians. Using your knowledge of calculus, find an expression for the voltage across the inductance. Then, use MATLAB to verify your answer for the voltage and to plot both the current and the voltage for $0 \le t \le 2$ s.

P78. A 1-H inductance has $i_L(0) = 0$ and $v_L(t) = t\exp(-t)$ for $0 \le t$. Using your calculus skills, find an expression for $i_L(t)$. Then, use MATLAB to verify your answer for $i_L(t)$ and to plot $v_L(t)$ and $i_L(t)$ for $0 \le t \le 10$ s.

Practice Test

Here is a practice test you can use to check your comprehension of the most important concepts in this chapter. Answers can be found in Appendix "Answers for the Practice Tests" and complete solutions are included in the Student Solutions files. See Appendix "On-Line Student Resources" for more information about the Student Solutions.

T1. The current flowing through a 10-μF capacitor having terminals labeled a and b is $i_{ab} = 0.3\exp(-2000t)$ A for $t \ge 0$. Given that $v_{ab}(0) = 0$, find an expression for $v_{ab}(t)$ for $t \ge 0$. Then, find the energy stored in the capacitor for $t = \infty$.

T2. Determine the equivalent capacitance C_{eq} for Figure T2.

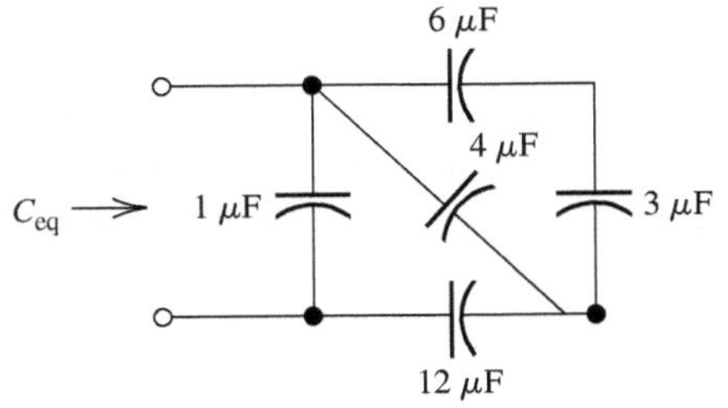

Figure T2

T3. A certain parallel-plate capacitor has plate length of 2 cm and width of 3 cm. The dielectric has a thickness of 0.1 mm and a relative dielectric constant of 80. Determine the capacitance.

T4. A 2-mH inductance has $i_{ab} = 0.3\sin(2000t)$ A. Find an expression for $v_{ab}(t)$. Then, find the peak energy stored in the inductance.

T5. Determine the equivalent inductance L_{eq} between terminals a and b in Figure T5.

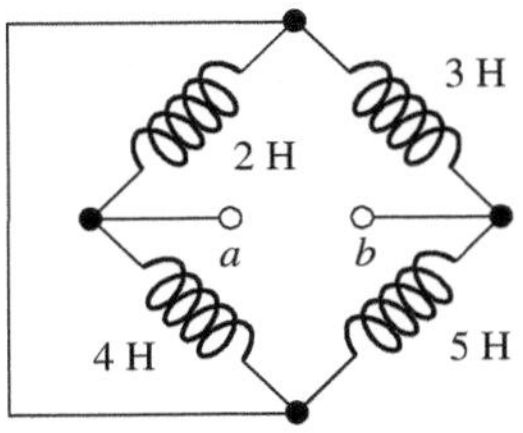

Figure T5

T6. Figure T6 has $L_1 = 40$ mH, $M = 20$ mH, and $L_2 = 30$ mH. Find expressions for $v_1(t)$ and $v_2(t)$.

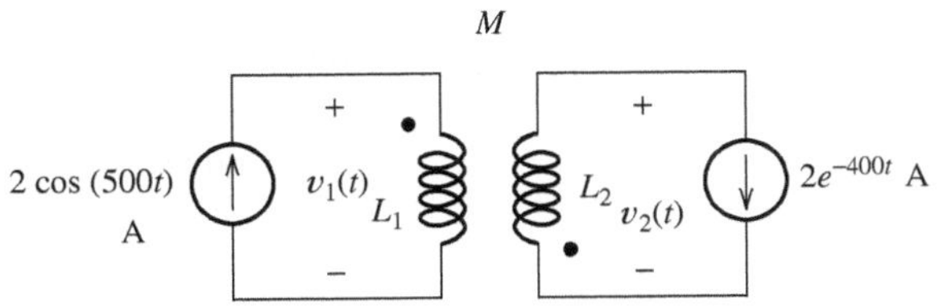

Figure T6

T7. The current flowing through a 20-μF capacitor having terminals labeled a and b is $i_{ab} = 3 \times 10^5 t^2 \exp(-2000t)$ A for $t \ge 0$. Given that $v_{ab}(0) = 5$ V, write a sequence of MATLAB commands to find the expression for $v_{ab}(t)$ for $t \ge 0$ and to produce plots of the current and voltage for $0 \le t \le 5$ ms.

ANSWERS FOR THE PRACTICE TESTS

Complete solutions for the practice tests are included in the Student Solutions files. See Appendix "On-Line Student Resources" for information on how to access these files.

T1. $v_{ab}(t) = 15 - 15\exp(-2000t)\,\text{V}$; $w_C(\infty) = 1.125\,\text{mJ}$.

T2. $C_{\text{eq}} = 5\,\mu\text{F}$.

T3. $C = 4248\,\text{pF}$.

T4. $v_{ab}(t) = 1.2\cos(2000t)\,\text{V}$; $w_{\text{peak}} = 90\,\mu\text{J}$.

T5. $L_{eq} = 3.208\,\text{H}$.

T6. $v_1(t) = -40\sin(500t) - 16\exp(-400t)\,\text{V}$;
$v_2(t) = 20\sin(500t) - 24\exp(-400t)\,\text{V}$.

T7. One set of commands and the result for $v_{ab}(t)$ are:

```
syms vab iab t
iab = 3*(10^5)*(t^2)*exp(-2000*t);
vab = (1/20e-6)*int(iab,t,0,t)
subplot(2,1,1)
ezplot(iab, [0 5e-3]), title('\iti_a_b\rm (A) versus \itt\rm (s)')
subplot(2,1,2)
ezplot(vab, [0 5e-3]), title('\itv_a_b\rm (V) versus \itt\rm (s)')
```

$$v_{ab} = \frac{15}{4} - \frac{15}{4}\exp(-2000t) - 7500t\exp(-2000t) - 7.5\times10^6 t^2\exp(-2000t)$$

You can test your commands using MATLAB to see if they produce this result for $v_{ab}(t)$ and plots like those in the Student Solutions.

ON-LINE STUDENT RESOURCES

Users of the text can access the Student Solutions Manual (and other folders mentioned below) in electronic form by following links starting from the website:

www.pearsonhighered.com/hambley

The MATLAB folder contains m-files. Except for the examples that use the Symbolic Toolbox, these files work equally well with MathScript, which is sometimes included with the LabVIEW program. The Hambley MathScript folder contains the m-files that work with MathScript.

The Virtual Instruments folder contains LabVIEW programs.

Transients

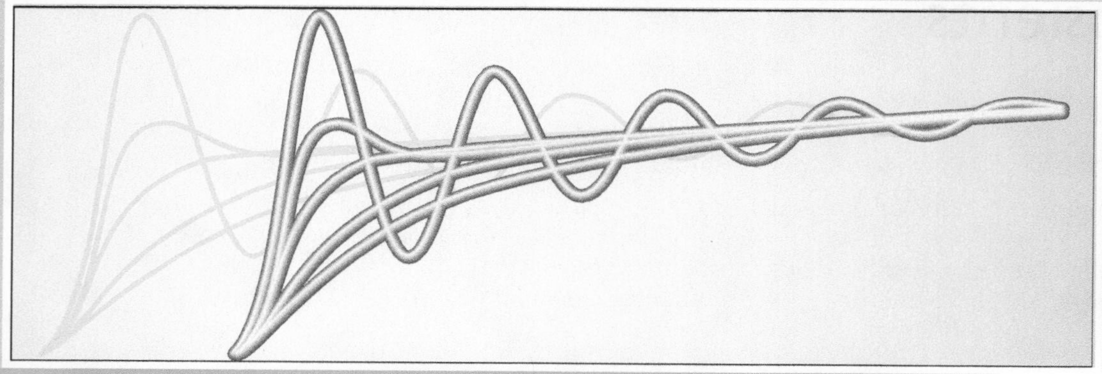

Transients

Study of this chapter will enable you to:

- Solve first-order *RC* or *RL* circuits.
- Understand the concepts of transient response and steady-state response.
- Relate the transient response of first-order circuits to the time constant.
- Solve *RLC* circuits in dc steady-state conditions.
- Solve second-order circuits.
- Relate the step response of a second-order system to its natural frequency and damping ratio.
- Use the MATLAB Symbolic Toolbox to solve differential equations.

Introduction to this chapter:

In this chapter, we study circuits that contain sources, switches, resistances, inductances, and capacitances. The time-varying currents and voltages resulting from the sudden application of sources, usually due to switching, are called **transients**.

In transient analysis, we start by writing circuit equations using concepts such as KCL, KVL, node-voltage analysis, and mesh-current analysis. Because the current–voltage relationships for inductances and capacitances involve integrals and derivatives, we obtain integrodifferential equations. These equations can be converted to pure differential equations by differentiating with respect to time. Thus, the study of transients requires us to solve differential equations.

1 FIRST-ORDER *RC* CIRCUITS

In this section, we consider transients in circuits that contain independent dc sources, resistances, and a single capacitance.

Discharge of a Capacitance through a Resistance

As a first example, consider the circuit shown in Figure 1(a). Prior to $t = 0$, the capacitor is charged to an initial voltage V_i. Then, at $t = 0$, the switch closes and current flows through the resistor, discharging the capacitor.

Writing a current equation at the top node of the circuit after the switch is closed yields

$$C\frac{dv_C(t)}{dt} + \frac{v_C(t)}{R} = 0$$

Multiplying by the resistance gives

$$RC\frac{dv_C(t)}{dt} + v_C(t) = 0 \qquad (1)$$

As expected, we have obtained a differential equation.

Equation 1 indicates that the solution for $v_C(t)$ must be a function that has the same form as its first derivative. Of course, a function with this property is an exponential. Thus, we anticipate that the solution is of the form

Equation 1 indicates that the solution for $v_C(t)$ must be a function that has the same form as its first derivative. The function with this property is an exponential.

$$v_C(t) = Ke^{st} \qquad (2)$$

in which K and s are constants to be determined.

Using Equation 2 to substitute for $v_C(t)$ in Equation 1, we have

$$RCKse^{st} + Ke^{st} = 0 \qquad (3)$$

Solving for s, we obtain

$$s = \frac{-1}{RC} \qquad (4)$$

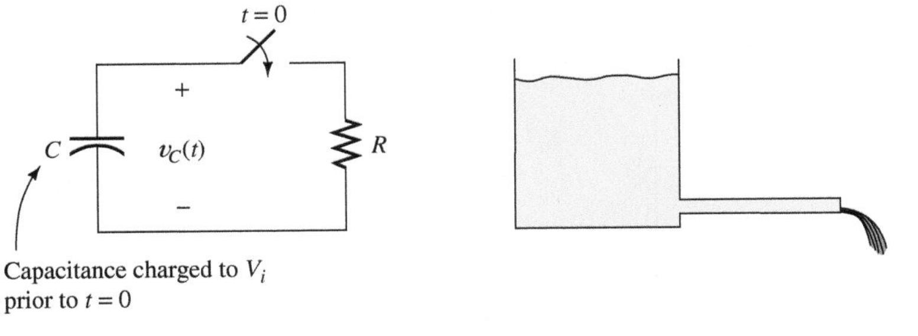

(a) Electrical circuit

(b) Fluid-flow analogy: a filled water tank discharging through a small pipe

Figure 1 A capacitance discharging through a resistance and its fluid-flow analogy. The capacitor is charged to V_i prior to $t = 0$ (by circuitry that is not shown). At $t = 0$, the switch closes and the capacitor discharges through the resistor.

Substituting this into Equation 2, we see that the solution is

$$v_C(t) = Ke^{-t/RC} \tag{5}$$

Because the current is finite, the voltage across the capacitor cannot change instantaneously when the switch closes.

Referring to Figure 1(a), we reason that the voltage across the capacitor cannot change instantaneously when the switch closes. This is because the current through the capacitance is $i_C(t) = C\,dv_C/dt$. In order for the voltage to change instantaneously, the current would have to be infinite. Since the voltage is finite, the current in the resistance must be finite, and we conclude that the voltage across the capacitor must be continuous. Thus, we write

$$v_C(0+) = V_i \tag{6}$$

in which $v_C(0+)$ represents the voltage immediately after the switch closes. Substituting into Equation 5, we have

$$v_C(0+) = V_i = Ke^0 = K \tag{7}$$

Hence, we conclude that the constant K equals the initial voltage across the capacitor. Finally, the solution for the voltage is

$$v_C(t) = V_i e^{-t/RC} \tag{8}$$

A plot of the voltage is shown in Figure 2. Notice that the capacitor voltage decays exponentially to zero.

The time interval $\tau = RC$ is called the time constant of the circuit.

The time interval

$$\tau = RC \tag{9}$$

is called the **time constant** of the circuit. In one time constant, the voltage decays by the factor $e^{-1} \cong 0.368$. After about five time constants, the voltage remaining on the capacitor is negligible compared with the initial value.

At one time constant, the voltage across a capacitance discharging through a resistance is $e^{-1} \cong 0.368$ times its initial value. After about three to five time constants, the capacitance is almost totally discharged.

An analogous fluid-flow system is shown in Figure 1(b). The tank initially filled with water is analogous to the charged capacitor. Furthermore, the small pipe is analogous to the resistor. At first, when the tank is full, the flow is large and the water level drops fast. As the tank empties, the flow decreases.

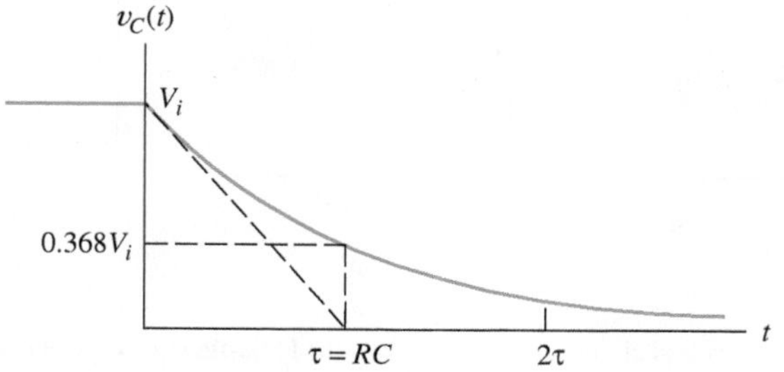

Figure 2 Voltage versus time for the circuit of Figure 1(a). When the switch is closed, the voltage across the capacitor decays exponentially to zero. At one time constant, the voltage is equal to 36.8 percent of its initial value.

In the past, engineers have frequently applied RC circuits in timing applications. For example, suppose that when a garage door opens or closes, a light is to be turned on and is to remain on for 30 s. To achieve this objective, we could design a circuit consisting of (1) a capacitor that is charged to an initial voltage V_i while the door opener is energized, (2) a resistor through which the capacitor discharges, and (3) a sensing circuit that keeps the light on as long as the capacitor voltage is larger than $0.368V_i$. If we choose the time constant $\tau = RC$ to be 30 s, the desired operation is achieved.

Charging a Capacitance from a DC Source through a Resistance

Next, consider the circuit shown in Figure 3. The source voltage V_s is constant—in other words, we have a dc source. The source is connected to the RC circuit by a switch that closes at $t = 0$. We assume that the initial voltage across the capacitor just before the switch closes is $v_C(0-) = 0$. Let us solve for the voltage across the capacitor as a function of time.

We start by writing a current equation at the node that joins the resistor and the capacitor. This yields

$$C\frac{dv_C(t)}{dt} + \frac{v_C(t) - V_s}{R} = 0 \tag{10}$$

The first term on the left-hand side is the current referenced downward through the capacitor. The second term is the current referenced toward the left through the resistor. KCL requires that the currents leaving the node sum to zero.

Rearranging Equation 10, we obtain

$$RC\frac{dv_C(t)}{dt} + v_C(t) = V_s \tag{11}$$

$v_C(0-)$ is the voltage across the capacitor the instant before the switch closes (at $t = 0$). Similarly, $v_C(0+)$ is the voltage across the capacitor the instant after the switch closes.

As expected, we have obtained a linear first-order differential equation with constant coefficients. As in the previous circuit, the voltage across the capacitance cannot change instantaneously because the voltages are finite, and thus, the current through the resistance (and therefore through the capacitance) is finite. Infinite current is required to change the voltage across a capacitance in an instant. Thus, we have

$$v_C(0+) = v_C(0-) = 0 \tag{12}$$

Now, we need to find a solution for $v_C(t)$ that (1) satisfies Equation 11 and (2) matches the initial conditions of the circuit stated in Equation 12. Notice that Equation 11 is the same as Equation 1, except for the constant on the right-hand side. Thus, we expect the solution to be the same as for Equation 1, except for an added constant term. Thus, we are led to try the solution

$$v_C(t) = K_1 + K_2e^{st} \tag{13}$$

in which K_1, K_2, and s are constants to be determined.

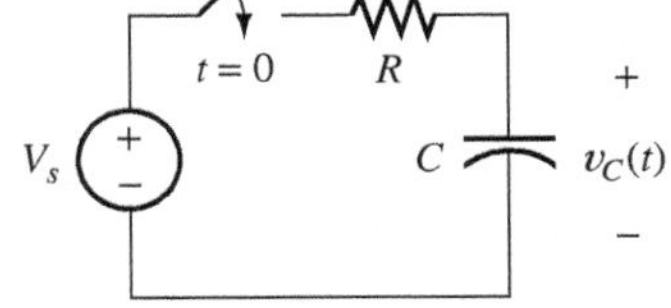

Figure 3 Capacitance charging through a resistance. The switch closes at $t = 0$, connecting the dc source V_s to the circuit.

If we use Equation 13 to substitute for $v_C(t)$ in Equation 11, we obtain

$$(1 + RCs)K_2e^{st} + K_1 = V_s \tag{14}$$

For equality, the coefficient of e^{st} must be zero. This leads to

$$s = \frac{-1}{RC} \tag{15}$$

From Equation 14, we also have

$$K_1 = V_s \tag{16}$$

Using Equations 15 and 16 to substitute into Equation 13, we obtain

$$v_C(t) = V_s + K_2e^{-t/RC} \tag{17}$$

in which K_2 remains to be determined.

Now, we use the initial condition (Equation 12) to find K_2. We have

$$v_C(0+) = 0 = V_s + K_2e^0 = V_s + K_2 \tag{18}$$

from which we find $K_2 = -V_s$. Finally, substituting into Equation 17, we obtain the solution

$$v_C(t) = V_s - V_se^{-t/RC} \tag{19}$$

When a dc source is contained in the circuit, the total response contains two parts: forced (or steady-state) and transient.

The second term on the right-hand side is called the **transient response**, which eventually decays to negligible values. The first term on the right-hand side is the **steady-state response**, also called the **forced response**, which persists after the transient has decayed.

Here again, the product of the resistance and capacitance has units of seconds and is called the time constant $\tau = RC$. Thus, the solution can be written as

$$v_C(t) = V_s - V_se^{-t/\tau} \tag{20}$$

In the case of a capacitance charging from a dc source through a resistance, a straight line tangent to the start of the transient reaches the final value at one time constant.

A plot of $v_C(t)$ is shown in Figure 4. Notice that $v_C(t)$ starts at 0 and approaches the final value V_s asymptotically as t becomes large. After one time constant, $v_C(t)$ has reached 63.2 percent of its final value. For practical purposes, $v_C(t)$ is equal to its final value V_s after about five time constants. Then, we say that the circuit has reached steady state.

It can be shown that if the initial slope of v_C is extended, it intersects the final value at one time constant as shown in Figure 4.

RC transients are the main limitation on the speed at which computer chips can operate.

We have seen in this section that several time constants are needed to charge or discharge a capacitance. This is the main limitation on the speed at which digital computers can process data. In a typical computer, information is represented by voltages that nominally assume values of either +1.8 or 0 V, depending on the data represented. When the data change, the voltages must change. It is impossible to build circuits that do not have some capacitance that is charged or discharged when voltages change in value. Furthermore, the circuits always have nonzero resistances that limit the currents available for charging or discharging the capacitances. Therefore, a nonzero time constant is associated with each circuit in the computer, limiting its speed.

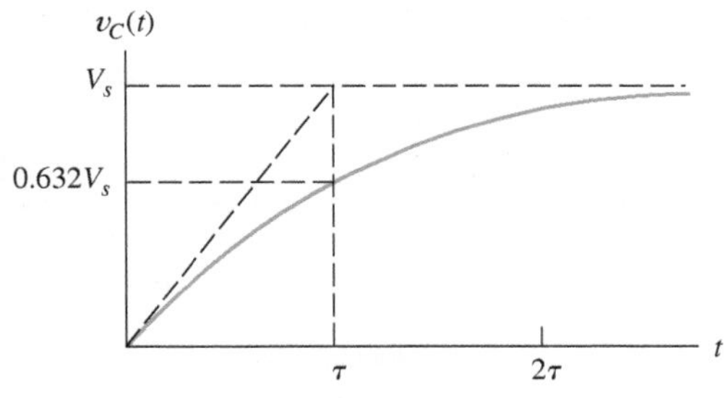

Figure 4 The charging transient for the RC circuit of Figure 3.

Exercise 1 Suppose that $R = 5000\ \Omega$ and $C = 1\ \mu$F in the circuit of Figure 1(a). Find the time at which the voltage across the capacitor reaches 1 percent of its initial value.

Answer $t = -5\ln(0.01)$ ms $\cong 23$ ms. □

Exercise 2 Show that if the initial slope of $v_C(t)$ is extended, it intersects the final value at one time constant, as shown in Figure 4. [The expression for $v_C(t)$ is given in Equation 20.] □

2 DC STEADY STATE

The transient terms in the expressions for currents and voltages in RLC circuits decay to zero with time. (An exception is LC circuits having no resistance.) For dc sources, the steady-state currents and voltages are also constant.

The transient terms in the expressions for currents and voltages in RLC circuits decay to zero with time.

Consider the equation for current through a capacitance:

$$i_C(t) = C\frac{dv_C(t)}{dt}$$

If the voltage $v_C(t)$ is constant, the current is zero. In other words, the capacitance behaves as an open circuit. Thus, we conclude that *for steady-state conditions with dc sources, capacitances behave as open circuits.*

Similarly, for an inductance, we have

$$v_L(t) = L\frac{di_L(t)}{dt}$$

When the current is constant, the voltage is zero. Thus, we conclude that *for steady-state conditions with dc sources, inductances behave as short circuits.*

These observations give us another approach to finding the steady-state solutions to circuit equations for RLC circuits with constant sources. First, we replace the capacitors by open circuits and the inductors by short circuits. The circuit then consists of dc sources and resistances. Finally, we solve the equivalent circuit for the steady-state currents and voltages.

The steps in determining the forced response for RLC circuits with dc sources are

1. Replace capacitances with open circuits.
2. Replace inductances with short circuits.
3. Solve the remaining circuit.

Example 1 Steady-State DC Analysis

Find v_x and i_x for the circuit shown in Figure 5(a) for $t >> 0$.

Solution After the switch has been closed a long time, we expect the transient response to have decayed to zero. Then the circuit is operating in dc steady-state

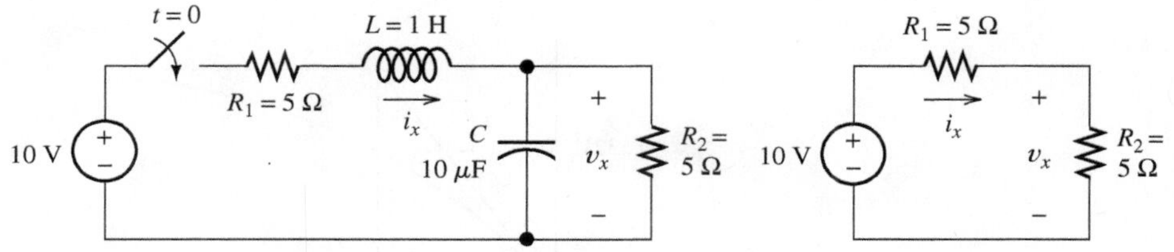

(a) Original circuit (b) Equivalent circuit for steady state

Figure 5 The circuit and its dc steady-state equivalent for Example 1.

Steps 1 and 2. conditions. We start our analysis by replacing the inductor by a short circuit and the capacitor by an open circuit. The equivalent circuit is shown in Figure 5(b).

Step 3. This resistive circuit is readily solved. The resistances R_1 and R_2 are in series. Thus, we have

$$i_x = \frac{10}{R_1 + R_2} = 1 \text{ A}$$

and

$$v_x = R_2 i_x = 5 \text{ V}$$

■

Sometimes, we are only interested in the steady-state operation of circuits with dc sources. For example, in analyzing the headlight circuits in an automobile, we are concerned primarily with steady state. On the other hand, we must consider transients in analyzing the operation of the ignition system.

In other applications, we are interested in steady-state conditions with sinusoidal ac sources. For sinusoidal sources, the steady-state currents and voltages are also sinusoidal. Instead of short and open circuits, we will replace inductances and capacitances by impedances, which are like resistances, except that impedances can have imaginary values.

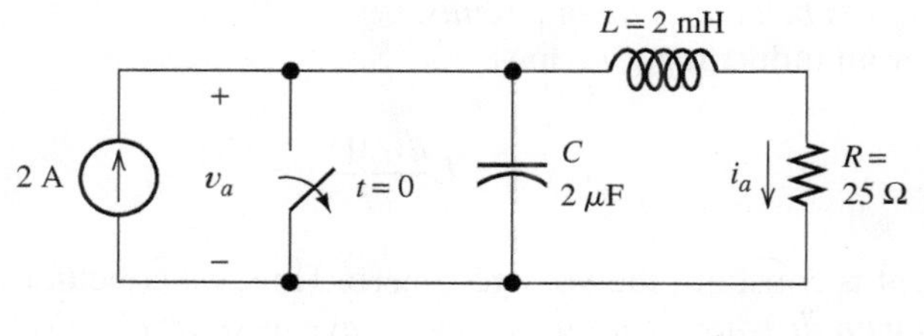

(a)

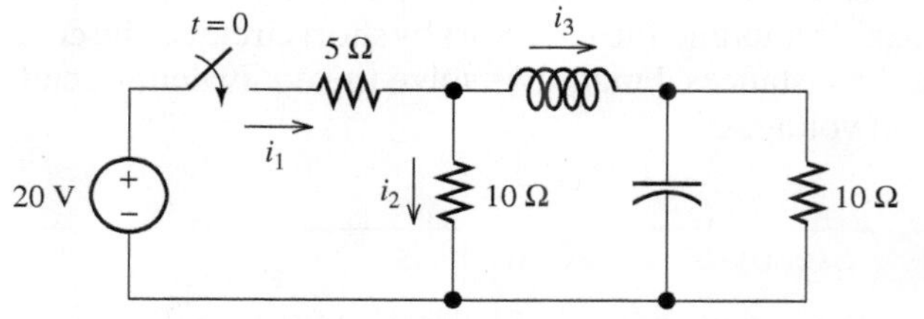

(b)

Figure 6 Circuits for Exercise 3.

Exercise 3 Solve for the steady-state values of the labeled currents and voltages for the circuits shown in Figure 6.
Answer **a.** $v_a = 50$ V, $i_a = 2$ A; **b.** $i_1 = 2$ A, $i_2 = 1$ A, $i_3 = 1$ A. □

3 *RL* CIRCUITS

In this section, we consider circuits consisting of dc sources, resistances, and a single inductance. The methods and solutions are very similar to those we studied for *RC* circuits in Section 1.

The steps involved in solving simple circuits containing dc sources, resistances, and one energy-storage element (inductance or capacitance) are as follows:

1. Apply Kirchhoff's current and voltage laws to write the circuit equation.
2. If the equation contains integrals, differentiate each term in the equation to produce a pure differential equation.
3. Assume a solution of the form $K_1 + K_2e^{st}$.
4. Substitute the solution into the differential equation to determine the values of K_1 and s. (Alternatively, we can determine K_1 by solving the circuit in steady state as discussed in Section 2.)
5. Use the initial conditions to determine the value of K_2.
6. Write the final solution.

Example 2 *RL* Transient Analysis

Consider the circuit shown in Figure 7. Find the current $i(t)$ and the voltage $v(t)$.

Solution First, we find the current $i(t)$. Of course, prior to $t = 0$, the switch is open and the current is zero:

$$i(t) = 0 \qquad \text{for } t < 0 \tag{21}$$

After the switch is closed, the current increases in value eventually reaching a steady-state value.

Writing a KVL equation around the loop, we have

Step 1.

$$Ri(t) + L\frac{di}{dt} = V_s \tag{22}$$

Step 2 is not needed in this case.

This is very similar to Equation 11, and we are, therefore, led to try a solution of the same form as that given by Equation 13. Thus, our trial solution is

Step 3.

$$i(t) = K_1 + K_2e^{st} \tag{23}$$

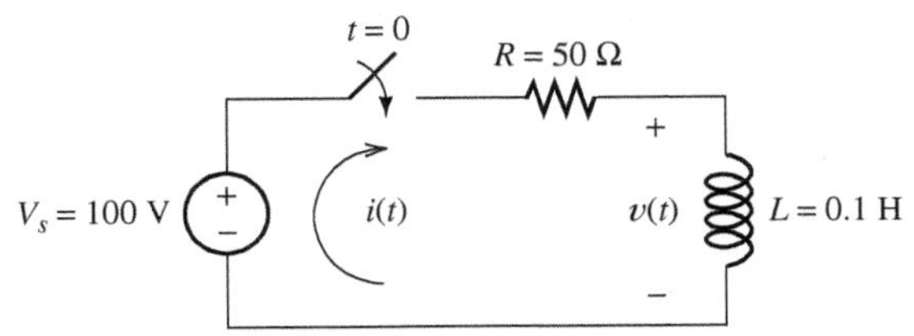

Figure 7 The circuit analyzed in Example 2.

Step 4. in which K_1, K_2, and s are constants that need to be determined. Following the procedure used in Section 1, we substitute the trial solution into the differential equation, resulting in

$$RK_1 + (RK_2 + sLK_2)e^{st} = V_s \tag{24}$$

from which we obtain

$$K_1 = \frac{V_s}{R} = 2 \tag{25}$$

and

$$s = \frac{-R}{L} \tag{26}$$

Substituting these values into Equation 23 results in

$$i(t) = 2 + K_2 e^{-tR/L} \tag{27}$$

Step 5. Next, we use the initial conditions to determine the value of K_2. The current in the inductor is zero prior to $t = 0$ because the switch is open. The applied voltage is finite, and the inductor current must be continuous (because $v_L = L\,di/dt$). Thus, immediately after the switch is closed, the current must be zero. Hence, we have

$$i(0+) = 0 = 2 + K_2 e^0 = 2 + K_2 \tag{28}$$

Solving, we find that $K_2 = -2$.

Substituting into Equation 27, we find that the solution for the current is

Step 6.

$$i(t) = 2 - 2e^{-t/\tau} \quad \text{for } t > 0 \tag{29}$$

in which the time constant is given by

$$\tau = \frac{L}{R} \tag{30}$$

A plot of the current versus time is shown in Figure 8(a). Notice that the current increases from zero to the steady-state value of 2 A. After five time constants, the current is within 99 percent of the final value. As a check, we verify that the steady-state current is 2 A. (As we saw in Section 2, this value can be obtained directly by treating the inductor as a short circuit.)

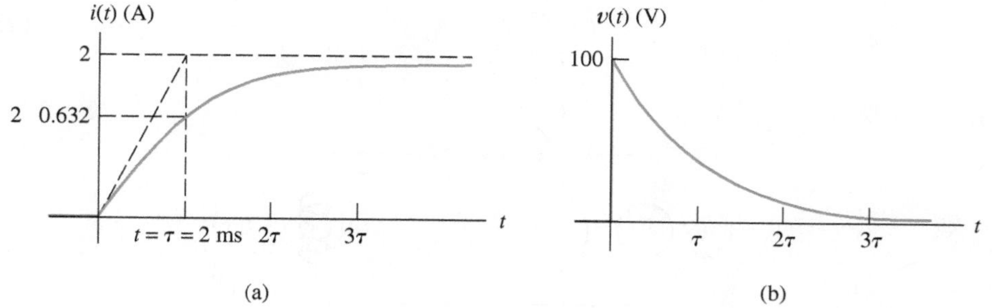

Figure 8 Current and voltage versus time for the circuit of Figure 7.

Now, we consider the voltage $v(t)$. Prior to $t = 0$, with the switch open, the voltage is zero.

$$v(t) = 0 \qquad \text{for } t < 0 \tag{31}$$

After $t = 0$, $v(t)$ is equal to the source voltage minus the drop across R. Thus, we have

$$v(t) = 100 - 50i(t) \qquad \text{for } t > 0 \tag{32}$$

Substituting the expression found earlier for $i(t)$, we obtain

$$v(t) = 100e^{-t/\tau} \tag{33}$$

A plot of $v(t)$ is shown in Figure 8(b).

At $t = 0$, the voltage across the inductor jumps from 0 to 100 V. As the current gradually increases, the drop across the resistor increases, and the voltage across the inductor falls. In steady state, we have $v(t) = 0$ because the inductor behaves as a short circuit. ■

After solving several circuits with a single energy-storage element, we can use our experience to skip some of the steps listed earlier in the section. We illustrate this in the next example.

Example 3 *RL* Transient Analysis

Consider the circuit shown in Figure 9 in which V_s is a dc source. Assume that the circuit is in steady state with the switch closed prior to $t = 0$. Find expressions for the current $i(t)$ and the voltage $v(t)$.

First, we use dc steady-state analysis to determine the current before the switch opens.

Solution Prior to $t = 0$, the inductor behaves as a short circuit. Thus, we have

$$v(t) = 0 \qquad \text{for } t < 0$$

and

$$i(t) = \frac{V_s}{R_1} \qquad \text{for } t < 0$$

Before the switch opens, current circulates clockwise through V_s, R_1, and the inductance. When the switch opens, current continues to flow through the inductance, but the return path is through R_2. Then, a voltage appears across R_2 and the inductance, causing the current to decay.

After the switch opens, the source is disconnected from the circuit, so the steady-state solution for $t > 0$ is zero.

Since there are no sources driving the circuit after the switch opens, the steady-state solution is zero for $t > 0$. Hence, the solution for $i(t)$ is given by

$$i(t) = Ke^{-t/\tau} \qquad \text{for } t > 0 \tag{34}$$

in which the time constant is

$$\tau = \frac{L}{R_2} \tag{35}$$

Unless an infinite voltage appears across the inductance, the current must be continuous. Recall that prior to $t = 0$, $i(t) = V_s/R_1$. Consequently, just after the switch opens, we have

$$i(0+) = \frac{V_s}{R_1} = Ke^{-0} = K$$

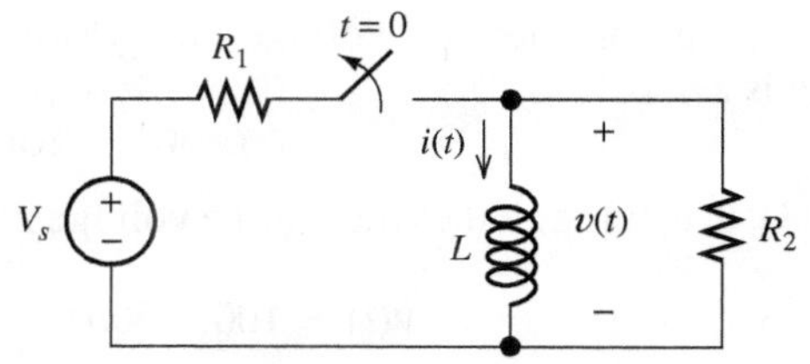

Figure 9 The circuit analyzed in Example 3.

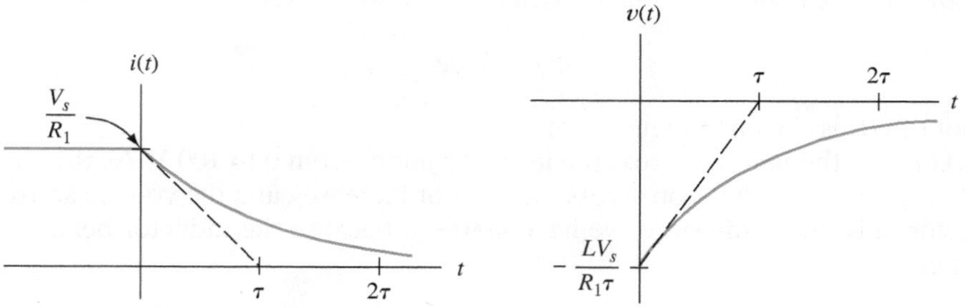

Figure 10 The current and voltage for the circuit of Figure 9.

Substituting the value of K into Equation 34, we find that the current is

$$i(t) = \frac{V_s}{R_1} e^{-t/\tau} \quad \text{for } t > 0 \tag{36}$$

The voltage is given by

$$\begin{aligned} v(t) &= L\frac{di(t)}{dt} \\ &= 0 \quad \text{for } t < 0 \\ &= -\frac{LV_s}{R_1\tau} e^{-t/\tau} \quad \text{for } t > 0 \end{aligned}$$

Plots of the voltage and current are shown in Figure 10. ■

Exercise 4 For the circuit of Example 3 (Figure 9), assume that $V_s = 15$ V, $R_1 = 10\ \Omega$, $R_2 = 100\ \Omega$, and $L = 0.1$ H. **a.** What is the value of the time constant (after the switch opens)? **b.** What is the maximum magnitude of $v(t)$? **c.** How does the maximum magnitude of $v(t)$ compare to the source voltage? **d.** Find the time t at which $v(t)$ is one-half of its value immediately after the switch opens.

Answer **a.** $\tau = 1$ ms; **b.** $|v(t)|_{\max} = 150$ V; **c.** the maximum magnitude of $v(t)$ is 10 times the value of V_s; **d.** $t = \tau \ln(2) = 0.693$ ms. □

Exercise 5 Consider the circuit shown in Figure 11, in which the switch opens at $t = 0$. Find expressions for $v(t)$, $i_R(t)$, and $i_L(t)$ for $t > 0$. Assume that $i_L(t)$ is zero before the switch opens.

Answer $v(t) = 20e^{-t/0.2}$, $i_R(t) = 2e^{-t/0.2}$, $i_L(t) = 2 - 2e^{-t/0.2}$. □

Exercise 6 Consider the circuit shown in Figure 12. Assume that the switch has been closed for a very long time prior to $t = 0$. Find expressions for $i(t)$ and $v(t)$.

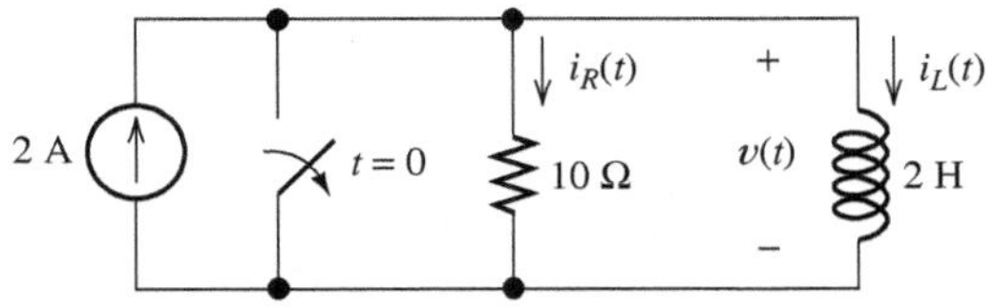

Figure 11 The circuit for Exercise 5.

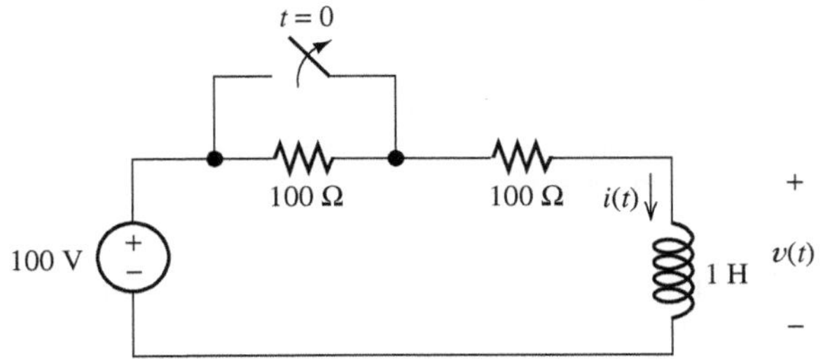

Figure 12 The circuit for Exercise 6.

Answer

$$\begin{aligned} i(t) &= 1.0 \qquad \text{for } t < 0 \\ &= 0.5 + 0.5e^{-t/\tau} \qquad \text{for } t > 0 \\ v(t) &= 0 \qquad \text{for } t < 0 \\ &= -100e^{-t/\tau} \qquad \text{for } t > 0 \end{aligned}$$

where the time constant is $\tau = 5$ ms. □

4 *RC* AND *RL* CIRCUITS WITH GENERAL SOURCES

Now that we have gained some familiarity with RL and RC circuits, we discuss their solution in general. In this section, we treat circuits that contain one energy-storage element, either an inductance or a capacitance.

Consider the circuit shown in Figure 13(a). The circuit inside the box can be any combination of resistances and sources. The single inductance L is shown explicitly. Recall that we can find a Thévenin equivalent for circuits consisting of sources and resistances. The Thévenin equivalent is an independent voltage source $v_t(t)$ in series with the Thévenin resistance R. Thus, any circuit composed of sources, resistances, and one inductance has the equivalent circuit shown in Figure 13(b). (Of course, we could reduce any circuit containing sources, resistances, and a single capacitance in a similar fashion.)

Writing a KVL equation for Figure 13(b), we obtain

$$L\frac{di(t)}{dt} + Ri(t) = v_t(t) \qquad (37)$$

If we divide through by the resistance R, we have

$$\frac{L}{R}\frac{di(t)}{dt} + i(t) = \frac{v_t(t)}{R} \qquad (38)$$

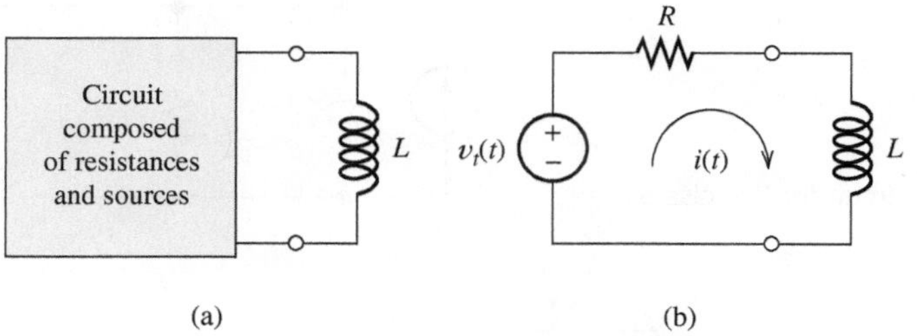

Figure 13 A circuit consisting of sources, resistances, and one inductance has an equivalent circuit consisting of a voltage source and a resistance in series with the inductance.

In general, the equation for any circuit containing one inductance or one capacitance can be put into the form

$$\tau \frac{dx(t)}{dt} + x(t) = f(t), \tag{39}$$

in which $x(t)$ represents the current or voltage for which we are solving. Then, we need to find solutions to Equation 39 that are consistent with the initial conditions (such as the initial current in the inductance).

The constant τ (which turns out to be the time constant) is a function of only the resistances and the inductance (or capacitance). The sources result in the term $f(t)$, which is called the **forcing function**. If we have a circuit without sources (such as Figure 1), the forcing function is zero. For dc sources, the forcing function is constant.

Equation 39 is called a first-order differential equation because the highest-order derivative is first order. It is a linear equation because it does not involve powers or other nonlinear functions of $x(t)$ or its derivatives. Thus, to solve an RL (or RC) circuit, we must find the general solution of a linear first-order differential equation with constant coefficients.

Solution of the Differential Equation

The general solution to Equation 39 consists of two parts.

An important result in differential equations states that the general solution to Equation 39 consists of two parts. The first part is called the **particular solution** $x_p(t)$ and is any expression that satisfies Equation 39. Thus,

The particular solution (also called the forced response) is any expression that satisfies the equation.

$$\tau \frac{dx_p(t)}{dt} + x_p(t) = f(t) \tag{40}$$

The particular solution is also called the **forced response** because it depends on the forcing function (which in turn is due to the independent sources).

In order to have a solution that satisfies the initial conditions, we must add the complementary solution to the particular solution.

(Even though the particular solution satisfies the differential equation, it may not be consistent with the initial conditions, such as the initial voltage on a capacitance or current through an inductance. By adding another term, known as the complementary solution, we obtain a general solution that satisfies both the differential equation and meets the initial conditions.)

For the forcing functions that we will encounter, we can often select the form of the particular solution by inspection. Usually, the particular solution includes terms with the same functional forms as the terms found in the forcing function and its derivatives.

Sinusoidal functions of time are one of the most important types of forcing functions in electrical engineering. For example, consider the forcing function

$$f(t) = 10\ \cos(200t)$$

Because the derivatives of sine and cosine functions are also sine and cosine functions, we would try a particular solution of the form

$$x_p(t) = A\ \cos(200t) + B\sin(200t)$$

where A and B are constants that must be determined. We find these constants by substituting the proposed solution into the differential equation and requiring the two sides of the equation to be identical. This leads to equations that can be solved for A and B.

The second part of the general solution is called the **complementary solution** $x_c(t)$ and is the solution of the **homogeneous equation**

The homogeneous equation is obtained by setting the forcing function to zero.

$$\tau\frac{dx_c(t)}{dt} + x_c(t) = 0 \qquad (41)$$

We obtain the homogeneous equation by setting the forcing function to zero. Thus, the form of the complementary solution does not depend on the sources. It is also called the **natural response** because it depends on the passive circuit elements. The complementary solution must be added to the particular solution in order to obtain a general solution that matches the initial values of the currents and voltages.

The complementary solution (also called the natural response) is obtained by solving the homogeneous equation.

We can rearrange the homogeneous equation into this form:

$$\frac{dx_c(t)/dt}{x_c(t)} = \frac{-1}{\tau} \qquad (42)$$

Integrating both sides of Equation 42, we have

$$\ln[x_c(t)] = \frac{-t}{\tau} + c \qquad (43)$$

in which c is the constant of integration. Equation 43 is equivalent to

$$x_c(t) = e^{(-t/\tau+c)} = e^c e^{-t/\tau}$$

Then, if we define $K = e^c$, we have the complementary solution

$$x_c(t) = Ke^{-t/\tau} \qquad (44)$$

Step-by-Step Solution

Next, we summarize an approach to solving circuits containing a resistance, a source, and an inductance (or a capacitance):

1. Write the circuit equation and reduce it to a first-order differential equation.
2. Find a particular solution. The details of this step depend on the form of the forcing function. We illustrate several types of forcing functions in examples, exercises, and problems.

3. Obtain the complete solution by adding the particular solution to the complementary solution given by Equation 44, which contains the arbitrary constant K.
4. Use initial conditions to find the value of K.

We illustrate this procedure with an example.

Example 4 Transient Analysis of an *RC* Circuit with a Sinusoidal Source

Solve for the current in the circuit shown in Figure 14. The capacitor is initially charged so that $v_C(0+) = 1$ V.

Step 1: Write the circuit equation and reduce it to a first-order differential equation.

Solution First, we write a voltage equation for $t > 0$. Traveling clockwise and summing voltages, we obtain

$$Ri(t) + \frac{1}{C}\int_0^t i(t)\,dt + v_C(0) - 2\sin(200t) = 0$$

We convert this to a differential equation by taking the derivative of each term. Of course, the derivative of the integral is simply the integrand. Because $v_C(0)$ is a constant, its derivative is zero. Thus, we have

$$R\frac{di(t)}{dt} + \frac{1}{C}i(t) = 400\cos(200t) \tag{45}$$

Multiplying by C, we get

$$RC\frac{di(t)}{dt} + i(t) = 400\,C\cos(200t) \tag{46}$$

Substituting values for R and C, we obtain

$$5 \times 10^{-3}\frac{di(t)}{dt} + i(t) = 400 \times 10^{-6}\cos(200t) \tag{47}$$

Step 2: Find a particular solution.

The particular solution for a sinusoidal forcing function always has the form given by Equation 48.

The second step is to find a particular solution $i_p(t)$. Often, we start by guessing at the form of $i_p(t)$, possibly including some unknown constants. Then, we substitute our guess into the differential equation and solve for the constants. In the present case, since the derivatives of $\sin(200t)$ and $\cos(200t)$ are $200\cos(200t)$ and $-200\sin(200t)$, respectively, we try a particular solution of the form

$$i_p(t) = A\cos(200t) + B\sin(200t) \tag{48}$$

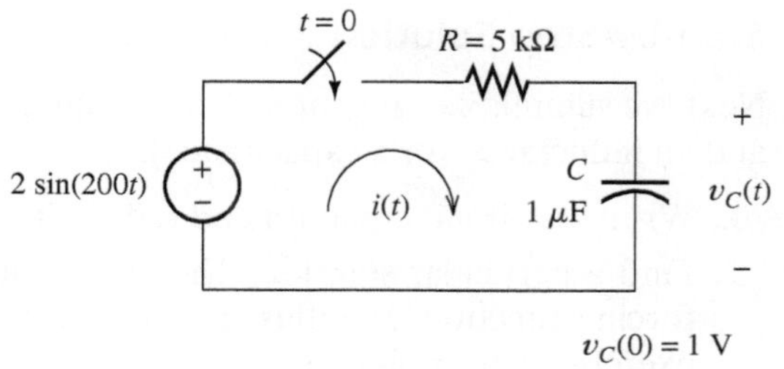

Figure 14 A first-order *RC* circuit with a sinusoidal source. See Example 4.

where A and B are constants to be determined so that i_p is indeed a solution to Equation 47.

Substituting the proposed solution into Equation 47, we obtain

We substitute Equation 48 into the differential equation, and solve for A and B.

$$-A\sin(200t) + B\cos(200t) + A\cos(200t) + B\sin(200t) = 400 \times 10^{-6}\cos(200t)$$

However, the left-hand side of this equation is required to be identical to the right-hand side. Equating the coefficients of the sine functions, we have

$$-A + B = 0 \tag{49}$$

Equating the coefficients of the cosine functions, we get

$$B + A = 400 \times 10^{-6} \tag{50}$$

These equations can be readily solved, yielding

$$A = 200 \times 10^{-6} = 200\ \mu\text{A}$$

and

$$B = 200 \times 10^{-6} = 200\ \mu\text{A}$$

Substituting these values into Equation 48, we obtain the particular solution

$$i_p(t) = 200\cos(200t) + 200\sin(200t)\ \mu\text{A} \tag{51}$$

which can also be written as

$$i_p(t) = 200\sqrt{2}\cos(200t - 45°)$$

We obtain the homogeneous equation by substituting 0 for the forcing function in Equation 46. Thus, we have

$$RC\frac{di(t)}{dt} + i(t) = 0 \tag{52}$$

The complementary solution is

$$i_c(t) = Ke^{-t/RC} = Ke^{-t/\tau} \tag{53}$$

Adding the particular solution and the complementary solution, we obtain the general solution

Step 3: Obtain the complete solution by adding the particular solution to the complementary solution.

$$i(t) = 200\cos(200t) + 200\sin(200t) + Ke^{-t/RC}\ \mu\text{A} \tag{54}$$

Finally, we determine the value of the constant K by using the initial conditions. The voltages and currents immediately after the switch closes are shown in Figure 15. The source voltage is 0 V and the voltage across the capacitor is

Step 4: Use initial conditions to find the value of K.

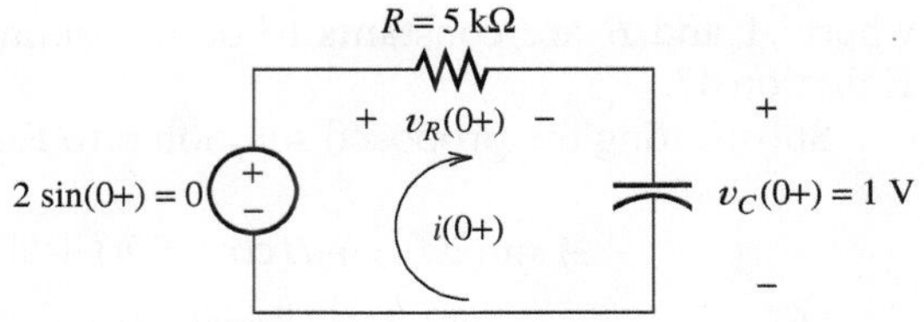

Figure 15 The voltages and currents for the circuit of Figure 14 immediately after the switch closes.

$v_C(0+) = 1$. Consequently, the voltage across the resistor must be $v_R(0+) = -1$ V. Thus, we get

$$i(0+) = \frac{v_R(0+)}{R} = \frac{-1}{5000} = -200\ \mu\text{A}$$

Substituting $t = 0$ into Equation 54, we obtain

$$i(0+) = -200 = 200 + K\ \mu\text{A} \tag{55}$$

Solving, we find that $K = -400\ \mu$A. Substituting this into Equation 54, we have the solution

$$i(t) = 200\cos(200t) + 200\sin(200t) - 400e^{-t/RC}\ \mu\text{A} \tag{56}$$

Plots of the particular solution and of the complementary solution are shown in Figure 16. The time constant for this circuit is $\tau = RC = 5$ ms. Notice that the natural response decays to negligible values in about 25 ms. As expected, the natural response has decayed in about five time constants. Furthermore, notice that for a sinusoidal forcing function, the forced response is also sinusoidal and persists after the natural response has decayed.

Notice that the forced response is sinusoidal for a sinusoidal forcing function.

A plot of the complete solution is shown in Figure 17. ■

Exercise 7 Repeat Example 4 if the source voltage is changed to $2\cos(200t)$ and the initial voltage on the capacitor is $v_C(0) = 0$. The circuit with these changes is shown in Figure 18.

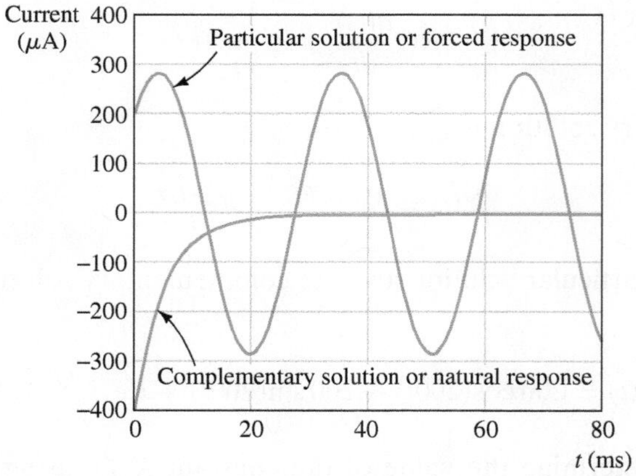

Figure 16 The complementary solution and the particular solution for Example 4.

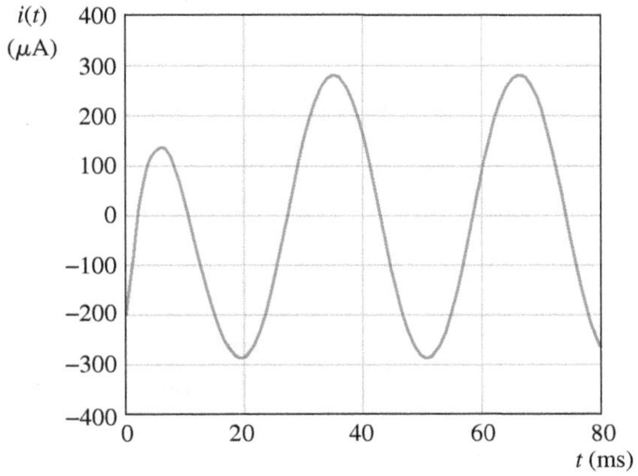

Figure 17 The complete solution for Example 4.

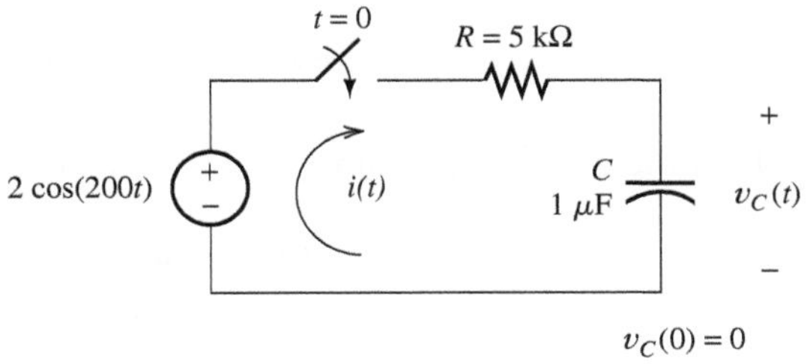

Figure 18 The circuit for Exercise 7.

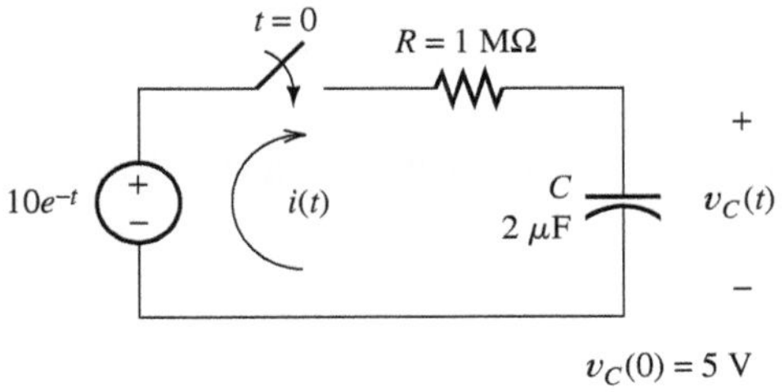

Figure 19 The circuit for Exercise 8.

Answer $i(t) = -200\sin(200t) + 200\cos(200t) + 200e^{-t/RC}$ μA, in which $\tau = RC =$ 5 ms. □

Exercise 8 Solve for the current in the circuit shown in Figure 19 after the switch closes. [*Hint:* Try a particular solution of the form $i_p(t) = Ae^{-t}$.]

Answer $i(t) = 20e^{-t} - 15e^{-t/2}$ μA. □

5 SECOND-ORDER CIRCUITS

In this section, we consider circuits that contain two energy-storage elements. In particular, we look at circuits that have one inductance and one capacitance, either in series or in parallel.

Differential Equation

To derive the general form of the equations that we encounter in circuits with two energy-storage elements, consider the series circuit shown in Figure 20(a). Writing

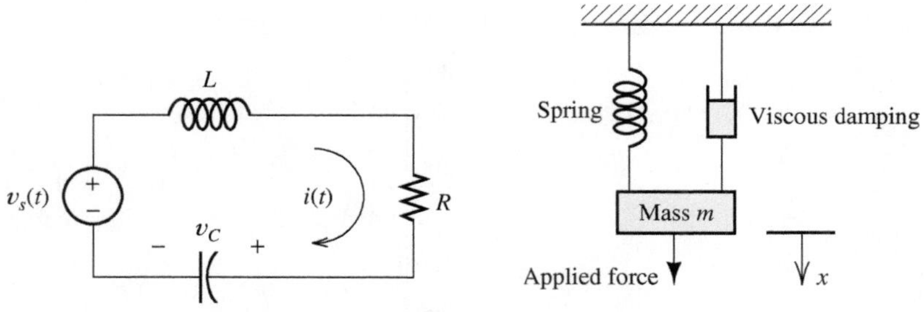

(a) Electrical circuit (b) Mechanical analog

Figure 20 The series *RLC* circuit and its mechanical analog.

a KVL equation, we have

$$L\frac{di(t)}{dt} + Ri(t) + \frac{1}{C}\int_0^t i(t)dt + v_C(0) = v_s(t) \quad (57)$$

We convert the integrodifferential equation to a pure differential equation by differentiating with respect to time.

Taking the derivative with respect to time, we get

$$L\frac{d^2i(t)}{dt^2} + R\frac{di(t)}{dt} + \frac{1}{C}i(t) = \frac{dv_s(t)}{dt} \quad (58)$$

Dividing through by L, we obtain

$$\frac{d^2i(t)}{dt^2} + \frac{R}{L}\frac{di(t)}{dt} + \frac{1}{LC}i(t) = \frac{1}{L}\frac{dv_s(t)}{dt} \quad (59)$$

Now, we define the **damping coefficient** as

$$\alpha = \frac{R}{2L} \quad (60)$$

and the **undamped resonant frequency** as

$$\omega_0 = \frac{1}{\sqrt{LC}} \quad (61)$$

The **forcing function** is

$$f(t) = \frac{1}{L}\frac{dv_s(t)}{dt} \quad (62)$$

Using these definitions, we find that Equation 59 can be written as

$$\frac{d^2i(t)}{dt^2} + 2\alpha\frac{di(t)}{dt} + \omega_0^2 i(t) = f(t) \quad (63)$$

If a circuit contains two energy-storage elements (after substituting all possible series or parallel equivalents), the circuit equations can always be reduced to the form given by Equation 63.

This is a linear second-order differential equation with constant coefficients. Thus, we refer to circuits having two energy-storage elements as second-order circuits. (An exception occurs if we can combine the energy-storage elements in series or parallel. For example, if we have two capacitors in parallel, we can combine them into a single equivalent capacitance, and then we would have a first-order circuit.)

Mechanical Analog

The mechanical analog of the series *RLC* circuit is shown in Figure 20(b). The displacement x of the mass is analogous to electrical charge, the velocity dx/dt is analogous to current, and force is analogous to voltage. The mass plays the role of the inductance, the spring plays the role of the capacitance, and the damper plays the role of the resistance. The equation of motion for the mechanical system can be put into the form of Equation 63.

Based on an intuitive consideration of Figure 20, we can anticipate that the sudden application of a constant force (dc voltage) can result in a displacement (current) that either approaches steady-state conditions asymptotically or oscillates before settling to the steady-state value. The type of behavior depends on the relative values of the mass, spring constant, and damping coefficient.

Solution of the Second-Order Equation

We will see that the circuit equations for currents and voltages in circuits having two energy-storage elements can always be put into the form of Equation 63. Thus, let us consider the solution of

$$\frac{d^2x(t)}{dt^2} + 2\alpha\frac{dx(t)}{dt} + \omega_0^2 x(t) = f(t) \qquad (64)$$

where we have used $x(t)$ for the variable, which could represent either a current or a voltage.

Here again, the general solution $x(t)$ to this equation consists of two parts: a particular solution $x_p(t)$ plus the complementary solution $x_c(t)$ and is expressed as

$$x(t) = x_p(t) + x_c(t) \qquad (65)$$

Particular Solution. The particular solution is any expression $x_p(t)$ that satisfies the differential equation

$$\frac{d^2x_p(t)}{dt^2} + 2\alpha\frac{dx_p(t)}{dt} + \omega_0^2 x_p(t) = f(t) \qquad (66)$$

The particular solution is also called the **forced response**. (Usually, we eliminate any terms from $x_p(t)$ that produce a zero net result when substituted into the left-hand side of Equation 66. In other words, we eliminate any terms that have the same form as the homogeneous solution.)

We will be concerned primarily with either constant (dc) or sinusoidal (ac) forcing functions. For dc sources, we can find the particular solution directly from the circuit by replacing the inductances by short circuits, replacing the capacitances by open circuits, and solving. This technique was discussed in Section 2.

For dc sources, we can find the particular solution by performing a dc steady-state analysis as discussed in Section 2.

Complementary Solution. The complementary solution $x_c(t)$ is found by solving the homogeneous equation, which is obtained by substituting 0 for the forcing function $f(t)$. Thus, the homogeneous equation is

$$\frac{d^2x_c(t)}{dt^2} + 2\alpha\frac{dx_c(t)}{dt} + \omega_0^2 x_c(t) = 0 \qquad (67)$$

In finding the solution to the homogeneous equation, we start by substituting the trial solution $x_c(t) = Ke^{st}$. This yields

$$s^2 Ke^{st} + 2\alpha s Ke^{st} + \omega_0^2 Ke^{st} = 0 \tag{68}$$

Factoring, we obtain

$$(s^2 + 2\alpha s + \omega_0^2)Ke^{st} = 0 \tag{69}$$

Since we want to find a solution Ke^{st} that is nonzero, we must have

$$s^2 + 2\alpha s + \omega_0^2 = 0 \tag{70}$$

This is called the **characteristic equation**.

The **damping ratio** is defined as

$$\zeta = \frac{\alpha}{\omega_0} \tag{71}$$

The form of the complementary solution depends on the value of the damping ratio.

The form of the complementary solution depends on the value of the damping ratio. The roots of the characteristic equation are given by

$$s_1 = -\alpha + \sqrt{\alpha^2 - \omega_0^2} \tag{72}$$

and

$$s_2 = -\alpha - \sqrt{\alpha^2 - \omega_0^2} \tag{73}$$

We have three cases depending on the value of the damping ratio ζ compared with unity.

If the damping ratio is greater than unity, we say that the circuit is overdamped, the roots of the characteristic equation are real, and the complementary solution has the form given in Equation 74.

1. *Overdamped case* ($\zeta > 1$). If $\zeta > 1$ (or equivalently, if $\alpha > \omega_0$), the roots of the characteristic equation are real and distinct. Then the complementary solution is

$$x_c(t) = K_1 e^{s_1 t} + K_2 e^{s_2 t} \tag{74}$$

In this case, we say that the circuit is **overdamped**.

If the damping ratio equals unity, the circuit is critically damped, the roots of the characteristic equation are real and equal, and the complementary solution has the form given in Equation 75.

2. *Critically damped case* ($\zeta = 1$). If $\zeta = 1$ (or equivalently, if $\alpha = \omega_0$), the roots are real and equal. Then, the complementary solution is

$$x_c(t) = K_1 e^{s_1 t} + K_2 t e^{s_1 t} \tag{75}$$

In this case, we say that the circuit is **critically damped**.

If the damping ratio is less than unity, the roots of the characteristic equation are complex conjugates, and the complementary solution has the form given in Equation 77.

3. *Underdamped case* ($\zeta < 1$). Finally, if $\zeta < 1$ (or equivalently, if $\alpha < \omega_0$), the roots are complex. (By the term *complex*, we mean that the roots involve the imaginary number $\sqrt{-1}$.) In other words, the roots are of the form

$$s_1 = -\alpha + j\omega_n \quad \text{and} \quad s_2 = -\alpha - j\omega_n$$

in which $j = \sqrt{-1}$ and the **natural frequency** is given by

$$\omega_n = \sqrt{\omega_0^2 - \alpha^2} \tag{76}$$

(In electrical engineering, we use j rather than i to stand for the imaginary number $\sqrt{-1}$ because we use i for current.)

For complex roots, the complementary solution is of the form

$$x_c(t) = K_1 e^{-\alpha t}\cos(\omega_n t) + K_2 e^{-\alpha t}\sin(\omega_n t) \tag{77}$$

In this case, we say that the circuit is **underdamped**.

Example 5 Analysis of a Second-Order Circuit with a DC Source

A dc source is connected to a series RLC circuit by a switch that closes at $t = 0$ as shown in Figure 21. The initial conditions are $i(0) = 0$ and $v_C(0) = 0$. Write the differential equation for $v_C(t)$. Solve for $v_C(t)$ if $R = 300, 200$, and $100\ \Omega$.

Solution First, we can write an expression for the current in terms of the voltage across the capacitance:

First, we write the circuit equations and reduce them to the form given in Equation 63.

$$i(t) = C\frac{dv_C(t)}{dt} \tag{78}$$

Then, we write a KVL equation for the circuit:

$$L\frac{di(t)}{dt} + Ri(t) + v_C(t) = V_s \tag{79}$$

Using Equation 78 to substitute for $i(t)$, we get

$$LC\frac{d^2v_C(t)}{dt^2} + RC\frac{dv_C(t)}{dt} + v_C(t) = V_s \tag{80}$$

Dividing through by LC, we have

$$\frac{d^2v_C(t)}{dt^2} + \frac{R}{L}\frac{dv_C(t)}{dt} + \frac{1}{LC}v_C(t) = \frac{V_s}{LC} \tag{81}$$

As expected, the differential equation for $v_C(t)$ has the same form as Equation 63.

Next, we find the particular solution. Since we have a dc source, we can find this part of the solution by replacing the inductance by a short circuit and the capacitance by an open circuit. This is shown in Figure 22. Then the current is zero, the drop across the resistance is zero, and the voltage across the capacitance (open circuit) is equal to the dc source voltage. Therefore, the particular solution is

Next, we find the particular solution by solving the circuit for dc steady-state conditions.

$$v_{Cp}(t) = V_s = 10 \text{ V} \tag{82}$$

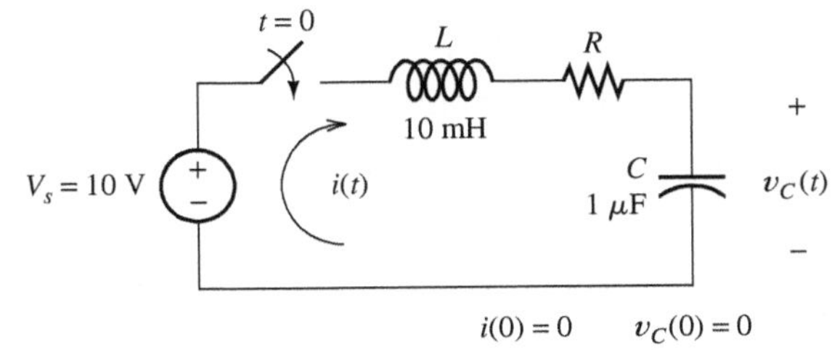

Figure 21 The circuit for Example 5.

Figure 22 The equivalent circuit for Figure 21 under steady-state conditions. The inductor has been replaced by a short circuit and the capacitor by an open circuit.

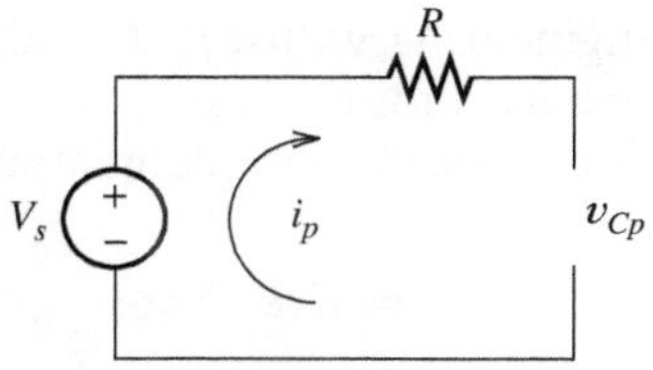

(It can be verified that this is a particular solution by substituting it into Equation 81.) Notice that in this circuit the particular solution for $v_C(t)$ is the same for all three values of resistance.

Next, we find the complementary solution for each value of R. For each resistance value, we

1. Determine the damping ratio and roots of the characteristic equation.
2. Select the appropriate form for the homogeneous solution, depending on the value of the damping ratio.
3. Add the homogeneous solution to the particular solution and determine the values of the coefficients (K_1 and K_2), based on the initial conditions.

Next, we find the homogeneous solution and general solution for each value of R. For all three cases, we have

$$\omega_0 = \frac{1}{\sqrt{LC}} = 10^4 \tag{83}$$

Case I ($R = 300\ \Omega$)

In this case, we get

$$\alpha = \frac{R}{2L} = 1.5 \times 10^4 \tag{84}$$

The damping ratio is $\zeta = \alpha/\omega_0 = 1.5$. Because we have $\zeta > 1$, this is the overdamped case. The roots of the characteristic equation are given by Equations 72 and 73. Substituting values, we find that

$$\begin{aligned} s_1 &= -\alpha + \sqrt{\alpha^2 - \omega_0^2} \\ &= -1.5 \times 10^4 + \sqrt{(1.5 \times 10^4)^2 - (10^4)^2} \\ &= -0.3820 \times 10^4 \end{aligned}$$

and

$$\begin{aligned} s_2 &= -\alpha - \sqrt{\alpha^2 - \omega_0^2} \\ &= -2.618 \times 10^4 \end{aligned}$$

The homogeneous solution has the form of Equation 74. Adding the particular solution given by Equation 82 to the homogeneous solution, we obtain the general solution

$$v_C(t) = 10 + K_1 e^{s_1 t} + K_2 e^{s_2 t} \tag{85}$$

Now, we must find values of K_1 and K_2 so the solution matches the known initial conditions in the circuit. It was given that the initial voltage on the capacitance is zero. Hence,

$$v_C(0) = 0$$

Evaluating Equation 85 at $t = 0$, we obtain

$$10 + K_1 + K_2 = 0 \tag{86}$$

Furthermore, the initial current was given as $i(0) = 0$. Since the current through the capacitance is given by

$$i(t) = C\frac{dv_C(t)}{dt}$$

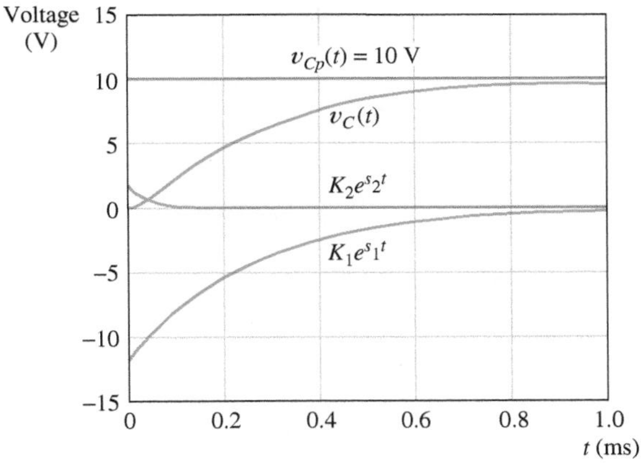

Figure 23 Solution for $R = 300\ \Omega$.

we conclude that

$$\frac{dv_C(0)}{dt} = 0$$

Taking the derivative of Equation 85 and evaluating at $t = 0$, we have

$$s_1K_1 + s_2K_2 = 0 \tag{87}$$

Now, we can solve Equations 86 and 87 for the values of K_1 and K_2. The results are $K_1 = -11.708$ and $K_2 = 1.708$. Substituting these values into Equation 85, we have the solution

$$v_C(t) = 10 - 11.708e^{s_1t} + 1.708e^{s_2t}$$

Plots of each of the terms of this equation and the complete solution are shown in Figure 23.

Case II ($R = 200\ \Omega$)

Now, we repeat the steps for $R = 200\ \Omega$.

In this case, we get

$$\alpha = \frac{R}{2L} = 10^4 \tag{88}$$

Because $\zeta = \alpha/\omega_0 = 1$, this is the critically damped case. The roots of the characteristic equation are given by Equations 72 and 73. Substituting values, we have

$$s_1 = s_2 = -\alpha + \sqrt{\alpha^2 - \omega_0^2} = -\alpha = -10^4$$

The homogeneous solution has the form of Equation 75. Adding the particular solution (Equation 82) to the homogeneous solution, we find that

$$v_C(t) = 10 + K_1e^{s_1t} + K_2te^{s_1t} \tag{89}$$

As in case I, the initial conditions require $v_C(0) = 0$ and $dv_C(0)/dt = 0$. Thus, substituting $t = 0$ into Equation 89, we get

$$10 + K_1 = 0 \tag{90}$$

Differentiating Equation 89 and substituting $t = 0$ yields

$$s_1K_1 + K_2 = 0 \tag{91}$$

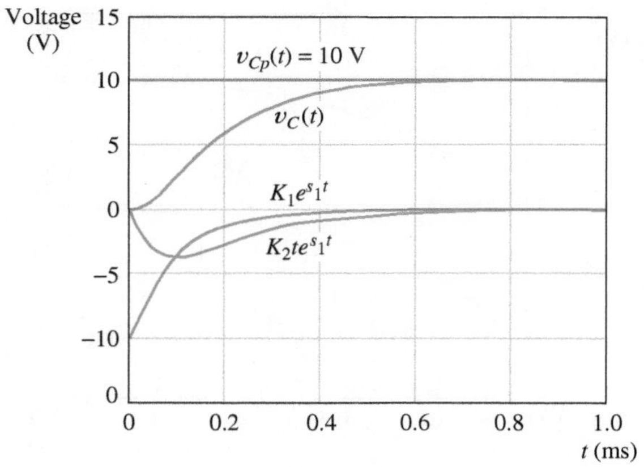

Figure 24 Solution for $R = 200\ \Omega$.

Solving Equations 90 and 91 yields $K_1 = -10$ and $K_2 = -10^5$. Thus, the solution is

$$v_C(t) = 10 - 10e^{s_1t} - 10^5te^{s_1t} \tag{92}$$

Plots of each of the terms of this equation and the complete solution are shown in Figure 24.

Finally, we repeat the solution for $R = 100\ \Omega$.

Case III ($R = 100\ \Omega$)

For this value of resistance, we have

$$\alpha = \frac{R}{2L} = 5000 \tag{93}$$

Because $\zeta = \alpha/\omega_0 = 0.5$, this is the underdamped case. Using Equation 76, we compute the natural frequency:

$$\omega_n = \sqrt{\omega_0^2 - \alpha^2} = 8660 \tag{94}$$

The homogeneous solution has the form of Equation 77. Adding the particular solution found earlier to the homogeneous solution, we obtain the general solution:

$$v_C(t) = 10 + K_1e^{-\alpha t}\cos(\omega_n t) + K_2e^{-\alpha t}\sin(\omega_n t) \tag{95}$$

As in the previous cases, the initial conditions are $v_C(0) = 0$ and $dv_C(0)/dt = 0$. Evaluating Equation 95 at $t = 0$, we obtain

$$10 + K_1 = 0 \tag{96}$$

Differentiating Equation 95 and evaluating at $t = 0$, we have

$$-\alpha K_1 + \omega_n K_2 = 0 \tag{97}$$

Solving Equations 96 and 97, we obtain $K_1 = -10$ and $K_2 = -5.774$. Thus, the complete solution is

$$v_C(t) = 10 - 10e^{-\alpha t}\cos(\omega_n t) - 5.774e^{-\alpha t}\sin(\omega_n t) \tag{98}$$

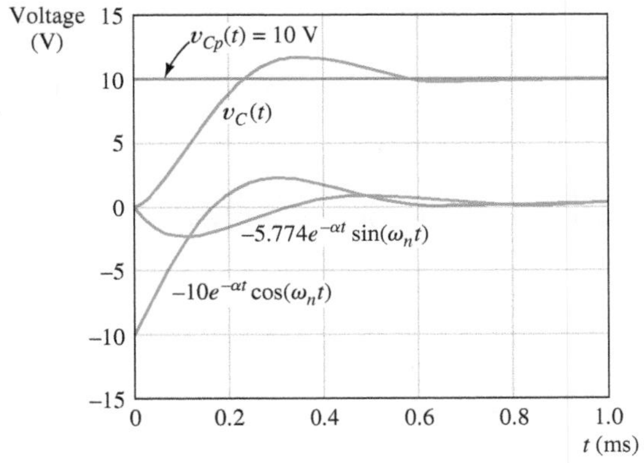

Figure 25 Solution for $R = 100\ \Omega$.

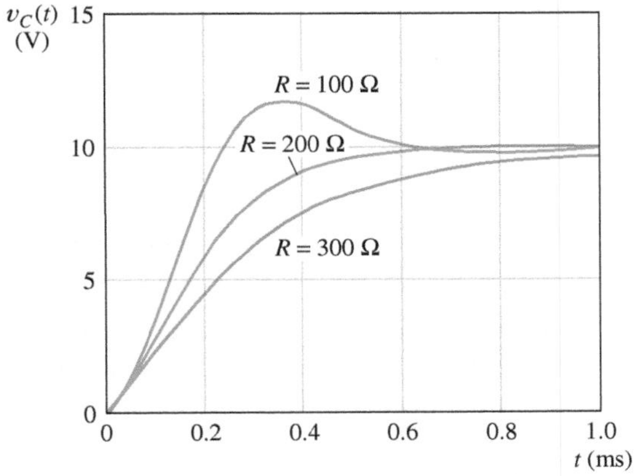

Figure 26 Solutions for all three resistances.

Plots of each of the terms of this equation and the complete solution are shown in Figure 25.

Figure 26 shows the complete response for all three values of resistance. ■

Normalized Step Response of Second-Order Systems

When we suddenly apply a constant source to a circuit, we say that the forcing function is a **step function**. A unit step function, denoted by $u(t)$, is shown in Figure 27. By definition, we have

$$\begin{aligned} u(t) &= 0 \quad & t < 0 \\ &= 1 \quad & t \geq 0 \end{aligned}$$

For example, if we apply a dc voltage of A volts to a circuit by closing a switch, the applied voltage is a step function, given by

$$v(t) = Au(t)$$

This is illustrated in Figure 28.

We often encounter situations, such as Example 5, in which step forcing functions are applied to second-order systems described by a differential equation

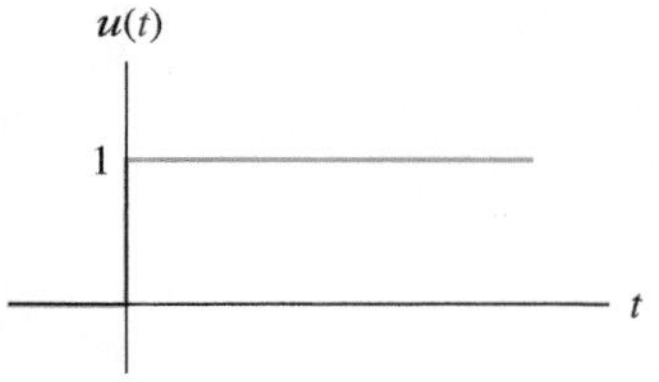

Figure 27 A unit step function $u(t)$. For $t < 0$, $u(t) = 0$. For $t \geq 0$, $u(t) = 1$.

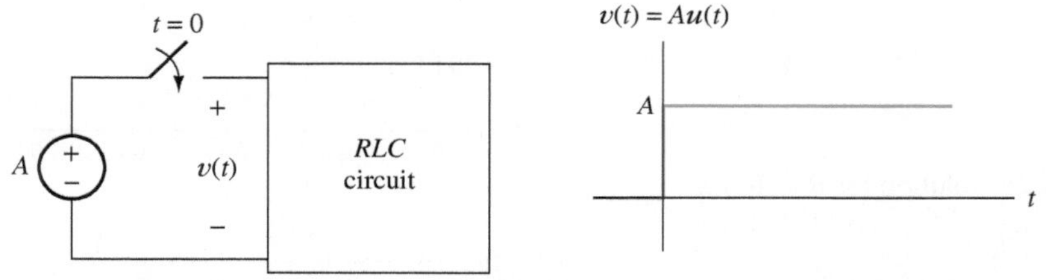

Figure 28 Applying a dc voltage by closing a switch results in a forcing function that is a step function.

of the form

$$\frac{d^2x(t)}{dt^2} + 2\alpha\frac{dx(t)}{dt} + \omega_0^2 x(t) = Au(t) \tag{99}$$

The differential equation is characterized by its undamped resonant frequency ω_0 and damping ratio $\zeta = \alpha/\omega_0$. [Of course, the solution for $x(t)$ also depends on the initial conditions.] Normalized solutions are shown in Figure 29 for the initial conditions $x(0) = 0$ and $x'(0) = 0$.

The system response for small values of the damping ratio ζ displays **overshoot** and **ringing** before settling to the steady-state value. On the other hand, if the damping ratio is large (compared to unity), the response takes a relatively long time to closely approach the final value.

Frequently, electrical control systems and mechanical systems are best designed with a damping ratio close to unity. For example, when the suspension system on your automobile becomes severely underdamped, it is time for new shock absorbers.

Sometimes, we want to design a second-order system that quickly settles to steady state. Then we try to design for a damping ratio close to unity. For example, the control system for a robot arm could be a second-order system. When a step signal calls for the arm to move, we probably want it to achieve the final position in the minimum time without excessive overshoot and ringing.

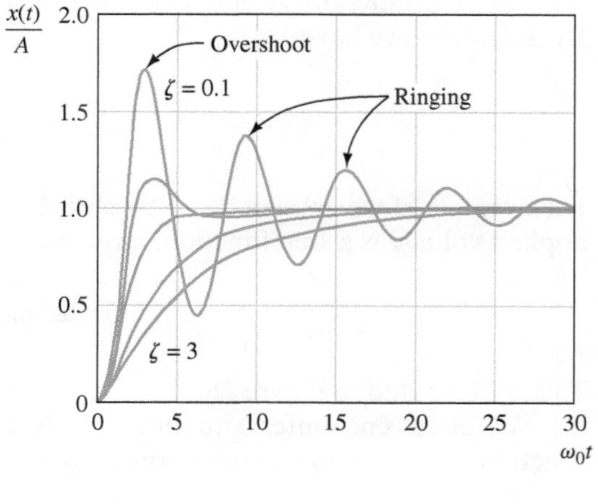

Figure 29 Normalized step responses for second-order systems described by Equation 99 with damping ratios of $\zeta = 0.1, 0.5, 1, 2,$ and 3. The initial conditions are assumed to be $x(0) = 0$ and $x'(0) = 0$.

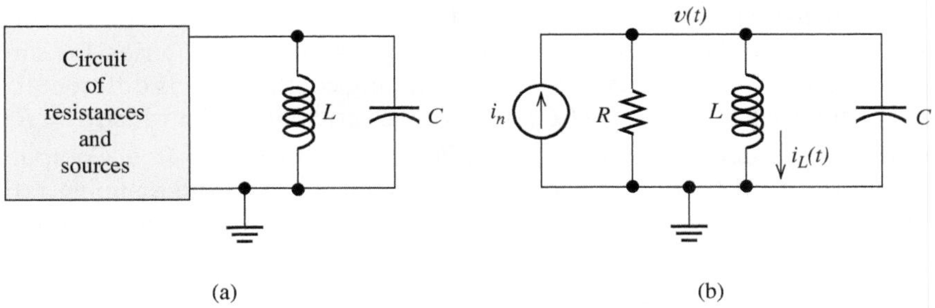

Figure 30 Any circuit consisting of sources, resistances, and a parallel LC combination can be reduced to the equivalent circuit shown in (b).

Circuits with Parallel *L* and *C*

The solution of circuits having an inductance and capacitance in parallel is very similar to the series case. Consider the circuit shown in Figure 30(a). The circuit inside the box is assumed to consist of sources and resistances. We can find a Norton equivalent circuit for any two-terminal circuit composed of resistances and sources. The equivalent circuit is shown in Figure 30(b).

We can analyze this circuit by writing a KCL equation at the top node of Figure 30(b) which results in

$$C\frac{dv(t)}{dt} + \frac{1}{R}v(t) + \frac{1}{L}\int_0^t v(t)\,dt + i_L(0) = i_n(t) \tag{100}$$

This can be converted into a pure differential equation by taking the derivative with respect to time:

$$C\frac{d^2v(t)}{dt^2} + \frac{1}{R}\frac{dv(t)}{dt} + \frac{1}{L}v(t) = \frac{di_n(t)}{dt} \tag{101}$$

Dividing through by the capacitance, we have

$$\frac{d^2v(t)}{dt^2} + \frac{1}{RC}\frac{dv(t)}{dt} + \frac{1}{LC}v(t) = \frac{1}{C}\frac{di_n(t)}{dt} \tag{102}$$

Now, if we define the damping coefficient

$$\alpha = \frac{1}{2RC} \tag{103}$$

the undamped resonant frequency

$$\omega_0 = \frac{1}{\sqrt{LC}} \tag{104}$$

and the forcing function

$$f(t) = \frac{1}{C}\frac{di_n(t)}{dt} \tag{105}$$

the differential equation can be written as

$$\frac{d^2v(t)}{dt^2} + 2\alpha\frac{dv(t)}{dt} + \omega_0^2 v(t) = f(t) \tag{106}$$

Notice that the equation for the damping coefficient of the parallel RLC circuit is different from that for the series circuit.

This equation has exactly the same form as Equation 64. Therefore, transient analysis of circuits with parallel LC elements is very similar to that of series LC circuits. However, notice that the equation for the damping coefficient α is different for the parallel circuit (in which $\alpha = 1/2RC$) than for the series circuit (in which $\alpha = R/2L$).

$v(0-)$ and $i_L(0-)$ are the voltage and current values immediately before the switch opens.

Exercise 9 Consider the circuit shown in Figure 31 with $R = 25\ \Omega$. **a.** Compute the undamped resonant frequency, the damping coefficient, and the damping ratio. **b.** The initial conditions are $v(0-) = 0$ and $i_L(0-) = 0$. Show that this requires that $v'(0+) = 10^6$ V/s. **c.** Find the particular solution for $v(t)$. **d.** Find the general solution for $v(t)$, including the numerical values of all parameters.

Answer **a.** $\omega_0 = 10^5, \alpha = 2 \times 10^5$, and $\zeta = 2$; **b.** KCL requires that $i_C(0) = 0.1$ A $= Cv'(0)$, thus $v'(0) = 10^6$; **c.** $v_p(t) = 0$; **d.** $v(t) = 2.89(e^{-0.268\times10^5 t} - e^{-3.73\times10^5 t})$. □

PRACTICAL APPLICATION 1

Electronics and the Art of Automotive Maintenance

Throughout much of the history of the automobile, ignition systems have been designed as a straightforward application of electrical transients. The basic ignition system used for many years is shown in Figure PA1. The coil is a pair of mutually coupled inductors known as the primary and the secondary. The points form a switch that opens and closes as the engine rotates, opening at the instant that an ignition spark is needed by one of the cylinders. While the points are closed, current builds up relatively slowly in the primary winding of the coil. Then, when the points open, the current is rapidly interrupted. The resulting high rate of change of current induces a large voltage across the secondary winding, which is connected to the appropriate spark plug by the distributor. The resistance is needed to limit the current in case the engine stops with the points closed.

The capacitor prevents the voltage across the points from rising too rapidly when they open. (Recall that the voltage across a capacitance cannot change instantaneously.) Otherwise, arcing would occur across the points, causing them to become burned and pitted. By slowing the rise of voltage, the capacitor gives the gap between the points time to become wide enough to withstand the voltage across them. (Even so, the peak voltage across the points is many times the battery voltage.)

The primary inductance, current-limiting resistance, and capacitance form an underdamped series RLC circuit. Thus, an oscillatory current flows through the primary when the points open, inducing the requisite voltage in the secondary.

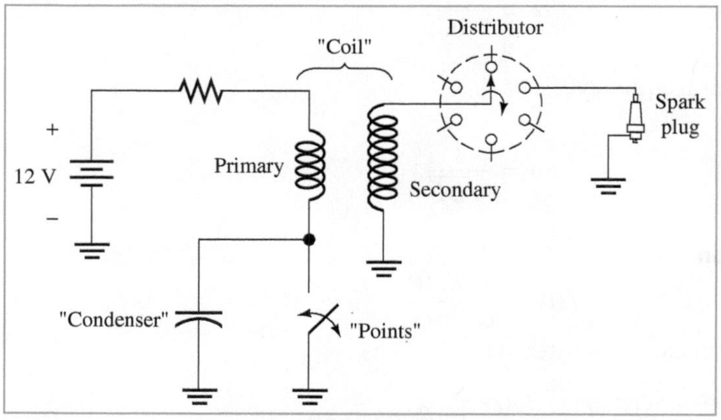

Figure PA1 Classic ignition for an internal-combustion engine.

In its early forms, the ignition system had mechanical or vacuum systems to make adjustments to the timing, depending on engine speed and throttle setting. In more recent years, the availability of complex electronics at reasonable costs plus the desire to adjust the ignition to obtain good performance and low pollution levels with varying air temperature, fuel quality, air pressure, engine temperature, and other factors have greatly affected the design of ignition systems. The basic principles remain the same as in the days of the classic automobile, but a complex network of electrical sensors, a digital computer, and an electronic switch have replaced the points and simple vacuum advance.

The complexity of modern engineering designs has become somewhat intimidating, even to practicing engineers. In the 1960s, as a new engineering graduate, one could study the design of an ignition system, a radio, or a home appliance, readily spotting and repairing malfunctions with the aid of a few tools and standard parts. Nowadays, if my car should fail to start due to ignition malfunction, at the end of a fishing trip into the backwoods of northern Michigan, I might very well have to walk back to civilization. Nevertheless, the improvements in performance provided by modern electronics make up for its difficulty of repair.

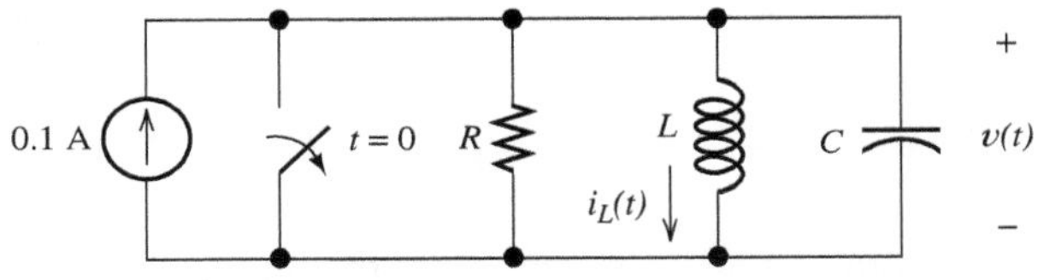

$L = 1$ mH $C = 0.1$ μF

Figure 31 Circuit for Exercises 9, 10, and 11.

Exercise 10 Repeat Exercise 9 for $R = 50\ \Omega$.
Answer **a.** $\omega_0 = 10^5$, $\alpha = 10^5$, and $\zeta = 1$; **b.** KCL requires that $i_C(0) = 0.1\text{ A} = Cv'(0)$, thus $v'(0) = 10^6$; **c.** $v_p(t) = 0$; **d.** $v(t) = 10^6 te^{-10^5 t}$. □

Exercise 11 Repeat Exercise 9 for $R = 250\ \Omega$.
Answer **a.** $\omega_0 = 10^5$, $\alpha = 0.2 \times 10^5$, and $\zeta = 0.2$; **b.** KCL requires that $i_C(0) = 0.1\text{ A} = Cv'(0)$, thus $v'(0) = 10^6$; **c.** $v_p(t) = 0$; **d.** $v(t) = 10.21e^{-2\times 10^4 t}\sin(97.98 \times 10^3 t)$. □

6 TRANSIENT ANALYSIS USING THE MATLAB SYMBOLIC TOOLBOX

The MATLAB Symbolic Toolbox greatly facilitates the solution of transients in electrical circuits. It makes the solution of systems of differential equations almost as easy as arithmetic using a calculator. A step-by-step process for solving a circuit in this manner is

1. Write the differential-integral equations for the mesh currents, node voltages, or other circuit variables of interest.
2. If necessary, differentiate the equations to eliminate integrals.
3. Analyze the circuit at $t = 0+$ (i.e., immediately after switches operate) to determine initial conditions for the circuit variables and their derivatives. For a first-order equation, we need the initial value of the circuit variable. For a second-order equation we need the initial values of the circuit variable and its first derivative.
4. Enter the equations and initial values into the `dsolve` command in MATLAB.

We illustrate with a few examples.

Example 6 Computer-Aided Solution of a First-Order Circuit

Solve for $v_L(t)$ in the circuit of Figure 32(a).

Solution First, we write a KCL equation at the node joining the resistance and inductance.

$$\frac{v_L(t) - 20\cos(100t)}{R} + \frac{1}{L}\int_0^t v_L(t)dt + i_L(0) = 0$$

Taking the derivative of the equation to eliminate the integral, multiplying each term by R, and substituting values, we eventually obtain

$$\frac{dv_L(t)}{dt} + 100v_L(t) = -2000\sin(100t)$$

Next, we need to determine the initial value of v_L. Because the switch is open prior to $t = 0$, the initial current in the inductance is zero prior to $t = 0$. Furthermore, the current cannot change instantaneously in this circuit. Thus, we have $i_L(0+) = 0$. Immediately after the switch closes, the voltage source has a value of 20 V, and the current flowing in the circuit is zero, resulting in zero volts across the resistor. Then KVL yields $v_L(0+) = 20\,\text{V}$. This is illustrated in Figure 32(b).

Now, we can write the MATLAB commands. As usual, we show the commands in **boldface**, comments in regular font, and MATLAB responses in color.

```
>> clear all
>> syms VL t
>> % Enter the equation and initial value in the dsolve command.
>> % DVL represents the derivative of VL with respect to time.
>> VL = dsolve('DVL + 100*VL = -2000*sin(100*t)', 'VL(0) = 20');
>> % Print answer with 4 decimal place accuracy for the constants:
>> vpa(VL,4)
     ans =
     10.0*cos(100.0*t)-10.0*sin(100.0*t)+10.0*exp(-100.0*t)
```

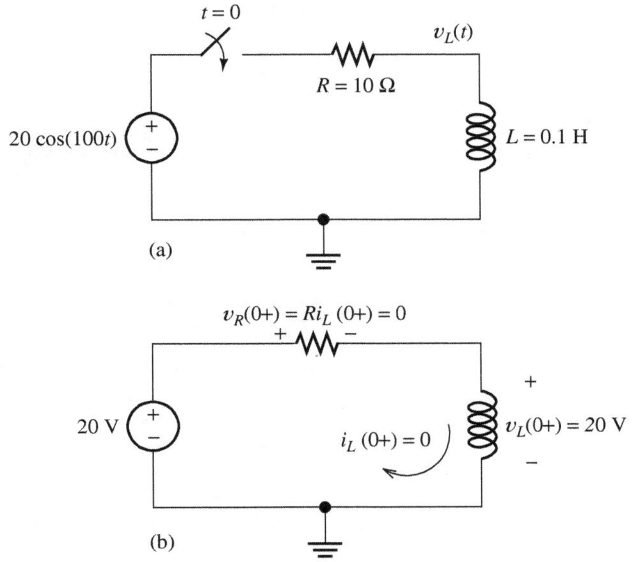

Figure 32 (a) Circuit of Example 6. (b) Circuit conditions at $t = 0+$.

In standard mathematical notation, the result becomes

$$v_L(t) = 10\cos(100t) - 10\sin(100t) + 10\exp(-100t)$$

An m-file named Example_6 containing the commands for this example can be found in the MATLAB folder. (See Appendix "On-Line Student Resources" for information about access to this folder.)

Example 7 Computer-Aided Solution of a Second-Order Circuit

The switch in the circuit of Figure 33(a) is closed for a long time prior to $t = 0$. Assume that $i_L(0+) = 0$. Use MATLAB to solve for $i_L(t)$ and plot the result for $0 \le t \le 2$ ms. (*Note:* The code for this example takes several minutes to run on the author's laptop using MATLAB version R2011b. It may not run at all with other versions.)

Solution Because this circuit contains two nodes and three meshes, node-voltage analysis is simpler than mesh analysis. We will solve for $v(t)$ and then take $1/L$ times the integral of the voltage to obtain the current through the inductance.

We start the node-voltage analysis by writing the KCL equation at the top node of the circuit (with the switch open).

$$C\frac{dv(t)}{dt} + \frac{v(t)}{R} + \frac{1}{L}\int_0^t v(t)dt + i_L(0+) = 0.2\exp(-1000t)$$

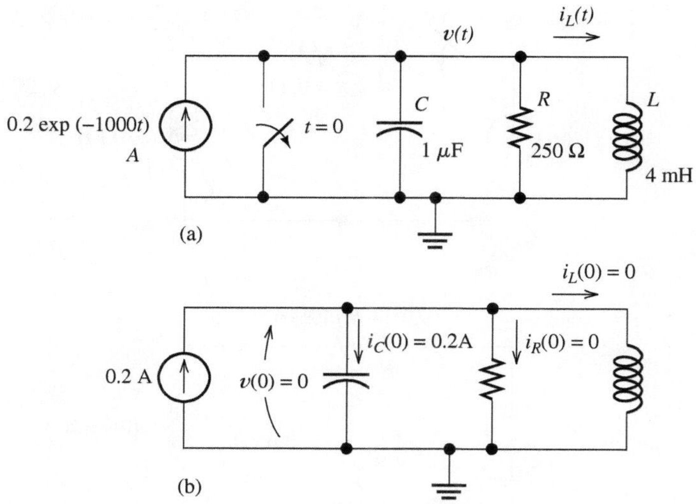

Figure 33 (a) Circuit of Example 7. (b) Circuit conditions at $t = 0+$.

Taking the derivative of the equation to eliminate the integral and substituting values, we eventually obtain

$$10^{-6}\frac{d^2v(t)}{dt^2} + 4 \times 10^{-3}\frac{dv(t)}{dt} + 250v(t) = -200\exp(-1000t)$$

Because this is a second-order equation, we need the initial value for both $v(t)$ and its first derivative. The circuit conditions at $t = 0+$ are shown in Figure 33(b). The problem states that the initial current in the inductance is zero. The initial voltage $v(0+)$ is zero, because, with the switch closed, the capacitor is shorted. When the switch opens, the voltage remains zero, because an infinite current would be required to change the capacitor voltage instantaneously. Furthermore, the current flowing through the resistor is zero because the voltage across it is zero. Thus, the 0.2 A from the source must flow through the capacitor, and we have

$$C\frac{dv(0+)}{dt} = 0.2$$

We have established that $v(0+) = 0$ and $v'(0+) = dv(0+)/dt = 0.2 \times 10^6$ V/s.

After the voltage is found, the current is given by

$$i_L(t) = \frac{1}{L}\int_0^t v(t)dt = 250\int_0^t v(t)dt$$

We use the following MATLAB commands to obtain the solution.

```
>> clear all
>> syms ILV t
>> % Enter the equation and initial values in the dsolve command.
>> % D2V represents the second derivative ofV.
>> V = dsolve('(1e-6)*D2V + (4e-3)*DV + 250*V = -200*exp(-1000*t)',...
           'DV(0)=0.2e6', 'V(0)=0');
>> % Calculate the inductor current by integratingV with respect to t
>> % from 0 to t and multiplying by 1/L:
>> IL = (250)*int(V,t,0,t);
```

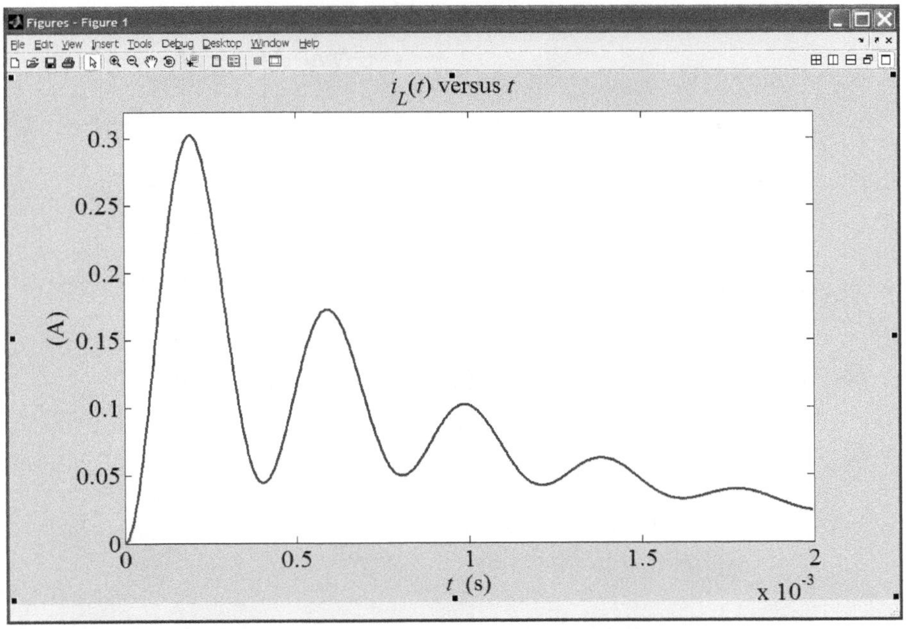

Figure 34 Plot of $i_L(t)$ versus t.

```
>> % Display the expression for current to 4 decimal place accuracy:
>> vpa(IL,4)
      ans =
      -(0.0008229*(246.0*cos(15688.0*t) - 246.0*exp(1000.0*t) +
         15.68*sin(15688.0*t)))/exp(2000.0*t)
>> ezplot(IL,[0 2e-3])
```

In standard mathematical notation, the result is

$$\begin{aligned} i_L(t) &= -0.2024\exp(-2000t)\cos(15680t) - \\ &\quad 0.01290\exp(-2000t)\sin(15680t) + 0.2024\exp(-1000t) \end{aligned}$$

The plot (after some editing to dress it up) is shown in Figure 34. An m-file named Example_7 containing the commands for this example can be found in the MATLAB folder. (See Appendix "On-Line Student Resources" for information about accessing this folder.) ■

Solving Systems of Linear Differential Equations

So far in this chapter, each of our examples has involved a single differential equation. Circuits that require two or more circuit variables (such as node voltages or mesh currents) result in systems of differential equations. While these systems can be rather formidable to solve by traditional methods, the MATLAB Symbolic Toolbox can solve them with relative ease.

Example 8 Computer-Aided Solution of a System of Differential Equations

Use MATLAB to solve for the node voltages in the circuit of Figure 35. The circuit has been connected for a long time prior to $t = 0$ with the switch open, so the initial values of the node voltages are zero.

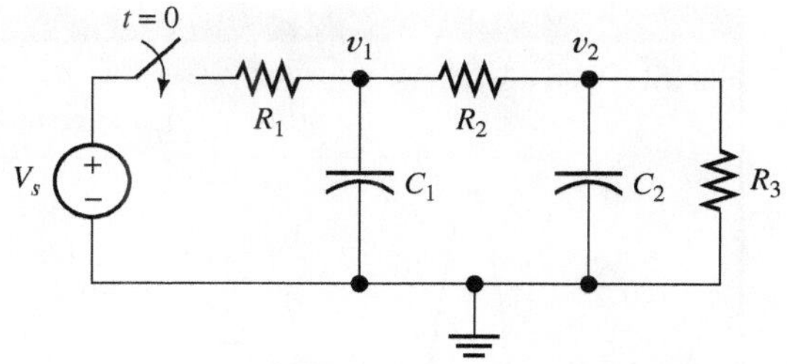

$V_s = 10$ V $R_1 = R_2 = R_3 = 1$ MΩ $C_1 = C_2 = 1$ μF

Figure 35 Circuit of Example 8.

Solution First, we write the KCL equations at nodes 1 and 2.

$$C_1 \frac{dv_1(t)}{dt} + \frac{v_1(t) - V_s}{R_1} + \frac{v_1(t) - v_2(t)}{R_2} = 0$$

$$C_2 \frac{dv_2(t)}{dt} + \frac{v_2(t) - v_1(t)}{R_2} + \frac{v_2(t)}{R_3} = 0$$

Now substituting values, multiplying each term by 10^6, and rearranging terms, we have

$$\frac{dv_1(t)}{dt} + 2v_1(t) - v_2(t) = 10$$

$$\frac{dv_2(t)}{dt} + 2v_2(t) - v_1(t) = 0$$

The MATLAB commands and results are:

```
>> clear all
>> syms v1 v2 t
>> [v1 v2] = dsolve('Dv1 + 2*v1 - v2 = 10','Dv2 + 2*v2 -v1 = 0',...
           'v1(0) = 0','v2(0)= 0');
>> v1
       v1 =
       ((5*exp(3*t))/3 + exp(2*t)*(5*exp(t) - 5) - 5/3)/exp(3*t)
>> v2
       v2 =
       (exp(2*t)*(5*exp(t) - 5) - (5*exp(3*t))/3 + 5/3)/exp(3*t)
```

Thus, the node voltages are given by

$$v_1(t) = 20/3 - 5\exp(-t) - (5/3)\exp(-3t)$$

$$v_2(t) = 10/3 - 5\exp(-t) + (5/3)\exp(-3t)$$

It is always a good idea to perform a few checks on our answers. First, we can verify that the MATLAB results are both zero at $t = 0$ as required by the initial conditions. Furthermore, at $t = \infty$, the capacitors act as open circuits, and the voltage division principle yields $v_1(\infty) = 20/3$V and $v_2(\infty) = 10/3$. The expressions delivered by MATLAB also yield these values. ■

Exercise 12 Use the MATLAB Symbolic Toolbox to solve Example 4, obtaining the result given in Equation 56 and a plot similar to Figure 17.

Answer A sequence of commands that produces the solution and the plot is:

```
clear all
syms ix t R C vCinitial w
ix = dsolve('(R*C)*Dix + ix = (w*C)*2*cos(w*t)', 'ix(0)=-vCinitial/R');
ians =subs(ix,[R C vCinitial w],[5000 1e-6 1 200]);
vpa(ians, 4)
ezplot(ians,[0 80e-3])
```

An m-file named Exercise_12 containing these commands can be found in the MATLAB folder. (See Appendix "On-Line Student Resources" for information about accessing this folder.) □

Exercise 13 Use the MATLAB Symbolic Toolbox to solve Example 5 obtaining the results given in the example for $v_C(t)$ and a plot similar to Figure 26.

Answer A list of commands that produces the solution and the plot is:

```
clear all
syms vc t
% Case I, R = 300:
vc = dsolve('(1e-8)*D2vc + (1e-6)*300*Dvc+ vc =10', 'vc(0) = 0','Dvc(0)=0');
vpa(vc,4)
ezplot(vc, [0 1e-3])
hold on % Turn hold on so all plots are on the same axes
% Case II, R = 200:
vc = dsolve('(1e-8)*D2vc + (1e-6)*200*Dvc+ vc =10', 'vc(0) = 0','Dvc(0)=0');
vpa(vc,4)
ezplot(vc, [0 1e-3])
% Case III, R = 100:
vc = dsolve('(1e-8)*D2vc + (1e-6)*100*Dvc+ vc =10', 'vc(0) = 0','Dvc(0)=0');
vpa(vc,4)
ezplot(vc, [0 1e-3])
```

An m-file named Exercise_13 containing these commands resides in the MATLAB folder. (See Appendix "On-Line Student Resources" for information about accessing this folder.) □

Summary

1. The transient part of the response for a circuit containing sources, resistances, and a single energy-storage element (L or C) is of the form $Ke^{-t/\tau}$. The time constant is given by $\tau = RC$ or by $\tau = L/R$, where R is the Thévenin resistance seen looking back into the circuit from the terminals of the energy-storage element.
2. In dc steady-state conditions, inductors behave as short circuits and capacitors behave as open circuits. We can find the steady-state (forced) response for dc sources by analyzing the dc equivalent circuit.
3. To find the transient currents and voltages, we must solve linear differential equations with constant coefficients. The solutions are the sum of two parts. The particular solution, also called the forced response, depends on the sources, as well as the other circuit elements. The homogeneous solution, also called the natural response, depends on the passive elements (R, L, and C), but not on the sources. In circuits that contain resistances, the natural response eventually decays to zero.
4. The natural response of a second-order circuit containing a series or parallel combination of inductance and capacitance depends on the damping ratio and undamped resonant frequency.

   If the damping ratio is greater than unity, the circuit is overdamped, and the natural response is of the form

$$x_c(t) = K_1 e^{s_1 t} + K_2 e^{s_2 t}$$

If the damping ratio equals unity, the circuit is critically damped, and the natural response is of the form

$$x_c(t) = K_1 e^{s_1 t} + K_2 t e^{s_1 t}$$

If the damping ratio is less than unity, the circuit is underdamped, and the natural response is of the form

$$x_c(t) = K_1 e^{-\alpha t} \cos(\omega_n t) + K_2 e^{-\alpha t} \sin(\omega_n t)$$

The normalized step response for second-order systems is shown in Figure 29 for several values of the damping ratio.

5. The MATLAB Symbolic Toolbox is a powerful tool for solving the equations for transient circuits. A step-by-step procedure is given.

Note: **You can check the answers to many of the problems in this chapter by using a computer-aided circuit-analysis program such as Multisim from National Instruments or OrCAD Capture from Cadence Inc.**

Problems

Section 1: First-Order *RC* Circuits

P1. A capacitance C discharges through a resistance R. Define and give an expression for the time constant. To attain a long time constant, do we need large or small values for R? For C?

P2. An initially charged capacitance discharges through a resistance. At one time constant, what percentage of the initial voltage remains? What percentage of the initial stored energy remains?

P3. The initial voltage across the capacitor shown in Figure P3 is $v_C(0+) = 0$. Find an expression for the voltage across the capacitor as a function of time, and sketch to scale versus time.

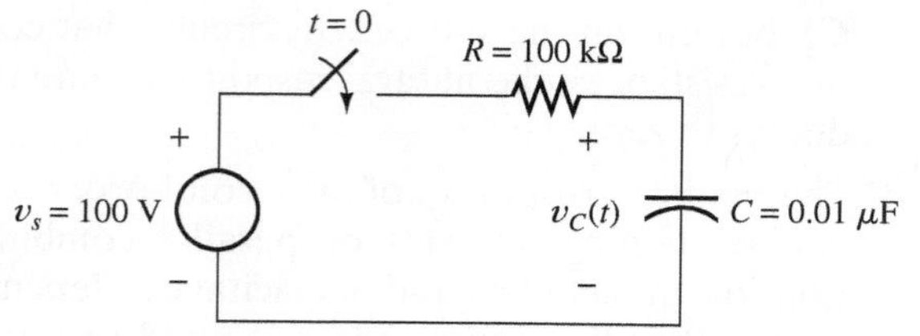

Figure P3

***P4.** Repeat Problem P3 for an initial voltage $v_C(0+) = -50$ V.

***P5.** The dielectric materials used in real capacitors are not perfect insulators. A resistance called a leakage resistance in parallel with the capacitance can model this imperfection. A 100-μF capacitor is initially charged to 100 V. We want 90 percent of the initial energy to remain after one minute. What is the limit on the leakage resistance for this capacitor?

P6. At $t = 0$, a 0.2-μF capacitance is charged to an unknown voltage V_i. The capacitance is in parallel with a 3-kΩ resistance. At $t = 1$ ms, the voltage across the capacitance is 10 V. Determine the value of V_i.

P7. The capacitor shown in Figure P7 is charged to a voltage of 50 V prior to $t = 0$. **a.** Find expressions for the voltage across the capacitor $v_C(t)$ and the voltage across the resistor $v_R(t)$. **b.** Find an expression for the power delivered to the resistor. **c.** Integrate the power from $t = 0$ to $t = \infty$ to find the energy delivered. **d.** Show that the energy delivered to the resistor is equal to the energy stored in the capacitor prior to $t = 0$.

* Denotes that answers are contained in the Student Solutions files. See Appendix "On-Line Student Resources" for more information about accessing the Student Solutions.

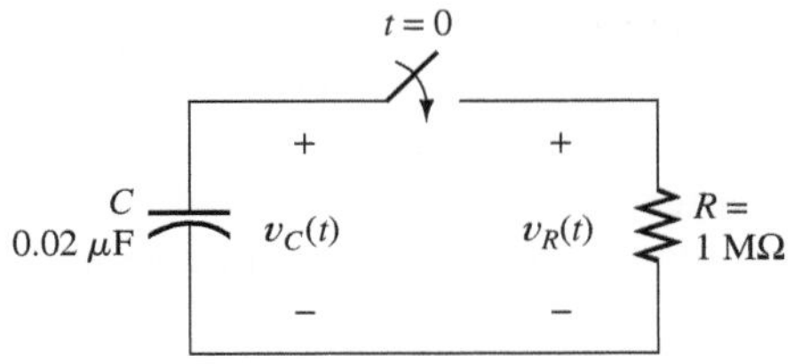

Figure P7

P8. We use the time constant to characterize transients in electric circuits. In physics, the half-life is often used to characterize the exponential decay of physical quantities such as radioactive substances. The half-life is the time required for the quantity to decay to half of its initial value. The time constant for the voltage on a capacitance discharging through a resistance is $\tau = RC$. Find an expression for the half-life of the voltage in terms of R and C.

P9. Find an expression for $v(t)$ for the circuit shown in Figure P9 and sketch $v(t)$ to scale versus time.

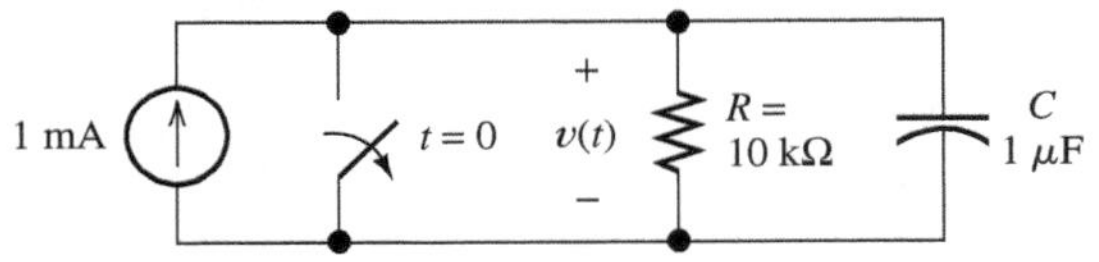

Figure P9

***P10.** A 100-μF capacitance is initially charged to 1000 V. At $t = 0$, it is connected to a 1-kΩ resistance. At what time t_2 has 50 percent of the initial energy stored in the capacitance been dissipated in the resistance?

***P11.** At $t = 0$, a charged 10-μF capacitance is connected to a voltmeter, as shown in Figure P11. The meter can be modeled as a resistance. At $t = 0$, the meter reads 50 V. At $t = 30$ s, the reading is 25 V. Find the resistance of the voltmeter.

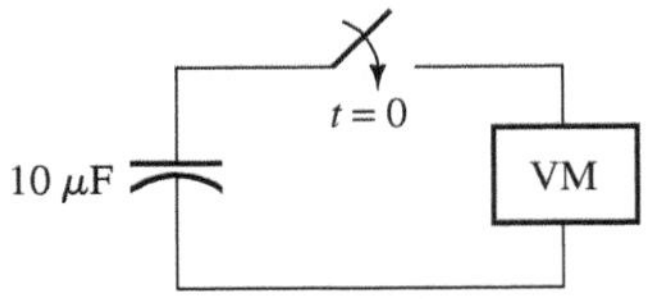

Figure P11

P12. The purchasing power P of a certain unit of currency declines by 3 percent per year. Determine the time constant associated with the purchasing power of this currency.

P13. At $t = 0$, an initially uncharged 10-μF capacitance is connected to a charging circuit consisting of a 1000-V voltage source in series with a 1-MΩ resistance. At $t = 25$ s, the capacitor is disconnected from the charging circuit and connected in parallel with a 2-MΩ resistor. Determine the voltage across the capacitor at $t = 25$ s and at $t = 50$ s. (*Hint*: You may find it convenient to redefine the time variable to be $t' = t - 25$ for the discharge interval so that the discharge starts at $t' = 0$.)

P14. A person shuffling across a dry carpet can be approximately modeled as a charged 100-pF capacitance with one end grounded. If the person touches a grounded metallic object such as a water faucet, the capacitance is discharged and the person experiences a brief shock. Typically, the capacitance may be charged to 20,000 V and the resistance (mainly of one's finger) is 100 Ω. Determine the peak current during discharge and the time constant of the current.

P15. A capacitance C is charged to an initial voltage V_i. At $t = 0$, a resistance R is connected across the capacitance. Write an expression for the current. Then, integrate the current from $t = 0$ to $t = \infty$, and show that the result is equal to the initial charge stored on the capacitance.

***P16.** At time t_1, a capacitance C is charged to a voltage of V_1. Then, the capacitance discharges through a resistance R. Write an expression for the voltage across the capacitance as a function of time for $t > t_1$ in terms of R, C, V_1, and t_1.

P17. In the circuit of Figure P17, the switch instantaneously moves back and forth between contacts A and B, spending 1 s in each position. Thus, the capacitor repeatedly charges for 1 s and then discharges for 1 s. Assume that $v_C(0) = 0$ and that the switch moves to position A at $t = 0$. Determine $v_C(1)$, $v_C(2)$, $v_C(3)$, and $v_C(4)$.

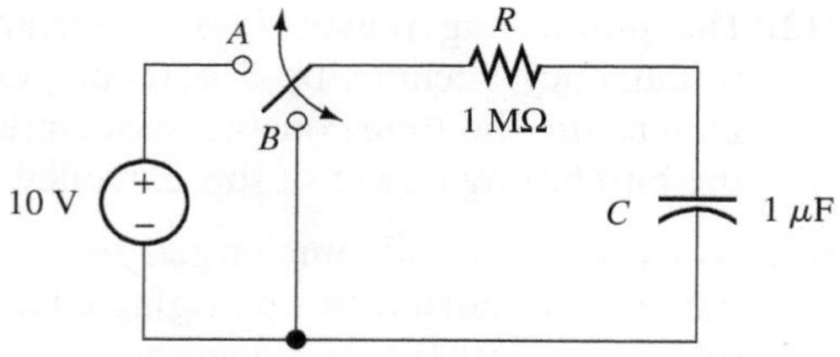

Figure P17

P18. Consider the circuit shown in Figure P18. Prior to $t = 0$, $v_1 = 100$ V and $v_2 = 0$. **a.** Immediately after the switch is closed, what is the value of the current [i.e., what is the value of $i(0+)$]? **b.** Write the KVL equation for the circuit in terms of the current and initial voltages. Take the derivative to obtain a differential equation. **c.** What is the value of the time constant in this circuit? **d.** Find an expression for the current as a function of time. **e.** Find the value that v_2 approaches as t becomes very large.

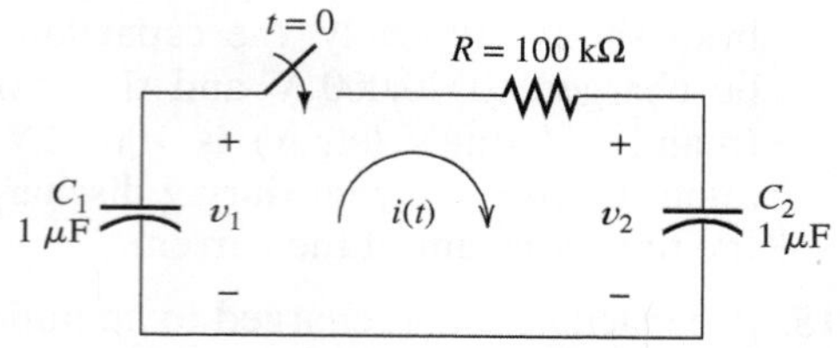

Figure P18

Section 2: DC Steady State

P19. List the steps for a dc steady-state analysis of *RLC* circuits.

P20. Explain why we replace capacitances with open circuits and inductances with short circuits in a dc steady-state analysis.

***P21.** Solve for the steady-state values of i_1, i_2, and i_3 for the circuit shown in Figure P21.

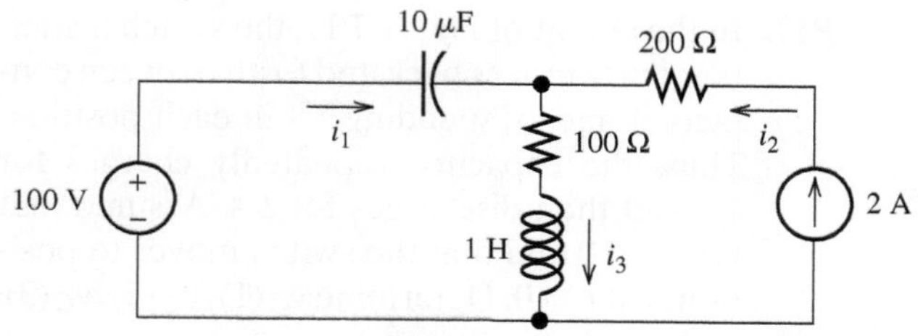

Figure P21

***P22.** Consider the circuit shown in Figure P22. What is the steady-state value of v_C after the switch opens? Determine how long it takes after the switch opens before v_C is within 1 percent of its steady-state value.

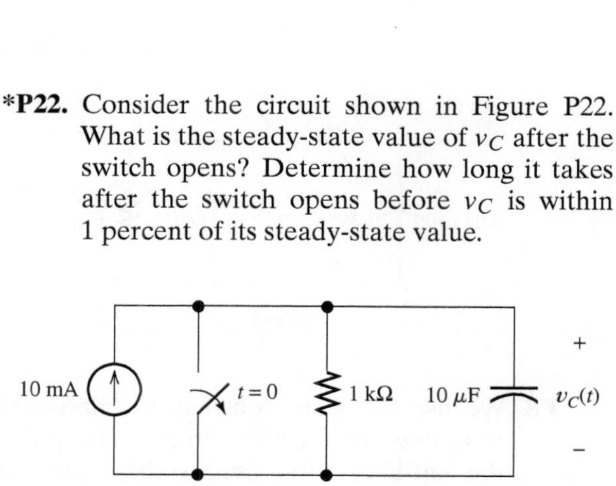

Figure P22

P23. Solve for the steady-state values of i_1, i_2, i_3, i_4, and v_C for the circuit shown in Figure P23, after the switch has been closed for a long time.

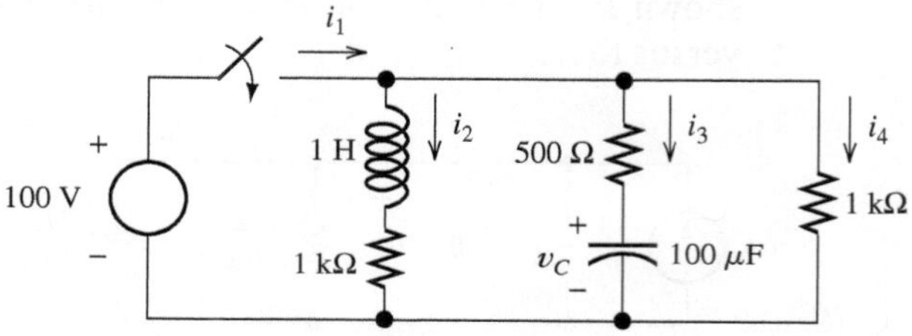

Figure P23

P24. The circuit shown in Figure P24 is operating in steady state. Determine the values of i_L, v_x, and v_C.

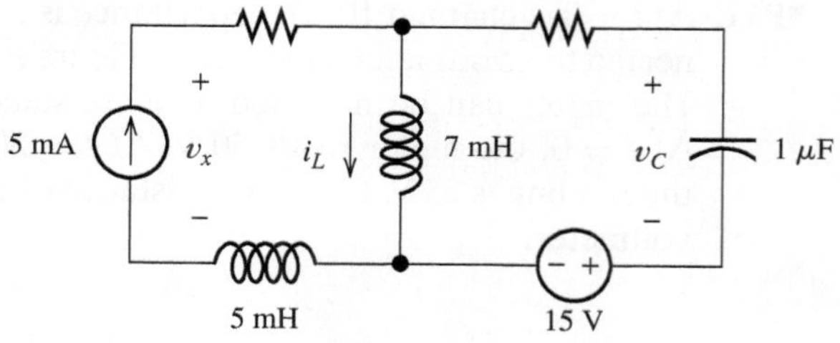

Figure P24

P25. The circuit shown in Figure P25 has been set up for a long time prior to $t = 0$ with the switch closed. Find the value of v_C prior to

$t = 0$. Find the steady-state value of v_C after the switch has been open for a long time.

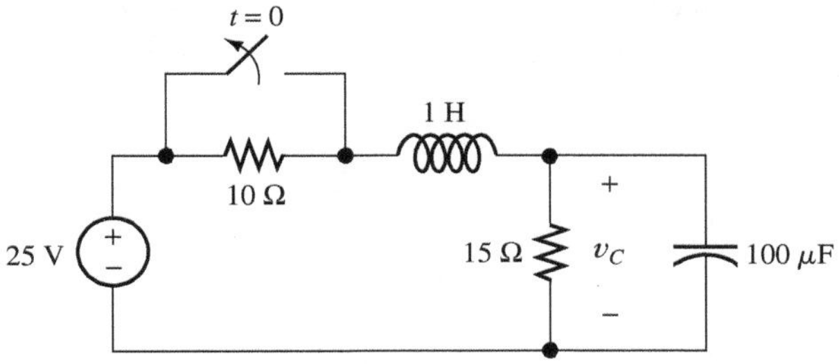

Figure P25

P26. Consider the circuit of Figure P26 in which the switch has been closed for a long time prior to $t = 0$. Determine the values of $v_C(t)$ just before $t = 0$ and a long time after $t = 0$. Also, determine the time constant after the switch opens and expressions for $v_C(t)$. Sketch $v_C(t)$ to scale versus time for $-0.2 \le t \le 1.0$ s.

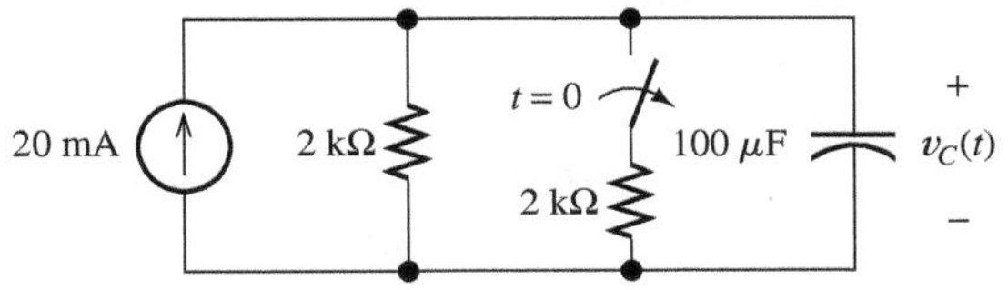

Figure P26

P27. Consider the circuit of Figure P27 in which the switch has been open for a long time prior to $t = 0$. Determine the values of $v_C(t)$ before $t = 0$ and a long time after $t = 0$. Also, determine the time constant after the switch closes and expressions for $v_C(t)$. Sketch $v_C(t)$ to scale versus time for $-2 \le t \le 5$ s.

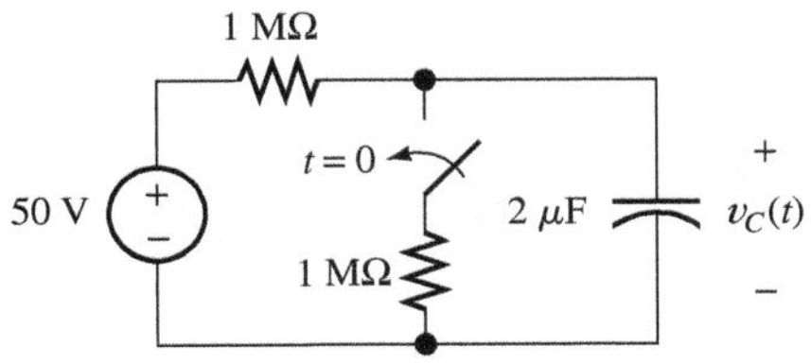

Figure P27

P28. The circuit of Figure P28 has been connected for a very long time. Determine the values of v_C and i_R.

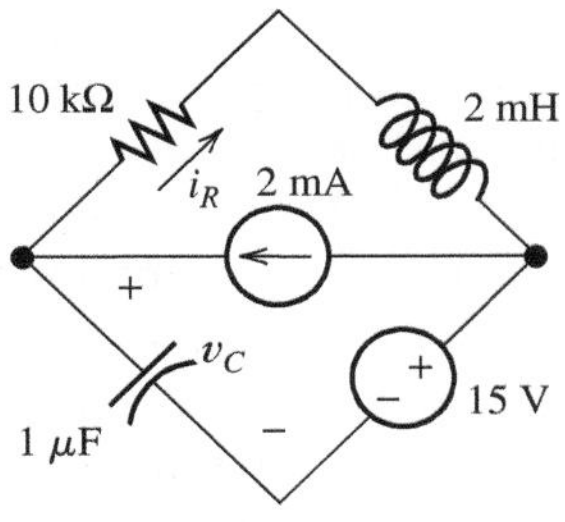

Figure P28

***P29.** In the circuit of Figure P29, the switch is in position A for a long time prior to $t = 0$. Find expressions for $v_R(t)$ and sketch it to scale for $-2 \le t \le 10$ s.

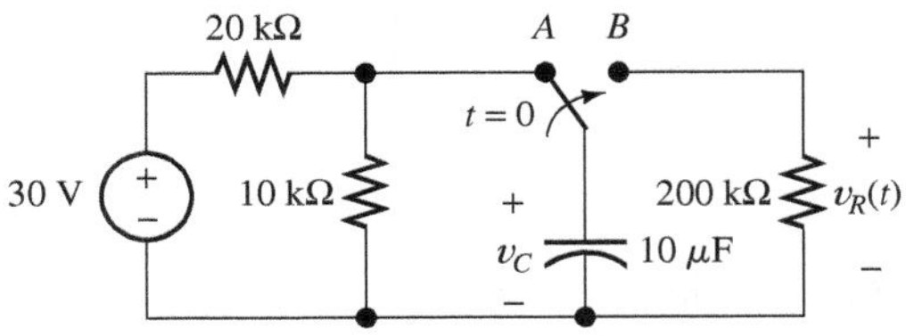

Figure P29

P30. For the circuit shown in Figure P30, the switch is closed for a long time prior to $t = 0$. Find expressions for $v_C(t)$ and sketch it to scale for $-60 \le t \le 300$ ms.

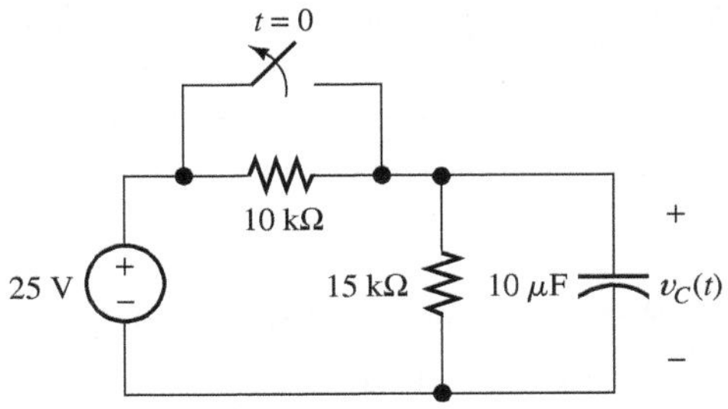

Figure P30

Section 3: *RL* **Circuits**

P31. Give the expression for the time constant of a circuit consisting of an inductance with an initial current in series with a resistance R. To attain a long time constant, do we need large or small values for R? For L?

P32. A circuit consists of switches that open or close at $t = 0$, resistances, dc sources, and a single-energy storage element—either an inductance or a capacitance. We wish to solve for a current or a voltage $x(t)$ as a function of time for $t \geq 0$. Write the general form for the solution. How is each unknown in the solution determined?

***P33.** The circuit shown in Figure P33 is operating in steady state with the switch closed prior to $t = 0$. Find $i(t)$ for $t < 0$ and for $t \geq 0$.

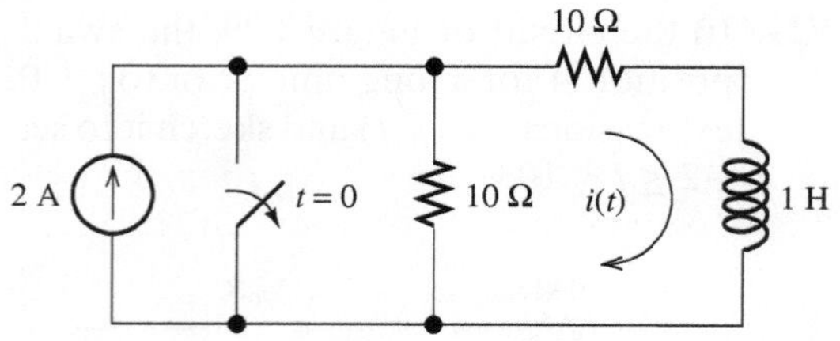

Figure P33

P34. Consider the circuit shown in Figure P34. The initial current in the inductor is $i_L(0-) = 0$. Find expressions for $i_L(t)$ and $v(t)$ for $t \geq 0$ and sketch to scale versus time.

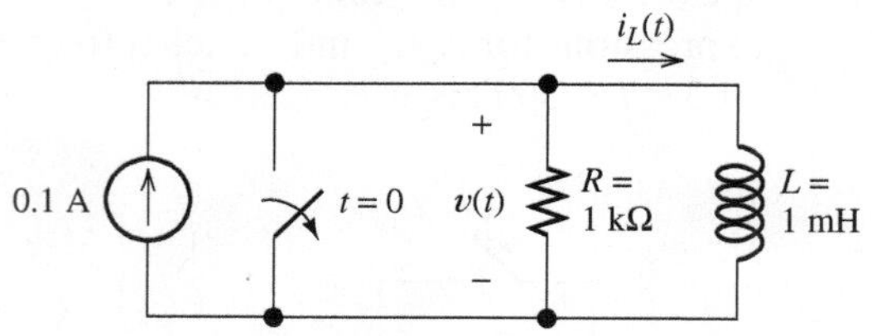

Figure P34

***P35.** Repeat Problem P34 with $i_L(0-) = -0.2$ A.

P36. For the circuit shown in Figure P36, find an expression for the current $i_L(t)$ and sketch it to scale versus time. Also, find an expression for $v_L(t)$ and sketch it to scale versus time.

P37. The circuit shown in Figure P37 is operating in steady state with the switch open prior to $t = 0$. Find expressions for $i(t)$ for $t < 0$ and for $t \geq 0$. Sketch $i(t)$ to scale versus time.

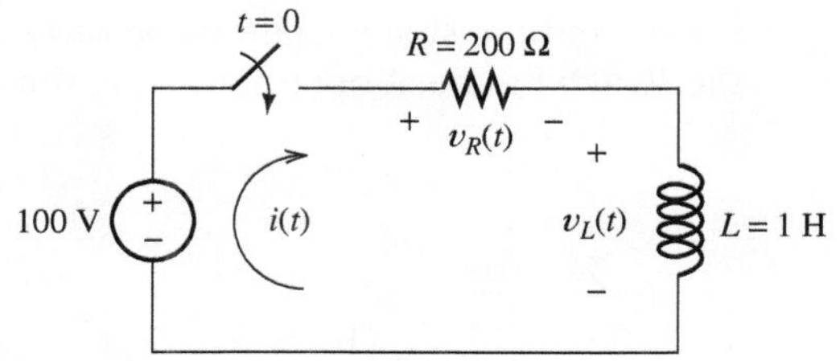

Figure P36

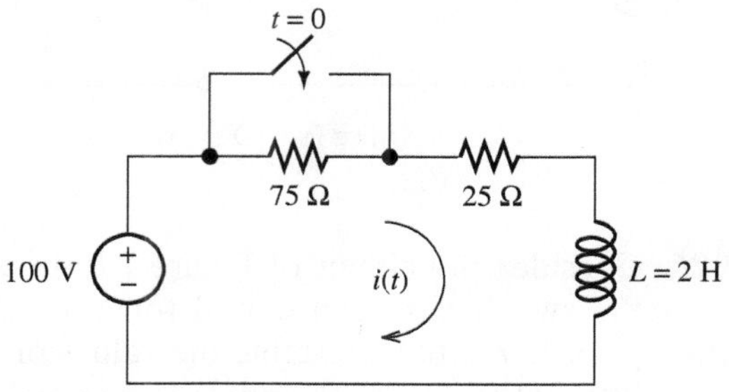

Figure P37

P38. Refer to the circuit of Figure P38. The current through the inductor is zero before $t = 0$. Determine expressions for and sketch $i(t)$ to scale versus time for $-0.2 \leq t \leq 1.0$ s.

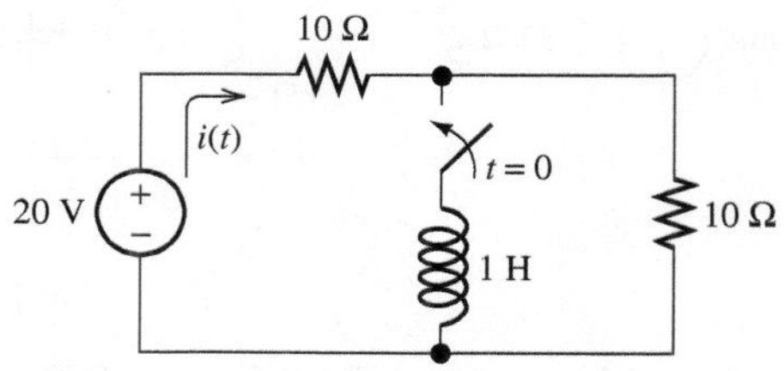

Figure P38

P39. The switch shown in Figure P39 has been closed for a long time prior to $t = 0$, then it opens at $t = 0$ and closes again at $t = 1$ s. Find $i_L(t)$ for all t.

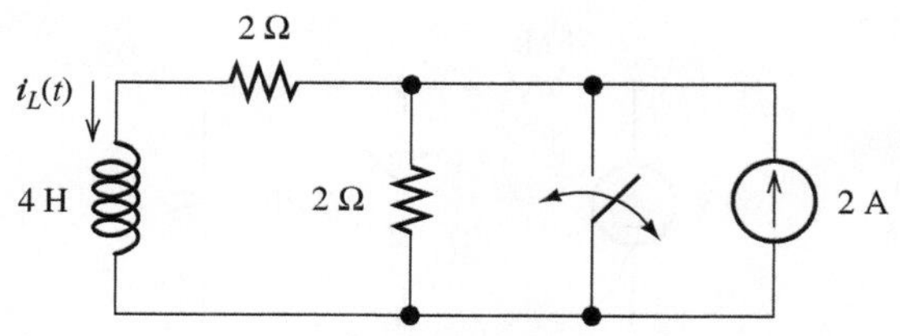

Figure P39

P40. We know that the circuit shown in Figure P40 has an initial current $i(0) = I_i$. **a.** Write an expression for $i(t)$ for $t \geq 0$. **b.** Find an expression for the power delivered to the resistance as a function of time. **c.** Integrate the power delivered to the resistance from $t = 0$ to $t = \infty$, and show that the result is equal to the initial energy stored in the inductance.

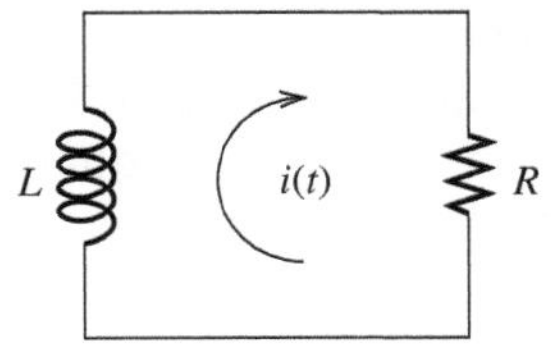

Figure P40

P41. Determine expressions for and sketch $v_R(t)$ to scale versus time for the circuit of Figure P41. The circuit is operating in steady state with the switch closed prior to $t = 0$. Consider the time interval $-0.2 \leq t \leq 1$ ms.

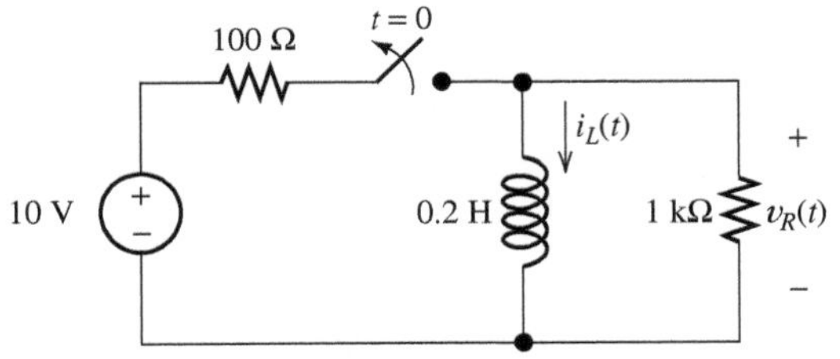

Figure P41

P42. Consider the circuit shown in Figure P42. A voltmeter VM is connected across the inductance. The switch has been closed for a long time. When the switch is opened, an arc appears across the switch contacts. Explain why. Assuming an ideal switch and inductor, what voltage appears across the inductor when the switch is opened? What could happen to the voltmeter when the switch opens?

***P43.** Real inductors have series resistance associated with the wire used to wind the coil. Suppose that we want to store energy in a 10-H inductor. Determine the limit on the series resistance so the energy remaining after one hour is at least 75 percent of the initial energy.

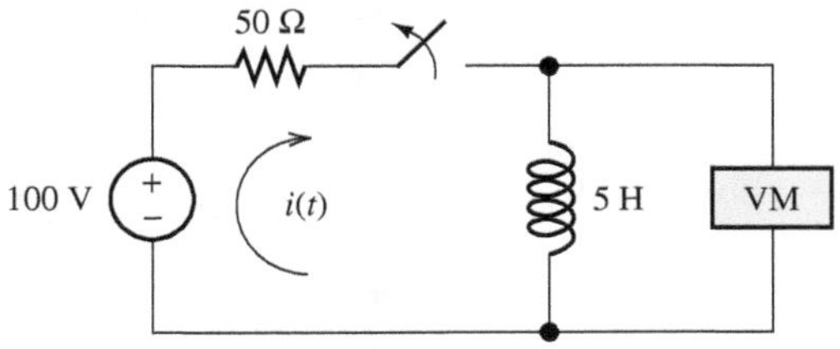

Figure P42

Section 4: ***RC* and *RL* Circuits with General Sources**

P44. What are the steps in solving a circuit having a resistance, a source, and an inductance (or capacitance)?

***P45.** Write the differential equation for $i(t)$ and find the complete solution for the circuit of Figure P45. [*Hint:* Try a particular solution of the form $i_p(t) = Ae^{-t}$.]

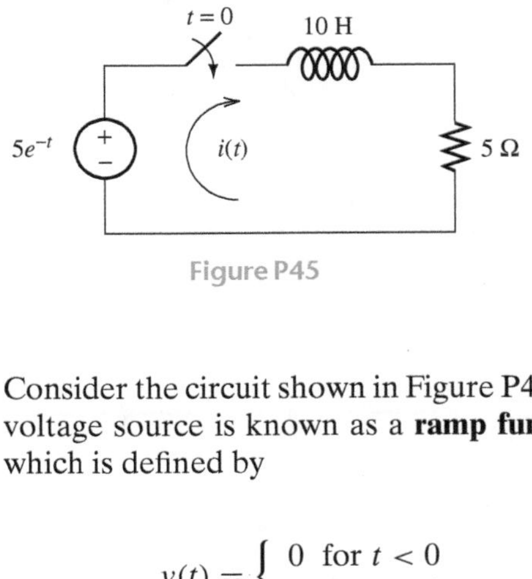

Figure P45

P46. Consider the circuit shown in Figure P46. The voltage source is known as a **ramp function,** which is defined by

$$v(t) = \begin{cases} 0 & \text{for } t < 0 \\ t & \text{for } t \geq 0 \end{cases}$$

Assume that $v_C(0) = 0$. Derive an expression for $v_C(t)$ for $t \geq 0$. Sketch $v_C(t)$ to scale versus time. [*Hint:* Write the differential equation for $v_C(t)$ and assume a particular solution of the form $v_{Cp}(t) = A + Bt$.]

***P47.** Solve for $v_C(t)$ for $t > 0$ in the circuit of Figure P47. [*Hint*: Try a particular solution of the form $v_{Cp}(t) = Ae^{-3t}$.]

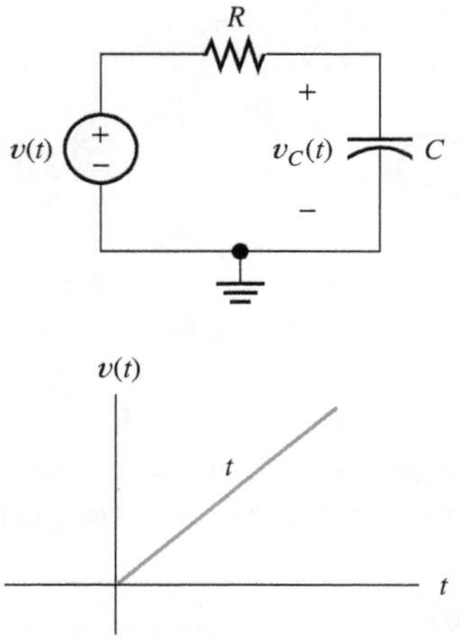

Figure P46

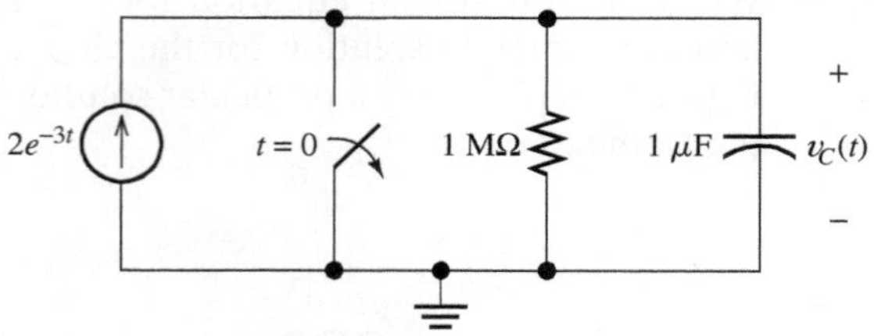

Figure P47

***P48.** Solve for $v(t)$ for $t > 0$ in the circuit of Figure P48, given that the inductor current is zero prior to $t = 0$. [*Hint:* Try a particular solution of the form $v_p = A\cos(10t) + B\sin(10t)$.]

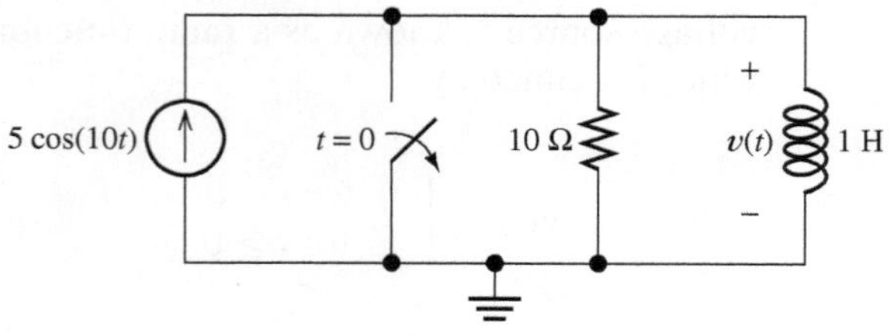

Figure P48

P49. Consider the circuit shown in Figure P49. The initial current in the inductor is $i(0+) = 0$. Write the differential equation for $i(t)$ and solve. [*Hint:* Try a particular solution of the form $i_p(t) = A\cos(300t) + B\sin(300t)$.]

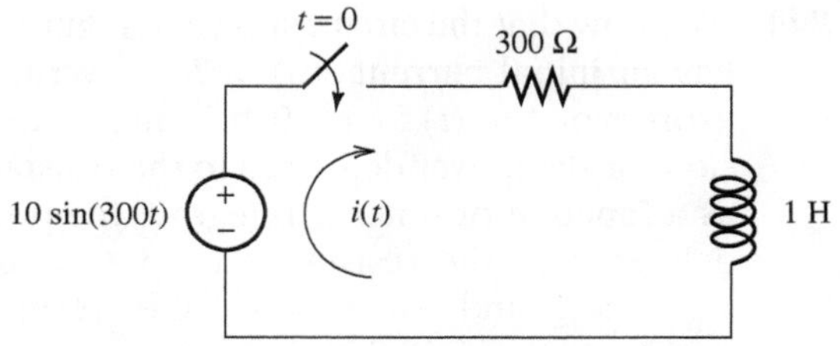

Figure P49

P50. The voltage source shown in Figure P50 is called a **ramp function**. Assume that $i(0) = 0$. Write the differential equation for $i(t)$, and find the complete solution. [*Hint:* Try a particular solution of the form $i_p(t) = A + Bt$.]

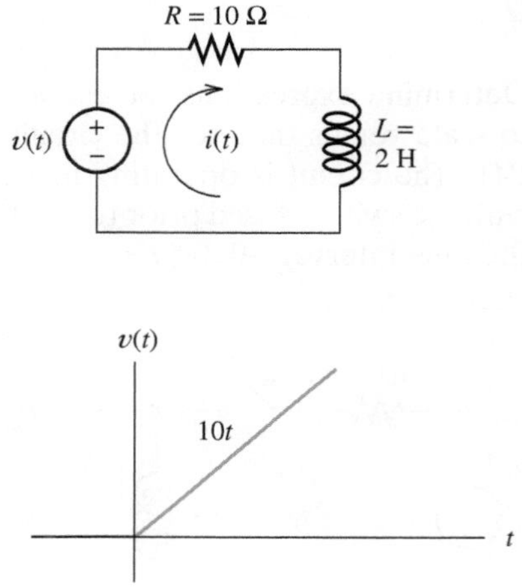

Figure P50

P51. Solve for $i_L(t)$ for $t > 0$ in the circuit of Figure P51. You will need to make an educated guess as to the form of the particular solution. (*Hint:* The particular solution includes terms with the same functional forms as the terms found in the forcing function and its derivatives.)

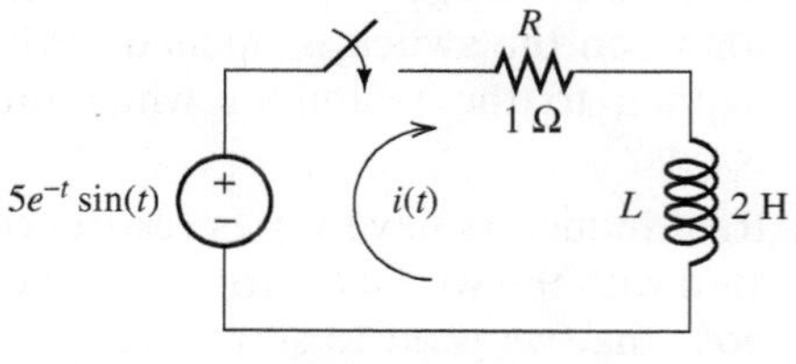

Figure P51

P52. Determine what form you would try for the particular solution for the differential equation

$$2\frac{dv(t)}{dt} + v(t) = 5t\sin(t)$$

Find the particular solution. (*Hint:* The particular solution includes terms with the same functional forms as the terms found in the forcing function and its derivatives.)

P53. Determine the form of the particular solution for the differential equation

$$\frac{dv(t)}{dt} + 3v(t) = t^2\exp(-t)$$

Then, find the particular solution. (*Hint:* The particular solution includes terms with the same functional forms as the terms found in the forcing function and its derivatives.)

P54. Consider the circuit shown in Figure P54. **a.** Write the differential equation for $i(t)$. **b.** Find the time constant and the form of the complementary solution. **c.** Usually, for an exponential-forcing function like this, we would try a particular solution of the form $i_p(t) = K\exp(-2t)$. Why doesn't that work in this case? **d.** Find the particular solution. [*Hint*: Try a particular solution of the form $i_p(t) = Kt\exp(-2t)$.] **e.** Find the complete solution for $i(t)$.

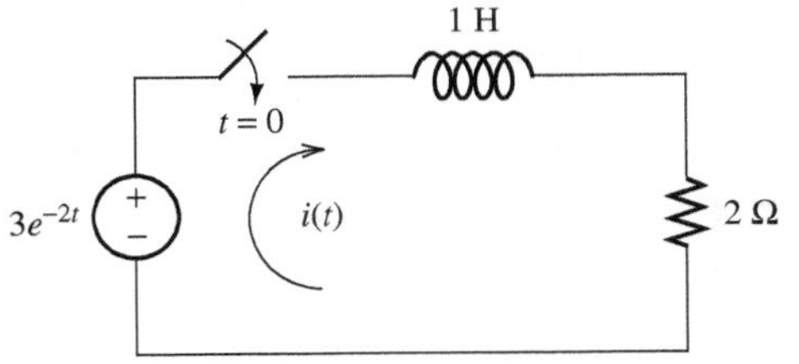

Figure P54

P55. Consider the circuit shown in Figure P55. **a.** Write the differential equation for $v(t)$. **b.** Find the time constant and the form of the complementary solution. **c.** Usually, for an exponential-forcing function like this, we would try a particular solution of the form $v_p(t) = K\exp(-10t)$. Why doesn't that work in this case? **d.** Find the particular solution. [*Hint*: Try a particular solution of the form $v_p(t) = Kt\exp(-10t)$.] **e.** Find the complete solution for $v(t)$.

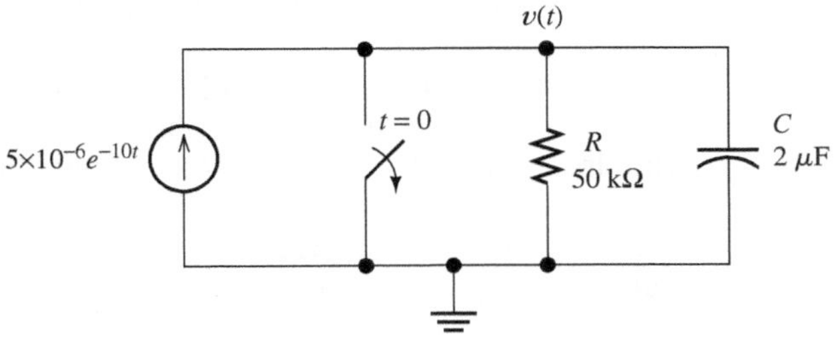

Figure P55

Section 5: Second-Order Circuits

P56. How can an underdamped second-order system be identified? What form does its complementary solution take? Repeat for a critically damped system and for an overdamped system.

P57. Discuss two methods that can be used to determine the particular solution of a circuit with constant dc sources.

P58. How can inspecting the circuit diagrams identify first- or second-order circuits?

P59. What is a unit step function?

P60. Sketch a step response for a second-order system that displays considerable overshoot and ringing. In what types of circuits do we find pronounced overshoot and ringing?

***P61.** A dc source is connected to a series RLC circuit by a switch that closes at $t = 0$, as shown in Figure P61. The initial conditions are $i(0+) = 0$ and $v_C(0+) = 0$. Write the differential equation for $v_C(t)$. Solve for $v_C(t)$ given that $R = 80\ \Omega$.

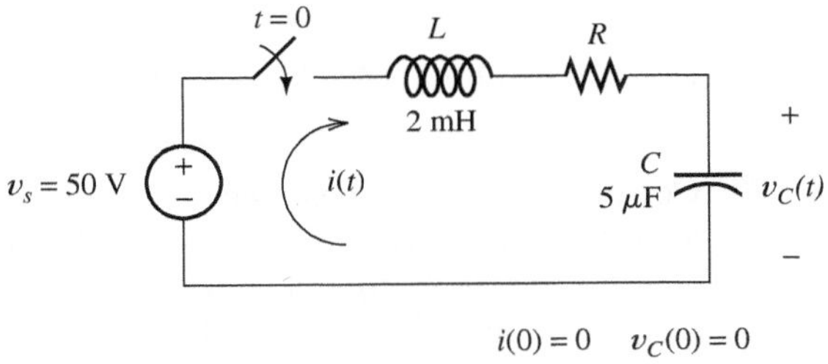

Figure P61

***P62.** Repeat Problem P61 for $R = 40\ \Omega$.

***P63.** Repeat Problem P61 for $R = 20\ \Omega$.

P64. Consider the circuit shown in Figure P64, with $R = 25\ \Omega$. **a.** Compute the undamped resonant frequency, the damping coefficient, and the damping ratio. **b.** The initial conditions are $v(0+) = 0$ and $i_L(0+) = 0$. Show that this requires that $v'(0+) = 10^9$ V/s. **c.** Find the particular solution for $v(t)$. **d.** Find the general solution for $v(t)$, including the numerical values of all parameters.

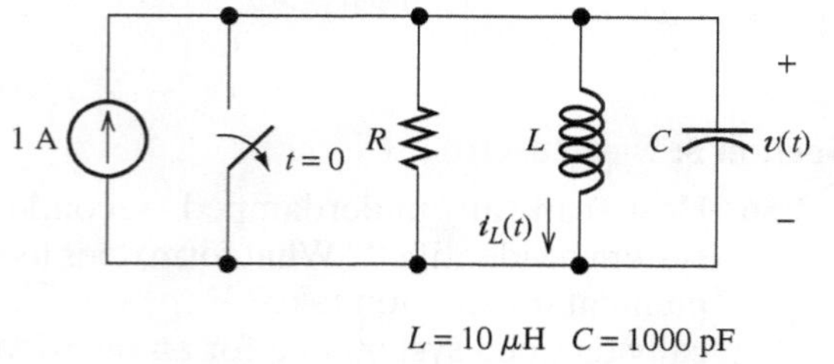

Figure P64

P65. Repeat Problem P64 for $R = 50\ \Omega$.

P66. Repeat Problem P64 for $R = 500\ \Omega$.

P67. Solve for $i(t)$ for $t > 0$ in the circuit of Figure P67, with $R = 50\ \Omega$, given that the inductor current and capacitor voltage are both zero prior to $t = 0$. [*Hint*: Try a particular solution of the form $i_p(t) = A\cos(100t) + B\sin(100t)$.]

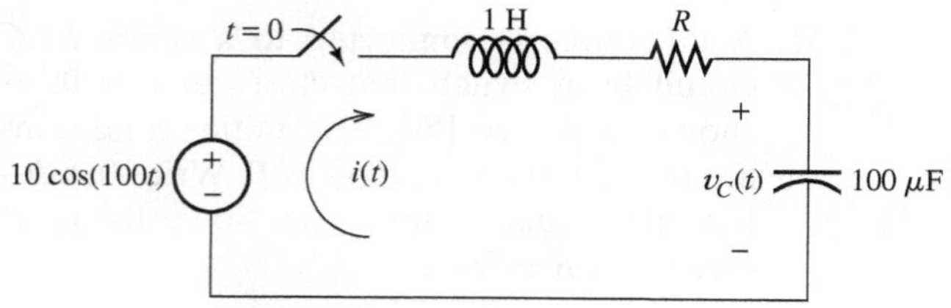

Figure P67

P68. Repeat Problem P67 with $R = 200\ \Omega$.

P69. Repeat Problem P67 with $R = 400\ \Omega$.

P70. Consider the circuit shown in Figure P70. **a.** Write the differential equation for $v(t)$. **b.** Find the damping coefficient, the natural frequency, and the form of the complementary solution. **c.** Usually, for this sinusoidal forcing function, we try a particular solution of the form $v_p(t) = A\cos(10^4 t) + B\sin(10^4 t)$. Why doesn't that work in this case? **d.** Find the particular solution. [*Hint*: Try a particular solution of the form $v_p(t) = At\cos(10^4 t) + Bt\sin(10^4 t)$.] **e.** Find the complete solution for $v(t)$.

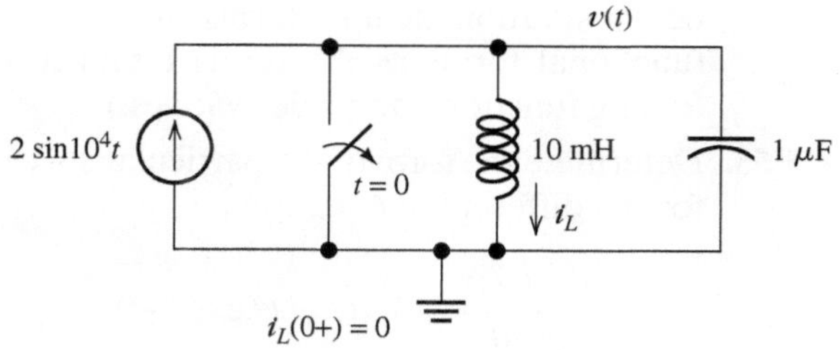

Figure P70

Section 6: Transient Analysis using the MATLAB Symbolic Toolbox

P71. Use MATLAB to derive an expression for $v(t)$ in the circuit of Figure P9 and plot $v(t)$ versus time for $0 < t < 50$ ms.

P72. Consider the circuit shown in Figure P46. The voltage source is known as a **ramp function,** which is defined by

$$v(t) = \begin{cases} 0 & \text{for } t < 0 \\ t & \text{for } t \geq 0 \end{cases}$$

Use MATLAB to derive an expression for $v_C(t)$ in terms of R, C, and t. Next, substitute $R = 1\ \text{M}\Omega$ and $C = 1\ \mu$F. Then, plot $v_C(t)$ and $v(t)$ on the same axes for $0 < t < 5$ s.

P73. Consider the circuit shown in Figure P49 in which the switch is open for a long time prior to $t = 0$. (Because lowercase "i" represents the square root of -1 in MATLAB, we need to avoid using it as the name of a variable, so denote the current as $i_s(t)$ instead of $i(t)$ for this problem and use "Is" for the current in MATLAB.) The initial current is $i_s(0+) = 0$. Write the differential equation for $i_s(t)$ and use MATLAB to solve. Then, plot $i_s(t)$ for t ranging from 0 to 80 ms.

P74. Consider the circuit shown in Figure P74 in which the switch has been open for a long time prior to $t = 0$ and we are given $R = 25\ \Omega$.

a. Write the differential equation for $v(t)$. **b.** Assume that the capacitor is initially charged by a 50-V dc source not shown in the figure, so we have $v(0+) = 50$ V. Determine the values of $i_L(0+)$ and $v'(0+)$. **c.** Use MATLAB to find the general solution for $v(t)$.

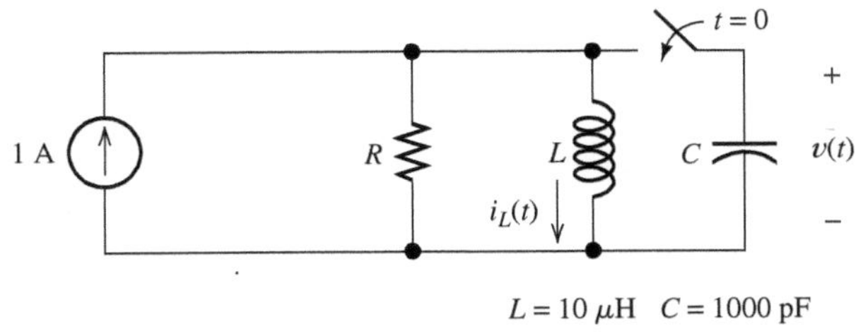

Figure P74

P75. Consider the circuit shown in Figure P70. **a.** Write the differential equation for $v(t)$. **b.** Determine the values for $v(0+)$ and $v'(0+)$. **c.** Use MATLAB to find the complete solution for $v(t)$.

P76. Use MATLAB to solve for the mesh currents in the circuit of Figure P76. The circuit has been connected for a long time prior to $t = 0$ with the switch open, so the initial values of the inductor currents are zero.

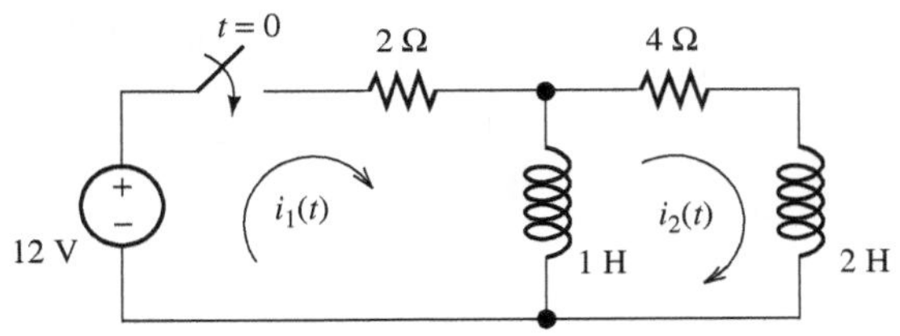

Figure P76

Practice Test

Here is a practice test you can use to check your comprehension of the most important concepts in this chapter. Answers can be found in Appendix "Answers for the Practice Tests" and complete solutions are included in the Student Solutions files. See Appendix "On-Line Student Resources" for more information about the Student Solutions.

T1. Consider the circuit shown in Figure T1. The circuit has been operating for a long time with the switch closed prior to $t = 0$. **a.** Determine the values of i_L, i_1, i_2, i_3, and v_C just before the switch opens. **b.** Determine the values of i_L, i_1, i_2, i_3, and v_C immediately after the switch opens. **c.** Find $i_L(t)$ for $t > 0$. **d.** Find $v_C(t)$ for $t > 0$.

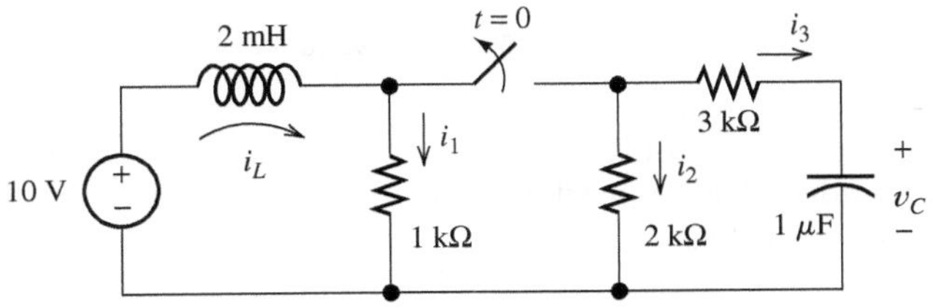

Figure T1

T2. Consider the circuit shown in Figure T2.

a. Write the differential equation for $i(t)$.

b. Find the time constant and the form of the complementary solution.

c. Find the particular solution.

d. Find the complete solution for $i(t)$.

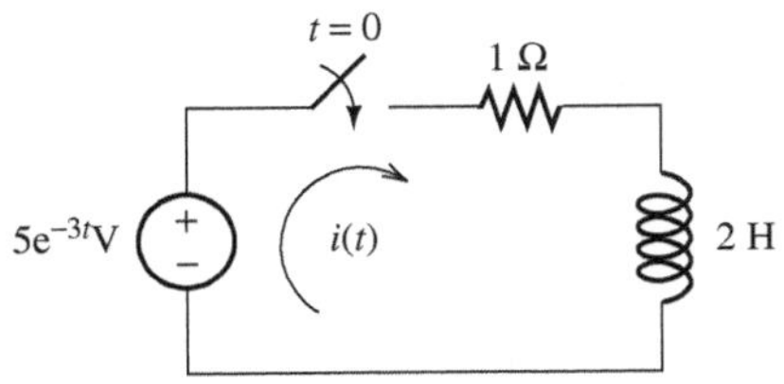

Figure T2

T3. Consider the circuit shown in Figure T3 in which the initial inductor current and capacitor voltage are both zero.

a. Write the differential equation for $v_C(t)$.

b. Find the particular solution.

c. Is this circuit overdamped, critically damped, or underdamped? Find the form of the complementary solution.

d. Find the complete solution for $v_C(t)$.

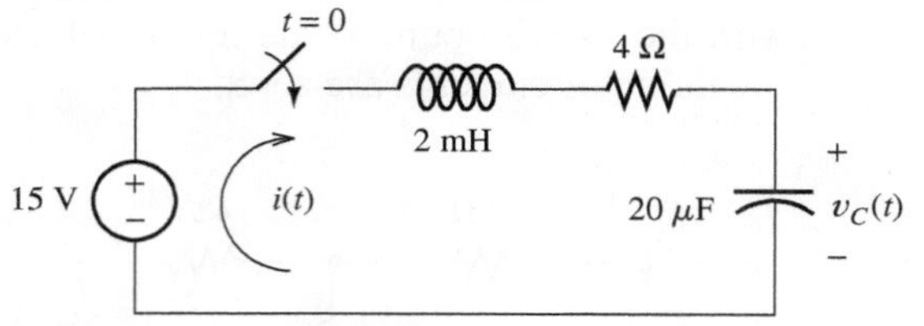

Figure T3

T4. Write the MATLAB commands to obtain the solution for the differential equation of question T3 with four decimal place accuracy for the constants.

ANSWERS FOR THE PRACTICE TESTS

Complete solutions for the practice tests are included in the Student Solutions files. See Appendix "On-Line Student Resources" for information on how to access these files.

T1. a. $i_1(0-) = 10\,\text{mA}$, $i_2(0-) = 5\,\text{mA}$, $i_3(0-) = 0$, $i_L(0-) = 15\,\text{mA}$, $v_C(0-) = 10\,\text{V}$;

b. $i_1(0+) = 15\,\text{mA}$, $i_2(0+) = 2\,\text{mA}$, and $i_3(0+) = -2\,\text{mA}$, $i_L(0+) = 15\,\text{mA}$, $v_C(0+) = 10\,\text{V}$;

c. $i_L(t) = 10 + 5\,\exp(-5 \times 10^5 t)\,\text{mA}$;

d. $v_C(t) = 10\,\exp(-200t)\,\text{V}$.

T2. a. $2\frac{di(t)}{dt} + i(t) = 5\,\exp(-3t)$;

b. $\tau = L/R = 2\,\text{s}$, $i_c(t) = A\exp(-0.5t)\,\text{A}$;

c. $i_p(t) = -\exp(-3t)\,\text{A}$;

d. $i(t) = \exp(-0.5t) - \exp(-3t)\,\text{A}$.

T3. a. $\frac{d^2v_C(t)}{dt^2} + 2000\frac{dv_C(t)}{dt} + 25 \times 10^6 v_C(t) = 375 \times 10^6$;

b. $v_{Cp}(t) = 15\,\text{V}$;

c. Underdamped; $v_{Cc}(t) = K_1 \exp(-1000t)\cos(4899t) + K_2 \exp(-1000t)\sin(4899t)$;

d. $v_C(t) = 15 - 15\,\exp(-1000t)\cos(4899t) - (3.062)\exp(-1000t)\sin(4899t)\,\text{V}$.

T4. The commands are

```
syms vC t
S = dsolve('D2vC + 2000*DvC + (25e6)*vC = 375e6', 'vC(0) = 0, DvC(0) = 0');
simple(vpa(S,4))
```

The commands are stored in the m-file named T_4 that can be found in the Hambley MATLAB folder. See Appendix "On-Line Student Resources" for information about accessing this folder.

ON-LINE STUDENT RESOURCES

Users of the text can access the Student Solutions Manual (and other folders mentioned below) in electronic form by following links starting from the website:

www.pearsonhighered.com/hambley

The MATLAB folder contains m-files. Except for the examples that use the Symbolic Toolbox, these files work equally well with MathScript, which is sometimes included with the LabVIEW program. The Hambley MathScript folder contains the m-files that work with MathScript.

The Virtual Instruments folder contains LabVIEW programs.

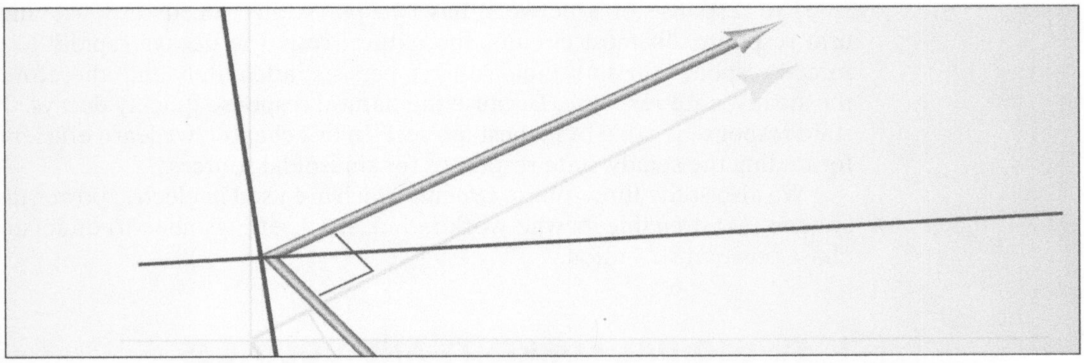

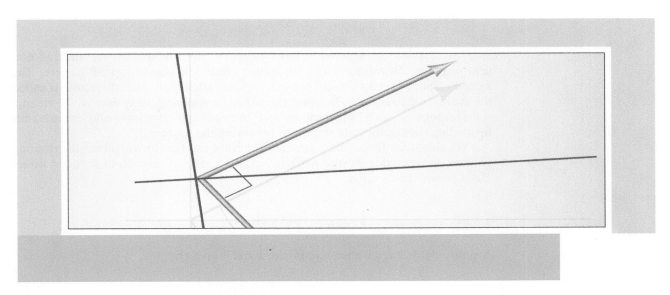

Steady-State Sinusoidal Analysis

Study of this chapter will enable you to:

- Identify the frequency, angular frequency, peak value, rms value, and phase of a sinusoidal signal.
- Determine the root-mean-square (rms) value of any periodic current or voltage.
- Solve steady-state ac circuits, using phasors and complex impedances.
- Compute power for steady-state ac circuits.
- Find Thévenin and Norton equivalent circuits.
- Determine load impedances for maximum power transfer.
- Discuss the advantages of three-phase power distribution.
- Solve balanced three-phase circuits.
- Use MATLAB to facilitate ac circuit calculations.

Introduction to this chapter:

Circuits with sinusoidal sources have many important applications. For example, electric power is distributed to residences and businesses by sinusoidal currents and voltages. Furthermore, sinusoidal signals have many uses in radio communication. Finally, a branch of mathematics known as Fourier analysis shows that all signals of practical interest are composed of sinusoidal components. Thus, the study of circuits with sinusoidal sources is a central theme in electrical engineering.

The response of a network has two parts: the forced response and the natural response. In most circuits, the natural response decays rapidly to zero. The forced response for sinusoidal sources persists indefinitely and, therefore, is called the steady-state response. Because the natural response quickly decays, the steady-state response is often of highest interest. In this chapter, we learn efficient methods for finding the steady-state responses for sinusoidal sources.

We also study three-phase circuits, which are used in electric power-distribution systems. Most engineers who work in industrial settings need to understand three-phase power distribution.

1 SINUSOIDAL CURRENTS AND VOLTAGES

A sinusoidal voltage is shown in Figure 1 and is given by

$$v(t) = V_m \cos(\omega t + \theta) \tag{1}$$

where V_m is the **peak value** of the voltage, ω is the **angular frequency** in radians per second, and θ is the **phase angle**.

Sinusoidal signals are periodic, repeating the same pattern of values in each **period** T. Because the cosine (or sine) function completes one cycle when the angle increases by 2π radians, we get

$$\omega T = 2\pi \tag{2}$$

The **frequency** of a periodic signal is the number of cycles completed in one second. Thus, we obtain

$$f = \frac{1}{T} \tag{3}$$

We refer to ω as angular frequency with units of radians per second and f simply as frequency with units of hertz (Hz).

The units of frequency are hertz (Hz). (Actually, the physical units of hertz are equivalent to inverse seconds.) Solving Equation 2 for the angular frequency, we have

$$\omega = \frac{2\pi}{T} \tag{4}$$

Using Equation 3 to substitute for T, we find that

$$\omega = 2\pi f \tag{5}$$

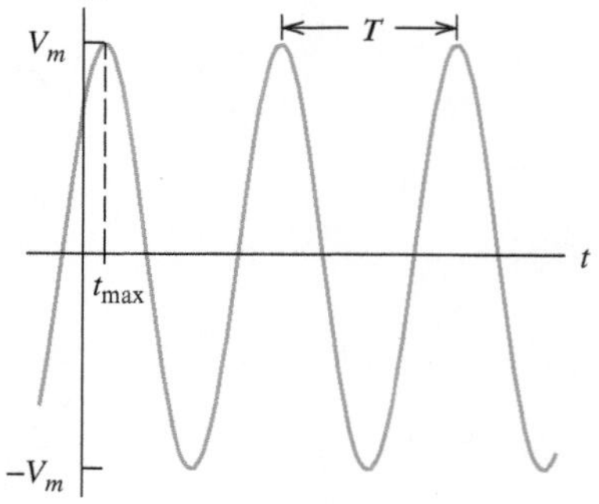

Figure 1 A sinusoidal voltage waveform given by $v(t) = V_m \cos(\omega t + \theta)$. *Note:* Assuming that θ is in degrees, we have $t_{max} = \frac{-\theta}{360} \times T$. For the waveform shown, θ is $-45°$.

Throughout our discussion, the argument of the cosine (or sine) function is of the form

$$\omega t + \theta$$

We assume that the angular frequency ω has units of radians per second (rad/s). However, we sometimes give the phase angle θ in degrees. Then, the argument has mixed units. If we wanted to evaluate $\cos(\omega t + \theta)$ for a particular value of time, we would have to convert θ to radians before adding the terms in the argument. Usually, we find it easier to visualize an angle expressed in degrees, and mixed units are not a problem.

Electrical engineers often write the argument of a sinusoid in mixed units: ωt is in radians and the phase angle θ is in degrees.

For uniformity, we express sinusoidal functions by using the cosine function rather than the sine function. The functions are related by the identity

$$\sin(z) = \cos(z - 90°) \tag{6}$$

For example, when we want to find the phase angle of

$$v_x(t) = 10\sin(200t + 30°)$$

we first write it as

$$\begin{aligned} v_x(t) &= 10\cos(200t + 30° - 90°) \\ &= 10\cos(200t - 60°) \end{aligned}$$

Thus, we state that the phase angle of $v_x(t)$ is $-60°$.

Root-Mean-Square Values

Consider applying a periodic voltage $v(t)$ with period T to a resistance R. The power delivered to the resistance is given by

$$p(t) = \frac{v^2(t)}{R} \tag{7}$$

Furthermore, the energy delivered in one period is given by

$$E_T = \int_0^T p(t)\, dt \tag{8}$$

The average power P_{avg} delivered to the resistance is the energy delivered in one cycle divided by the period. Thus,

$$P_{avg} = \frac{E_T}{T} = \frac{1}{T}\int_0^T p(t)\, dt \tag{9}$$

Using Equation 7 to substitute into Equation 9, we obtain

$$P_{avg} = \frac{1}{T}\int_0^T \frac{v^2(t)}{R}\, dt \tag{10}$$

This can be rearranged as

$$P_{avg} = \frac{\left[\sqrt{\frac{1}{T}\int_0^T v^2(t)\,dt}\right]^2}{R} \tag{11}$$

Now, we define the **root-mean-square** (rms) value of the periodic voltage $v(t)$ as

$$V_{rms} = \sqrt{\frac{1}{T}\int_0^T v^2(t)\,dt} \tag{12}$$

Using this equation to substitute into Equation 11, we get

$$P_{avg} = \frac{V_{rms}^2}{R} \tag{13}$$

Power calculations are facilitated by using rms values for voltage or current.

Thus, if the rms value of a periodic voltage is known, it is relatively easy to compute the average power that the voltage can deliver to a resistance. The rms value is also called the **effective value**.

Similarly for a periodic current $i(t)$, we define the rms value as

$$I_{rms} = \sqrt{\frac{1}{T}\int_0^T i^2(t)\,dt} \tag{14}$$

and the average power delivered if $i(t)$ flows through a resistance is given by

$$P_{avg} = I_{rms}^2 R \tag{15}$$

RMS Value of a Sinusoid

Consider a sinusoidal voltage given by

$$v(t) = V_m \cos(\omega t + \theta) \tag{16}$$

To find the rms value, we substitute into Equation 12, which yields

$$V_{rms} = \sqrt{\frac{1}{T}\int_0^T V_m^2 \cos^2(\omega t + \theta)\,dt} \tag{17}$$

Next, we use the trigonometric identity

$$\cos^2(z) = \frac{1}{2} + \frac{1}{2}\cos(2z) \tag{18}$$

to write Equation 17 as

$$V_{rms} = \sqrt{\frac{V_m^2}{2T}\int_0^T [1 + \cos(2\omega t + 2\theta)]\,dt} \tag{19}$$

Integrating, we get

$$V_{\text{rms}} = \sqrt{\frac{V_m^2}{2T}\left[t + \frac{1}{2\omega}\sin(2\omega t + 2\theta)\right]_0^T} \quad (20)$$

Evaluating, we have

$$V_{\text{rms}} = \sqrt{\frac{V_m^2}{2T}\left[T + \frac{1}{2\omega}\sin(2\omega T + 2\theta) - \frac{1}{2\omega}\sin(2\theta)\right]} \quad (21)$$

Referring to Equation 2, we see that $\omega T = 2\pi$. Thus, we obtain

$$\begin{aligned}\frac{1}{2\omega}\sin(2\omega T + 2\theta) - \frac{1}{2\omega}\sin(2\theta) &= \frac{1}{2\omega}\sin(4\pi + 2\theta) - \frac{1}{2\omega}\sin(2\theta)\\ &= \frac{1}{2\omega}\sin(2\theta) - \frac{1}{2\omega}\sin(2\theta)\\ &= 0\end{aligned}$$

Therefore, Equation 21 reduces to

$$V_{\text{rms}} = \frac{V_m}{\sqrt{2}} \quad (22)$$

This is a useful result that we will use many times in dealing with sinusoids.

Usually in discussing sinusoids, the rms or effective value is given rather than the peak value. For example, ac power in residential wiring is distributed as a 60-Hz 115-V rms sinusoid (in the United States). Most people are aware of this, but probably few know that 115 V is the rms value and that the peak value is $V_m = V_{\text{rms}} \times \sqrt{2} = 115 \times \sqrt{2} \cong 163$ V. (Actually, 115 V is the nominal residential distribution voltage. It can vary from approximately 105 to 130 V.)

Keep in mind that $V_{\text{rms}} = V_m/\sqrt{2}$ applies to sinusoids. To find the rms value of other periodic waveforms, we would need to employ the definition given by Equation 12.

The rms value for a sinusoid is the peak value divided by the square root of two. This is not true for other periodic waveforms such as square waves or triangular waves.

Example 1 Power Delivered to a Resistance by a Sinusoidal Source

Suppose that a voltage given by $v(t) = 100\cos(100\pi t)$ V is applied to a 50-Ω resistance. Sketch $v(t)$ to scale versus time. Find the rms value of the voltage and the average power delivered to the resistance. Find the power as a function of time and sketch to scale.

Solution By comparison of the expression given for $v(t)$ with Equation 1, we see that $\omega = 100\pi$. Using Equation 5, we find that the frequency is $f = \omega/2\pi = 50$ Hz. Then, the period is $T = 1/f = 20$ ms. A plot of $v(t)$ versus time is shown in Figure 2(a).

The peak value of the voltage is $V_m = 100$ V. Thus, the rms value is $V_{\text{rms}} = V_m/\sqrt{2} = 70.71$ V. Then, the average power is

$$P_{\text{avg}} = \frac{V_{\text{rms}}^2}{R} = \frac{(70.71)^2}{50} = 100 \text{ W}$$

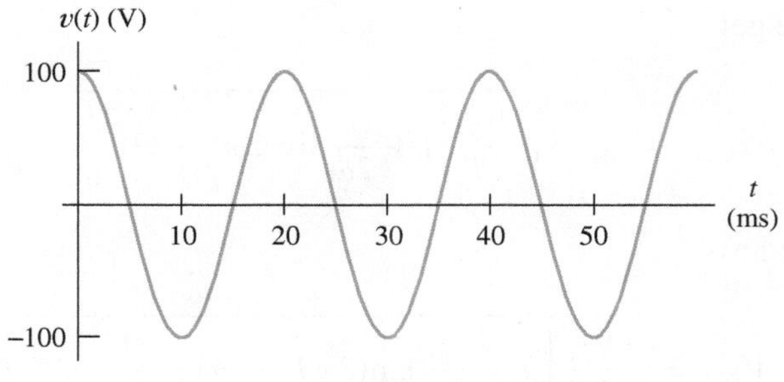

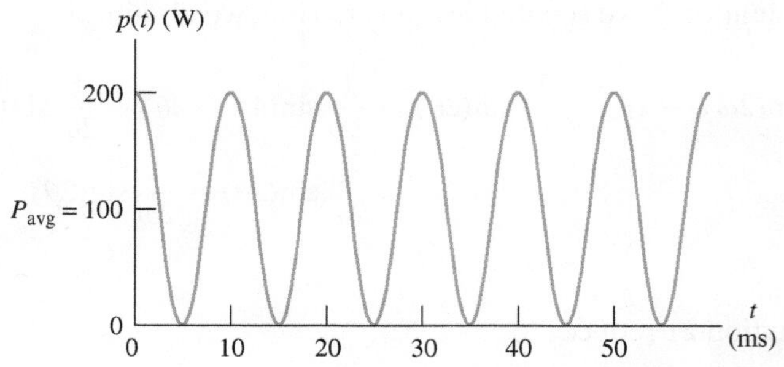

Figure 2 Voltage and power versus time for Example 1.

The power as a function of time is given by

$$p(t) = \frac{v^2(t)}{R} = \frac{100^2 \cos^2(100\pi t)}{50} = 200 \cos^2(100\pi t) \text{ W}$$

A plot of $p(t)$ versus time is shown in Figure 2(b). Notice that the power fluctuates from 0 to 200 W. However, the average power is 100 W, as we found by using the rms value. ■

For a sinusoidal current flowing in a resistance, power fluctuates periodically from zero to twice the average value.

RMS Values of Nonsinusoidal Voltages or Currents

Sometimes we need to determine the rms values of periodic currents or voltages that are not sinusoidal. We can accomplish this by applying the definition given by Equation 12 or 14 directly.

Example 2 RMS Value of a Triangular Voltage

The voltage shown in Figure 3(a) is known as a triangular waveform. Determine its rms value.

Solution First, we need to determine the equations describing the waveform between $t = 0$ and $t = T = 2$ s. As illustrated in Figure 3(b), the equations for the first period of the triangular wave are

$$v(t) = \begin{cases} 3t & \text{for} \quad 0 \le t \le 1 \\ 6 - 3t & \text{for} \quad 1 \le t \le 2 \end{cases}$$

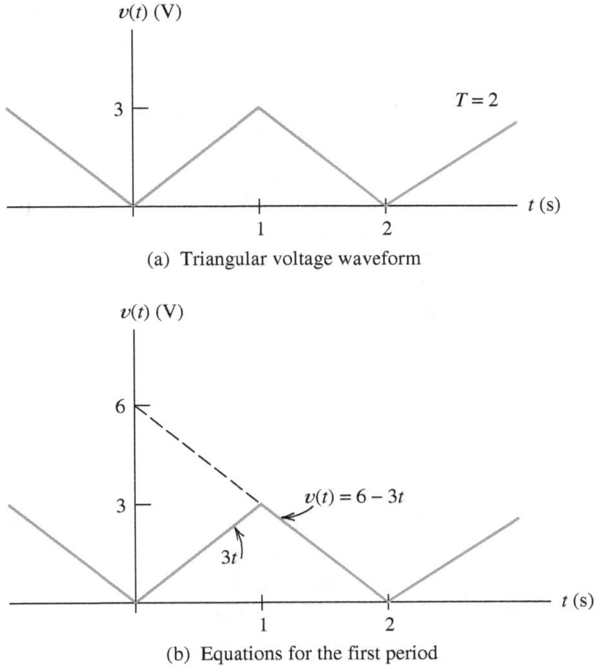

Figure 3 Triangular voltage waveform of Example 2.

Equation 12 gives the rms value of the voltage.

$$V_{\text{rms}} = \sqrt{\frac{1}{T}\int_0^T v^2(t)dt}$$

Dividing the interval into two parts and substituting for $v(t)$, we have

$$V_{\text{rms}} = \sqrt{\frac{1}{2}\left[\int_0^1 9t^2 dt + \int_1^2 (6-3t)^2 dt\right]}$$

$$V_{\text{rms}} = \sqrt{\frac{1}{2}\left[3t^3|_{t=0}^{t=1} + (36t - 18t^2 + 3t^3)|_{t=1}^{t=2}\right]}$$

Evaluating, we find

$$V_{\text{rms}} = \sqrt{\frac{1}{2}[3 + (72 - 36 - 72 + 18 + 24 - 3)]} = \sqrt{3}\,\text{V}$$

■

The integrals in this example are easy to carry out manually. However, when the integrals are more difficult, we can sometimes obtain answers using the MATLAB Symbolic Toolbox. Here are the MATLAB commands needed to perform the integrals in this example:

```
>> syms Vrms t
>> Vrms = sqrt((1/2)*(int(9*t^2,t,0,1) + int((6-3*t)^2,t,1,2)))
    Vrms =
    3^(1/2)
```

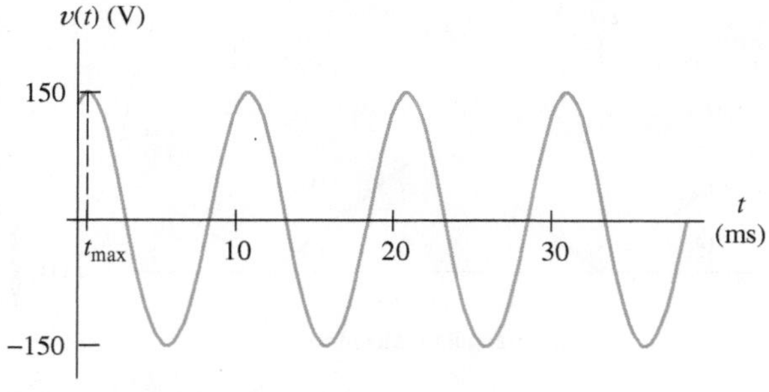

Figure 4 Answer for Exercise 1(c).

Exercise 1 Suppose that a sinusoidal voltage is given by

$$v(t) = 150\cos(200\pi t - 30^\circ)\text{ V}$$

a. Find the angular frequency, the frequency in hertz, the period, the peak value, and the rms value. Also, find the first value of time t_{max} after $t = 0$ such that $v(t)$ attains its positive peak. **b.** If this voltage is applied to a 50-Ω resistance, compute the average power delivered. **c.** Sketch $v(t)$ to scale versus time.

Answer **a.** $\omega = 200\pi$, $f = 100$ Hz, $T = 10$ ms, $V_m = 150$ V, $V_{rms} = 106.1$ V, $t_{max} = \frac{30^\circ}{360^\circ} \times T = 0.833$ ms; **b.** $P_{avg} = 225$ W; **c.** a plot of $v(t)$ versus time is shown in Figure 4. □

Exercise 2 Express $v(t) = 100\sin(300\pi t + 60^\circ)$ V as a cosine function.

Answer $v(t) = 100\cos(300\pi t - 30^\circ)$ V. □

Exercise 3 Suppose that the ac line voltage powering a computer has an rms value of 110 V and a frequency of 60 Hz, and the peak voltage is attained at $t = 5$ ms. Write an expression for this ac voltage as a function of time.

Answer $v(t) = 155.6\cos(377t - 108^\circ)$ V. □

2 PHASORS

In the next several sections, we will see that sinusoidal steady-state analysis is greatly facilitated if the currents and voltages are represented as vectors (called **phasors**) in the complex-number plane. In preparation for this material, you may wish to study the review of complex-number arithmetic in Appendix "Complex numbers".

We start with a study of convenient methods for adding (or subtracting) sinusoidal waveforms. We often need to do this in applying Kirchhoff's voltage law (KVL) or Kirchhoff's current law (KCL) to ac circuits. For example, in applying KVL to a network with sinusoidal voltages, we might obtain the expression

$$v(t) = 10\cos(\omega t) + 5\sin(\omega t + 60^\circ) + 5\cos(\omega t + 90^\circ) \tag{23}$$

To obtain the peak value of $v(t)$ and its phase angle, we need to put Equation 23 into the form

$$v(t) = V_m\cos(\omega t + \theta) \tag{24}$$

This could be accomplished by repeated substitution, using standard trigonometric identities. However, that method is too tedious for routine work. Instead, we will see that we can represent each term on the right-hand side of Equation 23 by a vector in the complex-number plane known as a **phasor**. Then, we can add the phasors with relative ease and convert the sum into the desired form.

Phasor Definition

For a sinusoidal voltage of the form

$$v_1(t) = V_1 \cos(\omega t + \theta_1)$$

we define the phasor as

$$\mathbf{V}_1 = V_1 \underline{/\theta_1}$$

Thus, the phasor for a sinusoid is a complex number having a magnitude equal to the peak value and having the same phase angle as the sinusoid. We use boldface letters for phasors. (Actually, engineers are not consistent in choosing the magnitudes of phasors. In this chapter, we take the peak values for the magnitudes of phasors, which is the prevailing custom in circuit-analysis courses for electrical engineers. We will take care to label rms phasors as such when we encounter them. If phasors are not labeled as rms, you can assume that they are peak values.)

Phasors are complex numbers that represent sinusoidal voltages or currents. The magnitude of a phasor equals the peak value and the angle equals the phase of the sinusoid (written as a cosine).

If the sinusoid is of the form

$$v_2(t) = V_2 \sin(\omega t + \theta_2)$$

we first convert to a cosine function by using the trigonometric identity

$$\sin(z) = \cos(z - 90^\circ) \tag{25}$$

Thus, we have

$$v_2(t) = V_2 \cos(\omega t + \theta_2 - 90^\circ)$$

and the phasor is

$$\mathbf{V}_2 = V_2 \underline{/\theta_2 - 90^\circ}$$

Phasors are obtained for sinusoidal currents in a similar fashion. Thus, for the currents

$$i_1(t) = I_1 \cos(\omega t + \theta_1)$$

and

$$i_2(t) = I_2 \sin(\omega t + \theta_2)$$

the phasors are

$$\mathbf{I}_1 = I_1 \underline{/\theta_1}$$

and

$$\mathbf{I}_2 = I_2 \underline{/\theta_2 - 90^\circ}$$

respectively.

Adding Sinusoids Using Phasors

Now, we illustrate how we can use phasors to combine the terms of the right-hand side of Equation 23. In this discussion, we proceed in small logical steps to illustrate clearly why sinusoids can be added by adding their phasors. Later, we streamline the procedure for routine work.

Our first step in combining the terms in Equation 23 is to write all the sinusoids as cosine functions by using Equation 25. Thus, Equation 23 can be written as

$$v(t) = 10\cos(\omega t) + 5\cos(\omega t + 60^\circ - 90^\circ) + 5\cos(\omega t + 90^\circ) \tag{26}$$

$$v(t) = 10\cos(\omega t) + 5\cos(\omega t - 30^\circ) + 5\cos(\omega t + 90^\circ) \tag{27}$$

Referring to Euler's formula (Equation 8) in Appendix "Complex numbers", we see that we can write

$$\cos(\theta) = \mathrm{Re}\left(e^{j\theta}\right) = \mathrm{Re}[\cos(\theta) + j\sin(\theta)] \tag{28}$$

where the notation Re( ) means that we retain only the real part of the quantity inside the parentheses. Thus, we can rewrite Equation 27 as

$$v(t) = 10\ \mathrm{Re}\left[e^{j\omega t}\right] + 5\ \mathrm{Re}\left[e^{j(\omega t - 30^\circ)}\right] + 5\ \mathrm{Re}\left[e^{j(\omega t + 90^\circ)}\right] \tag{29}$$

When we multiply a complex number Z by a real number A, both the real and imaginary parts of Z are multiplied by A. Thus, Equation 29 becomes

$$v(t) = \mathrm{Re}\left[10e^{j\omega t}\right] + \mathrm{Re}\left[5e^{j(\omega t - 30^\circ)}\right] + \mathrm{Re}\left[5e^{j(\omega t + 90^\circ)}\right] \tag{30}$$

Next, we can write

$$v(t) = \mathrm{Re}\left[10e^{j\omega t} + 5e^{j(\omega t - 30^\circ)} + 5e^{j(\omega t + 90^\circ)}\right] \tag{31}$$

because the real part of the sum of several complex quantities is equal to the sum of the real parts. If we factor out the common term $e^{j\omega t}$, Equation 31 becomes

$$v(t) = \mathrm{Re}\left[\left(10 + 5e^{-j30^\circ} + 5^{j90^\circ}\right)e^{j\omega t}\right] \tag{32}$$

Putting the complex numbers into polar form, we have

$$v(t) = \mathrm{Re}\left[(10\ \angle 0^\circ + 5\ \angle -30^\circ + 5\ \angle 90^\circ)e^{j\omega t}\right] \tag{33}$$

Now, we can combine the complex numbers as

$$\begin{aligned} 10\ \angle 0^\circ + 5\ \angle -30^\circ + 5\ \angle 90^\circ &= 10 + 4.33 - j2.50 + j5 \\ &= 14.33 + j2.5 \\ &= 14.54\ \angle 9.90^\circ \\ &= 14.54e^{j9.90^\circ} \end{aligned} \tag{34}$$

Using this result in Equation 33, we have

$$v(t) = \mathrm{Re}\left[\left(14.54e^{j9.90^\circ}\right)e^{j\omega t}\right]$$

which can be written as

$$v(t) = \text{Re}\left[14.54e^{j(\omega t+9.90^\circ)}\right] \quad (35)$$

Now, using Equation 28, we can write this as

$$v(t) = 14.54\cos(\omega t + 9.90^\circ) \quad (36)$$

Thus, we have put the original expression for $v(t)$ into the desired form. The terms on the left-hand side of Equation 34 are the phasors for the terms on the right-hand side of the original expression for $v(t)$. Notice that the essential part of the work needed to combine the sinusoids is to add the phasors.

Streamlined Procedure for Adding Sinusoids

From now on, to add sinusoids, we will first write the phasor for each term in the sum, add the phasors by using complex-number arithmetic, and then write the simplified expression for the sum.

To add sinusoids, we find the phasor for each term, add the phasors by using complex-number arithmetic, express the sum in polar form, and then write the corresponding sinusoidal time function.

Example 3 Using Phasors to Add Sinusoids

Suppose that

$$v_1(t) = 20\cos(\omega t - 45^\circ)$$
$$v_2(t) = 10\sin(\omega t + 60^\circ)$$

In using phasors to add sinusoids, all of the terms must have the same frequency.

Reduce the sum $v_s(t) = v_1(t) + v_2(t)$ to a single term.

Solution The phasors are

Step 1: Determine the phasor for each term.

$$\mathbf{V}_1 = 20\ \angle -45^\circ$$
$$\mathbf{V}_2 = 10\ \angle -30^\circ$$

Notice that we have subtracted 90° to find the phase angle for $\mathbf{V}_2$ because $v_2(t)$ is a sine function rather than a cosine function.

Next, we use complex-number arithmetic to add the phasors and convert the sum to polar form:

Step 2: Use complex arithmetic to add the phasors.

$$\begin{aligned}\mathbf{V}_s &= \mathbf{V}_1 + \mathbf{V}_2\\ &= 20\ \angle -45^\circ + 10\ \angle -30^\circ\\ &= 14.14 - j14.14 + 8.660 - j5\\ &= 22.80 - j19.14\\ &= 29.77\ \angle -40.01^\circ\end{aligned}$$

Step 3: Convert the sum to polar form.

Now, we write the time function corresponding to the phasor $\mathbf{V}_s$.

Step 4: Write the result as a time function.

$$v_s(t) = 29.77\cos(\omega t - 40.01^\circ)$$

■

Exercise 4 Reduce the following expressions by using phasors:

$$v_1(t) = 10\cos(\omega t) + 10\sin(\omega t)$$
$$i_1(t) = 10\cos(\omega t + 30°) + 5\sin(\omega t + 30°)$$
$$i_2(t) = 20\sin(\omega t + 90°) + 15\cos(\omega t - 60°)$$

Answer

$$v_1(t) = 14.14\cos(\omega t - 45°)$$
$$i_1(t) = 11.18\cos(\omega t + 3.44°)$$
$$i_2(t) = 30.4\cos(\omega t - 25.3°)$$

□

Phasors as Rotating Vectors

Consider a sinusoidal voltage given by

$$v(t) = V_m \cos(\omega t + \theta)$$

In developing the phasor concept, we write

$$v(t) = \text{Re}\left[V_m e^{j(\omega t+\theta)}\right]$$

The complex quantity inside the brackets is

$$V_m e^{j(\omega t+\theta)} = V_m \angle \omega t + \theta$$

Sinusoids can be visualized as the real-axis projection of vectors rotating in the complex plane. The phasor for a sinusoid is a snapshot of the corresponding rotating vector at $t = 0$.

This can be visualized as a vector of length V_m that rotates counterclockwise in the complex plane with an angular velocity of ω rad/s. Furthermore, the voltage $v(t)$ is the real part of the vector, which is illustrated in Figure 5. As the vector rotates, its projection on the real axis traces out the voltage as a function of time. The phasor is simply a "snapshot" of this rotating vector at $t = 0$.

Phase Relationships

We will see that the phase relationships between currents and voltages are often important. Consider the voltages

$$v_1(t) = 3\cos(\omega t + 40°)$$

To determine phase relationships from a phasor diagram, consider that the phasors rotate counterclockwise. Then, when standing at a fixed point, if $\mathbf{V}_1$ arrives first followed by $\mathbf{V}_2$ after a rotation of θ, we say that $\mathbf{V}_1$ leads $\mathbf{V}_2$ by θ. Alternatively, we could say that $\mathbf{V}_2$ lags $\mathbf{V}_1$ by θ. (Usually, we take θ as the smaller angle between the two phasors.)

and

$$v_2(t) = 4\cos(\omega t - 20°)$$

The corresponding phasors are

$$\mathbf{V}_1 = 3 \angle 40°$$

and

$$\mathbf{V}_2 = 4 \angle -20°$$

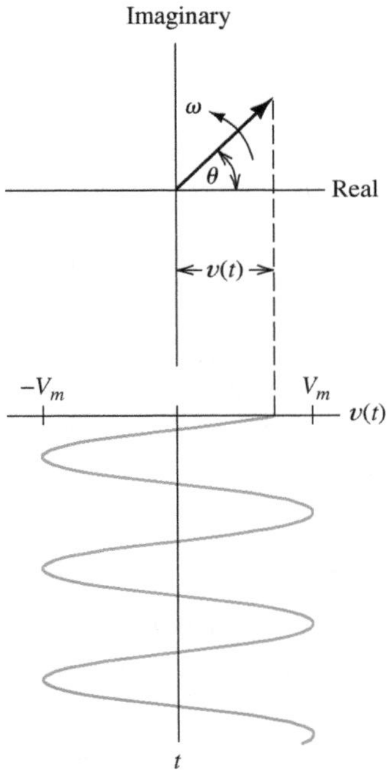

Figure 5 A sinusoid can be represented as the real part of a vector rotating counterclockwise in the complex plane.

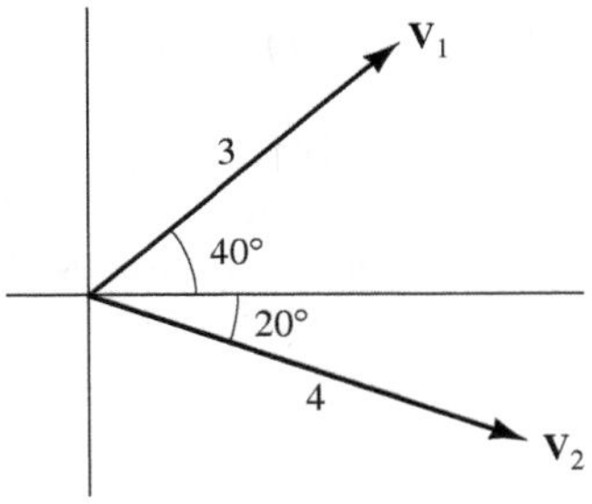

Figure 6 Because the vectors rotate counterclockwise, $\mathbf{V}_1$ leads $\mathbf{V}_2$ by 60° (or, equivalently, $\mathbf{V}_2$ lags $\mathbf{V}_1$ by 60°).

The phasor diagram is shown in Figure 6. Notice that the angle between $\mathbf{V}_1$ and $\mathbf{V}_2$ is 60°. Because the complex vectors rotate counterclockwise, we say that $\mathbf{V}_1$ *leads* $\mathbf{V}_2$ by 60°. (An alternative way to state the phase relationship is to state that $\mathbf{V}_2$ *lags* $\mathbf{V}_1$ by 60°.)

We have seen that the voltages versus time can be obtained by tracing the real part of the rotating vectors. The plots of $v_1(t)$ and $v_2(t)$ versus ωt are shown in Figure 7. Notice that $v_1(t)$ reaches its peak 60° earlier than $v_2(t)$. This is the meaning of the statement that $v_1(t)$ leads $v_2(t)$ by 60°.

To determine phase relationships between sinusoids from their plots versus time, find the shortest time interval t_p between positive peaks of the two waveforms. Then, the phase angle is $\theta = (t_p/T) \times 360°$. If the peak of $v_1(t)$ occurs first, we say that $v_1(t)$ leads $v_2(t)$ or that $v_2(t)$ lags $v_1(t)$.

Exercise 5 Consider the voltages given by

$$v_1(t) = 10\cos(\omega t - 30°)$$
$$v_2(t) = 10\cos(\omega t + 30°)$$
$$v_3(t) = 10\sin(\omega t + 45°)$$

State the phase relationship between each pair of the voltages. (*Hint:* Find the phasor for each voltage and draw the phasor diagram.)

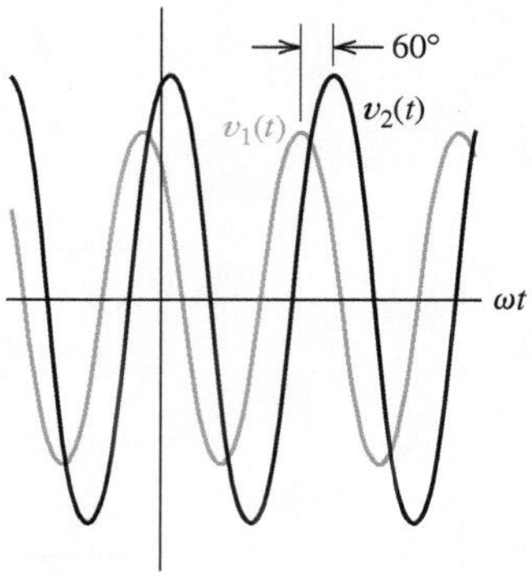

Figure 7 The peaks of $v_1(t)$ occur 60° before the peaks of $v_2(t)$. In other words, $v_1(t)$ leads $v_2(t)$ by 60°.

Answer

v_1 lags v_2 by 60° (or v_2 leads v_1 by 60°)
v_1 leads v_3 by 15° (or v_3 lags v_1 by 15°)
v_2 leads v_3 by 75° (or v_3 lags v_2 by 75°)

□

3 COMPLEX IMPEDANCES

In this section, we learn that by using phasors to represent sinusoidal voltages and currents, we can solve sinusoidal steady-state circuit problems with relative ease. Except for the fact that we use complex arithmetic, sinusoidal steady-state analysis is virtually the same as the analysis of resistive circuits.

Inductance

Consider an inductance in which the current is a sinusoid given by

$$i_L(t) = I_m \sin(\omega t + \theta) \tag{37}$$

Recall that the voltage across an inductance is

$$v_L(t) = L\frac{di_L(t)}{dt} \tag{38}$$

Substituting Equation 37 into Equation 38 and reducing, we obtain

$$v_L(t) = \omega L I_m \cos(\omega t + \theta) \tag{39}$$

Now, the phasors for the current and voltage are

$$\mathbf{I}_L = I_m \angle \theta - 90^\circ \tag{40}$$

and

$$\mathbf{V}_L = \omega L I_m \angle \theta = V_m \angle \theta \tag{41}$$

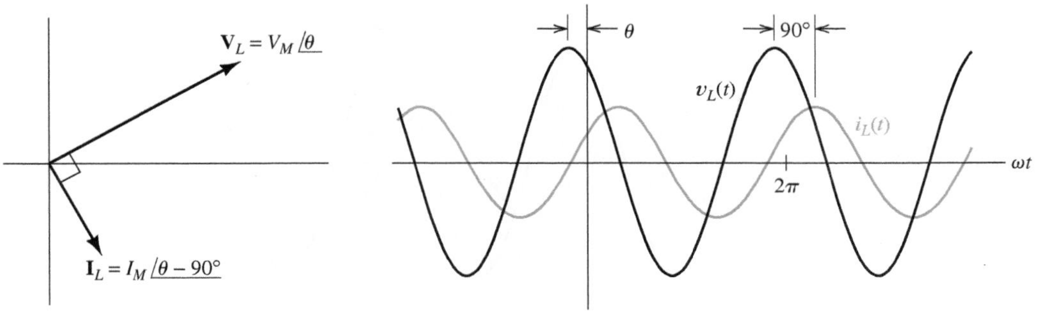

(a) Phasor diagram

(b) Current and voltage versus time

Figure 8 Current lags voltage by 90° in a pure inductance.

The phasor diagram of the current and voltage is shown in Figure 8(a). The corresponding waveforms of current and voltage are shown in Figure 8(b). *Notice that the current lags the voltage by 90° for a pure inductance.*

Current lags voltage by 90° for a pure inductance.

Equation 41 can be written in the form

$$\mathbf{V}_L = (\omega L \angle 90°) \times I_m \angle \theta - 90° \quad (42)$$

Using Equation 40 to substitute into Equation 42, we find that

$$\mathbf{V}_L = (\omega L \angle 90°) \times \mathbf{I}_L \quad (43)$$

which can also be written as

$$\mathbf{V}_L = j\omega L \times \mathbf{I}_L \quad (44)$$

We refer to the term $j\omega L = \omega L \angle 90°$ as the **impedance** of the inductance and denote it as Z_L. Thus, we have

$$Z_L = j\omega L = \omega L \angle 90° \quad (45)$$

and

$$\mathbf{V}_L = Z_L \mathbf{I}_L \quad (46)$$

Thus, the phasor voltage is equal to the impedance times the phasor current. This is Ohm's law in phasor form. However, for an inductance, the impedance is an imaginary number, whereas resistance is a real number. (Impedances that are pure imaginary are also called **reactances**.)

Equation 46 shows that phasor voltage and phasor current for an inductance are related in a manner analogous to Ohm's law.

Capacitance

In a similar fashion for a capacitance, we can show that if the current and voltage are sinusoidal, the phasors are related by

$$\mathbf{V}_C = Z_C \mathbf{I}_C \quad (47)$$

in which the impedance of the capacitance is

$$Z_C = -j\frac{1}{\omega C} = \frac{1}{j\omega C} = \frac{1}{\omega C} \angle -90° \quad (48)$$

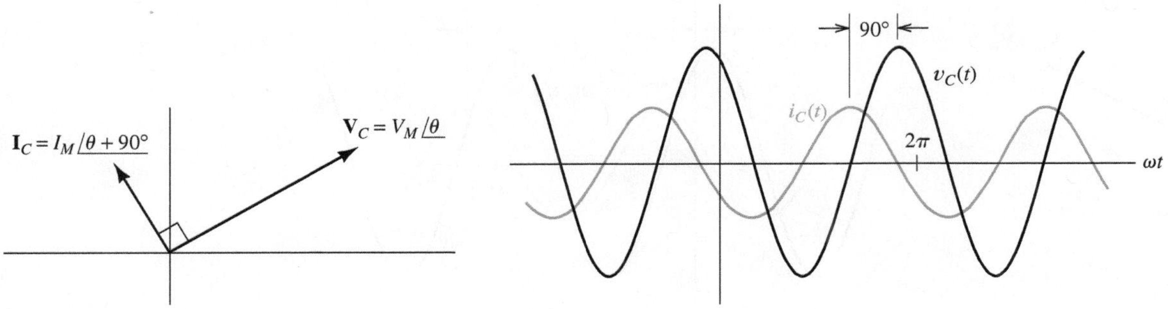

(a) Phasor diagram (b) Current and voltage versus time

Figure 9 Current leads voltage by 90° in a pure capacitance.

Notice that the impedance of a capacitance is also a pure imaginary number.

Suppose that the phasor voltage is

$$\mathbf{V}_C = V_m \angle \theta$$

Then, the phasor current is

$$\mathbf{I}_C = \frac{\mathbf{V}_C}{Z_C} = \frac{V_m \angle \theta}{(1/\omega C) \angle -90°} = \omega C V_m \angle \theta + 90°$$

$$\mathbf{I}_C = I_m \angle \theta + 90°$$

Current leads voltage by 90° for a pure capacitance.

where $I_m = \omega C V_m$. The phasor diagram for current and voltage in a pure capacitance is shown in Figure 9(a). The corresponding plots of current and voltage versus time are shown in Figure 9(b). Notice that the current leads the voltage by 90°. (On the other hand, current lags voltage for an inductance. This is easy to remember if you know *ELI* the *ICE* man. The letter *E* is sometimes used to stand for *electromotive force*, which is another term for voltage, *L* and *C* are used for inductance and capacitance, respectively, and *I* is used for current.)

Resistance

For a resistance, the phasors are related by

$$\mathbf{V}_R = R\mathbf{I}_R \tag{49}$$

Current and voltage are in phase for a resistance.

Because resistance is a real number, the current and voltage are in phase, as illustrated in Figure 10.

Exercise 6 A voltage $v_L(t) = 100\cos(200t)$ is applied to a 0.25-H inductance. (Notice that $\omega = 200$.) **a.** Find the impedance of the inductance, the phasor current, and the phasor voltage. **b.** Draw the phasor diagram.

Answer **a.** $Z_L = j50 = 50 \angle 90°$, $\mathbf{I}_L = 2 \angle -90°$, $\mathbf{V}_L = 100 \angle 0°$; **b.** the phasor diagram is shown in Figure 11(a). □

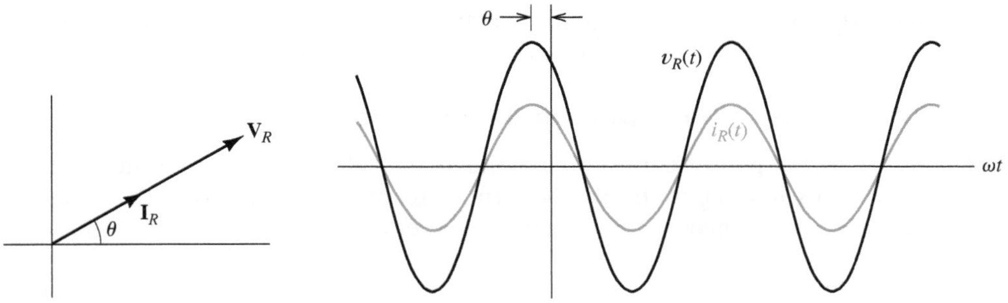

(a) Phasor diagram (b) Current and voltage versus time

Figure 10 For a pure resistance, current and voltage are in phase.

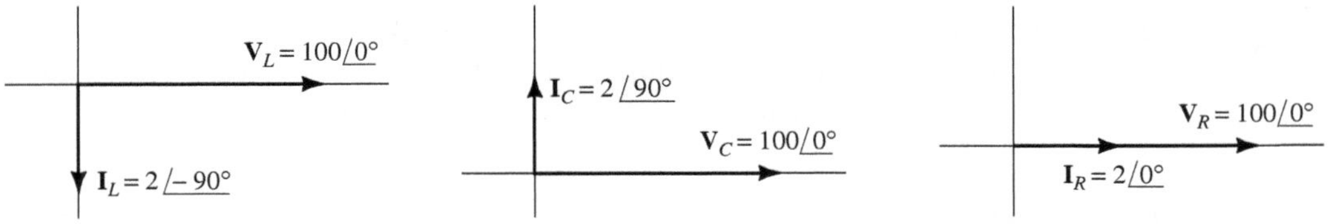

(a) Exercise 6 (0.25 H inductance) (b) Exercise 7 (100 μF capacitance) (c) Exercise 8 (50 Ω resistance)

Figure 11 Answers for Exercises 6, 7, and 8. The scale has been expanded for the currents compared with the voltages so the current phasors can be easily seen.

Exercise 7 A voltage $v_C(t) = 100\cos(200t)$ is applied to a 100-μF capacitance. **a.** Find the impedance of the capacitance, the phasor current, and the phasor voltage. **b.** Draw the phasor diagram.

Answer **a.** $Z_C = -j50 = 50\angle -90°$, $\mathbf{I}_C = 2\angle 90°$, $\mathbf{V}_C = 100\angle 0°$; **b.** the phasor diagram is shown in Figure 11(b). □

Exercise 8 A voltage $v_R(t) = 100\cos(200t)$ is applied to a 50-Ω resistance. **a.** Find the phasor for the current and the phasor voltage. **b.** Draw the phasor diagram.

Answer **a.** $\mathbf{I}_R = 2\angle 0°$, $\mathbf{V}_R = 100\angle 0°$; **b.** the phasor diagram is shown in Figure 11(c). □

4 CIRCUIT ANALYSIS WITH PHASORS AND COMPLEX IMPEDANCES

Kirchhoff's Laws in Phasor Form

Recall that KVL requires that the voltages sum to zero for any closed path in an electrical network. A typical KVL equation is

$$v_1(t) + v_2(t) - v_3(t) = 0 \tag{50}$$

If the voltages are sinusoidal, they can be represented by phasors. Then, Equation 50 becomes

$$\mathbf{V}_1 + \mathbf{V}_2 - \mathbf{V}_3 = 0 \tag{51}$$

Thus, we can apply KVL directly to the phasors. The sum of the phasor voltages equals zero for any closed path.

Similarly, KCL can be applied to currents in phasor form. The sum of the phasor currents entering a node must equal the sum of the phasor currents leaving.

Circuit Analysis Using Phasors and Impedances

We have seen that phasor currents and voltages are related by complex impedances, and Kirchhoff's laws apply in phasor form. Except for the fact that the voltages, currents, and impedances can be complex, the equations are exactly like those of resistive circuits.

A step-by-step procedure for steady-state analysis of circuits with sinusoidal sources is

1. Replace the time descriptions of the voltage and current sources with the corresponding phasors. (All of the sources must have the same frequency.)
2. Replace inductances by their complex impedances $Z_L = j\omega L = \omega L \angle 90^\circ$. Replace capacitances by their complex impedances $Z_C = 1/(j\omega C) = (1/\omega C) \angle -90^\circ$. Resistances have impedances equal to their resistances.

Example 4 Steady-State AC Analysis of a Series Circuit

Find the steady-state current for the circuit shown in Figure 12(a). Also, find the phasor voltage across each element and construct a phasor diagram.

Step 1: Replace the time description of the voltage source with the corresponding phasor.

Solution From the expression given for the source voltage $v_s(t)$, we see that the peak voltage is 100 V, the angular frequency is $\omega = 500$, and the phase angle is 30°. The phasor for the voltage source is

$$\mathbf{V}_s = 100 \angle 30^\circ$$

Step 2: Replace inductances and capacitances with their complex impedances.

The complex impedances of the inductance and capacitance are

$$Z_L = j\omega L = j500 \times 0.3 = j150\ \Omega$$

and

$$Z_C = -j\frac{1}{\omega C} = -j\frac{1}{500 \times 40 \times 10^{-6}} = -j50\ \Omega$$

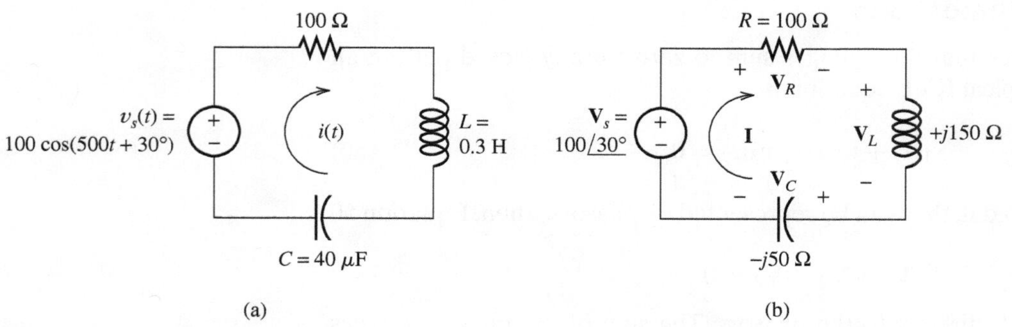

Figure 12 Circuit for Example 4.

The transformed circuit is shown in Figure 12(b). All three elements are in series. Thus, we find the equivalent impedance of the circuit by adding the impedances of all three elements:

Step 3: Use complex arithmetic to analyze the circuit.

$$Z_{\text{eq}} = R + Z_L + Z_C$$

Substituting values, we have

$$Z_{\text{eq}} = 100 + j150 - j50 = 100 + j100$$

Converting to polar form, we obtain

$$Z_{\text{eq}} = 141.4 \underline{/45^\circ}$$

Now, we can find the phasor current by dividing the phasor voltage by the equivalent impedance, resulting in

$$\mathbf{I} = \frac{\mathbf{V}_s}{Z} = \frac{100 \underline{/30^\circ}}{141.4 \underline{/45^\circ}} = 0.707 \underline{/-15^\circ}$$

As a function of time, the current is

$$i(t) = 0.707 \cos(500t - 15^\circ)$$

Next, we can find the phasor voltage across each element by multiplying the phasor current by the respective impedance:

$$\mathbf{V}_R = R \times \mathbf{I} = 100 \times 0.707 \underline{/-15^\circ} = 70.7 \underline{/-15^\circ}$$

$$\mathbf{V}_L = j\omega L \times \mathbf{I} = \omega L \underline{/90^\circ} \times \mathbf{I} = 150 \underline{/90^\circ} \times 0.707 \underline{/-15^\circ}$$
$$= 106.1 \underline{/75^\circ}$$

$$\mathbf{V}_C = -j\frac{1}{\omega C} \times \mathbf{I} = \frac{1}{\omega C} \underline{/-90^\circ} \times \mathbf{I} = 50 \underline{/-90^\circ} \times 0.707 \underline{/-15^\circ}$$
$$= 35.4 \underline{/-105^\circ}$$

The phasor diagram for the current and voltages is shown in Figure 13. Notice that the current **I** lags the source voltage $\mathbf{V}_s$ by 45°. As expected, the voltage $\mathbf{V}_R$ and current **I** are in phase for the resistance. For the inductance, the voltage $\mathbf{V}_L$ leads the current **I** by 90°. For the capacitance, the voltage $\mathbf{V}_C$ lags the current by 90°. ■

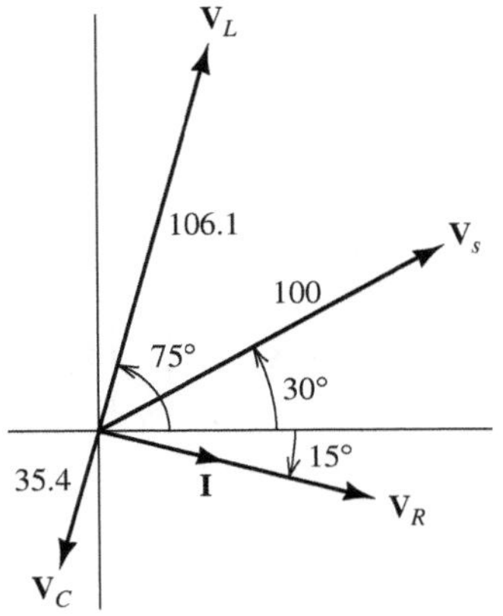

Figure 13 Phasor diagram for Example 4.

Example 5 Series and Parallel Combinations of Complex Impedances

Consider the circuit shown in Figure 14(a). Find the voltage $v_C(t)$ in steady state. Find the phasor current through each element, and construct a phasor diagram showing the currents and the source voltage.

Step 1: Replace the time description of the voltage source with the corresponding phasor.

Solution The phasor for the voltage source is $\mathbf{V}_s = 10\ \underline{/-90^\circ}$. [Notice that $v_s(t)$ is a sine function rather than a cosine function, and it is necessary to subtract 90° from the phase.] The angular frequency of the source is $\omega = 1000$. The impedances of the inductance and capacitance are

$$Z_L = j\omega L = j1000 \times 0.1 = j100\ \Omega$$

Step 2: Replace inductances and capacitances with their complex impedances.

and

$$Z_C = -j\frac{1}{\omega C} = -j\frac{1}{1000 \times 10 \times 10^{-6}} = -j100\ \Omega$$

The transformed network is shown in Figure 14(b).

Step 3: Use complex arithmetic to analyze the circuit.

To find $\mathbf{V}_C$, we will first combine the resistance and the impedance of the capacitor in parallel. Then, we will use the voltage-division principle to compute the voltage across the RC combination. The impedance of the parallel RC circuit is

$$Z_{RC} = \frac{1}{1/R + 1/Z_C} = \frac{1}{1/100 + 1/(-j100)}$$

$$= \frac{1}{0.01 + j0.01} = \frac{1\ \underline{/0^\circ}}{0.01414\ \underline{/45^\circ}} = 70.71\ \underline{/-45^\circ}$$

Converting to rectangular form, we have

$$Z_{RC} = 50 - j50$$

The equivalent network is shown in Figure 14(c).

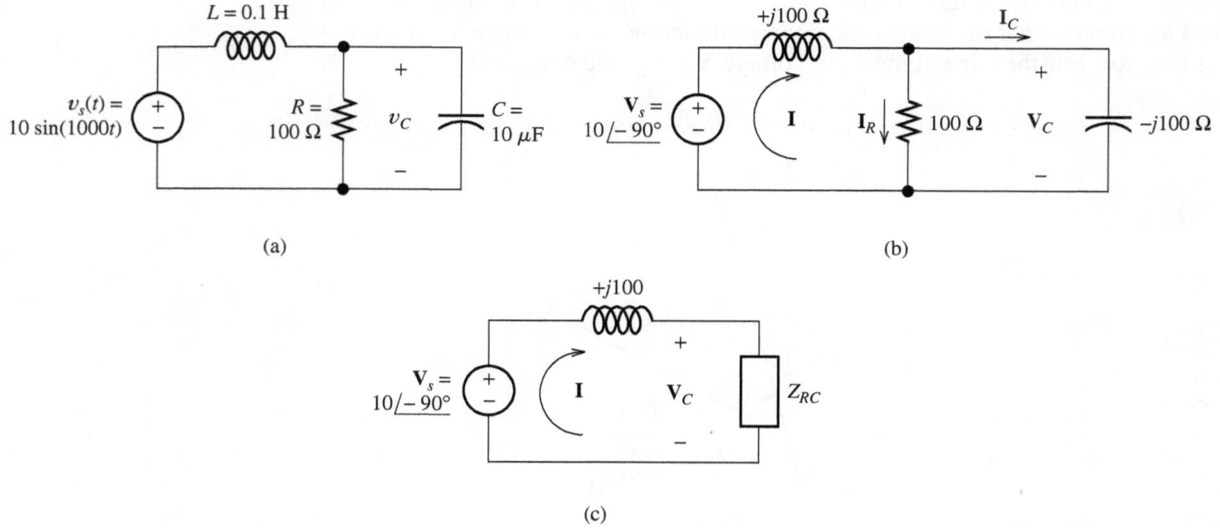

Figure 14 Circuit for Example 5.

Now, we use the voltage-division principle to obtain

$$\mathbf{V}_C = \mathbf{V}_s \frac{Z_{RC}}{Z_L + Z_{RC}} = 10\,\angle{-90^\circ}\,\frac{70.71\,\angle{-45^\circ}}{j100 + 50 - j50}$$

$$= 10\,\angle{-90^\circ}\,\frac{70.71\,\angle{-45^\circ}}{50 + j50} = 10\,\angle{-90^\circ}\,\frac{70.71\,\angle{-45^\circ}}{70.71\,\angle{45^\circ}}$$

$$= 10\,\angle{-180^\circ}$$

Converting the phasor to a time function, we have

$$v_C(t) = 10\cos(1000t - 180^\circ) = -10\cos(1000t)$$

Next, we compute the current in each element yielding

$$\mathbf{I} = \frac{\mathbf{V}_s}{Z_L + Z_{RC}} = \frac{10\,\angle{-90^\circ}}{j100 + 50 - j50} = \frac{10\,\angle{-90^\circ}}{50 + j50}$$

$$= \frac{10\,\angle{-90^\circ}}{70.71\,\angle{45^\circ}} = 0.1414\,\angle{-135^\circ}$$

$$\mathbf{I}_R = \frac{\mathbf{V}_C}{R} = \frac{10\,\angle{-180^\circ}}{100} = 0.1\,\angle{-180^\circ}$$

$$\mathbf{I}_C = \frac{\mathbf{V}_C}{Z_C} = \frac{10\,\angle{-180^\circ}}{-j100} = \frac{10\,\angle{-180^\circ}}{100\,\angle{-90^\circ}} = 0.1\,\angle{-90^\circ}$$

The phasor diagram is shown in Figure 15. ■

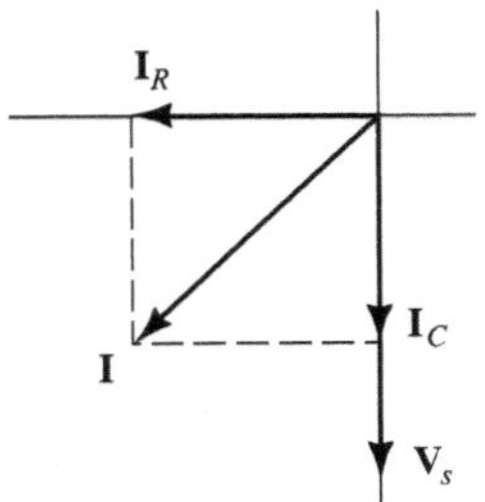

Figure 15 Phasor diagram for Example 5.

Node-Voltage Analysis

We can perform node-voltage analysis by using phasors. We illustrate with an example.

Example 6 Steady-State AC Node-Voltage Analysis

Use the node-voltage technique to find $v_1(t)$ in steady state for the circuit shown in Figure 16(a).

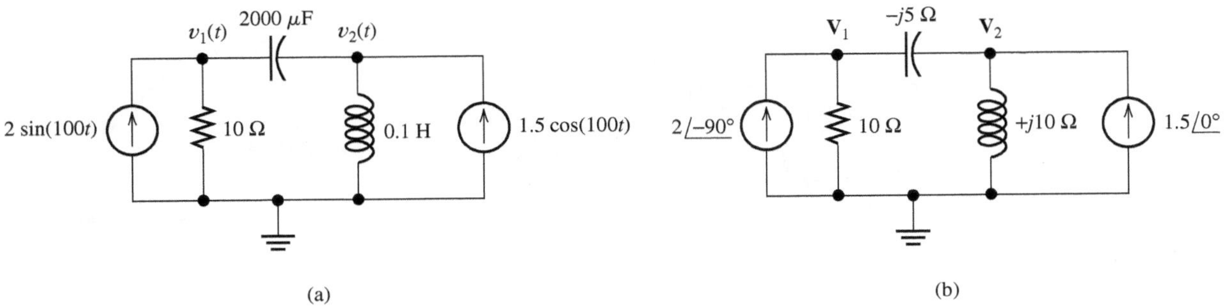

Figure 16 Circuit for Example 6.

Solution The transformed network is shown in Figure 16(b). We obtain two equations by applying KCL at node 1 and at node 2. This yields

$$\frac{\mathbf{V}_1}{10} + \frac{\mathbf{V}_1 - \mathbf{V}_2}{-j5} = 2\ \underline{/-90^\circ}$$

$$\frac{\mathbf{V}_2}{j10} + \frac{\mathbf{V}_2 - \mathbf{V}_1}{-j5} = 1.5\ \underline{/0^\circ}$$

These equations can be put into the standard form

$$(0.1 + j0.2)\mathbf{V}_1 - j0.2\mathbf{V}_2 = -j2$$

$$-j0.2\mathbf{V}_1 + j0.1\mathbf{V}_2 = 1.5$$

Now, we solve for $\mathbf{V}_1$ yielding

$$\mathbf{V}_1 = 16.1\ \underline{/29.7^\circ}$$

Then, we convert the phasor to a time function and obtain

$$v_1(t) = 16.1\cos(100t + 29.7^\circ)$$

■

Mesh-Current Analysis

In a similar fashion, you can use phasors to carry out mesh-current analysis in ac circuits. Exercise 11 gives you a chance to try this approach.

Exercise 9 Consider the circuit shown in Figure 17(a). **a.** Find $i(t)$. **b.** Construct a phasor diagram showing all three voltages and the current. **c.** What is the phase relationship between $v_s(t)$ and $i(t)$?

Answer **a.** $i(t) = 0.0283\cos(500t - 135^\circ)$; **b.** the phasor diagram is shown in Figure 17(b); **c.** $i(t)$ lags $v_s(t)$ by 45°. □

Exercise 10 Find the phasor voltage and the phasor current through each element in the circuit of Figure 18.

Answer $\mathbf{V} = 277\ \underline{/-56.3^\circ}$, $\mathbf{I}_C = 5.55\ \underline{/33.7^\circ}$, $\mathbf{I}_L = 1.39\ \underline{/-146.3^\circ}$, $\mathbf{I}_R = 2.77\ \underline{/-56.3^\circ}$. □

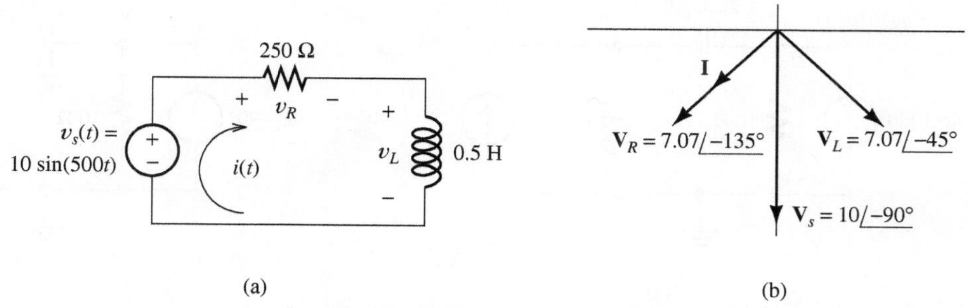

Figure 17 Circuit and phasor diagram for Exercise 9.

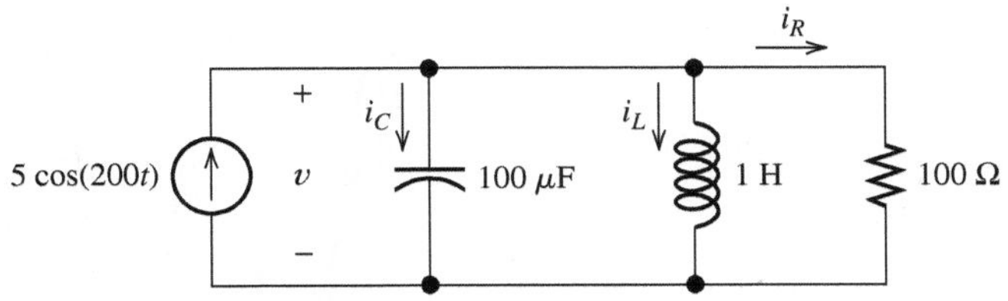

Figure 18 Circuit for Exercise 10.

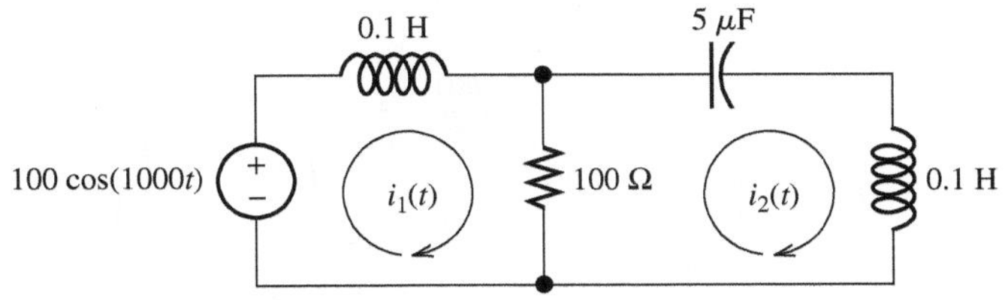

Figure 19 Circuit for Exercise 11.

Exercise 11 Solve for the mesh currents shown in Figure 19.
Answer $i_1(t) = 1.414\cos(1000t - 45°), i_2(t) = \cos(1000t)$. □

5 POWER IN AC CIRCUITS

Consider the situation shown in Figure 20. A voltage $v(t) = V_m \cos(\omega t)$ is applied to a network composed of resistances, inductances, and capacitances (i.e., an RLC network). The phasor for the voltage source is $\mathbf{V} = V_m \angle 0°$, and the equivalent impedance of the network is $Z = |Z| \angle \theta = R + jX$. The phasor current is

$$\mathbf{I} = \frac{\mathbf{V}}{Z} = \frac{V_m \angle 0°}{|Z| \angle \theta} = I_m \angle -\theta \tag{52}$$

where we have defined

$$I_m = \frac{V_m}{|Z|} \tag{53}$$

Before we consider the power delivered by the source to a general load, it is instructive to consider a pure resistive load, a pure inductive load, and a pure capacitive load.

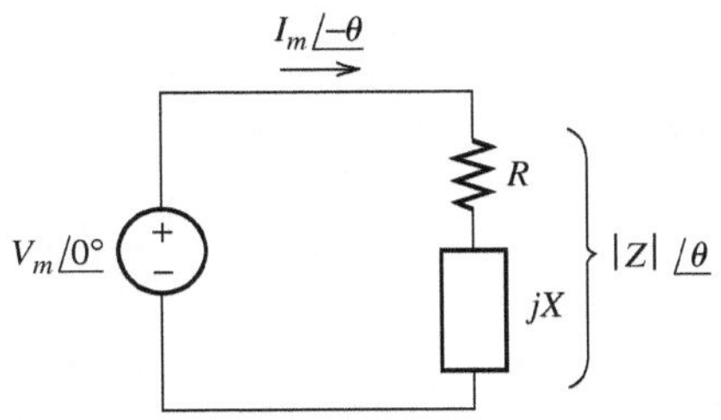

Figure 20 A voltage source delivering power to a load impedance $Z = R + jX$.

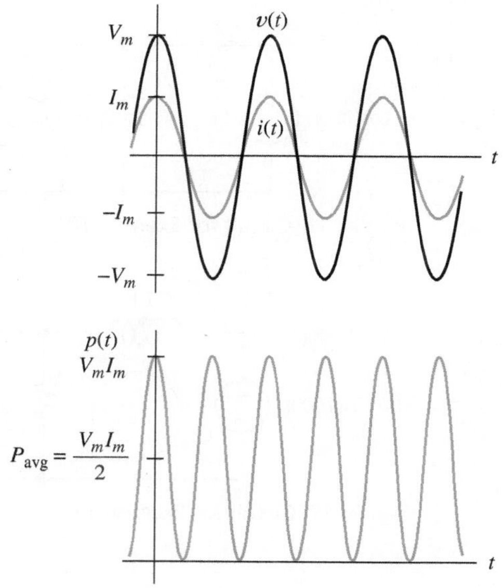

Figure 21 Current, voltage, and power versus time for a purely resistive load.

Current, Voltage, and Power for a Resistive Load

First, consider the case in which the network is a pure resistance. Then, $\theta = 0$, and we have

$$v(t) = V_m \cos(\omega t)$$
$$i(t) = I_m \cos(\omega t)$$
$$p(t) = v(t)i(t) = V_m I_m \cos^2(\omega t)$$

Average power is absorbed by resistances in ac circuits.

Plots of these quantities are shown in Figure 21. Notice that the current is in phase with the voltage (i.e., they both reach their peak values at the same time). Because $p(t)$ is positive at all times, we conclude that energy flows continually in the direction from the source to the load (where it is converted to heat). Of course, the value of the power rises and falls with the voltage (and current) magnitude.

Current, Voltage, and Power for an Inductive Load

Next, consider the case in which the load is a pure inductance for which $Z = \omega L \angle 90°$. Thus, $\theta = 90°$, and we get

$$v(t) = V_m \cos(\omega t)$$
$$i(t) = I_m \cos(\omega t - 90°) = I_m \sin(\omega t)$$
$$p(t) = v(t)i(t) = V_m I_m \cos(\omega t) \sin(\omega t)$$

Using the trigonometric identity $\cos(x)\sin(x) = (1/2)\sin(2x)$, we find that the expression for the power becomes

$$p(t) = \frac{V_m I_m}{2} \sin(2\omega t)$$

Power surges into and out of inductances in ac circuits. The average power absorbed by inductances is zero.

Plots of the current, voltage, and power are shown in Figure 22(a). Notice that the current lags the voltage by 90°. Half of the time the power is positive, showing

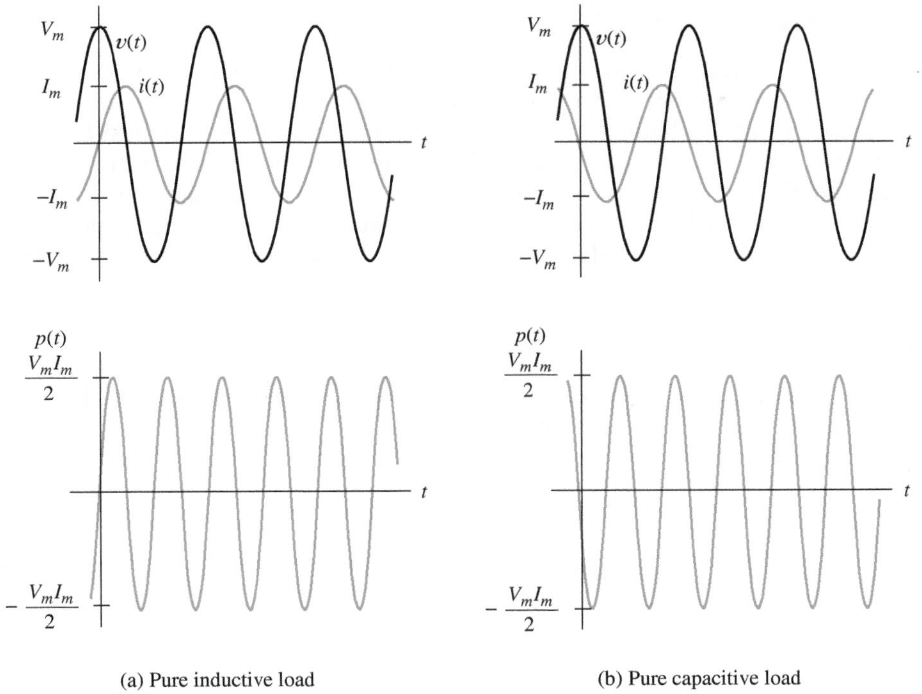

Figure 22 Current, voltage, and power versus time for pure energy-storage elements.

that energy is delivered to the inductance, where it is stored in the magnetic field. For the other half of the time, power is negative, showing that the inductance returns energy to the source. Notice that the average power is zero. In this case, we say that **reactive power** flows from the source to the load.

Current, Voltage, and Power for a Capacitive Load

Next, consider the case in which the load is a pure capacitance for which $Z = (1/\omega C)\ \angle -90°$. Then, $\theta = -90°$, and we have

$$\begin{aligned} v(t) &= V_m \cos(\omega t) \\ i(t) &= I_m \cos(\omega t + 90°) = -I_m \sin(\omega t) \\ p(t) &= v(t)i(t) = -V_m I_m \cos(\omega t)\sin(\omega t) \\ &= -\frac{V_m I_m}{2}\sin(2\omega t) \end{aligned}$$

Plots of the current, voltage, and power are shown in Figure 22(b). Here again, the average power is zero, and we say that reactive power flows. Notice, however, that the power for the capacitance carries the opposite sign as that for the inductance. Thus, we say that reactive power is positive for an inductance and is negative for a capacitance. If a load contains both inductance and capacitance with reactive powers of equal magnitude, the reactive powers cancel.

Power surges into and out of capacitances in ac circuits. The average power absorbed by capacitances is zero.

Importance of Reactive Power

The power flow back and forth to inductances and capacitances is called reactive power. Reactive power flow is important because it causes power dissipation in the lines and transformers of a power distribution system.

Even though no average power is consumed by a pure energy-storage element (inductance or capacitance), reactive power is still of concern to power-system engineers because transmission lines, transformers, fuses, and other elements must be capable of withstanding the current associated with reactive power. It is possible to have loads composed of energy-storage elements that draw large currents requiring heavy-duty wiring, even though little average power is consumed. Therefore, electric-power companies charge their industrial customers for reactive power (but at a lower rate) as well as for total energy delivered.

Power Calculations for a General Load

Now, let us consider the voltage, current, and power for a general *RLC* load for which the phase θ can be any value from $-90°$ to $+90°$. We have

$$v(t) = V_m \cos(\omega t) \tag{54}$$

$$i(t) = I_m \cos(\omega t - \theta) \tag{55}$$

$$p(t) = V_m I_m \cos(\omega t)\cos(\omega t - \theta) \tag{56}$$

Using the trigonometric identity

$$\cos(\omega t - \theta) = \cos(\theta)\cos(\omega t) + \sin(\theta)\sin(\omega t)$$

we can put Equation 56 into the form

$$p(t) = V_m I_m \cos(\theta)\cos^2(\omega t) + V_m I_m \sin(\theta)\cos(\omega t)\sin(\omega t) \tag{57}$$

Using the identities

$$\cos^2(\omega t) = \frac{1}{2} + \frac{1}{2}\cos(2\omega t)$$

and

$$\cos(\omega t)\sin(\omega t) = \frac{1}{2}\sin(2\omega t)$$

we find that Equation 57 can be written as

$$p(t) = \frac{V_m I_m}{2}\cos(\theta)[1 + \cos(2\omega t)] + \frac{V_m I_m}{2}\sin(\theta)\sin(2\omega t) \tag{58}$$

Notice that the terms involving $\cos(2\omega t)$ and $\sin(2\omega t)$ have average values of zero. Thus, the average power P is given by

$$P = \frac{V_m I_m}{2}\cos(\theta) \tag{59}$$

Using the fact that $V_{\text{rms}} = V_m/\sqrt{2}$ and $I_{\text{rms}} = I_m/\sqrt{2}$, we can write the expression for average power as

$$P = V_{\text{rms}} I_{\text{rms}} \cos(\theta) \tag{60}$$

As usual, the units of power are watts (W).

Power Factor

The term $\cos(\theta)$ is called the **power factor**:

$$\text{PF} = \cos(\theta) \tag{61}$$

To simplify our discussion, we assumed a voltage having zero phase. In general, the phase of the voltage may have a value other than zero. Then, θ should be taken as the phase of the voltage θ_v minus the phase of the current θ_i, or

Power factor is the cosine of the angle θ by which the current lags the voltage. (If the current leads the voltage, the angle is negative.)

$$\theta = \theta_v - \theta_i \tag{62}$$

Sometimes, θ is called the **power angle**.

Often, power factor is stated as a percentage. Also, it is common to state whether the current leads (capacitive load) or lags (inductive load) the voltage. A typical power factor would be stated to be 90 percent lagging, which means that $\cos(\theta) = 0.9$ and that the current lags the voltage.

Often, power factor is expressed as a percentage.

If the current lags the voltage, the power factor is said to be inductive or lagging. If the current leads the voltage, the power factor is said to be capacitive or leading.

Reactive Power

In ac circuits, energy flows into and out of energy storage elements (inductances and capacitances). For example, when the voltage magnitude across a capacitance is increasing, energy flows into it, and when the voltage magnitude decreases, energy flows out. Similarly, energy flows into an inductance when the current flowing through it increases in magnitude. Although instantaneous power can be very large, the net energy transferred per cycle is zero for either an ideal capacitance or inductance.

When a capacitance and an inductance are in parallel (or series) energy flows into one, while it flows out of the other. Thus, the power flow of a capacitance tends to cancel that of an inductance at each instant in time.

The peak instantaneous power associated with the energy storage elements contained in a general load is called **reactive power** and is given by

$$Q = V_{\text{rms}} I_{\text{rms}} \sin(\theta) \tag{63}$$

where θ is the power angle given by Equation 62, V_{rms} is the effective (or rms) voltage across the load, and I_{rms} is the effective current through the load. (Notice that if we had a purely resistive load, we would have $\theta = 0$ and $Q = 0$.)

The physical units of reactive power are watts. However, to emphasize the fact that Q does not represent the flow of net energy, its units are usually given as *V*olt *A*mperes *R*eactive (VARs).

The units of reactive power Q are VARs.

Apparent Power

Another quantity of interest is the **apparent power**, which is defined as the product of the effective voltage and the effective current, or

Apparent power equals the product of rms current and rms voltage. The units for apparent power are stated as volt-amperes (VA).

$$\text{apparent power} = V_{\text{rms}} I_{\text{rms}}$$

Its units are volt-amperes (VA).

Using Equations 60 and 63, we can write

$$P^2 + Q^2 = (V_{\text{rms}} I_{\text{rms}})^2 \cos^2(\theta) + (V_{\text{rms}} I_{\text{rms}})^2 \sin^2(\theta)$$

However, $\cos^2(\theta) + \sin^2(\theta) = 1$, so we have

$$P^2 + Q^2 = (V_{\text{rms}} I_{\text{rms}})^2 \qquad (64)$$

Units

Often, the units given for a quantity indicate whether the quantity is power (W), reactive power (VAR), or apparent power (VA). For example, if we say that we have a 5-kW load, this means that $P = 5$ kW. On the other hand, if we have a 5-kVA load, $V_{\text{rms}} I_{\text{rms}} = 5$ kVA. If we say that a load absorbs 5 kVAR, then $Q = 5$ kVAR.

Power Triangle

The power triangle is a compact way to represent ac power relationships.

The relationships between real power P, reactive power Q, apparent power $V_{\text{rms}} I_{\text{rms}}$, and the power angle θ can be represented by the **power triangle**. The power triangle is shown in Figure 23(a) for an inductive load, in which case θ and Q are positive. The power triangle for a capacitive load is shown in Figure 23(b), in which case θ and Q are negative.

Additional Power Relationships

The impedance Z is

$$Z = |Z| \angle \theta = R + jX$$

in which R is the resistance of the load and X is the reactance. This is illustrated in Figure 24. We can write

$$\cos(\theta) = \frac{R}{|Z|} \qquad (65)$$

and

$$\sin(\theta) = \frac{X}{|Z|} \qquad (66)$$

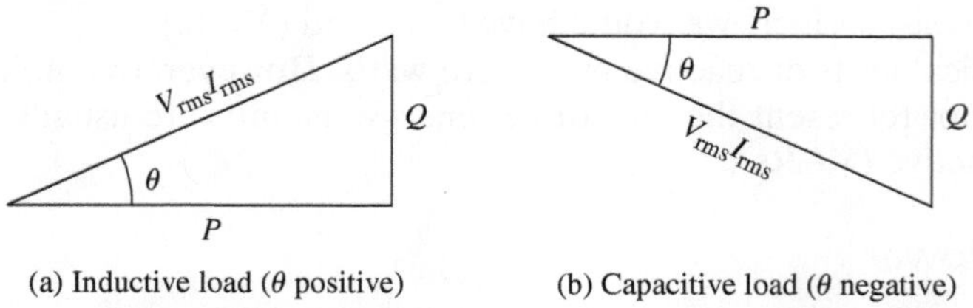

Figure 23 Power triangles for inductive and capacitive loads.

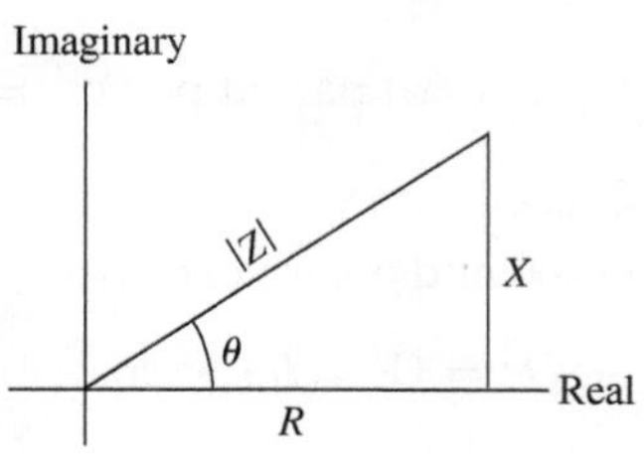

Figure 24 The load impedance in the complex plane.

Substituting Equation 65 into Equation 59, we find that

$$P = \frac{V_m I_m}{2} \times \frac{R}{|Z|} \tag{67}$$

However, Equation 53 states that $I_m = V_m/|Z|$, so we have

$$P = \frac{I_m^2}{2} R \tag{68}$$

Using the fact that $I_{\text{rms}} = I_m/\sqrt{2}$, we get

$$P = I_{\text{rms}}^2 R \tag{69}$$

In Equation 69, R is the real part of the impedance through which the current flows.

In a similar fashion, we can show that

$$Q = I_{\text{rms}}^2 X \tag{70}$$

In Equation 70, X is the imaginary part (including the algebraic sign) of the impedance through which the current flows.

In applying Equation 70, we retain the algebraic sign of X. For an inductive load, X is positive, whereas for a capacitive load, X is negative. This is not hard to remember if we keep in mind that Q is positive for inductive loads and negative for capacitive loads.

Reactive power Q is positive for inductive loads and negative for capacitive loads.

Furthermore, in Section 1, we showed that the average power delivered to a resistance is

$$P = \frac{V_{R\text{rms}}^2}{R} \tag{71}$$

In Equation 71, $V_{R\text{rms}}$ is the rms voltage across the resistance.

where $V_{R\text{rms}}$ is the rms value of the voltage *across the resistance.* (Notice in Figure 20 that the source voltage does not appear across the resistance, because the reactance is in series with the resistance.)

Similarly, we have

$$Q = \frac{V_{X\text{rms}}^2}{X} \tag{72}$$

In Equation 72, $V_{X\text{rms}}$ is the rms voltage across the reactance.

where $V_{X\text{rms}}$ is the rms value of the voltage *across the reactance*. Here again, X is positive for an inductance and negative for a capacitance.

Complex Power

Consider the portion of a circuit shown in Figure 25. The **complex power**, denoted as **S**, delivered to this circuit is defined as one half the product of the phasor voltage **V** and the complex conjugate of the phasor current **I***.

$$\mathbf{S} = \frac{1}{2}\mathbf{V}\mathbf{I}^* \tag{73}$$

The phasor voltage is $\mathbf{V} = V_m \angle \theta_v$ in which V_m is the peak value of the voltage and θ_v is the phase angle of the voltage. Furthermore, the phasor current is $\mathbf{I} = I_m \angle \theta_i$

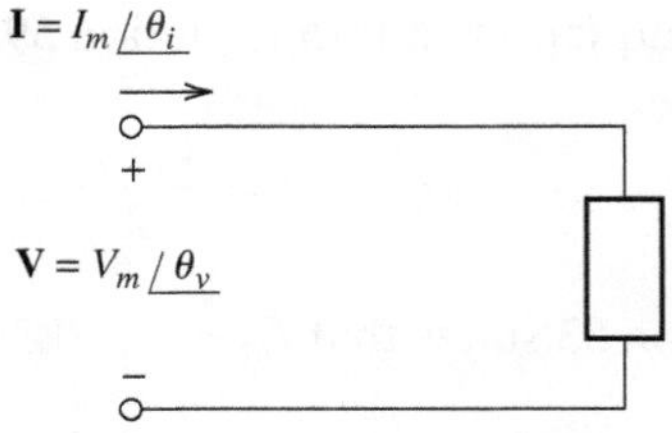

Figure 25 The complex power delivered to this circuit element is $\mathbf{S} = \frac{1}{2}\mathbf{VI}^*$.

where I_m is the peak value and θ_i is the phase angle of the current. Substituting into Equation 73, we have

$$\mathbf{S} = \frac{1}{2}\mathbf{VI}^* = \frac{1}{2}(V_m \angle \theta_v) \times (I_m \angle -\theta_i) = \frac{V_m I_m}{2} \angle \theta_v - \theta_i = \frac{V_m I_m}{2} \angle \theta \qquad (74)$$

where, as before, $\theta = \theta_v - \theta_i$ is the power angle. Expanding the right-hand term of Equation 74 into real and imaginary parts, we have

$$\mathbf{S} = \frac{V_m I_m}{2} \cos(\theta) + j\frac{V_m I_m}{2} \sin(\theta)$$

However, the first term on the right-hand side is the average power P delivered to the circuit and the second term is j times the reactive power. Thus, we can write:

$$\mathbf{S} = \frac{1}{2}\mathbf{VI}^* = P + jQ \qquad (75)$$

If we know the complex power $\mathbf{S}$, then we can find the power, reactive power, and apparent power:

$$P = \text{Re}(\mathbf{S}) = \text{Re}\left(\frac{1}{2}\mathbf{VI}^*\right) \qquad (76)$$

$$Q = \text{Im}(\mathbf{S}) = \text{Im}\left(\frac{1}{2}\mathbf{VI}^*\right) \qquad (77)$$

$$\text{apparent power} = |\mathbf{S}| = \left|\frac{1}{2}\mathbf{VI}^*\right| \qquad (78)$$

where $\text{Re}(\mathbf{S})$ denotes the real part of $\mathbf{S}$ and $\text{Im}(\mathbf{S})$ denotes the imaginary part of $\mathbf{S}$.

Example 7 AC Power Calculations

Compute the power and reactive power taken from the source for the circuit of Example 5. Also, compute the power and reactive power delivered to each element in the circuit. For convenience, the circuit and the currents that were computed in Example 5 are shown in Figure 26.

Solution To find the power and reactive power for the source, we must first find the power angle which is given by Equation 62:

$$\theta = \theta_v - \theta_i$$

The angle of the source voltage is $\theta_v = -90°$, and the angle of the current delivered by the source is $\theta_i = -135°$. Therefore, we have

$$\theta = -90° - (-135°) = 45°$$

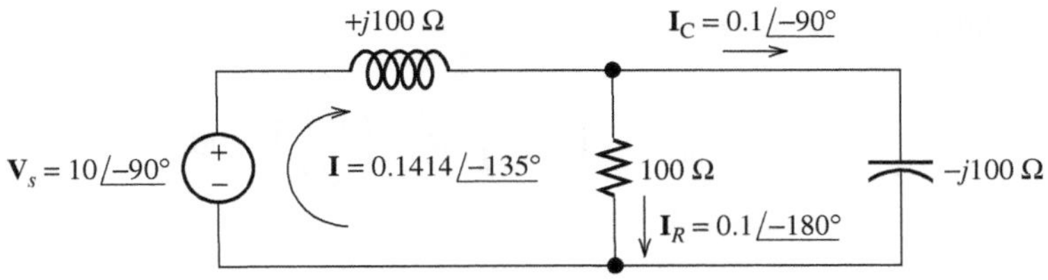

Figure 26 Circuit and currents for Example 7.

The rms source voltage and current are

$$V_{srms} = \frac{|\mathbf{V}_s|}{\sqrt{2}} = \frac{10}{\sqrt{2}} = 7.071 \text{ V}$$

$$I_{rms} = \frac{|\mathbf{I}|}{\sqrt{2}} = \frac{0.1414}{\sqrt{2}} = 0.1 \text{ A}$$

Now, we use Equations 60 and 63 to compute the power and reactive power delivered by the source:

$$\begin{aligned} P &= V_{srms} I_{rms} \cos(\theta) \\ &= 7.071 \times 0.1 \cos(45°) = 0.5 \text{ W} \\ Q &= V_{srms} I_{rms} \sin(\theta) \\ &= 7.071 \times 0.1 \sin(45°) = 0.5 \text{ VAR} \end{aligned}$$

An alternative and more compact method for computing P and Q is to first find the complex power and then take the real and imaginary parts:

$$\begin{aligned} \mathbf{S} &= \frac{1}{2}\mathbf{V}_s\mathbf{I}^* = \frac{1}{2}(10\angle -90°)(0.1414\angle 135°) = 0.707\angle 45° = 0.5 + j0.5 \\ P &= \text{Re}(\mathbf{S}) = 0.5 \text{ W} \\ Q &= \text{Im}(\mathbf{S}) = 0.5 \text{ VAR} \end{aligned}$$

We can use Equation 70 to compute the reactive power delivered to the inductor, yielding

$$Q_L = I_{rms}^2 X_L = (0.1)^2(100) = 1.0 \text{ VAR}$$

For the capacitor, we have

$$Q_C = I_{Crms}^2 X_C = \left(\frac{0.1}{\sqrt{2}}\right)^2 (-100) = -0.5 \text{ VAR}$$

Notice that we have used the rms value of the current through the capacitor in this calculation. Furthermore, notice that the reactance X_C of the capacitance is negative. As expected, the reactive power is negative for a capacitance. The reactive power for the resistance is zero. As a check, we can verify that the reactive power delivered by the source is equal to the sum of the reactive powers absorbed by the inductance and capacitance. This is demonstrated by

$$Q = Q_L + Q_C$$

The power delivered to the resistance is

$$P_R = I_{R\text{rms}}^2 R = \left(\frac{|\mathbf{I}_R|}{\sqrt{2}}\right)^2 R = \left(\frac{0.1}{\sqrt{2}}\right)^2 100$$
$$= 0.5 \text{ W}$$

The power absorbed by the capacitance and inductance is given by

$$P_L = 0$$
$$P_C = 0$$

Thus, all of the power delivered by the source is absorbed by the resistance. ■

In power distribution systems, we typically encounter much larger values of power, reactive power, and apparent power than the small values of the preceding example. For example, a large power plant may generate 1000 MW. A 100-hp motor used in an industrial application absorbs approximately 85 kW of electrical power under full load.

A typical residence absorbs a *peak* power in the range of 10 to 40 kW. The *average* power for my home (which is of average size, has two residents, and does not use electrical heating) is approximately 600 W. It is interesting to keep your average power consumption and the power used by various appliances in mind because it gives you a clear picture of the economic and environmental impact of turning off lights, computers, and so on, that are not being used.

Example 8 Using Power Triangles

Consider the situation shown in Figure 27. Here, a voltage source delivers power to two loads connected in parallel. Find the power, reactive power, and power factor for the source. Also, find the phasor current **I**.

Solution By the units given in the figure, we see that load A has an *apparent power* of 10 kVA. On the other hand, the *power* for load B is specified as 5 kW.

Furthermore, load A has a power factor of 0.5 leading, which means that the current leads the voltage in load A. Another way to say this is that load A is capacitive. Similarly, load B has a power factor of 0.7 lagging (or inductive).

Our approach is to find the power and reactive power for each load. Then, we add these values to find the power and reactive power for the source. Finally, we compute the power factor for the source and then find the current.

Calculations for load A

Because load A has a leading (capacitive) power factor, we know that the reactive power Q_A and power angle θ_A are negative. The power triangle for load A is shown

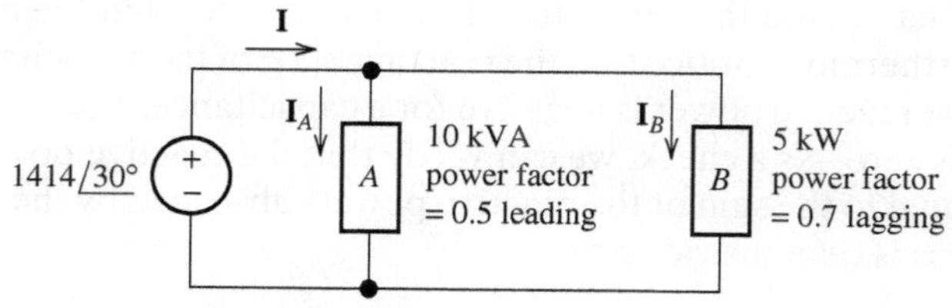

Figure 27 Circuit for Example 8.

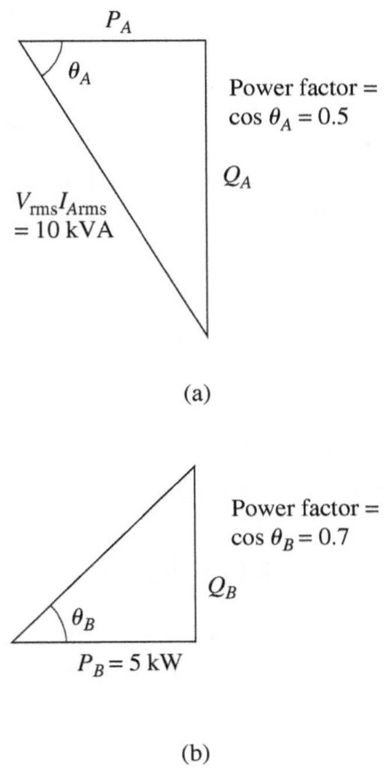

Figure 28 Power triangles for loads A and B of Example 8.

in Figure 28(a). The power factor is

$$\cos(\theta_A) = 0.5$$

The power is

$$P_A = V_{\text{rms}} I_{A\text{rms}} \cos(\theta_A) = 10^4(0.5) = 5 \text{ kW}$$

Solving Equation 64 for reactive power, we have

$$\begin{aligned} Q_A &= \sqrt{(V_{\text{rms}} I_{A\text{rms}})^2 - P_A^2} \\ &= \sqrt{(10^4)^2 - (5000)^2} \\ &= -8.660 \text{ kVAR} \end{aligned}$$

Notice that we have selected the negative value for Q_A, because we know that reactive power is negative for a capacitive (leading) load.

Calculations for load B

The power triangle for load B is shown in Figure 28(b). Since load B has a lagging (inductive) power factor, we know that the reactive power Q_B and power angle θ_B are positive. Thus,

$$\theta_B = \arccos(0.7) = 45.57^\circ$$

Applying trigonometry, we can write

$$\begin{aligned} Q_B &= P_B \tan(\theta_B) = 5000\tan(45.57^\circ) \\ Q_B &= 5.101 \text{ kVAR} \end{aligned}$$

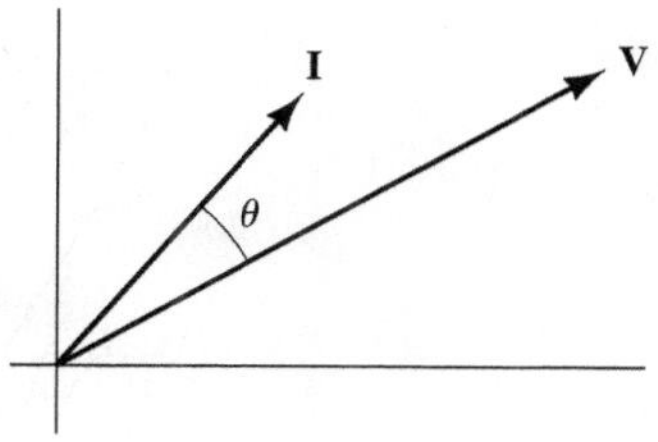

Figure 29 Phasor diagram for Example 8.

Total power is obtained by adding the powers for the various loads. Similarly, the reactive powers are added.

At this point, as shown here we can find the power and reactive power delivered by the source:

$$P = P_A + P_B = 5 + 5 = 10 \text{ kW}$$
$$Q = Q_A + Q_B = -8.660 + 5.101 = -3.559 \text{ kVAR}$$

Power calculations for the source.

Because Q is negative, we know that the power angle is negative. Thus, we have

$$\theta = \arctan\left(\frac{Q}{P}\right) = \arctan\left(\frac{-3.559}{10}\right) = -19.59^\circ$$

The power factor is

$$\cos(\theta) = 0.9421$$

Power-system engineers frequently express power factors as percentages and would state this power factor as 94.21 percent leading.

The complex power delivered by the source is

$$\mathbf{S} = P + jQ = 10 - j3.559 = 10.61 \angle -19.59^\circ \text{ kVA}$$

Thus, we have

$$\mathbf{S} = \frac{1}{2}\mathbf{V}_s\mathbf{I}^* = \frac{1}{2}(1414 \angle 30^\circ)\mathbf{I}^* = 10.61 \times 10^3 \angle -19.59^\circ \text{ kVA}$$

Solving for the phasor current, we obtain:

$$\mathbf{I} = 15.0 \angle 49.59^\circ \text{ A}$$

The phasor diagram for the current and voltage is shown in Figure 29. Notice that the current is leading the voltage. ■

Power-Factor Correction

We have seen that large currents can flow in energy-storage devices (inductance and capacitance) without average power being delivered. In heavy industry, many loads are partly inductive, and large amounts of reactive power flow. This reactive power causes higher currents in the power distribution system. Consequently, the lines and transformers must have higher ratings than would be necessary to deliver the same average power to a resistive (100 percent power factor) load.

Power-factor correction can provide a significant economic advantage for consumers of large amounts of electrical energy.

Energy rates charged to industry depend on the power factor, with higher charges for energy delivered at lower power factors. (Power factor is not taken into account for residential customers.) Therefore, it is advantageous to choose loads that operate at near unity power factor. A common approach is to place capacitors in parallel with an inductive load to increase the power factor.

Example 9 Power-Factor Correction

A 50-kW load operates from a 60-Hz 10-kV-rms line with a power factor of 60 percent lagging. Compute the capacitance that must be placed in parallel with the load to achieve a 90 percent lagging power factor.

Solution First, we find the load power angle:

$$\theta_L = \arccos(0.6) = 53.13^\circ$$

Then, we use the power-triangle concept to find the reactive power of the load. Hence,

$$Q_L = P_L \tan(\theta_L) = 66.67 \text{ kVAR}$$

After adding the capacitor, the power will still be 50 kW and the power angle will become

$$\theta_{\text{new}} = \arccos(0.9) = 25.84^\circ$$

The new value of the reactive power will be

$$Q_{\text{new}} = P_L \tan(\theta_{\text{new}}) = 24.22 \text{ kVAR}$$

Thus, the reactive power of the capacitance must be

$$Q_C = Q_{\text{new}} - Q_L = -42.45 \text{ kVAR}$$

Now, we find that the reactance of the capacitor is

$$X_C = -\frac{V_{\text{rms}}^2}{Q_C} = \frac{(10^4)^2}{42{,}450} = -2356\ \Omega$$

Finally, the angular frequency is

$$\omega = 2\pi 60 = 377.0$$

and the required capacitance is

$$C = \frac{1}{\omega |X_C|} = \frac{1}{377 \times 2356} = 1.126\ \mu\text{F}$$

Exercise 12 **a.** A voltage source $\mathbf{V} = 707.1\,\angle 40^\circ$ delivers 5 kW to a load with a power factor of 100 percent. Find the reactive power and the phasor current. **b.** Repeat if the power factor is 20 percent lagging. **c.** For which power factor would the current ratings of the conductors connecting the source to the load be higher? In which case could the wiring be a lower cost?

Answer **a.** $Q = 0, \mathbf{I} = 14.14 \angle 40°$; **b.** $Q = 24.49$ kVAR, $\mathbf{I} = 70.7 \angle -38.46°$; **c.** The current ratings for the conductors would need to be five times higher for part (b) than for part (a). Clearly, the wiring could be a lower cost for 100 percent power factor. □

Exercise 13 A 1-kV-rms 60-Hz voltage source delivers power to two loads in parallel. The first load is a 10-μF capacitor, and the second load absorbs an apparent power of 10 kVA with an 80 percent lagging power factor. Find the total power, the total reactive power, the power factor for the source, and the rms source current.

Answer $P = 8$ kW, $Q = 2.23$ kVAR, PF = 96.33 percent lagging, $I_{rms} = 8.305$ A. □

6 THÉVENIN AND NORTON EQUIVALENT CIRCUITS

Thévenin Equivalent Circuits

A two-terminal network composed of sources and resistances has a Thévenin equivalent circuit consisting of a voltage source in series with a resistance. We can apply this concept to circuits composed of sinusoidal sources (all having a common frequency), resistances, inductances, and capacitances. Here, the Thévenin equivalent consists of a phasor voltage source in series with a complex impedance as shown in Figure 30. Recall that phasors and complex impedances apply only for steady-state operation; therefore, these Thévenin equivalents are valid for only steady-state operation of the circuit.

The Thévenin voltage is equal to the open-circuit phasor voltage of the original circuit.

As in resistive circuits, the Thévenin voltage is equal to the open-circuit voltage of the two-terminal circuit. In ac circuits, we use phasors, so we can write

$$\mathbf{V}_t = \mathbf{V}_{oc} \quad (79)$$

We can find the Thévenin impedance by zeroing the independent sources and determining the impedance looking into the circuit terminals.

The Thévenin impedance Z_t can be found by zeroing the *independent* sources and looking back into the terminals to find the equivalent impedance. (Recall that in zeroing a voltage source, we reduce its voltage to zero, and it becomes a short circuit. On the other hand, in zeroing a current source, we reduce its current to zero, and it becomes an open circuit.) Also, keep in mind that we must not zero the *dependent* sources.

The Thévenin impedance equals the open-circuit voltage divided by the short-circuit current.

Another approach to determining the Thévenin impedance is first to find the short-circuit phasor current $\mathbf{I}_{sc}$ and the open-circuit voltage $\mathbf{V}_{oc}$. Then, the Thévenin impedance is given by

$$Z_t = \frac{\mathbf{V}_{oc}}{\mathbf{I}_{sc}} = \frac{\mathbf{V}_t}{\mathbf{I}_{sc}} \quad (80)$$

Thus, except for the use of phasors and complex impedances, the concepts and procedures for Thévenin equivalents of steady-state ac circuits are the same as for resistive circuits.

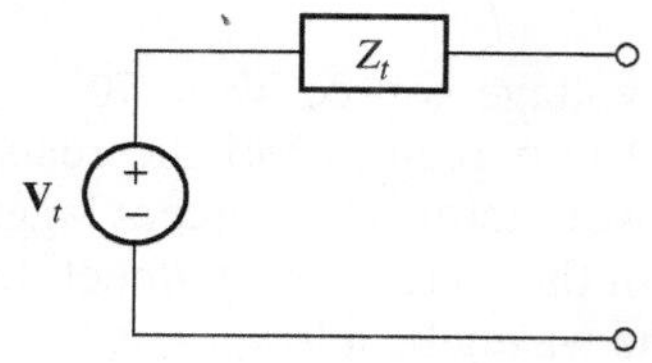

Figure 30 The Thévenin equivalent for an ac circuit consists of a phasor voltage source $\mathbf{V}_t$ in series with a complex impedance Z_t.

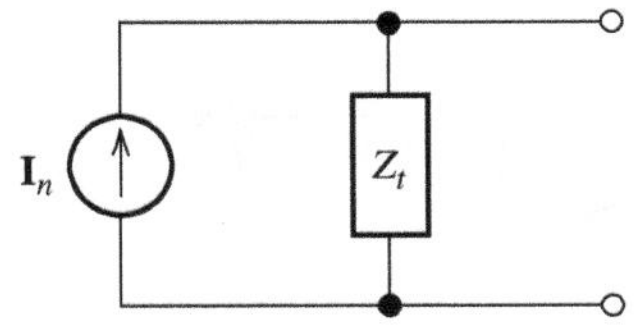

Figure 31 The Norton equivalent circuit consists of a phasor current source $\mathbf{I}_n$ in parallel with the complex impedance Z_t.

Norton Equivalent Circuits

Another equivalent for a two-terminal steady-state ac circuit is the Norton equivalent, which consists of a phasor current source $\mathbf{I}_n$ in parallel with the Thévenin impedance. This is shown in Figure 31. The Norton current is equal to the short-circuit current of the original circuit:

$$\mathbf{I}_n = \mathbf{I}_{sc} \tag{81}$$

Example 10 Thévenin and Norton Equivalents

Find the Thévenin and Norton equivalent circuits for the circuit shown in Figure 32(a).

Solution We must find two of the three quantities: $\mathbf{V}_{oc}$, $\mathbf{I}_{sc}$, or Z_t. Often, it pays to look for the two that can be found with the least amount of work. In this case, we elect to start by zeroing the sources to find Z_t. After that part of the problem is finished, we will find the short-circuit current.

First, look to see which two of the three quantities $\mathbf{V}_{oc}$, $\mathbf{I}_{sc}$, or Z_t are easiest to determine.

If we zero the sources, we obtain the circuit shown in Figure 32(b). The Thévenin impedance is the impedance seen looking back into terminals a–b. This is the parallel

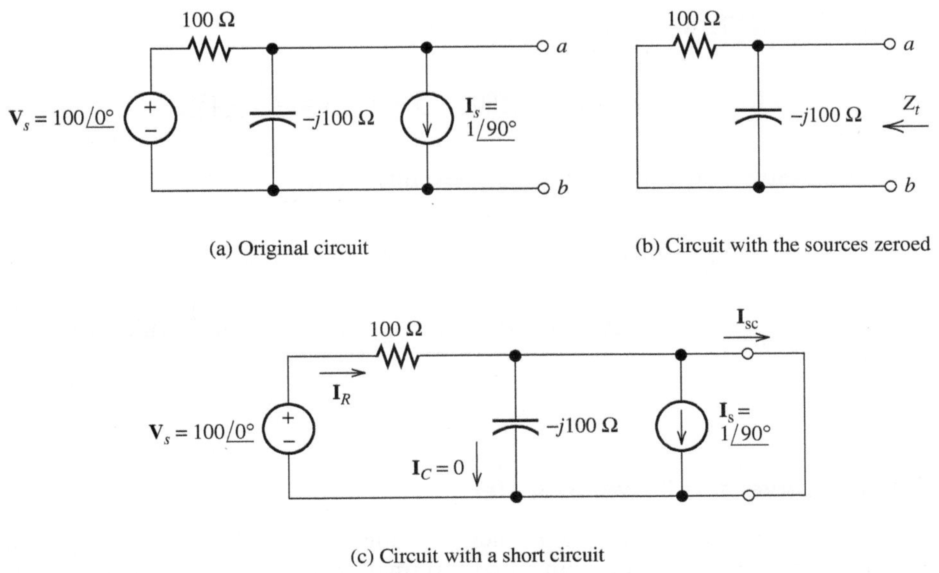

Figure 32 Circuit of Example 10.

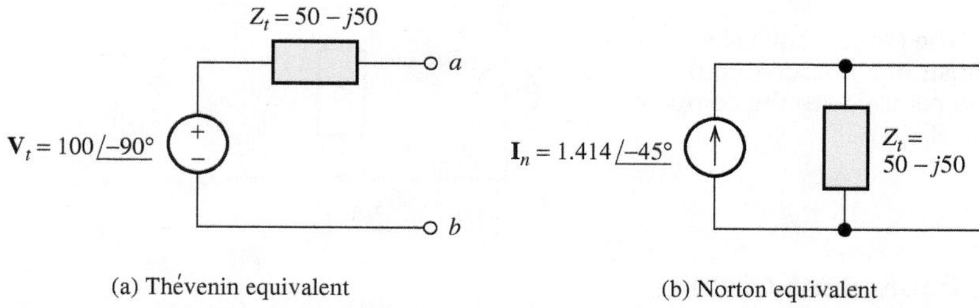

Figure 33 Thévenin and Norton equivalents for the circuit of Figure 32(a).

combination of the resistance and the impedance of the capacitance. Thus, we have

$$\begin{aligned} Z_t &= \frac{1}{1/100 + 1/(-j100)} \\ &= \frac{1}{0.01 + j0.01} \\ &= \frac{1}{0.01414\ \angle 45^\circ} \\ &= 70.71\ \angle{-45^\circ} \\ &= 50 - j50\ \Omega \end{aligned}$$

Now, we apply a short circuit to terminals a–b and find the current, which is shown in Figure 32(c). With a short circuit, the voltage across the capacitance is zero. Therefore, $\mathbf{I}_C = 0$. Furthermore, the source voltage $\mathbf{V}_s$ appears across the resistance, so we have

$$\mathbf{I}_R = \frac{\mathbf{V}_s}{100} = \frac{100}{100} = 1\ \angle 0^\circ\ \text{A}$$

Then applying KCL, we can write

$$\mathbf{I}_{sc} = \mathbf{I}_R - \mathbf{I}_s = 1 - 1\ \angle 90^\circ = 1 - j = 1.414\ \angle{-45^\circ}\ \text{A}$$

Next, we can solve Equation 80 for the Thévenin voltage:

$$\mathbf{V}_t = \mathbf{I}_{sc} Z_t = 1.414\ \angle{-45^\circ} \times 70.71\ \angle{-45^\circ} = 100\ \angle{-90^\circ}\ \text{V}$$

Finally, we can draw the Thévenin and Norton equivalent circuits, which are shown in Figure 33. ■

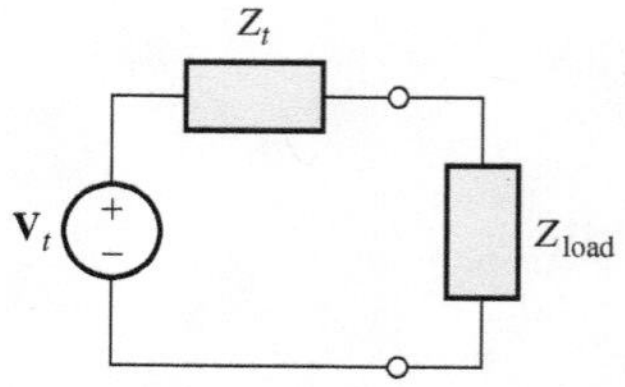

Figure 34 The Thévenin equivalent of a two-terminal circuit delivering power to a load impedance.

Maximum Average Power Transfer

Sometimes we are faced with the problem of adjusting a load impedance to extract the maximum average power from a two-terminal circuit. This situation is shown in Figure 34, in which we have represented the two-terminal circuit by its Thévenin equivalent. Of course, the power delivered to the load depends on the load impedance. A short-circuit load receives no power because the voltage across it is zero. Similarly, an open-circuit load receives no power because the current through it is zero. Furthermore, a pure reactive load (inductance or capacitance) receives no power because the load power factor is zero.

Two situations are of interest. First, suppose that the load impedance can take any complex value. Then, it turns out that the load impedance for maximum-power transfer is the complex conjugate of the Thévenin impedance:

If the load can take on any complex value, maximum-power transfer is attained for a load impedance equal to the complex conjugate of the Thévenin impedance.

$$Z_{\text{load}} = Z_t^*$$

Let us consider why this is true. Suppose that the Thévenin impedance is

$$Z_t = R_t + jX_t$$

Then, the load impedance for maximum-power transfer is

$$Z_{\text{load}} = Z_t^* = R_t - jX_t$$

Of course, the total impedance seen by the Thévenin source is the sum of the Thévenin impedance and the load impedance:

$$\begin{aligned} Z_{\text{total}} &= Z_t + Z_{\text{load}} \\ &= R_t + jX_t + R_t - jX_t \\ &= 2R_t \end{aligned}$$

Thus, the reactance of the load cancels the internal reactance of the two-terminal circuit. Maximum power is transferred to a given load resistance by maximizing the current. For given resistances, maximum current is achieved by choosing the reactance to minimize the total impedance magnitude. Of course, for fixed resistances, the minimum impedance magnitude occurs for zero total reactance.

Having established the fact that the total reactance should be zero, we have a resistive circuit.

The second case of interest is a load that is constrained to be a pure resistance. In this case, it can be shown that the load resistance for maximum-power transfer is equal to the magnitude of the Thévenin impedance:

$$Z_{\text{load}} = R_{\text{load}} = |Z_t|$$

Example 11 Maximum Power Transfer

Determine the maximum power that can be delivered to a load by the two-terminal circuit of Figure 32(a) if **a.** the load can have any complex value and **b.** the load must be a pure resistance.

Solution In Example 10, we found that the circuit has the Thévenin equivalent shown in Figure 33(a). The Thévenin impedance is

$$Z_t = 50 - j50\ \Omega$$

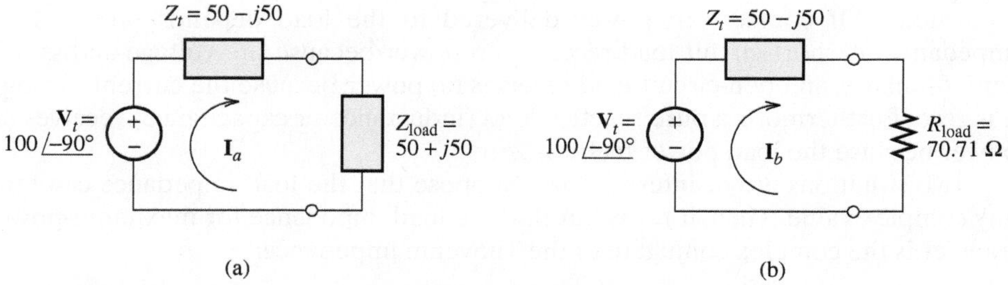

Figure 35 Thévenin equivalent circuit and loads of Example 11.

a. The complex load impedance that maximizes power transfer is

$$Z_{load} = Z_t^* = 50 + j50$$

The Thévenin equivalent with this load attached is shown in Figure 35(a). The current is

$$\mathbf{I}_a = \frac{\mathbf{V}_t}{Z_t + Z_{load}} = \frac{100\ \angle{-90°}}{50 - j50 + 50 + j50} = 1\ \angle{-90°}\ \text{A}$$

The rms load current is $I_{arms} = 1/\sqrt{2}$. Finally, the power delivered to the load is

$$P = I_{arms}^2 R_{load} = \left(\frac{1}{\sqrt{2}}\right)^2 (50) = 25\ \text{W}$$

b. The purely resistive load for maximum power transfer is

$$R_{load} = |Z_t| = |50 - j50| = \sqrt{50^2 + (-50)^2} = 70.71\ \Omega$$

The Thévenin equivalent with this load attached is shown in Figure 35(b). The current is

$$\mathbf{I}_b = \frac{\mathbf{V}_t}{Z_t + Z_{load}} = \frac{100\ \angle{-90°}}{50 - j50 + 70.71} = \frac{100\ \angle{-90°}}{130.66\ \angle{-22.50°}} = 0.7654\ \angle{-67.50°}\ \text{A}$$

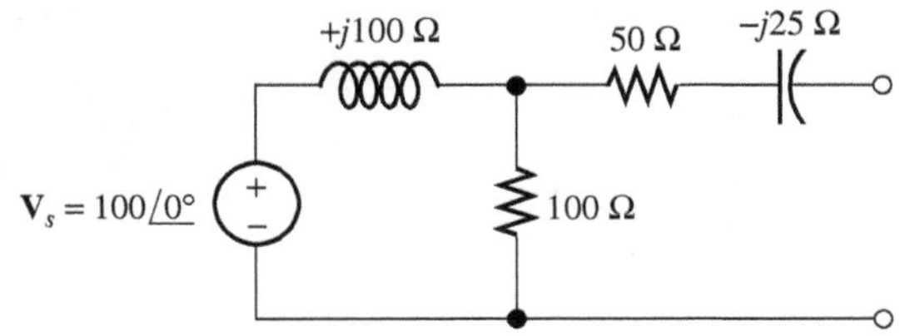

Figure 36 Circuit of Exercises 14 and 15.

The power delivered to this load is

$$P = I^2_{brms} R_{load}$$
$$= \left(\frac{0.7653}{\sqrt{2}}\right)^2 70.71$$
$$= 20.71 \text{ W}$$

Notice that the power available to a purely resistive load is less than that for a complex load. ■

Exercise 14 Find the Thévenin impedance, the Thévenin voltage, and the Norton current for the circuit shown in Figure 36.

Answer $Z_t = 100 + j25\ \Omega$, $\mathbf{V}_t = 70.71\ \angle{-45°}$, $\mathbf{I}_n = 0.686\ \angle{-59.0°}$. □

Exercise 15 Determine the maximum power that can be delivered to a load by the two-terminal circuit of Figure 36 if **a.** the load can have any complex value and **b.** the load must be a pure resistance.

Answer **a.** 6.25 W; **b.** 6.16 W. □

7 BALANCED THREE-PHASE CIRCUITS

Much of the power used by business and industry is supplied by three-phase distribution systems. Plant engineers need to be familiar with three-phase power.

We will see that there are important advantages in generating and distributing power with multiple ac voltages having different phases. We consider the most common case: three equal-amplitude ac voltages having phases that are 120° apart. This is known as a **balanced three-phase source**, an example of which is illustrated in Figure 37. [Recall that in double-subscript notation for voltages the first subscript is the positive reference. Thus, $v_{an}(t)$ is the voltage between nodes a and n with the positive reference at node a.]

The source shown in Figure 37(a) is said to be **wye connected (Y connected)**. Later in this chapter, we consider another configuration, known as the delta (Δ) connection.

The three voltages shown in Figure 37(b) are given by

$$v_{an}(t) = V_Y \cos(\omega t) \tag{82}$$

$$v_{bn}(t) = V_Y \cos(\omega t - 120°) \tag{83}$$

$$v_{cn}(t) = V_Y \cos(\omega t + 120°) \tag{84}$$

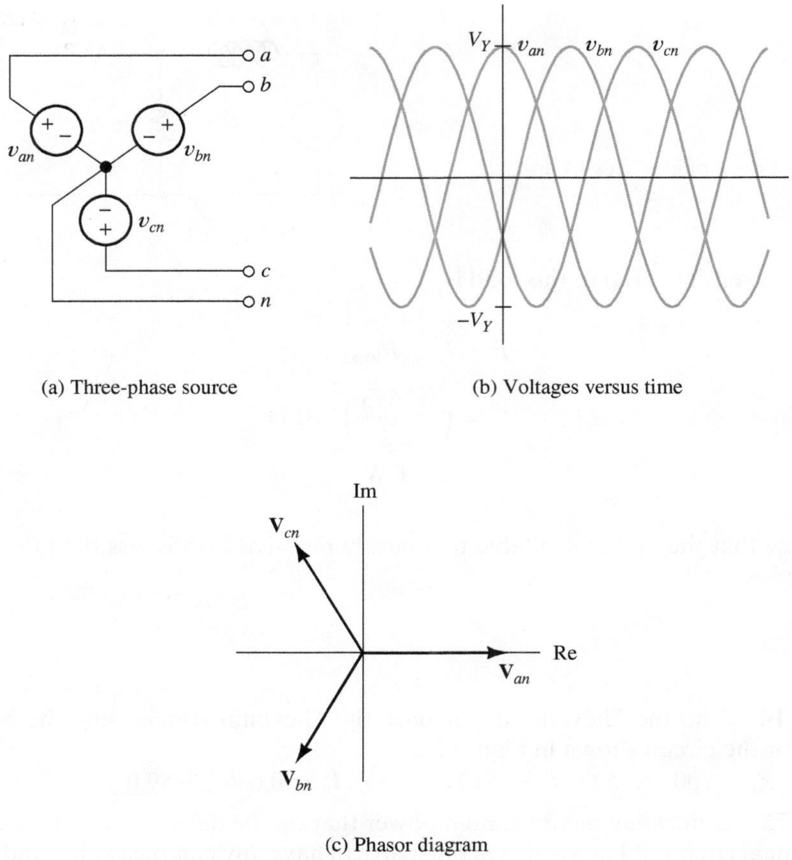

Figure 37 A balanced three-phase voltage source.

where V_Y is the magnitude of each source in the wye-connected configuration. The corresponding phasors are

$$\mathbf{V}_{an} = V_Y \angle 0^\circ \tag{85}$$

$$\mathbf{V}_{bn} = V_Y \angle -120^\circ \tag{86}$$

$$\mathbf{V}_{cn} = V_Y \angle 120^\circ \tag{87}$$

The phasor diagram is shown in Figure 37(c).

Phase Sequence

Three-phase sources can have either a positive or negative phase sequence.

This set of voltages is said to have a **positive phase sequence** because the voltages reach their peak values in the order *abc*. Refer to Figure 37(c) and notice that v_{an} leads v_{bn}, which in turn leads v_{cn}. (Recall that we think of the phasors as rotating counterclockwise in determining phase relationships.) If we interchanged b and c, we would have a **negative phase sequence**, in which the order is *acb*.

We will see later in the text that the direction of rotation of certain three-phase motors can be reversed by changing the phase sequence.

Phase sequence can be important. For example, if we have a three-phase induction motor, the direction of rotation is opposite for the two phase sequences. To reverse the direction of rotation of such a motor, we would interchange the b and c connections. (You may find this piece of information useful if you ever work with three-phase motors, which are very common in industry.) Because circuit analysis is very similar for both phase sequences, we consider only the positive phase sequence in most of the discussion that follows.

Wye–Wye Connection

Consider the three-phase source connected to a balanced three-phase load shown in Figure 38. The wires a–A, b–B, and c–C are called **lines**, and the wire n–N is called the **neutral**. This configuration is called a wye–wye (Y–Y) connection with neutral. By the term *balanced load*, we mean that the three load impedances are equal.

Three-phase sources and loads can be connected either in a wye configuration or in a delta configuration.

Later, we will see that other configurations are useful. For example, the neutral wire n–N can be omitted. Furthermore, the source and load can be connected in the form of a delta. We will see that currents, voltages, and power can be computed for these other configurations by finding an equivalent wye–wye circuit. Thus, the key to understanding three-phase circuits is a careful examination of the wye–wye circuit.

The key to understanding the various three-phase configurations is a careful examination of the wye–wye circuit.

Often, we use the term *phase* to refer to part of the source or the load. Thus, phase A of the source is $v_{an}(t)$, and phase A of the load is the impedance connected between A and N. We refer to V_Y as the **phase voltage** or as the **line-to-neutral voltage** of the wye-connected source. (Power-systems engineers usually specify rms values rather than peak magnitudes. Unless stated otherwise, we use phasors having magnitudes equal to the peak values rather than the rms values.) Furthermore, $\mathbf{I}_{aA}$, $\mathbf{I}_{bB}$, and $\mathbf{I}_{cC}$ are called **line currents**. (Recall that in the double-subscript notation for currents, the reference direction is from the first subscript to the second. Thus, $\mathbf{I}_{aA}$ is the current referenced from node a to node A, as illustrated in Figure 38.)

The current in phase A of the load is given by

$$\mathbf{I}_{aA} = \frac{\mathbf{V}_{an}}{Z\,\angle\theta} = \frac{V_Y\,\angle 0^\circ}{Z\,\angle\theta} = I_L\,\angle{-\theta}$$

where $I_L = V_Y/Z$ is the magnitude of the line current. Because the load impedances are equal, all of the line currents are the same, except for phase. Thus, the currents are given by

$$i_{aA}(t) = I_L \cos(\omega t - \theta) \tag{88}$$

$$i_{bB}(t) = I_L \cos(\omega t - 120^\circ - \theta) \tag{89}$$

$$i_{cC}(t) = I_L \cos(\omega t + 120^\circ - \theta) \tag{90}$$

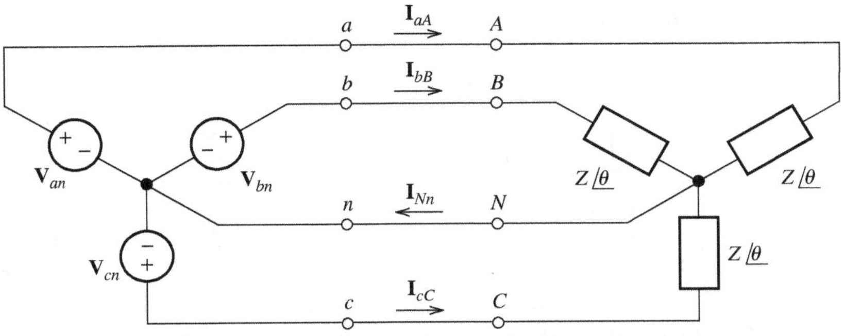

Figure 38 A three-phase wye–wye connection with neutral.

The neutral current in Figure 38 is given by

$$i_{Nn}(t) = i_{aA}(t) + i_{bB}(t) + i_{cC}(t)$$

In terms of phasors, this is

$$\begin{aligned}
\mathbf{I}_{Nn} &= \mathbf{I}_{aA} + \mathbf{I}_{bB} + \mathbf{I}_{cC} \\
&= I_L \underline{/-\theta} + I_L \underline{/-120^\circ - \theta} + I_L \underline{/120^\circ - \theta} \\
&= I_L \underline{/-\theta} \times (1 + 1 \underline{/-120^\circ} + 1 \underline{/120^\circ}) \\
&= I_L \underline{/-\theta} \times (1 - 0.5 - j0.866 - 0.5 + j0.866) \\
&= 0
\end{aligned}$$

The sum of three equal magnitude phasors 120° apart in phase is zero.

The neutral current is zero in a balanced wye–wye system. Thus in theory, the neutral wire can be inserted or removed without affecting load currents or voltages. This is *not* true if the load is unbalanced, which is often the case in real power distribution systems.

Thus, the sum of three phasors with equal magnitudes and 120° apart in phase is zero. (We make use of this fact again later in this section.)

We have shown that the neutral current is zero in a balanced three-phase system. Consequently, the neutral wire can be eliminated without changing any of the voltages or currents. Then, the three source voltages are delivered to the three load impedances with three wires.

An important advantage of three-phase systems compared with single phase is that the wiring for connecting the sources to the loads is less expensive. As shown in Figure 39, it would take six wires to connect three single-phase sources to three loads separately, whereas only three wires (four if the neutral wire is used) are needed for the three-phase connection to achieve the same power transfer.

Power

Another advantage of balanced three-phase systems, compared with single-phase systems, is that the total power is constant (as a function of time) rather than pulsating. (Refer to Figure 2 to see that power pulsates in the single-phase case.) To show that the power is constant for the balanced wye–wye connection shown in Figure 38, we write an expression for the total power. The power delivered to phase A of the load is $v_{an}(t)i_{aA}(t)$. Similarly, the power for each of the other phases of the load is the product of the voltage and the current. Thus, the total power is

$$p(t) = v_{an}(t)i_{aA}(t) + v_{bn}(t)i_{bB}(t) + v_{cn}(t)i_{cC}(t) \tag{91}$$

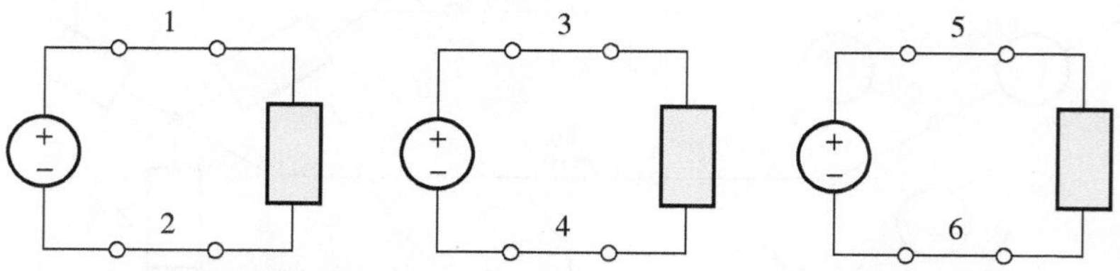

Figure 39 Six wires are needed to connect three single-phase sources to three loads. In a three-phase system, the same power transfer can be accomplished with three wires.

Using Equations 82, 83, and 84 to substitute for the voltages and Equations 88, 89, and 90 to substitute for the currents, we obtain

$$\begin{aligned} p(t) &= V_Y \cos(\omega t) I_L \cos(\omega t - \theta) \\ &\quad + V_Y \cos(\omega t - 120°) I_L \cos(\omega t - \theta - 120°) \\ &\quad + V_Y \cos(\omega t + 120°) I_L \cos(\omega t - \theta + 120°) \end{aligned} \tag{92}$$

Using the trigonometric identity

$$\cos(x)\cos(y) = \frac{1}{2}\cos(x-y) + \frac{1}{2}\cos(x+y)$$

we find that Equation 92 can be written as

$$\begin{aligned} p(t) &= 3\frac{V_Y I_L}{2}\cos(\theta) + \frac{V_Y I_L}{2}[\cos(2\omega t - \theta) \\ &\quad + \cos(2\omega t - \theta - 240°) + \cos(2\omega t - \theta + 480°)] \end{aligned} \tag{93}$$

However, the term in brackets is

$$\begin{aligned} &\cos(2\omega t - \theta) + \cos(2\omega t - \theta - 240°) + \cos(2\omega t - \theta + 480°) \\ &= \cos(2\omega t - \theta) + \cos(2\omega t - \theta + 120°) + \cos(2\omega t - \theta - 120°) \\ &= 0 \end{aligned}$$

(Here, we have used the fact, established earlier, that the sum is zero for three sine waves of equal amplitude and 120° apart in phase.) Thus, the expression for power becomes

$$p(t) = 3\frac{V_Y I_L}{2}\cos(\theta) \tag{94}$$

Notice that the total power is constant with respect to time. A consequence of this fact is that the torque required to drive a three-phase generator connected to a balanced load is constant, and vibration is lessened. Similarly, the torque produced by a three-phase motor is constant rather than pulsating as it is for a single-phase motor.

In balanced three-phase systems, total power flow is constant with respect to time.

The rms voltage from each line to neutral is

$$V_{Y\text{rms}} = \frac{V_Y}{\sqrt{2}} \tag{95}$$

Similarly, the rms value of the line current is

$$I_{L\text{rms}} = \frac{I_L}{\sqrt{2}} \tag{96}$$

Using Equations 95 and 96 to substitute into Equation 94, we find that

$$P_{\text{avg}} = p(t) = 3V_{Y\text{rms}} I_{L\text{rms}} \cos(\theta) \tag{97}$$

In Equations 97 and 98, $V_{Y\text{rms}}$ is the rms line-to-neutral voltage, $I_{L\text{rms}}$ is the rms line current, and θ is the angle of the load impedances.

Reactive Power

As in single-phase circuits, power flows back and forth between the sources and energy-storage elements contained in a three-phase load. This power is called *reactive power*. The higher currents that result because of the presence of reactive power require wiring and other power-distribution components having higher ratings. The reactive power delivered to a balanced three-phase load is given by

$$Q = 3\frac{V_Y I_L}{2}\sin(\theta) = 3V_{Y\text{rms}}I_{L\text{rms}}\sin(\theta) \tag{98}$$

Line-to-Line Voltages

As we have mentioned earlier, the voltages between terminals $a, b,$ or c and the neutral point n are called **line-to-neutral voltages**. On the other hand, voltages between a and b, b and c, or a and c are called **line-to-line voltages** or, more simply, **line voltages**. Thus $\mathbf{V}_{an}$, $\mathbf{V}_{bn}$, and $\mathbf{V}_{cn}$ are line-to-neutral voltages, whereas $\mathbf{V}_{ab}$, $\mathbf{V}_{bc}$, and $\mathbf{V}_{ca}$ are line-to-line voltages. (For consistency, we choose the subscripts cyclically in the order *abcabc*.) Let us consider the relationships between line-to-line voltages and line-to-neutral voltages.

We can obtain the following relationship by applying KVL to Figure 38:

$$\mathbf{V}_{ab} = \mathbf{V}_{an} - \mathbf{V}_{bn}$$

Using Equations 85 and 86 to substitute for $\mathbf{V}_{an}$ and $\mathbf{V}_{bn}$, we obtain

$$\mathbf{V}_{ab} = V_Y \angle 0^\circ - V_Y \angle -120^\circ \tag{99}$$

which is equivalent to

$$\mathbf{V}_{ab} = V_Y \angle 0^\circ + V_Y \angle 60^\circ \tag{100}$$

This relationship is illustrated in Figure 40. It can be shown that Equation 100 reduces to

$$\mathbf{V}_{ab} = \sqrt{3}V_Y \angle 30^\circ \tag{101}$$

We denote the magnitude of the line-to-line voltage as V_L. The magnitude of the line-to-line voltage is $\sqrt{3}$ times the magnitude of the line-to-neutral voltage:

$$V_L = \sqrt{3}V_Y \tag{102}$$

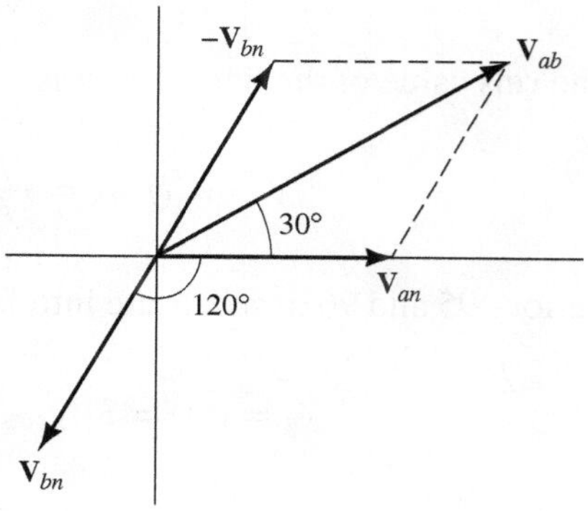

Figure 40 Phasor diagram showing the relationship between the line-to-line voltage $\mathbf{V}_{ab}$ and the line-to-neutral voltages $\mathbf{V}_{an}$ and $\mathbf{V}_{bn}$.

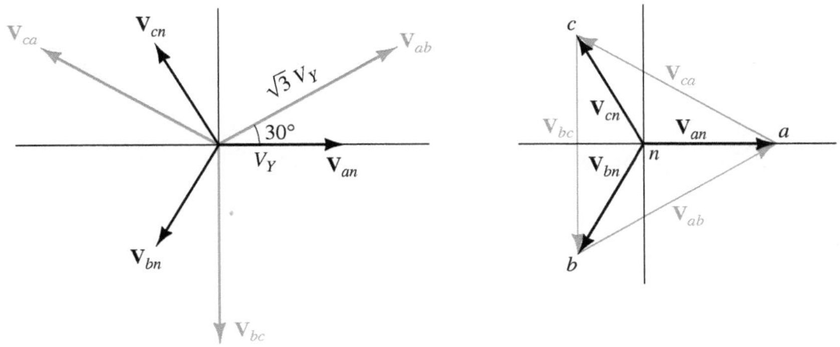

(a) All phasors starting from the origin

(b) A more intuitive way to draw the phasor diagram

Figure 41 Phasor diagram showing line-to-line voltages and line-to-neutral voltages.

Figure 41(b) provides a convenient way to remember the phase relationships between line-to-line and line-to-neutral voltages.

Thus, the relationship between the line-to-line voltage $\mathbf{V}_{ab}$ and the line-to-neutral voltage $\mathbf{V}_{an}$ is

$$\mathbf{V}_{ab} = \mathbf{V}_{an} \times \sqrt{3}\ \underline{/30^\circ} \tag{103}$$

Similarly, it can be shown that

$$\mathbf{V}_{bc} = \mathbf{V}_{bn} \times \sqrt{3}\ \underline{/30^\circ} \tag{104}$$

and

$$\mathbf{V}_{ca} = \mathbf{V}_{cn} \times \sqrt{3}\ \underline{/30^\circ} \tag{105}$$

These voltages are shown in Figure 41.

Example 12 Analysis of a Wye–Wye System

A balanced positive-sequence wye-connected 60-Hz three-phase source has line-to-neutral voltages of $V_Y = 1000$ V. This source is connected to a balanced wye-connected load. Each phase of the load consists of a 0.1-H inductance in series with a 50-Ω resistance. Find the line currents, the line-to-line voltages, the power, and the reactive power delivered to the load. Draw a phasor diagram showing the line-to-neutral voltages, the line-to-line voltages, and the line currents. Assume that the phase angle of $\mathbf{V}_{an}$ is zero.

Solution First, by computing the complex impedance of each phase of the load, we find that

$$Z = R + j\omega L = 50 + j2\pi(60)(0.1) = 50 + j37.70$$
$$= 62.62\ \underline{/37.02^\circ}$$

Next, we draw the circuit as shown in Figure 42(a). In balanced wye–wye calculations, we can assume that n and N are connected. (The currents and voltages are the same whether or not the neutral connection actually exists.) Thus, $\mathbf{V}_{an}$ appears across phase A of the load, and we can write

$$\mathbf{I}_{aA} = \frac{\mathbf{V}_{an}}{Z} = \frac{1000\ \underline{/0^\circ}}{62.62\ \underline{/37.02^\circ}} = 15.97\ \underline{/-37.02^\circ}$$

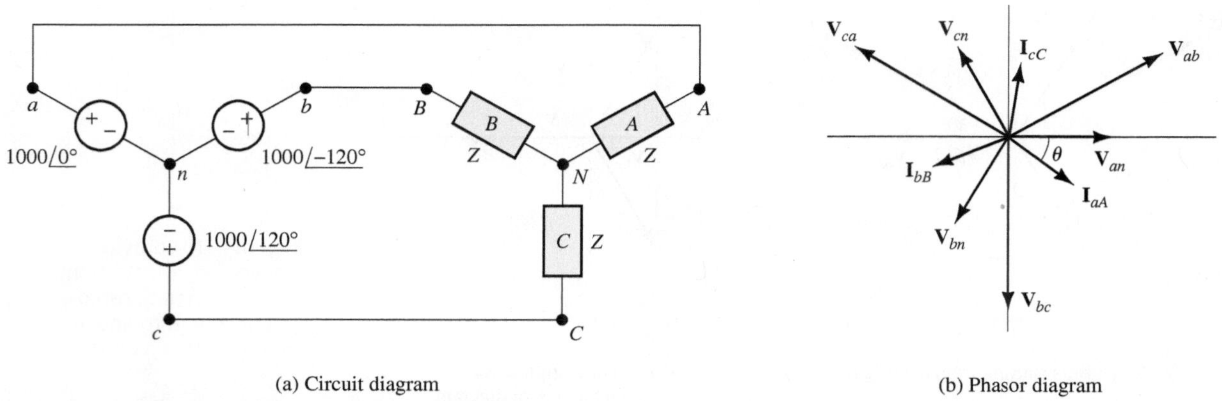

Figure 42 Circuit and phasor diagram for Example 12.

Similarly,

$$\mathbf{I}_{bB} = \frac{\mathbf{V}_{bn}}{Z} = \frac{1000\ \angle -120^\circ}{62.62\ \angle 37.02^\circ} = 15.97\ \angle -157.02^\circ$$

$$\mathbf{I}_{cC} = \frac{\mathbf{V}_{cn}}{Z} = \frac{1000\ \angle 120^\circ}{62.62\ \angle 37.02^\circ} = 15.97\ \angle 82.98^\circ$$

We use Equations 103, 104, and 105 to find the line-to-line phasors:

$$\mathbf{V}_{ab} = \mathbf{V}_{an} \times \sqrt{3}\ \angle 30^\circ = 1732\ \angle 30^\circ$$

$$\mathbf{V}_{bc} = \mathbf{V}_{bn} \times \sqrt{3}\ \angle 30^\circ = 1732\ \angle -90^\circ$$

$$\mathbf{V}_{ca} = \mathbf{V}_{cn} \times \sqrt{3}\ \angle 30^\circ = 1732\ \angle 150^\circ$$

The power delivered to the load is given by Equation 94:

$$P = 3\frac{V_Y I_L}{2}\cos(\theta) = 3\left(\frac{1000 \times 15.97}{2}\right)\cos(37.02^\circ) = 19.13\ \text{kW}$$

The reactive power is given by Equation 98:

$$Q = 3\frac{V_Y I_L}{2}\sin(\theta) = 3\left(\frac{1000 \times 15.97}{2}\right)\sin(37.02^\circ) = 14.42\ \text{kVAR}$$

The phasor diagram is shown in Figure 42(b). As usual, we have chosen a different scale for the currents than for the voltages. ■

Exercise 16 A balanced positive-sequence wye-connected 60-Hz three-phase source has line-to-line voltages of $V_L = 1000$ V. This source is connected to a balanced wye-connected load. Each phase of the load consists of a 0.2-H inductance in series with a 100-Ω resistance. Find the line-to-neutral voltages, the line currents, the power, and the reactive power delivered to the load. Assume that the phase of $\mathbf{V}_{an}$ is zero.

Answer $\mathbf{V}_{an} = 577.4\ \underline{/0^\circ}$, $\mathbf{V}_{bn} = 577.4\ \underline{/-120^\circ}$, $\mathbf{V}_{cn} = 577.4\ \underline{/120^\circ}$; $\mathbf{I}_{aA} = 4.61\ \underline{/-37^\circ}$, $\mathbf{I}_{bB} = 4.61\ \underline{/-157^\circ}$, $\mathbf{I}_{cC} = 4.61\ \underline{/83^\circ}$; $P = 3.19$ kW; $Q = 2.40$ kVAR. □

Delta-Connected Sources

A set of balanced three-phase voltage sources can be connected in the form of a delta, as shown in Figure 43. Ordinarily, we avoid connecting voltage sources in closed loops. However, in this case, it turns out that the sum of the voltages is zero:

$$\mathbf{V}_{ab} + \mathbf{V}_{bc} + \mathbf{V}_{ca} = 0$$

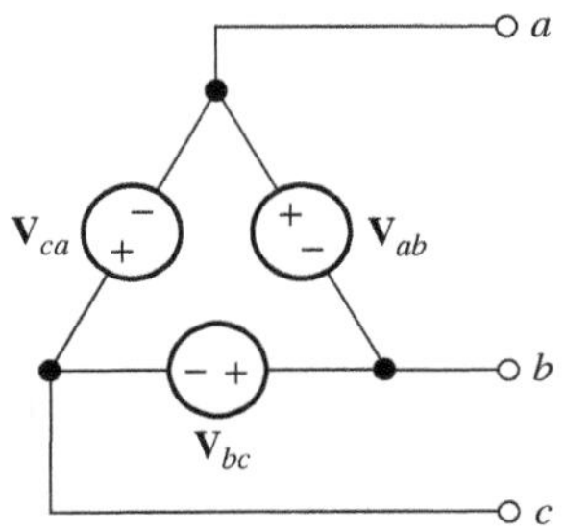

Figure 43 Delta-connected three-phase source.

Thus, the current circulating in the delta is zero. (Actually, this is a first approximation. There are many subtleties of power distribution systems that are beyond the scope of our discussion. For example, the voltages in actual power distribution systems are not exactly sinusoidal; instead, they are the sum of several harmonic components. The behavior of harmonic components is an important factor in making a choice between wye- and delta-connected sources or loads.)

For a given delta-connected source, we can find an equivalent wye-connected source (or vice versa) by using Equations 103 through 105. Clearly, a delta-connected source has no neutral point, so a four-wire connection is possible for only a wye-connected source.

Wye- and Delta-Connected Loads

Load impedances can be either wye connected or delta connected, as shown in Figure 44. It can be shown that the two loads are equivalent if

$$Z_\Delta = 3Z_Y \tag{106}$$

Thus, we can convert a delta-connected load to an equivalent wye-connected load, or vice versa.

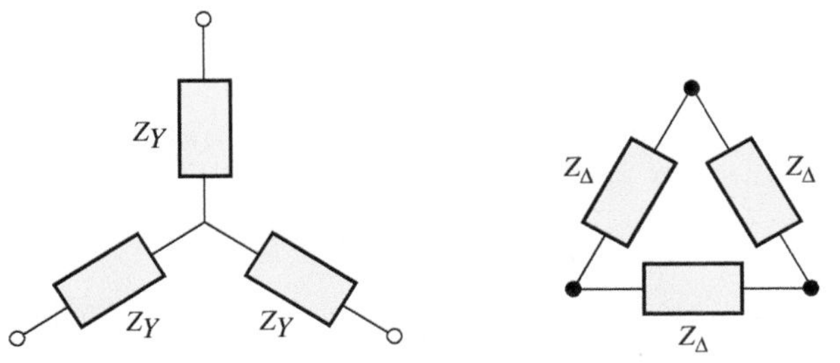

(a) Wye-connected load (b) Delta-connected load

Figure 44 Loads can be either wye connected or delta connected.

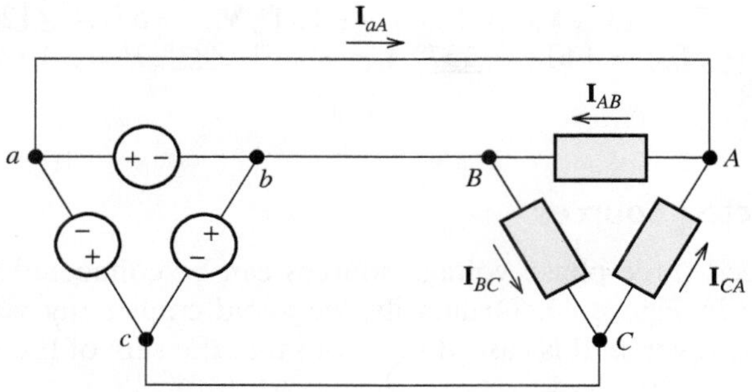

Figure 45 A delta-connected source delivering power to a delta-connected load.

Delta–Delta Connection

Figure 45 shows a delta-connected source delivering power to a delta-connected load. We assume that the source voltages are given by

$$\mathbf{V}_{ab} = V_L \angle 30^\circ \tag{107}$$

$$\mathbf{V}_{bc} = V_L \angle -90^\circ \tag{108}$$

$$\mathbf{V}_{ca} = V_L \angle 150^\circ \tag{109}$$

These phasors are shown in Figure 41. (We have chosen the phase angles of the delta-connected source to be consistent with our earlier discussion.)

If the impedances of the connecting wires are zero, the line-to-line voltages at the load are equal to those at the source. Thus $\mathbf{V}_{AB} = \mathbf{V}_{ab}$, $\mathbf{V}_{BC} = \mathbf{V}_{bc}$, and $\mathbf{V}_{CA} = \mathbf{V}_{ca}$.

We assume that the impedance of each phase of the load is $Z_\Delta \angle \theta$. Then, the load current for phase AB is

$$\mathbf{I}_{AB} = \frac{\mathbf{V}_{AB}}{Z_\Delta \angle \theta} = \frac{\mathbf{V}_{ab}}{Z_\Delta \angle \theta} = \frac{V_L \angle 30^\circ}{Z_\Delta \angle \theta} = \frac{V_L}{Z_\Delta} \angle 30^\circ - \theta$$

We define the magnitude of the current as

$$I_\Delta = \frac{V_L}{Z_\Delta} \tag{110}$$

Hence,

$$\mathbf{I}_{AB} = I_\Delta \angle 30^\circ - \theta \tag{111}$$

Similarly,

$$\mathbf{I}_{BC} = I_\Delta \angle -90^\circ - \theta \tag{112}$$

$$\mathbf{I}_{CA} = I_\Delta \angle 150^\circ - \theta \tag{113}$$

The current in line a–A is

$$\begin{aligned}\mathbf{I}_{aA} &= \mathbf{I}_{AB} - \mathbf{I}_{CA} \\ &= I_\Delta \angle 30^\circ - \theta - I_\Delta \angle 150^\circ - \theta \\ &= (I_\Delta \angle 30^\circ - \theta) \times (1 - 1 \angle 120^\circ)\end{aligned}$$

$$= (I_\Delta \angle 30^\circ - \theta) \times (1.5 - j0.8660)$$
$$= (I_\Delta \angle 30^\circ - \theta) \times (\sqrt{3} \angle -30^\circ)$$
$$= \mathbf{I}_{AB} \times \sqrt{3} \angle -30^\circ$$

The magnitude of the line current is

$$I_L = \sqrt{3} I_\Delta \tag{114}$$

For a balanced delta-connected load, the line-current magnitude is equal to the square root of three times the current magnitude in any arm of the delta.

Example 13 Analysis of a Balanced Delta–Delta System

Consider the circuit shown in Figure 46(a). A delta-connected source supplies power to a delta-connected load through wires having impedances of $Z_{\text{line}} = 0.3 + j0.4\ \Omega$. The load impedances are $Z_\Delta = 30 + j6$. The source voltages are

$$\mathbf{V}_{ab} = 1000 \angle 30^\circ$$
$$\mathbf{V}_{bc} = 1000 \angle -90^\circ$$
$$\mathbf{V}_{ca} = 1000 \angle 150^\circ$$

Find the line current, the line-to-line voltage at the load, the current in each phase of the load, the power delivered to the load, and the power dissipated in the line.

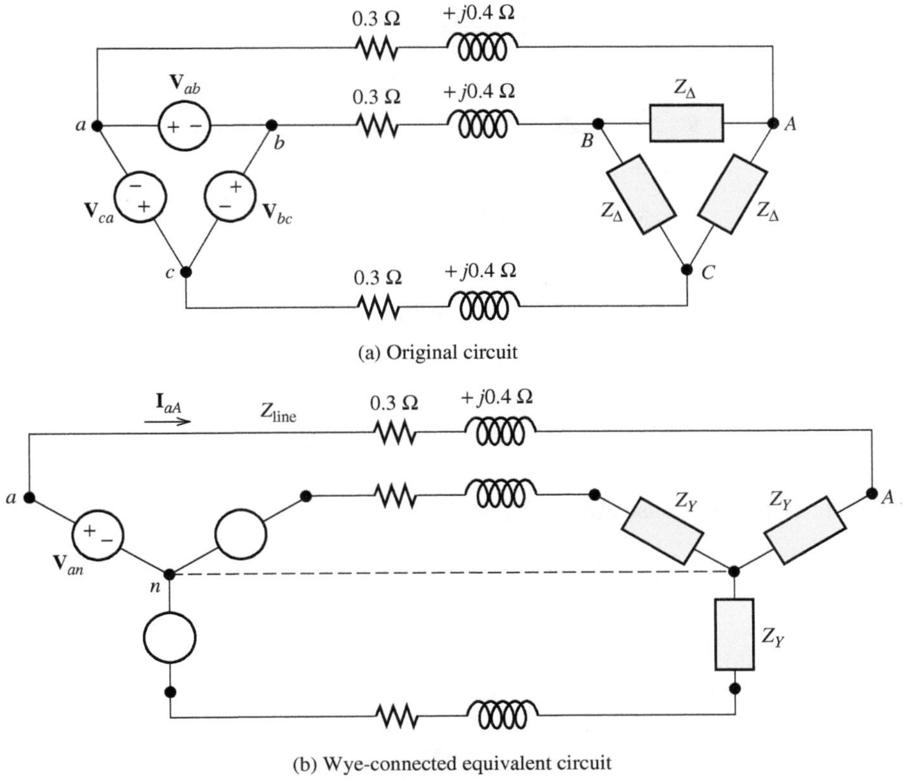

Figure 46 Circuit of Example 13.

Often, it is convenient to start an analysis by finding the wye–wye equivalent of a system.

Solution First, we find the wye-connected equivalents for the source and the load. (Actually, we only need to work with one third of the circuit because the other two thirds are the same except for phase angles.) We choose to work with the A phase of the wye-equivalent circuit. Solving Equation 103 for $\mathbf{V}_{an}$, we find that

$$\mathbf{V}_{an} = \frac{\mathbf{V}_{ab}}{\sqrt{3}\ \underline{/30^\circ}} = \frac{1000\ \underline{/30^\circ}}{\sqrt{3}\ \underline{/30^\circ}} = 577.4\ \underline{/0^\circ}$$

Using Equation 106, we have

$$Z_Y = \frac{Z_\Delta}{3} = \frac{30 + j6}{3} = 10 + j2$$

Now, we can draw the wye-equivalent circuit, which is shown in Figure 46(b).

In a balanced wye–wye system, we can consider the neutral points to be connected together as shown by the dashed line in Figure 46(b). This reduces the three-phase circuit to three single-phase circuits. For phase A of Figure 46(b), we can write

$$\mathbf{V}_{an} = (Z_{\text{line}} + Z_Y)\mathbf{I}_{aA}$$

Therefore,

$$\begin{aligned}\mathbf{I}_{aA} &= \frac{\mathbf{V}_{an}}{Z_{\text{line}} + Z_Y} = \frac{577.4\ \underline{/0^\circ}}{0.3 + j0.4 + 10 + j2} \\ &= \frac{577.4\ \underline{/0^\circ}}{10.3 + j2.4} = \frac{577.4\ \underline{/0^\circ}}{10.58\ \underline{/13.12^\circ}} \\ &= 54.60\ \underline{/-13.12^\circ}\end{aligned}$$

To find the line-to-neutral voltage at the load, we write

$$\begin{aligned}\mathbf{V}_{An} &= \mathbf{I}_{Aa}Z_Y = 54.60\ \underline{/-13.12^\circ} \times (10 + j2) \\ &= 54.60\ \underline{/-13.12^\circ} \times 10.20\ \underline{/11.31^\circ} \\ &= 556.9\ \underline{/-1.81^\circ}\end{aligned}$$

Now, we compute the line-to-line voltage at the load:

$$\begin{aligned}\mathbf{V}_{AB} &= \mathbf{V}_{An} \times \sqrt{3}\ \underline{/30^\circ} = 556.9\ \underline{/-1.81^\circ} \times \sqrt{3}\ \underline{/30^\circ} \\ &= 964.6\ \underline{/28.19^\circ}\end{aligned}$$

The current through phase AB of the load is

$$\begin{aligned}\mathbf{I}_{AB} &= \frac{\mathbf{V}_{AB}}{Z_\Delta} = \frac{964.6\ \underline{/28.19^\circ}}{30 + j6} = \frac{964.6\ \underline{/28.19^\circ}}{30.59\ \underline{/11.31^\circ}} \\ &= 31.53\ \underline{/16.88^\circ}\end{aligned}$$

The power delivered to phase AB of the load is the rms current squared times the resistance:

$$P_{AB} = I_{AB\text{rms}}^2 R = \left(\frac{31.53}{\sqrt{2}}\right)^2 (30) = 14.91\ \text{kW}$$

The powers delivered to the other two phases of the load are the same, so the total power is

$$P = 3P_{AB} = 44.73 \text{ kW}$$

The power lost in line A is

$$P_{\text{line}A} = I^2_{aA\text{rms}} R_{\text{line}} = \left(\frac{54.60}{\sqrt{2}}\right)^2 (0.3) = 0.447 \text{ kW}$$

The power lost in the other two lines is the same, so the total line loss is

$$P_{\text{line}} = 3 \times P_{\text{line}A} = 1.341 \text{ kW}$$

■

Exercise 17 A delta-connected source has voltages given by

$$\mathbf{V}_{ab} = 1000 \angle 30^\circ$$

$$\mathbf{V}_{bc} = 1000 \angle -90^\circ$$

$$\mathbf{V}_{ca} = 1000 \angle 150^\circ$$

This source is connected to a delta-connected load consisting of 50-Ω resistances. Find the line currents and the power delivered to the load.

Answer $\mathbf{I}_{aA} = 34.6 \angle 0^\circ$, $\mathbf{I}_{bB} = 34.6 \angle -120^\circ$, $\mathbf{I}_{cC} = 34.6 \angle 120^\circ$; $P = 30$ kW. □

8 AC ANALYSIS USING MATLAB

In this section, we will illustrate how MATLAB can greatly facilitate the analysis of complicated ac circuits. In fact, a practicing engineer working at a computer might have little use for a calculator, as it is easy to keep a MATLAB window open for all sorts of engineering calculations. Of course, you will probably need to use calculators for course exams and when you take the Professional Engineer (PE) exams. The PE exams allow only fairly simple scientific calculators, and you should practice with one of those allowed before attempting the exams.

Complex Data in MATLAB

By default, MATLAB assumes that $i = j = \sqrt{-1}$. However, I have encountered at least one bug in the software attributable to using j instead of i, and therefore I recommend using i in MATLAB and the Symbolic Toolbox. We need to be careful to avoid using i for other purposes when using MATLAB to analyze ac circuits. For example, if we were to use i as the name of a current or other variable, we would later experience errors if we also used i for the imaginary unit without reassigning its value.

Complex numbers are represented in rectangular form (such as 3 + 4i or alternatively 3 + i*4) in MATLAB.

We can use the fact that $M \angle \theta = M \exp(j\theta)$ to enter polar data. In MATLAB, angles are assumed to be in radians, so we need to multiply angles that are expressed in degrees by $\pi/180$ to convert to radians before entering them. For example, we use the following command to enter the voltage $V_s = 5\sqrt{2} \angle 45^\circ$:

```
>> Vs = 5*sqrt(2)*exp(i*45*pi/180)
Vs =
   5.0000 + 5.0000i
```

We can readily verify that MATLAB has correctly computed the rectangular form of $5\sqrt{2}\ \angle 45^\circ$.

Alternatively, we could use Euler's formula

$$M \angle \theta = M \exp(j\theta) = M\cos(\theta) + jM\sin(\theta)$$

to enter polar data, again with angles in radians. For example, $V_s = 5\sqrt{2}\ \angle 45^\circ$ can be entered as:

```
>> Vs = 5*sqrt(2)*cos(45*pi/180) + i*5*sqrt(2)*sin(45*pi/180)
Vs =
   5.0000 + 5.0000i
```

Values that are already in rectangular form can be entered directly. For example, to enter $Z = 3 + j4$, we use the command:

```
>> Z = 3 + i*4
Z =
   3.0000 + 4.0000i
```

Then, if we enter

```
>> Ix = Vs/Z
Ix =
   1.4000 - 0.2000i
```

MATLAB performs the complex arithmetic and gives the answer in rectangular form.

Finding the Polar Form of MATLAB Results

Frequently, we need the polar form of a complex value calculated by MATLAB. We can find the magnitude using the `abs` command and the angle in radians using the `angle` command. To obtain the angle in degrees, we must convert the angle from radians by multiplying by $180/\pi$. Thus, to obtain the magnitude and angle in degrees for Vs, we would enter the following commands:

```
>> abs(Vs) % Find the magnitude of Vs.
ans =
    7.0711
>> (180/pi)*angle(Vs) % Find the angle of Vs in degrees.
ans =
   45.0000
```

Adding New Functions to MATLAB

Because we often want to enter values or see results in polar form with the angles in degrees, it is convenient to add two new functions to MATLAB. Thus, we write an m-file, named pin.m, containing the commands to convert from polar to rectangular form, and store it in our working MATLAB folder. The commands in the m-file are:

```
function z = pin(magnitude, angleindegrees)
z = magnitude*exp(i*angleindegrees*pi/180)
```

Then, we can enter Vs $= 5\sqrt{2}\,\angle 45^\circ$ simply by typing the command:

```
>> Vs = pin(5*sqrt(2),45)
Vs =
   5.0000 + 5.0000i
```

We have chosen pin as the name of this new function to suggest "polar input." This file is included in the MATLAB folder. (See Appendix "On-Line Student Resources" for information about accessing this folder.)

Similarly, to obtain the polar form of an answer, we create a new function, named pout (to suggest "polar out"), with the commands:

```
function [y] = pout(x);
magnitude = abs(x);
angleindegrees = (180/pi)*angle(x);
y = [magnitude angleindegrees];
```

which are stored in the m-file named pout.m. Then, to find the polar form of a result, we can use the new function. For example,

```
>> pout(Vs)
ans =
   7.0711   45.0000
```

Here is another simple example:

```
>> pout(i*200)
ans =
   200   90
```

Solving Network Equations with MATLAB

We can readily solve node voltage or mesh equations and perform other calculations for ac circuits in MATLAB. The steps are:

1. Write the mesh current or node voltage equations.
2. Put the equations into matrix form, which is $\mathbf{ZI} = \mathbf{V}$ for mesh currents, in which $\mathbf{Z}$ is the coefficient matrix, $\mathbf{I}$ is the column vector of mesh current variables to be found, and $\mathbf{V}$ is the column vector of constant terms. For node voltages, the matrix equations take the form $\mathbf{YV} = \mathbf{I}$ in which $\mathbf{Y}$ is the coefficient matrix, $\mathbf{V}$ is the column vector of node voltage variables to be determined, and $\mathbf{I}$ is the column vector of constants.
3. Enter the matrices into MATLAB and compute the mesh currents or node voltages using the inverse matrix approach. $\mathbf{I} = \text{inv}(\mathbf{Z}) \times \mathbf{V}$ for mesh currents or $\mathbf{V} = \text{inv}(\mathbf{Y}) \times \mathbf{I}$ for node voltages, where inv denotes the matrix inverse.
4. Use the results to compute any other quantities of interest.

Example 14 Phasor Mesh-Current Analysis with MATLAB

Determine the values for the mesh currents, the real power supplied by $\mathbf{V}_1$, and the reactive power supplied by $\mathbf{V}_1$ in the circuit of Figure 47.

Solution First, we apply KVL to each loop obtaining the mesh-current equations:

$$(5 + j3)\mathbf{I}_1 + (50\,\angle -10^\circ)(\mathbf{I}_1 - \mathbf{I}_2) = 2200\sqrt{2}$$

$$(50\,\angle -10^\circ)(\mathbf{I}_2 - \mathbf{I}_1) + (4 + j)\mathbf{I}_2 + 2000\sqrt{2}\,\angle 30 = 0$$

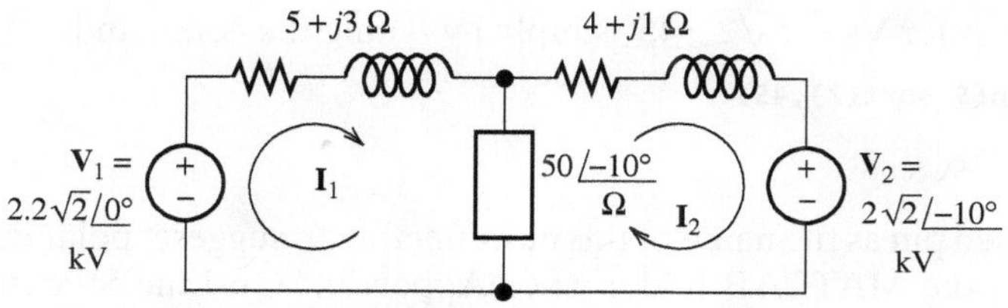

Figure 47 Cirucit for Example 14.

In matrix form, these equations become

$$\begin{bmatrix} (5+j3+50\,\angle{-10^\circ}) & -50\,\angle{-10^\circ} \\ -50\,\angle{-10^\circ} & (4+j+50\,\angle{-10^\circ}) \end{bmatrix} \begin{bmatrix} \mathbf{I}_1 \\ \mathbf{I}_2 \end{bmatrix} = \begin{bmatrix} 2200\sqrt{2} \\ -2000\sqrt{2}\,\angle{-10^\circ} \end{bmatrix}$$

We will solve these equations for $\mathbf{I}_1$ and $\mathbf{I}_2$. Then, we will compute the complex power delivered by $\mathbf{V}_1$

$$\mathbf{S}_1 = \frac{1}{2}\mathbf{V}_1\mathbf{I}_1^*$$

Finally, the power is the real part of $\mathbf{S}_1$ and the reactive power is the imaginary part.

We enter the coefficient matrix $\mathbf{Z}$ and the voltage matrix $\mathbf{V}$ into MATLAB, making use of our new pin function to enter polar values. Then, we calculate the current matrix.

```
>> Z = [(5 + i*3 + pin(50,-10)) (-pin(50,-10));...
   (-pin(50,-10)) (4 + i + pin(50,-10))];
>> V = [2200*sqrt(2); -pin(2000*sqrt(2),-10)];
>> I = inv(Z)*V
I =
   74.1634 + 29.0852i
   17.1906 + 26.5112i
```

This has given us the values of the mesh currents in rectangular form. Next, we obtain the polar form for the mesh currents, making use of our new pout function:

```
>> pout(I(1))
ans =
   79.6628  21.4140
>> pout(I(2))
ans =
   31.5968  57.0394
```

Thus, the currents are $\mathbf{I}_1 = 79.66\,\angle{21.41^\circ}$ A and $\mathbf{I}_2 = 31.60\,\angle{57.04^\circ}$ A, rounded to two decimal places. Next, we compute the complex power, real power, and reactive power for the first source.

$$\mathbf{S}_1 = \frac{1}{2}\mathbf{V}_1\mathbf{I}_1^*$$

```
>> S1 = (1/2)*(2200*sqrt(2))*conj(I(1));
>> P1 = real(S1)
P1 =
  1.1537e + 005
>> Q1 = imag(S1)
Q1 =
  -4.5246e + 004
```

Thus, the power supplied by $\mathbf{V}_1$ is 115.37 kW and the reactive power is −45.25 kVAR. The commands for this example appear in the m-file named Example_14. ■

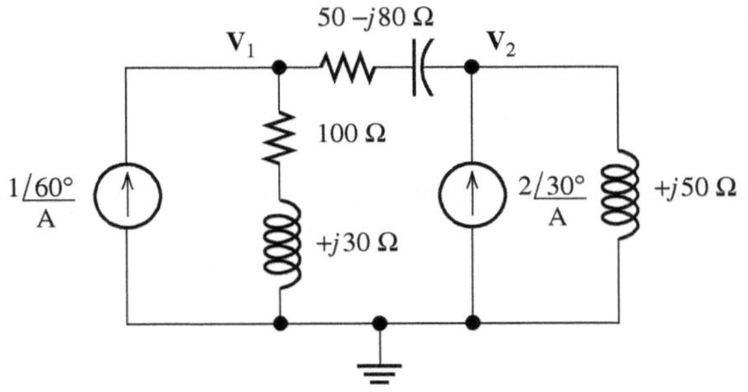

Figure 48 Circuit for Exercise 18.

Exercise 18 Use MATLAB to solve for the phasor node voltages in polar form for the circuit of Figure 48.

Answer The MATLAB commands are:

```
clear
Y = [(1/(100+i*30)+1/(50-i*80)) (-1/(50-i*80));...
        (-1/(50-i*80)) (1/(i*50)+1/(50-i*80))];
I = [pin(1,60); pin(2,30)];
V = inv(Y)*I;
pout(V(1))
pout(V(2))
```

and the results are $\mathbf{V}_1 = 79.98\angle 106.21^\circ$ and $\mathbf{V}_2 = 124.13\angle 116.30^\circ$. □

Summary

1. A sinusoidal voltage is given by $v(t) = V_m \cos(\omega t + \theta)$, where V_m is the peak value of the voltage, ω is the angular frequency in radians per second, and θ is the phase angle. The frequency in hertz is $f = 1/T$, where T is the period. Furthermore, $\omega = 2\pi f$.
2. For uniformity, we express sinusoidal voltages in terms of the cosine function. A sine function can be converted to a cosine function by use of the identity $\sin(z) = \cos(z - 90^\circ)$.
3. The root-mean-square (rms) value (or effective value) of a periodic voltage $v(t)$ is

$$V_{\text{rms}} = \sqrt{\frac{1}{T}\int_0^T v^2(t)\, dt}$$

The average power delivered to a resistance by $v(t)$ is

$$P_{\text{avg}} = \frac{V_{\text{rms}}^2}{R}$$

Similarly, for a current $i(t)$, we have

$$I_{\text{rms}} = \sqrt{\frac{1}{T}\int_0^T i^2(t)\, dt}$$

and the average power delivered if $i(t)$ flows through a resistance is

$$P_{\text{avg}} = I_{\text{rms}}^2 R$$

For a sinusoid, the rms value is the peak value divided by $\sqrt{2}$.

4. We can represent sinusoids with phasors. The magnitude of the phasor is the peak value of the sinusoid. The phase angle of the phasor is the phase angle of the sinusoid (assuming that we have written the sinusoid in terms of a cosine function).
5. We can add (or subtract) sinusoids by adding (or subtracting) their phasors.
6. The phasor voltage for a passive circuit is the phasor current times the complex impedance of the circuit. For a resistance, $\mathbf{V}_R = R\mathbf{I}_R$, and the voltage is in phase with the current. For an

inductance, $\mathbf{V}_L = j\omega L\mathbf{I}_L$, and the voltage leads the current by 90°. For a capacitance, $\mathbf{V}_C = -j(1/\omega C)\mathbf{I}_C$, and the voltage lags the current by 90°.

7. Many techniques learned for resistive circuits can be applied directly to sinusoidal circuits if the currents and voltages are replaced by phasors and the passive circuit elements are replaced by their complex impedances. For example, complex impedances can be combined in series or parallel in the same way as resistances (except that complex arithmetic must be used). Node voltages, the current-division principle, and the voltage-division principle also apply to ac circuits.

8. When a sinusoidal current flows through a sinusoidal voltage, the average power delivered is $P = V_{\text{rms}} I_{\text{rms}} \cos(\theta)$, where θ is the power angle, which is found by subtracting the phase angle of the current from the phase angle of the voltage (i.e., $\theta = \theta_v - \theta_i$). The power factor is $\cos(\theta)$.

9. Reactive power is the flow of energy back and forth between the source and energy-storage elements (L and C). We define reactive power to be positive for an inductance and negative for a capacitance. The net energy transferred per cycle by reactive power flow is zero. Reactive power is important because a power distribution system must have higher current ratings if reactive power flows than would be required for zero reactive power.

10. Apparent power is the product of rms voltage and rms current. Many useful relationships between power, reactive power, apparent power, and the power angle can be obtained from the power triangles shown in Figure 23.

11. In steady state, a network composed of resistances, inductances, capacitances, and sinusoidal sources (all of the same frequency) has a Thévenin equivalent consisting of a phasor voltage source in series with a complex impedance. The Norton equivalent consists of a phasor current source in parallel with the Thévenin impedance.

12. For maximum-power transfer from a two-terminal ac circuit to a load, the load impedance is selected to be the complex conjugate of the Thévenin impedance. If the load is constrained to be a pure resistance, the value for maximum power transfer is equal to the magnitude of the Thévenin impedance.

13. Because of savings in wiring, three-phase power distribution is more economical than single phase. The power flow in balanced three-phase systems is smooth, whereas power pulsates in single-phase systems. Thus, three-phase motors generally have the advantage of producing less vibration than single-phase motors.

Problems

Section 1: Sinusoidal Currents and Voltages

P1. Give the units for angular frequency, ω, and frequency, f. What is the relationship between f and ω?

P2. In terms of physical units, such as m, kg, C, and s, what are the units of radians? What are the *physical* units for angular frequency?

P3. Consider the plot of the sinusoidal voltage $v(t) = V_m \cos(\omega t + \theta)$ shown in Figure 1. Which of the numbered statements below best describes **a.** Increasing the peak amplitude V_m? **b.** Increasing the frequency f? **c.** Increasing θ? **d.** Decreasing the angular frequency ω? **e.** Decreasing the period?

1. Stretches the sinusoidal curve horizontally.
2. Compresses the sinusoidal curve horizontally.
3. Translates the sinusoidal curve to the right.
4. Translates the sinusoidal curve to the left.
5. Stretches the sinusoidal curve vertically.
6. Compresses the sinusoidal curve vertically.

* Denotes that answers are contained in the Student Solutions files. See Appendix "On-Line Student Resources" for more information about accessing the Student Solutions.

***P4.** A voltage is given by $v(t) = 10\sin(1000\pi t + 30°)$ V. First, use a cosine function to express $v(t)$. Then, find the angular frequency, the frequency in hertz, the phase angle, the period, and the rms value. Find the power that this voltage delivers to a 50-Ω resistance. Find the first value of time after $t = 0$ that $v(t)$ reaches its peak value. Sketch $v(t)$ to scale versus time.

P5. Repeat Problem P4 for $v(t) = 5\sin(500\pi t + 120°)$.

***P6.** A sinusoidal voltage $v(t)$ has an rms value of 20 V, a period of 100 μs, and reaches a positive peak at $t = 20$ μs. Write an expression for $v(t)$.

P7. We have a sinusoidal current $i(t)$ that has an rms value of 20 A, a period of 1 ms, and reaches a positive peak at $t = 0.3$ ms. Write an expression for $i(t)$.

P8. The voltage $v(t) = 10\sin(250\pi t)$ V appears across a 20-Ω resistance. Sketch $v(t)$ and $p(t)$ to scale versus time. Find the average power delivered to the resistance.

P9. A sinusoidal voltage has a peak value of 15 V, a frequency of 500 Hz, and crosses zero with positive slope at $t = 0.1$ ms. Write an expression for the voltage.

P10. A current $i(t) = 2\cos(1000\pi t)$ A flows through a 5-Ω resistance. Sketch $i(t)$ and $p(t)$ to scale versus time. Find the average power delivered to the resistance.

P11. Is the rms value of a periodic waveform always equal to the peak value divided by the square root of two? When is it?

***P12.** Find the rms value of the current waveform shown in Figure P12.

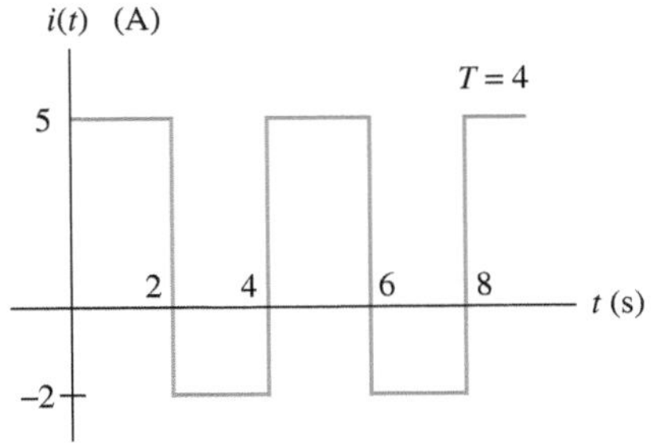

Figure P12

P13. Find the rms value of the voltage waveform shown in Figure P13.

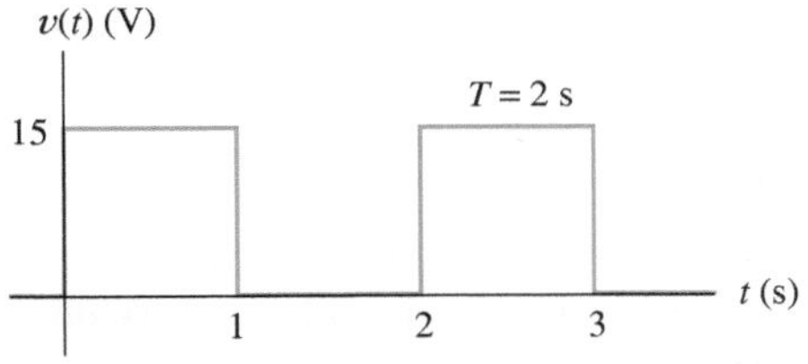

Figure P13

P14. Compute the rms value of the periodic waveform shown in Figure P14.

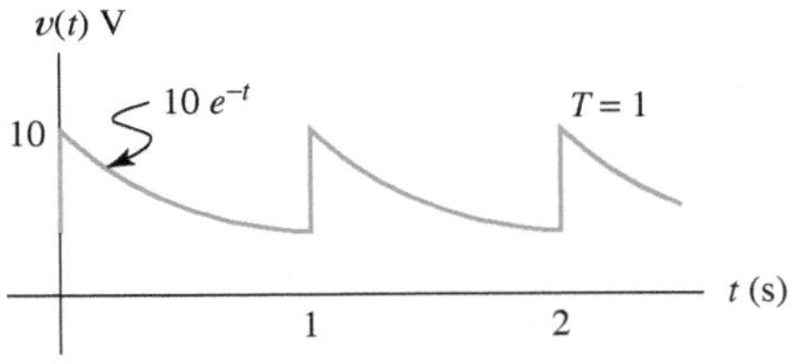

Figure P14

P15. Determine the rms value of $v(t) = A\cos(2\pi t) + 2B\sin(2\pi t)$.

P16. Calculate the rms value of the full-wave rectified sinusoidal wave shown in Figure P16, which is given by $v(t) = 4|\cos(20\pi t)|$.

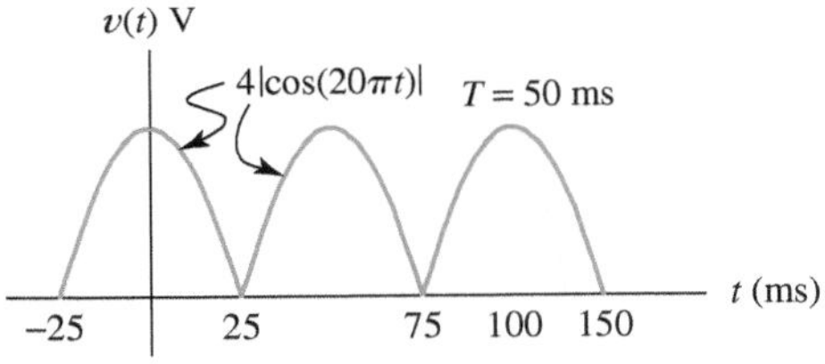

Figure P16

P17. Find the rms value of the voltage waveform shown in Figure P17.

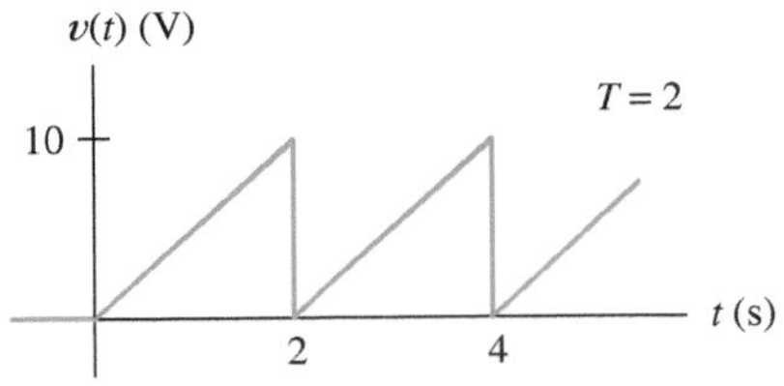

Figure P17

P18. Determine the rms value of $v(t) = 3 + 4\sqrt{2}\cos(20\pi t)$ V.

Section 2: Phasors

P19. What are the steps we follow in adding sinusoidal currents or voltages? What must be true of the sinusoids?

P20. **a.** Explain how the phase relationship between two sinusoids of the same frequency can be determined working from the phasor diagram. **b.** Explain how to determine the phase relationship between two sinusoids of the same frequency working from plots of the sinusoids versus time.

***P21.** Reduce $5\cos(\omega t + 75°) - 3\cos(\omega t - 75°) + 4\sin(\omega t)$ to the form $V_m \cos(\omega t + \theta)$.

***P22.** Suppose that $v_1(t) = 100\cos(\omega t)$ and $v_2(t) = 100\sin(\omega t)$. Use phasors to reduce the sum $v_s(t) = v_1(t) + v_2(t)$ to a single term of the form $V_m \cos(\omega t + \theta)$. Draw a phasor diagram, showing $\mathbf{V}_1$, $\mathbf{V}_2$, and $\mathbf{V}_s$. State the phase relationships between each pair of these phasors.

***P23.** Consider the phasors shown in Figure P23. The frequency of each signal is $f = 200$ Hz. Write a time-domain expression for each voltage in the form $V_m \cos(\omega t + \theta)$. State the phase relationships between pairs of these phasors.

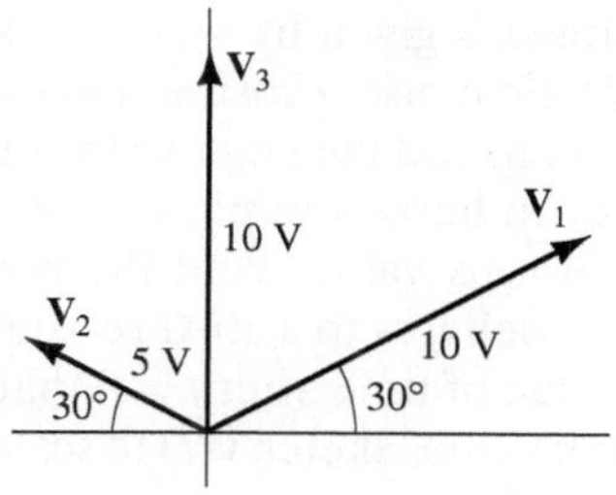

Figure P23

P24. Suppose we have two sinusoidal voltages of the same frequency with rms values of 12 V and 7 V, respectively. The phase angles are unknown. What is the smallest rms value that the sum of these voltages could have? The largest? Justify your answers.

P25. Find an expression for the sinusoid shown in Figure P25 of the form $v(t) = V_m \cos(\omega t + \theta)$, giving the numerical values of V_m, ω, and θ. Also, determine the phasor and the rms value of $v(t)$.

P26. A sinusoidal current $i_1(t)$ has a phase angle of $-30°$. Furthermore, $i_1(t)$ attains its positive peak 0.25 ms later than current $i_2(t)$ does. Both the currents have a frequency of 1000 Hz. Determine the phase angle of $i_2(t)$.

P27. Suppose that $v_1(t) = 90\cos(\omega t - 15°)$ and $v_2(t) = 50\sin(\omega t - 60°)$. Use phasors to

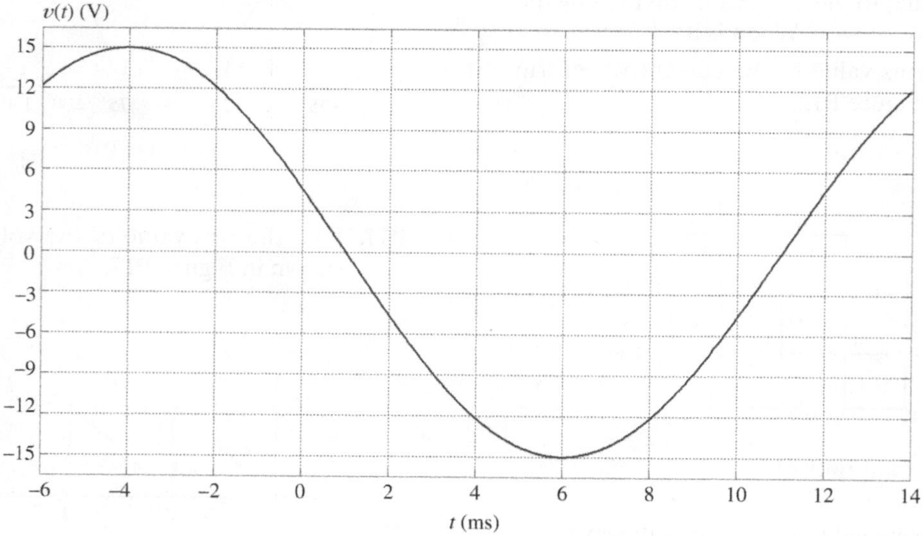

Figure P25

reduce the difference $v_s(t) = v_1(t) - v_2(t)$ to a single term of the form $V_m \cos(\omega t + \theta)$. State the phase relationships between each pair of these phasors.

P28. Reduce the expression

$$5 \sin(\omega t + 45°) + 15 \cos(\omega t - 30°) + 10 \cos(\omega t - 120°)$$

to the form $V_m \cos(\omega t + \theta)$.

P29. Suppose we have a circuit in which the voltage is $v_1(t) = 15 \cos(\omega t + 30°)$ V. Furthermore, the current $i_1(t)$ has an rms value of 5 A and lags $v_1(t)$ by 40°. (The current and the voltage have the same frequency.) Draw a phasor diagram and write an expression for $i_1(t)$ of the form $I_m \cos(\omega t + \theta)$.

Section 3: Complex Impedances

P30. What is the phase relationship between current and voltage for a pure resistance? For an inductance? For a capacitance?

P31. Write the relationship between the phasor voltage and phasor current for an inductance. Repeat for capacitance. Repeat for a resistance.

***P32.** A voltage $v_L(t) = 10 \cos(2000\pi t)$ is applied to a 100-mH inductance. Find the complex impedance of the inductance. Find the phasor voltage and current, and construct a phasor diagram. Write the current as a function of time. Sketch the voltage and current to scale versus time. State the phase relationship between the current and voltage.

***P33.** A voltage $v_C(t) = 10 \cos(2000\pi t)$ is applied to a 10-μF capacitance. Find the complex impedance of the capacitance. Find the phasor voltage and current, and construct a phasor diagram. Write the current as a function of time. Sketch the voltage and current to scale versus time. State the phase relationship between the current and voltage.

P34. A certain circuit element is known to be a pure resistance, a pure inductance, or a pure capacitance. Determine the type and value (in ohms, henrys, or farads) of the element if the voltage and current for the element are given by: **a.** $v(t) = 100 \cos(200t + 30°)$ V, $i(t) = 2.5 \sin(200t + 30°)$ A; **b.** $v(t) = 100 \sin(200t + 30°)$V, $i(t) = 4 \cos(200t + 30°)$ A; **c.** $v(t) = 100 \cos(100t + 30°)$ V, $i(t) = 5 \cos(100t + 30°)$ A.

P35. **a.** The current and voltage for a certain circuit element are shown in Figure P35(a). Determine the nature and value of the element. **b.** Repeat for Figure P35(b).

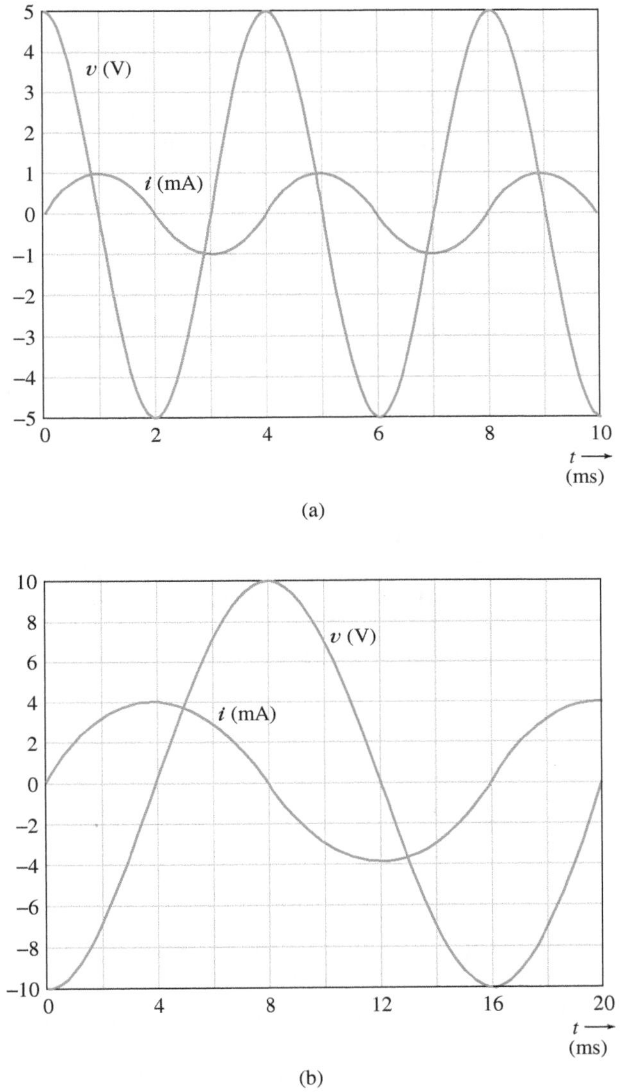

Figure P35

P36. **a.** A certain element has a phasor voltage of $\mathbf{V} = 100 \angle 30°$ V and current of $\mathbf{I} = 5 \angle 120°$ A. The angular frequency is 1000 rad/s. Determine the nature and value of the element. **b.** Repeat for $\mathbf{V} = 20 \angle -45°$ V and current of $\mathbf{I} = 2 \angle -135°$ A. **c.** Repeat for $\mathbf{V} = 50 \angle 45°$ V and current of $\mathbf{I} = 10 \angle 45°$ A.

Section 4: Circuit Analysis with Phasors and Complex Impedances

P37. Explain the step-by-step procedure for steady-state analysis of circuits with sinusoidal sources. What condition must be true of the sources?

***P38.** Find the phasors for the current and for the voltages of the circuit shown in Figure P38. Construct a phasor diagram showing $\mathbf{V}_s$, $\mathbf{I}$, $\mathbf{V}_R$, and $\mathbf{V}_L$. What is the phase relationship between $\mathbf{V}_s$ and $\mathbf{I}$?

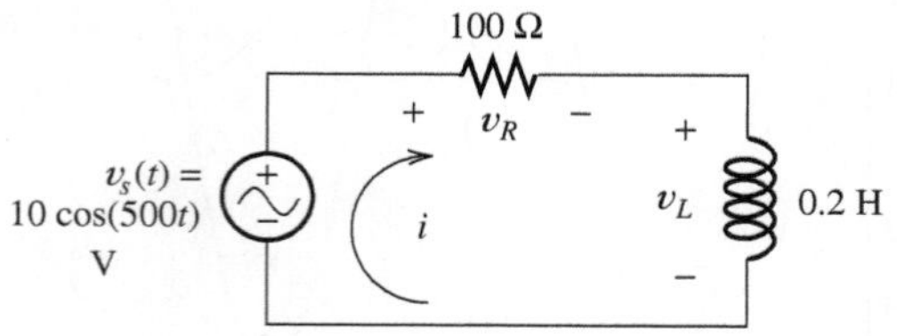

Figure P38

P39. Change the inductance to 0.4 H, and repeat Problem P38.

***P40.** Find the phasors for the current and the voltages for the circuit shown in Figure P40. Construct a phasor diagram showing $\mathbf{V}_s$, $\mathbf{I}$, $\mathbf{V}_R$, and $\mathbf{V}_C$. What is the phase relationship between $\mathbf{V}_s$ and $\mathbf{I}$?

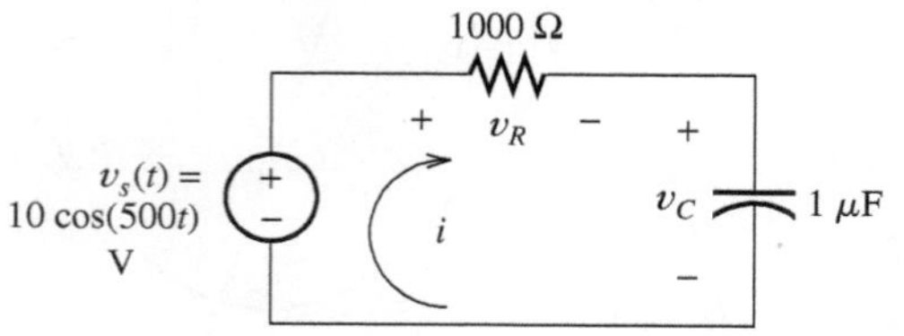

Figure P40

P41. Repeat Problem P40, changing the capacitance value to 2 μF.

***P42.** Find the complex impedance in polar form of the network shown in Figure P42 for $\omega = 500$. Repeat for $\omega = 1000$ and $\omega = 2000$.

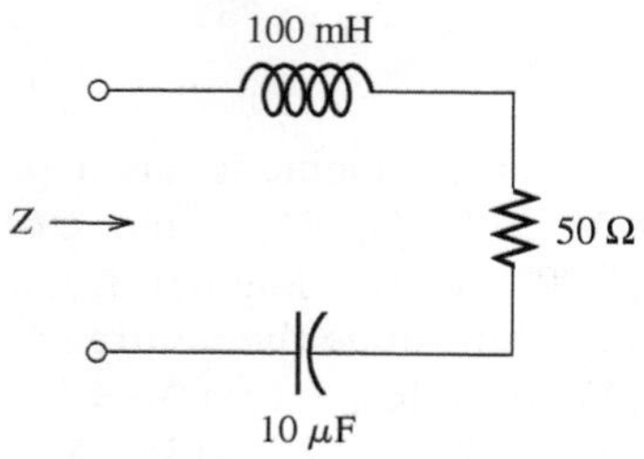

Figure P42

P43. Compute the complex impedance of the network shown in Figure P43 for $\omega = 500$. Repeat for $\omega = 1000$ and $\omega = 2000$. Give the answers in both polar and rectangular forms.

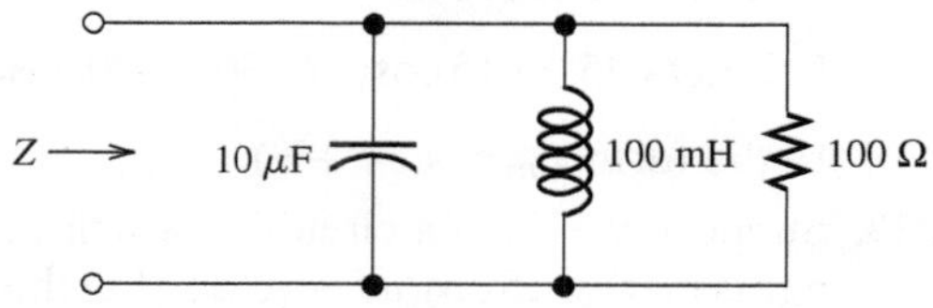

Figure P43

P44. A 100-μF capacitance is connected in parallel with the series combination of a 10-mH inductance and a 5-Ω resistance. Calculate the impedance of the combination in rectangular form and in polar form for angular frequencies of 500, 1000, and 2000 radians per second.

***P45.** Consider the circuit shown in Figure P45. Find the phasors $\mathbf{I}_s$, $\mathbf{V}$, $\mathbf{I}_R$, $\mathbf{I}_L$, and $\mathbf{I}_C$. Compare the peak value of $i_L(t)$ with the peak value of $i_s(t)$. Do you find the answer surprising? Explain.

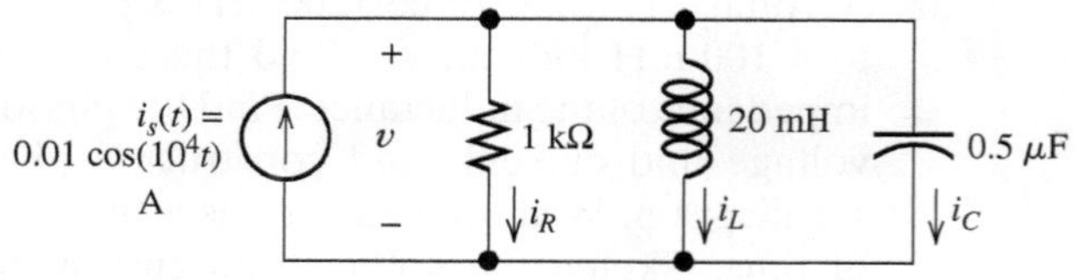

Figure P45

P46. Find the phasors for the voltage and the currents of the circuit shown in Figure P46. Construct a phasor diagram showing $\mathbf{I}_s$, $\mathbf{V}$, $\mathbf{I}_R$, and $\mathbf{I}_L$. What is the phase relationship between $\mathbf{V}$ and $\mathbf{I}_s$?

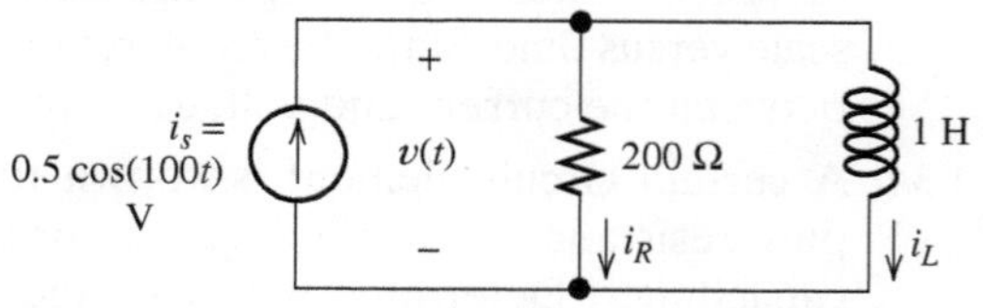

Figure P46

P47. Consider the circuit shown in Figure P47. Find the phasors $\mathbf{V}_s$, $\mathbf{I}$, $\mathbf{V}_L$, $\mathbf{V}_R$, and $\mathbf{V}_C$ in polar form. Compare the peak value of $v_L(t)$ with the peak value of $v_s(t)$. Do you find the answer surprising? Explain.

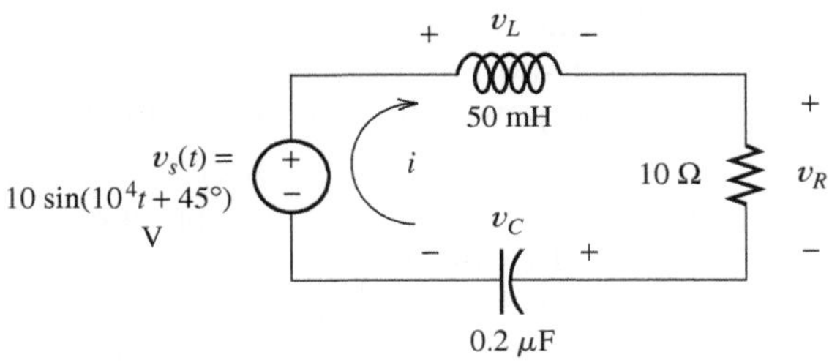

Figure P47

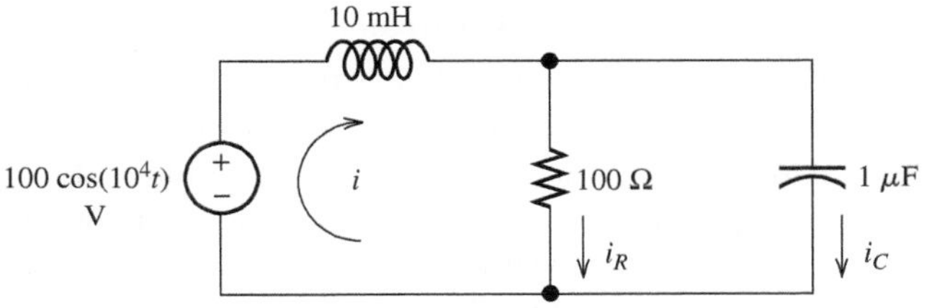

Figure P51

***P48.** Find the phasors for the voltage and the currents for the circuit shown in Figure P48. Construct a phasor diagram showing $\mathbf{I}_s$, $\mathbf{V}$, $\mathbf{I}_R$, and $\mathbf{I}_C$. What is the phase relationship between $\mathbf{V}$ and $\mathbf{I}_s$?

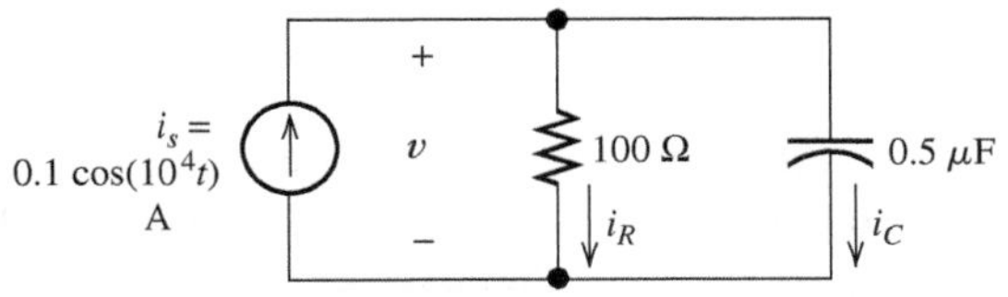

Figure P48

P49. Consider the circuit shown in Figure P49. Find the phasors $\mathbf{V}_1$, $\mathbf{V}_2$, $\mathbf{V}_R$, $\mathbf{V}_L$, and $\mathbf{I}$. Draw the phasor diagram to scale. What is the phase relationship between $\mathbf{I}$ and $\mathbf{V}_1$? Between $\mathbf{I}$ and $\mathbf{V}_L$?

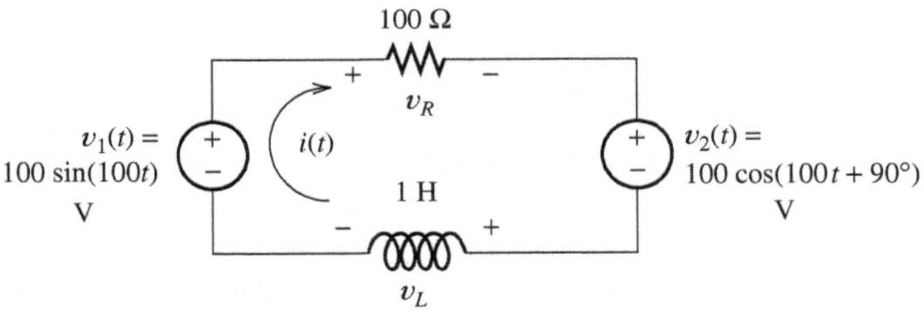

Figure P49

P50. Solve for the node voltage shown in Figure P50.

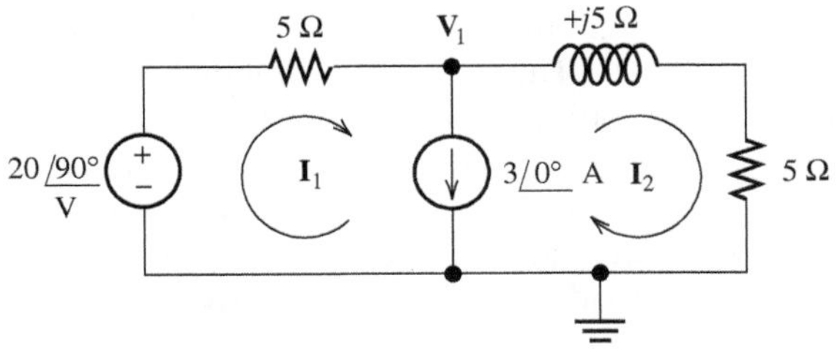

Figure P50

P51. Find the phasors $\mathbf{I}$, $\mathbf{I}_R$, and $\mathbf{I}_C$ for the circuit shown in Figure P51. Also, draw the phasor diagram for the currents.

P52. **a.** At what frequency or frequencies is the series combination of elements shown in Figure P52 equivalent to an open circuit? A short circuit? **b.** Repeat with the elements in parallel.

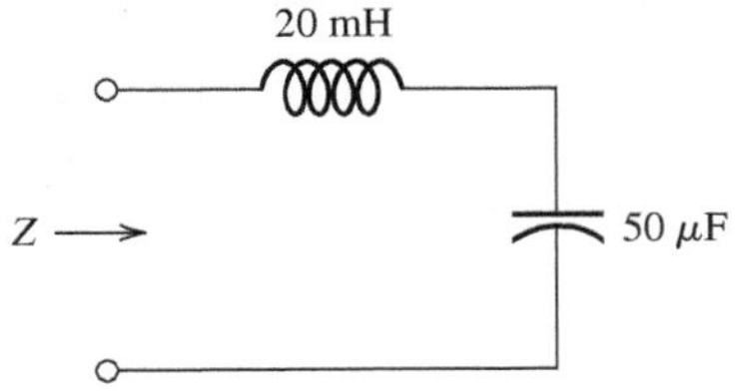

Figure P52

P53. Solve for the node voltage shown in Figure P53.

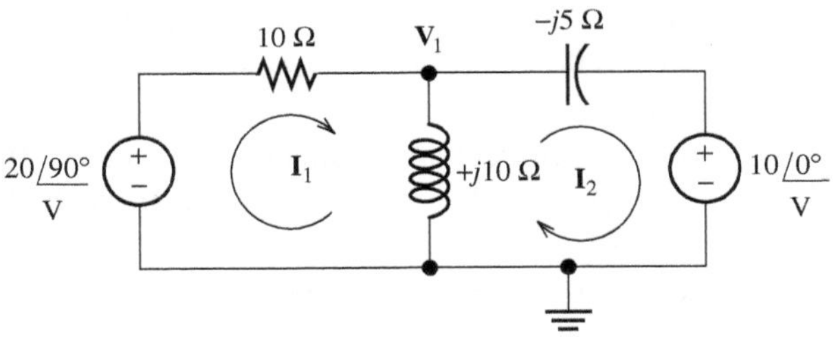

Figure P53

P54. **a.** At what frequency or frequencies is the series combination of elements shown in Figure P54 equivalent to an open circuit? A short circuit? **b.** Repeat with the elements in parallel.

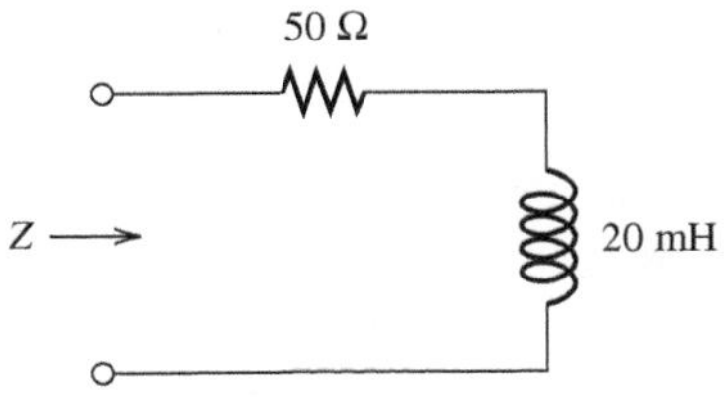

Figure P54

Section 5: Power in AC Circuits

P55. What are the customary units for real power? For reactive power? For apparent power?

P56. How do we compute the complex power delivered to a circuit component? How are average power and reactive power related to complex power?

P57. Explain how power factor and power angle are related. How is the power angle determined if we know the phasors for the current through and voltage across a load?

P58. A load is said to have a leading power factor. Is it capacitive or inductive? Is the reactive power positive or negative? Repeat for a load with lagging power factor.

P59. Assuming that a nonzero ac source is applied, state whether the power and reactive power are positive, negative, or zero for: **a.** a pure resistance; **b.** a pure inductance; **c.** a pure capacitance.

P60. Define what we mean by "power-factor correction." For power-factor correction of an inductive load, what type of element should we place in parallel with the load?

P61. **a.** Sketch a power triangle for an inductive load, label the sides, and show the power angle. **b.** Repeat for a capacitive load.

P62. Discuss why power plant and distribution system engineers are concerned with: **a.** the real power absorbed by a load; **b.** with the reactive power.

***P63.** Consider the circuit shown in Figure P63. Find the phasor current **I**. Find the power, reactive power, and apparent power delivered by the source. Find the power factor and state whether it is lagging or leading.

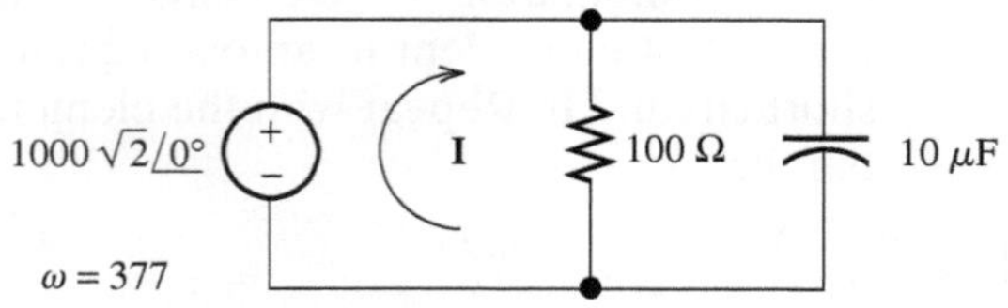

Figure P63

P64. Repeat Problem P63, replacing the capacitance by a 1-H inductance.

***P65.** Consider a load that has an impedance given by $Z = 100 - j50\ \Omega$. The current flowing through this load is $\mathbf{I} = 15\sqrt{2}\angle 30°$ A. Is the load inductive or capacitive? Determine the power factor, power, reactive power, and apparent power delivered to the load.

P66. Determine the complex power, power factor, power, reactive power, and apparent power delivered to the load shown in Figure P66, given that $\mathbf{I} = 15\sqrt{2}\angle 75°$ A. Also, determine the load impedance. Is the power factor leading or lagging?

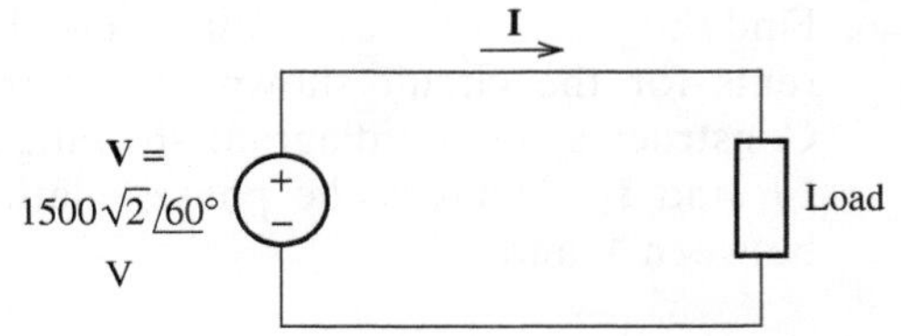

Figure P66

P67. Determine the power for each element, including the sources, shown in Figure P67. Also, state whether each element is delivering or absorbing energy.

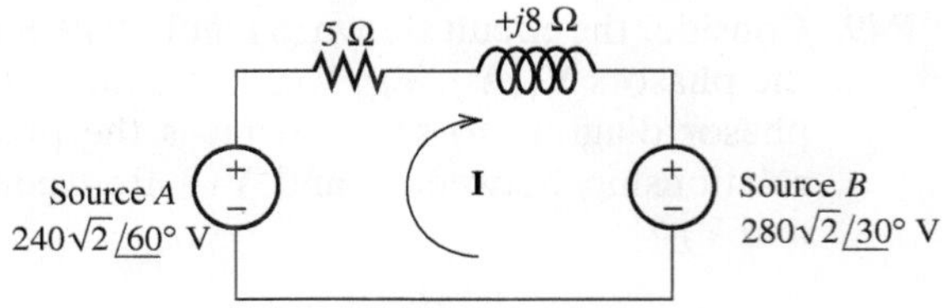

Figure P67

P68. Suppose that the load impedance shown in Figure P66 is given by $Z = 40 - j30\Omega$. (This is a different value from that of Problem P66.) Is the load inductive or capacitive? Determine the power factor, complex power, real power, reactive power, and apparent power delivered to the load.

P69. The voltage across a load is $v(t) = 10^4\sqrt{2}\cos(\omega t + 75°)$ V, and the current through the load is $i(t) = 25\sqrt{2}\cos(\omega t + 30°)$ A. The reference direction for the current points into the positive reference for the voltage. Determine the complex power, the power factor, the real power, the reactive power, and the apparent power of the load. Is this load inductive or capacitive?

P70. Given that a nonzero ac voltage source is applied, state whether the power and reactive power are positive, negative, or zero for: **a.** a pure capacitance; **b.** a resistance in series with an inductance; **c.** a resistance in series with a capacitance; **d.** a pure resistance. (Assume that the resistances, inductance, and capacitance are nonzero and finite in value.)

P71. Given that a nonzero ac voltage source is applied, what can you say about whether the power and reactive power are positive, negative, or zero for a pure capacitance in series with a pure inductance? Consider cases in which the impedance magnitude of the capacitance is greater than, equal to, or less than the impedance magnitude of the inductance.

P72. Repeat Problem P71 for the inductance and capacitance in parallel.

P73. A 60-Hz 240-V-rms source supplies power to a load consisting of a resistance in series with an inductance. The real power is 1500 W, and the apparent power is 2500 VA. Determine the value of the resistance and the value of the inductance.

P74. Determine the power for each element, including the sources, shown in Figure P74. Also, state whether each element is delivering or absorbing energy.

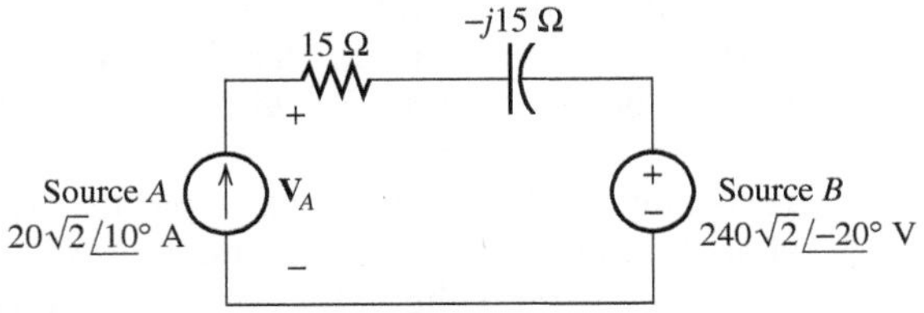

Figure P74

***P75.** Two loads—A and B—are connected in parallel across a 1-kV rms 60-Hz line, as shown in Figure P75. Load A consumes 10 kW with a 90-percent-lagging power factor. Load B has an apparent power of 15 kVA with an 80-percent-lagging power factor. Find the power, reactive power, and apparent power delivered by the source. What is the power factor seen by the source?

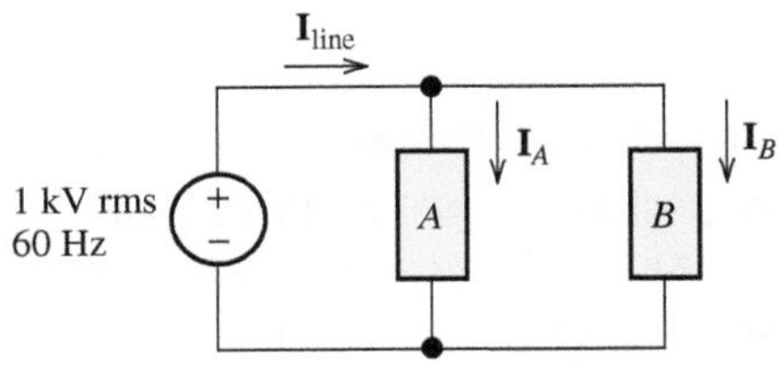

Figure P75

P76. Repeat Problem P75 given that load A consumes 50 kW with a 60-percent-lagging power factor and load B consumes 75 kW with an 80-percent-leading power factor.

P77. Find the power, reactive power, and apparent power delivered by the source in Figure P77. Find the power factor seen by the source and state whether it is leading or lagging.

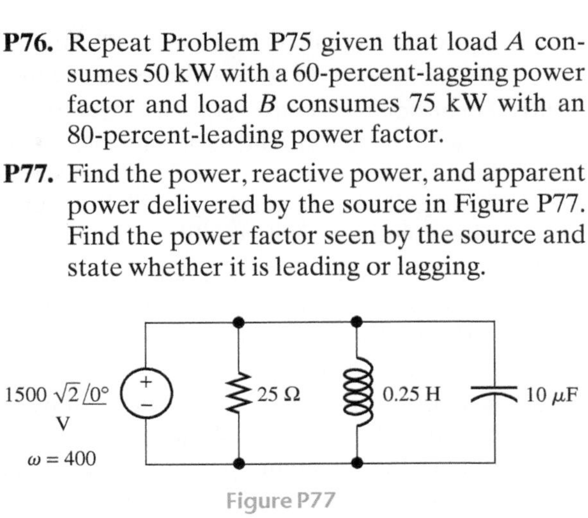

Figure P77

P78. Repeat Problem P77 with the resistance, inductance, and capacitance connected in series rather than in parallel.

***P79.** Consider the situation shown in Figure P79. A 1000-V rms source delivers power to a load. The load consumes 100 kW with a power factor of 25 percent lagging. **a.** Find the phasor **I**, assuming that the capacitor is not connected to the circuit. **b.** Find the value of the capacitance that must be connected in parallel with the load to achieve a power factor of 100 percent. Usually, power-systems engineers rate capacitances used for power-factor correction in terms of their reactive power rating. What is the rating of this capacitance in kVAR? Assuming that this capacitance is connected, find the new value for the phasor **I**. **c.** Suppose that the source is connected to the load by a long distance. What are the potential advantages and disadvantages of connecting the capacitance across the load?

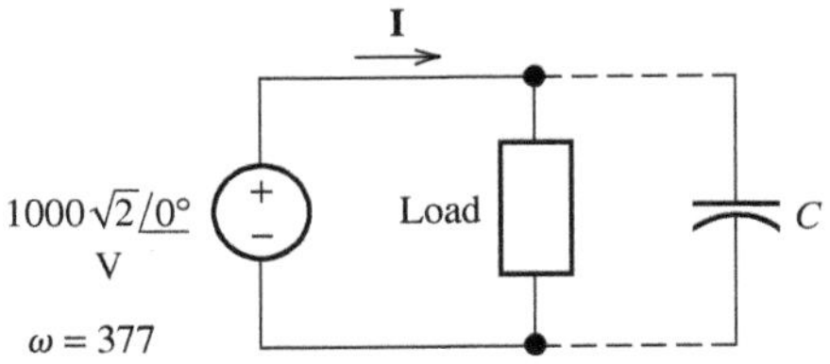

Figure P79

Section 6: Thévenin and Norton Equivalent Circuits

P80. Of what does an ac steady-state Thévenin equivalent circuit consist? A Norton equivalent circuit? How are the values of the parameters of these circuits determined?

P81. For an ac circuit consisting of a load connected to a Thévenin circuit, is it possible for the load voltage to exceed the Thévenin voltage in magnitude? If not, why not? If so, under what conditions is it possible? Explain.

P82. To attain maximum power delivered to a load, what value of load impedance is required if: **a.** the load can have any complex value; **b.** the load must be pure resistance?

***P83.** **a.** Find the Thévenin and Norton equivalent circuits for the circuit shown in Figure P83. **b.** Find the maximum power that this circuit can deliver to a load if the load can have any complex impedance; **c.** if the load is purely resistive.

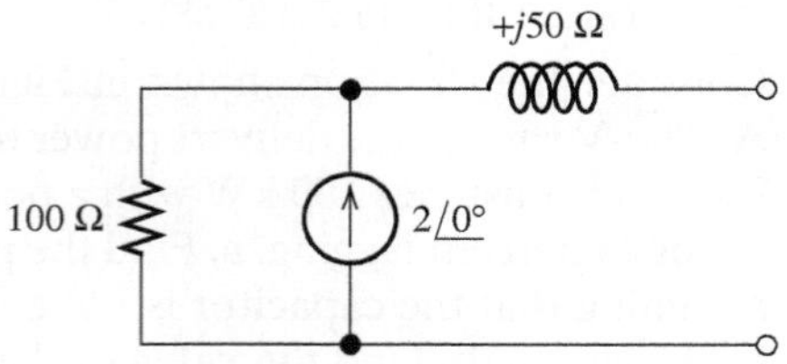

Figure P83

P84. Draw the Thévenin and Norton equivalent circuits for Figure P84, labeling the elements and terminals.

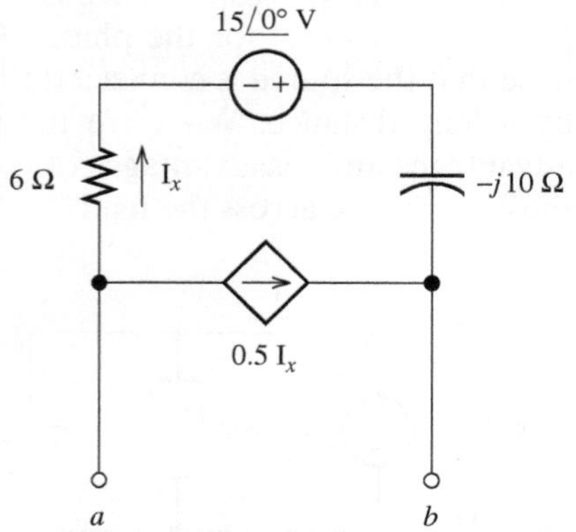

Figure P84

P85. Find the Thévenin voltage, Thévenin impedance, and Norton current for the two-terminal circuit shown in Figure P85.

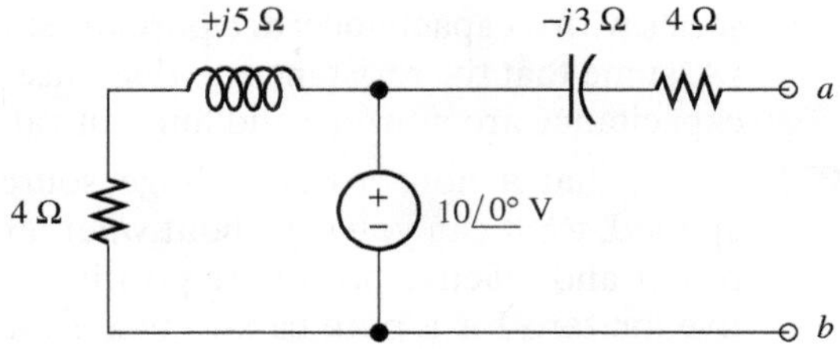

Figure P85

P86. Find the Thévenin and Norton equivalent circuits for the circuit shown in Figure P86. Find the maximum power that this circuit can deliver to a load if the load can have any complex impedance. Repeat if the load must be purely resistive.

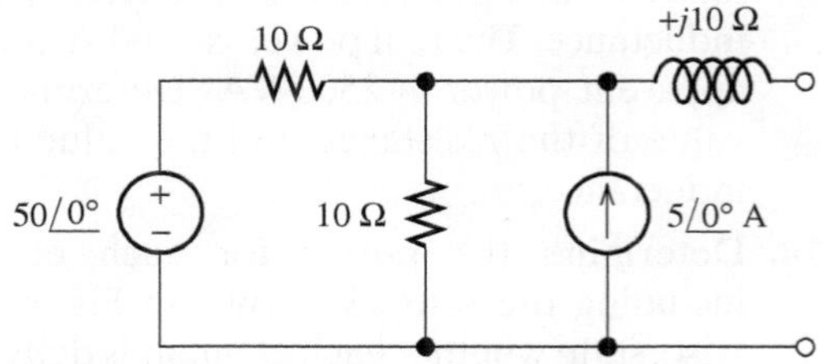

Figure P86

***P87.** The Thévenin equivalent of a two-terminal network is shown in Figure P87. The frequency is $f = 60$ Hz. We wish to connect a load across terminals *a*–*b* that consists of a resistance and a capacitance in parallel such that the power delivered to the resistance is maximized. Find the value of the resistance and the value of the capacitance.

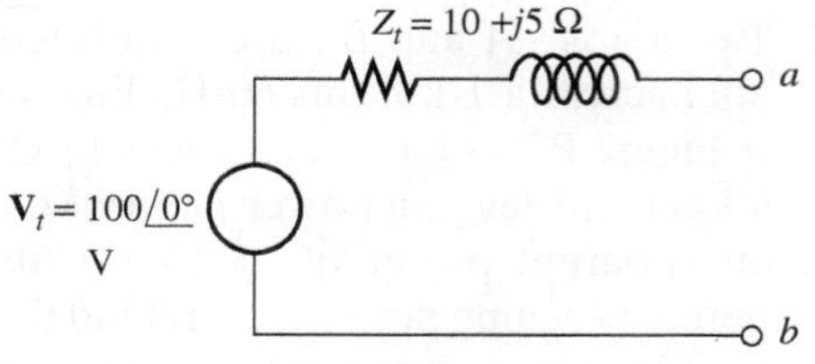

Figure P87

P88. Repeat Problem P87 with the load required to consist of a resistance and a capacitance in series.

Section 7: Balanced Three-Phase Circuits

P89. A positive-sequence three-phase source has $v_{an}(t) = 200\cos(\omega t + 120°)$ V. Find time-domain expressions for $v_{bn}(t)$, $v_{cn}(t)$, $v_{ab}(t)$, $v_{bc}(t)$, and $v_{ca}(t)$ and sketch their phasor diagram.

P90. We have a balanced positive-sequence three-phase source for which

$$v_{an}(t) = 150\cos(400\pi t + 15°)\text{ V}$$

a. Find the frequency of this source in Hz. **b.** Give expressions for $v_{bn}(t)$ and $v_{cn}(t)$. **c.** Repeat part (b) for a negative-sequence source.

***P91.** Each phase of a wye-connected load consists of a 50-Ω resistance in parallel with a 100-μF capacitance. Find the impedance of each phase of an equivalent delta-connected load. The frequency of operation is 60 Hz.

***P92.** A balanced wye-connected three-phase source has line-to-neutral voltages of 440 V rms. Find the rms line-to-line voltage magnitude. If this source is applied to a wye-connected load composed of three 30-Ω resistances, find the rms line-current magnitude and the total power delivered.

P93. What can you say about the flow of power as a function of time between a balanced three-phase source and a balanced load? Is this true of a single-phase source and a load? How is this a potential advantage for the three-phase system? What is another advantage of three-phase power distribution compared with single phase?

P94. A delta-connected source delivers power to a delta-connected load, as shown in Figure P94. The rms line-to-line voltage at the source is $V_{ab\text{rms}} = 440$ V. The load impedance is $Z_\Delta = 12 + j3$. Find $\mathbf{I}_{aA}$, $\mathbf{V}_{AB}$, $\mathbf{I}_{AB}$, the total power delivered to the load, and the power lost in the line.

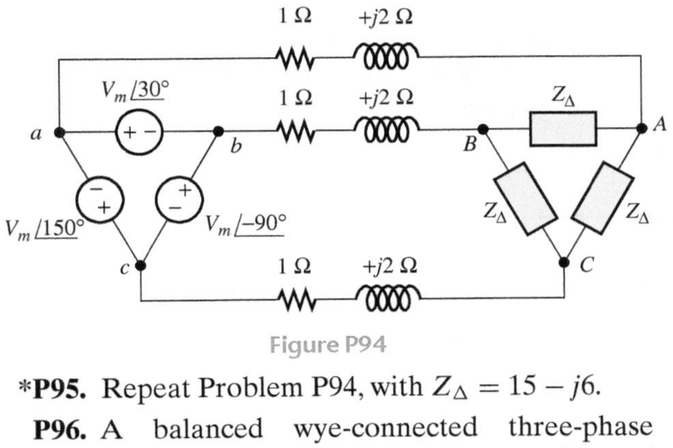

Figure P94

***P95.** Repeat Problem P94, with $Z_\Delta = 15 - j6$.

P96. A balanced wye-connected three-phase source has line-to-neutral voltages of 277 V rms. Find the rms line-to-line voltage. This source is applied to a delta-connected load, each arm of which consists of a 15-Ω resistance in parallel with a $+j30$-Ω reactance. Determine the rms line current magnitude, the power factor, and the total power delivered.

P97. A negative-sequence wye-connected source has line-to-neutral voltages $V_{an} = V_Y\angle 180°$, $V_{bn} = V_Y\angle -60°$, and $V_{cn} = V_Y\angle 60°$. Find the line-to-line voltages $\mathbf{V}_{ab}$, $\mathbf{V}_{bc}$, and $\mathbf{V}_{ca}$. Construct a phasor diagram showing both sets of voltages and compare with Figure 41.

P98. A balanced positive-sequence wye-connected 60-Hz three-phase source has line-to-line voltages of $V_L = 208$ V rms. This source is connected to a balanced wye-connected load. Each phase of the load consists of an impedance of $30 + j40$ Ω. Find the line-to-neutral voltage phasors, the line-to-line voltage phasors, the line-current phasors, the power, and the reactive power delivered to the load. Assume that the phase of $\mathbf{V}_{an}$ is zero.

P99. In this chapter, we have considered balanced loads only. However, it is possible to determine an equivalent wye for an unbalanced delta, and vice versa. Consider the equivalent circuits shown in Figure P99. Derive formulas for the impedances of the wye in terms of the impedances of the delta. (*Hint*: Equate the impedances between corresponding pairs of terminals of the two circuits with the third terminal open. Then, solve the equations for Z_a, Z_b, and Z_c in terms of Z_A, Z_B, and Z_C. Take care in distinguishing between upper- and lowercase subscripts.)

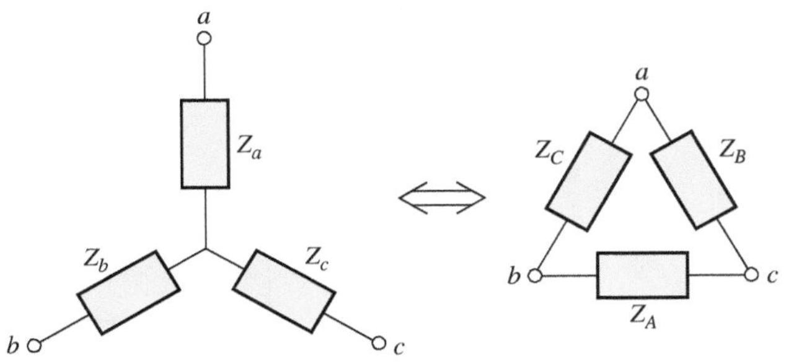

Figure P99

P100. Repeat Problem P99, but solve for the impedances of the delta in terms of those of the wye. [*Hint*: Start by working in terms of the admittances of the delta (Y_A, Y_B, and Y_C) and the impedances of the wye (Z_a, Z_b, and Z_c). Short terminals b and c for each circuit. Then, equate the admittances between terminal a and the shorted terminals for the two circuits. Repeat this twice more with shorts between the remaining two pairs of terminals. Solve the equations to determine Y_A, Y_B, and Y_C in terms of Z_a, Z_b, and Z_c. Finally, invert the equations for Y_A, Y_B, and Y_C to obtain equations relating the impedances. Take care in distinguishing between upper- and lowercase subscripts.]

Section 8: AC Analysis using MATLAB

***P101.** Use MATLAB to solve for the node voltages shown in Figure P101.

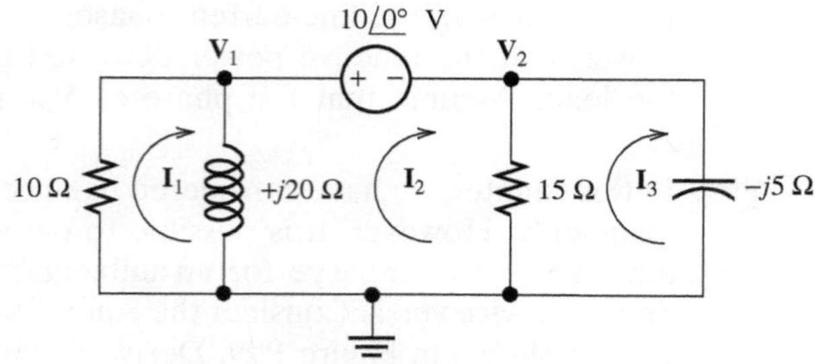

Figure P101

P102. Use MATLAB to solve for the mesh currents shown in Figure P101.

***P103.** Use MATLAB to solve for the mesh currents shown in Figure P53.

P104. Use MATLAB to solve for the mesh currents shown in Figure P50.

P105. Use MATLAB to solve for the node voltages shown in Figure P105.

P106. A **Lissajous figure** results if one sinusoid is plotted versus another. Consider $x(t) = \cos(\omega_x t)$ and $y(t) = \cos(\omega_y t + \theta)$. Use MATLAB to generate values of x and y for 20 seconds at 100 points per second and obtain a plot of y versus x for: **a.** $\omega_x = \omega_y = 2\pi$ and $\theta = 0°$; **b.** $\omega_x = \omega_y = 2\pi$ and $\theta = 45°$; **c.** $\omega_x = \omega_y = 2\pi$ and $\theta = 90°$; **d.** $\omega_x = 6\pi$, $\omega_y = 2\pi$, and $\theta = 90°$.

P107. Use the MATLAB Symbolic Toolbox to determine the rms value of $v(t)$ which has a period of 1 s and is given by $v(t) = 10\exp(-5t)\sin(20\pi t)$ V for $0 \le t \le 1$ s.

P108. Use MATLAB to obtain a plot of $v(t) = \cos(19\pi t) + \cos(21\pi t)$ for t ranging from 0 to 2 seconds. Explain why the terms in this expression cannot be combined by using phasors. Then, considering that the two terms can be represented as the real projection of the sum of two vectors rotating at different speeds in the complex plane, comment on the plot.

P109. Use MATLAB or manually produce plots of the magnitudes of the impedances of a 20-mH inductance, a 10-μF capacitance, and a 40-Ω resistance to scale versus frequency for the range from zero to 1000 Hz.

P110. **a.** Use MATLAB to produce a plot of the impedance magnitude versus angular frequency for the circuit of Figure P52. Allow ω to range from zero to 2000 rad/s and the vertical axis to range from 0 to 100 Ω. **b.** Repeat with the inductance and capacitance in parallel.

P111. **a.** Use MATLAB to produce a plot of the impedance magnitude versus angular frequency for the circuit shown in Figure P54. Allow ω to range from zero to 5000 rad/s. **b.** Repeat with the inductance and resistance in parallel.

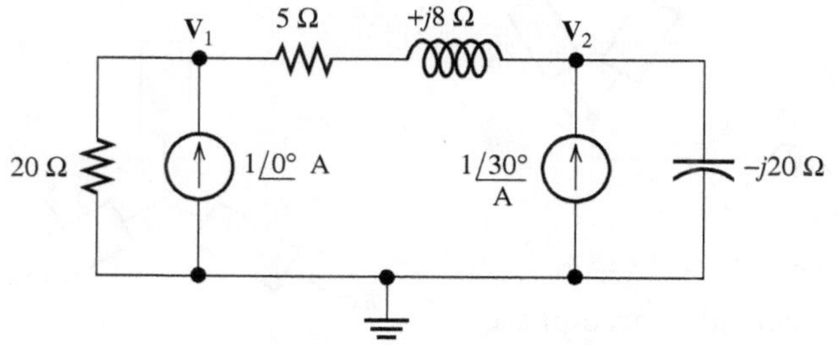

Figure P105

Practice Test

Here is a practice test you can use to check your comprehension of the most important concepts in this chapter. Answers can be found in Appendix "Answers for the Practice Tests" and complete solutions are included in the Student Solutions files. See Appendix "On-Line Student Resources" for more information about the Student Solutions.

T1. Determine the rms value of the current shown in Figure T1 and the average power delivered to the 50-Ω resistance.

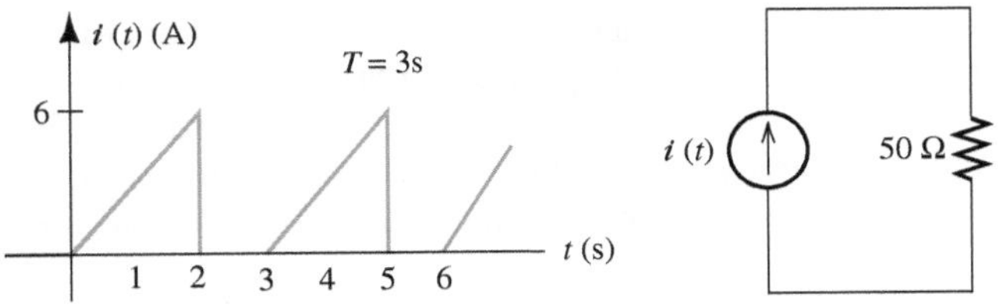

Figure T1

T2. Reduce the expression

$$v(t) = 5\sin(\omega t + 45°) + 5\cos(\omega t - 30°)$$

to the form $V_m \cos(\omega t + \theta)$.

T3. We have two voltages $v_1(t) = 15\sin(400\pi t + 45°)$ V and $v_2(t) = 5\cos(400\pi t - 30°)$ V. Determine (including units): **a.** the rms value of $v_1(t)$; **b.** the frequency of the voltages; **c.** the angular frequency of the voltages; **d.** the period of the voltages; **e.** the phase relationship between $v_1(t)$ and $v_2(t)$.

T4. Find the phasor values of $\mathbf{V}_R$, $\mathbf{V}_L$, and $\mathbf{V}_C$ in polar form for the circuit of Figure T4.

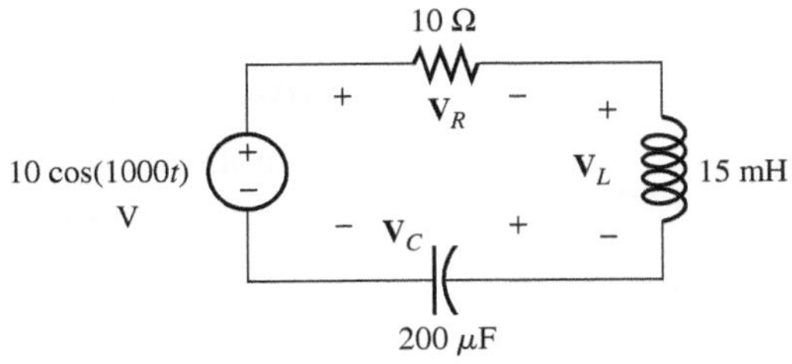

Figure T4

T5. Determine the complex power, power, reactive power, and apparent power absorbed by the load in Figure T5. Also, determine the power factor for the load.

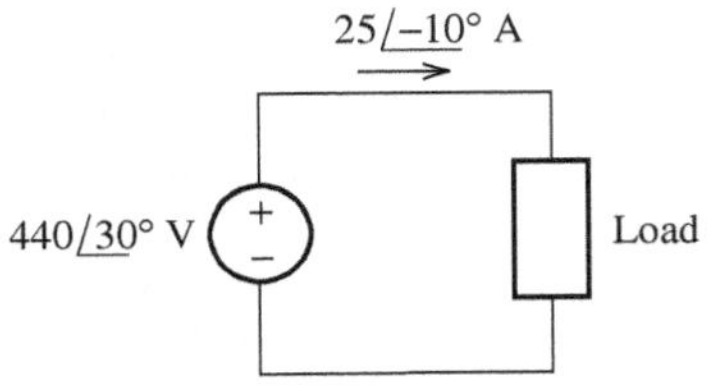

Figure T5

T6. Determine the line current $\mathbf{I}_{aA}$ in polar form for the circuit of Figure T6. This is a positive-sequence, balanced, three-phase system with $\mathbf{V}_{an} = 208\angle 30°$ V and $Z_\Delta = 6 + j8\ \Omega$.

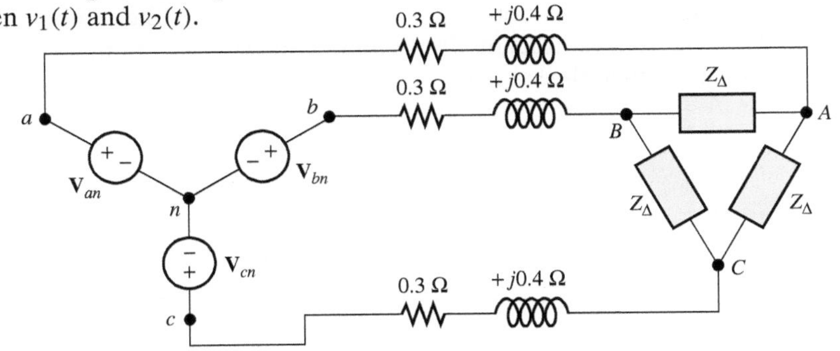

Figure T6

T7. Write the MATLAB commands to obtain the values of the mesh currents of Figure T7 in polar form. You may use the pin and pout functions defined in this chapter if you wish.

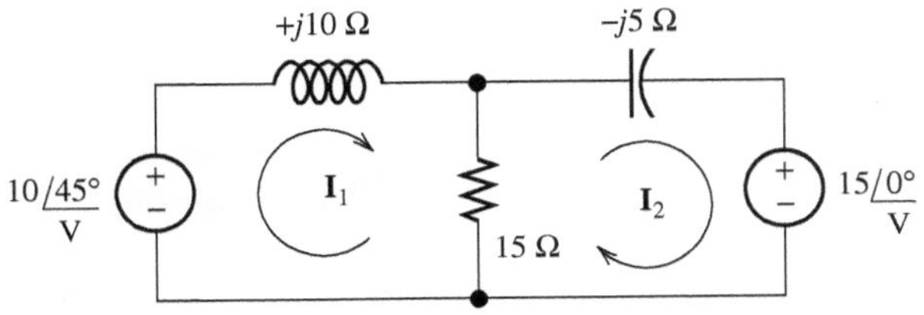

Figure T7

COMPLEX NUMBERS

Sinusoidal steady-state analysis is greatly facilitated if the currents and voltages are represented as complex numbers known as **phasors**. In this appendix, we review complex numbers.

Basic Complex-Number Concepts

Complex numbers involve the imaginary number $j = \sqrt{-1}$. (Electrical engineers use j to represent the square root of -1 rather than i, because i is often used for currents.) Several examples of complex numbers are

$$3 + j4 \quad \text{and} \quad -2 + j5$$

We say that a complex number $Z = x + jy$ has a **real part** x and an **imaginary part** y. We can represent complex numbers by points in the **complex plane**, in which the real part is the horizontal coordinate and the imaginary part is the vertical coordinate. We often show the complex number by an arrow directed from the origin of the complex plane to the point defined by the real and imaginary components. This is illustrated in Figure 1.

A **pure imaginary number**, $j6$ for example, has a real part of zero. On the other hand, a **pure real number**, such as 5, has an imaginary part of zero.

We say that complex numbers of the form $x + jy$ are in **rectangular form**. The **complex conjugate** of a number in rectangular form is obtained by changing the sign of the imaginary part. For example, if

$$Z_2 = 3 - j4$$

then the complex conjugate of Z_2 is

$$Z_2^* = 3 + j4$$

(Notice that we denote the complex conjugate by the symbol *.)

We add, subtract, multiply, and divide complex numbers that are in rectangular form in much the same way as we do algebraic expressions, making the substitution $j^2 = -1$.

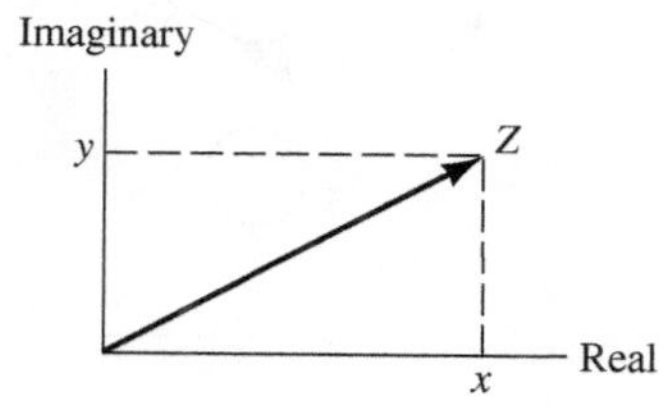

Figure 1 Complex plane.

Example 1 Complex Arithmetic in Rectangular Form

Given that $Z_1 = 5 + j5$ and $Z_2 = 3 - j4$, reduce $Z_1 + Z_2$, $Z_1 - Z_2$, $Z_1 Z_2$, and Z_1/Z_2 to rectangular form.

Solution For the sum, we have

$$Z_1 + Z_2 = (5 + j5) + (3 - j4) = 8 + j1$$

Notice that we add (algebraically) real part to real part and imaginary part to imaginary part.

The difference is

$$Z_1 - Z_2 = (5 + j5) - (3 - j4) = 2 + j9$$

In this case, we subtract each part of Z_2 from the corresponding part of Z_1.

For the product, we get

$$\begin{aligned} Z_1 Z_2 &= (5 + j5)(3 - j4) \\ &= 15 - j20 + j15 - j^2 20 \\ &= 15 - j20 + j15 + 20 \\ &= 35 - j5 \end{aligned}$$

Notice that we expanded the product in the usual way for binomial expressions. Then, we used the fact that $j^2 = -1$.

To divide the numbers, we obtain

$$\frac{Z_1}{Z_2} = \frac{5 + j5}{3 - j4}$$

We can reduce this expression to rectangular form by multiplying the numerator and denominator by the complex conjugate of the denominator. This causes the denominator of the fraction to become pure real. Then, we divide each part of the numerator by the denominator. Thus, we find that

$$\begin{aligned} \frac{Z_1}{Z_2} &= \frac{5 + j5}{3 - j4} \times \frac{Z_2^*}{Z_2^*} \\ &= \frac{5 + j5}{3 - j4} \times \frac{3 + j4}{3 + j4} \\ &= \frac{15 + j20 + j15 + j^2 20}{9 + j12 - j12 - j^2 16} \\ &= \frac{15 + j20 + j15 - 20}{9 + j12 - j12 + 16} \\ &= \frac{-5 + j35}{25} \\ &= -0.2 + j1.4 \end{aligned}$$

■

Exercise 1 Given that $Z_1 = 2 - j3$ and $Z_2 = 8 + j6$, reduce $Z_1 + Z_2$, $Z_1 - Z_2$, $Z_1 Z_2$, and Z_1/Z_2 to rectangular form.

Answer $Z_1 + Z_2 = 10 + j3$, $Z_1 - Z_2 = -6 - j9$, $Z_1 Z_2 = 34 - j12$, $Z_1/Z_2 = -0.02 - j0.36$. □

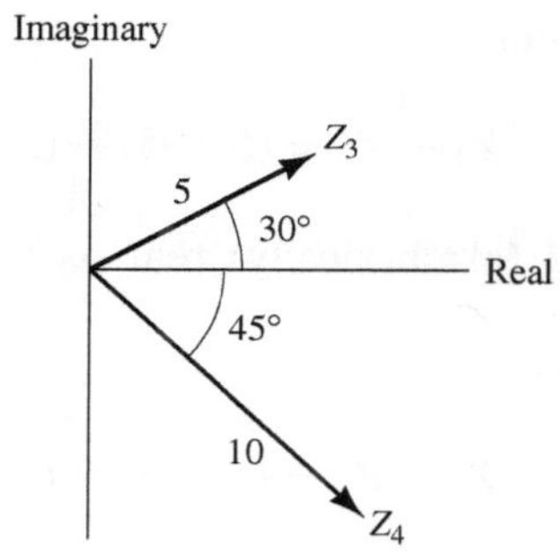

Figure 2 Complex numbers in polar form.

Complex Numbers in Polar Form

Complex numbers can be expressed in **polar form** by giving the length of the arrow that represents the number and the angle between the arrow and the positive real axis. Examples of complex numbers in polar form are

$$Z_3 = 5\underline{/30^\circ} \quad \text{and} \quad Z_4 = 10\underline{/-45^\circ}$$

These numbers are shown in Figure 2. The length of the arrow that represents a complex number Z is denoted as $|Z|$ and is called the **magnitude** of the complex number.

Complex numbers can be converted from polar to rectangular form, or vice versa, by using the fact that the magnitude $|Z|$, the real part x, and the imaginary part y form a right triangle. This is illustrated in Figure 3. Using trigonometry, we can write the following relationships:

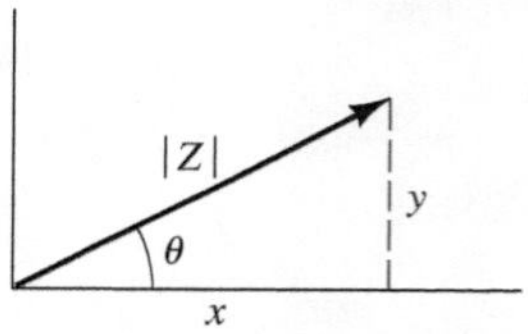

Figure 3 Complex number representation.

$$|Z|^2 = x^2 + y^2 \quad (1)$$

$$\tan(\theta) = \frac{y}{x} \quad (2)$$

$$x = |Z|\cos(\theta) \quad (3)$$

$$y = |Z|\sin(\theta) \quad (4)$$

These equations can be used to convert numbers from polar to rectangular form, or vice versa.

Example 2 Polar-to-Rectangular Conversion

Convert $Z_3 = 5\underline{/30^\circ}$ to rectangular form.

Solution Using Equations A.3 and A.4, we have

$$x = |Z|\cos(\theta) = 5\cos(30^\circ) = 4.33$$

and

$$y = |Z|\sin(\theta) = 5\sin(30^\circ) = 2.5$$

Thus, we can write

$$Z_3 = 5\underline{/30^\circ} = x + jy = 4.33 + j2.5$$

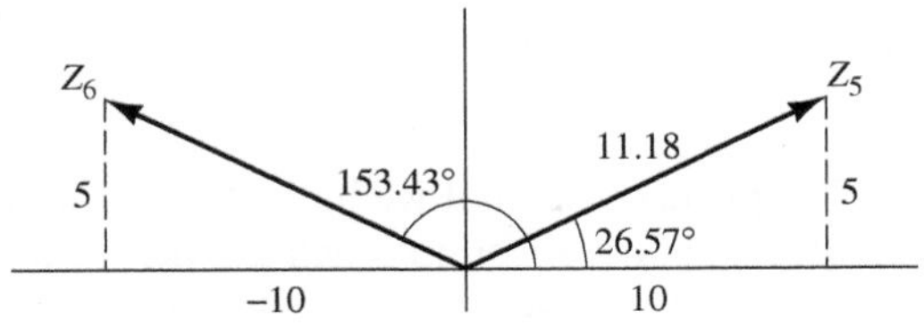

Figure 4 Complex numbers of Example 3.

Example 3 Rectangular-to-Polar Conversion

Convert $Z_5 = 10 + j5$ and $Z_6 = -10 + j5$ to polar form.

Solution The complex numbers are illustrated in Figure 4. First, we use Equation 1 to find the magnitudes of each of the numbers. Thus,

$$|Z_5| = \sqrt{x_5^2 + y_5^2} = \sqrt{10^2 + 5^2} = 11.18$$

and

$$|Z_6| = \sqrt{x_6^2 + y_6^2} = \sqrt{(-10)^2 + 5^2} = 11.18$$

To find the angles, we use Equation 2.

$$\tan(\theta_5) = \frac{y_5}{x_5} = \frac{5}{10} = 0.5$$

Taking the arctangent of both sides, we have

$$\theta_5 = \arctan(0.5) = 26.57°$$

Thus, we can write

$$Z_5 = 10 + j5 = 11.18\angle 26.57°$$

This is illustrated in Figure 4.

Evaluating Equation 2 for Z_6, we have

$$\tan(\theta_6) = \frac{y_6}{x_6} = \frac{5}{-10} = -0.5$$

Now if we take the arctan of both sides, we obtain

$$\theta_6 = -26.57°$$

However, $Z_6 = -10 + j5$ is shown in Figure 4. Clearly, the value that we have found for θ_6 is incorrect. The reason for this is that the arctangent function is multivalued. The value actually given by most calculators or computer programs is the principal value. *If the number falls to the left of the imaginary axis (i.e., if the real part is negative), we must add (or subtract)* 180° *to* $\arctan(y/x)$ *to obtain the correct angle.* Thus, the true angle for Z_6 is

$$\theta_6 = 180 + \arctan\left(\frac{y_6}{x_6}\right) = 180 - 26.57 = 153.43°$$

Finally, we can write

$$Z_6 = -10 + j5 = 11.18\underline{/153.43^\circ}$$

■

The procedures that we have illustrated in Examples A.2 and A.3 can be carried out with a relatively simple calculator. However, if we find the angle by taking the arctangent of y/x, we must consider the fact that the principal value of the arctangent is the true angle only if the real part x is positive. If x is negative, we have

$$\theta = \arctan\left(\frac{y}{x}\right) \pm 180^\circ \tag{5}$$

Many scientific calculators are capable of converting complex numbers from polar to rectangular, and vice versa, in a single operation. Practice with your calculator to become proficient using this feature. *It is always a good idea to make a sketch of the number in the complex plane as a check on the conversion process.*

Exercise 2 Convert the numbers $Z_1 = 15\underline{/45^\circ}$, $Z_2 = 10\underline{/-150^\circ}$, and $Z_3 = 5\underline{/90^\circ}$ to rectangular form.

Answer $Z_1 = 10.6 + j10.6$, $Z_2 = -8.66 - j5$, $Z_3 = j5$. □

Exercise 3 Convert the numbers $Z_1 = 3 + j4$, $Z_2 = -j10$, and $Z_3 = -5 - j5$ to polar form.

Answer $Z_1 = 5\underline{/53.13^\circ}$, $Z_2 = 10\underline{/-90^\circ}$, $Z_3 = 7.07\underline{/-135^\circ}$. □

Euler's Identities

Equations A.6 through A.9 are the bridge between sinusoidal currents or voltages and complex numbers.

You may have been wondering what complex numbers have to do with sinusoids. The connection is through Euler's identities, which state that

$$\cos(\theta) = \frac{e^{j\theta} + e^{-j\theta}}{2} \tag{6}$$

and

$$\sin(\theta) = \frac{e^{j\theta} - e^{-j\theta}}{2j} \tag{7}$$

Another form of these identities is

$$e^{j\theta} = \cos(\theta) + j\sin(\theta) \tag{8}$$

and

$$e^{-j\theta} = \cos(\theta) - j\sin(\theta) \tag{9}$$

Thus, $e^{j\theta}$ is a complex number having a real part of $\cos(\theta)$ and an imaginary part of $\sin(\theta)$. This is illustrated in Figure 5. The magnitude is

$$|e^{j\theta}| = \sqrt{\cos^2(\theta) + \sin^2(\theta)}$$

By the well-known identity $\cos^2(\theta) + \sin^2(\theta) = 1$, this becomes

$$|e^{j\theta}| = 1 \tag{10}$$

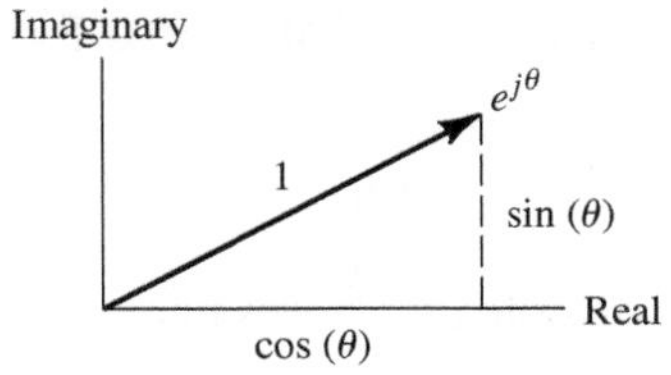

Figure 5 Euler's identity.

Furthermore, the angle of $e^{j\theta}$ is θ. Thus, we can write

$$e^{j\theta} = 1\angle\theta = \cos(\theta) + j\sin(\theta) \tag{11}$$

Similarly, we have

$$e^{-j\theta} = 1\angle-\theta = \cos(\theta) - j\sin(\theta) \tag{12}$$

Notice that $e^{-j\theta}$ is the complex conjugate of $e^{j\theta}$.

A complex number such as $A\angle\theta$ can be written as

$$A\angle\theta = A \times (1\angle\theta) = Ae^{j\theta} \tag{13}$$

We call $Ae^{j\theta}$ the **exponential form** of a complex number. Hence, a given complex number can be written in three forms: the rectangular form, the polar form, and the exponential form. Using Equation 11 to substitute for $e^{j\theta}$ on the right-hand side of Equation 13, we obtain the three forms of a complex number:

$$A\angle\theta = Ae^{j\theta} = A\cos(\theta) + jA\sin(\theta) \tag{14}$$

Example 4 Exponential Form of a Complex Number

Express the complex number $Z = 10\angle 60^\circ$ in exponential and rectangular forms. Sketch the number in the complex plane.

Solution Conversion from polar to exponential forms is based on Equation 13. Thus, we have

$$Z = 10\angle 60^\circ = 10e^{j60^\circ}$$

The rectangular form can be found by using Equation 8:

$$\begin{aligned} Z &= 10 \times (e^{j60^\circ}) \\ &= 10 \times [\cos(60^\circ) + j\sin(60^\circ)] \\ &= 5 + j8.66 \end{aligned}$$

The graphical representation of Z is shown in Figure 6. ■

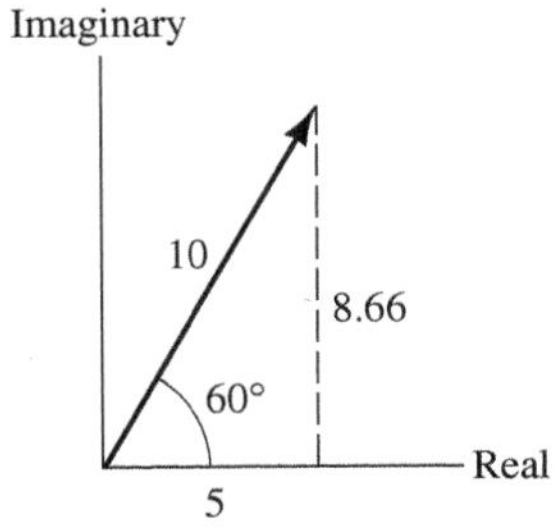

Figure 6 See Example 4.

Exercise 4 Express $Z_1 = 10 + j10$ and $Z_2 = -10 + j10$ in polar and exponential forms.

Answer $Z_1 = 14.14\angle 45^\circ = 14.14e^{j45^\circ}$, $Z_2 = 14.14\angle 135^\circ = 14.14e^{j135^\circ}$. □

Arithmetic Operations in Polar and Exponential Form

To add (or subtract) complex numbers, we must first convert them to rectangular form. Then, we add (or subtract) real part to real part and imaginary to imaginary.

Consider two complex numbers in exponential form given by

$$Z_1 = |Z_1|e^{j\theta_1} \quad \text{and} \quad Z_2 = |Z_2|e^{j\theta_2}$$

The polar forms of these numbers are

$$Z_1 = |Z_1|\underline{/\theta_1} \quad \text{and} \quad Z_2 = |Z_2|\underline{/\theta_2}$$

For multiplication of numbers in exponential form, we have

$$Z_1 \times Z_2 = |Z_1|e^{j\theta_1} \times |Z_2|e^{j\theta_2} = |Z_1||Z_2|e^{j(\theta_1+\theta_2)}$$

As usual, in multiplying exponentials, we add the exponents. In polar form, this is

$$Z_1 \times Z_2 = |Z_1|\underline{/\theta_1} \times |Z_2|\underline{/\theta_2} = |Z_1||Z_2|\underline{/\theta_1 + \theta_2}$$

Thus, to multiply numbers in polar form, we multiply the magnitudes and add the angles.

Now consider division:

$$\frac{Z_1}{Z_2} = \frac{|Z_1|e^{j\theta_1}}{|Z_2|e^{j\theta_2}} = \frac{|Z_1|}{|Z_2|}e^{j(\theta_1-\theta_2)}$$

As usual, in dividing exponentials, we subtract the exponents. In polar form, this is

$$\frac{Z_1}{Z_2} = \frac{|Z_1|\underline{/\theta_1}}{|Z_2|\underline{/\theta_2}} = \frac{|Z_1|}{|Z_2|}\underline{/\theta_1 - \theta_2}$$

Thus, to divide numbers in polar form, we divide the magnitudes and subtract the angle of the divisor from the angle of the dividend.

Example 5 Complex Arithmetic in Polar Form

Given $Z_1 = 10\underline{/60^\circ}$ and $Z_2 = 5\underline{/45^\circ}$, find Z_1Z_2, Z_1/Z_2, and $Z_1 + Z_2$ in polar form.

Solution For the product, we have

$$Z_1 \times Z_2 = 10\underline{/60^\circ} \times 5\underline{/45^\circ} = 50\underline{/105^\circ}$$

Dividing the numbers, we have

$$\frac{Z_1}{Z_2} = \frac{10\underline{/60^\circ}}{5\underline{/45^\circ}} = 2\underline{/15^\circ}$$

Before we can add (or subtract) the numbers, we must convert them to rectangular form. Using Equation 14 to convert the polar numbers to rectangular, we get

$$Z_1 = 10\underline{/60^\circ} = 10\cos(60^\circ) + j10\sin(60^\circ)$$

$$= 5 + j8.66$$
$$Z_2 = 5\angle 45^\circ = 5\cos(45^\circ) + j5\sin(45^\circ)$$
$$= 3.54 + j3.54$$

Now, we can add the numbers. We denote the sum as Z_s:

$$Z_s = Z_1 + Z_2 = 5 + j8.66 + 3.54 + j3.54$$
$$= 8.54 + j12.2$$

Next, we convert the sum to polar form:

$$|Z_s| = \sqrt{(8.54)^2 + (12.2)^2} = 14.9$$
$$\tan\theta_s = \frac{12.2}{8.54} = 1.43$$

Taking the arctangent of both sides, we have

$$\theta_s = \arctan(1.43) = 55^\circ$$

Because the real part of Z_s is positive, the correct angle is the principal value of the arctangent (i.e., 55° is the correct angle). Thus, we obtain

$$Z_s = Z_1 + Z_2 = 14.9\angle 55^\circ$$ ■

Exercise 5 Given $Z_1 = 10\angle 30^\circ$ and $Z_2 = 20\angle 135^\circ$, find Z_1Z_2, Z_1/Z_2, $Z_1 - Z_2$, and $Z_1 + Z_2$ in polar form.

Answer $Z_1Z_2 = 200\angle 165^\circ$, $Z_1/Z_2 = 0.5\angle -105^\circ$, $Z_1 - Z_2 = 24.6\angle -21.8^\circ$, $Z_1 + Z_2 = 19.9\angle 106^\circ$. □

Summary

1. Complex numbers can be expressed in rectangular, polar, or exponential forms. Addition, subtraction, multiplication, and division of complex numbers are necessary operations in solving steady-state ac circuits by the phasor method.
2. Sinusoids and complex numbers are related through Euler's identities.

Problems*

P1. Given that $Z_1 = 2 + j3$ and $Z_2 = 4 - j3$, reduce $Z_1 + Z_2$, $Z_1 - Z_2$, Z_1Z_2, and Z_1/Z_2 to rectangular form.

P2. Given that $Z_1 = 1 - j2$ and $Z_2 = 2 + j3$, reduce $Z_1 + Z_2$, $Z_1 - Z_2$, Z_1Z_2, and Z_1/Z_2 to rectangular form.

* Solutions for these problems are contained in the Student Solutions files. See Appendix "On-Line Student Resources" for more information about accessing the Student Solutions.

P3. Given that $Z_1 = 10 + j5$ and $Z_2 = 20 - j20$, reduce $Z_1 + Z_2, Z_1 - Z_2, Z_1Z_2$, and Z_1/Z_2 to rectangular form.

P4. Express each of these complex numbers in polar form and in exponential form: **a.** $Z_a = 5 - j5$; **b.** $Z_b = -10 + j5$; **c.** $Z_c = -3 - j4$; **d.** $Z_d = -j12$.

P5. Express each of these complex numbers in rectangular form and in exponential form: **a.** $Z_a = 5\angle 45°$; **b.** $Z_b = 10\angle 120°$; **c.** $Z_c = -15\angle -90°$; **d.** $Z_d = -10\angle 60°$.

P6. Express each of these complex numbers in rectangular form and in polar form: **a.** $Z_a = 5e^{j30°}$; **b.** $Z_b = 10e^{-j45°}$; **c.** $Z_c = 100e^{j135°}$; **d.** $Z_d = 6e^{j90°}$.

P7. Reduce each of the following to rectangular form:

a. $Z_a = 5 + j5 + 10\angle 30°$

b. $Z_b = 5\angle 45° - j10$

c. $Z_c = \dfrac{10\angle 45°}{3 + j4}$

d. $Z_d = \dfrac{15}{5\angle 90°}$

ANSWERS FOR THE PRACTICE TESTS

Complete solutions for the practice tests are included in the Student Solutions files. See Appendix "On-Line Student Resources" for information on how to access these files.

T1. $I_{rms} = \sqrt{8} = 2.828\,\text{A}; P = 400\,\text{W}$.

T2. $v(t) = 9.914\ \cos(\omega t - 37.50°)$

T3. **a.** $V_{1rms} = 10.61\,\text{V}$; **b.** $f = 200$ Hz; **c.** $\omega = 400\pi$ radians/s; **d.** $T = 5$ ms; **e.** $\mathbf{V}_1$ lags $\mathbf{V}_2$ by 15° or $\mathbf{V}_2$ leads $\mathbf{V}_1$ by 15°.

T4. $\mathbf{V}_R = 7.071\ \angle -45°$ V; $\mathbf{V}_L = 10.606\ \angle 45°$ V; $\mathbf{V}_C = 5.303\ \angle -135°$ V.

T5. $\mathbf{S} = 5500\ \angle 40° = 4213 + j3535\,\text{VA}$;
$P = 4213\,\text{W}; Q = 3535\,\text{VAR}$; apparent power = 5500 VA;
Power factor = 76.6 percent lagging.

T6. $\mathbf{I}_{aA} = 54.26\ \angle -23.13°$ A.

T7. The commands are:

```
Z = [(15+i*10) -15; -15 (15-i*5)]
V = [pin(10,45); -15]
I = inv(Z)*V
pout(I(1))
pout(I(2))
```

ON-LINE STUDENT RESOURCES

Users of the text can access the Student Solutions Manual (and other folders mentioned below) in electronic form by following links starting from the website:

www.pearsonhighered.com/hambley

The MATLAB folder contains m-files. Except for the examples that use the Symbolic Toolbox, these files work equally well with MathScript, which is sometimes included with the LabVIEW program. The Hambley MathScript folder contains the m-files that work with MathScript.

The Virtual Instruments folder contains LabVIEW programs.

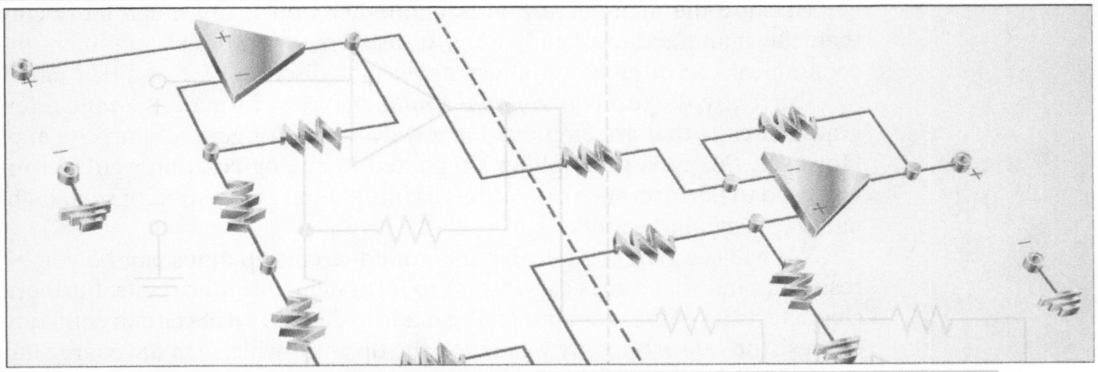

Operational Amplifiers

Study of this chapter will enable you to:

- List the characteristics of ideal op amps.
- Identify negative feedback in op-amp circuits.
- Use the summing-point constraint to analyze ideal op-amp circuits that have negative feedback.
- Select op-amp circuit configurations suitable for various applications.
- Use op amps to design useful circuits.
- Identify practical op-amp limitations and recognize potential inaccuracies in instrumentation applications.
- Work with instrumentation amplifiers.
- Apply integrators, differentiators, and active filters.

Introduction to this chapter:

In this chapter, we introduce an important device known as the **operational amplifier**, which finds application in a wide range of engineering instrumentation.

An operational amplifier is a circuit composed of perhaps 30 BJTs or FETs, 10 resistors, and several capacitors. These components are manufactured concurrently on a single piece of silicon crystal (called a chip) by a sequence of processing steps. Circuits manufactured in this way are called **integrated circuits** (ICs).

From Chapter 14 of *Electrical Engineering: Principles and Applications*, Sixth Edition. Allan R. Hambley.

Because the manufacture of integrated circuits is not much more complicated than the manufacture of individual transistors, operational amplifiers provide an economical and often better alternative to the discrete FET and BJT circuits.

Currently, the term *operational amplifier*, or less formally *op amp*, refers to integrated circuits that are employed in a wide variety of general-purpose applications. However, this type of amplifier originated in analog-computer circuits in which it was used to perform such operations as integration or addition of signals—hence, the name *operational* amplifier.

We will see that inexpensive integrated-circuit op amps can be combined with resistors (and sometimes capacitors) to form many useful circuits. Furthermore, the characteristics of these circuits can be made to depend on the circuit configuration and the resistor values but only weakly on the op amp—which can have large unit-to-unit variations in some of its parameters.

1 IDEAL OPERATIONAL AMPLIFIERS

The circuit symbol for the operational amplifier is shown in Figure 1. The operational amplifier is a differential amplifier having both inverting and noninverting input terminals. The input signals are denoted as $v_1(t)$ and $v_2(t)$. (As usual, we use lowercase letters to represent general time-varying voltages. Often, we will omit the time dependence and refer to the voltages simply as v_1, v_2, and so on.)

The input signal of a differential amplifier consists of a differential component and a common-mode component.

Recall that the average of the input voltages is called the **common-mode signal** and is given by

$$v_{icm} = \frac{1}{2}(v_1 + v_2)$$

Also, the difference between the input voltages is called the **differential signal**, given by

$$v_{id} = v_1 - v_2$$

An ideal operational amplifier has the following characteristics:

Characteristics of ideal op amps.

- Infinite input impedances
- Infinite gain for the differential input signal
- Zero gain for the common-mode input signal

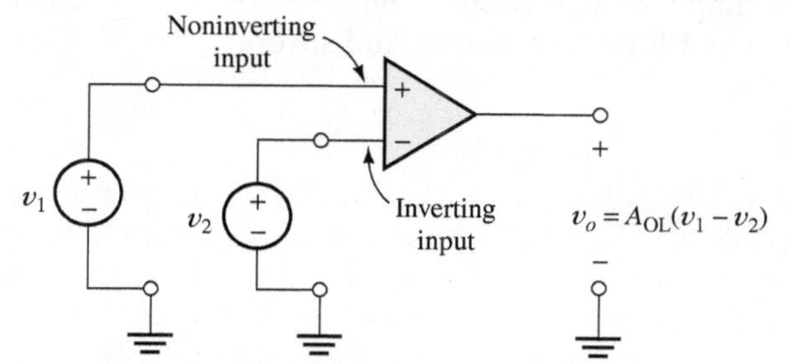

Figure 1 Circuit symbol for the op amp.

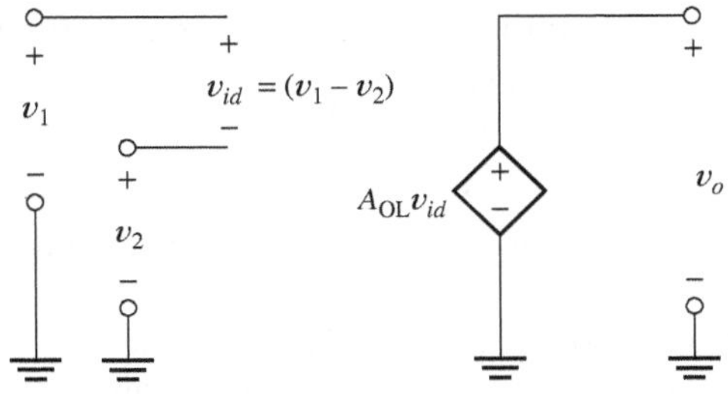

Figure 2 Equivalent circuit for the ideal op amp. The open-loop gain A_{OL} is very large (approaching infinity).

- Zero output impedance
- Infinite bandwidth

An equivalent circuit for the ideal operational amplifier consists simply of a controlled source as shown in Figure 2. The **open-loop gain** A_{OL} is very large in magnitude—ideally, infinite.

As we will shortly see, op amps are generally used with feedback networks that return part of the output signal to the input. Thus, a *loop* is created in which signals flow through the amplifier to the output and back through the feedback network to the input. A_{OL} is the gain of the op amp without a feedback network. That is why we call it the *open-loop gain.*

For now, we assume that the open-loop gain A_{OL} is constant. Thus, there is no distortion, either linear or nonlinear, and the output voltage v_o has a waveshape identical to that of the differential input $v_{id} = v_1 - v_2$. (Later, we will see that A_{OL} is actually a function of frequency. Furthermore, we will learn that real op amps suffer from nonlinear imperfections.)

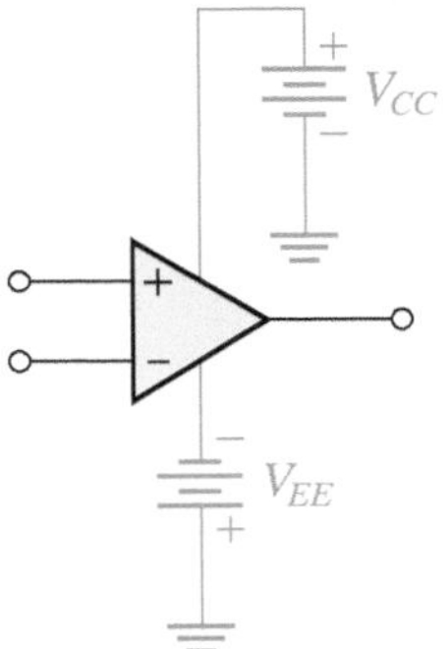

Figure 3 Op-amp symbol showing the dc power supplies, V_{CC} and V_{EE}.

Power-Supply Connections

For a real op amp to function properly, one or more dc supply voltages must be applied, as shown in Figure 3. Often, however, we do not explicitly show the power-supply connections in circuit diagrams. (As indicated in the figure, it is standard practice to use uppercase symbols with repeated uppercase subscripts, such as V_{CC} and V_{EE}, to represent dc power-supply voltages.)

2 INVERTING AMPLIFIERS

Operational amplifiers are almost always used with **negative feedback**, in which part of the output signal is returned to the input in opposition to the source signal. (It is also possible to have *positive* feedback, in which the signal returned to the input *aids* the original source signal. However, negative feedback turns out to be more useful in amplifier circuits.) Frequently, we analyze op-amp circuits by assuming an ideal op amp and employing a concept that we call the summing-point constraint.

Operational amplifiers are almost always used with negative feedback, in which part of the output signal is returned to the input in opposition to the source signal.

For an ideal op amp, the open-loop differential gain is assumed to approach infinity, and even a very tiny input voltage results in a very large output voltage. In a negative-feedback circuit, a fraction of the output is returned to the inverting input terminal. This forces the differential input voltage toward zero. If we assume infinite gain, the differential input voltage is driven to zero exactly. Since the differential input voltage of the op amp is zero, the input current is also zero. The fact that the differential input voltage and the input current are forced to zero is called the **summing-point constraint**.

In a negative feedback system, the ideal op-amp output voltage attains the value needed to force the differential input voltage and input current to zero. We call this fact the summing-point constraint.

Ideal op-amp circuits are analyzed by the following steps:

1. Verify that *negative* feedback is present.
2. Assume that the differential input voltage and the input current of the op amp are forced to zero. (This is the summing-point constraint.)
3. Apply standard circuit-analysis principles, such as Kirchhoff's laws and Ohm's law, to solve for the quantities of interest.

Next, we illustrate this type of analysis for some important circuits that are commonly used in engineering and scientific instrumentation.

The Basic Inverter

An op-amp circuit known as the **inverting amplifier** is shown in Figure 4. We will determine the voltage gain $A_v = v_o/v_{\text{in}}$ by assuming an ideal op amp and employing the summing-point constraint. However, before starting analysis of an op-amp circuit, we should always check to make sure that negative feedback is present rather than positive feedback.

In Figure 4, the feedback is negative, as we shall demonstrate. For example, suppose that due to the input source v_{in}, a positive voltage v_x appears at the inverting input. Then a negative output voltage of large (theoretically infinite) magnitude results at the output. Part of this output voltage is returned to the inverting input by the feedback path through R_2. Thus, the initially positive voltage at the inverting input is driven toward zero by the feedback action. A similar chain of events occurs for the appearance of a negative voltage at the inverting input terminal. Hence, the output voltage of the op amp takes precisely the value needed to oppose the source and produce (nearly) zero voltage at the op-amp input. Since we assume that the gain of the op amp is infinite, a negligible (theoretically zero) input voltage v_x is needed to produce the required output.

Figure 5 shows the inverting amplifier, including the conditions of the summing-point constraint at the input of the op amp. Notice that the input voltage v_{in} appears across R_1. Thus, the current through R_1 is

$$i_1 = \frac{v_{\text{in}}}{R_1} \tag{1}$$

Because the current flowing into the op-amp input terminals is zero, the current flowing through R_2 is

$$i_2 = i_1 \tag{2}$$

Thus, from Equations 1 and 2, we have

$$i_2 = \frac{v_{\text{in}}}{R_1} \tag{3}$$

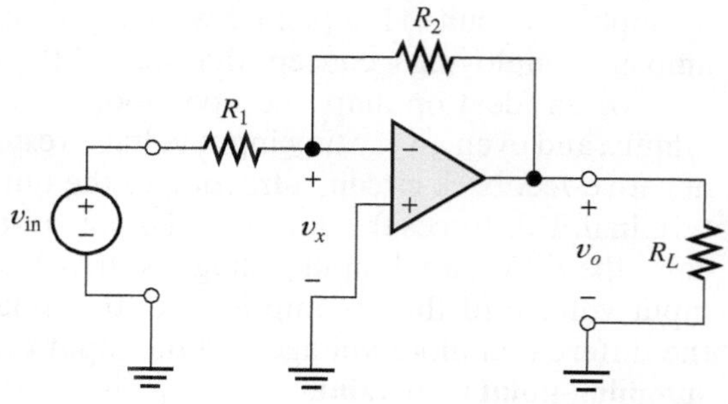

Figure 4 The inverting amplifier.

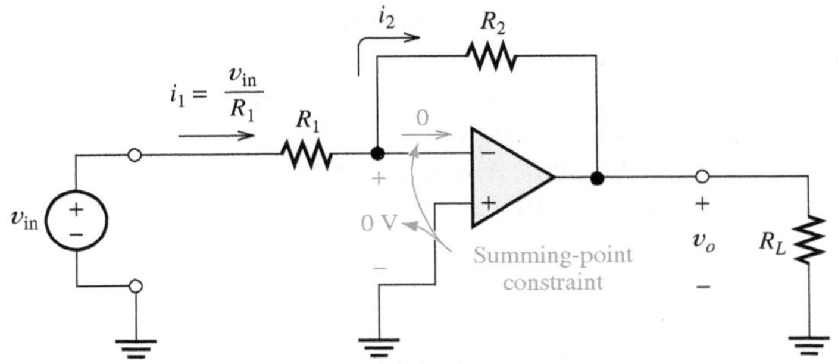

Figure 5 We make use of the summing-point constraint in the analysis of the inverting amplifier.

Writing a voltage equation around the loop by including the output terminals, the resistor R_2, and the op-amp input, we obtain

$$v_o + R_2 i_2 = 0 \tag{4}$$

Using Equation 3 to substitute for i_2 in Equation 4 and solving for the circuit voltage gain, we have

$$A_v = \frac{v_o}{v_{in}} = -\frac{R_2}{R_1} \tag{5}$$

We refer to A_v as the **closed-loop gain** because it is the gain of the circuit with the feedback network in place.

Under the ideal-op-amp assumption, the closed-loop voltage gain is determined solely by the ratio of the resistances. This is a very desirable situation because resistors are available with precise and stable values. Notice that the voltage gain is negative, indicating that the amplifier is inverting (i.e., the output voltage is out of phase with the input voltage).

Under the ideal op-amp assumption, the closed-loop voltage gain of the inverter is determined solely by the ratio of the resistances.

The input impedance of the inverting amplifier is

$$Z_{in} = \frac{v_{in}}{i_1} = R_1 \tag{6}$$

Thus, we can easily control the input impedance of the circuit by our choice of R_1.

Rearranging Equation 5, we have

$$v_o = -\frac{R_2}{R_1} v_{in} \tag{7}$$

Consequently, we see that the output voltage is independent of the load resistance R_L. We conclude that the output acts as an ideal voltage source (as far as R_L is concerned). *In other words, the output impedance of the inverting amplifier is zero.*

Later, we will see that the characteristics of the inverting amplifier are influenced by nonideal properties of the op amp. Nevertheless, in many applications, the departure of actual performance from the ideal is insignificant.

The inverter has a closed-loop voltage gain $A_v = -R_2/R_1$, an input impedance equal to R_1, and zero output impedance.

Virtual-Short-Circuit Concept

Sometimes, the condition at the op-amp input terminals of Figure 5 is called a **virtual short circuit**. That terminology is used because even though the differential input voltage of the op amp is forced to zero (as if by a short circuit to ground), the op-amp input current is also zero.

This terminology can be confusing unless it is realized that it is the action at the output of the op amp acting through the feedback network that enforces zero differential input voltage. (Possibly, it would be just as valid to call the condition at the op-amp input terminals a "virtual open circuit" because no current flows.)

Variations of the Inverter Circuit

Several useful versions of the inverter circuit exist. Analysis of these circuits follows the same pattern that we have used for the basic inverter: Verify that *negative* feedback is present, assume the summing-point constraint, and then apply basic circuit laws.

Example 1 Analysis of an Inverting Amplifier

Figure 6 shows a version of the inverting amplifier that can have high gain magnitude without resorting to as wide a range of resistor values as is needed in the standard inverter configuration. Derive an expression for the voltage gain under the ideal-op-amp assumption. Also, find the input impedance and output impedance. Evaluate the results for $R_1 = R_3 = 1\ \text{k}\Omega$ and $R_2 = R_4 = 10\ \text{k}\Omega$. Then, consider the standard inverter configuration of Figure 5 with $R_1 = 1\ \text{k}\Omega$, and find the value of R_2 required to achieve the same gain.

Solution First, we verify that negative feedback is present. Assume a positive value for v_i, which results in a negative output voltage of very large magnitude. Part of this negative voltage is returned through the resistor network and opposes the original input voltage. Thus, we conclude that negative feedback is present.

Generally, if a network of resistors is connected between the inverting input and the output, negative feedback exists.

Next, we assume the conditions of the summing-point constraint:

$$v_i = 0 \quad \text{and} \quad i_i = 0$$

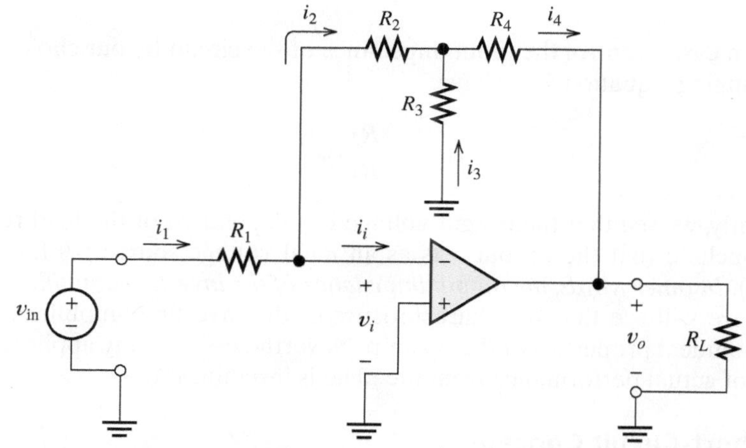

Figure 6 An inverting amplifier that achieves high gain magnitude with a smaller range of resistance values than required for the basic inverter. See Example 1.

Then, we apply Kirchhoff's current law, Kirchhoff's voltage law, and Ohm's law to analyze the circuit. To begin, we notice that v_{in} appears across R_1 (because $v_i = 0$). Hence, we can write

$$i_1 = \frac{v_{\text{in}}}{R_1} \tag{8}$$

Next, we apply Kirchhoff's current law to the node at the right-hand end of R_1, to obtain

$$i_2 = i_1 \tag{9}$$

(Here, we have used the fact that $i_i = 0$.)

Writing a voltage equation around the loop through v_i, R_2, and R_3, we obtain

$$R_2 i_2 = R_3 i_3 \tag{10}$$

(In writing this equation, we have used the fact that $v_i = 0$.) Applying Kirchhoff's current law at the top end of R_3 yields

$$i_4 = i_2 + i_3 \tag{11}$$

Writing a voltage equation for the loop containing v_o, R_4, and R_3 gives

$$v_o = -R_4 i_4 - R_3 i_3 \tag{12}$$

Next, we use substitution to eliminate the current variables (i_1, i_2, i_3, and i_4) and obtain an equation relating the output voltage to the input voltage. First, from Equations 8 and 9, we obtain

$$i_2 = \frac{v_{\text{in}}}{R_1} \tag{13}$$

Then, we use Equation 13 to substitute for i_2 in Equation 10 and rearrange terms to obtain

$$i_3 = v_{\text{in}} \frac{R_2}{R_1 R_3} \tag{14}$$

Using Equations 13 and 14 to substitute for i_2 and i_3 in Equation 11, we find that

$$i_4 = v_{\text{in}} \left(\frac{1}{R_1} + \frac{R_2}{R_1 R_3} \right) \tag{15}$$

Finally, using Equations 14 and 15 to substitute into 12, we obtain

$$v_o = -v_{\text{in}} \left(\frac{R_2}{R_1} + \frac{R_4}{R_1} + \frac{R_2 R_4}{R_1 R_3} \right) \tag{16}$$

Therefore, the voltage gain of the circuit is

$$A_v = \frac{v_o}{v_{\text{in}}} = -\left(\frac{R_2}{R_1} + \frac{R_4}{R_1} + \frac{R_2 R_4}{R_1 R_3} \right) \tag{17}$$

The input impedance is obtained from Equation 8:

$$R_{\text{in}} = \frac{v_{\text{in}}}{i_1} = R_1 \tag{18}$$

Inspection of Equation 16 shows that the output voltage is independent of the load resistance. Thus, the output appears as an ideal voltage source to the load. In other words, the output impedance of the amplifier is zero.

Evaluating the voltage gain for the resistor values given ($R_1 = R_3 = 1$ kΩ and $R_2 = R_4 = 10$ kΩ) yields

$$A_v = -120$$

In the basic inverter circuit of Figure 5, the voltage gain is given by Equation 5, which states that

$$A_v = -\frac{R_2}{R_1}$$

Therefore, to achieve a voltage gain of −120 with $R_1 = 1$ kΩ, we need $R_2 =$ 120 kΩ. Notice that a resistance ratio of 120 : 1 is required for the basic inverter, whereas the circuit of Figure 6 has a ratio of only 10 : 1. Sometimes, there are significant practical advantages in keeping the ratio of resistances in a circuit as close to unity as possible. Then, the circuit of Figure 6 is preferable to the basic inverter shown in Figure 5. ■

Now that we have demonstrated how to make use of the summing-point constraint in analysis of ideal-op-amp circuits having negative feedback, we provide some exercises for you to practice applying the technique. Each of these circuits has negative feedback, and if we assume ideal op amps, the summing-point constraint can be used in analysis.

Exercise 1 A circuit known as a summer is shown in Figure 7. **a.** Use the ideal-op-amp assumption to solve for the output voltage in terms of the input voltages and resistor values. **b.** What is the input resistance seen by v_A? **c.** By v_B? **d.** What is the output resistance seen by R_L?

Answer **a.** $v_o = -(R_f/R_A)v_A - (R_f/R_B)v_B$; **b.** the input resistance for v_A is equal to R_A; **c.** the input resistance for v_B is equal to R_B; **d.** the output resistance is zero. □

Exercise 2 Solve for the currents and voltages labeled in the circuits of Figure 8.

Answer **a.** $i_1 = 1$ mA, $i_2 = 1$ mA, $i_o = -10$ mA, $i_x = -11$ mA, $v_o = -10$ V; **b.** $i_1 =$ 5 mA, $i_2 = 5$ mA, $i_3 = 5$ mA, $i_4 = 10$ mA, $v_o = -15$ V. □

Exercise 3 Find an expression for the output voltage of the circuit shown in Figure 9.

Answer $v_o = 4v_1 - 2v_2$. □

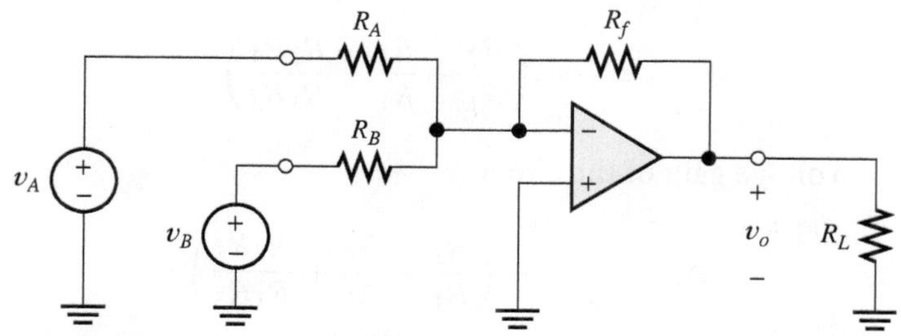

Figure 7 Summing amplifier. See Exercise 1.

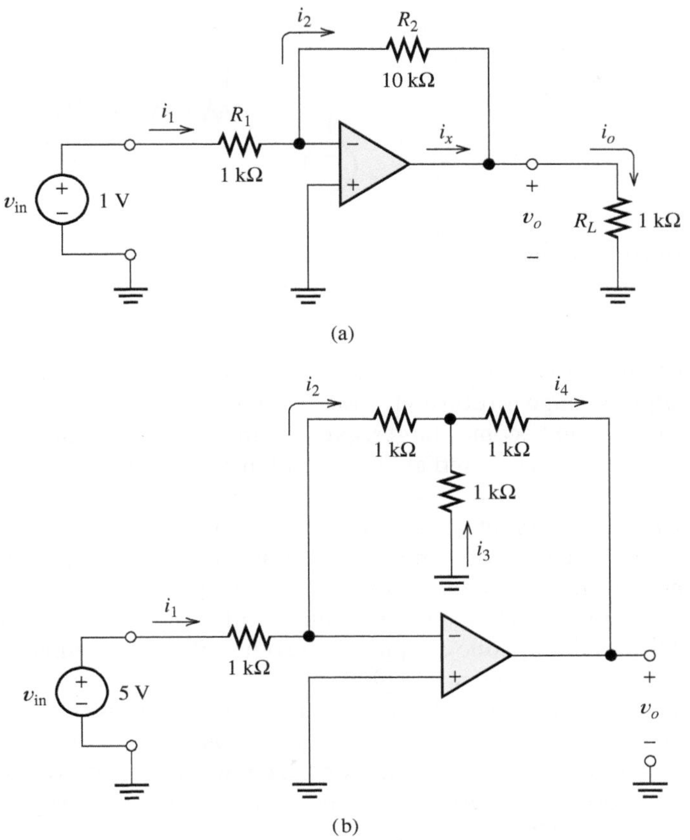

Figure 8 Circuits for Exercise 2.

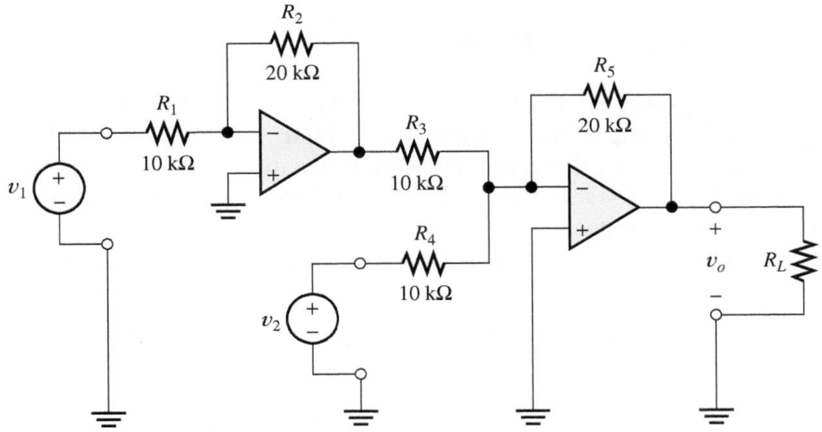

Figure 9 Circuit for Exercise 3.

Positive Feedback

It is interesting to consider the inverting amplifier configuration with the input terminals of the op amp interchanged as shown in Figure 10. In this case, the feedback is positive–in other words, the feedback signal *aids* the original input signal. For

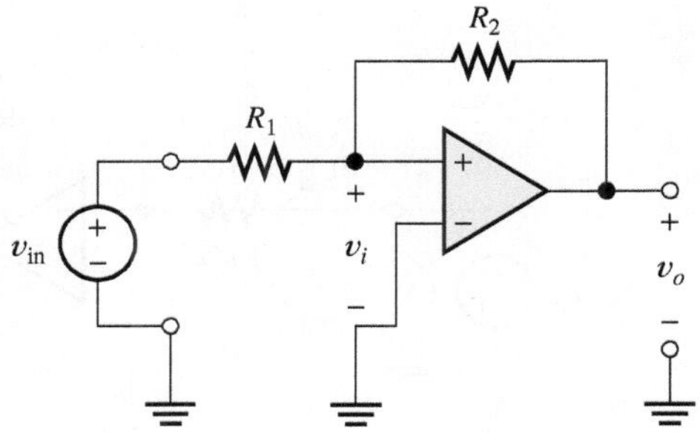

Figure 10 Circuit with positive feedback.

example, if the input voltage v_i is positive, a very large positive output voltage results. Part of the output voltage is returned to the op-amp input by the feedback network. Thus, the input voltage becomes larger, causing an even larger output voltage. The output quickly becomes saturated at the maximum possible voltage that the op amp can produce.

If an initial negative input voltage is present, the output saturates at its negative extreme. Hence, the circuit does not function as an amplifier–the output voltage is stuck at one extreme or the other and does not respond to the input voltage v_{in}. (However, if the input voltage v_{in} becomes sufficiently large in magnitude, the output can be forced to switch from one extreme to the other. Positive-feedback circuits [i.e., flip-flops] are useful for memory in digital systems.)

With positive feedback, the op-amp's input and output voltages increase in magnitude until the output voltage reaches one of its extremes.

If we were to ignore the fact that the circuit of Figure 10 has positive rather than negative feedback and to apply the summing-point constraint erroneously, we would obtain $v_o = -(R_2/R_1)v_{in}$, just as we did for the circuit with negative feedback. This illustrates the importance of verifying that negative feedback is present before using the summing-point constraint.

3 NONINVERTING AMPLIFIERS

The circuit configuration for a noninverting amplifier is shown in Figure 11. We assume an ideal op amp to analyze the circuit. First, we check to see whether the feedback is negative or positive. In this case, it is negative. To see this, assume that v_i becomes positive and notice that it produces a very large positive output voltage. Part of the output voltage appears across R_1. Since $v_i = v_{in} - v_1$, the voltage v_i becomes smaller as v_o and v_1 become larger. Thus, the amplifier and feedback network act to

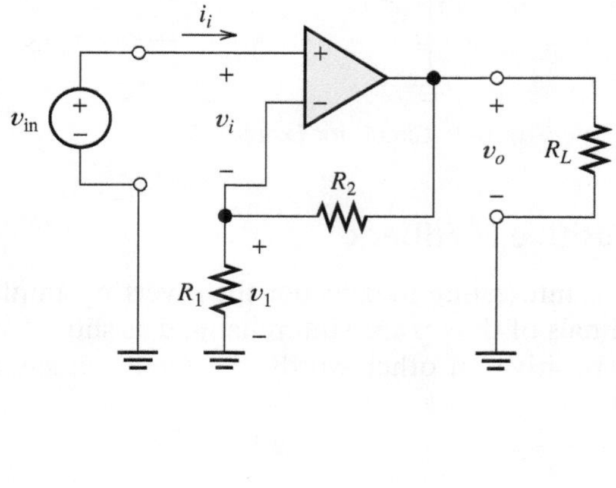

Figure 11 Noninverting amplifier.

drive v_i toward zero. This is negative feedback because the feedback signal opposes the original input.

Having verified that negative feedback is present, we utilize the summing-point constraint: $v_i = 0$ and $i_i = 0$. Applying Kirchhoff's voltage law and the fact that $v_i = 0$, we can write

$$v_{in} = v_1 \tag{19}$$

Since i_i is zero, the voltage across R_1 is given by the voltage-division principle:

$$v_1 = \frac{R_1}{R_1 + R_2} v_o \tag{20}$$

Using Equation 20 to substitute into 19 and rearranging, we find that the closed-loop voltage gain is:

$$A_v = \frac{v_o}{v_{in}} = 1 + \frac{R_2}{R_1} \tag{21}$$

Notice that the circuit is a noninverting amplifier (A_v is positive), and the gain is set by the ratio of the feedback resistors.

The input impedance of the circuit is theoretically infinite because the input current i_i is zero. Since the voltage gain is independent of the load resistance, the output voltage is independent of the load resistance. Thus, the output impedance is zero. *Therefore, under the ideal-op-amp assumption, the noninverting amplifier is an ideal voltage amplifier.*

Under the ideal-op-amp assumption, the noninverting amplifier is an ideal voltage amplifier having infinite input resistance and zero output resistance.

Voltage Follower

Notice from Equation 21 that the minimum gain magnitude is unity, which is obtained with $R_2 = 0$. Usually, we choose R_1 to be an open circuit for unity gain. The resulting circuit, called a **voltage follower**, is shown in Figure 12.

Exercise 4 Find the voltage gain $A_v = v_o/v_{in}$ and input impedance of the circuit shown in Figure 13: **a.** with the switch open; **b.** with the switch closed.

Answer **a.** $A_v = +1, R_{in} = \infty$; **b.** $A_v = -1, R_{in} = R/2$. □

Exercise 5 Assume an ideal op amp and use the summing-point constraint to find an expression for the output current i_o in the circuit of Figure 14. Also find the input and output resistances of the circuit.

Answer $i_o = v_{in}/R_F, R_{in} = \infty, R_o = \infty$ (because the output current is independent of the load resistance). □

Exercise 6 **a.** Derive an expression for the voltage gain v_o/v_{in} of the circuit shown in Figure 15. **b.** Evaluate for $R_1 = 10\ \text{k}\Omega$ and $R_2 = 100\ \text{k}\Omega$. **c.** Find the input resistance of this circuit. **d.** Find the output resistance.

Answer **a.** $A_v = 1 + 3(R_2/R_1) + (R_2/R_1)^2$; **b.** $A_v = 131$; **c.** $R_{in} = \infty$; **d.** $R_o = 0$. □

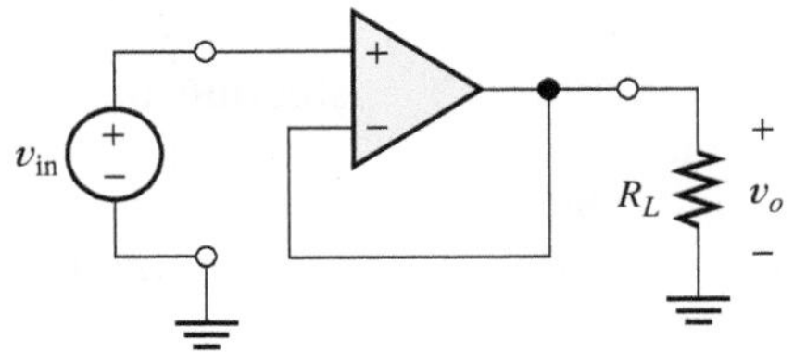

Figure 12 The voltage follower which has $A_v = 1$.

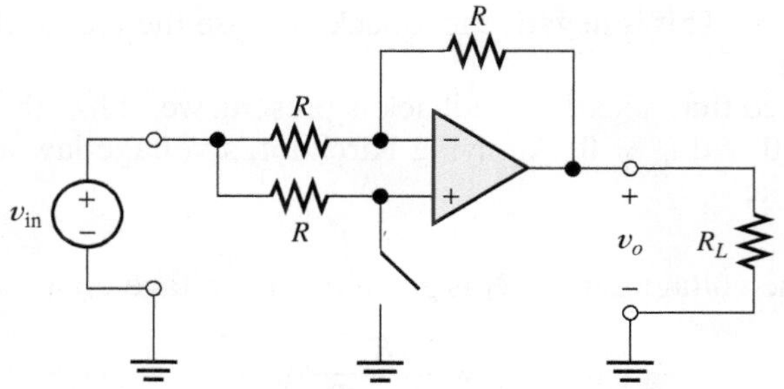

Figure 13 Inverting or noninverting amplifier. See Exercise 4.

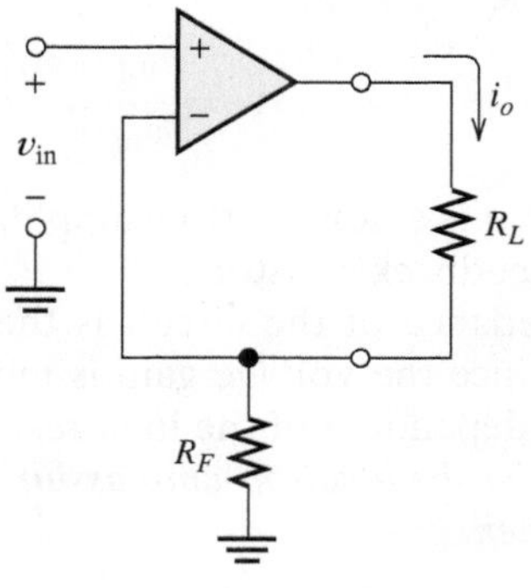

Figure 14 Voltage-to-current converter (also known as a transconductance amplifier). See Exercise 5.

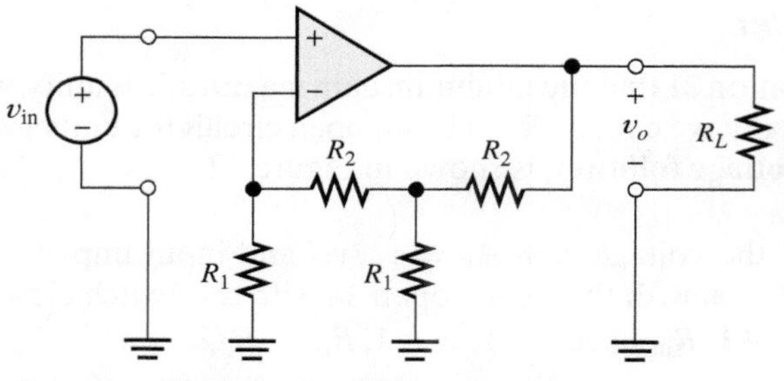

Figure 15 Circuit for Exercise 6.

PRACTICAL APPLICATION 1

Mechanical Application of Negative Feedback: Power Steering

Besides its use in op-amp circuits, negative feedback has many other applications in engineering–automotive power-assisted steering systems provide one example. A simplified diagram of a typical system is shown in Figure PA1. A hydraulic pump driven by the engine continuously supplies pressure to a control valve that routes the fluid to two sides of the booster cylinder. For straight-ahead steering, pressure is applied equally to both sides of the cylinder and no turning force results. As the steering wheel is moved by the driver, more pressure is applied to one side of the cylinder or the other to help turn the wheels in the desired direction. (The fluid path for one direction is illustrated in the figure.) A mechanical feedback arm from the steering linkage causes the valve to return to its neutral position as the wheels turn. Thus, there is a negative feedback path from the booster cylinder through the mechanical linkage back to the control valve.

Negative feedback is an important aspect of the power-steering system. Consider what would happen if the mechanical linkage between the output of the booster cylinder and the control valve is removed. Then, if the steering wheel were moved slightly off center, pressure would be applied continuously to the booster cylinder and the wheels would eventually move all the way to their extreme position. It would be very difficult for the driver to make a gradual turn.

On the other hand, with the feedback linkage in place, the wheels move only far enough to return the valve (nearly) to its neutral position. As the steering wheel is turned, the wheels move a proportional amount.

Notice that the control valve responds to the difference between the input from the steering wheel and the position of the steering linkage. This is similar to the way that the op amp responds to its differential input signal. The pump is analogous to the power supply in an op-amp circuit. Furthermore, the booster cylinder position is analogous to the op-amp output signal, and the mechanical linkage back to the control valve is analogous to a feedback circuit.

Steer-by-wire systems are a more modern alternative for mechanical/hydraulic steering systems and are under intense development. Here, the mechanical/hydraulic steering components are replaced by electrical sensors, microcontrollers, software, and electrical motors. Just as in the mechanical system, negative feedback is used in steer-by-wire systems. Actual and desired wheel positions are derived from sensors connected to the wheels and to the steering wheel. The software compares the actual wheel position to the desired position and uses the difference to control motors that turn the wheels. There is no steering column or actual mechanical path from the steering wheel to the vehicle wheels. These new electronic steering systems have the potential to significantly reduce weight and increase fuel economy of a vehicle. However, they also have some new safety issues. After all, loss of steering due to a software glitch could be very serious.

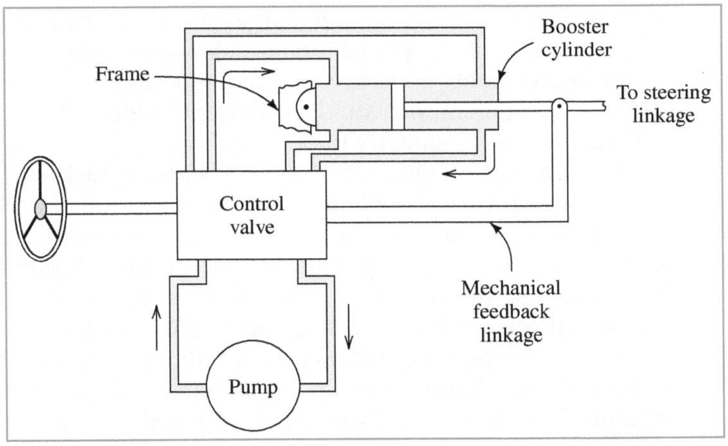

Figure PA1 A simplified diagram of an automotive power-assisted steering system illustrating the importance of negative feedback.

4 DESIGN OF SIMPLE AMPLIFIERS

Many useful amplifiers can be designed by using resistive feedback networks with op amps.

Many useful amplifiers can be designed by using resistive feedback networks with op amps. For now, we consider the op amps to be ideal. Later, we consider the effects of the nonideal properties of real op amps. Often in practice, the performance requirements of the circuits to be designed are not extreme, and design can be carried out assuming ideal op amps.

Amplifier design using op amps mainly consists of selecting a suitable circuit configuration and values for the feedback resistors.

We illustrate design by using the op-amp circuits that we have considered in previous sections (including the exercises). For these circuits, design consists primarily of selecting a suitable circuit configuration and values for the feedback resistors.

Example 2 Design of a Noninverting Amplifier

Design a noninverting amplifier that has a voltage gain of 10, using an ideal op amp. The input signals lie in the range −1 to +1 V. Use standard 5-percent-tolerance resistors in the design. (See Appendix "Nominal Values and the Color Code for Resistors" for a list of standard 5-percent-tolerance resistor values.)

Solution We use the noninverting amplifier configuration of Figure 11. The gain is given by Equation 21. Thus, we have

$$A_v = 10 = 1 + \frac{R_2}{R_1}$$

Theoretically, any resistor values would provide the proper gain, provided that $R_2 = 9R_1$. However, very small resistances are not practical because the current through the resistors must be supplied by the output of the op amp, and ultimately, by the power supply. For example, if $R_1 = 1\ \Omega$ and $R_2 = 9\ \Omega$, for an output voltage of 10 V, the op amp must supply 1 A of current. This is illustrated in Figure 16. Most integrated-circuit op amps are not capable of such a large output current, and even if they were, the load on the power supply would be unwarranted. In the circuit at hand, we would want to keep $R_1 + R_2$ large enough so the current that must be supplied to them is reasonable. For general design with power supplies operated from the ac power line, currents up to several milliamperes are usually acceptable. (In battery-operated equipment, we would try harder to reduce the current and avoid having to replace batteries frequently.)

If the resistances are too small, an impractical amount of current and power will be needed to operate the amplifier.

On the other hand, very large resistances, such as $R_1 = 10\ \text{M}\Omega$ and $R_2 = 90\ \text{M}\Omega$, also present problems. Such large resistances are unstable in value, particularly in a humid environment. Later, we will see that large resistances lead to problems due to an op-amp imperfection known as bias current. Furthermore, high-impedance circuits are prone to injection of unwanted signals from nearby circuits through stray capacitive coupling. This is illustrated in Figure 17.

Very large resistance may be unstable in value and lead to stray coupling of undesired signals.

Generally, resistance values between about 100 Ω and 1 MΩ are suitable for use in op-amp circuits. Since the problem statement calls for standard 5-percent-tolerance resistors (see Appendix "Nominal Values and the Color Code for Resistors"), we

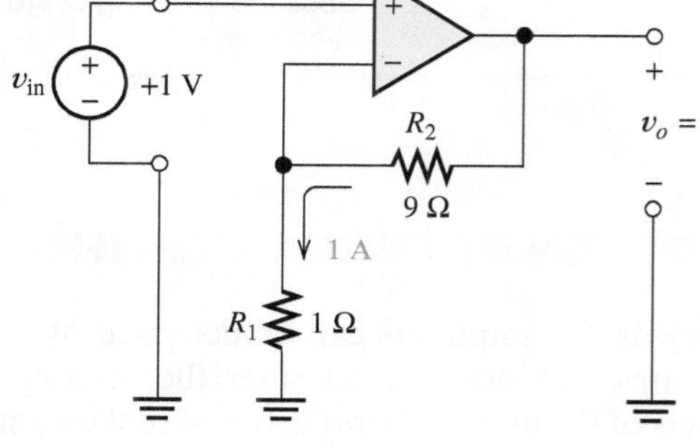

Figure 16 If low resistances are used, an excessively large current is required.

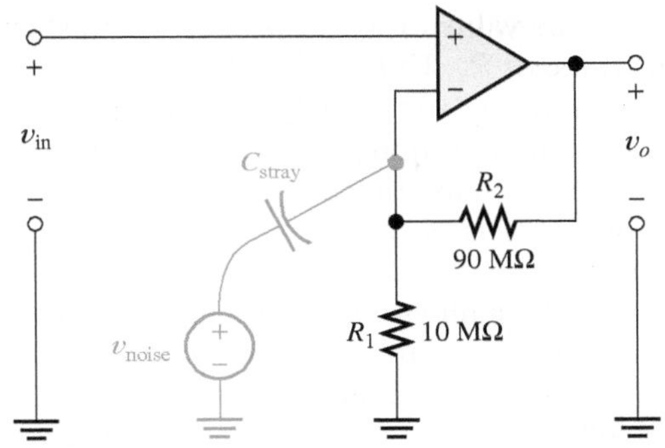

Figure 17 If very high resistances are used, stray capacitance can couple unwanted signals into the circuit.

look for a pair of resistor values such that the ratio R_2/R_1 is 9. One possibility is $R_2 = 180$ kΩ and $R_1 = 20$ kΩ. However, for many applications, we would find that $R_2 = 18$ kΩ and $R_1 = 2$ kΩ would work just as well. Of course, if 5-percent-tolerance resistors are used, we can expect unit-to-unit variations of about ±10 percent in the ratio R_2/R_1. This is because R_2 could be 5-percent low while R_1 is 5 percent high, or vice versa. Thus, the gain of the amplifier (which is $A_v = 1 + R_2/R_1$) varies by about ±9 percent.

If more precision is needed, 1-percent-tolerance resistors can be used. Another possibility is an adjustable resistor to set the gain to the desired value. ■

Example 3 Amplifier Design

A transducer for instrumentation of vibrations in a forge hammer has an internal impedance that is always less than 500 Ω but is variable over time. An amplifier that produces an amplified version of the internal source voltage v_s is required. The voltage gain should be -10 ± 5 percent. Design an amplifier for this application.

Solution Since an inverting gain is specified, we choose to use the inverting amplifier of Figure 4. The proposed amplifier and the signal source are shown in Figure 18.

Using the summing-point constraint and conventional circuit analysis, we can show that

$$v_o = -\frac{R_2}{R_1 + R_s} v_s$$

Hence, we must select resistance values so that

$$\frac{R_2}{R_1 + R_s} = 10 \pm 5\%$$

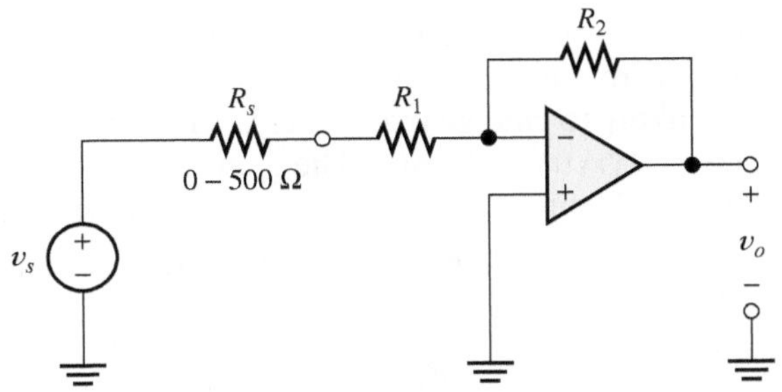

Figure 18 Circuit of Example 3.

Because the value of R_s is variable, we must choose R_1 much greater than the maximum value of R_s. Thus, we are led to choose $R_1 \cong 100R_{s\,\max} = 50$ kΩ. (Then, as R_s ranges from zero to 500 Ω, the sum $R_1 + R_s$ varies by only 1 percent.) To achieve the desired gain, we require that $R_2 \cong 500$ kΩ.

Since a gain tolerance of ±5 percent is specified, we resort to the use of 1 percent resistors. This is necessary because gain variations occur due to variations in R_s, variations in R_1, and variations in R_2. If each of these causes a ±1 percent gain variation, the gain varies by about ±3 percent, which is within the allowed range.

Consulting a table of standard values for 1 percent resistors (see Appendix "Nominal Values and the Color Code for Resistors"), we choose $R_1 = 49.9$ kΩ and $R_2 = 499$ kΩ. As well as ensuring that the gain does not vary outside the specified limits, these values are not so small that large currents occur or so large that undue coupling of unwanted signals into the circuit is likely to be a problem.

Another solution would be to use 5-percent-tolerance resistors, but choose $R_1 =$ 51 kΩ and R_2 as the series combination of a 430-kΩ fixed resistor and a 200-kΩ adjustable resistor. Then the gain could be set initially to the desired value. Some gain fluctuation would occur in operation due to variation of R_s and drift of the other resistance values due to aging, temperature changes, and so on. ■

Exercise 7 Find the maximum and minimum values of the gain $A_{vs} = v_o/v_s$ for the circuit designed in Example 3. The nominal resistor values are $R_1 = 49.9$ kΩ and $R_2 = 499$ kΩ. Assume that the resistors R_1 and R_2 range as far as ±1 percent from their nominal values and that R_s ranges from 0 to 500 Ω.

Answer The extreme gain values are −9.71 and −10.20. □

Close-Tolerance Designs

When designing amplifiers with tight gain tolerances (1 percent or better), it is necessary to employ adjustable resistors. We might be tempted to use lower cost 5-percent-tolerance resistors rather than 1-percent-tolerance resistors and use the adjustable resistor to offset the larger variations. However, this is not good practice because 5-percent-tolerance resistors tend to be less stable than 1-percent-tolerance resistors. Furthermore, fixed resistors tend to be more stable than adjustable resistors. The best approach from the standpoint of long-term precision is to use 1-percent-tolerance fixed resistors and design for only enough adjustment to overcome the resulting gain variations.

Often, we combine various types of op-amp circuits in the design of a desired function. These points are illustrated in the next example.

Example 4 Summing Amplifier Design

Two signal sources have internal voltages $v_1(t)$ and $v_2(t)$, respectively. The internal resistances of the sources are known always to be less than 1 kΩ, but the exact values are not known and are likely to change over time. Design an amplifier for which the output voltage is $v_o(t) = A_1v_1(t) + A_2v_2(t)$. The gains are to be $A_1 = 5 \pm 1$ percent and $A_2 = -2 \pm 1$ percent. Assume that ideal op amps are available.

Solution The summer circuit of Figure 7 can be used to form the weighted sum of the input voltages given by

$$v_o = -\frac{R_f}{R_A}v_A - \frac{R_f}{R_B}v_B$$

in which the gains for both input signals are negative. However, the problem statement calls for a positive gain for v_1 and a negative gain for v_2. Thus, we first pass v_1 through an inverting amplifier. The output of this inverter and v_2 are then applied to the summer. The proposed circuit diagram is shown in Figure 19.

It can be shown that the output voltage of this circuit is given by

$$v_o = \frac{R_2}{R_{s1} + R_1}\frac{R_f}{R_A}v_1 - \frac{R_f}{R_{s2} + R_B}v_2 \quad (22)$$

We must select values for the resistances so that the gain for the v_1 input is +5 and the gain for the v_2 input is −2. Many combinations of resistances can be used to meet these specifications. However, we should keep the input impedances seen by the sources much larger than the internal source impedances, to avoid gain variations due to loading. This implies that we should choose large values for R_1 and R_B. (However, keep in mind that extremely large values are not practical.) Since we want the gain values to remain within ±1 percent of the design values, we choose $R_1 = R_B \cong 500\ \text{k}\Omega$. Then, as the source impedances change, the gains change by only about 0.2 percent (because the input impedances are approximately 500 times larger than the highest value of the source impedances).

Even if we choose to use 1-percent-tolerance resistors, we must use adjustable resistors to trim the gain. For example, with 1 percent resistors, the gain

$$A_1 = \frac{R_2}{R_{s1} + R_1}\frac{R_f}{R_A}$$

varies by about ±4 percent, due to the resistance tolerances. Thus, to provide for adjustment of A_1, we use the combination of a fixed resistance in series with a variable resistance for R_1. Similarly, to provide for adjustment of A_2, we use a second variable resistance in series with a fixed resistance for R_B.

Suppose that we select R_1 as a 453-kΩ (this is a standard nominal value for 1-percent-tolerance resistors) fixed resistor in series with a 100-kΩ trimmer (i.e., an adjustable resistor having a maximum value of 100 kΩ). We use the same combination for R_B. (Recall that we plan to design for nominal values of R_1 and R_B of 500 kΩ each.) The trimmers allow for approximately a ±10 percent adjustment, which is more than adequate to allow for variations of the fixed resistors.

The gain for the v_2 input is

$$A_2 = -\frac{R_f}{R_{s2} + R_B}$$

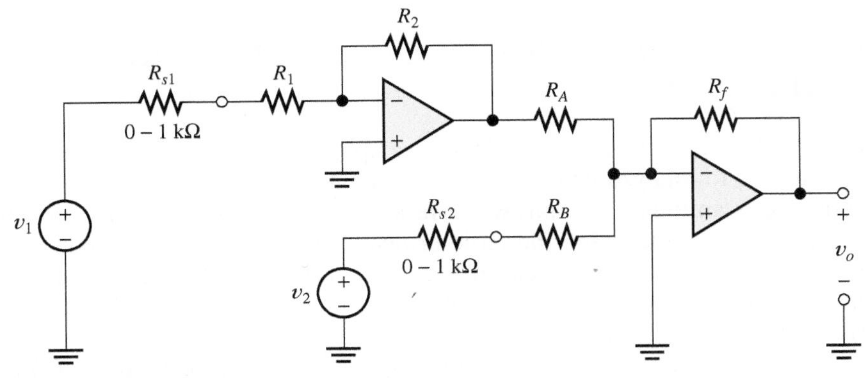

Figure 19 Amplifier designed in Example 4.

Because $R_{s2} + R_B$ has a nominal value 500 kΩ and we want to have $A_2 = -2$, R_f is selected to be a 1-MΩ 1-percent-tolerance resistor. Now, since we want to achieve

$$A_1 = \frac{R_2}{R_{s1} + R_1}\frac{R_f}{R_A} = 5$$

and the values we have already selected result in $R_f/(R_{s1} + R_1) = 2$, we must choose values of R_2 and R_A such that $R_2/R_A \cong 2.5$. Thus, we choose R_2 as a 1-MΩ resistor and R_A as a 402-kΩ resistor. This completes the design. The following values are selected:

R_1 = a 453-kΩ fixed resistor in series with a 100-kΩ trimmer (500-kΩ nominal design value).

R_B is the same as R_1.

$R_2 = 1$ MΩ.

$R_A = 402$ kΩ.

$R_f = 1$ MΩ.

Usually, design problems have many "right" answers.

These are by no means the only values that can be used to meet the specifications. Usually, design problems have many "right" answers. ■

Exercise 8 Derive Equation 22. □

Exercise 9 A certain source has an internal impedance of 600 Ω±20 percent. Design an amplifier whose output voltage is $v_o = A_{vs}v_s$, where v_s is the internal voltage of the source. Assume ideal op amps and design for $A_{vs} = 20 \pm 5$ percent.

Answer Many answers are possible. A good solution is the circuit of Figure 11 with $R_2 \cong 19 \times R_1$. For example, we could use 1-percent-tolerance resistors having nominal values of $R_1 = 1$ kΩ and $R_2 = 19.1$ kΩ. □

Exercise 10 Repeat Exercise 9 for $A_{vs} = -25 \pm 3$ percent.

Answer Many answers are possible. A good solution is the circuit of Figure 18 with $R_1 \geq 20R_s$ and with $R_2 \cong 25(R_1+R_s)$. For example, we could use 1-percent-tolerance resistors having nominal values of $R_1 = 20$ kΩ and $R_2 = 515$ kΩ. □

Exercise 11 Repeat Example 4 if $A_1 = +1 \pm 1$ percent and $A_2 = -3 \pm 1$ percent.

Answer Many answers can be found by following the approach taken in Example 4. □

5 OP-AMP IMPERFECTIONS IN THE LINEAR RANGE OF OPERATION

In Sections 1 through 4, we introduced the op amp, learned how to use the summing-point constraint to analyze negative-feedback amplifier circuits, and learned how to design simple amplifiers. So far, we have assumed ideal op amps. This assumption is appropriate for learning the basic principles of op-amp circuits, but not for high-performance circuits using real op amps. Therefore, in this and the next few sections, we consider the imperfections of real op amps and how to allow for these imperfections in circuit design.

Real op amps have several categories of imperfections compared with ideal op amps.

The nonideal characteristics of real op amps fall into three categories: (1) nonideal properties in linear operation, (2) nonlinear characteristics, and (3) dc offsets.

We discuss the imperfections for the linear range of operation in this section. In the next several sections, we consider nonlinear operation and dc offsets.

Input and Output Impedances

Real op amps have finite input impedance and nonzero output impedance.

An ideal op amp has infinite input impedance and zero output impedance. However, a real op amp has finite input impedance and nonzero output impedance. The input impedances of IC op amps having BJT input stages are usually about 1 MΩ. Op amps having FET input stages have much higher input impedances, as much as 10^{12} Ω. Output impedance is ordinarily between 1 and 100 Ω for an IC op amp, although it can be as high as several thousand ohms for a low-power op amp.

In circuits with negative feedback, the impedances are drastically altered by the feedback action, and the input or output impedances of the op amps rarely place serious limits on closed-loop circuit performance.

Gain and Bandwidth Limitations

Real op amps have finite open-loop gain and finite bandwidth.

Ideal op amps have infinite gain magnitude and unlimited bandwidth. Real op amps have finite open-loop gain magnitude, typically between 10^4 and 10^6. (We are referring to the open-circuit voltage gain of the op amp without feedback resistors.) Furthermore, the bandwidth of real op amps is limited. The gain of a real op amp is a function of frequency, becoming smaller in magnitude at higher frequencies.

Usually, the bandwidth of an IC op amp is intentionally limited by the op-amp designer. This is called *frequency compensation* and is necessary to avoid oscillation in feedback amplifiers. However, it turns out that the open-loop gain of most integrated-circuit op amps is of the form

$$A_{\text{OL}}(f) = \frac{A_{0\text{OL}}}{1 + j(f/f_{B\text{OL}})} \tag{23}$$

in which $A_{0\text{OL}}$ is the dc open-loop gain of the amplifier, and $f_{B\text{OL}}$ is the open-loop break frequency.

In a Bode plot for $A_{\text{OL}}(f)$, the gain magnitude is approximately constant up to $f_{B\text{OL}}$. Above $f_{B\text{OL}}$, the gain magnitude falls at 20 dB per decade. This is illustrated in Figure 20.

Closed-Loop Bandwidth

We will show that negative feedback reduces the dc gain of an op amp and extends its bandwidth. Consider the noninverting amplifier circuit shown in Figure 21. The phasor output voltage $\mathbf{V}_o$ is the open-loop gain times the phasor differential input voltage $\mathbf{V}_{id}$:

$$\mathbf{V}_o = A_{\text{OL}}(f)\mathbf{V}_{id} \tag{24}$$

We assume that the input impedance of the op amp is infinite, so the input current is zero. Then, the voltage across R_1 can be found by applying the voltage-division principle to the feedback network (which is composed of R_1 in series with R_2). The voltage across R_1 is shown as $\beta\mathbf{V}_o$, in which β is the voltage-division ratio of R_1 and R_2:

$$\beta = \frac{R_1}{R_1 + R_2} \tag{25}$$

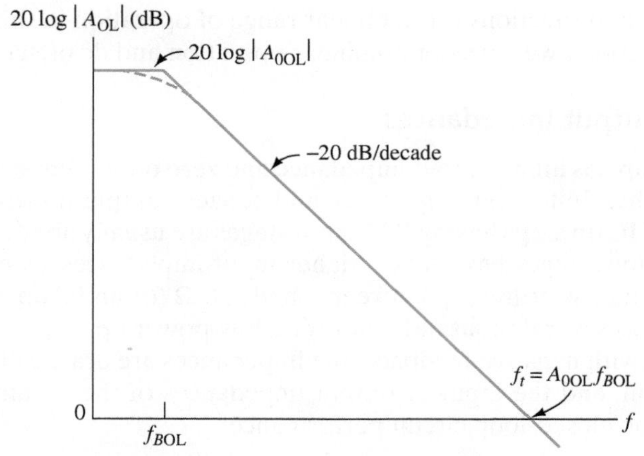

Figure 20 Bode plot of open-loop gain for a typical op amp.

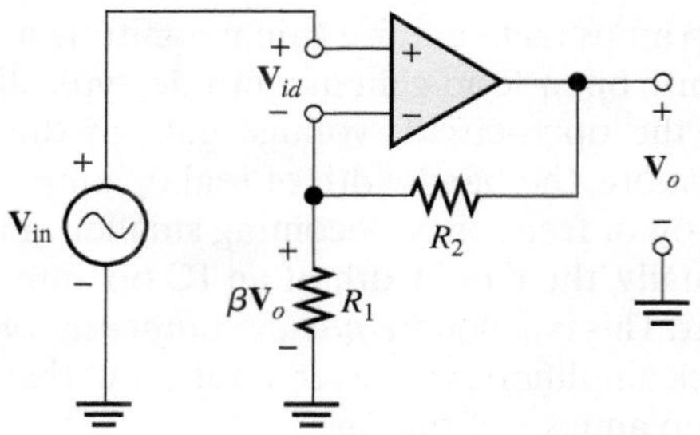

Figure 21 Noninverting amplifier circuit used for analysis of closed-loop bandwidth.

Applying Kirchhoff's voltage law to Figure 21, we have

$$\mathbf{V}_{in} = \mathbf{V}_{id} + \beta \mathbf{V}_o$$

Solving for $\mathbf{V}_{id}$ and substituting into Equation 24, we have

$$\mathbf{V}_o = A_{OL}(\mathbf{V}_{in} - \beta \mathbf{V}_o) \tag{26}$$

Now, we can solve for the gain of the circuit including the feedback resistors, which is called the **closed-loop gain**. This is given by

$$A_{CL} = \frac{\mathbf{V}_o}{\mathbf{V}_{in}} = \frac{A_{OL}}{1 + \beta A_{OL}} \tag{27}$$

Using Equation 23 to substitute for the open-loop gain, we get

$$A_{CL}(f) = \frac{A_{0OL}/[1 + j(f/f_{BOL})]}{1 + \{\beta A_{0OL}/[1 + j(f/f_{BOL})]\}} \tag{28}$$

This can be put into the form

$$A_{CL}(f) = \frac{A_{0OL}/(1 + \beta A_{0OL})}{1 + \{jf/[f_{BOL}(1 + \beta A_{0OL})]\}} \tag{29}$$

Now, we define the closed-loop dc gain as

$$A_{0CL} = \frac{A_{0OL}}{1 + \beta A_{0OL}} \tag{30}$$

and the closed-loop bandwidth as

$$f_{BCL} = f_{BOL}(1 + \beta A_{0OL}) \tag{31}$$

Using these definitions in Equation 29, we obtain

$$A_{CL}(f) = \frac{A_{0CL}}{1 + j(f/f_{BCL})} \tag{32}$$

Comparing this with Equation 23, we see that the closed-loop gain takes exactly the same form as the open-loop gain. The dc open-loop gain A_{0OL} is very large, and we usually have $(1 + \beta A_{0OL}) >> 1$. Thus, from Equation 30, we see that the closed-loop gain is much smaller than the open-loop gain. Furthermore, Equation 31 shows that the closed-loop bandwidth is much greater than the open-loop bandwidth. *In sum, we see that negative feedback reduces the gain magnitude and increases bandwidth.*

Negative feedback reduces gain magnitude and increases bandwidth.

Gain–Bandwidth Product

Now, consider the product of the closed-loop gain and closed-loop bandwidth. From Equations 30 and 31, we have

$$A_{0CL}f_{BCL} = \frac{A_{0OL}}{1 + \beta A_{0OL}} \times f_{BOL}(1 + \beta A_{0OL}) = A_{0OL}f_{BOL} \tag{33}$$

Hence, we see that the product of dc gain and bandwidth is independent of the feedback ratio β. We denote the **gain–bandwidth** as f_t. Thus, we have

$$f_t = A_{0CL}f_{BCL} = A_{0OL}f_{BOL} \tag{34}$$

As indicated in Figure 20, it turns out that f_t is the frequency at which the Bode plot of the open-loop gain crosses 0 dB. Recall that 0 dB corresponds to unity-gain magnitude. Consequently, f_t is also called the **unity-gain bandwidth**. General-purpose IC op amps have gain–bandwidth products of several megahertz.

The gain–bandwidth product is constant for the noninverting amplifier. As we reduce the gain (by choosing a lower value for $1 R_2/R_1$), the bandwidth becomes greater.

Example 5 Open-Loop and Closed-Loop Bode Plots

A certain op amp has a dc open-loop gain of $A_{0OL} = 10^5$ and $f_{BOL} = 40$ Hz. Find the closed-loop bandwidth if this op amp is used with feedback resistors to form a noninverting amplifier having a closed-loop dc gain of 10. Then, construct a Bode plot of the open-loop gain and a Bode plot of the closed-loop gain.

Solution The gain–bandwidth product is

$$f_t = A_{0OL}f_{BOL} = 10^5 \times 40 \text{ Hz} = 4 \text{ MHz} = A_{0CL}f_{BCL}$$

Thus, if feedback is used to reduce the gain to $A_{0CL} = 10$, the bandwidth is $f_{BCL} = 400$ kHz.

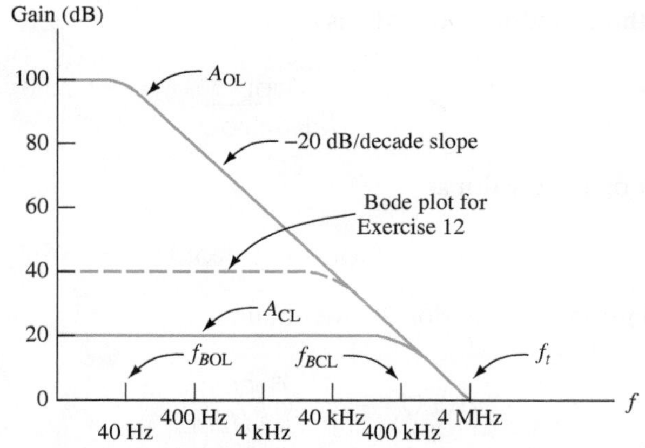

Figure 22 Bode plots for Example 5 and Exercise 12.

In decibels, the dc open-loop gain becomes

$$A_{0OL} = 20 \log(10^5) = 100 \text{ dB}$$

The break frequency is $f_{BOL} = 40$ Hz. Here, the gain function is approximated as being constant below the break frequency and falls at 20 dB/decade above the break frequency. The Bode plot is shown in Figure 22.

Converting $A_{0CL} = 10$ to decibels, we have

$$A_{0CL} = 10 \log(10) = 20 \text{ dB}$$

and the break frequency is $f_{BCL} = 400$ kHz. The resulting Bode plot is shown in Figure 22. Notice that the closed-loop gain plot is constant until it reaches the open-loop plot and then the closed-loop plot rolls off. ■

Exercise 12 Repeat Example 5 for $A_{0CL} = 100$.
Answer $f_{BCL} = 40$ kHz. The Bode plot is shown in Figure 22. □

6 NONLINEAR LIMITATIONS

Output Voltage Swing

The output voltage of a real op amp is limited to the range between certain limits that depend on the internal design of the op amp. When the output voltage tries to go beyond these limits, clipping occurs.

There are several nonlinear limitations of the outputs of real op amps. First, the output voltage range is limited. If an input signal is sufficiently large that the output voltage would be driven beyond these limits, clipping occurs.

The range of allowed output voltage depends on the type of op amp in use, on the load resistance value, and on the values of the power-supply voltages. For example, with supply voltages of +15 V and −15 V, the LM741 op amp (LM741 is the manufacturer's type number for a popular op amp) is capable of producing output voltages in the range from approximately −14 to +14 V. If smaller power-supply voltages are used, the linear range is reduced. (These are *typical* limits for load resistances greater than 10 kΩ. The *guaranteed* output range for the LM741 is only from −12 to +12 V. Smaller load resistances further restrict the range.)

Consider the noninverting amplifier with a sinusoidal input signal shown in Figure 23. Assuming an ideal op amp, the voltage gain is given by Equation 21, which is repeated here for convenience:

$$A_v = 1 + \frac{R_2}{R_1}$$

Substituting the values shown in Figure 23 ($R_1 = 1$ kΩ and $R_2 = 3$ kΩ), we find $A_v = 4$. The output waveform for $R_L = 10$ kΩ and $V_{im} = 1$ V is shown in Figure 24. The output waveform is sinusoidal because none of the nonlinear limits of the op amp have been exceeded. On the other hand, for $V_{im} = 5$ V, the output reaches the maximum output voltage limits and the output waveform is clipped. This is shown in Figure 25.

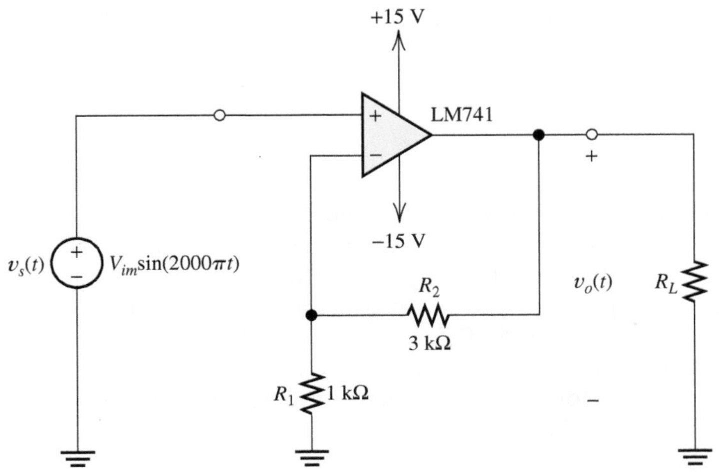

Figure 23 Noninverting amplifier used to demonstrate various nonlinear limitations of op amps.

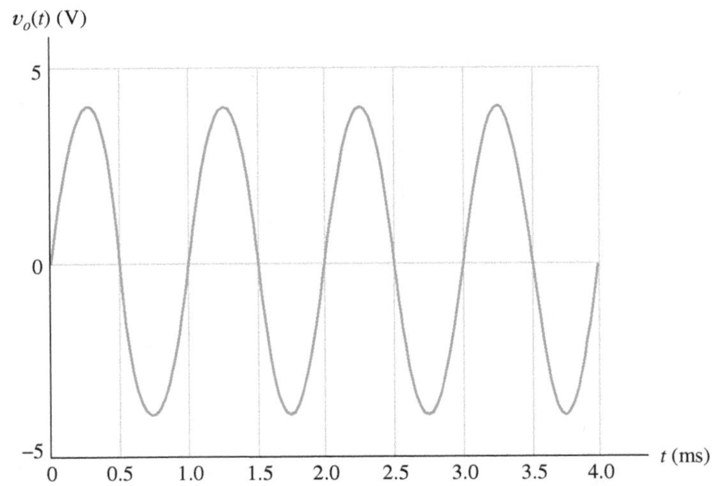

Figure 24 Output of the circuit of Figure 23 for $R_L = 10$ kΩ and $V_{im} = 1$ V. None of the limitations are exceeded, and $v_o(t) = 4v_s(t)$.

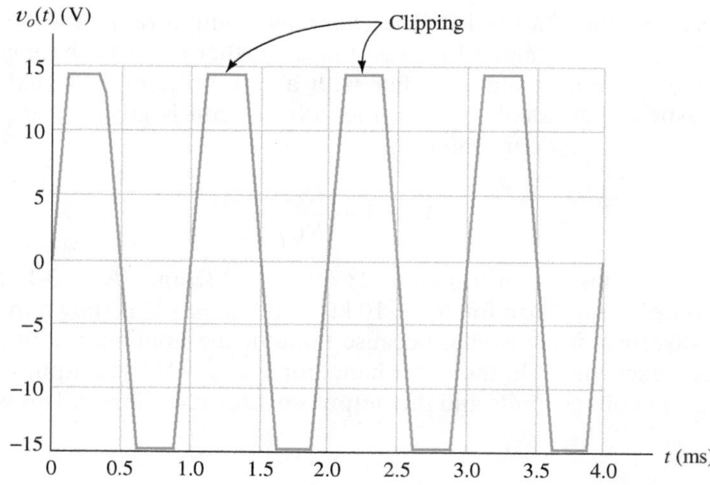

Figure 25 Output of the circuit of Figure 23 for $R_L = 10$ kΩ and $V_{im} = 5$ V. Clipping occurs because the maximum possible output voltage magnitude is reached.

Output Current Limits

The output current range of a real op amp is limited. If an input signal is sufficiently large that the output current would be driven beyond these limits, clipping occurs.

A second limitation is the maximum current that an op amp can supply to a load. For the LM741, the limits are ±40 mA. If a small-value load resistance would draw a current outside these limits, the output waveform becomes clipped.

For example, suppose that we set the peak input voltage to $V_{im} = 1$ V and adjust the load resistance to $R_L = 50\ \Omega$ for the circuit of Figure 23. For an ideal op amp, we would expect a peak output voltage of $V_{om} = 4$ V and a peak load current of $V_{om}/R_L = 80$ mA. However, output current magnitude of the LM741 is limited to 40 mA. Therefore, clipping occurs due to current limiting. The output voltage

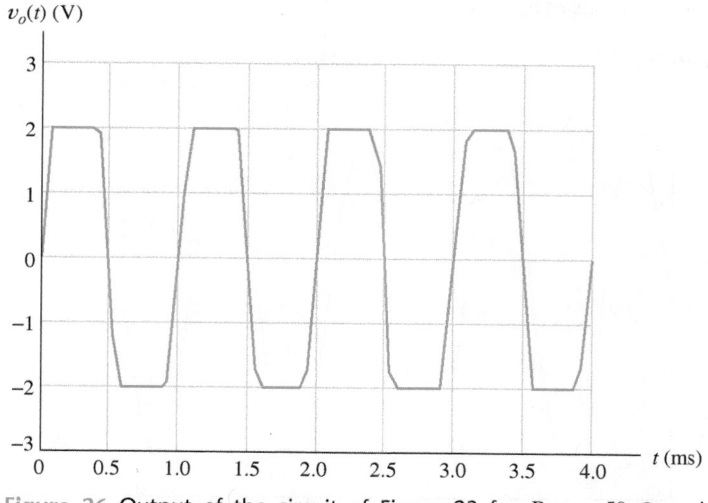

Figure 26 Output of the circuit of Figure 23 for $R_L = 50\ \Omega$ and $V_{im} = 1$ V. Clipping occurs because the maximum output current limit is reached.

waveform of the circuit is shown in Figure 26. Notice that the peak output voltage is 40 mA $\times R_L = 2$ V.

Slew-Rate Limitation

Another nonlinear limitation of actual op amps is that the magnitude of the rate of change of the output voltage is limited. This is called the **slew-rate limitation**. The output voltage cannot increase (or decrease) in magnitude at a rate exceeding this limit. In equation form, the slew-rate limit is

Another nonlinear limitation of actual op amps is that the magnitude of the rate of change of the output voltage is limited.

$$\left|\frac{dv_o}{dt}\right| \le \text{SR} \tag{35}$$

For various types of IC op amps, the slew-rate limit ranges from SR $= 10^5$ V/s to SR $= 10^8$ V/s. For the LM741 with $\pm$15-V supplies and $R_L > 2$ kΩ, the typical value is 5×10^5 V/s (which is often stated as 0.5 V/μs).

For example, consider the circuit of Figure 23, except that the input source voltage is changed to a 2.5-V-peak 50-kHz sine wave given by

$$v_s(t) = 2.5\sin(10^5\pi t)$$

starting at $t = 0$. [$v_s(t)$ is assumed to be zero prior to $t = 0$.] The output waveform is shown in Figure 27. Also plotted in the figure is four times the input voltage, which is the output assuming an ideal op amp. At $t = 0$, the output voltage is zero. The ideal output increases at a rate exceeding the slew-rate limit of the LM741, so the LM741 output increases at its maximum rate, which is approximately 0.5 V/μs. At point A, the actual output finally "catches up" with the ideal output, but by then, the ideal output is decreasing at a rate that exceeds the slew-rate limit. Thus, at point A, the output of the LM741 begins to decrease at its maximum possible rate. Notice that because of slew-rate limiting, the actual op-amp output is a triangular waveform rather than a sinusoid.

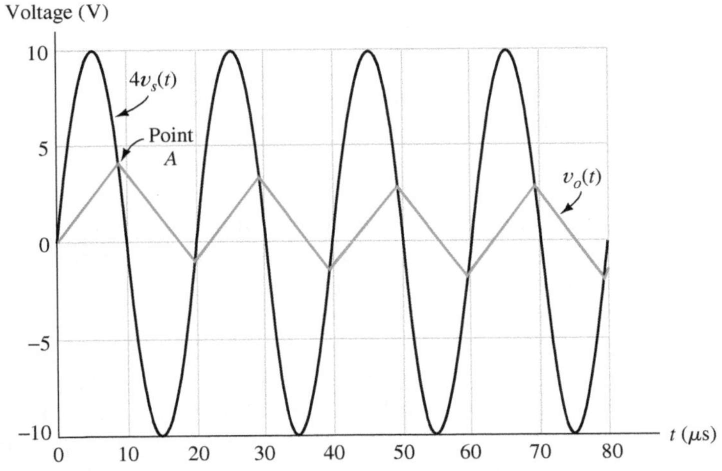

Figure 27 Output of the circuit of Figure 23 for $R_L = 10$ kΩ and $v_s(t) = 2.5\sin(10^5\pi t)$. The output waveform is a triangular waveform because the slew-rate limit is exceeded. The output for an ideal op amp, which is equal to $4v_s(t)$, is shown for comparison.

Full-Power Bandwidth

The full-power bandwidth of an op amp is the range of frequencies for which the op amp can produce an undistorted sinusoidal output with peak amplitude equal to the guaranteed maximum output voltage.

The **full-power bandwidth** of an op amp is the range of frequencies for which the op amp can produce an undistorted sinusoidal output with peak amplitude equal to the guaranteed maximum output voltage.

Next, we derive an expression for the full-power bandwidth in terms of the slew rate and peak amplitude. The output voltage is given by

$$v_o(t) = V_{om}\sin(\omega t)$$

Taking the derivative with respect to time, we have

$$\frac{dv_o(t)}{dt} = \omega V_{om}\cos(\omega t)$$

The maximum magnitude of the rate of change is $\omega V_{om} = 2\pi f V_{om}$. Setting this equal to the slew-rate limit, we get

$$2\pi f V_{om} = \text{SR}$$

Solving for frequency, we obtain

$$f_{\text{FP}} = \frac{\text{SR}}{2\pi V_{om}} \quad (36)$$

where we have denoted the full-power bandwidth as f_{FP}. An undistorted full-amplitude sinusoidal output waveform is possible only for frequencies less than f_{FP}.

Example 6 Full-Power Bandwidth

Find the full-power bandwidth of the LM741 op amp given that the slew rate is $\text{SR} = 0.5\ \text{V}/\mu\text{s}$ and the guaranteed maximum output amplitude is $V_{om} = 12$ V.

Solution We substitute the given data into Equation 36 to obtain

$$f_{\text{FP}} = \frac{\text{SR}}{2\pi V_{om}} \cong 6.63\ \text{kHz}$$

Thus, we can obtain an undistorted 12-V-peak sinusoidal output from the LM741 only for frequencies less than 6.63 kHz. ■

Exercise 13 A certain op amp has a maximum output voltage range from −4 to +4 V. The maximum current magnitude is 10 mA. The slew-rate limit is $\text{SR} = 5\ \text{V}/\mu\text{s}$. This op amp is used in the circuit of Figure 28. Assume a sinusoidal input signal for all parts of this exercise. **a.** Find the full-power bandwidth of the op amp. **b.** For a frequency of 1 kHz and $R_L = 1\ \text{k}\Omega$, what peak output voltage is possible without distortion (i.e., clipping or slew-rate limiting)? **c.** For a frequency of 1 kHz and $R_L = 100\ \Omega$, what peak output voltage is possible without distortion? **d.** For a frequency of 1 MHz and $R_L = 1\ \text{k}\Omega$, what peak output voltage is possible without distortion? **e.** If $R_L = 1\ \text{k}\Omega$ and $v_s(t) = 5\sin(2\pi 10^6 t)$, sketch the steady-state output waveform to scale versus time.

Answer **a.** $f_{\text{FP}} = 199$ kHz; **b.** 4 V; **c.** 1 V; **d.** 0.796 V; **e.** the output waveform is a triangular wave with a peak amplitude of 1.25 V. □

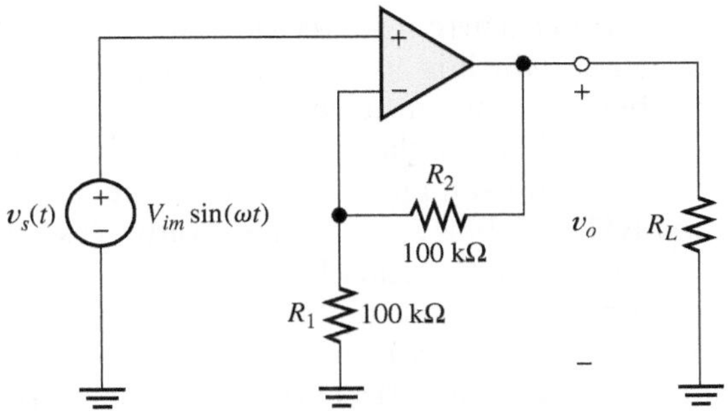

Figure 28 Circuit for Exercise 13.

7 DC IMPERFECTIONS

Op amps have direct-coupled input circuits. Thus, dc bias currents that flow into (or from) the input devices of the op amp must flow through the elements that are connected to the input terminals, such as the signal source or feedback resistors.

The dc current flowing into the noninverting input is denoted as I_{B+}, and the dc current flowing into the inverting input is I_{B-}. The average of the dc currents is called **bias current** and is denoted as I_B. Thus, we have

$$I_B = \frac{I_{B+} + I_{B-}}{2} \tag{37}$$

Nominally, the input circuit of the op amp is symmetrical, and the bias currents flowing into the inverting and noninverting inputs are equal. However, in practice, the devices are not perfectly matched, and the bias currents are not equal. The difference between the bias currents, called the **offset current**, is denoted as

$$I_{\text{off}} = I_{B+} - I_{B-} \tag{38}$$

Another dc imperfection of op amps is that the output voltage may not be zero for zero input voltage. The op amp behaves as if a small dc source known as the **offset voltage** is in series with one of the input terminals.

The three dc imperfections (bias current, offset current, and offset voltage) can be modeled by placing dc sources at the input of the op amp as shown in Figure 29. The I_B current sources model the bias current. The $I_{\text{off}}/2$ current source models the offset current, and the V_{off} voltage source models the offset voltage.

The three dc imperfections (bias current, offset current, and offset voltage) can be modeled by placing dc sources at the input of the op amp as shown in Figure 29.

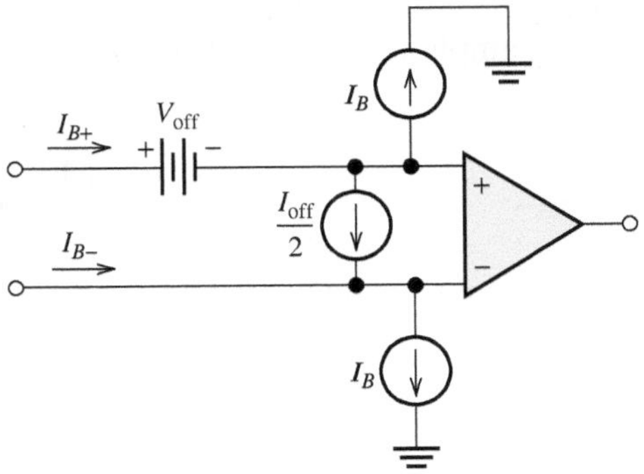

Figure 29 Three current sources and a voltage source model the dc imperfections of an op amp.

The bias-current sources are equal in magnitude and are referenced in the same direction (which is away from the input terminals in Figure 29). In some op amps, the bias current can have a negative value, so the currents flow toward the input terminals. Usually, the direction of the bias current is predictable for a given type of op amp. For example, if the input terminals of an op amp are the base terminals of *npn* BJTs, the bias current I_B is positive (assuming the reference directions shown in Figure 29). On the other hand, *pnp* BJTs would result in a negative value for I_B.

Since the bias-current sources are matched in magnitude and direction, it is possible to design circuits in such a way that their effects cancel. On the other hand, the polarity of the offset voltage and the direction of the offset current are unpredictable—varying from unit to unit. For example, if the offset voltage of a given type of op amp is specified as a maximum of 2 mV, the value of V_{off} ranges from -2 to $+2$ mV from unit to unit. Usually, most units have offset values close to zero, and only a few have values close to the maximum specification. A typical specification for the maximum offset voltage magnitude for IC op amps is several millivolts.

Bias currents are usually on the order of 100 nA for op amps with BJT input devices. Bias currents are much lower for op amps with FET inputs—a typical specification is 100 pA at 25°C for a device with JFET input devices. Usually, offset current specifications range from 20 to 50 percent of the bias current.

The effect of bias current, offset current, and offset voltage on inverting or noninverting amplifiers is to add a (usually undesirable) dc voltage to the intended output signal.

The effect of bias current, offset current, and offset voltage on inverting or noninverting amplifiers is to add a (usually undesirable) dc voltage to the intended output signal. We can analyze these effects by including the sources shown in Figure 29 and assuming an otherwise ideal op amp.

Example 7 Determining Worst-Case DC Output

Find the worst-case dc output voltage of the inverting amplifier shown in Figure 30(a), assuming that $v_{\text{in}} = 0$. The maximum bias current of the op amp is 100 nA, the maximum offset current magnitude is 40 nA, and the maximum offset-voltage magnitude is 2 mV.

First, we calculate the output voltage resulting from each of the dc sources acting individually. Then, we use superposition.

Solution Our approach is to calculate the output voltage due to each of the dc sources acting individually. Then by using superposition, the worst-case output can be found by adding the outputs due to the various sources.

First, we consider the offset voltage. The circuit, including the offset voltage source, is shown in Figure 30(b). The offset voltage source can be placed in series with either input. We have elected to place it in series with the noninverting input. Then, the circuit takes the form of a noninverting amplifier. [Notice that although it is drawn differently, the circuit of Figure 30(b) is electrically equivalent to the noninverting amplifier of Figure 11.] Thus, the output voltage is the gain of the noninverting amplifier, given by Equation 21, times the offset voltage:

$$V_{o,\text{voff}} = -\left(1 + \frac{R_2}{R_1}\right) V_{\text{off}}$$

Substituting values, we find that

$$V_{o,\text{voff}} = -11 V_{\text{off}}$$

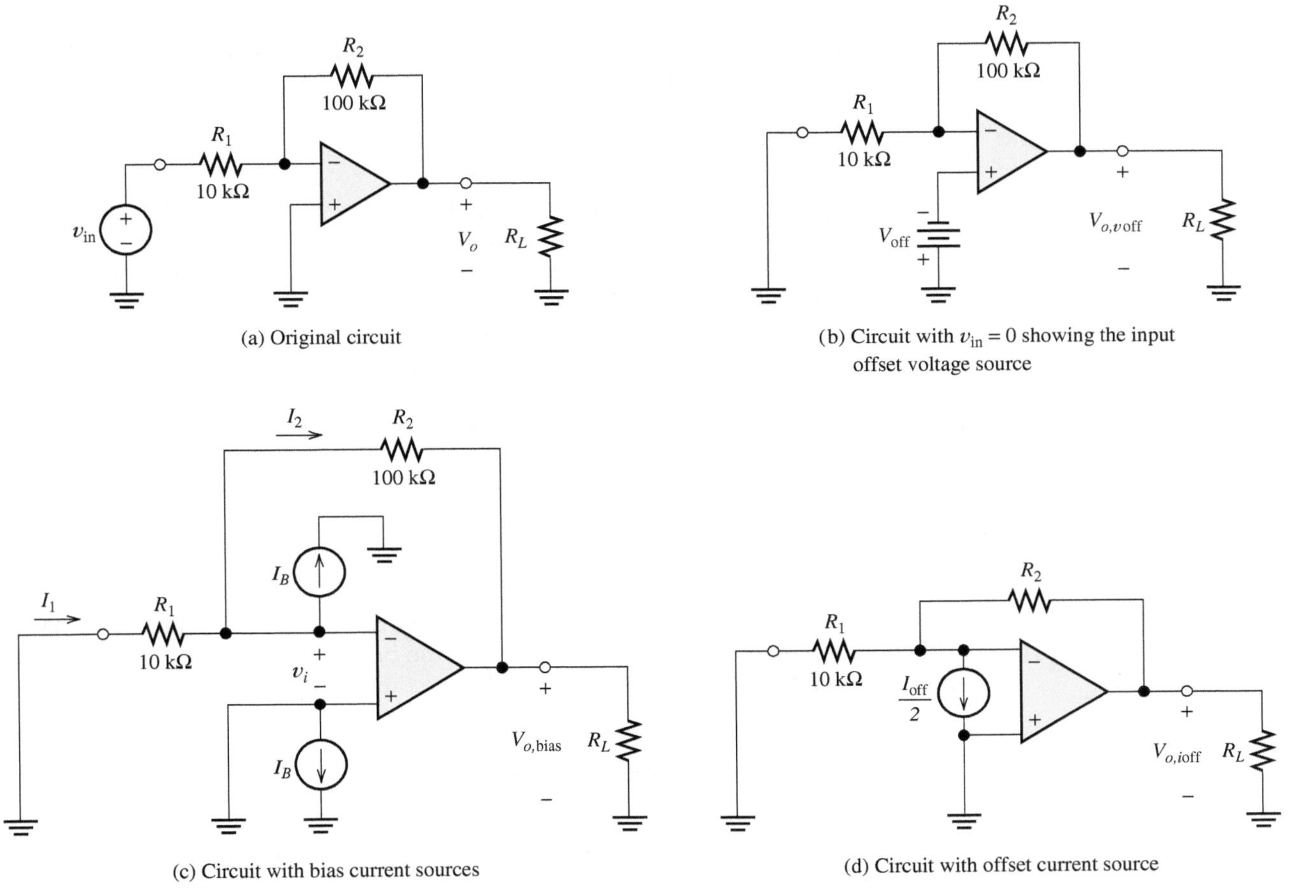

Figure 30 Circuits of Example 7.

Since the offset voltage V_{off} is specified to have a maximum value of 2 mV, the value of $V_{o,v\text{off}}$ ranges between extremes of -22 and $+22$ mV. However, most units would have $V_{o,v\text{off}}$ closer to zero.

Next, we consider the bias-current sources. The circuit, including the bias-current sources, is shown in Figure 30(c). Because the noninverting input is connected directly to ground, one of the bias-current sources is short circuited and has no effect. Since we assume an ideal op amp (aside from the dc sources), the summing-point constraint applies, and $v_i = 0$. Thus, the current I_1 is zero. Applying Kirchhoff's current law, we have $I_2 = -I_B$. Writing a voltage equation from the output through R_2 and R_1, we have

$$V_{o,\text{bias}} = -R_2 I_2 - R_1 I_1$$

Substituting $I_1 = 0$ and $I_2 = -I_B$, we obtain

$$V_{o,\text{bias}} = R_2 I_B$$

Because the maximum value of I_B is 100 nA, the maximum value of $V_{o,\text{bias}}$ is 10 mV. As is often the case, the maximum value of I_B is specified, but the minimum is not. Thus, $V_{o,\text{bias}}$ ranges from some small indeterminate voltage (perhaps a few millivolts) up to 10 mV. (We will conservatively assume that the minimum value of $V_{o,\text{bias}}$ is zero.)

Next, we consider the offset-current source. The circuit is shown in Figure 30(d). By an analysis similar to that for the bias current, we can show that

$$V_{o,ioff} = R_2\left(\frac{I_{off}}{2}\right)$$

The specification for the maximum magnitude of I_{off} is 40 nA. Therefore, the value of $V_{o,ioff}$ ranges between extremes of −2 and +2 mV.

By superposition, the dc output voltage is the sum of the contributions of the various sources acting individually.

By superposition, the dc output voltage is the sum of the contributions of the various sources acting individually, yielding

$$V_o = V_{o,voff} + V_{o,bias} + V_{o,ioff}$$

Hence, the extreme values of the output voltage are

$$V_o = 22 + 10 + 2 = 34\text{ mV}$$

and

$$V_o = -22 + 0 - 2 = -24\text{ mV}$$

Thus, the output voltage ranges from −24 to +34 mV from unit to unit. (We have assumed a minimum contribution of zero for the bias current.) Typical units would have total output voltages closer to zero than to these extreme values. ■

Cancellation of the Effects of Bias Currents

As mentioned earlier, it is possible to design circuits in which the effects of the two bias-current sources cancel. For example, consider the inverting amplifier configuration. Adding a resistor R_{bias} in series with the noninverting op-amp input, as shown in Figure 31, does not affect the gain of the amplifier, but results in cancellation of the effects of the I_B sources. Notice that the value of R_{bias} is equal to the parallel combination of R_1 and R_2.

Exercise 14 Consider the amplifier shown in Figure 31. **a.** Assume an ideal op amp, and derive an expression for the voltage gain v_o/v_{in}. Notice that the result is the same as Equation 5, which was derived for the inverting amplifier without the bias-current-compensating resistor R_{bias}. **b.** Redraw the circuit with $v_{in} = 0$, but include the bias-current sources. Show that the output voltage is zero. **c.** Assume that $R_1 = 10\text{ k}\Omega$, $R_2 = 100\text{ k}\Omega$, and a specification of 3 mV for the maximum magnitude

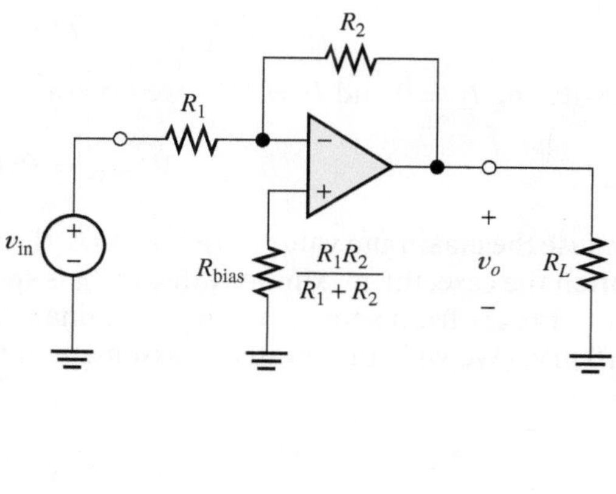

Figure 31 Adding the resistor R_{bias} to the inverting amplifier circuit causes the effects of bias currents to cancel.

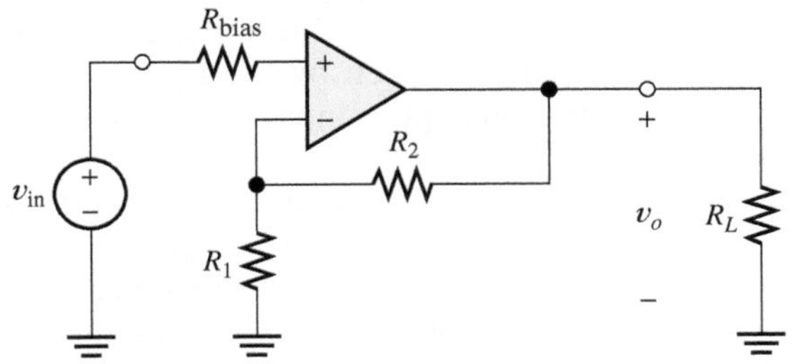

Figure 32 Noninverting amplifier, including resistor R_{bias} to balance the effects of the bias currents. See Exercise 15.

of V_{off}. Find the range of output voltages resulting from the offset voltage source V_{off}. **d.** Assume that $R_1 = 10$ kΩ, $R_2 = 100$ kΩ, and a specification of 40 nA for the maximum magnitude of I_{off}. Find the range of output voltages resulting from the offset current. **e.** Assuming the values given in parts (c) and (d), what range of output voltages results from the combined action of the bias current, offset voltage, and offset current?

Answer **a.** $v_o/v_{in} = -R_2/R_1$; **b.** ±33 mV; **c.** ±4 mV; **d.** ±37 mV. □

Exercise 15 Consider the noninverting amplifier shown in Figure 32. **a.** Derive an expression for the voltage gain v_o/v_{in}. Does the gain depend on the value of R_{bias}? Explain. **b.** Derive an expression for R_{bias} in terms of the other resistance values so that the output voltage due to the bias currents is zero.

Answer **a.** $v_o/v_{in} = 1 + R_2/R_1$. The gain is independent of R_{bias} because the current through R_{bias} is zero (assuming an ideal op amp). **b.** $R_{bias} = R_1 || R_2 = 1/(1/R_1 + 1/R_2)$. □

8 DIFFERENTIAL AND INSTRUMENTATION AMPLIFIERS

Figure 33 shows a differential amplifier. Assuming an ideal op amp and that $R_4/R_3 = R_2/R_1$, the output voltage is a constant times the differential input signal $(v_1 - v_2)$. The gain for the common-mode signal is zero. To minimize the effects of bias current, we should choose $R_2 = R_4$ and $R_1 = R_3$.

Differential amplifiers are widely used in engineering instrumentation.

The output impedance of the circuit is zero. The input impedance for the v_1 source is $R_3 + R_4$.

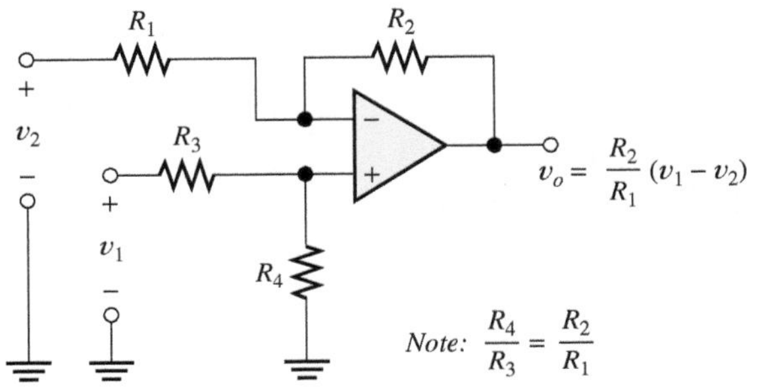

Figure 33 Differential amplifier.

A current that depends on v_1 flows back through the feedback network (R_1 and R_2) into the input source v_2. Thus, as seen by the v_2 source, the circuit does not appear to be passive. Hence, the concept of input impedance does not apply for the v_2 source (unless v_1 is zero).

In some applications, the signal sources contain internal impedances, and the desired signal is the difference between the internal source voltages. Then, we could design the circuit by including the internal source resistances of v_2 and v_1 as part of R_1 and R_3, respectively. However, to obtain very high common-mode rejection, it is necessary to match the ratios of the resistances closely. This can be troublesome if the source impedances are not small enough to be neglected and are not predictable.

Instrumentation-Quality Differential Amplifier

Figure 34 shows an improved differential amplifier circuit for which the common-mode rejection ratio is not dependent on the internal resistances of the sources. Because of the summing-point constraint at the inputs of X_1 and X_2, the currents drawn from the signal sources are zero. Hence, the input impedances seen by both sources are infinite, and the output voltage is unaffected by the internal source impedances. This is an important advantage of this circuit compared to the simpler differential amplifier of Figure 33. Notice that the second stage of the instrumentation amplifier is a unity-gain version of the differential amplifier.

A subtle point concerning this circuit is that the differential-mode signal experiences a higher gain in the first stage (X_1 and X_2) than the common-mode signal does. To illustrate this point, first consider a pure differential input (i.e., $v_1 = -v_2$). Then, because the circuit is symmetrical, point A remains at zero voltage. Hence, in the analysis for a purely differential input signal, point A can be considered to be grounded. In this case, the input amplifiers X_1 and X_2 are configured as noninverting

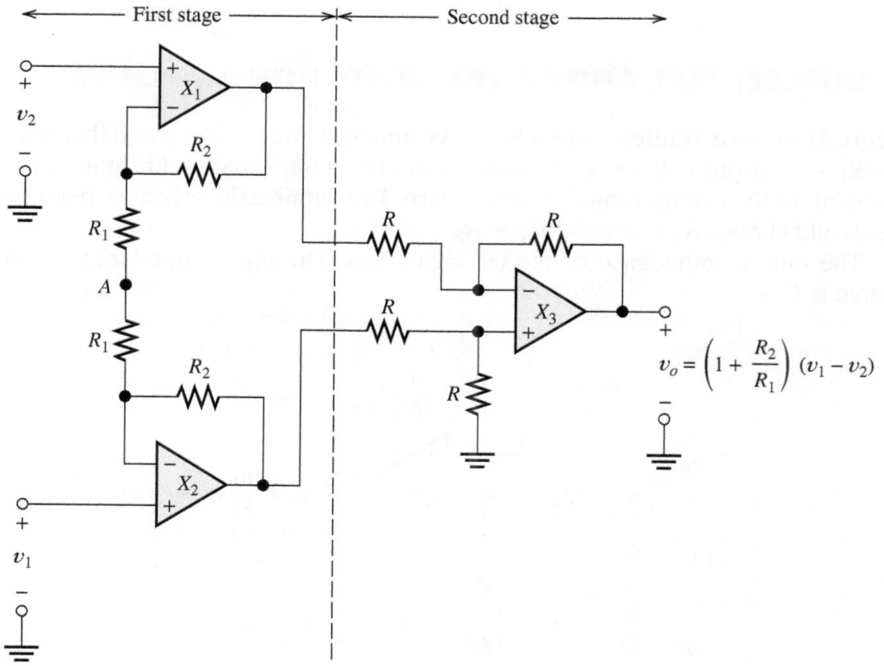

Figure 34 Instrumentation-quality differential amplifier.

amplifiers having gains of $(1 + R_2/R_1)$. The differential gain of the second stage is unity. Thus, the overall gain for the differential signal is $(1 + R_2/R_1)$.

Now, consider a pure common-mode signal (i.e., $v_1 = v_2 = v_{cm}$). Because of the summing-point constraint, the voltage between the input terminals of X_1 (or X_2) is zero. Thus, the voltages at the inverting input terminals of X_1 and X_2 are both equal to v_{cm}. Hence, the voltage across the series-connected R_1 resistors is zero, and no current flows through the R_1 resistors. Therefore, no current flows through the R_2 resistors. Thus, the output voltages of X_1 and X_2 are equal to v_{cm}, and we have shown that the first-stage gain is unity for the common-mode signal. On the other hand, the differential gain of the first stage is $(1 + R_2/R_1)$, which can be much larger than unity, thereby achieving a reduction of the common-mode signal amplitude relative to the differential signal. [Notice that if point A were actually grounded, the gain for the common-mode signal would be the same as for the differential signal, namely $(1 + R_2/R_1)$.]

In practice, the series combination of the two R_1 resistors is implemented by a single resistor (equal in value to $2R_1$) because it is not necessary to have access to point A. Thus, matching of component values for R_1 is not required. Furthermore, it can be shown that close matching of the R_2 resistors is not required to achieve a higher differential gain than common-mode gain in the first stage. Since the first stage reduces the relative amplitude of the common-mode signal, matching of the resistors in the second stage is not as critical.

Thus, although it is more complex, the differential amplifier of Figure 34 has better performance than that of Figure 33. Specifically, the common-mode rejection ratio is independent of the internal source resistances, the input impedance seen by both sources is infinite, and resistor matching is not as critical.

Exercise 16 Assume an ideal op amp, and derive the expression shown for the output voltage of the differential amplifier of Figure 33. Assume that $R_4/R_3 = R_2/R_1$. □

9 INTEGRATORS AND DIFFERENTIATORS

Figure 35 shows the diagram of an **integrator**, which is a circuit that produces an output voltage proportional to the running-time integral of the input voltage. (By the term *running time integral*, we mean that the upper limit of integration is t.)

Integrators produce output voltages that are proportional to the running-time integral of the input voltages. In a running time integral, the upper limit of integration is t.

The integrator circuit is often useful in instrumentation applications. For example, consider a signal from an accelerometer that is proportional to acceleration. By integrating the acceleration signal, we obtain a signal proportional to velocity. Another integration yields a signal proportional to position.

In Figure 35, negative feedback occurs through the capacitor. Thus, assuming an ideal op amp, the voltage at the inverting op-amp input is zero. The input current is given by

$$i_{in}(t) = \frac{v_{in}(t)}{R} \tag{39}$$

The current flowing into the input terminal of the (ideal) op amp is zero. Therefore, the input current i_{in} flows through the capacitor. We assume that the reset switch is opened at $t = 0$. Therefore, the capacitor voltage is zero at $t = 0$. The voltage across the capacitor is given by

$$v_C(t) = \frac{1}{C}\int_0^t i_{in}(t)\, dt \tag{40}$$

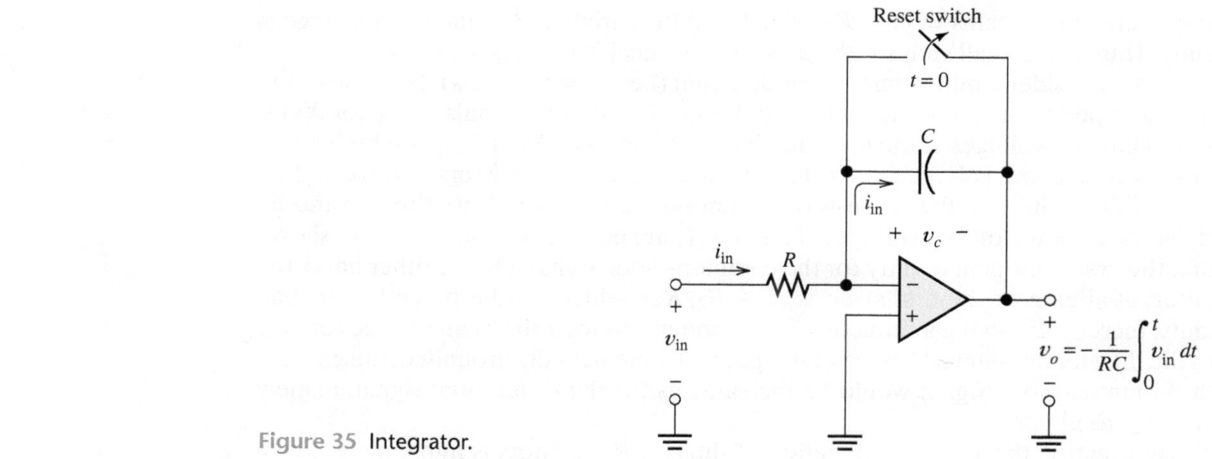

Figure 35 Integrator.

Writing a voltage equation from the output terminal through the capacitor and then to ground through the op-amp input terminals, we obtain

$$v_o(t) = -v_C(t) \tag{41}$$

Using Equation 39 to substitute into 40 and the result into 41, we obtain

$$v_o(t) = -\frac{1}{RC}\int_0^t v_{in}(t)\,dt \tag{42}$$

Thus, the output voltage is $-1/RC$ times the running integral of the input voltage. If an integrator having positive gain is desired, we can cascade the integrator with an inverting amplifier.

The magnitude of the gain can be adjusted by the choice of R and C. Of course, in selecting a capacitor, we usually want to use as small a value as possible to minimize cost, volume, and mass. However, for a given gain constant $(1/RC)$, smaller C leads to larger R and smaller values of i_{in}. Therefore, the bias current of the op amp becomes more significant as the capacitance becomes smaller. As usual, we try to design for the best compromise.

Exercise 17 Consider the integrator of Figure 35 with the square-wave input signal shown in Figure 36. **a.** If $R = 10$ kΩ, $C = 0.1$ μF, and the op amp is ideal, sketch the output waveform to scale. **b.** If $R = 10$ kΩ, what value of C is required for the peak-to-peak output amplitude to be 2 V?

Answer **a.** See Figure 37; **b.** $C = 0.5$ μF. □

Exercise 18 Consider the circuit of Figure 35 with $v_{in} = 0$, $R = 10$ kΩ, and $C = 0.01$ μF. As indicated in the figure, the reset switch opens at $t = 0$. The op amp is ideal except for a bias current of $I_B = 100$ nA. **a.** Find an expression for the output voltage of the circuit as a function of time. **b.** Repeat for $C = 1$ μF.

Answer **a.** $v_o(t) = 10t$; **b.** $v_o(t) = 0.1t$. □

Exercise 19 Add a resistance R in series with the noninverting input of the op amp in Figure 35 and repeat Exercise 18.

Answer **a.** $v_o(t) = -1$ mV; **b.** $v_o(t) = -1$ mV. □

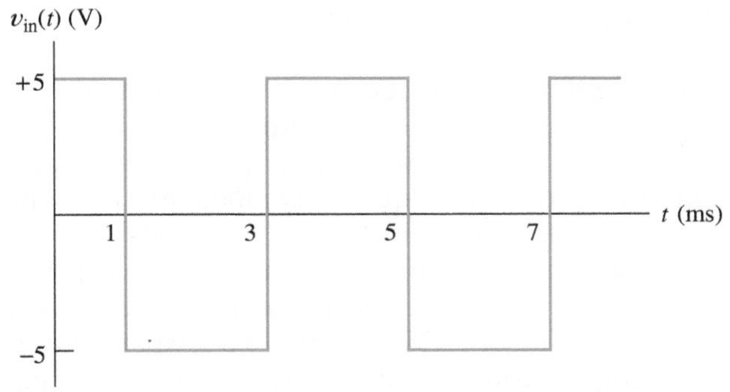

Figure 36 Square-wave input signal for Exercise 17.

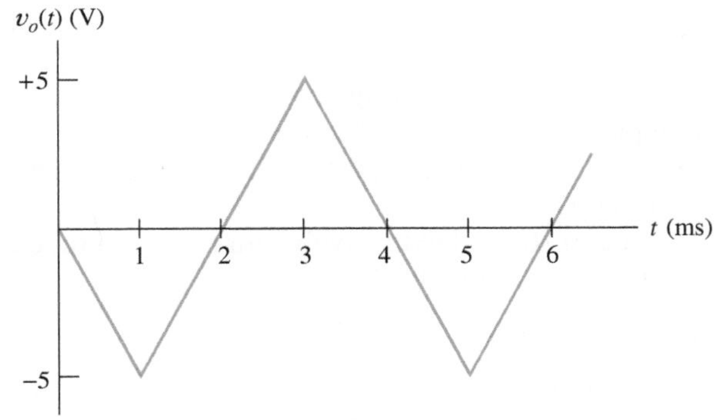

Figure 37 Answer for Exercise 17.

Differentiator Circuit

Figure 38 shows a **differentiator** that produces an output voltage proportional to the time derivative of the input voltage. By an analysis similar to that used for the integrator, we can show that the circuit produces an output voltage given by

$$v_o(t) = -RC\frac{dv_{in}}{dt} \tag{43}$$

Exercise 20 Derive Equation 43. □

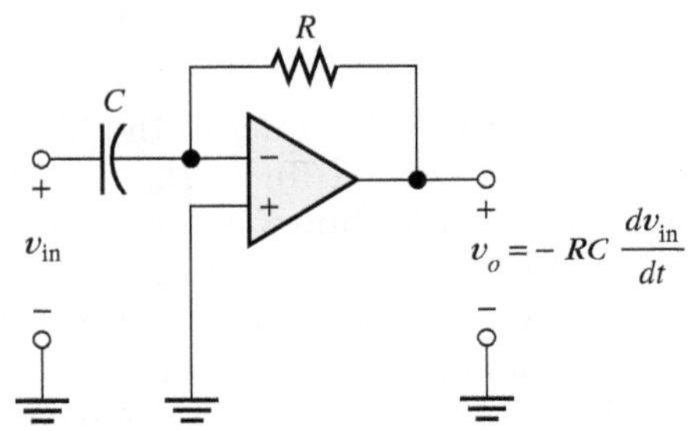

Figure 38 Differentiator.

10 ACTIVE FILTERS

Filters are circuits designed to pass input components with frequencies in one range to the output and prevent input components with frequencies in other ranges from reaching the output. For example, a lowpass filter passes low-frequency input components to the output but not high-frequency components. A common application for filters is to separate a signal of interest from other signals and noise. For example, in an electrocardiograph, we need a filter that passes the heart signals, which have frequencies below about 100 Hz, and rejects higher frequency noise that can be created by contraction of other muscles. We might use a lowpass filter to remove noise from historical phonograph recordings. In radio receivers, filters separate one station from the others. In digital instrumentation systems, a lowpass filter is often needed to remove noise and signal components that have frequencies higher than half of the sampling frequency in order to avoid a type of distortion, known as aliasing, during sampling and analog-to-digital conversion.

Filters can be very useful in separating desired signals from noise.

In this section, we show how to design lowpass filters composed of resistors, capacitors, and op amps. Filters composed of op amps, resistors, and capacitors are said to be **active filters**. In many respects, active filters have improved performance compared to passive circuits.

Active filters have been studied extensively and many useful circuits have been found. Ideally, an active filter circuit should:

1. Contain few components.
2. Have a transfer function that is insensitive to component tolerances.
3. Place modest demands on the op amp's gain–bandwidth product, output impedance, slew rate, and other specifications.
4. Be easily adjusted.
5. Require a small spread of component values.
6. Allow a wide range of useful transfer functions to be realized.

Various circuits have been described in the literature that meet these goals to varying degrees. Many complete books have been written that deal exclusively with active filters. In this section, we confine our attention to a particular (but practical) means for implementing lowpass filters.

Butterworth Transfer Function

The magnitude of the **Butterworth transfer function** is given by

$$|H(f)| = \frac{H_0}{\sqrt{1 + (f/f_B)^{2n}}} \qquad (44)$$

in which the integer n is the *order* of the filter and f_B is the 3-dB cutoff frequency. Substituting $f = 0$ yields $|H(0)| = H_0$; thus, H_0 is the dc gain magnitude. Plots of this transfer function are shown in Figure 39. Notice that as the order of the filter increases, the transfer function approaches that of an ideal lowpass filter.

An active lowpass Butterworth filter can be implemented by cascading modified **Sallen–Key circuits**, one of which is shown in Figure 40. In this version of the Sallen–Key circuit, the resistors labeled R have equal values. Similarly, the capacitors

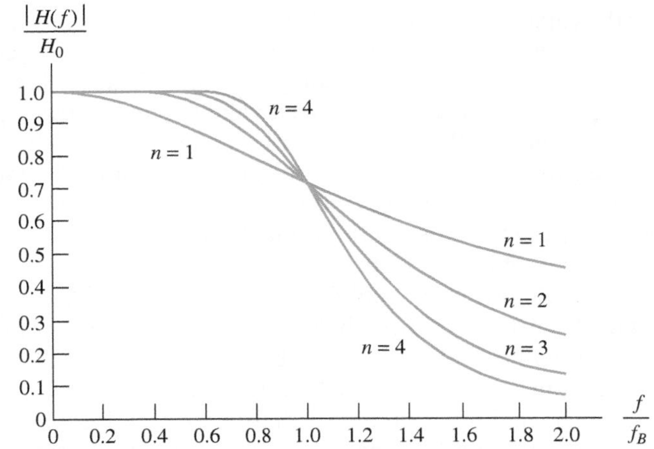

Figure 39 Transfer-function magnitude versus frequency for lowpass Butterworth filters.

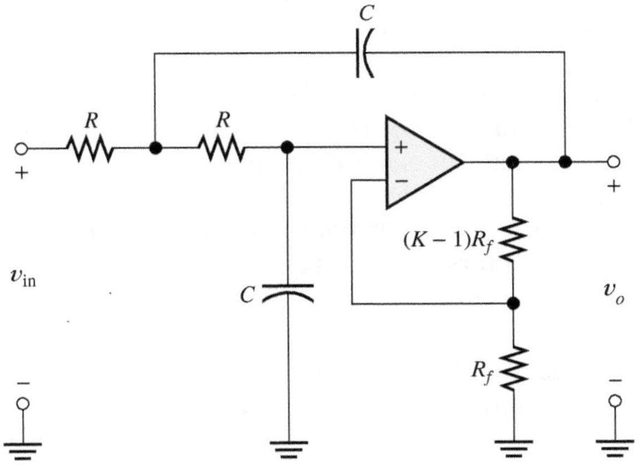

Figure 40 Equal-component Sallen–Key lowpass active-filter section.

labeled C have equal values. Useful circuits having unequal components are possible, but equal components are convenient.

The Sallen–Key circuit shown in Figure 40 is a second-order lowpass filter. To obtain an nth-order filter, $n/2$ circuits must be cascaded. (We assume that n is even.)

The 3-dB cutoff frequency of the overall filter is related to R and C by

$$f_B = \frac{1}{2\pi RC} \qquad (45)$$

Usually, we wish to design for a given cutoff frequency. We try to select small capacitance values because this leads to small physical size and low cost. However, Equation 45 shows that as the capacitances become small, the resistance values become larger (for a given cutoff frequency). If the capacitance is selected too small, the resistance becomes unrealistically large. Furthermore, stray wiring capacitance can easily affect a high-impedance circuit. Thus, we select a capacitance value that is small, but not too small (say not smaller than 1000 pF).

In selecting the capacitor, we should select a value that is readily available in the tolerance required. Then, we use Equation 45 to compute the resistance. It is helpful to select the capacitance first and then compute the resistance, because resistors are commonly available in more finely spaced values than capacitors. Possibly, we cannot find nominal values of R and C that yield exactly the desired break frequency; however, it is a rare situation for which the break frequency must be controlled to an accuracy less than a few percent. Thus, 1-percent-tolerance resistors usually result in a break frequency sufficiently close to the value desired.

Notice in the circuit of Figure 40 that the op amp and the feedback resistors R_f and $(K-1)R_f$ form a noninverting amplifier having a gain of K. At dc, the capacitors act as open circuits. Then, the resistors labeled R are in series with the input terminals of the noninverting amplifier and have no effect on gain. Thus, the dc gain of the circuit is K. As K is varied from zero to three, the transfer function displays more and more peaking (i.e., the gain magnitude increases with frequency and reaches a peak before falling off). For $K = 3$, infinite peaking occurs. It turns out that for K greater than three, the circuit is unstable—it oscillates.

The most critical issue in selection of the feedback resistors R_f and $(K-1)R_f$ is their ratio. If desired, a precise ratio can be achieved by including a potentiometer, which is adjusted to yield the required dc gain for each section. To minimize the effects of bias current, we should select values such that the parallel combination of R_f and $(K-1)R_f$ is equal to $2R$. However, with FET input op amps, input bias current is often so small that this is not necessary.

An nth-order Butterworth lowpass filter is obtained by cascading $n/2$ stages having proper values for K. (Here again, we assume that n is even.) Table 1 shows the required K values for filters of various orders. The dc gain H_0 of the overall filter is the product of the K values of the individual stages.

Table 1. *K* Values for Lowpass or Highpass Butterworth Filters of Various Orders

Order	*K*
2	1.586
4	1.152
	2.235
6	1.068
	1.586
	2.483
8	1.038
	1.337
	1.889
	2.610

Example 8 Lowpass Active Filter Design

Design a fourth-order lowpass Butterworth filter having a cutoff frequency of 100 Hz.

Solution We arbitrarily choose capacitor values of $C = 0.1\ \mu$F. This is a standard value and not prohibitively large. (Perhaps we could achieve an equally good design by using smaller capacitances, say 0.01 μF. However, as we have mentioned earlier, there is a practical limit to how small the capacitances can be.)

Active lowpass filters such as this are useful as antialias filters in computer-based instrumentation systems.

Next, we solve Equation 45 for R. Substituting $f_B = 100$ Hz and $C = 0.1\ \mu$F results in $R = 15.92$ kΩ. In practice, we would select a 15.8-kΩ 1-percent-tolerance resistor. This results in a nominal cutoff frequency slightly higher than the design objective.

Consulting Table 1, we find that a fourth-order filter requires two sections having gains of $K = 1.152$ and 2.235. This results in an overall dc gain of $H_0 = 1.152 \times 2.235 \cong 2.575$. We arbitrarily select $R_f = 10$ kΩ for both sections. The complete circuit diagram is shown in Figure 41. The resistors R_3 and R_{13} consist of fixed resistors in series with small trimmers that can be adjusted to obtain the required gain for each stage. ■

A Bode plot of the overall gain magnitude for the filter designed in Example 8 is shown in Figure 42. It can be verified that the dc gain in decibels is $20 \log H_0 \cong 8.2$ dB. As desired, the 3-dB frequency is very nearly 100 Hz.

Figure 43 shows the gain of each section normalized by its dc gain. The figure also shows the normalized overall gain. Of course, the overall normalized gain is the product of the normalized gains of the individual stages. (Notice that the gains are plotted as ratios rather than in decibels.) The transfer function of the first stage—which is the low-gain stage—rolls off without peaking. However, considerable peaking occurs in the second stage. It is this peaking that squares up the shoulder of the overall transfer characteristic.

Exercise 21 Show that for frequencies much greater than f_B, the magnitude of the lowpass Butterworth transfer function given in Equation 44 rolls off at $20 \times n$ decibels per decade. □

Exercise 22 Design a sixth-order Butterworth lowpass filter having a cutoff frequency of 5 kHz.

Answer Many answers are possible. For a sixth-order filter, three stages like Figure 40 need to be cascaded. A good choice is to use capacitors in the range

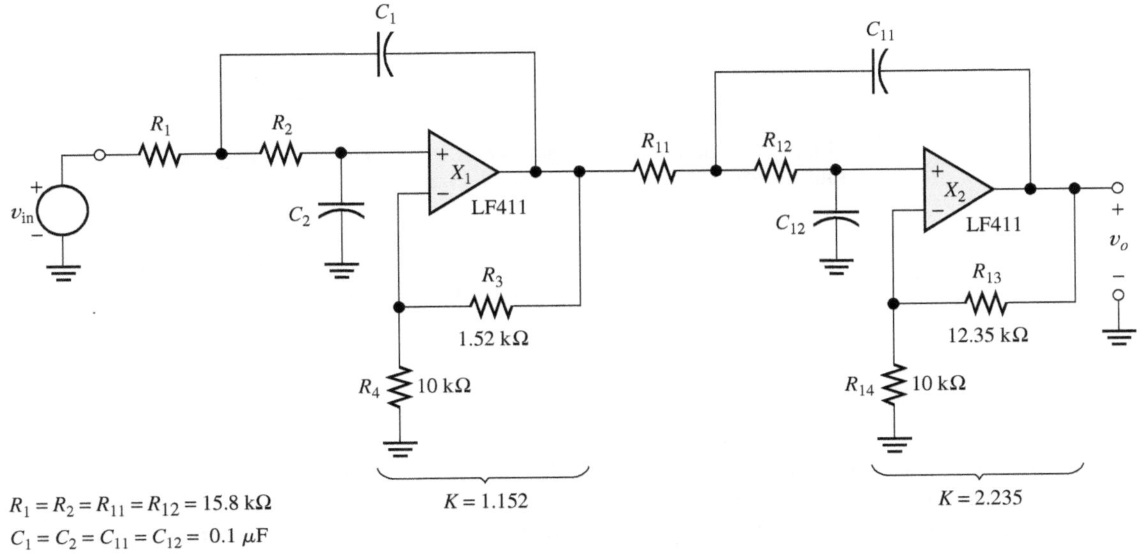

Figure 41 Fourth-order Butterworth lowpass filter designed in Example 8.

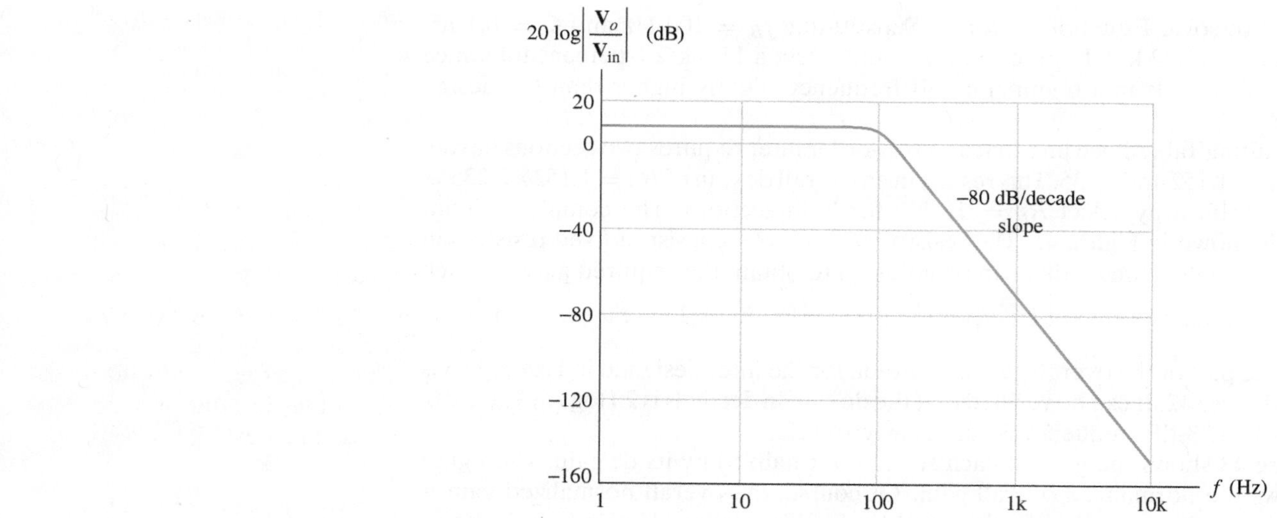

Figure 42 Bode magnitude plot of the gain for the fourth-order lowpass filter of Example 8.

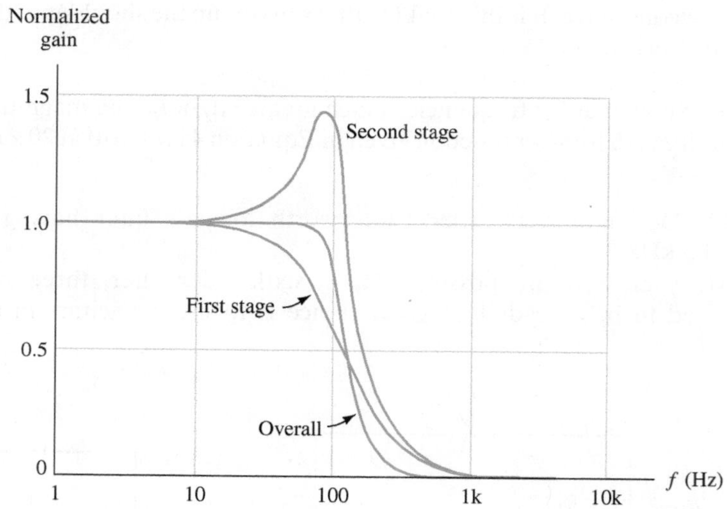

Figure 43 Comparison of gain versus frequency for the stages of the fourth-order lowpass filter of Example 8.

from 1000 pF to 0.01 μF. With $C = 0.01\ \mu$F, we need $R = 3.183$ kΩ. $R_f = 10$ kΩ is a good choice. From Table 1, we find the gain values to be 1.068, 1.586, and 2.483. □

Summary

1. If a differential amplifier has input voltages v_1 and v_2, the common-mode input is $v_{icm} = \frac{1}{2}(v_1 + v_2)$ and the differential input signal is $v_{id} = v_1 - v_2$.

2. An ideal operational amplifier has infinite input impedance, infinite gain for the differential input signal, zero gain for the common-mode input

signal, zero output impedance, and infinite bandwidth.

3. In an amplifier circuit with negative feedback, part of the output is returned to the input. The feedback signal opposes the input source.
4. To analyze ideal op-amp circuits with negative feedback, we assume that the differential input voltage and the input current of the op amp are driven to zero (this is the summing-point constraint), and then we use basic circuit principles to analyze the circuit.
5. The basic inverting amplifier configuration is shown in Figure 4. Its closed-loop voltage gain is $A_v = -R_2/R_1$.
6. The basic noninverting amplifier configuration is shown in Figure 11. Its closed-loop voltage gain is $A_v = 1 + R_2/R_1$.
7. Many useful amplifier circuits can be designed with the use of op amps. First, we select a suitable circuit configuration, and then we determine the resistor values that achieve the desired gain values.
8. In the design of op-amp circuits, very large resistances are unsuitable because their values are unstable and because high-impedance circuits are vulnerable to capacitive coupling of noise. Very low resistances are unsuitable because large currents flow in them for the voltages typically encountered in op-amp circuits.
9. In the linear range of operation, the imperfections of real op amps include finite input impedance, nonzero output impedance, and finite open-loop gain magnitude, which falls off with increasing frequency.
10. Negative feedback reduces gain magnitude and extends bandwidth. For the noninverting amplifier, the product of dc gain magnitude and bandwidth is constant for a given op-amp type.
11. The output voltage range and the output current range of any op amp are limited. If the output waveform reaches (and tries to exceed) either of these limits, clipping occurs.
12. The rate of change of the output voltage of any op amp is limited in magnitude. This is called the slew-rate limitation. The full-power bandwidth is the highest frequency for which the op amp can produce a full-amplitude sinusoidal output signal.
13. Dc imperfections of op amps are bias current, offset current, and offset voltage. These effects can be modeled by the sources shown in Figure 29. The effect of dc imperfections is a (usually undesirable) dc component added to the intended output signal.
14. A single op amp can be used as a differential amplifier as shown in Figure 33. However, the instrumentation amplifier shown in Figure 34 has better performance.
15. The integrator circuit shown in Figure 35 produces an output voltage that is proportional to the running time integral of the input voltage. A differentiator circuit is shown in Figure 38.
16. Active filters often have better performance than passive filters. Active Butterworth lowpass filters can be obtained by cascading several Sallen–Key circuits having the proper gains.

Problems

Section 1: Ideal Operational Amplifiers

P1. Suppose that a real op amp has five terminals. List the probable functions of the terminals.

P2. List the characteristics of an ideal operational amplifier.

P3. Explain the distinction between *open-loop gain* and *closed-loop gain*.

P4. Give the definitions of the differential input voltage and of the common-mode input voltage for a differential amplifier having input voltages v_1 and v_2.

* Denotes that answers are contained in the Student Solutions files. See Appendix "On-Line Student Resources" for more information about accessing the Student Solutions.

***P5.** The input voltages (in units of volts) of a differential amplifier are

$$v_1(t) = 0.5\cos(2000\pi t) + 20\cos(120\pi t)$$

$$v_2(t) = -0.5\cos(2000\pi t) + 20\cos(120\pi t)$$

Find expressions for the common-mode and differential components of the input signal.

Section 2: Inverting Amplifiers

***P6.** What are the steps in analyzing an amplifier containing an ideal op amp?

P7. Draw the circuit diagram of the basic inverting amplifier configuration. Give an expression for the closed-loop voltage gain of the circuit in terms of the resistances, assuming an ideal op amp. Give expressions for the input impedance and output impedance of the circuit.

P8. Define the term *summing-point constraint.* Does it apply when negative feedback is present? When positive feedback is present?

***P9.** Determine the closed-loop voltage gain of the circuit shown in Figure P9, assuming an ideal op amp.

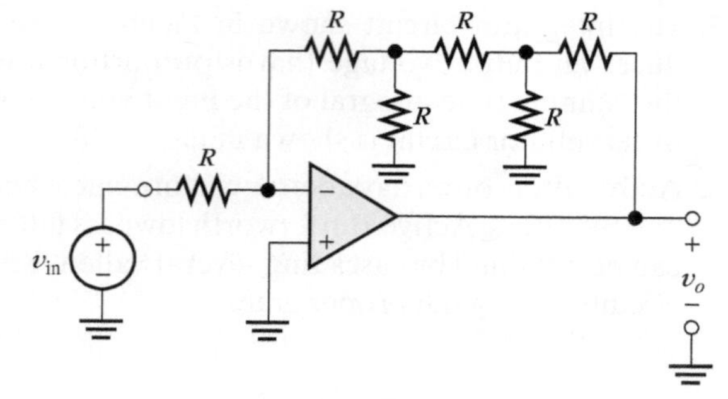

Figure P9

P10. Sketch $v_{in}(t)$ and $v_o(t)$ to scale versus time for the circuit shown in Figure P10. The op amp is ideal.

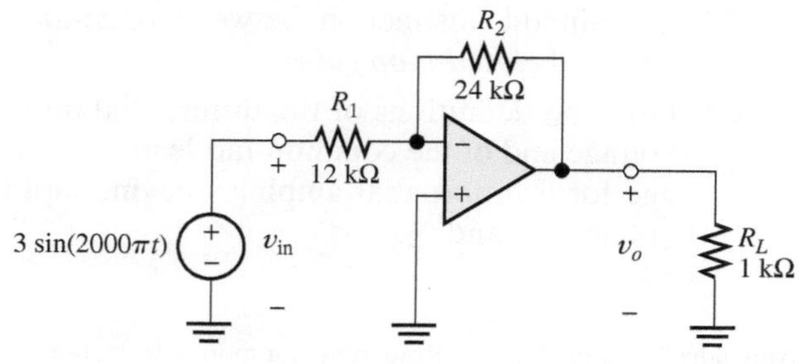

Figure P10

P11. Determine the closed-loop voltage gain of the circuit shown in Figure P11, assuming an ideal op amp.

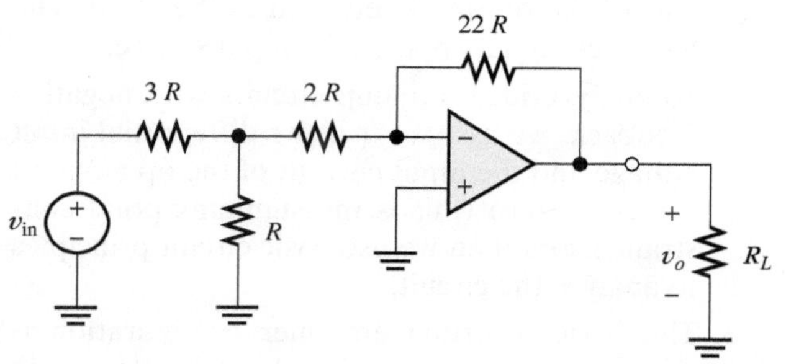

Figure P11

P12. The amplifier shown in Figure P12 is called an **exponential amplifier**. The circuit has negative feedback, and the summing-point constraint applies. Assume an ideal op amp, that v_{in} is positive, and that the diode current given by the equation $i_D \cong I_s \exp\left(\frac{v_D}{nV_T}\right)$, which states that $i_D = I_s \exp(v_D/nV_T)$. Derive an expression for v_o in terms of v_{in}, R, I_s, n, and V_T.

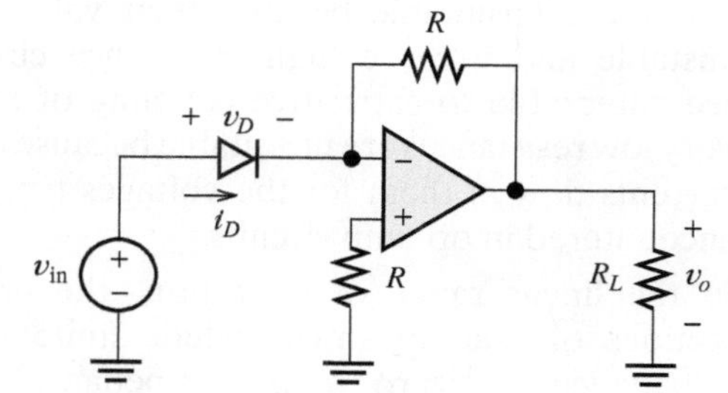

Figure P12

P13. The amplifier shown in Figure P13 is called a **logarithmic amplifier**. The circuit has negative feedback, and the summing-point constraint applies. Assume an ideal op amp, that v_{in} is positive, and that the

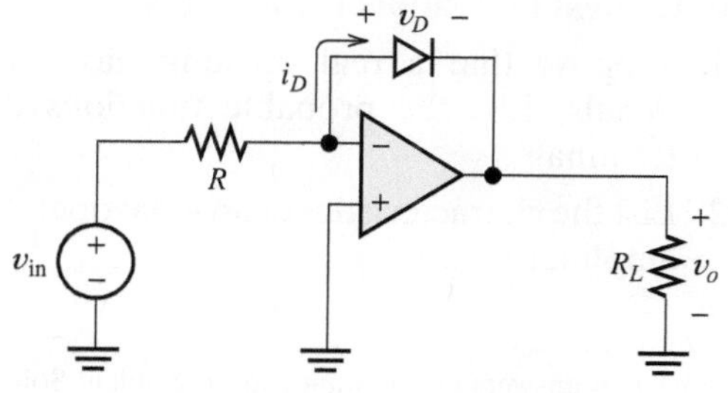

Figure P13

diode current given by the equation $i_D \cong I_s \exp\left(\frac{v_D}{nV_T}\right)$, which states that $i_D = I_s \exp(v_D/nV_T)$. Derive an expression for v_o in terms of v_{in}, R, I_s, n, and V_T.

P14. Consider the inverting amplifier shown in Figure P14. Assuming an ideal op amp, solve for the currents and voltages shown. According to Kirchhoff's current law, the sum of the currents entering a closed surface must equal the sum of the currents leaving. Explain how the law is satisfied for the closed surface shown when we use a real op amp in this circuit.

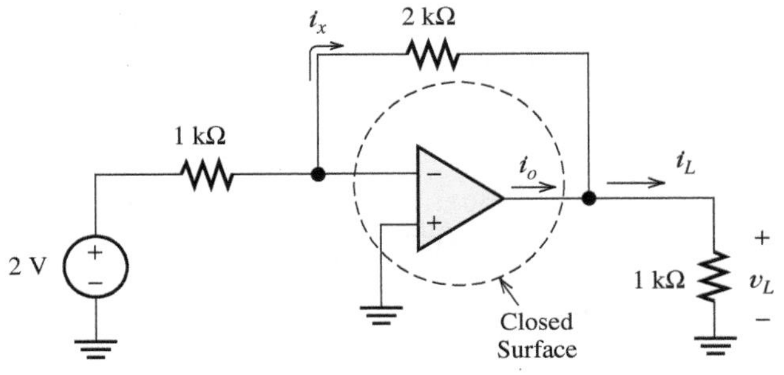

Figure P14

P15. Consider the circuit shown in Figure P13, with an unusual diode that has $i_D = Kv_D^3$. Assume that the summing-point constraint applies, and derive an expression for v_o in terms of v_{in}, R, and K.

P16. The op amp shown in Figure P16 is ideal, except that the extreme output voltages that it can produce are ±5 V. Determine two possible values for each of the voltages shown, assuming that the input current to the inverting input of the op amp is negligible. (*Hint*: Notice that this circuit has *positive* feedback so the summing-point constraint does not apply.)

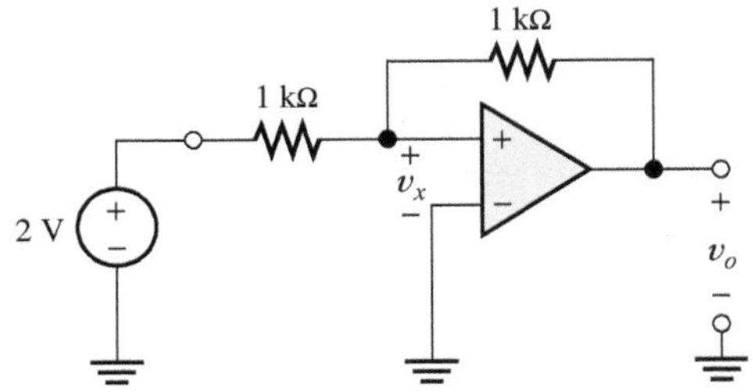

Figure P16

Section 3: Noninverting Amplifiers

***P17.** The voltage follower of Figure 12 has unity voltage gain so that $v_o = v_{in}$. Why not simply connect the load directly to the source, thus eliminating the op amp? Give an example of a situation in which the voltage follower is particularly good compared with the direct connection.

***P18.** Draw the circuit diagram of an op-amp voltage follower. What value is its voltage gain? Input impedance? Output impedance?

***P19.** Analyze the ideal op-amp circuit shown in Figure P19 to find an expression for v_o in terms of v_A, v_B, and the resistance values.

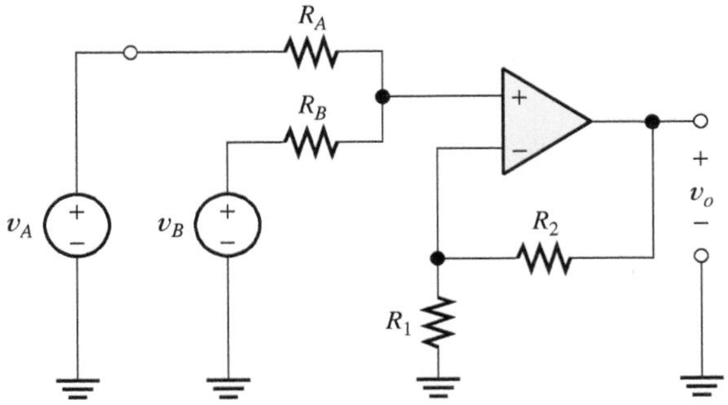

Figure P19

***P20.** Consider the circuit shown in Figure P20. **a.** Find an expression for the output voltage in terms of the source current and resistance values. **b.** What value is the output impedance of this circuit? **c.** What value is the input impedance of this circuit? **d.** This circuit can be classified as an ideal amplifier. What is the amplifier type?

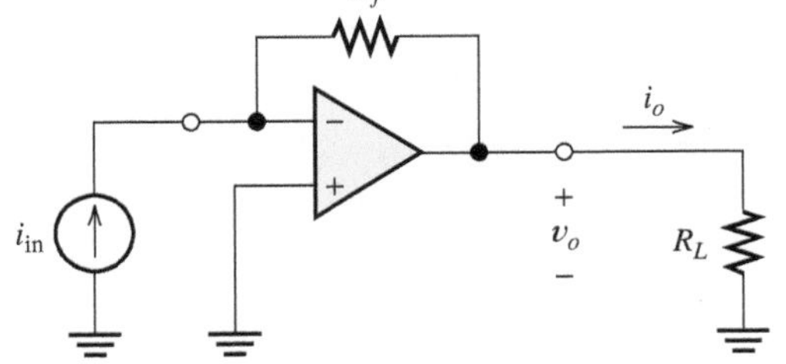

Figure P20

P21. Draw the circuit diagram of the basic noninverting amplifier configuration. Give an expression for the closed-loop voltage gain of the circuit in terms of the resistances, assuming an ideal op amp. Give expressions for the input impedance and output impedance of the circuit.

P22. For each of the circuits shown in Figure P22, assume that the op amp is ideal and find the value of v_o. Each of the circuits has negative feedback, and the summing-point constraint applies.

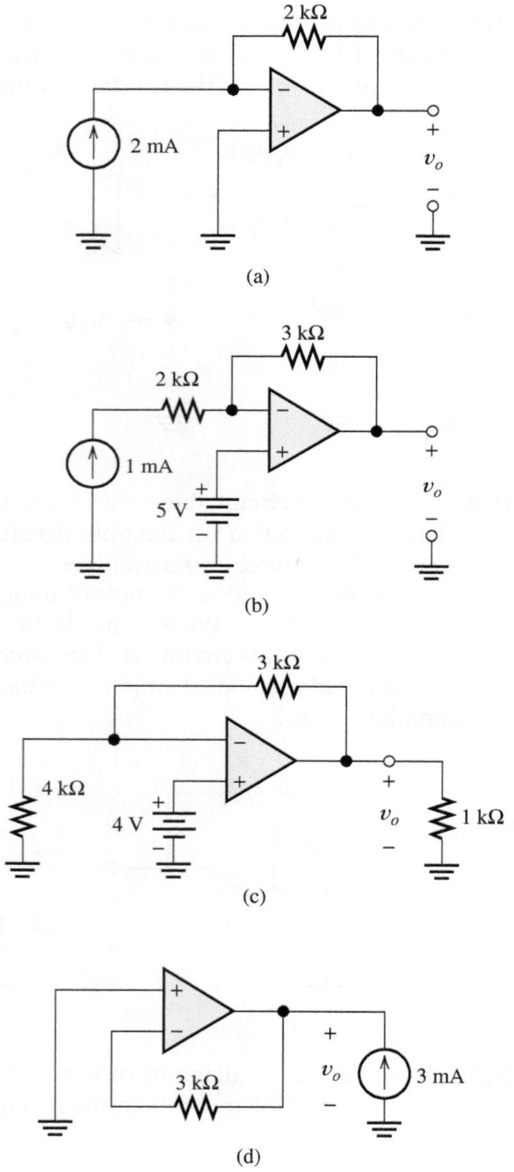

Figure P22

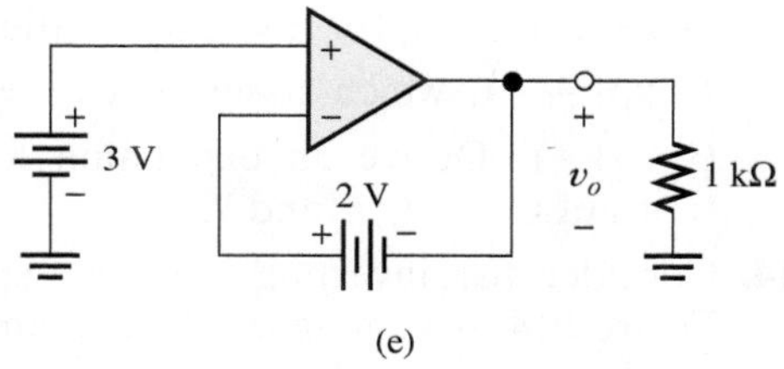

Figure P22 *(Cont.)*

P23. The circuit shown in Figure P23 has

$$v_{\text{in}}(t) = 3 + 3\cos(2000\pi t)$$

Determine the value required for R_2 so that the dc component of the output $v_o(t)$ is zero. What is the resulting output voltage?

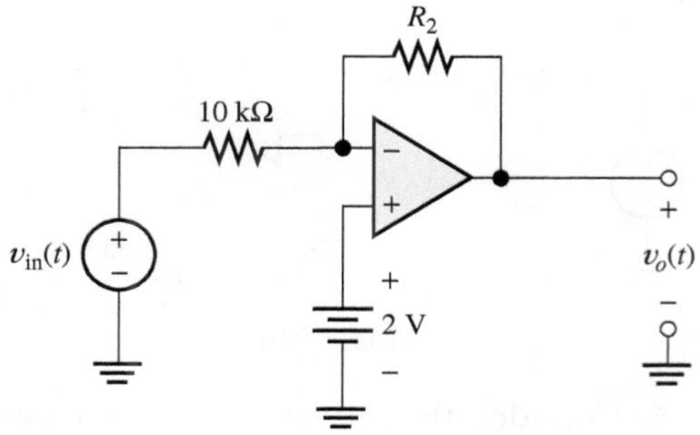

Figure P23

P24. Consider the circuit shown in Figure P24. **a.** Find an expression for the output current i_o in terms of the input current i_{in} and resistance values. **b.** What value is the output impedance of this circuit? **c.** What value is the input impedance of this circuit? **d.** This circuit can be classified as an ideal amplifier. What is the amplifier type?

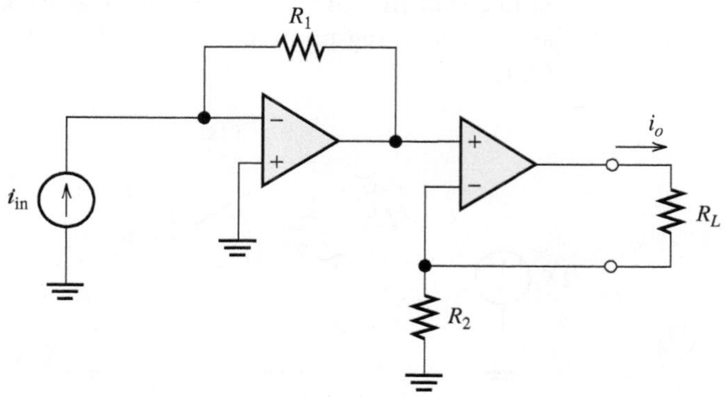

Figure P24

P25. Analyze each of the ideal-op-amp circuits shown in Figure P25 to find expressions for i_o. What is the value of the output impedance for each of these circuits? Why? [*Note:* The bottom end of the input voltage source is *not* grounded in part (b) of the figure. Thus, we say that this source is *floating*.]

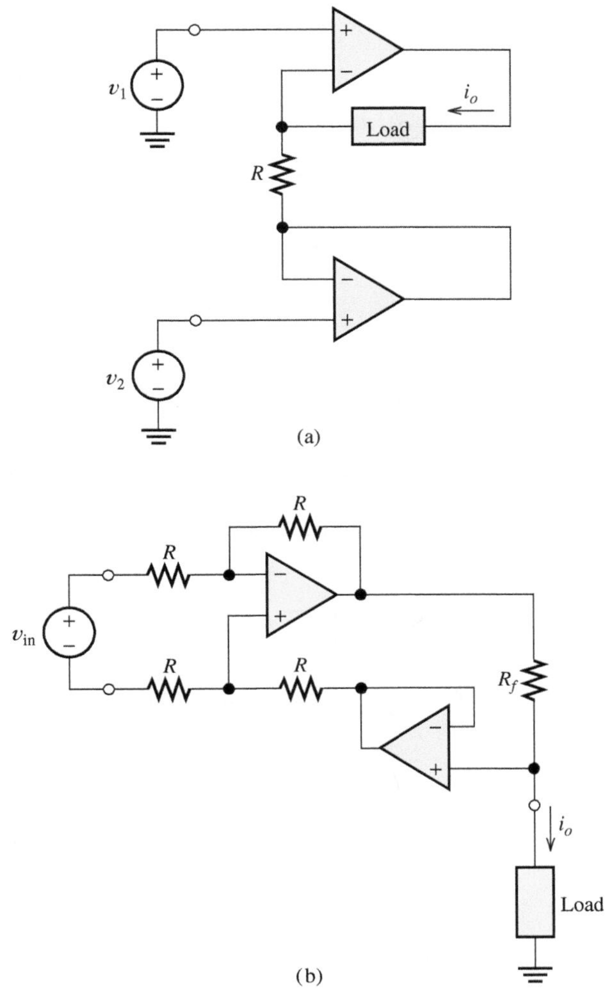

Figure P25

P26. Consider the circuit shown in Figure P26. **a.** Find an expression for the output voltage in terms of the source current and resistance values. **b.** What value is the output impedance of this circuit? **c.** What value is the input impedance of this circuit? **d.** This circuit can be classified as an ideal amplifier. What is the amplifier type?

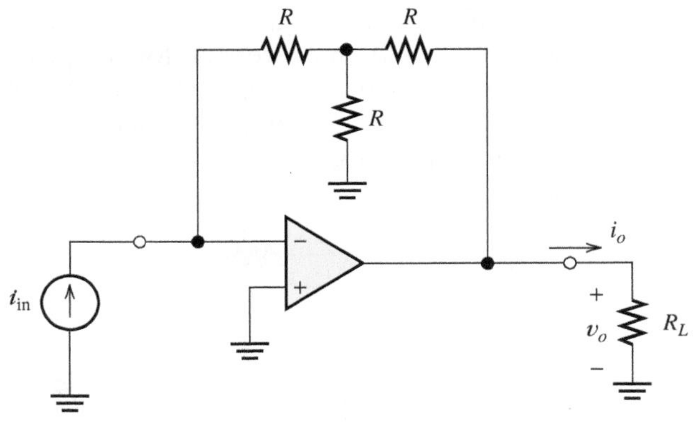

Figure P26

P27. We have an inverting amplifier using 1-percent-tolerance resistors and an ideal op amp. The nominal amplifier gain is −2. What are the minimum and maximum gains possible, assuming that the resistances are within the stated tolerance? What is the percentage tolerance of the gain?

P28. Consider the circuit shown in Figure P28. **a.** Find an expression for the output current i_o in terms of the input voltage v_{in} and resistance values. **b.** What value is the output impedance of this circuit? **c.** What value is the input impedance of this circuit? **d.** This circuit can be classified as an ideal amplifier. What is the amplifier type?

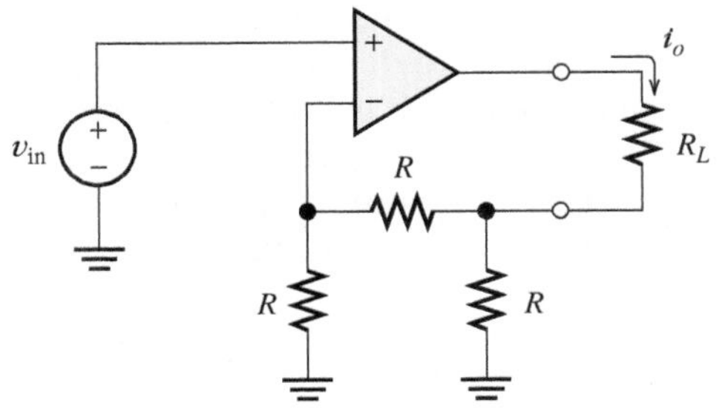

Figure P28

P29. The power gain G of an amplifier is defined to be the power delivered to the load R_L

divided by the power delivered by the signal source v_s. Find an expression for the power gain of each of the amplifiers shown in Figure P29. Assume ideal op amps. Which circuit has the larger power gain?

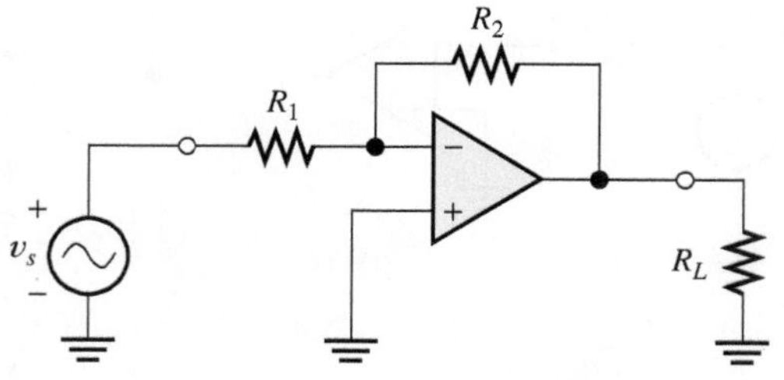

(a) Inverting amplifier

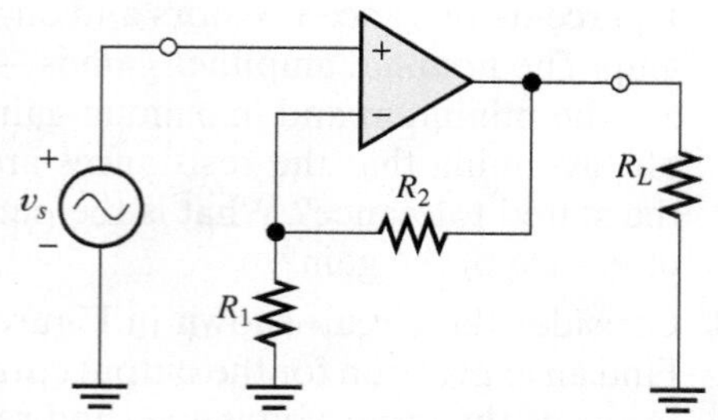

(b) Noninverting amplifier

Figure P29

***P30.** Consider the circuits shown in Figure P30(a) and (b). One of the circuits has negative feedback, and the other circuit has positive feedback. Assume that the op amps are ideal, except that the output voltage is limited to extremes of ± 5 V. For the input voltage waveform shown in Figure P30(c), sketch the output voltage $v_o(t)$ to scale versus time for each circuit.

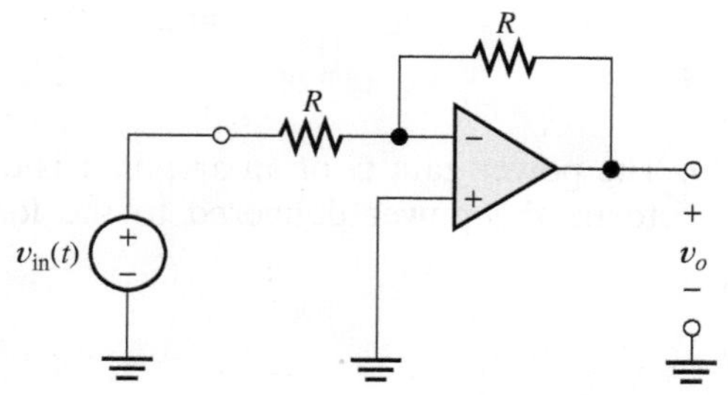

(a)

Figure P30

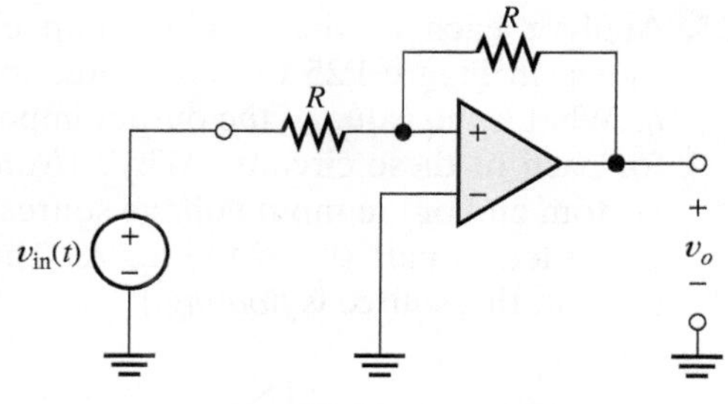

(b)

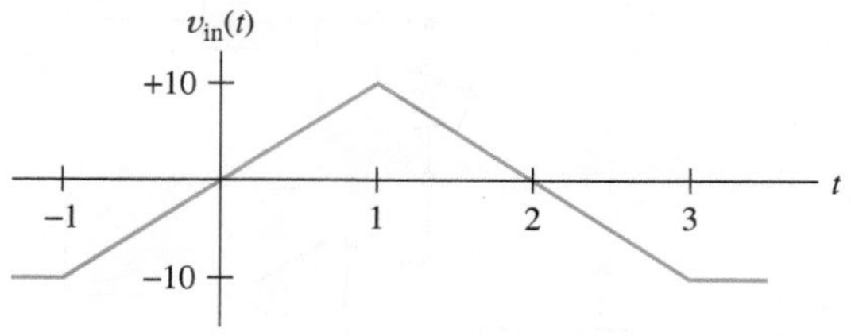

(c)

Figure P30 (*Cont.*)

P31. Repeat Problem P30 for the circuits of Figure P31(a) and (b). [The input voltage waveform is shown in Figure P30(c).]

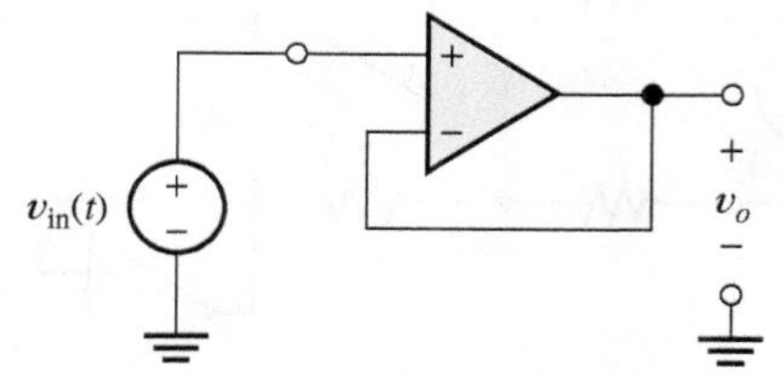

(a)

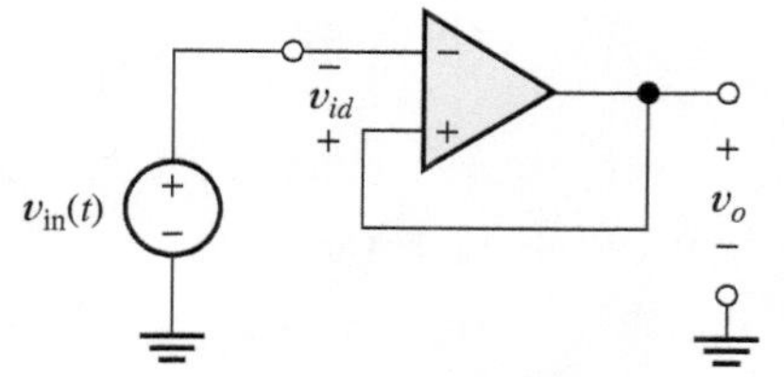

(b)

Figure P31

P32. The circuit shown in Figure P32 employs negative feedback. Use the summing-point constraint (for both op amps) to derive expressions for the voltage gains $A_1 = v_{o1}/v_{in}$ and $A_2 = v_{o2}/v_{in}$.

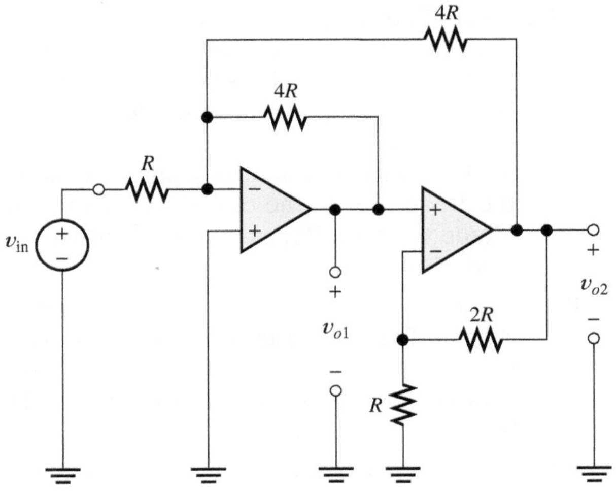

Figure P32

P33. We have a noninverting amplifier using 1-percent-tolerance resistors and an ideal op amp. The nominal amplifier gain is 2. What are the minimum and maximum gains possible, assuming that the resistances are within the stated tolerance? What is the percentage tolerance of the gain?

***P34.** Consider the amplifier shown in Figure P34. Find an expression for the output current i_o. What is the input impedance? What is the output impedance seen by R_L?

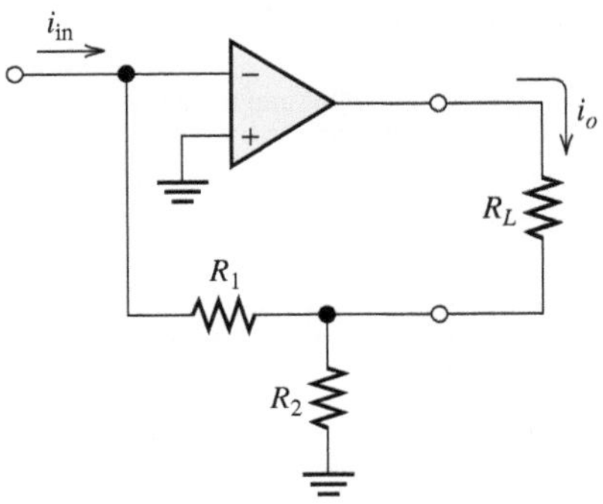

Figure P34

P35. Derive an expression for the voltage gain of the circuit shown in Figure P35 as a function of T, assuming an ideal op amp. (T varies from 0 to unity, depending on the position of the wiper of the potentiometer.)

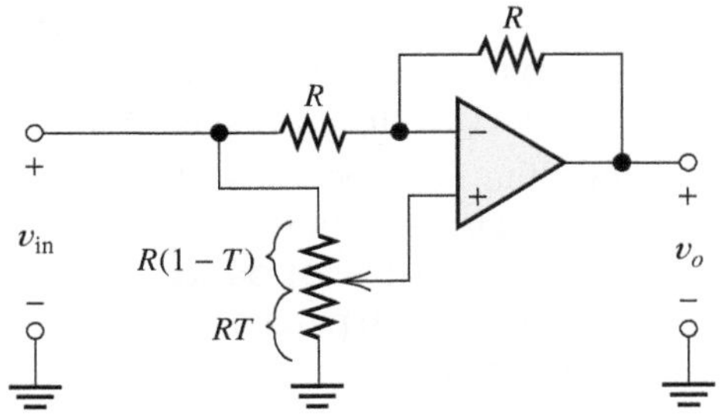

Figure P35

Section 4: Design of Simple Amplifiers

P36. Suppose that we are designing an amplifier, using an op amp. What problems are associated with using very small feedback resistances? With very large feedback resistances?

***P37.** Using the components listed in Table P37, design an amplifier having a voltage gain of -10 ± 20 percent. The input impedance is required to be as large as possible (ideally, an open circuit). Remember to use practical resistance values. (*Hint:* Cascade a noninverting stage with an inverting stage.)

Table P37. Available Parts for Design Problems

Standard 5%-tolerance resistors. (See Appendix "Nominal Values and the Color Code for Resistors".)
Standard 1%-tolerance resistors. (Don't use these if a 5%-tolerance resistor will do, because 1%-tolerance resistors are more expensive.)
Ideal op amps.
Adjustable resistors (trimmers) having maximum values ranging from 100 Ω to 1 MΩ in a 1–2–5 sequence (i.e., 100 Ω, 200 Ω, 500 Ω, 1 kΩ, etc.). Don't use trimmers if fixed resistors will suffice.

***P38.** For Example 4, it is possible to achieve a design that requires only one op amp. Find a suitable circuit configuration and resistance values. For this problem, the gain tolerances are relaxed to ± 5 percent.

***P39.** Using the components listed in Table P37, design a circuit for which the output voltage is $v_o = A_1 v_1 + A_2 v_2$. The voltages v_1 and v_2 are input voltages. Design to achieve $A_1 =$

5 ± 5 percent and $A_2 = -10 \pm 5$ percent. The input impedances are required to be as large as possible (ideally, open circuits).

P40. Using the components listed in Table P37, design an amplifier having an input impedance of at least 50 kΩ and a voltage gain of: **a.** -2 ± 20 percent; **b.** -2 ± 5 percent; **c.** -2 ± 0.5 percent.

P41. Using the components listed in Table P37, design a circuit for which the output voltage is $v_o = A_1 v_1 + A_2 v_2$. The voltages v_1 and v_2 are input voltages. Design to achieve $A_1 = -4 \pm 5$ percent and $A_2 = -4 \pm 5$ percent. The input impedances are required to be as large as possible (ideally, open circuits).

P42. Design an amplifier having a voltage gain of $+5 \pm 3$ percent and an input impedance of 2 kΩ ± 1 percent, using the components listed in Table P37.

P43. Two signal sources have internal voltages $v_1(t)$ and $v_2(t)$, respectively. The internal (i.e., Thévenin) resistances of the sources are known always to be less than 2 kΩ, but the exact values are not known and are likely to change over time. Using the components listed in Table P37, design an amplifier for which the output voltage is $v_o(t) = A_1 v_1(t) + A_2 v_2(t)$. The gains are to be $A_1 = -10 \pm 1$ percent and $A_2 = 3 \pm 1$ percent.

P44. Suppose we have a signal source with an internal (i.e., Thévenin) impedance that is always less than 1000 Ω, but is variable over time. Using the components listed in Table P37, design an amplifier that produces an amplified version of the internal source voltage. The voltage gain should be -10 ± 5 percent.

Section 5: Op-Amp Imperfections in the Linear Range of Operation

P45. List the imperfections of real op amps in their linear range of operation.

***P46.** A certain op amp has a unity-gain bandwidth of $f_t = 15$ MHz. If this op amp is used in a noninverting amplifier having a closed-loop dc gain of $A_{0CL} = 10$, determine the closed-loop break frequency f_{BCL}. Repeat for a dc gain of 100.

***P47.** A certain op amp has an open-loop dc gain of $A_{0OL} = 200{,}000$ and an open-loop 3-dB bandwidth of $f_{BOL} = 5$ Hz. Sketch the Bode plot of the open-loop gain magnitude to scale. If this op amp is used in a noninverting amplifier having a closed-loop dc gain of 100, sketch the Bode plot of the closed-loop gain magnitude to scale. Repeat for a closed-loop dc gain of 10.

P48. A certain op amp has an open-loop dc gain of $A_{0OL} = 400{,}000$ and an open-loop 3-dB bandwidth of $f_{BOL} = 10$ Hz. Find the open-loop gain magnitude at a frequency of: **a.** 10 Hz; **b.** 1000 Hz; **c.** 4 MHz.

P49. The objective of this problem is to investigate the effects of finite open-loop gain, finite input impedance, and nonzero output impedance of the op amp on the voltage follower. The circuit, including the op-amp model, is shown in Figure P49. **a.** Derive an expression for the circuit voltage gain v_o/v_s. Evaluate for $A_{OL} = 10^5$, $R_{in} = 1$ MΩ, and $R_o = 25$ Ω. Compare this result to the gain with an ideal op amp. **b.** Derive an expression for the circuit input impedance $Z_{in} = v_s/i_s$. Evaluate for $A_{OL} = 10^5$, $R_{in} = 1$ MΩ, and $R_o = 25$ Ω. Compare this result to the input impedance with an ideal op amp. **c.** Derive an expression for the circuit output impedance Z_o. Evaluate for $A_{OL} = 10^5$, $R_{in} = 1$ MΩ, and $R_o = 25$ Ω. Compare this result to the output impedance with an ideal op amp.

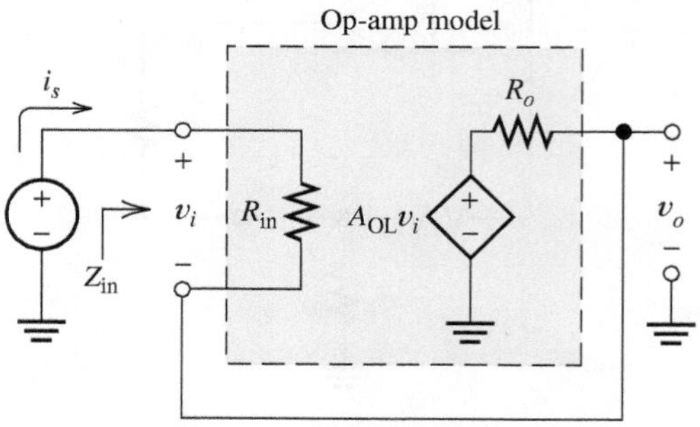

Figure P49

P50. We need a noninverting amplifier that has a dc gain of 10, and the gain magnitude at 5 kHz must be not less than 9.5. Determine the minimum gain–bandwidth specification required for the op amp.

P51. We need a noninverting amplifier that has a dc gain of 5, and the phase shift for the 100-kHz component must not exceed 10° in magnitude. Determine the minimum gain–bandwidth specification required for the op amp.

P52. We have the following two alternatives for designing an amplifier having a dc gain of 25. The first alternative is to use a single noninverting stage, having a gain of 25. The second alternative is to cascade two noninverting stages, each having a gain of 5. Op amps having a gain–bandwidth product of 10^6 are to be used. Draw the circuit diagram, write an expression for the gain as a function of frequency, and find the 3-dB bandwidth for each alternative. Which alternative has the greater bandwidth?

P53. The objective of this problem is to investigate the effects of finite gain, finite input impedance, and nonzero output impedance of the op amp on the inverting amplifier. The circuit, including the op-amp model, is shown in Figure P53. **a.** Derive an expression for the circuit voltage gain v_o/v_s. Evaluate for $A_{OL} = 10^5$, $R_{in} = 1\ \text{M}\Omega$, $R_o = 25\ \Omega$, $R_1 = 1\ \text{k}\Omega$, and $R_2 = 10\ \text{k}\Omega$. Compare this result to the gain with an ideal op amp. **b.** Derive an expression for the circuit input impedance $Z_{in} = v_s/i_s$. Evaluate for $A_{OL} = 10^5$, $R_{in} = 1\ \text{M}\Omega$, $R_o = 25\ \Omega$, $R_1 = 1\ \text{k}\Omega$, and $R_2 = 10\ \text{k}\Omega$. Compare this result to the input impedance with an ideal op amp.

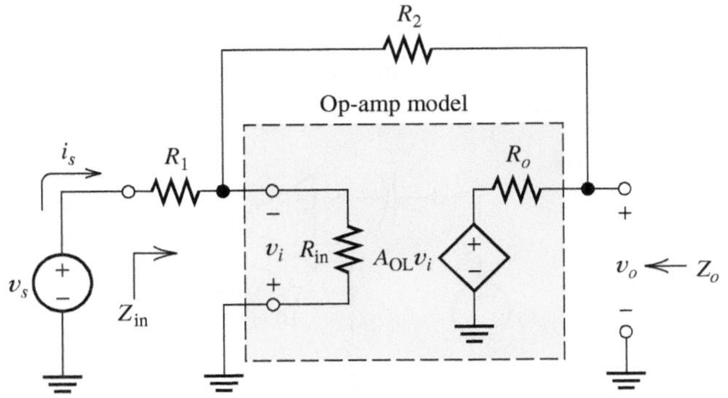

Figure P53

c. Derive an expression for the circuit output impedance Z_o. Evaluate for $A_{OL} = 10^5$, $R_{in} = 1\ \text{M}\Omega$, $R_o = 25\ \Omega$, $R_1 = 1\ \text{k}\Omega$, and $R_2 = 10\ \text{k}\Omega$. Compare this result to the output impedance with an ideal op amp.

Section 6: Nonlinear Limitations

P54. What are the nonlinear limitations of real op amps?

***P55.** Suppose that we have an op amp with a maximum output voltage range from −10 to +10 V. The maximum output current magnitude is 20 mA. The slew-rate limit is SR = 10 V/μs. This op amp is used in the circuit of Figure 28. **a.** Find the full-power bandwidth of the op amp. **b.** For a frequency of 1 kHz and $R_L = 1\ \text{k}\Omega$, what peak output voltage is possible without distortion? **c.** For a frequency of 1 kHz and $R_L = 100\ \Omega$, what peak output voltage is possible without distortion? **d.** For a frequency of 1 MHz and $R_L = 1\ \text{k}\Omega$, what peak output voltage is possible without distortion? **e.** If $R_L = 1\ \text{k}\Omega$ and $v_s(t) = 5\sin(2\pi 10^6 t)$, sketch the steady-state output waveform to scale versus time.

***P56.** One way to measure the slew-rate limitation of an op amp is to apply a sine wave (or square wave) as the input to an amplifier and then increase the frequency until the output waveform becomes triangular. Suppose that a 1-MHz input signal produces a triangular output waveform having a peak-to-peak amplitude of 4 V. Determine the slew rate of the op amp.

P57. Discuss what we mean by the term *full-power bandwidth.*

P58. If the ideal output, with a sinusoidal input signal, greatly exceeds the full-power bandwidth, what is the waveform of the output signal? Under these conditions, if the slew rate of the op amp is 10 V/μs and the frequency of the input is 1 MHz, what is the peak-to-peak amplitude of the output signal?

P59. We need an amplifier that can produce a 200-kHz sine-wave output having a peak amplitude of 5 V. What is the minimum slew-rate specification allowed for the op amp?

P60. We need a noninverting amplifier with a dc gain of 5 to amplify an input signal, in volts, given by

$$v_{\text{in}}(t) = 0 \quad t \leq 0$$
$$= [1 - \exp(-t)] \quad t \geq 0$$

in which t is in μs. Determine the minimum slew-rate specification required for the op amp if distortion must be avoided.

P61. The circuit shown in Figure P61 is known as a **bridge amplifier**. **a.** Assuming ideal op amps, derive an expression for the voltage gain v_o/v_s. **b.** If $v_s(t) = 3\sin(\omega t)$, sketch $v_1(t)$, $v_2(t)$, and $v_o(t)$ to scale versus time. **c.** If the op amps are supplied from ± 15 V and clip at output voltages of ± 13 V, what is the peak value of $v_o(t)$ just at the threshold of clipping? (*Comment:* This circuit can be useful if a peak output voltage greater than the magnitude of the supply voltages is required.)

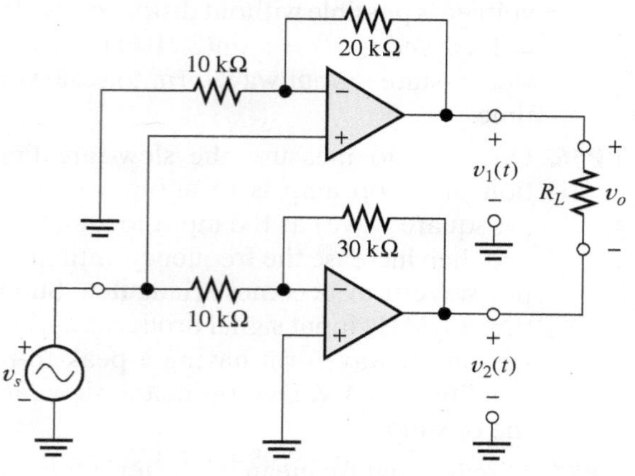

Figure P61

P62. A voltage follower is needed to amplify an input signal given by

$$v_{\text{in}}(t) = 0 \quad t \leq 0$$
$$= t^3 \quad 0 \leq t \leq 2$$
$$= 8 \quad 2 \leq t$$

in which t is in μs. Determine the minimum slew-rate specification required for the op amp if distortion must be avoided.

P63. The op amp shown in Figure P63 has a maximum output voltage range from -5 to $+5$ V. The maximum output current magnitude of the op amp is 20 mA. The slew-rate limit is 5 V/μs. **a.** Find the full-power bandwidth of the op amp. **b.** For a frequency of 5 kHz and $R_L = 50\ \Omega$, what peak output voltage is possible without distortion? **c.** For a frequency of 5 kHz and $R_L = 10$ kΩ, what peak output voltage is possible without distortion? **d.** For a frequency of 1 MHz and $R_L = 10$ kΩ, what peak output voltage is possible without distortion?

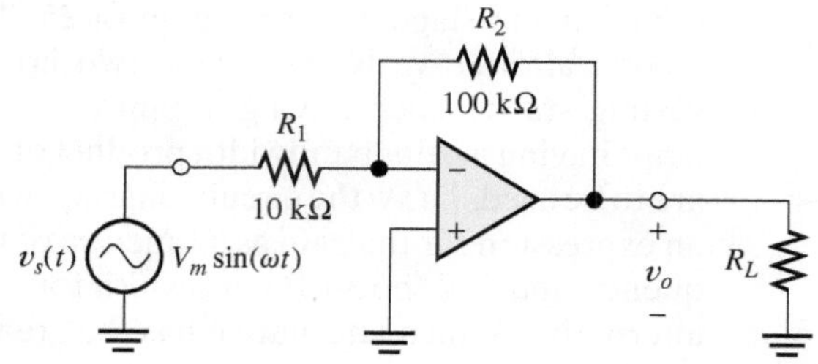

Figure P63

Section 7: DC Imperfections

***P64.** Draw the circuit symbol for an op amp, adding sources to account for dc imperfections.

P65. Name the advantage of a FET-input op amp compared with a BJT-input op amp.

P66. What are the dc imperfections of real op amps and the net effect of these dc imperfections?

***P67.** Find the worst-case dc output voltages of the inverting amplifier shown in Figure 30(a) for $v_{\text{in}} = 0$. The bias current ranges from 100 to 200 nA, the maximum offset current magnitude is 50 nA, and the maximum offset voltage magnitude is 4 mV.

P68. Sometimes, an ac-coupled amplifier is needed. The circuit shown in Figure P68

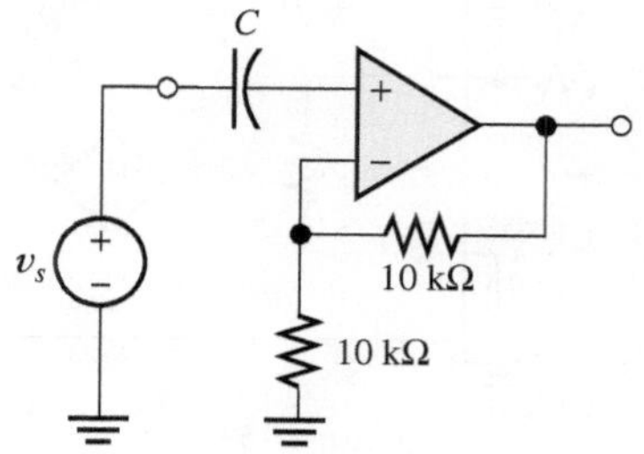

Figure P68

is a poor way to accomplish ac coupling. Explain why. (*Hint:* Consider the effect of bias current.) Show how to add a component (including its value) so that bias current has no effect on the output voltage of this circuit.

P69. Consider the amplifier shown in Figure P63. With zero dc input voltage from the signal source, it is desired that the dc output voltage be no greater than 50 mV. **a.** Ignoring other dc imperfections, what is the maximum offset voltage allowed for the op amp? **b.** Ignoring other dc imperfections, what is the maximum bias current allowed for the op amp? **c.** Show how to add a resistor to the circuit (including its value) so that the effects of the bias currents cancel. **d.** Assuming that the resistor of part (c) is in place, and ignoring offset voltage, what is the maximum offset current allowed for the op amp?

Section 8: Differential and Instrumentation Amplifiers

P70. In terms of the differential and common-mode components of a signal, what is the function of a differential amplifier?

***P71.** Using the parts listed in Table P37, design a single-op-amp differential amplifier having a nominal differential gain of 10.

P72. Repeat Problem P71, using the instrumentation-quality circuit shown in Figure 34.

P73. We have an instrumentation-quality differential amplifier as shown in Figure 34, with $R_1 = 1\ \text{k}\Omega$, $R_2 = 4\ \text{k}\Omega$, and $R = 10\ \text{k}\Omega$. The input signals, in volts, are given by

$$v_1(t) = 0.2\cos(2000\pi t) + \cos(120\pi t)$$

$$v_2(t) = -0.2\cos(2000\pi t) + \cos(120\pi t)$$

a. Find expressions for the differential and common-mode components of the input signal.

b. Assuming ideal op amps, find expressions for the voltages at the output terminals of X_1 and X_2.

c. Again assuming ideal op amps, find an expression for the output voltage $v_o(t)$.

Section 9: Integrators and Differentiators

P74. What do we mean by the term *running time integral*?

***P75.** Sketch the output voltage of the circuit shown in Figure P75 to scale versus time. Sometimes, an integrator circuit is used as a (approximate) pulse counter. Suppose that the output voltage is −10 V. How many input pulses have been applied (assuming that the pulses have an amplitude of 5 V and a duration of 2 ms, as shown in the figure)?

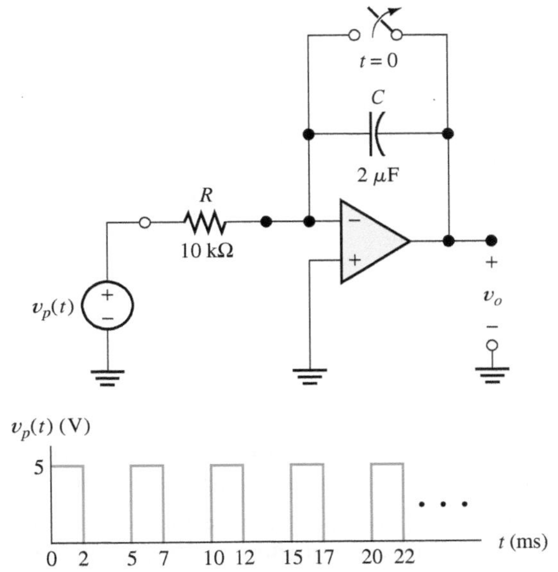

Figure P75

P76. Sketch the output voltage of the ideal op-amp circuit shown in Figure P76 to scale versus time.

P77. The displacement of a robot arm in a given direction is represented by a voltage signal $v_{in}(t)$. The voltage is proportional to displacement, and 1 V corresponds to a displacement of 10 mm from the reference position. Design a circuit that produces a voltage $v_1(t)$ that is proportional to the velocity of the robot arm such that 1 m/s corresponds to 1 V. Design an additional circuit that produces a voltage v_2 that is proportional to the acceleration of the robot arm such that 1 m/s^2 corresponds to 1 V. Use the components listed in Table P37, plus as many capacitors as needed.

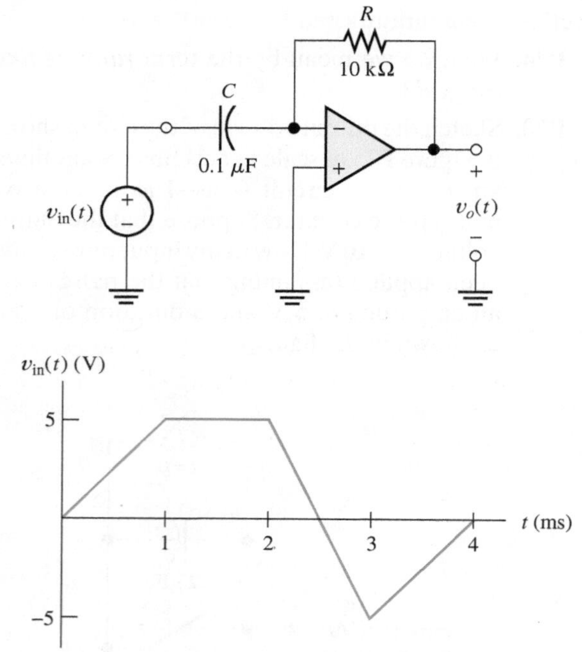

Figure P76

Section 10: Active Filters

P78. What is the function of a filter? What is a typical application? What is an active filter?

***P79.** Derive an expression for the voltage transfer ratio of each of the circuits shown in Figure P79. Also, sketch the magnitude Bode plots to scale. Assume that the op amps are ideal.

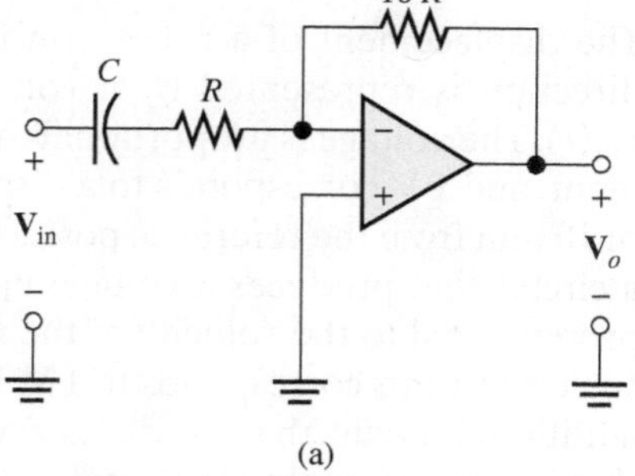

(a)

Figure P79

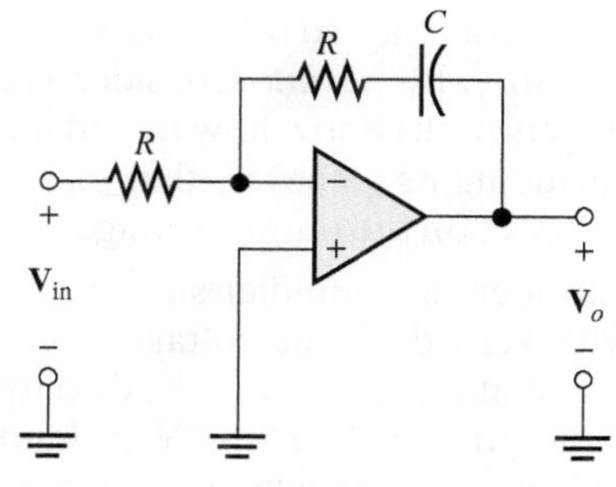

(b)

Figure P79 *(Cont.)*

P80. It is illuminating to look at the integrator circuit as a filter. Derive the transfer function for the integrator of Figure P75, and sketch the magnitude Bode plot to scale.

P81. Repeat Problem P80 for the differentiator circuit shown in Figure P76.

P82. Derive an expression for the voltage transfer ratio for the circuit shown in Figure P82. Also, sketch the magnitude Bode plot to scale. Assume that the op amp is ideal.

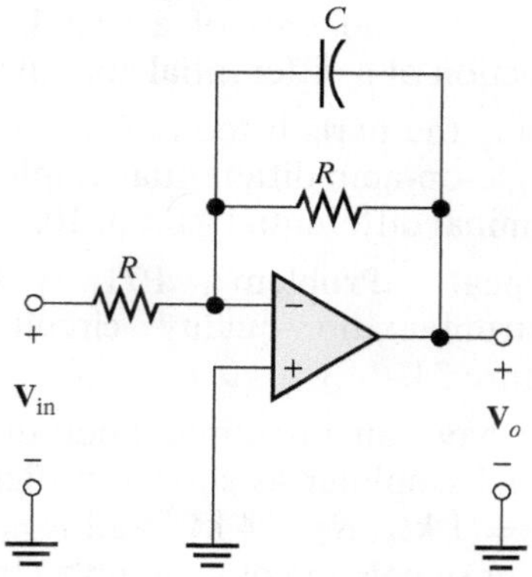

Figure P82

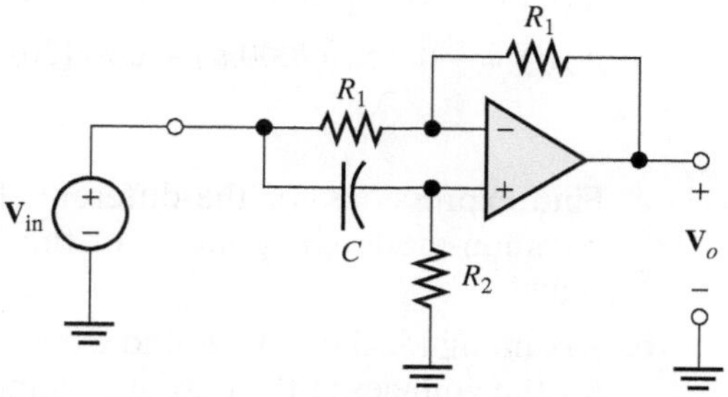

Figure P83

P83. Derive an expression for the voltage transfer ratio for the circuit shown in Figure P83. Then find expressions for the magnitude and phase of the transfer function. What effect does this filter have on the amplitude of a sinusoidal input? On the phase?

Practice Test

Here is a practice test you can use to check your comprehension of the most important concepts in this chapter. Answers can be found in Appendix "Answers for the Practice Tests" and complete solutions are included in the Student Solutions files. See Appendix "On-Line Student Resources" for more information about the Student Solutions.

T1. Draw the circuit diagram for each of the following amplifiers. Clearly label the op amp input terminals and any resistances needed. Also, give the equation for the voltage gain of the amplifier in terms of the resistances on your diagram. **a.** The basic inverter. **b.** The noninverting amplifier. **c.** The voltage follower.

T2. Derive an expression for voltage gain $A_v = v_o/v_{\text{in}}$ of the circuit shown in Figure T2 assuming that the summing-point constraint applies. (There are both negative and positive feedback paths, but the resistances have been carefully selected so the circuit has net negative feedback and the summing-point constraint does apply.)

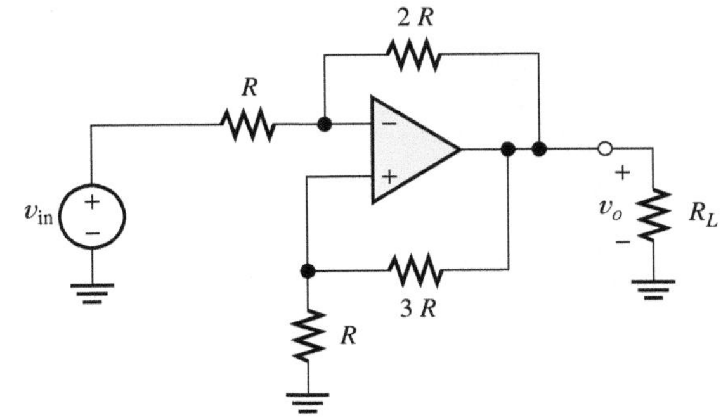

Figure T2

T3. A certain op amp has an open-loop dc gain of $A_{0\text{OL}} = 200{,}000$ and an open-loop 3-dB bandwidth of $f_{B\text{OL}} = 5$ Hz. This op amp is used in a noninverting amplifier having a closed-loop dc gain of $A_{0\text{CL}} = 100$. **a.** Determine the closed-loop break frequency $f_{B\text{CL}}$. **b.** Given that the input voltage to the noninverting amplifier is $v_{\text{in}}(t) = 0.05\cos(2\pi \times 10^5 t)$ V, find the expression for the output voltage.

T4. We have an op amp with a maximum output voltage range from −4.5 to +4.5 V. The maximum output current magnitude is 5 mA. The slew-rate limit is SR = 20 V/μs. This op amp is used in the circuit of Figure 28. **a.** Find the full-power bandwidth of the op amp. **b.** For a frequency of 1 kHz and $R_L = 200\ \Omega$, what peak output voltage, V_{om}, is possible without distortion? **c.** For a frequency of 1 kHz and $R_L = 10$ kΩ, what peak output voltage, V_{om}, is possible without distortion? **d.** For a frequency of 5 MHz and $R_L = 10$ kΩ, what peak output voltage, V_{om}, is possible without distortion?

T5. Draw an op amp symbol including sources to account for offset voltage, offset current, and bias current. What is the principal effect of these sources in an amplifier circuit?

T6. Draw the circuit diagram of a differential amplifier using one op amp and resistances as needed. Give the output voltage in terms of the input voltages and resistances.

T7. Draw the circuit diagrams for an integrator and for a differentiator. Also give an expression for the output voltage in terms of the input voltage and component values.

T8. What is a filter? An active filter? Give one application for an active filter.

NOMINAL VALUES AND THE COLOR CODE FOR RESISTORS

Several types of resistors are available for use in electronic circuits. Carbon-film and carbon-composition resistors with tolerances of 5 percent, 10 percent, or 20 percent are available with various power ratings (such as 1/8, 1/4, and 1/2 W). These resistors are used in noncritical applications such as biasing.

Metal-film 1-percent-tolerance resistors are used where greater precision is required. For example, we often choose metal-film resistors in applications such as the feedback resistors of an op amp.

Wire-wound resistors are available with high power-dissipation ratings. Wire-wound resistors often have significant series inductance because they consist of resistance wire that is wound on a form, such as ceramic. Thus, they are often not suitable for use as a resistance at high frequencies.

The value and tolerance are marked on 5-percent, 10-percent, and 20-percent-tolerance resistors by color bands as shown in Figure 1. The first band is closest to one end of the resistor. The first and second bands give the significant digits of the resistance value. The third band gives the exponent of the multiplier. The fourth band indicates the tolerance. The fifth band is optional and indicates whether the resistors meet certain military reliability specifications.

Table 1 shows the combinations of significant figures available as nominal values for 5-percent, 10-percent, and 20-percent-tolerance resistors. Table 2 shows the standard nominal significant digits for 1-percent-tolerance resistors.

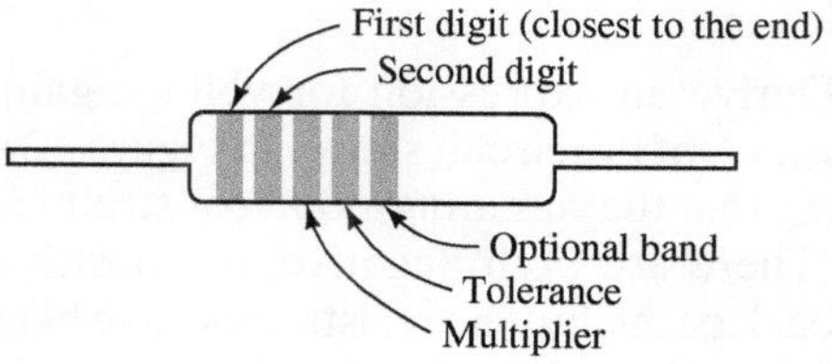

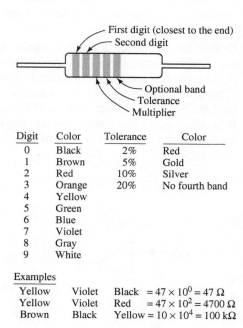

Digit	Color	Tolerance	Color
0	Black	2%	Red
1	Brown	5%	Gold
2	Red	10%	Silver
3	Orange	20%	No fourth band
4	Yellow		
5	Green		
6	Blue		
7	Violet		
8	Gray		
9	White		

Examples

Yellow	Violet	Black	$= 47 \times 10^0 = 47\ \Omega$
Yellow	Violet	Red	$= 47 \times 10^2 = 4700\ \Omega$
Brown	Black	Yellow	$= 10 \times 10^4 = 100\ \text{k}\Omega$

Figure 1 Resistor color code.

Table 1. Standard Nominal Values for 5-percent-Tolerance Resistors[a]

10	16	**27**	43	**68**
11	**18**	30	**47**	75
12	20	**33**	51	**82**
13	**22**	36	**56**	91
15	24	**39**	62	

[a] Resistors having tolerances of 10 percent and 20 percent are available only for the values given in boldface.

Table 2. Standard Values for 1-percent-Tolerance Metal-Film Resistors

100	140	196	274	383	536	750
102	143	200	280	392	549	768
105	147	205	287	402	562	787
107	150	210	294	412	576	806
110	154	215	301	422	590	825
113	158	221	309	432	604	845
115	162	226	316	442	619	866
118	165	232	324	453	634	887
121	169	237	332	464	649	909
124	174	243	340	475	665	931
127	178	249	348	487	681	953
130	182	255	357	499	698	976
133	187	261	365	511	715	
137	191	267	374	523	732	

ANSWERS FOR THE PRACTICE TESTS

Complete solutions for the practice tests are included in the Student Solutions files. See Appendix "On-Line Student Resources" for information on how to access these files.

T1. **a.** The circuit diagram is shown in Figure 4, and the voltage gain is $A_v = -R_2/R_1$. (Of course, you could use different resistance labels, such as R_A and R_B, so long as your equation for the gain is modified accordingly.) **b.** The circuit diagram is shown in Figure 11 and the voltage gain is $A_v = 1 + R_2/R_1$. **c.** The circuit diagram is shown in Figure 12 and the voltage gain is $A_v = 1$.

T2. $A_v = -8$.

T3. **a.** $f_{BCL} = 10\,\text{kHz}$; **b.** $v_o(t) = 0.4975\cos(2\pi \times 10^5 t - 84.29°)$.

T4. **a.** $f_{FP} = 707.4\,\text{kHz}$; **b.** $V_{om} = 1\,\text{V}$. **c.** $V_{om} = 4.5\,\text{V}$; **d.** $V_{om} = 0.637\,\text{V}$.

T5. See Figure 29 for the circuit diagram. The principal effect of bias current, offset current, and offset voltage in amplifier circuits is to add a (usually undesirable) dc voltage to the intended output signal.

T6. See Figure 33. Usually, we would have $R_1 = R_3$ and $R_2 = R_4$.

T7. See Figures 35 and 38.

T8. Filters are circuits designed to pass input components with frequencies in one range to the output and prevent input components with frequencies in other ranges from reaching the output. An active filter is a filter composed of op amps, resistors, and capacitors. Several filter applications are mentioned in the first paragraph of Section 10.

ON-LINE STUDENT RESOURCES

Users of the text can access the Student Solutions Manual (and other folders mentioned below) in electronic form by following links starting from the website:

`www.pearsonhighered.com/hambley`

The MATLAB folder contains m-files. Except for the examples that use the Symbolic Toolbox, these files work equally well with MathScript, which is sometimes included with the LabVIEW program. The Hambley MathScript folder contains the m-files that work with MathScript.

The Virtual Instruments folder contains LabVIEW programs.

Magnetic Circuits and Transformers

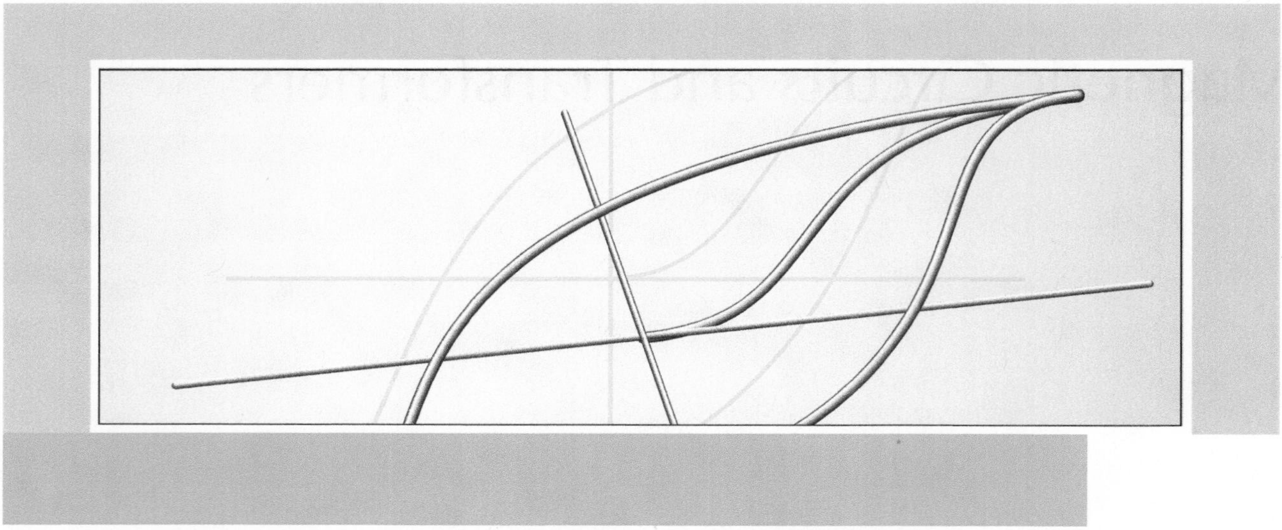

Magnetic Circuits and Transformers

Study of this chapter will enable you to:

- Understand magnetic fields and their interactions with moving charges.
- Use the right-hand rule to determine the direction of the magnetic field around a current-carrying wire or coil.
- Calculate forces on moving charges and current-carrying wires due to magnetic fields.
- Calculate the voltage induced in a coil by a changing magnetic flux or in a conductor cutting through a magnetic field.
- Use Lenz's law to determine the polarities of induced voltages.
- Apply magnetic-circuit concepts to determine the magnetic fields in practical devices.
- Determine the inductance and mutual inductance of coils, given their physical parameters.
- Understand hysteresis, saturation, core loss, and eddy currents in cores composed of magnetic materials such as iron.
- Understand ideal transformers and solve circuits that include transformers.
- Use the equivalent circuits of real transformers to determine their regulations and power efficiencies.

Introduction to this chapter:

In describing interactions of matter, we often employ field concepts. For example, masses are attracted by gravitation. We envision gravitational fields produced by masses and explain the forces on other masses in terms of their interaction with these fields. Another example is stationary electrical charges. Charges of like sign repel one another, and unlike charges attract one another. Conceptually, each charge creates an electric field, and the other charge interacts with the field, resulting in a force.

In this chapter, we study some important engineering applications of **magnetic fields**, which are created by electrical charges in motion. Charges moving through magnetic fields experience forces. Furthermore, changing magnetic fields induce voltages in nearby conductors.

In this chapter, we start by reviewing basic magnetic-field concepts. Then, we consider the relationships between magnetic fields and inductance, including mutual inductance. Next, we study **transformers**, which greatly facilitate the distribution of electrical power.

Magnetic fields also form the basis of most practical devices for converting energy between electrical and mechanical forms.

1 MAGNETIC FIELDS

Magnetic fields exist in the space around permanent magnets and around wires that carry current. In both cases, the basic source of the magnetic field is electrical charge in motion. In an iron permanent magnet, fields are created by the spin of electrons in atoms. These fields aid one another, producing the net external field that we observe. (In most other materials, the magnetic fields of the electrons tend to cancel one another.) If a current-carrying wire is formed into a multiturn coil, the magnetic field is greatly intensified, particularly if the coil is wound around an iron core.

We can visualize a magnetic field as **lines of magnetic flux** that form closed paths. The lines are close together where the magnetic field is strong and farther apart where the field is weaker. This is illustrated in Figure 1. The units of magnetic flux are webers (Wb).

Magnetic flux lines form closed paths that are close together where the field is strong and farther apart where the field is weak.

The earth has a natural magnetic field that is relatively weak compared with those in typical transformers, motors, or generators. Due to interactions of the fields, magnets tend to align with the earth's field. Thus, a magnet has a north-seeking end (N) and a south-seeking end (S). Unlike ends of magnets are attracted. By convention, flux lines leave the north-seeking end (N) of a magnet and enter its south-seeking end (S). A compass can be used to investigate the direction of the lines of flux. The compass needle indicates north in the direction of the flux [i.e., the compass points toward the south-seeking (S) end of the magnet]. (Note that the earth's field lines are directed from south to north. Thus, if we were to place N and S marks on the earth as we do on a magnet, S would appear near the *north* geographic pole, because that is where the field lines enter the earth.)

Flux lines leave the north-seeking end of a magnet and enter the south-seeking end.

In equations, we represent the **magnetic flux density** as the vector quantity **B**. (Throughout our discussion, we use boldface for vector quantities. The corresponding lightface italic symbols represent the magnitudes of the vectors. Thus, B represents the magnitude of the vector **B**. We also use boldface for phasors. However, it will be clear from the context which quantities are spatial vectors and which are phasors.) Furthermore, we use the International System of Units (SI), in which the units of **B** are webers/meter^2 (Wb/m^2) or, equivalently, teslas (T). The flux density vector **B** has a direction tangent to the flux lines, as illustrated in Figure 1.

When placed in a magnetic field, a compass indicates north in the direction of the flux lines.

Right-Hand Rule

The direction of the magnetic field produced by a current can be determined by the right-hand rule. There are several interpretations of this rule. For example, as

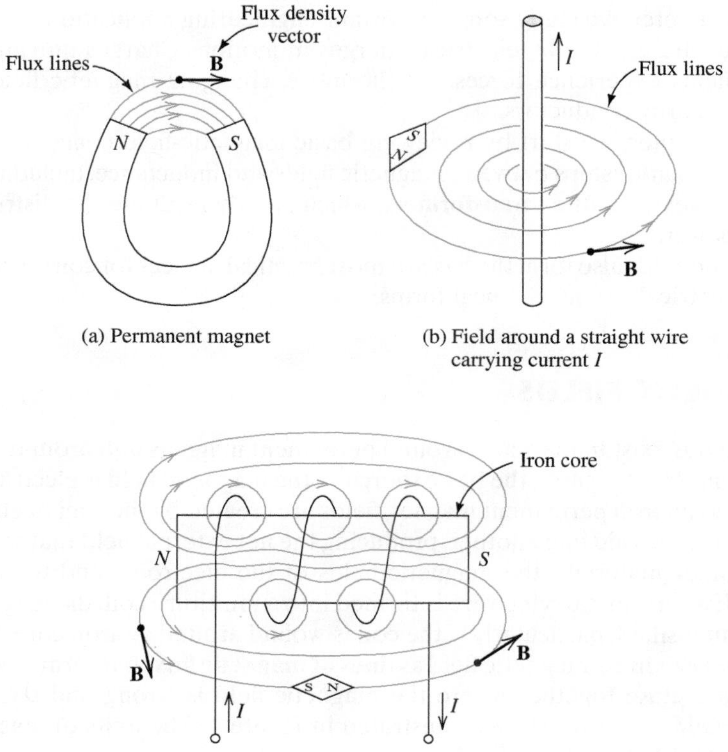

Figure 1 Magnetic fields can be visualized as lines of flux that form closed paths. Using a compass, we can determine the direction of the flux lines at any point. Note that the flux density vector **B** is tangent to the lines of flux.

illustrated in Figure 2(a), if a wire is grasped with the thumb pointing in the direction of the current, the fingers encircle the wire, pointing in the direction of the magnetic field. Moreover, as illustrated in Figure 2(b), if the fingers are wrapped around a coil in the direction of current flow, the thumb points in the direction of the magnetic field that is produced inside the coil.

The right-hand rule is used to determine the directions of magnetic fields.

Exercise 1 A wire horizontal to the ground carries current toward the north. (Neglect the earth's field.) **a.** Directly underneath the wire, what is the direction of **B**? **b.** Directly above the wire, what is the direction of **B**?

Answer **a.** west; **b.** east. □

Exercise 2 A coil is wound around the periphery of a clock. If current flows clockwise, what is the direction of **B** in the center of the clock face?

Answer Into the clock face. □

Forces on Charges Moving in Magnetic Fields

An electrical charge q moving with velocity vector **u** through a magnetic field **B** experiences a force **f** as illustrated in Figure 3. The force vector is given by

$$\mathbf{f} = q\mathbf{u} \times \mathbf{B} \quad (1)$$

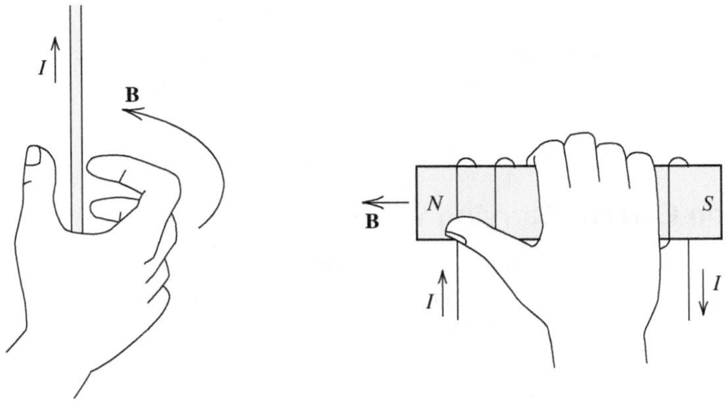

(a) If a wire is grasped with the thumb pointing in the current direction, the fingers encircle the wire in the direction of the magnetic field

(b) If a coil is grasped with the fingers pointing in the current direction, the thumb points in the direction of the magnetic field inside the coil

Figure 2 Illustrations of the right-hand rule.

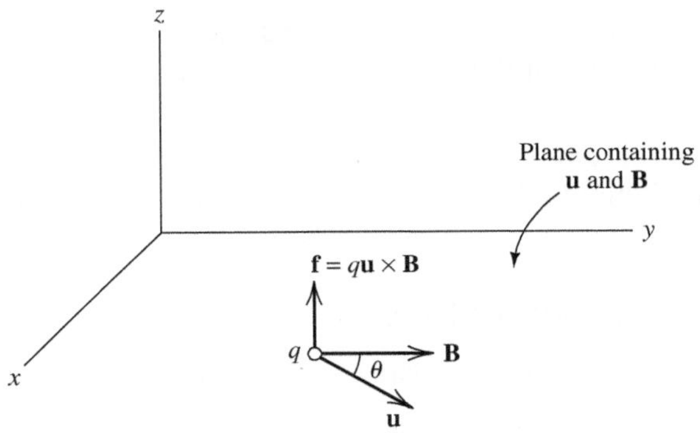

Figure 3 A charge moving through a magnetic field experiences a force **f** perpendicular to both the velocity **u** and flux density **B**.

in which × represents the vector cross product. Note that due to the definition of the cross product, the force is perpendicular to the plane containing the magnetic flux density **B** and the velocity **u**. Furthermore, the magnitude of the force is given by

Force is exerted on a charge as it moves through a magnetic field.

$$f = quB \sin(\theta) \tag{2}$$

in which θ is the angle between **u** and **B**, as illustrated in the figure.

In the SI system, the force vector **f** has units of newtons (N), the charge is in coulombs (C), and the velocity vector **u** is in meters/second (m/s). Thus, for dimensional consistency in Equations 1 and 2, the magnetic field vector **B** must have units of newton seconds per coulomb meter (Ns/Cm), which is the dimensional equivalent of the tesla (T).

Exercise 3 An electron ($q = -1.602 \times 10^{-19}$ C) travels at 10^5 m/s in the positive x direction. The magnetic flux density is 1 T in the positive y direction. Find the magnitude and direction of the force on the electron. (Assume a right-hand coordinate system such as that shown in Figure 3.)
Answer $f = 1.602 \times 10^{-14}$ N in the negative z direction. □

Forces on Current-Carrying Wires

Force is exerted on a current-carrying conductor when it is immersed in a magnetic field.

Current flowing in a conductor consists of charge (usually, electrons) in motion. Thus, forces appear on a current-carrying wire immersed in a magnetic field. The force on an incremental length of the wire is given by

$$d\mathbf{f} = i\, d\mathbf{l} \times \mathbf{B} \tag{3}$$

in which the direction of $d\mathbf{l}$ and the reference direction for the current are the same.

For a straight wire of length l and a constant magnetic field, we have

$$f = ilB \sin(\theta) \tag{4}$$

in which θ is the angle between the wire and the field. Notice that the force is maximized if the direction of the field is perpendicular to the wire.

Exercise 4 A wire of length $l = 1$ m carries a current of 10 A perpendicular to a field of $B = 0.5$ T. Compute the magnitude of the force on the wire.
Answer $f = 5$ N. □

Flux Linkages and Faraday's Law

The magnetic flux passing through a surface area A is given by the surface integral

$$\phi = \int_A \mathbf{B} \cdot d\mathbf{A} \tag{5}$$

The magnetic flux passing through a surface is determined by integrating the dot product of **B** and incremental area over the surface.

in which $d\mathbf{A}$ is an increment of area on the surface. The direction of the vector $d\mathbf{A}$ is perpendicular to the surface. If the magnetic flux density is constant and perpendicular to the surface, Equation 5 reduces to

$$\phi = BA \tag{6}$$

We say that the flux passing through the surface bounded by a coil **links** the coil. If the coil has N turns, then the total flux linkages are given by

$$\lambda = N\phi \tag{7}$$

Here, we have assumed that the same flux links each turn of the coil. This is a good approximation when the turns are close together on an iron form, which is often the case in transformers and electrical machines.

According to **Faraday's law of magnetic induction**, a voltage

$$e = \frac{d\lambda}{dt} \tag{8}$$

is induced in a coil whenever its flux linkages are changing. This can occur either because the magnetic field is changing with time or because the coil is moving relative to a magnetic field.

Lenz's law states that the polarity of the induced voltage is such that the voltage would produce a current (through an external resistance) that opposes the original change in flux linkages. (Think of the induced voltage as a voltage source.) For example, suppose that the magnetic field linking the coil shown in Figure 4 is pointing into the page and increasing in magnitude. (This field is the result of a coil or moving permanent magnet not shown in the figure.) Then, the voltage induced in the coil produces a counterclockwise current. According to the right-hand rule, this current produces a magnetic field directed out of the page, opposing the initial field change.

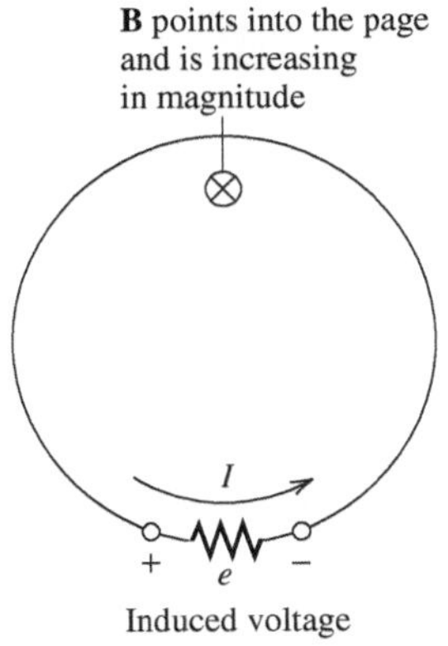

Figure 4 When the flux linking a coil changes, a voltage is induced in the coil. The polarity of the voltage is such that if a circuit is formed by placing a resistance across the coil terminals, the resulting current produces a field that tends to oppose the original change in the field.

Voltages Induced in Field-Cutting Conductors

Voltage is also induced in a conductor moving through a magnetic field in a direction such that the conductor cuts through magnetic lines of flux. For example, consider Figure 5. A uniform magnetic field is directed into the page. The sliding conductor and the stationary rails form a loop having an area of $A = lx$. The flux linkages of the coil are

$$\lambda = BA = Blx$$

According to Faraday's law, the voltage induced in the coil is given by

$$e = \frac{d\lambda}{dt} = Bl\frac{dx}{dt}$$

However, $u = dx/dt$ is the velocity of the sliding conductor, so we have

$$e = Blu \tag{9}$$

Voltage is induced across the terminals of a coil if the flux linkages are changing with time. Moreover, voltage is induced between the ends of a conductor moving so as to cut through flux lines.

Equation 9 can be used to compute the voltage induced across the ends of a straight conductor moving in uniform magnetic field, provided that the velocity, the conductor, and the magnetic-field vector are mutually perpendicular.

For example, a conductor in a typical dc generator rated for 1 kW has a length of 0.2 m, a velocity of 12 m/s, and cuts through a field of 0.5 T. This results in an

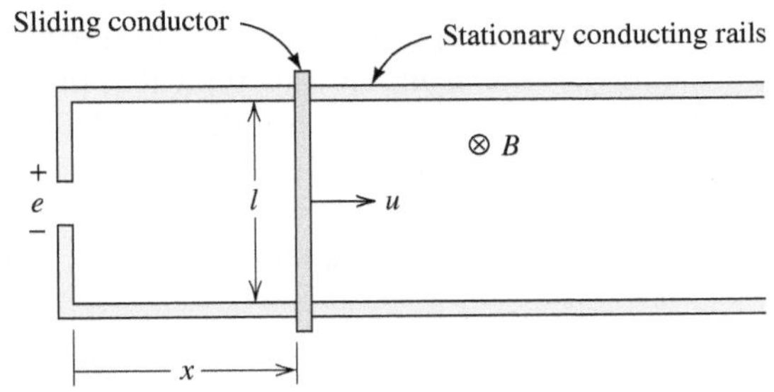

Figure 5 A voltage is induced in a conductor moving so as to cut through magnetic flux lines.

induced voltage of 1.2 V. (Higher output voltages are produced by connecting many such conductors in series.)

Exercise 5 **a.** A 10-turn circular coil has a radius of 5 cm. A flux density of 0.5 T is directed perpendicular to the plane of the coil. Evaluate the flux linking the coil and the flux linkages. **b.** Suppose that the flux is reduced to zero at a uniform rate during an interval of 1 ms. Determine the voltage induced in the coil.

Answer **a.** $\phi = 3.927$ mWb, $\lambda = 39.27$ mWb turns; **b.** $e = 39.27$ V. □

Magnetic Field Intensity and Ampère's Law

So far, we have considered the magnetic flux density **B** and its effects. To summarize, **B** produces forces on moving charges and current-carrying conductors. It also induces voltage in a coil if the flux linkages are changing with time. Furthermore, voltage is induced across a moving conductor when it cuts through flux lines.

Now, we introduce another field vector, known as the **magnetic field intensity H**, and consider how magnetic fields are established. In general, magnetic fields are set up by charges in motion. In most of the applications that we consider, the magnetic fields are established by currents flowing in coils. We will see that **H** is determined by the currents and the configuration of the coils. Furthermore, we will see that the resulting flux density **B** depends on **H**, as well as the properties of the material filling the space around the coils.

The magnetic field intensity **H** and magnetic flux density **B** are related by

$$\mathbf{B} = \mu \mathbf{H} \tag{10}$$

in which μ is the magnetic permeability of the material. The units of **H** are amperes/meter (A/m), and the units of μ are webers/ampere-meter (Wb/Am).

B is magnetic flux density with units of webers per square meter ($\mathrm{Wb/m^2}$) or teslas (T), and **H** is magnetic field intensity with units of amperes per meter (A/m).

For free space, we have

$$\mu = \mu_0 = 4\pi \times 10^{-7}\ \mathrm{Wb/Am} \tag{11}$$

Some materials, most notably iron and certain rare-earth alloys, have a much higher magnetic permeability than free space. The relative permeability of a material is the ratio of its permeability to that of free space:

$$\mu_r = \frac{\mu}{\mu_0} \tag{12}$$

The types of iron used in typical motors and transformers have relative permeabilities of several thousand.

The value of μ_r ranges from several hundred to 1 million for various iron and rare-earth alloys. The iron used in typical transformers, motors, and generators has a relative permeability of several thousand.

Ampère's law states that the line integral of the magnetic field intensity around a closed path is equal to the algebraic sum of the currents flowing through the area enclosed by the path.

Ampère's law states that the line integral of the magnetic field intensity around a closed path is equal to the algebraic sum of the currents flowing through the area enclosed by the path. In equation form, we have

$$\oint \mathbf{H} \cdot d\mathbf{l} = \sum i \tag{13}$$

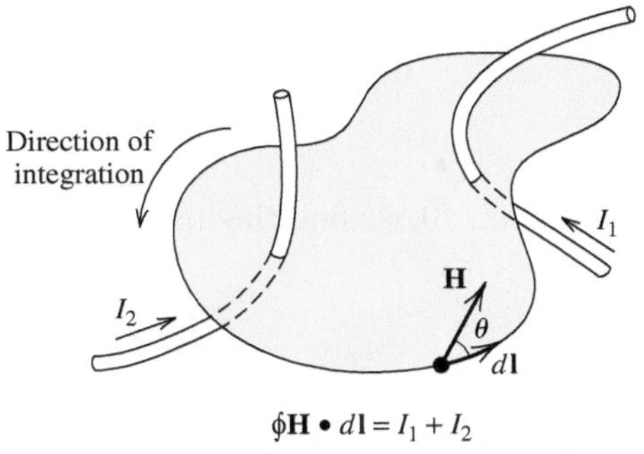

Figure 6 Ampère's law states that the line integral of magnetic field intensity around a closed path is equal to the sum of the currents flowing through the surface bounded by the path.

in which $d\mathbf{l}$ is a vector element of length having its direction tangent to the path of integration. Recall that the vector dot product is given by

$$\mathbf{H} \cdot d\mathbf{l} = H\,dl\,\cos(\theta) \tag{14}$$

in which θ is the angle between $\mathbf{H}$ and $d\mathbf{l}$.

Depending on its reference direction, a given current carries either a plus sign or a minus sign in the summation of Equation 13. If the reference direction for a current is related to the direction of integration by the right-hand rule, it carries a plus sign. (According to the right-hand rule, if you place the thumb of your right hand on the wire pointing in the reference direction, your fingers encircle the wires in the direction of integration.) Currents that are referenced in the opposite direction carry a negative sign in Equation 13. Ampère's law is illustrated by example in Figure 6, in which case the reference directions of both currents are related to the direction of integration by the right-hand rule.

If the magnetic intensity has constant magnitude and points in the same direction as the incremental length $d\mathbf{l}$ everywhere along the path, Ampère's law reduces to

$$Hl = \sum i \tag{15}$$

in which l is the length of the path.

In some cases, we can use Ampère's law to find formulas for the magnetic field in the space around a current-carrying wire or coil.

Example 1 Magnetic Field around a Long Straight Wire

Consider a long straight wire carrying current I out of the page as shown in Figure 7. Find expressions for the magnetic field intensity and magnetic flux density in the space around the wire. Assume that the material surrounding the wire has permeability μ.

Solution By symmetry and the right-hand rule, we conclude that $\mathbf{B}$ and $\mathbf{H}$ fall in a plane perpendicular to the wire (i.e., in the plane of the paper) and are tangent to circles having their centers at the wire. This is illustrated in Figure 7. Furthermore, the magnitude of H is constant for a given radius r. Applying Ampère's law (Equation 15) to the circular path shown in the figure, we have

$$Hl = H2\pi r = I$$

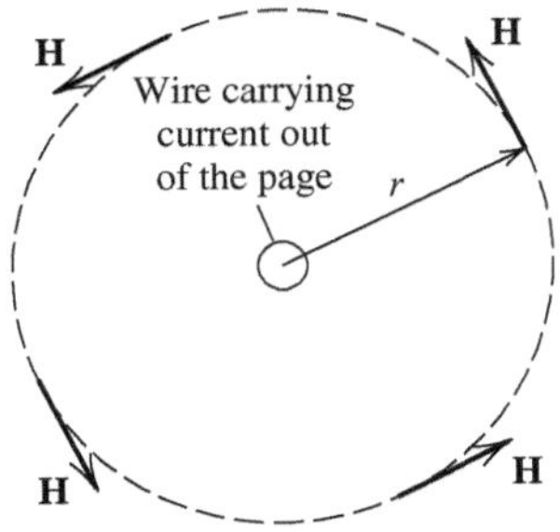

Figure 7 The magnetic field around a long straight wire carrying a current can be determined with Ampère's law aided by considerations of symmetry.

Solving for the magnetic intensity, we obtain

$$H = \frac{I}{2\pi r}$$

Then by Equation 10, we find the magnetic flux density as

$$B = \mu H = \frac{\mu I}{2\pi r}$$

■

Example 2 Flux Density in a Toroidal Core

Consider the toroidal coil shown in Figure 8. Find an expression for the magnetic flux density B on the center line of the core in terms of the number of coil turns N, the current I, the permeability μ of the core, and the physical dimensions. Then, assuming that the flux density is constant throughout the core (this is approximately true if $R >> r$), find expressions for the total flux and the flux linkages.

Solution By symmetry, the field intensity is constant in magnitude along the dashed circular center line shown in the figure. (We assume that the coil is wound in a symmetrical manner all the way around the toroidal core. For clarity, only part of the coil is shown in the figure.) Applying Ampère's law to the dashed path, we obtain

$$Hl = H2\pi R = NI$$

Solving for H and using Equation 10 to determine B, we have

$$H = \frac{NI}{2\pi R} \tag{16}$$

and

$$B = \frac{\mu NI}{2\pi R} \tag{17}$$

Assuming that R is much greater than r, the flux density is nearly constant over the cross section of the core. Then, according to Equation 6, the flux is equal to the product of the flux density and the area of the cross section:

$$\phi = BA = \frac{\mu NI}{2\pi R}\pi r^2 = \frac{\mu NIr^2}{2R} \tag{18}$$

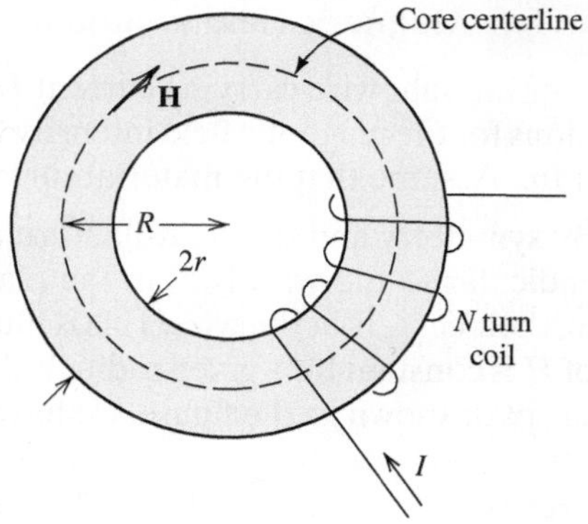

Figure 8 Toroidal coil analyzed in Examples 2, 3, and 4.

Finally, we note that all of the flux links all of the turns, and we have

$$\lambda = N\phi = \frac{\mu N^2 I r^2}{2R} \quad (19)$$

■

Example 3 Flux and Flux Linkages for a Toroidal Core

Suppose that we have a toroidal core with $\mu_r = 5000$, $R = 10$ cm, $r = 2$ cm, and $N = 100$. The current is

$$i(t) = 2\sin(200\pi t)$$

Compute the flux and the flux linkages. Then, use Faraday's law of induction to determine the voltage induced in the coil.

Solution First, the permeability of the core material is

$$\mu = \mu_r \mu_0 = 5000 \times 4\pi \times 10^{-7}$$

Using Equation 18, we compute the flux:

$$\phi = \frac{\mu N I r^2}{2R} = \frac{5000 \times 4\pi \times 10^{-7} \times 100 \times 2\sin(200\pi t) \times (2 \times 10^{-2})^2}{2 \times 10 \times 10^{-2}}$$
$$= (2.513 \times 10^{-3})\sin(200\pi t) \text{ Wb}$$

The flux linkages are

$$\lambda = N\phi$$
$$= 100 \times (2.513 \times 10^{-3})\sin(200\pi t)$$
$$= 0.2513\sin(200\pi t) \text{ weber turns}$$

Finally, using Faraday's law (Equation 8), we can find the voltage induced in the coil by the changing field:

$$e = \frac{d\lambda}{dt} = 0.2513 \times 200\pi\cos(200\pi t)$$
$$= 157.9\cos(200\pi t) \text{ V}$$

■

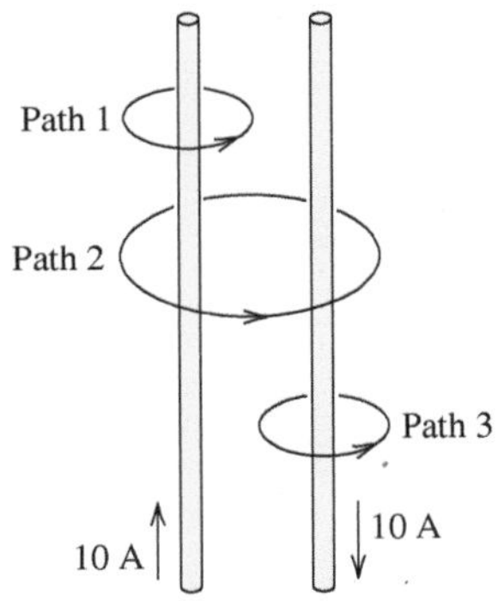

Figure 9 See Exercises 7 and 8.

Exercise 6 A long straight wire surrounded by air ($\mu_r \cong 1$) carries a current of 20 A. Compute the magnetic flux density at a point 1 cm from the wire.
Answer 4×10^{-4} T. □

Exercise 7 Figure 9 shows two wires carrying equal currents in opposite directions. Find the value of

$$\oint \mathbf{H} \cdot d\mathbf{l}$$

for each path shown in the direction indicated.
Answer Path 1, 10 A; path 2, 0; path 3, −10 A. □

Exercise 8 Find the force between a 1-m length of the wires shown in Figure 9 if the distance between the wires is 10 cm. Is this a force of attraction or of repulsion?
Answer $f = 2 \times 10^{-4}$ N; repulsion. □

2 MAGNETIC CIRCUITS

In many engineering applications, we need to compute the magnetic fields for structures that lack sufficient symmetry for straight-forward application of Ampère's law. Then, we use an approximate method known as magnetic-circuit analysis.

We will see that many useful devices (such as transformers, motors, and generators) contain coils wound on iron cores. In this section, we learn how to calculate the magnetic fields in these devices. A simple example, discussed in the preceding section, is the toroidal coil shown in Figure 8 and analyzed in Example 2. The toroid possesses sufficient symmetry that we readily applied Ampère's law to find an expression for the field intensity. However, in many applications, we need to analyze more complex configurations (such as cores that lack symmetry and those with multiple coils) for which the direct application of Ampère's law is not feasible. Instead, we use **magnetic circuit concepts**, which are analogous to those used to analyze electrical circuits.

The **magnetomotive force** (mmf) of an N-turn current-carrying coil is given by

$$\mathcal{F} = Ni \tag{20}$$

A current-carrying coil is the magnetic-circuit analog of a voltage source in an electrical circuit. Magnetomotive force is analogous to source voltage. Usually, we give the units of magnetomotive force as A·turns; however, the number of turns is actually a pure number without physical units.

The **reluctance** of a path for magnetic flux, such as the bar of iron shown in Figure 10, is given by

$$\mathcal{R} = \frac{l}{\mu A} \tag{21}$$

in which l is the length of the path (in the direction of the magnetic flux), A is the cross-sectional area, and μ is the permeability of the material. Reluctance is analogous to resistance in an electrical circuit. When the bar is not straight, the length of the path is somewhat ambiguous, and then we estimate its value as the length of the centerline. Thus, l is sometimes called the **mean length** of the path.

Magnetic flux ϕ in a magnetic circuit is analogous to current in an electrical circuit. Magnetic flux, reluctance, and magnetomotive force are related by

$$\mathcal{F} = \mathcal{R}\phi \tag{22}$$

which is the counterpart of Ohm's law ($V = Ri$). The units of reluctance are A·turns/Wb.

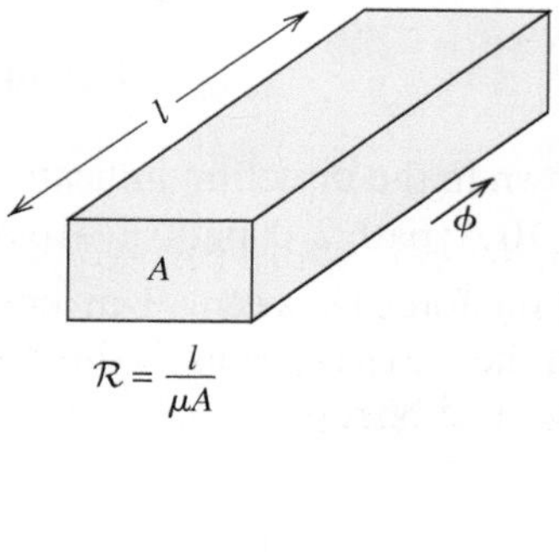

Figure 10 The reluctance $\mathcal{R}$ of a magnetic path depends on the mean length l, the area A, and the permeability μ of the material.

Example 4 The Toroidal Coil as a Magnetic Circuit

Using magnetic circuit concepts, analyze the toroidal coil shown in Figure 8 to find an expression for the flux.

Solution As indicated in Figure 11, the magnetic circuit of the toroidal coil is analogous to a simple electrical circuit with a resistance connected across a voltage source.

The mean length of the magnetic path is

$$l = 2\pi R$$

The cross section of the core is circular with radius r. Thus, the area of the cross section is

$$A = \pi r^2$$

Substituting into Equation 21, we find the reluctance to be

$$\mathcal{R} = \frac{l}{\mu A} = \frac{2\pi R}{\mu \pi r^2} = \frac{2R}{\mu r^2}$$

The magnetomotive force is

$$\mathcal{F} = NI$$

Solving Equation 22 for the flux, we have

$$\phi = \frac{\mathcal{F}}{\mathcal{R}}$$

Substituting the expressions for $\mathcal{F}$ and $\mathcal{R}$ found earlier, we get

$$\phi = \frac{\mu N r^2 I}{2R}$$

This is the same expression for the flux that we obtained in Examples 2 and 3 by applying Ampère's law. ■

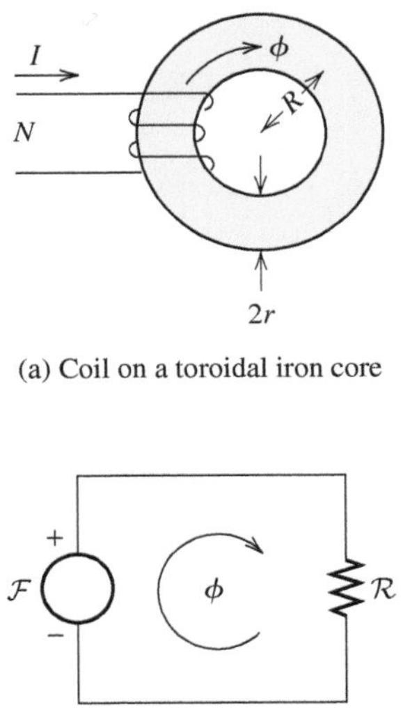

Figure 11 The magnetic circuit for the toroidal coil.

Advantage of the Magnetic-Circuit Approach

The advantage of the magnetic-circuit approach is that it can be applied to unsymmetrical magnetic cores with multiple coils. Coils are sources of magnetomotive forces that can be manipulated as source voltages are in an electrical circuit. Reluctances in series or parallel are combined as resistances are. Fluxes are analogous to currents. The magnetic-circuit approach is not an exact method for determining magnetic fields, but it is sufficiently accurate for many engineering applications. We illustrate these methods with a few examples.

The advantage of the magnetic-circuit approach is that it can be applied to unsymmetrical magnetic cores with multiple coils.

Example 5 A Magnetic Circuit with an Air Gap

Consider the magnetic core with an air gap as shown in Figure 12(a). The core material has a relative permeability of 6000 and a rectangular cross section 2 cm by 3 cm. The coil has 500 turns. Determine the current required to establish a flux density of $B_{gap} = 0.25$ T in the air gap.

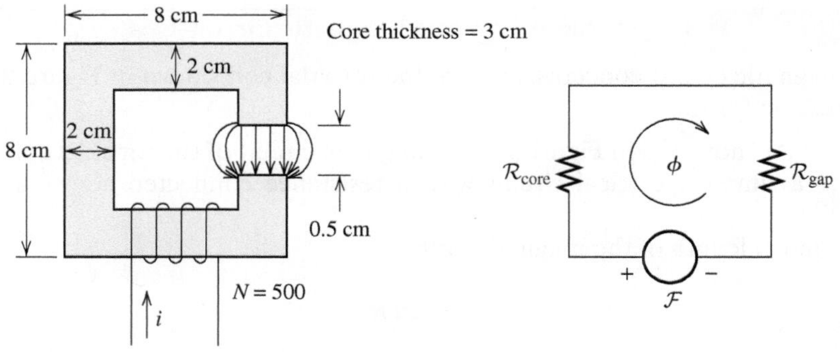

(a) Iron core with an air gap (b) Magnetic circuit

Figure 12 Magnetic circuit of Example 5.

Solution As shown in Figure 12(b), this magnetic circuit is analogous to an electrical circuit with one voltage source and two resistances in series. First, we compute the reluctance of the core. Notice that the centerline of the flux path is a square 6 cm by 6 cm. Thus, the mean length of the iron core is

$$l_{core} = 4 \times 6 - 0.5 = 23.5 \text{ cm}$$

The cross-sectional area of the core is

$$A_{core} = 2 \text{ cm } \times 3 \text{ cm } = 6 \times 10^{-4} \text{ m}^2$$

The permeability of the core is

$$\mu_{core} = \mu_r \mu_0 = 6000 \times 4\pi \times 10^{-7} = 7.540 \times 10^{-3}$$

Finally, the reluctance of the core is

$$\mathcal{R}_{core} = \frac{l_{core}}{\mu_{core} A_{core}} = \frac{23.5 \times 10^{-2}}{7.540 \times 10^{-3} \times 6 \times 10^{-4}}$$
$$= 5.195 \times 10^4 \text{ A·turns/Wb}$$

We approximately account for fringing by adding the length of the gap to the depth and width in computing effective gap area.

Now, we compute the reluctance of the air gap. The flux lines tend to bow out in the air gap as shown in Figure 12(a). This is called **fringing**. *Thus, the effective area of the air gap is larger than that of the iron core. Customarily, we take this into account by adding the length of the gap to each of the dimensions of the air-gap cross section.* Thus, the effective area of the gap is

$$A_{gap} = (2 \text{ cm } + 0.5 \text{ cm}) \times (3 \text{ cm } + 0.5 \text{ cm}) = 8.75 \times 10^{-4} \text{ m}^2$$

The permeability of air is approximately the same as that of free space:

$$\mu_{gap} \cong \mu_0 = 4\pi \times 10^{-7}$$

Thus, the reluctance of the gap is

$$\mathcal{R}_{gap} = \frac{l_{gap}}{\mu_{gap} A_{gap}} = \frac{0.5 \times 10^{-2}}{4\pi \times 10^{-7} \times 8.75 \times 10^{-4}}$$
$$= 4.547 \times 10^6 \text{ A·turns/Wb}$$

The total reluctance is the sum of the reluctance of the core and that of the gap:

$$\mathcal{R} = \mathcal{R}_{gap} + \mathcal{R}_{core} = 4.547 \times 10^6 + 5.195 \times 10^4 = 4.600 \times 10^6$$

Even though the gap is much shorter than the iron core, the reluctance of the gap is higher than that of the core because of the much higher permeability of the iron. Most of the magnetomotive force is dropped across the air gap. (This is analogous to the fact that the largest fraction of the applied voltage is dropped across the largest resistance in a series electrical circuit.)

Now, we can compute the flux:

$$\phi = B_{gap}A_{gap} = 0.25 \times 8.75 \times 10^{-4} = 2.188 \times 10^{-4}\ \text{Wb}$$

The flux in the core is the same as that in the gap. However, the flux density is higher in the core, because the area is smaller. The magnetomotive force is given by

$$\mathcal{F} = \phi\mathcal{R} = 4.600 \times 10^6 \times 2.188 \times 10^{-4} = 1006\ \text{A·turns}$$

According to Equation 20, we have

$$\mathcal{F} = Ni$$

Solving for the current and substituting values, we get

$$i = \frac{\mathcal{F}}{N} = \frac{1006}{500} = 2.012\ \text{A}$$

■

Example 6 A Magnetic Circuit with Reluctances in Series and Parallel

The iron core shown in Figure 13(a) has a cross section of 2 cm by 2 cm and a relative permeability of 1000. The coil has 500 turns and carries a current of $i = 2$ A. Find the flux density in each air gap.

Solution The magnetic circuit is depicted in Figure 13(b). First, we compute the reluctances of the three paths. For the center path, we have

$$\mathcal{R}_c = \frac{l_c}{\mu_r\mu_0 A_{core}} = \frac{10 \times 10^{-2}}{1000 \times 4\pi \times 10^{-7} \times 4 \times 10^{-4}}$$
$$= 1.989 \times 10^5\ \text{A·turns/Wb}$$

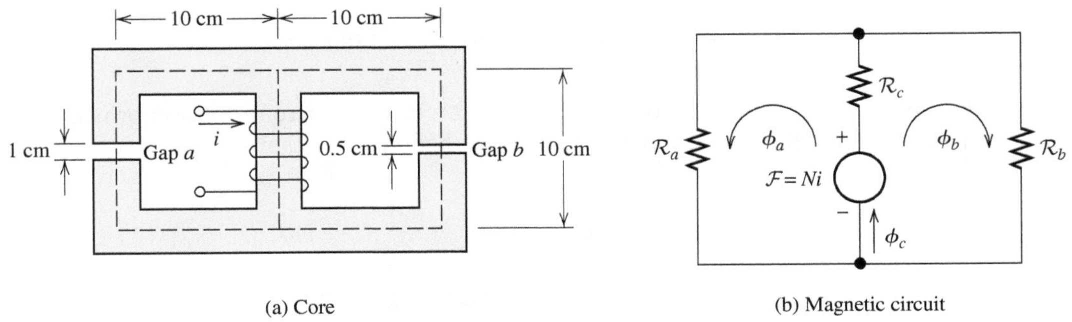

Figure 13 Magnetic circuit of Example 6.

For the left-hand path, the total reluctance is the sum of the reluctance of the iron core plus the reluctance of gap a. We take fringing into account by adding the gap length to its width and depth in computing area of the gap. Thus, the area of gap a is $A_a = 3\text{ cm} \times 3\text{ cm} = 9 \times 10^{-4}\text{ m}^2$. Then, the total reluctance of the left-hand path is

$$\begin{aligned}\mathcal{R}_a &= \mathcal{R}_{\text{gap}} + \mathcal{R}_{\text{core}}\\ &= \frac{l_{\text{gap}}}{\mu_0 A_a} + \frac{l_{\text{core}}}{\mu_r \mu_0 A_{\text{core}}}\\ &= \frac{1 \times 10^{-2}}{4\pi \times 10^{-7} \times 9 \times 10^{-4}} + \frac{29 \times 10^{-2}}{1000 \times 4\pi \times 10^{-7} \times 4 \times 10^{-4}}\\ &= 8.842 \times 10^6 + 5.769 \times 10^5\\ &= 9.420 \times 10^6\text{ A·turns/Wb}\end{aligned}$$

Similarly, the reluctance of the right-hand path is

$$\begin{aligned}\mathcal{R}_b &= \mathcal{R}_{\text{gap}} + \mathcal{R}_{\text{core}}\\ &= \frac{l_{\text{gap}}}{\mu_0 A_b} + \frac{l_{\text{core}}}{\mu_r \mu_0 A_{\text{core}}}\\ &= \frac{0.5 \times 10^{-2}}{4\pi \times 10^{-7} \times 6.25 \times 10^{-4}} + \frac{29.5 \times 10^{-2}}{1000 \times 4\pi \times 10^{-7} \times 4 \times 10^{-4}}\\ &= 6.366 \times 10^6 + 5.869 \times 10^5\\ &= 6.953 \times 10^6\text{ A·turns/Wb}\end{aligned}$$

Next, we can combine the reluctances $\mathcal{R}_a$ and $\mathcal{R}_b$ in parallel. Then, the total reluctance is the sum of $\mathcal{R}_c$ and this parallel combination:

$$\begin{aligned}\mathcal{R}_{\text{total}} &= \mathcal{R}_c + \frac{1}{1/\mathcal{R}_a + 1/\mathcal{R}_b}\\ &= 1.989 \times 10^5 + \frac{1}{1/(9.420 \times 10^6) + 1/(6.953 \times 10^6)}\\ &= 4.199 \times 10^6\text{ A·turns/Wb}\end{aligned}$$

Now, the flux in the center leg of the coil can be found by dividing the magnetomotive force by the total reluctance:

$$\phi_c = \frac{Ni}{\mathcal{R}_{\text{total}}} = \frac{500 \times 2}{4.199 \times 10^6} = 238.1\ \mu\text{Wb}$$

Fluxes are analogous to currents. Thus, we use the current-division principle to determine the flux in the left-hand and right-hand paths, resulting in

$$\begin{aligned}\phi_a &= \phi_c \frac{\mathcal{R}_b}{\mathcal{R}_a + \mathcal{R}_b}\\ &= 238.1 \times 10^{-6} \times \frac{6.953 \times 10^6}{6.953 \times 10^6 + 9.420 \times 10^6}\\ &= 101.1\ \mu\text{Wb}\end{aligned}$$

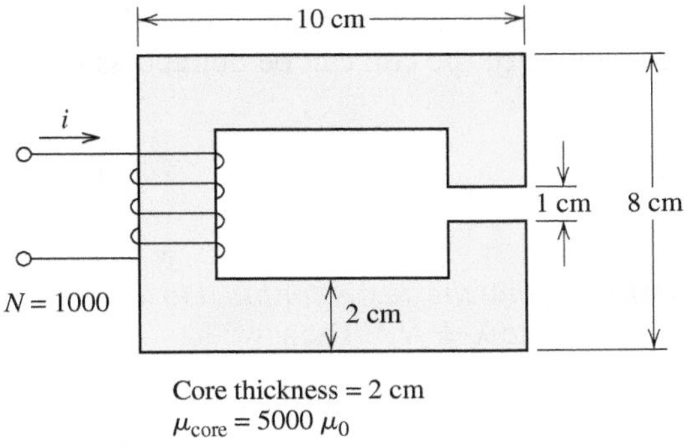

Figure 14 Magnetic circuit of Exercise 9.

Similarly, for gap b we have

$$\phi_b = \phi_c \frac{\mathcal{R}_a}{\mathcal{R}_a + \mathcal{R}_b}$$
$$= 238.1 \times 10^{-6} \frac{9.420 \times 10^6}{6.953 \times 10^6 + 9.420 \times 10^6}$$
$$= 137.0\ \mu\text{Wb}$$

As a check on these calculations, we note that $\phi_c = \phi_a + \phi_b$.

Now, we find the flux densities in the gaps by dividing the fluxes by the areas:

$$B_a = \frac{\phi_a}{A_a} = \frac{101.1\ \mu\text{Wb}}{9 \times 10^{-4}\ \text{m}^2} = 0.1123\ \text{T}$$
$$B_b = \frac{\phi_b}{A_b} = \frac{137.0\ \mu\text{Wb}}{6.25 \times 10^{-4}\ \text{m}^2} = 0.2192\ \text{T}$$

■

Typically, we find that in magnetic circuits consisting of iron cores with air gaps, the reluctance of the iron has a negligible effect on the results. Furthermore, we usually do not have a precise value of the permeability for the iron. Thus, it is often sufficiently accurate to assume zero reluctance for the iron cores. This is the counterpart of assuming zero resistance for the wires in an electrical circuit.

Exercise 9 Consider the magnetic circuit shown in Figure 14. Determine the current required to establish a flux density of 0.5 T in the air gap.
Answer $i = 4.03$ A. □

Exercise 10 Repeat Example 6, taking the reluctance of the iron paths to be zero. Determine the error as a percentage of the flux densities computed in the example.
Answer $\phi_a = 113.1\ \mu$Wb, $B_a = 0.1257$ T, 11.9 percent error; $\phi_b = 157.1\ \mu$Wb, $B_b = 0.2513$ T, 14.66 percent error. □

3 INDUCTANCE AND MUTUAL INDUCTANCE

We have seen that when a coil carries current, a magnetic flux is produced that links the coil. If the current changes with time, the flux also changes, inducing a voltage in the coil. Now, we relate inductance to the physical parameters of the coil and the core upon which it is wound.

Consider a coil carrying a current i that sets up a flux ϕ linking the coil. The inductance of the coil can be defined as flux linkages divided by current:

$$L = \frac{\lambda}{i} \tag{23}$$

Assuming that the flux is confined to the core so that all of the flux links all of the turns, we can write $\lambda = N\phi$. Then, we have

$$L = \frac{N\phi}{i} \tag{24}$$

Equation 25 is valid only if all of the flux links all of the turns.

Substituting $\phi = Ni/\mathcal{R}$, we obtain

$$L = \frac{N^2}{\mathcal{R}} \tag{25}$$

Thus, we see that the inductance depends on the number of turns, the core dimensions, and the core material. Notice that inductance is proportional to the square of the number of turns.

According to Faraday's law, voltage is induced in a coil when its flux linkages change:

$$e = \frac{d\lambda}{dt} \tag{26}$$

Rearranging Equation 23, we have $\lambda = Li$. Substituting this for λ in Equation 26, we get

$$e = \frac{d(Li)}{dt} \tag{27}$$

For a coil wound on a stationary core, the inductance is constant with time, and Equation 27 reduces to

$$e = L\frac{di}{dt} \tag{28}$$

Of course, this is the equation relating voltage and current that we used to analyze circuits containing inductance.

Example 7 Calculation of Inductance

Determine the inductance of the 500-turn coil shown in Figure 12 and analyzed in Example 5.

Solution In Example 5, we found that the reluctance of the magnetic path is

$$\mathcal{R} = 4.600 \times 10^6 \text{ A·turns/Wb}$$

Substituting into Equation 25, we obtain

$$L = \frac{N^2}{\mathcal{R}} = \frac{500^2}{4.6 \times 10^6} = 54.35 \text{ mH}$$

■

Mutual Inductance

When two coils are wound on the same core, some of the flux produced by one coil links the other coil. We denote the flux linkages of coil 2 caused by the current in coil 1 as λ_{21}. Correspondingly, the flux linkages of coil 1 produced by its own current are denoted as λ_{11}. Similarly, the current in coil 2 produces flux linkages λ_{22} in coil 2 and λ_{12} in coil 1.

The **self inductances** of the coils are defined as

$$L_1 = \frac{\lambda_{11}}{i_1} \tag{29}$$

and

$$L_2 = \frac{\lambda_{22}}{i_2} \tag{30}$$

The **mutual inductance** between the coils is

$$M = \frac{\lambda_{21}}{i_1} = \frac{\lambda_{12}}{i_2} \tag{31}$$

The total fluxes linking the coils are

$$\lambda_1 = \lambda_{11} \pm \lambda_{12} \tag{32}$$

and

$$\lambda_2 = \pm\lambda_{21} + \lambda_{22} \tag{33}$$

where the + sign applies if the fluxes are aiding and the − sign applies if the fluxes are opposing.

Dot Convention

It is standard practice to place a dot on one end of each coil in a circuit diagram to indicate how the fluxes interact. An example of this is shown in Figure 15. The dots are placed such that currents entering the dotted terminals produce aiding magnetic flux. Notice that (according to the right-hand rule) a current entering either of the dotted terminals in Figure 15 produces flux in a clockwise direction in the core. Thus, if both currents enter (or if both leave) the dotted terminals, the mutual flux linkages add to the self flux linkages. On the other hand, if one current enters a dotted terminal and the other leaves, the mutual flux linkages carry a minus sign.

Aiding fluxes are produced by currents entering like-marked terminals.

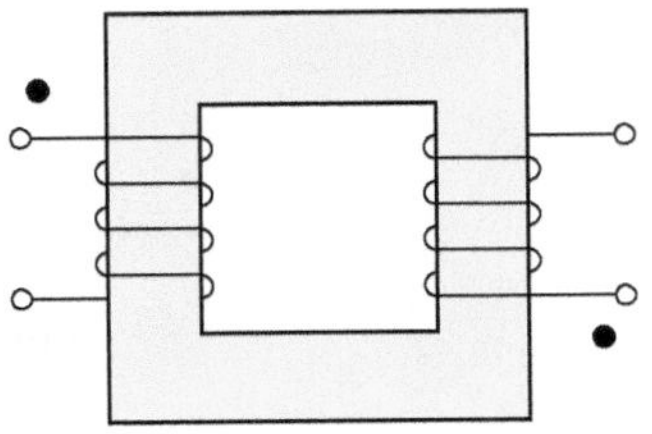

Figure 15 According to convention, currents entering the dotted terminals produce aiding fluxes.

Circuit Equations for Mutual Inductance

Solving Equations 29 through 31 for the flux linkages and substituting into Equations 32 and 33, we have

$$\lambda_1 = L_1 i_1 \pm M i_2 \tag{34}$$

and

$$\lambda_2 = \pm M i_1 + L_2 i_2 \tag{35}$$

Applying Faraday's law to find the voltages induced in the coils, we get

$$e_1 = \frac{d\lambda_1}{dt} = L_1 \frac{di_1}{dt} \pm M \frac{di_2}{dt} \tag{36}$$

and

$$e_2 = \frac{d\lambda_2}{dt} = \pm M \frac{di_1}{dt} + L_2 \frac{di_2}{dt} \tag{37}$$

Here again, we have assumed that the coils and core are stationary, so the inductances are constant with respect to time. These are the basic equations used to analyze circuits having mutual inductance.

Example 8 Calculation of Inductance and Mutual Inductance

Two coils are wound on a toroidal core as illustrated in Figure 16. The reluctance of the core is 10^7 (ampere-turns)/Wb. Determine the self inductances and mutual inductance of the coils. Assume that the flux is confined to the core so that all of the flux links both coils.

Solution The self inductances can be computed using Equation 25. For coil 1, we have

$$L_1 = \frac{N_1^2}{\mathcal{R}} = \frac{100^2}{10^7} = 1 \text{ mH}$$

Similarly, for coil 2 we get

$$L_2 = \frac{N_2^2}{\mathcal{R}} = \frac{200^2}{10^7} = 4 \text{ mH}$$

To compute the mutual inductance, we find the flux produced by i_1:

$$\phi_1 = \frac{N_1 i_1}{\mathcal{R}} = \frac{100 i_1}{10^7} = 10^{-5} i_1$$

The flux linkages of coil 2 resulting from the current in coil 1 are given by

$$\lambda_{21} = N_2 \phi_1 = 200 \times 10^{-5} i_1$$

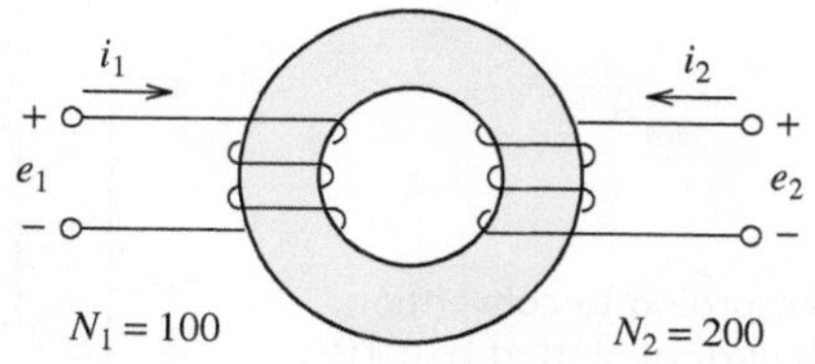

Figure 16 Coils of Example 8.

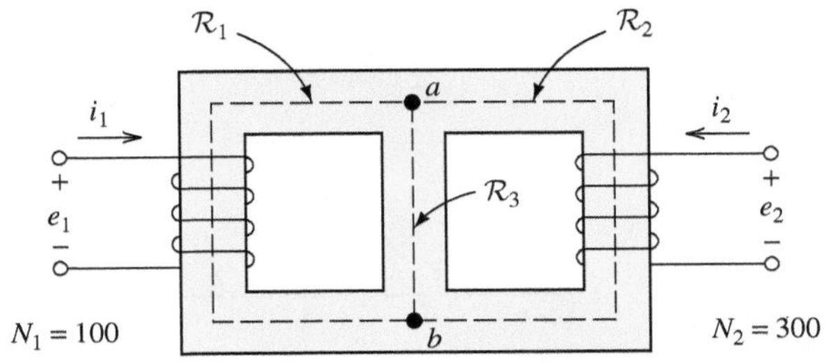

Figure 17 Magnetic circuit of Exercise 13.

Finally, the mutual inductance is

$$M = \frac{\lambda_{21}}{i_1} = 2 \text{ mH}$$

Exercise 11 Compute the mutual inductance in Example 8 by use of the formula $M = \lambda_{12}/i_2$.

Answer $M = 2$ mH. Notice that we get the same value from $M = \lambda_{21}/i_1$ and from $M = \lambda_{12}/i_2$.

Exercise 12 Does the flux produced by i_2 aid or oppose the flux produced by i_1 for the coils shown in Figure 16? If a dot is placed on the top terminal of coil 1, which end of coil 2 should have a dot? Write the expressions for e_1 and e_2, taking care to select the proper sign for the mutual term.

Answer The fluxes oppose one another. The dot should be on the bottom terminal of coil 2, so the correct expressions are

$$e_1 = L_1 \frac{di_1}{dt} - M \frac{di_2}{dt} \quad \text{and} \quad e_2 = -M \frac{di_1}{dt} + L_2 \frac{di_2}{dt}$$

Exercise 13 For the core shown in Figure 17, the reluctances of all three paths between points a and b are equal.

$$\mathcal{R}_1 = \mathcal{R}_2 = \mathcal{R}_3 = 10^6 \text{ (A·turns)/Wb}$$

Assume that all of the flux is confined to the core. **a.** Do the fluxes produced by i_1 and i_2 aid or oppose one another in path 1? In path 2? In path 3? If a dot is placed on the top end of coil 1, which end of coil 2 should carry a dot? **b.** Determine the values of L_1, L_2, and M. **c.** Should the mutual term for the voltages (in Equations 36 and 37) carry a plus sign or a minus sign?

Answer **a.** Aid in paths 1 and 2, oppose in path 3; the dot should be on the top end of coil 2; **b.** $L_1 = 6.667$ mH, $L_2 = 60$ mH, $M = 10$ mH; **c.** a plus sign.

4 MAGNETIC MATERIALS

So far, we have assumed that the relationship between B and H is linear (i.e., $B = \mu H$). Actually, for the iron alloys used in motors, permanent magnets, and transformers, the relationship between B and H is not linear.

The relationship between B and H is not linear for the types of iron used in motors and transformers.

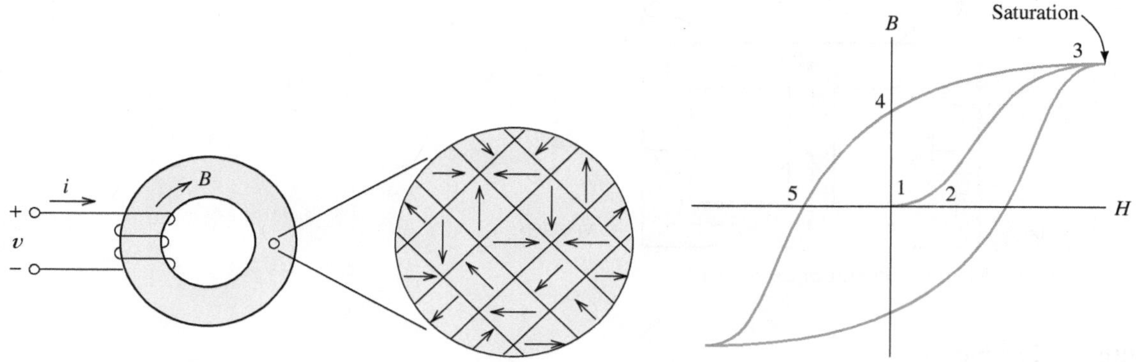

(a) Sample and coil for applying H (b) Magnetic domains (c) Hysteresis loop in the $B-H$ plane

Figure 18 Materials such as iron display a B–H relationship with hysteresis and saturation.

Figure 18(a) shows a coil used to apply magnetic field intensity H to a sample of iron. Suppose that we start with a sample that is not magnetized. If we look at the material on a microscopic scale, we see that the magnetic fields of the atoms in small **domains** are aligned. However, the field directions are random for the various domains, and the external macroscopic field is zero. This is illustrated in Figure 18(b).

Figure 18(c) shows a plot of B versus H. At point 1, both B and H are zero. As H is increased by applying current to the coil, the magnetic fields of the domains tend to align with the applied field. At first (point 1 to point 2), this is a reversible process, so that if the applied field is reduced to zero, the domains return to their original random orientations. However, for greater applied field intensities, the domains align with the applied field such that they tend to maintain their alignment even if the applied field is reduced to zero (point 2 to point 3). Eventually, for sufficiently high fields, all of the domains are aligned with the applied field and the slope of the B–H curve approaches μ_0. We say that the material is **saturated**. For typical iron core materials, saturation occurs for B in the range of 1 to 2 T.

For typical iron cores, saturation occurs for B in the range from 1 to 2 T.

If starting from point 3, the applied field H is reduced to zero, a residual flux density B remains in the core (point 4). This occurs because the magnetic domains continue to point in the direction imposed earlier by the applied field. If H is increased in the reverse direction, B is reduced to zero (point 5). Eventually, saturation occurs in the reverse direction. If an ac current is applied to the coil, a **hysteresis loop** is traced in the B–H plane.

Energy Considerations

Let us consider the energy flow to and from the coil shown in Figure 18(a). We assume that the coil has zero resistance. As the current is increasing, the increasing flux density induces a voltage, resulting in energy flow into the coil. The energy W delivered to the coil is the integral of power. Thus, we get

$$W = \int_0^t vi\,dt = \int_0^t N\frac{d\phi}{dt} i\,dt = \int_0^\phi Ni\,d\phi \qquad (38)$$

Now $Ni = Hl$ and $d\phi = AdB$, where l is the mean path length and A is the cross-sectional area. Making these substitutions in the expression on the right-hand

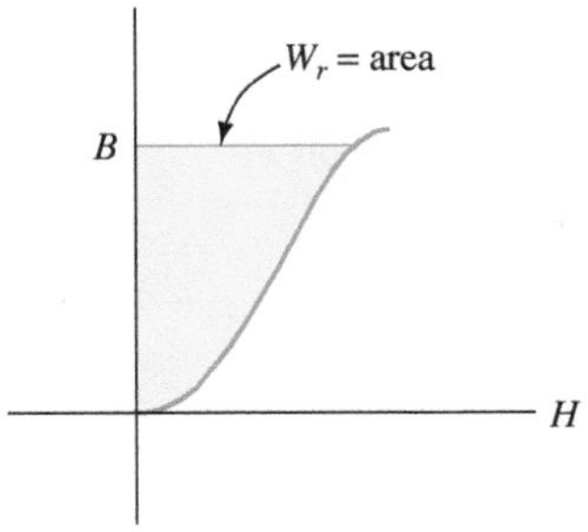

Figure 19 The area between the B–H curve and the B axis represents the volumetric energy supplied to the core.

side of Equation 38, we have

$$W = \int_0^B AlH \, dB \tag{39}$$

However, the product of the cross-sectional area A and the length of the core l is the volume of the core. Dividing both sides of Equation 39 by the volume results in

$$W_v = \frac{W}{Al} = \int_0^B H \, dB \tag{40}$$

in which W_v represents energy per unit volume of the core. As illustrated in Figure 19, the volumetric energy delivered to the coil is the area between the B–H curve and the B-axis. Part of this energy is returned to the circuit when H is reduced to zero, part of it remains stored in the residual field, and part of it is converted to heat in the process of magnetizing the core.

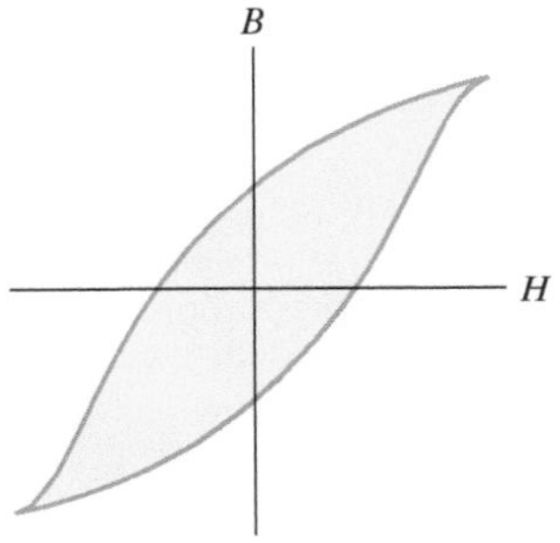

Figure 20 The area of the hysteresis loop is the volumetric energy converted to heat per cycle.

Core Loss

When an ac current is applied to a coil having an iron core, more energy is put into the coil on each cycle than is returned to the circuit. Part of the energy is converted to heat in reversing the directions of the magnetic domains. This is similar to the heat produced when we repeatedly bend a piece of metal. The volumetric energy converted to heat per cycle is equal to the area of the hysteresis loop as illustrated in Figure 20. This energy loss is called **core loss**. Since a fixed amount of energy is converted to heat for each cycle, the power loss due to hysteresis is proportional to frequency.

Power loss due to hysteresis is proportional to frequency, assuming constant peak flux.

In motors, generators, and transformers, conversion of energy into heat is undesirable. Therefore, we would choose an alloy having a thin hysteresis loop as in Figure 21(a). On the other hand, for a permanent magnet, we would choose a material having a large residual field, such as in Figure 21(b).

Eddy-Current Loss

Besides hysteresis, there is another effect that leads to core loss for ac operation. First, let us consider a solid iron core. Of course, the core itself is an electrical conductor, acting much like shorted turns. As the magnetic fields change, voltages are induced in the core, causing currents, known as **eddy currents**, to circulate in the core material. As a result, power is dissipated in the core according to $P = v^2/R$.

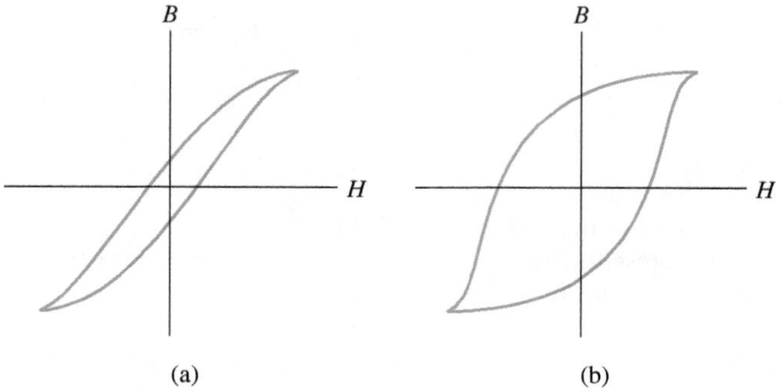

Figure 21 When we want to minimize core loss (as in a transformer or motor), we choose a material having a thin hysteresis loop. On the other hand, for a permanent magnet, we should choose a material with a wide loop.

A partial solution to eddy-current loss is to laminate the core with thin sheets of iron that are electrically insulated from one another. The orientation of the sheets is selected to interrupt the flow of current. Thus, the resistance is higher for eddy currents, and the loss is greatly reduced. Another approach is to make the core with powdered iron held together by an insulating binder.

Power loss due to eddy currents is proportional to the square of frequency, assuming constant peak flux.

For operation with a given peak flux density, the voltages induced in the core are proportional to frequency (because of Faraday's law). Therefore, power loss due to eddy currents increases with the square of frequency (because $P = v^2/R$).

Energy Stored in the Magnetic Field

Even though many core materials do not have a linear B–H characteristic, we often perform initial design calculations assuming that $B = \mu H$. The properties of the core material are usually not accurately known, so the calculations for motor or transformer design are approximate. The linear approximation is convenient and sufficiently accurate as long as the cores are operated below the saturation level.

Substituting $H = B/\mu$ into Equation 40 and integrating, we obtain

$$W_v = \int_0^B \frac{B}{\mu}\, dB = \frac{B^2}{2\mu} \tag{41}$$

Notice that for a given flux density, the volumetric energy stored in the field is inversely proportional to the permeability.

In a magnetic circuit having an air gap, the flux density is roughly the same in the iron core as in the air gap. (It is usually a little less in the air gap, due to fringing.) The permeability of an iron core is much greater (by a factor of several thousand or more) than that of air. Thus, the volumetric energy of the gap is much higher than that of the core. *In a magnetic circuit consisting of an iron core with a substantial air gap, nearly all of the stored energy resides in the gap.*

Exercise 14 Consider a coil wound on an iron core. For 60-Hz ac operation with a given applied current, the hysteresis loop of the core material has an area of 40 J/m^3. The core volume is 200 cm^3. Find the power converted to heat because of hysteresis.

Answer 0.48 W. □

Exercise 15 A certain iron core has an air gap with an effective area of 2 cm by 3 cm and a length of 0.5 cm. The applied magnetomotive force is 1000 ampere turns and the reluctance of the iron is negligible. Find the flux density and the energy stored in the air gap.
Answer $B = 0.2513$ T, $W = 0.0754$ J. □

5 IDEAL TRANSFORMERS

A transformer consists of several coils wound on a common core that usually consists of laminated iron (to reduce eddy-current loss). We will see that transformers can be used to adjust the values of ac voltages. A voltage can be *stepped up* by using a transformer. For example, 2400 V can be stepped up to 48 kV. Transformers can also be used to *step a voltage down*, such as 2400 V to 240 V.

Transformers find many applications in electric power distribution. In transporting power over long distances (from a hydroelectric power-generating station to a distant city, for example), it is desirable to use relatively large voltages, typically hundreds of kilovolts. Recall that the power delivered by an ac source is given by

$$P = V_{\text{rms}} I_{\text{rms}} \cos(\theta) \qquad (42)$$

For a fixed power factor ($\cos \theta$), many combinations of voltage and current can be used in transferring a given amount of power. The wires that carry the current have nonzero resistances. Thus, some power is lost in the transmission lines, given by

$$P_{\text{loss}} = R_{\text{line}} I_{\text{rms}}^2 \qquad (43)$$

in which R_{line} is the resistance of the transmission line. By designing the power distribution system with a large voltage value and a small current value, the line loss can be made to be a small fraction of the power transported. Thus, larger voltage yields higher efficiency in power distribution.

For safety and other reasons, relatively small voltages must be employed where the power is consumed. For example, in U.S. residences, the nominal voltages are either 110 or 220 V rms. Thus, transformers are useful in stepping voltage levels up or down as needed in a power distribution system.

Transformers greatly facilitate power distribution by stepping voltage up and down at various points in the distribution system.

Voltage Ratio

A transformer is illustrated in Figure 22. An ac voltage source is connected to the primary coil, which consists of N_1 turns of wire. Current flows into the primary side and causes an ac magnetic flux $\phi(t)$ to appear in the core. This flux induces a voltage in the N_2-turn secondary coil, which delivers power to the load. Depending on the turns ratio N_2/N_1, the rms secondary voltage can be greater or less than the rms primary voltage.

For now, we neglect the resistances of the coils and the core loss. Furthermore, we assume that the reluctance of the core is very small and that all of the flux links all of the turns of both coils.

The primary voltage is given by

$$v_1(t) = V_{1m} \cos(\omega t) \qquad (44)$$

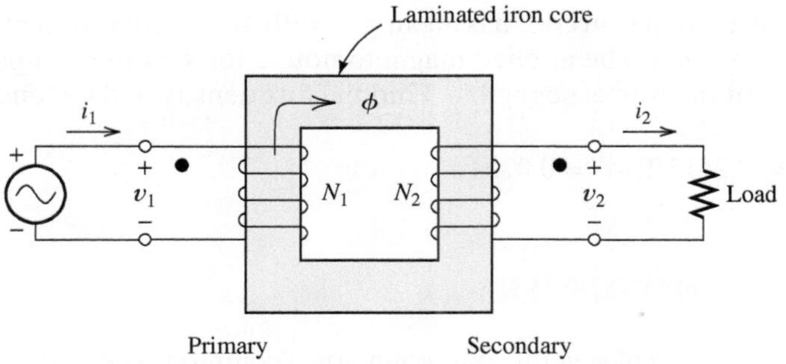

Figure 22 A transformer consists of several coils wound on a common core.

According to Faraday's law, we have

$$v_1(t) = V_{im}\cos(\omega t) = N_1 \frac{d\phi}{dt} \tag{45}$$

which can be rearranged and integrated to yield

$$\phi(t) = \frac{V_{1m}}{N_1 \omega}\sin(\omega t) \tag{46}$$

Assuming that all of the flux links all of the turns, the secondary voltage is given by

$$v_2(t) = N_2 \frac{d\phi}{dt} \tag{47}$$

Using Equation 46 to substitute for $\phi(t)$, we have

$$v_2(t) = N_2 \frac{V_{1m}}{N_1 \omega}\frac{d}{dt}[\sin(\omega t)] \tag{48}$$

$$v_2(t) = \frac{N_2}{N_1} V_{1m}\cos(\omega t) \tag{49}$$

$$v_2(t) = \frac{N_2}{N_1} v_1(t) \tag{50}$$

In an ideal transformer, all of the flux links all of the turns, and the voltage across each coil is proportional to its number of turns.

Notice that the voltage across each coil is proportional to its number of turns. This is an important relationship to know when working with transformers.

Also, notice that we have included a dot on the end of each winding in Figure 22. As usual, the dots are placed so that if the currents entered the dotted terminals, they would produce aiding magnetic fields. Furthermore, application of Lenz's law shows that the induced voltages have positive polarity at both dotted terminals when ϕ is increasing, and negative polarity at both dotted terminals when ϕ is decreasing. *Thus in a transformer, the polarities of the voltages at the dotted terminals agree. When a voltage with positive polarity at the dotted terminal appears across coil 1, the voltage across coil 2 is also positive at the dotted terminal.*

Voltage polarities are the same at like-dotted terminals.

Hence, we have established the fact that the voltage across each winding is proportional to the number of turns. Clearly, the peak and rms values of the voltages are also related by the turns ratio:

$$V_{2\text{rms}} = \frac{N_2}{N_1} V_{1\text{rms}} \tag{51}$$

Example 9 Determination of Required Turns Ratio

Suppose that we have a 4700-V-rms ac source and we need to deliver 220 V rms to a load. Determine the turns ratio N_1/N_2 of the transformer needed.

Solution Rearranging Equation 51, we have

$$\frac{N_1}{N_2} = \frac{V_{1rms}}{V_{2rms}} = \frac{4700}{220} = 21.36$$

■

Current Ratio

Again let us consider the transformer shown in Figure 22. Notice that the currents i_1 and i_2 produce opposing magnetic fields (because i_1 enters a dotted terminal and i_2 leaves a dotted terminal). Thus, the total mmf applied to the core is

$$\mathcal{F} = N_1 i_1(t) - N_2 i_2(t) \tag{52}$$

Furthermore, the mmf is related to the flux and the reluctance of the core by

$$\mathcal{F} = \mathcal{R}\phi \tag{53}$$

In a well-designed transformer, the core reluctance is very small. Ideally, the reluctance is zero, and the mmf required to establish the flux in the core is zero. Then, Equation 52 becomes

The net mmf is zero for an ideal transformer.

$$\mathcal{F} = N_1 i_1(t) - N_2 i_2(t) = 0 \tag{54}$$

Rearranging this equation, we obtain

$$i_2(t) = \frac{N_1}{N_2} i_1(t) \tag{55}$$

This relationship also applies for the rms values of the currents:

$$I_{2rms} = \frac{N_1}{N_2} I_{1rms} \tag{56}$$

Compare Equation 51 for the voltages to Equation 56 for the currents. Notice that if the voltage is stepped up (i.e., $N_2/N_1 > 1$), the current is stepped down, and vice versa.

Power in an Ideal Transformer

Again consider Figure 22. The power delivered to the load by the secondary winding is

$$p_2(t) = v_2(t) i_2(t) \tag{57}$$

Using Equations 50 and 55 to substitute for $v_2(t)$ and $i_2(t)$, respectively, we have

$$p_2(t) = \frac{N_2}{N_1} v_1(t) \frac{N_1}{N_2} i_1(t) = v_1(t) i_1(t) \tag{58}$$

However, the power delivered to the primary winding by the source is $p_1(t) = v_1(t)i_1(t)$, and we get

$$p_2(t) = p_1(t) \tag{59}$$

Power is neither generated nor consumed by an ideal transformer.

Thus, we have established the fact that the power delivered to the primary winding by the source is delivered in turn to the load by the secondary winding. *Net power is neither generated nor consumed by an ideal transformer.*

Summary. Let us summarize the idealizing assumptions and their consequences for the transformer.

1. We assumed that all of the flux links all of the windings of both coils and that the resistance of the coils is zero. Thus, the voltage across each coil is proportional to the number of turns on the coil. This led to the voltage relationship

$$v_2(t) = \frac{N_2}{N_1} v_1(t)$$

2. We assumed that the reluctance of the core is negligible, so the total mmf of both coils is zero. This led to the current relationship

$$i_2(t) = \frac{N_1}{N_2} i_1(t)$$

3. A consequence of the voltage and current relationships is that all of the power delivered to an ideal transformer by the source is transferred to the load. Thus, an ideal transformer has a power efficiency of 100 percent.

The circuit symbol for the transformer is shown in Figure 23(a).

Mechanical Analog of the Transformer: The Lever

The lever illustrated in Figure 23(b) is a mechanical analog of the electrical transformer. The velocities of the ends of the lever are related by the length ratio of the lever, $v_2 = v_1(l_2/l_1)$, just as transformer voltages are related by the turns ratio. Similarly, the forces are related by $F_2 = F_1(l_1/l_2)$, which is analogous to the relationship between currents in the transformer. As in a transformer, the frictionless lever neither generates nor consumes energy. On one end of the lever, we have small force and large velocity, while on the other end the force is large and the velocity is small. This mirrors the effects of the transformer on current and voltage.

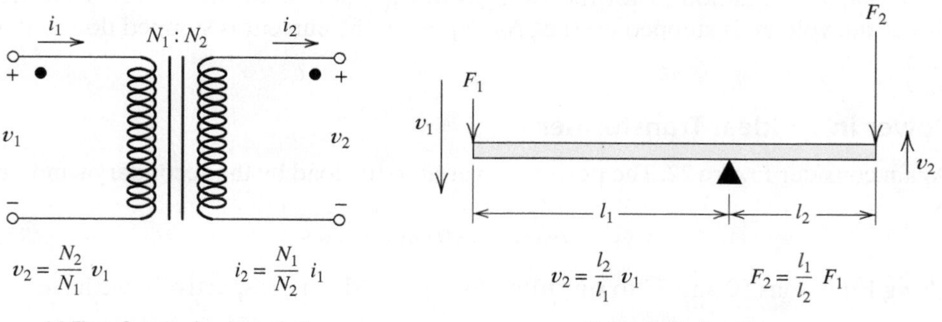

Figure 23 The circuit symbol for a transformer and its mechanical analog.

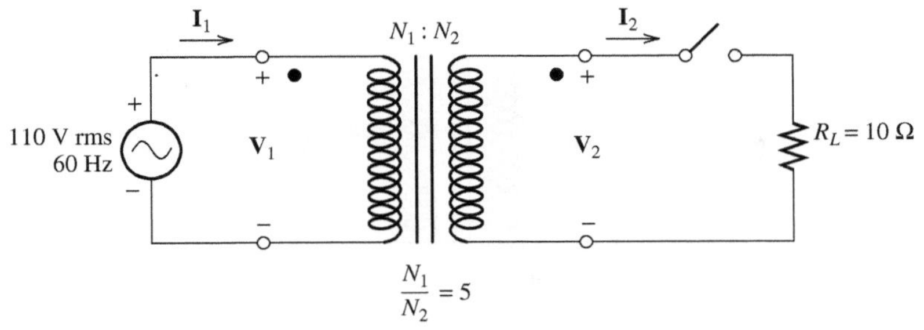

Figure 24 Circuit of Example 10.

Example 10 Analysis of a Circuit Containing an Ideal Transformer

Consider the source, transformer, and load shown in Figure 24. Determine the rms values of the currents and voltages: **a.** with the switch open; **b.** with the switch closed.

Solution Because of the applied source, the primary voltage is $V_{1rms} = 110$ V. The primary and secondary voltages are related by Equation 51:

$$V_{2rms} = \frac{N_2}{N_1} V_{1rms} = \frac{1}{5} \times 110 = 22 \text{ V}$$

Rearranging Equation 56, we have

$$I_{1rms} = \frac{N_2}{N_1} I_{2rms}$$

a. With the switch open, the secondary current is zero. Therefore, the primary current I_{1rms} is also zero, and no power is taken from the source.

b. With the switch closed, the secondary current is

$$I_{2rms} = \frac{V_{2rms}}{R_L} = \frac{22}{10} = 2.2 \text{ A}$$

Then, the primary current is

$$I_{1rms} = \frac{N_2}{N_1} I_{2rms} = \frac{1}{5} \times 2.2 = 0.44 \text{ A}$$

Let us consider the sequence of events in this example. When the source voltage is applied to the primary winding, a very small primary current (ideally zero) flows, setting up the flux in the core. The flux induces the voltage in the secondary winding. Before the switch is closed, no current flows in the secondary. After the switch is closed, current flows in the secondary opposing the flux in the core. However, because of the voltage applied to the primary, the flux must be maintained in the core. (Otherwise, Kirchhoff's voltage law would not be satisfied in the primary circuit.) Thus, current must begin to flow into the primary to offset the magnetomotive force of the secondary winding. ■

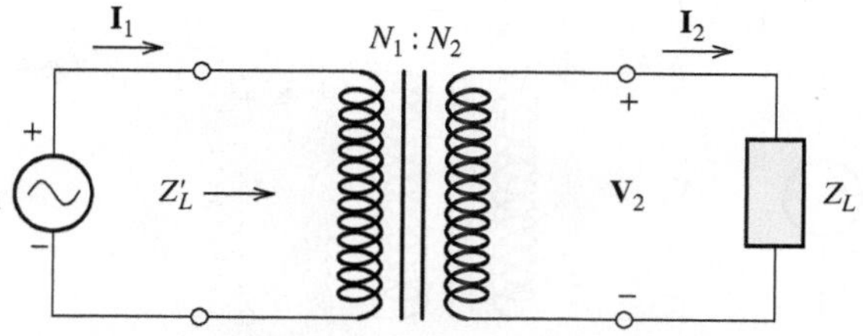

Figure 25 The impedance seen looking into the primary is $Z'_L = (N_1/N_2)^2 \times Z_L$.

Impedance Transformations

Consider the circuit shown in Figure 25. The phasor current and voltage in the secondary are related to the load impedance by

$$\frac{\mathbf{V}_2}{\mathbf{I}_2} = Z_L \tag{60}$$

Using Equations 51 and 56 to substitute for $\mathbf{I}_2$ and $\mathbf{V}_2$, we have

$$\frac{(N_2/N_1)\mathbf{V}_1}{(N_1/N_2)\mathbf{I}_1} = Z_L \tag{61}$$

Rearranging this, we get

$$Z'_L = \frac{\mathbf{V}_1}{\mathbf{I}_1} = \left(\frac{N_1}{N_2}\right)^2 Z_L \tag{62}$$

in which Z'_L is the impedance *seen* by the source. We say that the load impedance is *reflected* to the primary side by the square of the turns ratio.

Example 11 Using Impedance Transformations

Consider the circuit shown in Figure 26(a). Find the phasor currents and voltages. Also, find the power delivered to the load.

Solution First, we reflect the load impedance Z_L to the primary side of the transformer as shown in Figure 26(b). The impedance seen from the primary side is

$$Z'_L = \left(\frac{N_1}{N_2}\right)^2 Z_L = (10)^2(10 + j20) = 1000 + j2000$$

The total impedance seen by the source is

$$Z_s = R_1 + Z'_L = 1000 + 1000 + j2000 = 2000 + j2000$$

Converting to polar form, we have

$$Z_s = 2828\angle 45^\circ$$

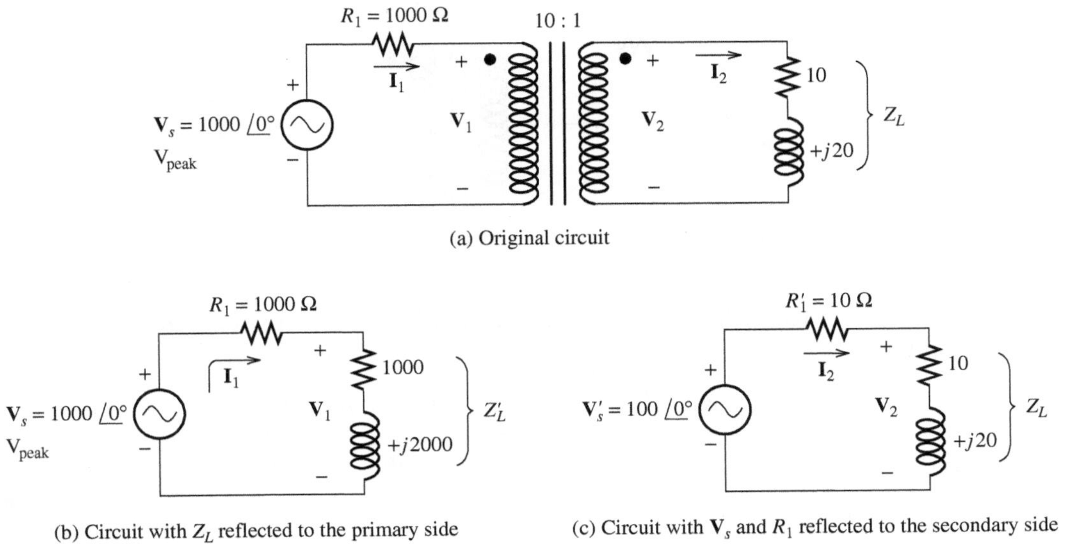

Figure 26 The circuit of Examples 11 and 12.

Now, we can compute the primary current and voltage:

$$\mathbf{I}_1 = \frac{\mathbf{V}_s}{Z_s} = \frac{1000\angle 0°}{2828\angle 45°} = 0.3536\angle -45° \text{ A peak}$$

$$\mathbf{V}_1 = \mathbf{I}_1 Z_L' = 0.3536\angle -45° \times (1000 + j2000)$$

$$= 0.3536\angle -45° \times (2236\angle 63.43°) = 790.6\angle 18.43° \text{ V peak}$$

Next, we can use the turns ratio to compute the secondary current and voltage:

$$\mathbf{I}_2 = \frac{N_1}{N_2}\mathbf{I}_1 = \frac{10}{1} 0.3536\angle -45° = 3.536\angle -45° \text{ A peak}$$

$$\mathbf{V}_2 = \frac{N_2}{N_1}\mathbf{V}_1 = \frac{1}{10} 790.6\angle 18.43° = 79.06\angle 18.43° \text{ V peak}$$

Finally, we compute the power delivered to the load:

$$P_L = I_{2\text{rms}}^2 R_L = \left(\frac{3.536}{\sqrt{2}}\right)^2 (10) = 62.51 \text{ W}$$

■

Besides transferring impedances from one side of a transformer to the other by using the square of the turns ratio, we can also reflect voltage sources or current sources by using the turns ratio.

Example 12 Reflecting the Source to the Secondary

Consider Figure 26(a). Reflect V_s and R_1 to the secondary side.

Solution The voltage is reflected by using the turns ratio. Thus, we have

$$\mathbf{V}_s' = \frac{N_2}{N_1}\mathbf{V}_s = \frac{1}{10} 1000\angle 0° = 100\angle 0°$$

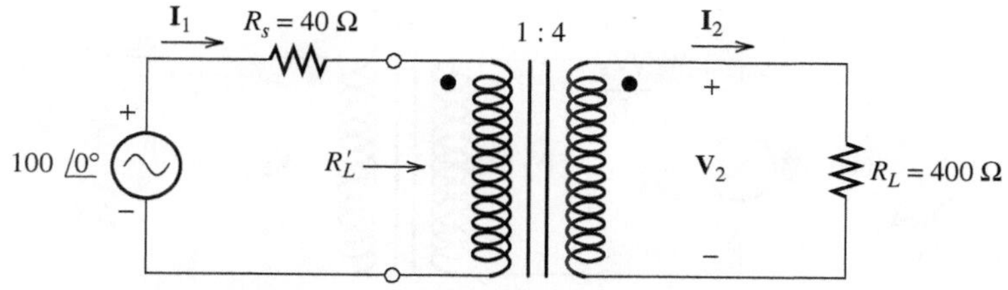

Figure 27 Circuit of Exercises 16 and 17.

On the other hand, the resistance is reflected using the square of the turns ratio. This yields

$$R_1' = \left(\frac{N_2}{N_1}\right)^2 R_1 = \left(\frac{1}{10}\right)^2 (1000) = 10\ \Omega$$

The circuit with $\mathbf{V}_s$ and R_1 transferred to the secondary side is shown in Figure 26(c). ■

Exercise 16 Working from the circuit of Figure 26(c), find the values of $\mathbf{V}_2$ and the power delivered to the load. (Of course, the answers should be the same as the values found in Example 11.)

Answer $\mathbf{V}_2 = 79.06\angle 18.43°$, $P_L = 62.51$ W. □

Exercise 17 Consider the circuit shown in Figure 27. Compute the values of $\mathbf{I}_1$, $\mathbf{I}_2$, $\mathbf{V}_2$, the power delivered to R_L, and R_L'.

Answer $\mathbf{I}_1 = 1.538\angle 0°$, $\mathbf{I}_2 = 0.3846\angle 0°$, $\mathbf{V}_2 = 153.8\angle 0°$, $P_L = 29.60$ W, $R_L' = 25\ \Omega$. □

Exercise 18 Recall that to achieve maximum power transfer from a source with an internal resistance of R_s, we want the effective load resistance R_L' to equal R_s. Find the turns ratio that would result in maximum power delivered to the load in Figure 27.

Answer $N_1/N_2 = 1/\sqrt{10}$. □

6 REAL TRANSFORMERS

Well-designed transformers approximately meet the conditions that we assumed in our discussion of the ideal transformer. Often for initial design calculations, we can assume that a transformer is ideal. However, a better model is needed for accurate calculations in the final stages of design. Moreover, a better understanding of transformers and their limitations is gained by considering a refined model.

The equivalent circuit of a real transformer is shown in Figure 28. The resistances R_1 and R_2 account for the resistance of the wires used to wind the coils of the transformer.

For the ideal transformer, we assumed that all of the flux links all of the turns of both coils. In fact, some of the flux produced by each coil leaves the core and does not link the other coil. We account for this **leakage flux** by adding the inductances L_1 and L_2 to the ideal transformer, as shown in Figure 28.

In discussing the ideal transformer, we assumed that the core reluctance was zero and ignored core loss. This meant that zero magnetomotive force was required

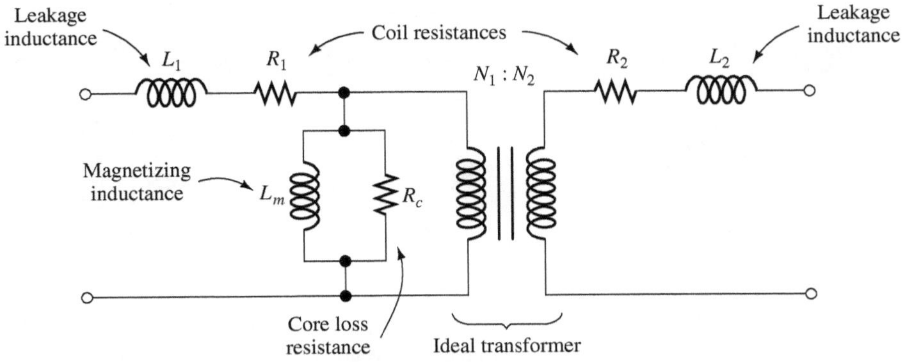

Figure 28 The equivalent circuit of a real transformer.

Table 1. Circuit Values of a 60-Hz 20-kVA 2400/240-V Transformer Compared with Those of an Ideal Transformer

Element Name	*Symbol*	*Ideal*	*Real*
Primary resistance	R_1	0	3.0 Ω
Secondary resistance	R_2	0	0.03 Ω
Primary leakage reactance	$X_1 = \omega L_1$	0	6.5 Ω
Secondary leakage reactance	$X_2 = \omega L_2$	0	0.07 Ω
Magnetizing reactance	$X_m = \omega L_m$	∞	15 kΩ
Core-loss resistance	R_c	∞	100 kΩ

to establish the flux in the core. Neither of these assumptions is exactly true. The **magnetizing inductance** L_m shown in Figure 28 accounts for the nonzero core reluctance. The current needed to establish the flux flows through L_m. Finally, the resistance R_c accounts for power dissipated in the core due to hysteresis and eddy currents.

Table 1 compares the values of the circuit elements of a real transformer with those of an ideal transformer.

Variations of the Transformer Model

Figure 29 shows several variations of the transformer equivalent circuit. In Figure 29(a), the secondary inductance and resistance have been referred to the primary side. In Figure 29(b), the magnetizing inductance and loss resistance have been moved to the input side of the circuit. [Actually, the circuit in Figure 29(b) is not precisely equivalent to that in Figure 29(a). However, in normal operation, the voltage drop across L_1 and R_1 is very small compared to either the input voltage or the voltage across L_m and R_m. Thus, for normal operating conditions, virtually identical results are obtained from either circuit.] Other equivalent circuits can be obtained by moving the circuit elements to the secondary side and by moving L_m and R_c to the right-hand side. Usually, we select the equivalent circuit configuration that is most convenient for the problem at hand.

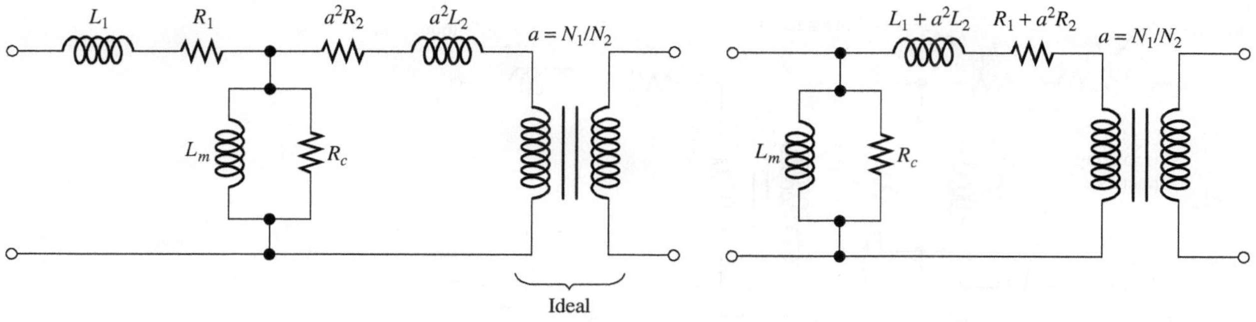

(a) All elements referred to the primary side

(b) Approximate equivalent circuit that is sometimes more convenient to use than that of part (a)

Figure 29 Variations of the transformer equivalent circuit. The circuit of (b) is not exactly equivalent to that of (a), but is sufficiently accurate for practical applications.

Regulation and Efficiency

Because of the elements L_1, L_2, R_1, and R_2, the voltage delivered to the load side of a transformer varies with the load current. Usually, this is an undesirable effect. The regulation of a transformer is defined as

$$\text{percent regulation} = \frac{V_{\text{no-load}} - V_{\text{load}}}{V_{\text{load}}} \times 100\%$$

in which $V_{\text{no-load}}$ is the rms voltage across the load terminals for an open-circuit load and V_{load} is the rms voltage across the actual load.

Ideally, we usually want the percentage regulation to be zero. For instance, poor regulation in a residence would mean that the lights dim when an electric clothes dryer is started. Clearly, this is not a desirable situation.

Because of the resistances in the transformer equivalent circuit, not all of the power input to the transformer is delivered to the load. We define the power efficiency as

$$\text{power efficiency} = \frac{P_{\text{load}}}{P_{\text{in}}} \times 100\% = \left(1 - \frac{P_{\text{loss}}}{P_{\text{in}}}\right) \times 100\%$$

in which P_{load} is the power delivered to the load, P_{loss} is the power dissipated in the transformer, and P_{in} is the power delivered by the source to the transformer primary terminals.

In this example, we are taking the rms values of currents and voltages (rather than peak values) as the phasor magnitudes. This is often done by power-distribution engineers. We will clearly indicate when phasors represent rms values rather than peak values.

Example 13 Regulation and Efficiency Calculations

Find the percentage regulation and power efficiency for the transformer of Table 1 for a rated load having a lagging power factor of 0.8.

Solution First, we draw the circuit as shown in Figure 30. Notice that we have placed the magnetizing reactance X_m and core loss resistance R_c on the left-hand side of R_1 and X_1, because this makes the calculations a bit simpler and is sufficiently accurate. We assume a zero phase reference for the load voltage. It is customary in

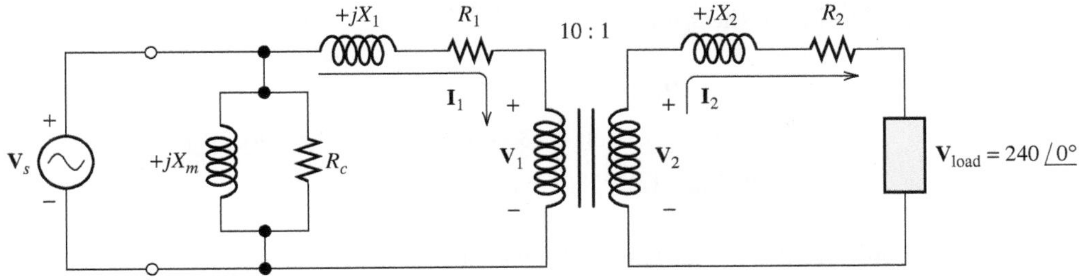

Figure 30 Circuit of Example 13.

power-system engineering to take the values of phasors as the rms values (rather than the peak values) of the currents and voltages. Thus, as a phasor, we have

$$\mathbf{V}_{\text{load}} = 240\angle 0^\circ \text{ V rms}$$

For rated load (20 kVA), the load current is

$$I_2 = \frac{20 \text{ kVA}}{240 \text{ V}} = 83.33 \text{ A rms}$$

The load power factor is

$$\text{power factor } = \cos(\theta) = 0.8$$

Solving, we find that

$$\theta = 36.87^\circ$$

Thus, the phasor load current is

$$\mathbf{I}_2 = 83.33\angle -36.87^\circ \text{ A rms}$$

where the phase angle is negative because the load was stated to have a lagging power factor.

The primary current is related to the secondary current by the turns ratio:

$$\mathbf{I}_1 = \frac{N_2}{N_1}\mathbf{I}_2 = \frac{1}{10} \times 83.33\angle -36.87^\circ = 8.333\angle -36.87^\circ \text{ A rms}$$

Next, we can compute the voltages:

$$\begin{aligned}\mathbf{V}_2 &= \mathbf{V}_{\text{load}} + (R_2 + jX_2)\mathbf{I}_2 \\ &= 240 + (0.03 + j0.07)83.33\angle -36.87^\circ \\ &= 240 + 6.346\angle 29.93^\circ \\ &= 245.50 + j3.166 \text{ V rms}\end{aligned}$$

The primary voltage is related to the secondary voltage by the turns ratio:

$$\begin{aligned}\mathbf{V}_1 &= \frac{N_1}{N_2}\mathbf{V}_2 = 10 \times (245.50 + j3.166) \\ &= 2455.0 + j31.66 \text{ V rms}\end{aligned}$$

Now, we can compute the source voltage:

$$\begin{aligned}\mathbf{V}_s &= \mathbf{V}_1 + (R_1 + jX_1)\mathbf{I}_1\\ &= 2455.0 + j31.66 + (3 + j6.5) \times (8.333\angle -36.87^\circ)\\ &= 2508.2\angle 1.37^\circ \text{ V rms}\end{aligned}$$

Next, we compute the power loss in the transformer:

$$\begin{aligned}P_{\text{loss}} &= \frac{V_s^2}{R_c} + I_1^2 R_1 + I_2^2 R_2\\ &= 62.91 + 208.3 + 208.3\\ &= 479.5 \text{ W}\end{aligned}$$

The power delivered to the load is given by

$$\begin{aligned}P_{\text{load}} &= V_{\text{load}} I_2 \times \text{ power factor}\\ &= 20 \text{ kVA } \times 0.8 = 16{,}000 \text{ W}\end{aligned}$$

The input power is given by

$$\begin{aligned}P_{\text{in}} &= P_{\text{load}} + P_{\text{loss}}\\ &= 16{,}000 + 479.5 = 16{,}479.5 \text{ W}\end{aligned}$$

At this point, we can compute the power efficiency:

$$\begin{aligned}\text{efficiency} &= \left(1 - \frac{P_{\text{loss}}}{P_{\text{in}}}\right) \times 100\%\\ &= \left(1 - \frac{479.5}{16{,}479.5}\right) \times 100\% = 97.09\%\end{aligned}$$

Next, we can determine the no-load voltages. Under no-load conditions, we have

$$\begin{aligned}I_1 &= I_2 = 0\\ V_1 &= V_s = 2508.2\\ V_{\text{no-load}} &= V_2 = V_1 \frac{N_2}{N_1} = 250.82 \text{ V rms}\end{aligned}$$

Finally, the percentage regulation is

$$\begin{aligned}\text{percent regulation} &= \frac{V_{\text{no-load}} - V_{\text{load}}}{V_{\text{load}}} \times 100\%\\ &= \frac{250.82 - 240}{240} \times 100\%\\ &= 4.51\%\end{aligned}$$

■

Summary

1. The right-hand rule can be used to determine the direction of the magnetic field produced by a current. This is illustrated in Figure 2.
2. Force is exerted on a charge moving through a magnetic field according to the equation

$$\mathbf{f} = q\mathbf{u} \times \mathbf{B}$$

Similarly, forces appear on a current-carrying wire immersed in a magnetic field. The force on an incremental length of wire is given by

$$d\mathbf{f} = i d\mathbf{l} \times \mathbf{B}$$

3. According to Faraday's law of induction, voltage is induced in a coil when its magnetic flux linkages change with time. Similarly, voltages are induced in conductors that cut through magnetic flux lines. We can determine the polarity of the induced voltage by using Lenz's law.
4. Magnetic flux density **B** and the magnetic field intensity **H** are related by

$$\mathbf{B} = \mu\mathbf{H}$$

where μ is the magnetic permeability of the material. For air or vacuum, $\mu = \mu_0 = 4\pi \times 10^{-7}$.
5. According to Ampère's law, the line integral of **H** around a closed path is equal to the algebraic sum of the currents flowing through the area bounded by the path. We can use this law to find the field around a long straight wire or inside a toroidal coil.
6. Practical magnetic devices can be approximately analyzed by using circuit concepts. Magnetomotive forces are analogous to voltage sources, reluctance is analogous to resistance, and flux is analogous to current.
7. The inductance and mutual inductance of coils can be computed from knowledge of the physical parameters of the coils and the core on which they are wound.
8. The B–H relationship for iron takes the form of a hysteresis loop, which displays saturation in the neighborhood of 1 to 2 T. The area of the loop represents energy converted to heat per cycle. Eddy currents are another cause of core loss. Energy can be stored in magnetic fields. In a magnetic circuit consisting of an iron core with an air gap, most of the energy is stored in the gap.
9. In an ideal transformer, the voltage across each coil is proportional to its number of turns, the net mmf is zero, and the power efficiency is 100 percent.
10. Equivalent circuits for real transformers are shown in Figures 28 and 29.
11. Efficiency and regulation are important aspects of transformer operation.

Problems

Section 1: Magnetic Fields

P1. State Faraday's law of magnetic induction and Lenz's law.

P2. State Ampère's law, including the reference directions for the currents.

P3. State the right-hand rule as it applies to: **a.** a current-carrying conductor; **b.** a current-carrying coil.

P4. What is the fundamental cause of magnetic fields?

***P5.** A bar magnet is inserted into a single-turn coil as illustrated in Figure P5. Is the voltage v_{ab} positive or negative as the bar approaches the coil?

***P6.** The magnetic field of the earth is approximately 3×10^{-5} T. At what distance from a

* Denotes that answers are contained in the Student Solutions files. See Appendix "On-Line Student Resources" for more information about accessing the Student Solutions.

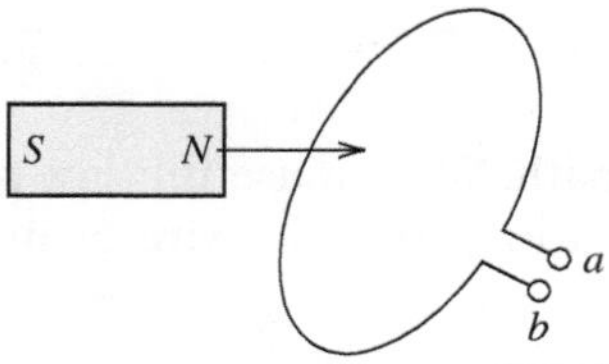

Figure P5

long straight wire carrying a steady current of 10 A is the field equal to 10 percent of the earth's field? Suggest at least two ways to help reduce the effect of electrical circuits on the navigation compass in a boat or airplane.

***P7.** A 0.5-m length of wire carries a 10-A current perpendicular to a magnetic field. Determine the magnetic flux density needed so that the force on the wire is 3 N.

P8. A long copper pipe carries a dc current. Is there a magnetic field inside the pipe due to the current? Outside? Justify your answers.

P9. An irregular loop of wire carries an electrical current as illustrated in Figure P9. Is there a *net* force on the loop due to the magnetic fields created? Justify your answer. (*Hint:* Consider Newton's third law of motion.)

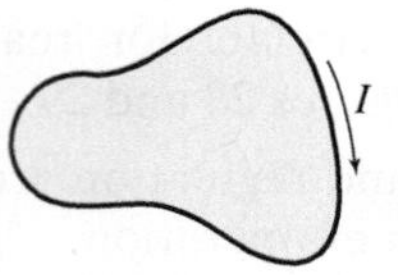

Figure P9

P10. Using equations given in Section 1, perform dimensional analyses to determine the units of μ, **B**, and **H** in terms of meters, kilograms, seconds, and coulombs.

P11. Use the right-hand rule to find the direction of the magnetic flux for each coil shown in Figure P11. Mark the N and S ends of each coil. Do the coils attract or repel one another?

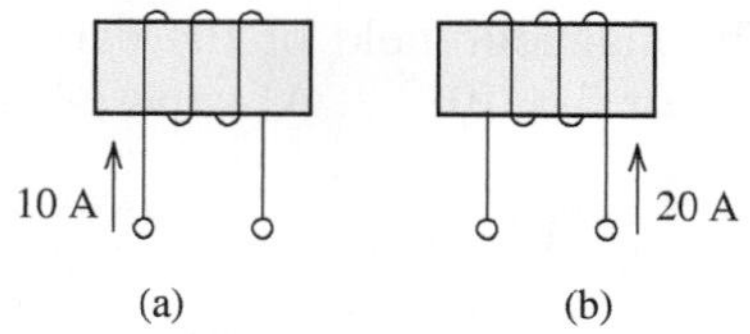

Figure P11

P12. Suppose that the flux ϕ linking the coils shown in Figure P12 is increasing in magnitude. Find the polarity of the voltage across each coil.

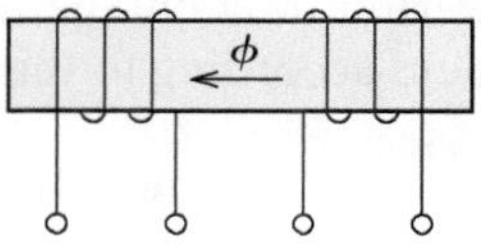

Figure P12

P13. Two very long parallel wires are 1 cm apart and carry currents of 10 A in the same direction. The material surrounding the wires has $\mu_r = 1$. Determine the force on a 0.5-m section of one of the wires. Do the wires attract or repel one another?

***P14.** A uniform flux density of 1 T is perpendicular to the plane of a five-turn circular coil of radius 10 cm. Find the flux linking the coil and the flux linkages. Suppose that the field is decreased to zero at a uniform rate in 1 ms. Find the magnitude of the voltage induced in the coil.

***P15.** Suppose that we test a material and find that $B = 0.1$ Wb/m^2 for an applied H of 50 A/m. Compute the relative permeability of the material.

P16. Consider two coils which are wound on nonmagnetic forms such that part of the flux produced by each coil links the other, as shown in Figure P16. Assume that the inductance of

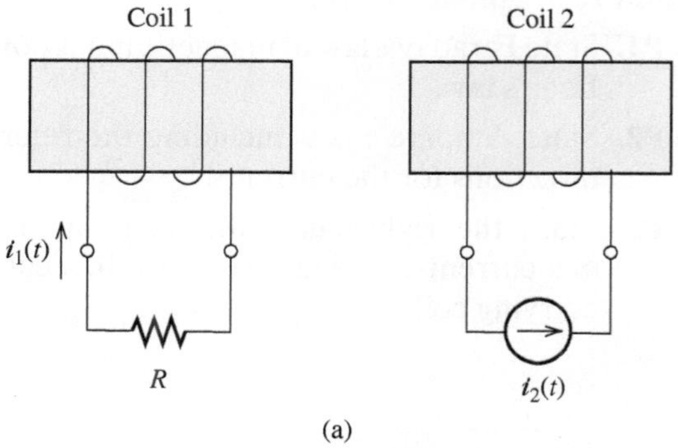

Figure P16

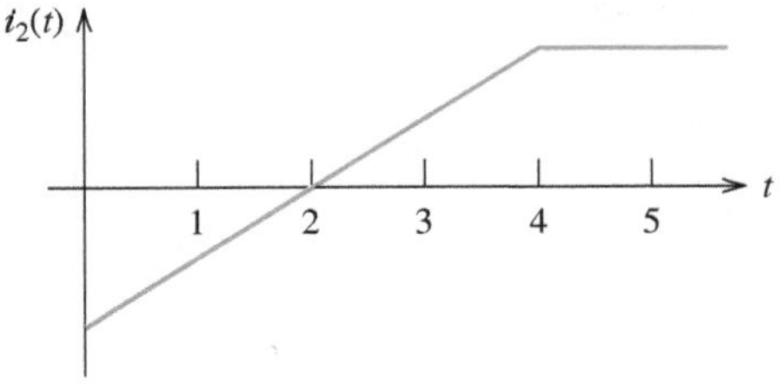

(b)

Figure P16 (Cont.)

the left-hand coil is small enough so that $i_1(t)$ is equal to the voltage induced by the magnetic field of the right-hand coil divided by the resistance. At $t = 1$ s, is the force between the coils attraction, repulsion, or zero? Explain your reasoning. Repeat for $t = 2, 3,$ and 5 s.

P17. A 200-turn toroidal coil (see Figure 8) has $r = 1$ cm and $R = 10$ cm. When a current given by $0.05 \sin(200t)$A flows in the coil, the voltage is $0.5 \cos(200t)$A. Determine the flux ϕ as a function of time and the relative permeability of the core material.

P18. A uniform flux density given by $B = 0.3 \sin(377t)$ T is perpendicular to the plane of a 1000-turn circular coil of radius 20 cm. Find the flux linkages and the voltage as functions of time.

P19. Suppose that, in designing an electrical generator, we need to produce a voltage of 120 V by moving a straight conductor through a uniform magnetic field of 0.5 T at a speed of 30 m/s. The conductor, its motion, and the field are mutually perpendicular. What is the required length of the conductor? It turns out that in generator design, a conductor of this length is impractical, and we must use N conductors of length 0.1 m. However, by connecting the conductors in series, we can obtain the required 120 V. What is the number N of conductors needed?

P20. Two infinitely long, very thin wires lie on the x and y axes and carry currents as shown in Figure P20. **a.** Show the direction of the forces on the wires due to the magnetic fields on the positive and negative part of each axis, assuming that I_x and I_y are both positive. **b.** Compute the torque on the wire that lies on the y axis.

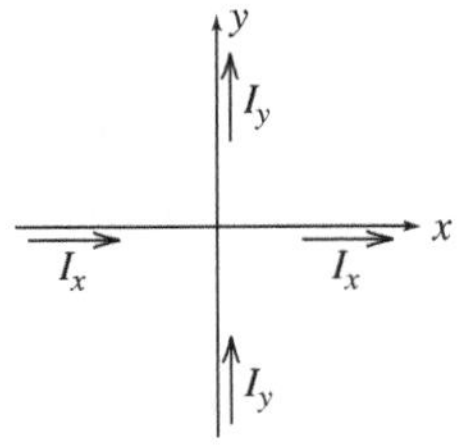

Figure P20

P21. A very long, straight wire carrying a constant current $i(t) = I_1$ and a rectangular single-turn coil lie in the same plane, as illustrated in Figure P22. The wire and the coil are surrounded by air. A source is applied to the coil causing a constant clockwise current I_2 to flow in the loop. **a.** Derive an expression for the net force exerted on the coil due to the magnetic field of the wire. **b.** Evaluate the force given that $I_1 = I_2 = 10$ A, $l = 10$ cm, $r_1 = 1$ cm, and $r_2 = 10$ cm. **c.** Is the loop attracted or repelled by the wire?

P22. A very long, straight wire carrying current $i(t)$ and a rectangular single-turn coil lie in the same plane, as illustrated in Figure P22. The wire and the coil are surrounded by air. **a.** Derive an expression for the flux linking the coil. **b.** Derive an expression for the voltage $v_{ab}(t)$ induced in the coil. **c.** Determine the rms value of v_{ab}, given that $i(t)$ is a 10-A rms 60-Hz sinusoid, $l = 10$ cm, $r_1 = 1$ cm, and $r_2 = 10$ cm.

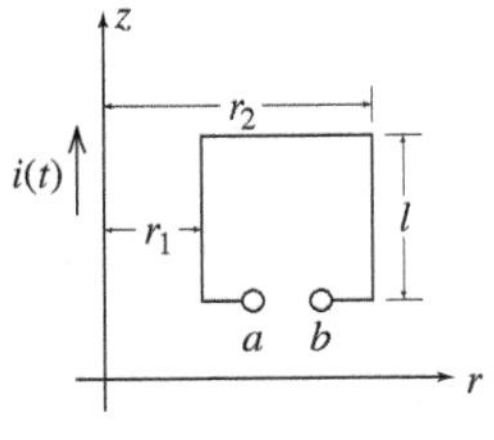

Figure P22

P23. A 120-V-rms 60-Hz sinusoidal voltage appears across a 500-turn coil. Determine the peak and rms values of the flux linking the coil.

Section 2: Magnetic Circuits

***P24.** Consider the magnetic circuit of Figure 13 that was analyzed in Example 6. Suppose that the length of gap *a* is reduced to zero. Compute the flux in gap *b*. Why is the result less than that found in Example 6?

***P25.** An air gap has a length of 0.1 cm. What length of iron core has the same reluctance as the air gap? The relative permeability of the iron is 5000. Assume that the cross-sectional areas of the gap and the core are the same.

***P26.** What quantity in a magnetic circuit is analogous to a voltage source in an electrical circuit? To resistance? To current?

P27. What happens to the reluctance of a magnetic path if its length is doubled? If the cross-sectional area is doubled? If the relative permeability is doubled?

P28. What are the physical units of reluctance in terms of kilograms, coulombs, meters, and seconds?

P29. Draw the electrical circuit analog for the magnetic circuit shown in Figure P29. Pay special attention to the polarities of the voltage sources. Determine the flux density in the core.

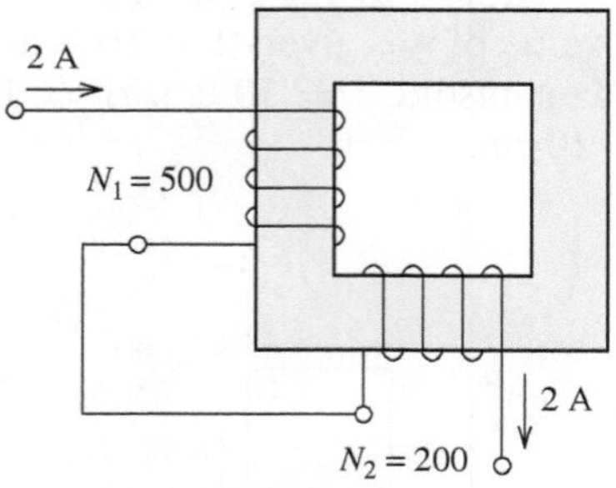

Cross-section = 3 cm × 3 cm
Path length = 36 cm
$\mu_r = 1000$

Figure P29

P30. Compute the flux in each leg of the magnetic core shown in Figure P30.

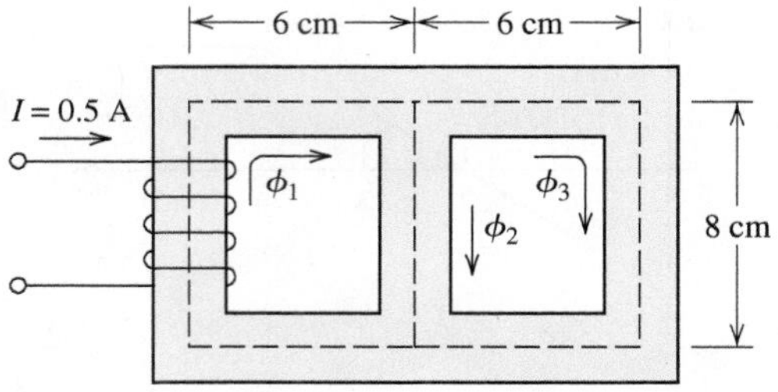

$N = 1000$ turns
Core cross-section: 2 cm × 2 cm
$\mu_r = 5000$

Figure P30

P31. Consider the magnetic circuit shown in Figure P31. Assume that the reluctance of the iron is small enough so it can be neglected. The lengths of the air gaps are 0.1 cm, and the effective area of each gap is 20 cm^2. Determine the total number of turns needed to produce a flux density of 0.5 T in the gaps.

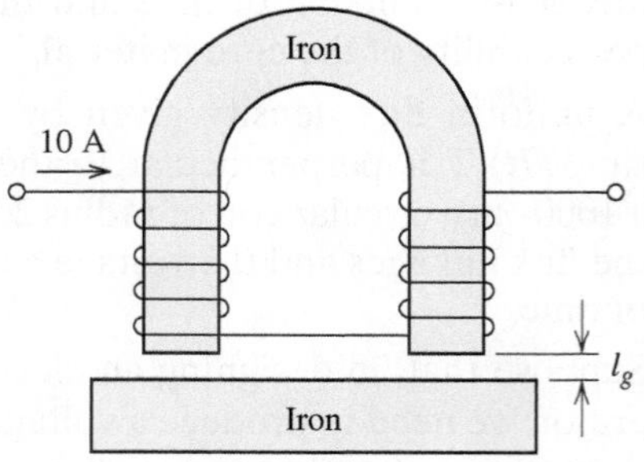

Figure P31

P32. Compute the flux in each leg of the core shown in Figure P32. Account for fringing by adding the gap length to each of the cross-sectional dimensions of the gap.

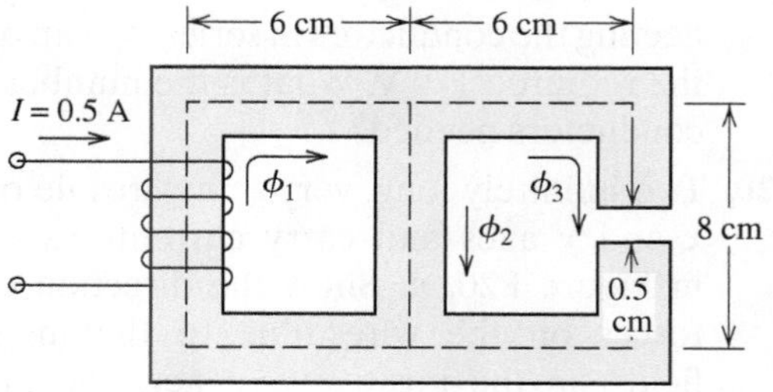

$N = 1000$ turns
Core cross-section: 2 cm × 2 cm
$\mu_r = 5000$

Figure P32

***P33.** Consider the *solenoid* shown in Figure P33, which is typical of those commonly used as actuators for mechanisms and for operating valves in chemical processes. Neglect fringing and the reluctance of the core. Derive an expression for the flux as a function of the physical dimensions, μ_0, the number of turns N, and the current.

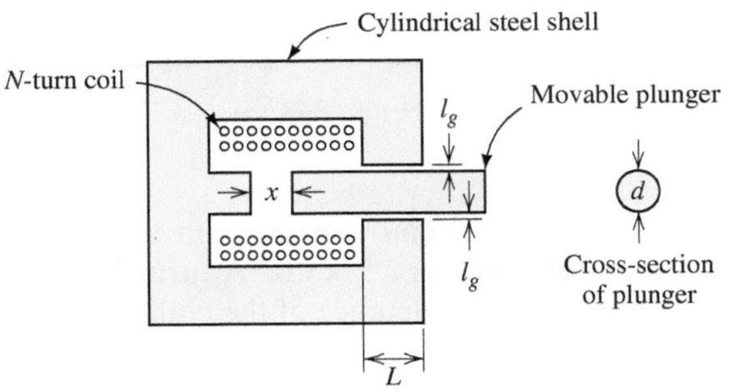

Figure P33

P34. Consider the core shown in Figure P34, which has two coils of N turns, each connected so that the fluxes aid in the center leg. Determine the value of N so that $I = 2$ A produces a flux density of 0.25 T in the gap. The gap and the core have square cross-sections 2 cm on each side. Account for fringing by adding the gap length to the length of each side of the gap.

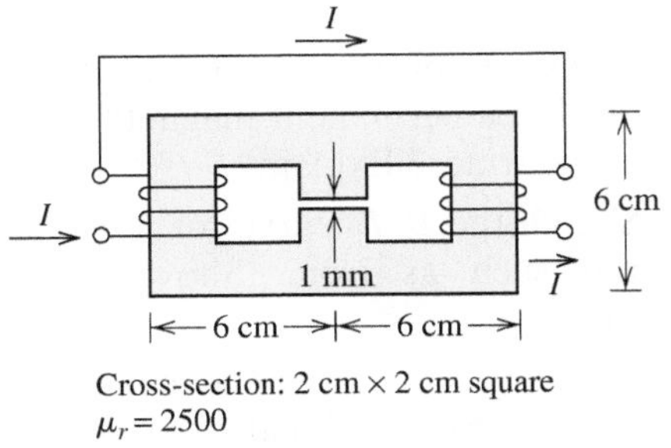

Figure P34

P35. Consider a toroidal core, as shown in Figure 11, that has a relative permeability of 1000, $R = 5$ cm, and $r = 2$ cm. Two windings are wound on the core, one with 200 turns and the other with 400 turns. A voltage source described by $v(t) = 10\cos(10^5 t)$ is applied to the 200-turn coil, and the 400-turn coil is open circuited. Determine the current in the 200-turn coil and the voltage across the 400-turn coil. Assume that all of the magnetic flux is confined to the core and that the current is a pure sine wave.

Section 3: Inductance and Mutual Inductance

***P36.** A 500-turn coil is wound on an iron core. When a 120-V-rms 60-Hz voltage is applied to the coil, the current is 1 A rms. Neglect the resistance of the coil. Determine the reluctance of the core. Given that the cross-sectional area of the core is 5 cm^2 and the length is 20 cm, determine the relative permeability of the core material.

***P37.** A 100-turn coil wound on a magnetic core is found to have an inductance of 200 mH. What inductance will be obtained if the number of turns is increased to 200, assuming that all of the flux links all of the turns?

P38. Write one or two paragraphs that explain the voltage–current relationship of an inductor in terms of basic principles of magnetic fields.

***P39.** Consider the circuit shown in Figure P39. The two coils have $L_1 = 0.1$ H, $L_2 = 10$ H, and $M = 0.5$ H. Prior to $t = 0$, the currents in the coils are zero. At $t = 0$, the switch closes. Determine and sketch $i_1(t)$ and $i_2(t)$ to scale versus time.

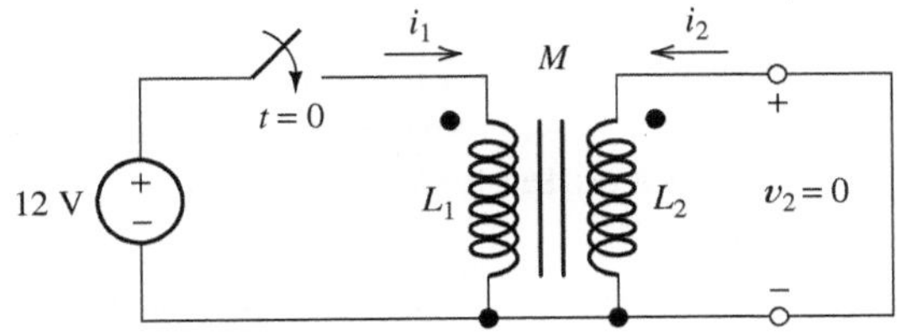

Figure P39

***P40.** Two coils wound on a common core have $L_1 = 1$ H, $L_2 = 2$ H, and $M = 0.5$ H. The currents are $i_1 = \cos(377t)$ A and $i_2 = 0.5\cos(377t)$ A. Both of the currents enter dotted terminals. Find expressions for the voltages across the coils.

P41. A symmetrical toroidal coil is wound on a plastic core ($\mu_r \cong 1$) and is found to have an inductance of 1 mH. What inductance will result if the core material is changed to a ferrite having $\mu_r = 200$? Assume that the entire magnetic path is composed of ferrite.

P42. A 100-turn coil is wound on a toroidal core and has an inductance of 100 mH. Suppose that a 200-turn coil is wound on a second toroidal core having dimensions (r and R as shown in Figure 11) that are double those of the first core. Both cores are made of the same material, which has very high permeability. Determine the inductance of the second coil.

P43. A relay has a 500-turn coil that draws 50 mA rms when a 60-Hz voltage of 24 V rms is applied. Assume that the resistance of the coil is negligible. Determine the peak flux linking the coil, the reluctance of the core, and the inductance of the coil.

P44. Consider the coils shown in Figure P12. Suppose that a dot is placed on the leftmost terminal. Place a dot on the appropriate terminal of the right-hand coil to indicate the sense of the coupling.

P45. Two coils wound on a common core have $L_1 = 0.2$ H, $L_2 = 0.5$ H, and $M = 0.1$ H. The currents are $i_1 = \exp(-1000t)$ A and $i_2 = 2\exp(-1000t)$ A. Both of the currents enter dotted terminals. Find expressions for the voltages across the coils.

P46. Two coils wound on a common core have $L_1 = 1$ H, $L_2 = 2$ H, and $M = 0.5$ H. The currents are $i_1 = 1$ A and $i_2 = 0.5$ A. If both currents enter dotted terminals, find the flux linkages of both coils. Repeat if i_1 enters a dotted terminal and i_2 leaves a dotted terminal.

P47. Two coils having inductances L_1 and L_2 are wound on a common core. The fraction of the flux produced by one coil that links the other coil is called the *coefficient of coupling* and is denoted by k. Derive an expression for the mutual inductance M in terms of L_1, L_2, and k.

P48. Consider the circuit shown in Figure P48. The two coils have $L_1 = 0.1$ H, $L_2 = 10$ H, and $M = 1$ H. Prior to $t = 0$, the currents in the coils are zero. At $t = 0$, the switch closes. Determine and sketch $i_1(t)$ and $v_2(t)$ to scale versus time.

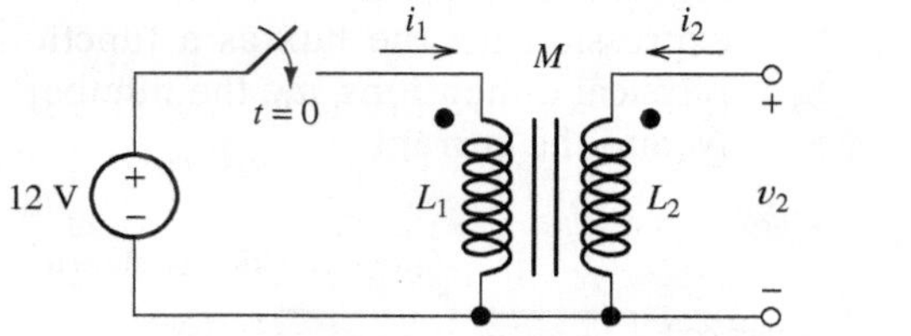

Figure P48

P49. A 200-turn coil is wound on a core having a reluctance of 5×10^5 A·turns/Wb. Determine the inductance of the coil.

Section 4: Magnetic Materials

***P50.** For operation at 60 Hz and a given peak flux density, the core loss of a given core is 1 W due to hysteresis and 0.5 W due to eddy currents. Estimate the core loss for 400-Hz operation with the same peak flux density.

***P51.** What are two causes of core loss for a coil with an iron core excited by an ac current? What considerations are important in minimizing loss due to each of these causes? What happens to the power loss in each case if the frequency of operation is doubled while maintaining constant peak flux density?

P52. What characteristic is desirable in the B–H curve for a prospective material to be used in a permanent magnet? In a motor or transformer? Explain.

P53. Sketch the B–H curve for a magnetic material such as iron. Show hysteresis and saturation.

P54. A magnetic core has a mean length of 20 cm, a cross-sectional area of 4 cm^2, and a relative permeability of 2000. A 500-turn coil wound on the core carries a dc current of 0.1 A. **a.** Determine the reluctance of the core, the flux density in the core, and the inductance. **b.** Compute the energy stored in the magnetic field as $W = (1/2)LI^2$. **c.** Use Equation 41 to compute the energy density in the core. Then, compute the energy by taking the product of energy density and volume. Compare to the value found in part (b).

P55. At a frequency of 60 Hz, the core loss of a certain coil with an iron core is 1.8 W, and at a frequency of 120 Hz, it is 5.6 W. The peak flux density is the same for both cases. Determine the power loss due to hysteresis and that due to eddy currents for 60-Hz operation.

P56. A certain iron core has an air gap with an effective area of 2 cm × 3 cm and a length l_g. The applied magnetomotive force is 1000 A·turns, and the reluctance of the iron is negligible. Find the flux density and the energy stored in the air gap as a function of l_g.

P57. Consider a coil wound on an iron core. Suppose that for operation with a given 60-Hz ac current, the hysteresis loop of the core material takes the form of a rectangle, as shown in Figure P57. The core volume is 1000 cm^3. Find the power converted to heat because of hysteresis.

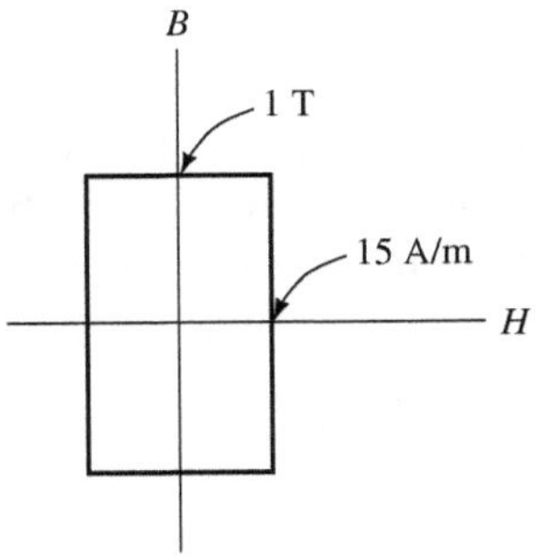

Figure P57

Section 5: Ideal Transformers

P58. What assumptions did we make in deriving the relationships between the voltages and currents in an ideal transformer?

***P59.** Suppose that we need to cause a 25-Ω load resistance to appear as a 100-Ω resistance to the source. Instead of using a transformer, we could place a 75-Ω resistance in series with the 25-Ω resistance. From the standpoint of power efficiency, which approach is better? Explain.

***P60.** In U.S. residences, electrical power is generally utilized at a nominal voltage of 120 V rms. What problems would become pronounced if the power distribution system and household appliances had been designed for a lower voltage (say, 12 V rms)? For a higher voltage (say, 12 kV)?

***P61.** Consider the transformer having three windings, as shown in Figure P61. **a.** Place dots on windings to indicate the sense of the coupling between coil 1 and coil 2; between coil 1 and coil 3. **b.** Assuming that all of the flux links all of the turns, determine the voltages $\mathbf{V}_2$ and $\mathbf{V}_3$. **c.** Assuming that the net mmf required to establish the core flux is zero, find an expression for $\mathbf{I}_1$ in terms of $\mathbf{I}_2$, $\mathbf{I}_3$, and the turns ratios. Then, compute the value of $\mathbf{I}_1$.

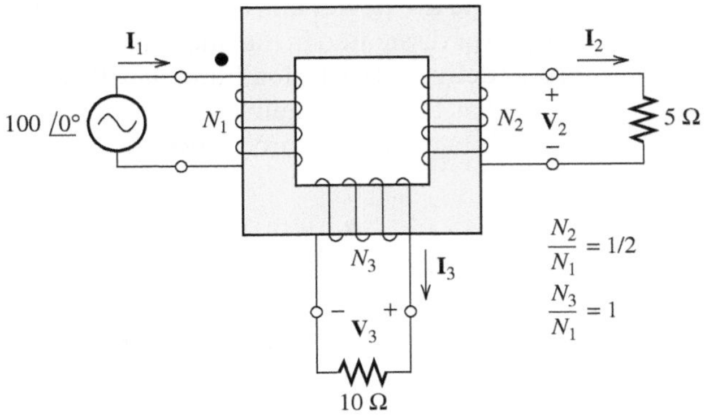

Figure P61

P62. Consider the circuit shown in Figure P62. Find the secondary voltage $V_{2\text{rms}}$, the secondary current $I_{2\text{rms}}$, and the power delivered to the load if the turns ratio is $N_1/N_2 = 10$. Repeat for $N_1/N_2 = 1$ and for $N_1/N_2 = 0.1$.

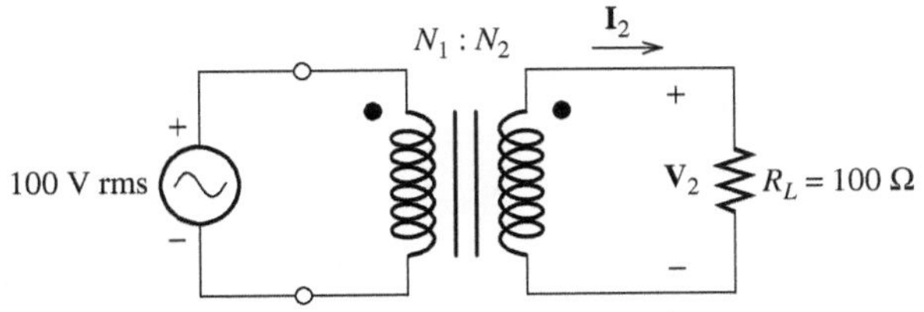

Figure P62

P63. A transformer is needed that will cause an actual load resistance of 25 Ω to appear as 100 Ω to an ac voltage source of 240 V rms. Draw the diagram of the circuit required. What turns ratio is required for the transformer? Find the current taken from the source, the current flowing through the load, and the load voltage.

P64. A voltage source V_s is to be connected to a resistive load $R_L = 10\ \Omega$ by a transmission line having a resistance $R_{\text{line}} = 10\ \Omega$, as shown in Figure P64. In part (a) of the figure, no transformers are used. In part (b) of the figure, one transformer is used to step up the source voltage at the sending end of the line, and another transformer is used to step the voltage back down at the load. For each case, determine the power delivered by the source; the power dissipated in the line resistance; the power delivered to the load; and the efficiency, defined as the power delivered to the load as a percentage of the source power.

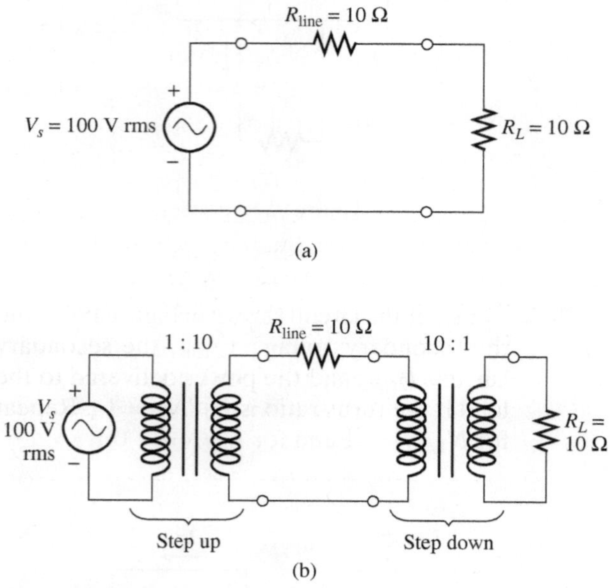

Figure P64

P65. Consider the circuit shown in Figure P65. **a.** Determine the values of $\mathbf{I}_1$ and $\mathbf{V}_2$. **b.** For each of the sources, determine the average power and state whether power is delivered by or absorbed by the source. **c.** Move the dot on the secondary to the bottom end of the coil and repeat parts (a) and (b).

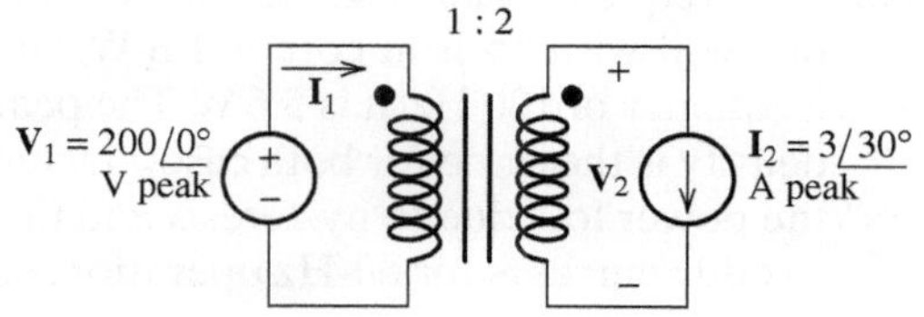

Figure P65

P66. **a.** Reflect the resistances and voltage sources to the left-hand side of the circuit shown in Figure P66 and solve for the current $\mathbf{I}_1$. **b.** Repeat with the dot moved to the top of the right-hand coil.

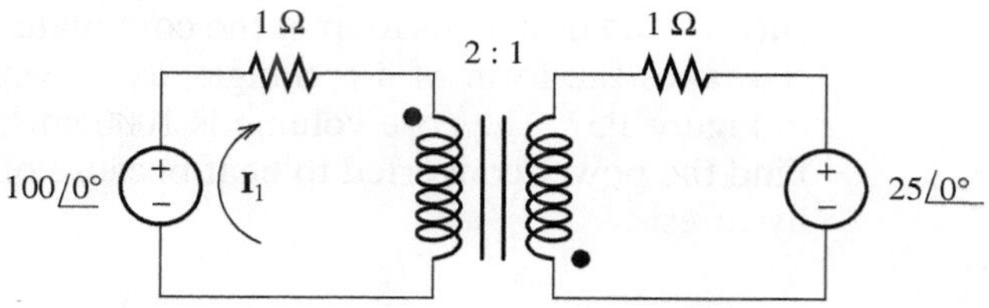

Figure P66

P67. A type of transformer known as an *autotransformer* is shown in Figure P67. **a.** Assuming that all of the flux links all of the turns, determine the relationship between v_1, v_2, and the

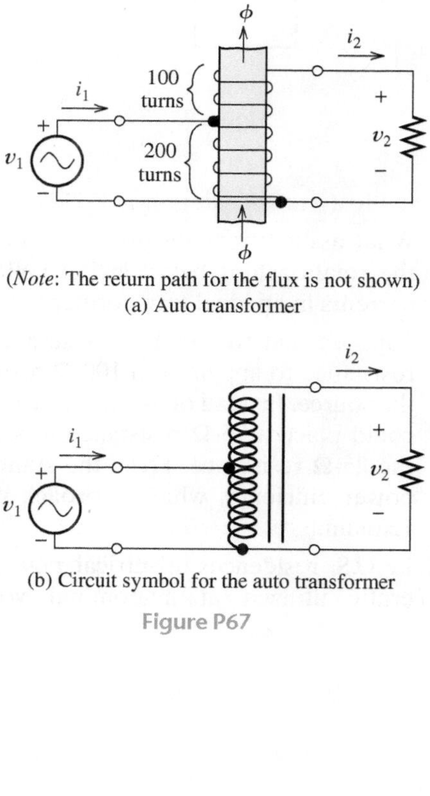

Figure P67

number of turns. **b.** Assuming that the total mmf required to establish the flux is zero, find the relationship between the currents i_1 and i_2.

P68. Find the equivalent resistance R'_L and capacitance C'_L seen looking into the transformers in Figure P68. (*Hint:* Keep in mind that it is the *impedance* that is reflected by the square of the turns ratio.)

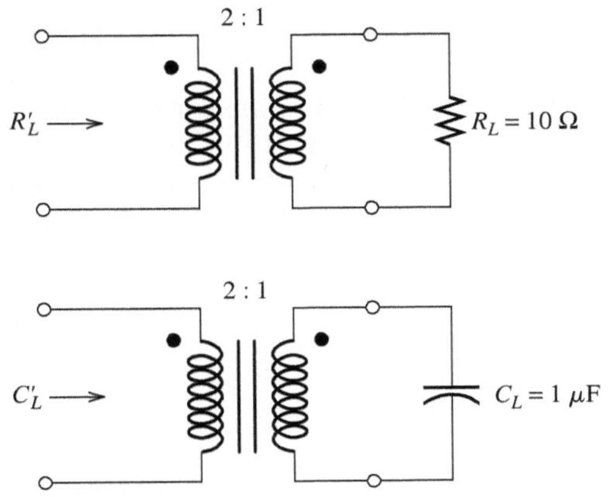

Figure P68

P69. An autotransformer is shown in Figure P69. Assume that all of the flux links all of the turns and that negligible mmf is needed to establish the flux. Determine the values of $\mathbf{I}_1, \mathbf{I}_2, \mathbf{I}_3$, and $\mathbf{V}_2$.

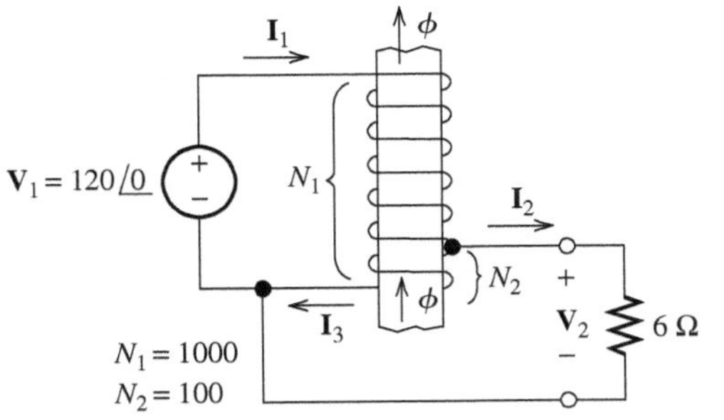

Figure P69

Section 6: Real Transformers

***P70.** Draw an equivalent circuit for a real transformer. Briefly discuss the reason that each element appears in the equivalent circuit.

***P71.** A 60-Hz 20-kVA 8000/240-V-rms transformer has the following equivalent-circuit parameters:

Primary resistance	R_1	15 Ω
Secondary resistance	R_2	0.02 Ω
Primary leakage reactance	$X_1 = \omega L_1$	120 Ω
Secondary leakage reactance	$X_2 = \omega L_2$	0.15 Ω
Magnetizing reactance	$X_m = \omega L_m$	30 kΩ
Core-loss resistance	R_c	200 kΩ

Find the percentage regulation and power efficiency for the transformer for a 2-kVA load (i.e., 10 percent of rated capacity) having a lagging power factor of 0.8.

P72. When operating with an open-circuit load and with rated primary voltage, a certain 60-Hz 20-kVA 8000/240-V-rms transformer has a primary current of 0.315 A rms and absorbs 360 W. Which of the elements of the equivalent circuit of Figure 29(b) can be determined from this data? Find the numerical values of these elements.

***P73.** Usually, transformers are designed to operate with peak flux densities just below saturation of the core material. Why would we not want to design them to operate far below the saturation point? Far above the saturation point? Assume that the voltage and current ratings are to remain constant.

P74. Under the assumptions that we made for the ideal transformer, we determined that $v_2 = (N_2/N_1)v_1$. Theoretically, if a dc voltage is applied to the primary of an ideal transformer, a dc voltage should appear across the secondary winding. However, real transformers are ineffective for dc. Use the equivalent circuit of Figure 28 to explain.

P75. A 60-Hz 20-kVA 8000/240-V-rms transformer has the following equivalent-circuit parameters:

Primary resistance	R_1	15 Ω
Secondary resistance	R_2	0.02 Ω
Primary leakage reactance	$X_1 = \omega L_1$	120 Ω
Secondary leakage reactance	$X_2 = \omega L_2$	0.15 Ω
Magnetizing reactance	$X_m = \omega L_m$	30 kΩ
Core-loss resistance	R_c	200 kΩ

Find the percentage regulation and power efficiency for the transformer for a rated load having a lagging power factor of 0.8.

P76. A certain 60-Hz, 20-kVA, 8000/240 V-rms transformer is operated with a short-circuited secondary and reduced primary voltage. It is found that, for an applied primary voltage of 500 V rms, the primary current is 2.5 A rms (i.e., this is the rated primary current) and the transformer absorbs 270 W. Consider the equivalent circuit of Figure 29(b). Under the stated conditions, the current and power for L_m and R_c can be neglected. Explain why. Determine the values of the total leakage inductance referred to the primary ($L_1 + a^2L_2$) and the total resistance referred to the primary ($R_1 + a^2R_2$).

P77. A certain residence is supplied with electrical power by the transformer of Table 1. The residence uses 400 kWh of electrical energy per month. From the standpoint of energy efficiency, which of the equivalent circuit elements listed in the table are most significant? You will need to use good judgment and make some assumptions in obtaining an answer.

P78. We have a transformer designed to operate at 60 Hz. The voltage ratings are 4800 V rms and 240 V rms for the primary and secondary windings, respectively. The transformer is rated for 10 kVA. Now, we want to use this transformer at 120 Hz. Discuss the factors that must be considered in setting ratings appropriate for operation at the new frequency. (Keep in mind that for best utilization of the material in the transformer, we want the peak flux density to be nearly at saturation for both frequencies.)

Practice Test

Here is a practice test you can use to check your comprehension of the most important concepts in this chapter. Answers can be found in Appendix "Answers for the Practice Tests" and complete solutions are included in the Student Solutions files. See Appendix "On-Line Student Resources" for more information about the Student Solutions.

T1. Consider a right-hand Cartesian coordinate system as shown in Figure 3. We have a wire along the x-axis carrying 12 A in the positive x direction and a constant flux density of 0.3 T directed in the positive z direction. **a.** Determine the force and its direction on a 0.2 m length of the wire. **b.** Repeat if the field is directed in the positive x direction.

T2. Suppose we have a ten-turn square coil 25 cm on each side lying in the x-y plane. A magnetic flux density is directed in the positive z direction and is given by $0.7 \sin(120\pi t)$ T. The flux is constant with respect to x, y, and z. Determine the voltage induced in the coil.

T3. A 20-cm length of wire moves at 15 m/s in a constant flux density of 0.4 T. The wire, direction of motion, and direction of the flux are mutually perpendicular. Determine the voltage induced in the wire segment.

T4. Consider the magnetic circuit shown in Figure T4. The core has a relative permeability of 1500. **a.** Carefully estimate the flux density in the air gap. **b.** Determine the inductance of the coil.

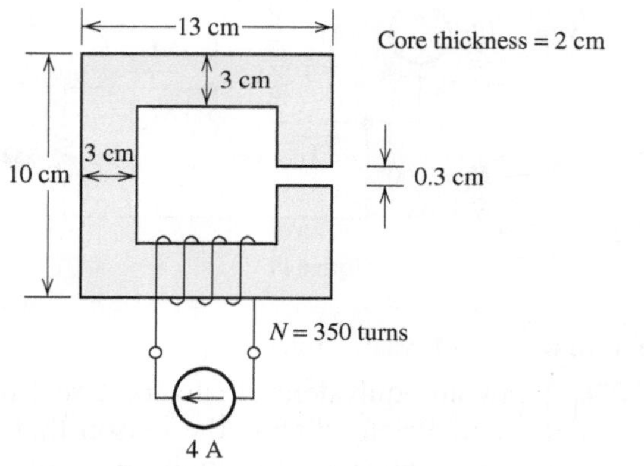

Figure T4

T5. Suppose we have an ac current flowing through a coil wound on an iron core. Name two mechanisms by which energy is converted to heat in the core material. For each, how is the core material selected to minimize the power loss? How does each power loss depend on the frequency of the ac current?

T6. Consider the circuit shown in Figure T6 which has $R_s = 0.5\,\Omega$, $R_L = 1000\,\Omega$, and $N_1/N_2 = 0.1$. **a.** Determine the rms values of the currents and voltages with the switch open. **b.** Repeat with the switch closed.

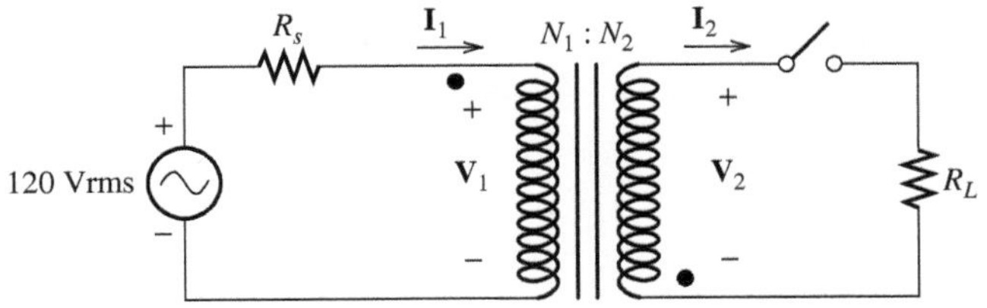

Figure T6

T7. You have been assigned to select a transformer to supply a peak power of 100 kW to a load that draws peak power only a very small percentage of the time and draws very little power the rest of the time. Two transformers, A and B, are both suitable. While both transformers have the same efficiency at peak load, most of the loss in A is due to core loss, and most of the loss in B is due to the resistances of the coils. From the standpoint of operating costs, which transformer is better? Why?

ANSWERS FOR THE PRACTICE TESTS

Complete solutions for the practice tests are included in the Student Solutions files. See Appendix "On-Line Student Resources" for information on how to access these files.

T1. **a.** The force is 0.72 N pointing in the negative y direction. **b.** The force is zero.

T2. $v = 164.9\cos(120\pi t)$ V.

T3. 1.2 V.

T4. **a.** $B_{gap} = 0.5357$ T; **b.** $L = 35.58$ mH.

T5. The two mechanisms by which power is converted to heat in an iron core are hysteresis and eddy currents. To minimize loss due to hysteresis, we choose a material for which the plot of B versus H displays a thin hysteresis loop. To minimize loss due to eddy currents, we make the core from laminated sheets or from powdered iron held together by an insulating binder. Hysteresis loss is proportional to frequency and eddy-current loss is proportional to the square of frequency.

T6. **a.** $I_{1rms} = 0$, $I_{2rms} = 0$, $V_{1rms} = 120$ V, $V_{2rms} = 1200$ V. **b.** $I_{1rms} = 11.43$ A, $I_{2rms} = 1.143$ A, $V_{1rms} = 114.3$ V, $V_{2rms} = 1143$ V.

T7. Transformer B is better from the standpoint of total energy loss and operating costs.

ON-LINE STUDENT RESOURCES

Users of the text can access the Student Solutions Manual (and other folders mentioned below) in electronic form by following links starting from the website:

`www.pearsonhighered.com/hambley`

The MATLAB folder contains m-files. Except for the examples that use the Symbolic Toolbox, these files work equally well with MathScript, which is sometimes included with the LabVIEW program. The Hambley MathScript folder contains the m-files that work with MathScript.

The Virtual Instruments folder contains LabVIEW programs.

DC Machines

From Chapter 16 of *Electrical Engineering: Principles and Applications*, Sixth Edition. Allan R. Hambley.

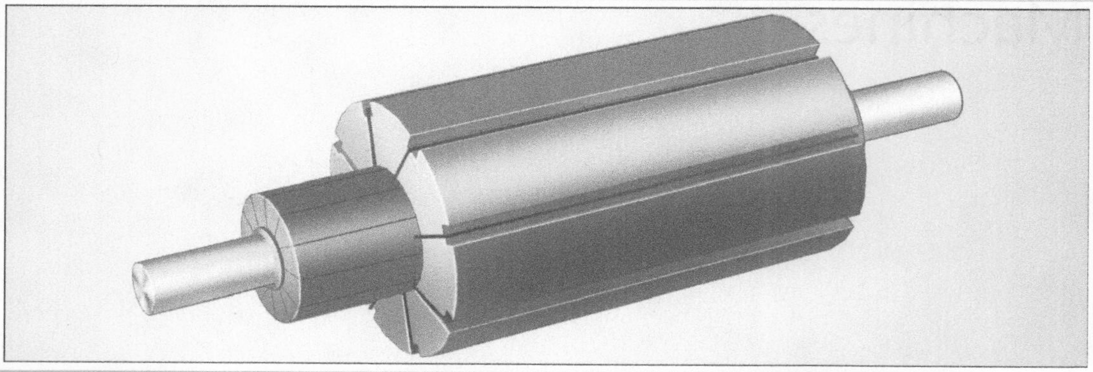

DC Machines

Study of this chapter will enable you to:

- Select the proper motor type for various applications.
- State how torque varies with speed for various motors.
- Use the equivalent circuit for dc motors to compute electrical and mechanical quantities.
- Use motor nameplate data.
- Understand the operation and characteristics of shunt-connected dc motors, series-connected dc motors, and universal motors.

Introduction to this chapter:

In this chapter, we consider machines that convert mechanical energy to and from electrical energy. **Motors** convert electrical energy into rotational mechanical energy. Conversely, **generators** convert mechanical energy into electrical energy. Most electrical machines can be used either as motors or as generators.

Electrical motors are used to power hundreds of the devices that we use in everyday life, such as computer disks, refrigerators, garage-door openers, washing machines, food mixers, vacuum cleaners, DVD players, ventilation fans, automotive power windows, windshield wipers, elevators, and so on. Industrial applications include bulk material handling, machining operations, pumps, rock crushers, fans, compressors, and hoists. Electrical motors are the best choice in the vast majority of stationary applications where mechanical energy is needed, whether it is a tiny fraction of a horsepower or thousands of horsepower. It is important for designers of mechanical systems that employ motors to have a good understanding of the external characteristics of various motors so they can choose the proper types to power their systems.

1 OVERVIEW OF MOTORS

We will see that there are many kinds of electrical motors. In this section, we give a brief overview of electrical motors, their specifications, and operating characteristics. Then, in the remainder of this chapter, we discuss dc machines in detail. We cite the three-phase ac induction motor as an example frequently in this section because it is the type in most widespread use. However, many of the concepts discussed in this section apply to other types of electrical motors as well.

You will find this section useful both as a preview of motor characteristics and as a convenient summary after you finish studying this chapter.

Basic Construction

An electrical motor consists of a stationary part, or **stator**, and a **rotor**, which is the rotating part connected to a shaft that couples the machine to its mechanical load. The shaft and rotor are supported by bearings so that they can rotate freely. This is illustrated in Figure 1.

Depending on the type of machine, either the stator or the rotor (or both) contain current-carrying conductors configured into coils. Slots are cut into the stator and rotor to contain the windings and their insulation. Currents in the windings set up magnetic fields and interact with fields to produce torque.

Usually, the stator and the rotor are made of iron to intensify the magnetic field. As in transformers, if the magnetic field alternates in direction through the iron with time, the iron must be laminated to avoid large power losses due to eddy currents. (In certain parts of some machines, the field is steady and lamination is not necessary.)

The characteristics of several common types of machines are summarized in Table 1. At this point, many of the entries in the table will probably not be very meaningful to you, particularly if this is the first time that you have studied rotating

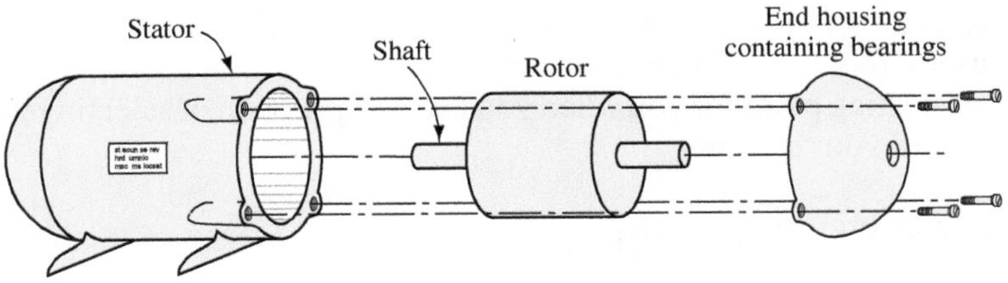

Figure 1 An electrical motor consists of a cylindrical rotor that spins inside a stator.

Table 1. Characteristics of Electrical Motors

		Type	Power Range (hp)	Rotor	Stator	Comments and Applications
Ac motors	Three phase	Induction	1–5000	Squirrel cage	Three-phase armature windings	Simple rugged construction; very common; fans, pumps
				Wound field		Adjustable speed using rotor resistance; cranes, hoists
		Synchronous	1–5	Permanent magnet		Precise speed; transport sheet materials
			1000–50,000	Dc field winding		Large constant loads; potential for power-factor correction
	Single phase	Induction	$\frac{1}{3}$–5	Squirrel cage	Main and auxiliary windings	Several types: split phase, capacitor start, capacitor run; simple and rugged; many household applications: fans, water pumps, refrigerators
		Synchronous	$\frac{1}{10}$ or less	Reluctance or hysteresis	Armature winding	Low torque, fixed speed; timing applications
Dc motors	Wound field	Shunt connected	10–200	Armature winding	Field winding	Industrial applications, grinding, machine tools, hoists
		Series connected				High torque at low speed; dangerous if not loaded; drills, automotive starting motors, (universal motor used for single-phase ac has high power/weight ratio)
		Compound connected				Can be designed to tailor torque–speed characteristic; traction motors
	Permanent-magnet field		$\frac{1}{20}$–10	Armature winding	Permanent magnets	Servo applications, machine tools, computer peripherals, automotive fans, window motors

electrical machinery. However, as we progress through this chapter, the table will become a useful tool for comparing the various types of motors. Also, it will provide a convenient starting point for you when you face the problem of selecting the proper motor for one of your systems.

Armature and Field Windings

As we have mentioned, a machine may contain several sets of windings. In most types of machines, a given winding can be classed either as a **field winding** or as an **armature winding**. (We avoid classification of armature and field windings for induction motors and simply refer to stator windings and rotor conductors.) The primary purpose of a field winding is to set up the magnetic field in the machine. The current in the field winding is independent of the mechanical load imposed on the motor (except in series-connected motors). On the other hand, the armature winding carries a current that depends on the mechanical power produced. Typically, the armature current amplitude is small when the load is light and larger for heavier loads. If the machine acts as a generator, the electrical output is taken from the armature. In some machines, the field is produced by permanent magnets (PM), and a field winding is not needed.

The purpose of the field winding is to set up the magnetic field required to produce torque.

The armature windings carry currents that vary with mechanical load. When the machine is used as a generator, the output is taken from the armature windings.

Table 1 shows the location (stator or rotor) of the field and armature windings for some common machine types. For example, in three-phase synchronous ac machines, the field winding is on the rotor, and the armature is on the stator. In other machines, such as the wound-field dc machine, the locations are reversed. You may find it convenient to refer to Table 1 from time to time throughout this chapter to help avoid confusion between the different types of machines.

AC Motors

Motors can be powered from either ac or dc sources. Ac power can be either single phase or three phase. Ac motors include several types:

1. Induction motors, which are the most common type because they have relatively simple rugged construction and good operating characteristics.
2. Synchronous motors, which run at constant speed regardless of load torque, assuming that the frequency of the electrical source is constant, which is usually the case. Three-phase synchronous machines generate most of the electrical energy used in the world.
3. A variety of special-purpose types.

About two-thirds of the electrical energy generated in the United States is consumed by motors. Of this, well over half is used by induction motors. Thus, you are likely to encounter ac induction motors very frequently.

DC Motors

Dc motors are those that are powered from dc sources. One of the difficulties with dc motors is that nearly all electrical energy is distributed as ac. If only ac power is available and we need to use a dc motor, a rectifier or some other converter must be used to convert ac to dc. This adds to the expense of the system. Thus, ac machines are usually preferable if they meet the needs of the application.

Dc motors are common in automotive applications.

Exceptions are automotive applications in which dc is readily available from the battery. Dc motors are employed for starting, windshield wipers, fans, and power windows.

In the most common types of dc motors, the direction of the current in the armature conductors on the rotor is reversed periodically during rotation. This is accomplished with a mechanical switch composed of **brushes** mounted on the stator and a **commutator** mounted on the shaft. The commutator consists of conducting segments insulated from one another. Each commutator segment is connected to some of the armature conductors (on the rotor). The brushes are in sliding contact with the commutator. As the commutator rotates, switching action caused by the brushes moving from one segment to another changes the direction of current in the armature conductors. We explain this in more detail later; the important point here is that the brushes and commutator are subject to wear, and a significant disadvantage of dc motors is their relatively frequent need for maintenance.

A significant disadvantage of dc motors is the need for relatively frequent maintenance of brushes and commutators.

Until recently, an important advantage of dc motors was that their speed and direction could be controlled more readily than those of ac motors. However, this advantage is rapidly disappearing because electronic systems that can vary the frequency of an ac source have become economically advantageous. These variable-frequency sources can be used with simple rugged ac induction motors to achieve speed control.

Nevertheless, dc motors are still useful in some control applications and wherever dc power is readily available, such as in vehicles. Later in this chapter, we examine the various types of dc motors in more detail.

Losses, Power Ratings, and Efficiency

Figure 2 depicts the flow of power from a three-phase electrical source through an induction motor to a mechanical load such as a pump. Part of the electrical power is lost (converted to heat) due to resistance of the windings, hysteresis, and eddy currents. Similarly, some of the power that is converted to mechanical form is lost to friction and windage (i.e., moving the air surrounding the rotor and shaft). Part of the power loss to windage is sometimes intentional, because fan blades to promote cooling are fabricated as an integral part of the rotor.

The electrical input power P_{in}, in watts, supplied by the three-phase source is given by

$$P_{\text{in}} = \sqrt{3}V_{\text{rms}}I_{\text{rms}}\cos(\theta) \tag{1}$$

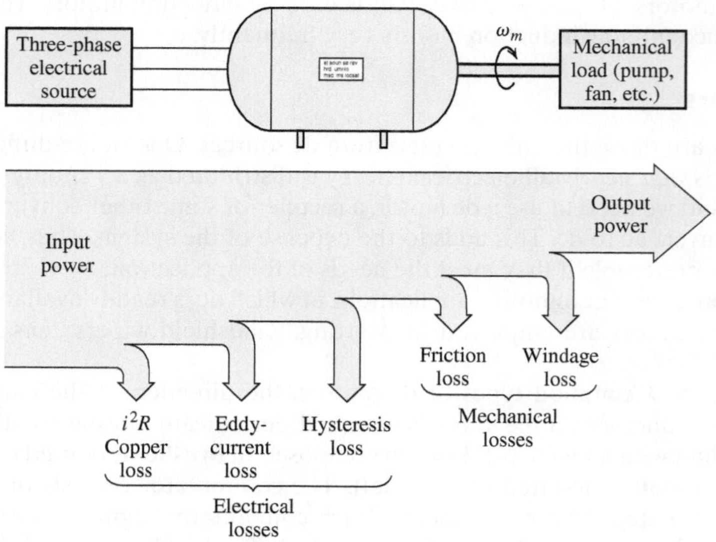

Figure 2 Power flows left to right from a three-phase electrical source into an induction motor and then to a mechanical load. Some of the power is lost along the way due to various causes.

where V_{rms} is the rms value of the line-to-line voltage, I_{rms} is the rms value of the line current, and $\cos(\theta)$ is the power factor.

The mechanical output power is

$$P_{out} = T_{out}\omega_m \tag{2}$$

in which P_{out} is the output power in watts, T_{out} is the output torque in newton-meters, and ω_m is the angular speed of the load in radians per second.

Rotational speed may be given in revolutions per minute denoted by n_m, or in radians per second denoted by ω_m. These quantities are related by

$$\omega_m = n_m \times \frac{2\pi}{60} \tag{3}$$

Also, torque may be given in foot-pounds instead of in newton-meters. The conversion relationship is

$$T_{\text{foot-pounds}} = T_{\text{newton-meters}} \times 0.7376 \tag{4}$$

In the United States, the mechanical output power for a given electric motor is frequently stated in horsepower (hp). To convert from watts to horsepower, we have

$$P_{\text{horsepower}} = \frac{P_{\text{watts}}}{746} \tag{5}$$

The **power rating** of a motor is the output power that the motor can safely produce on a continuous basis. For example, we can safely operate a 5-hp motor with a load that absorbs 5 hp of mechanical power. If the power required by the load is reduced, the motor draws less input power from the electrical source, and in the case of an induction motor, speeds up slightly. It is important to realize that most motors can supply output power varying from zero to several times their rated power, depending on the mechanical load. It is up to the system designer to ensure that the motor is not overloaded.

It is up to the system designer to ensure that the motor is not overloaded.

The chief output power limitation of motors is their temperature rise due to losses. Thus, a brief overload that does not cause significant rise in temperature is often acceptable.

The power **efficiency** of a motor is given by

$$\eta = \frac{P_{out}}{P_{in}} \times 100\% \tag{6}$$

Well-designed electrical motors operating close to their rated capacity have efficiencies in the range of 85 to 95 percent. On the other hand, if the motor is called upon to produce only a small fraction of its rated power, its efficiency is generally much lower.

Torque–Speed Characteristics

Consider a system in which a three-phase induction motor drives a load such as a pump. Figure 3 shows the torque produced by the motor versus speed.

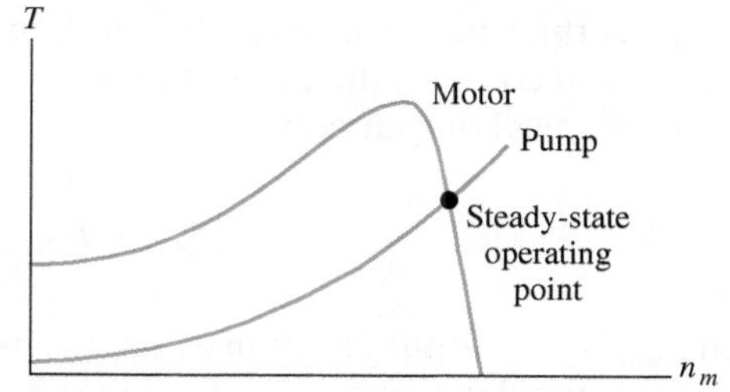

Figure 3 The torque–speed characteristics of an induction motor and a load consisting of a pump. In steady state, the system operates at the point for which the torque produced by the motor equals the torque required by the load.

The torque required to drive the load is also shown. Suppose that the system is at a standstill and then a switch is closed connecting the electrical source to the motor. At low speeds, the torque produced by the motor is larger than that needed to drive the load. The excess torque causes the system to accelerate. Eventually, the speed stabilizes at the point for which the torque produced by the motor equals the torque needed to drive the load.

Now consider the torque–speed characteristics for a three-phase induction motor and a load consisting of a hoist shown in Figure 4. Here, the starting torque of the motor is less than that demanded by the load. Thus, if power is applied from a standing start, the system does not move. In this case, excessive currents are drawn by the motor, and unless fuses or other protection equipment disconnect the source, the motor could overheat and be destroyed.

Even though the motor cannot start the load shown in Figure 4, notice that the motor is capable of keeping the load moving once the speed exceeds n_1. Perhaps this could be accomplished with a mechanical clutch.

Designers must be able to choose motors having torque–speed characteristics appropriate for various loads.

The various types of motors have different torque–speed characteristics. Some examples are shown in Figure 5. It is important for the system designer to choose a motor suitable for the load requirements.

Speed Regulation

Depending on the torque–speed characteristics, a motor may slow down as the torque demanded by the load increases. Speed regulation is defined as the difference between the no-load speed and the full-load speed, expressed as a percentage of the full-load speed:

$$\text{speed regulation} = \frac{n_{\text{no-load}} - n_{\text{full-load}}}{n_{\text{full-load}}} \times 100\% \tag{7}$$

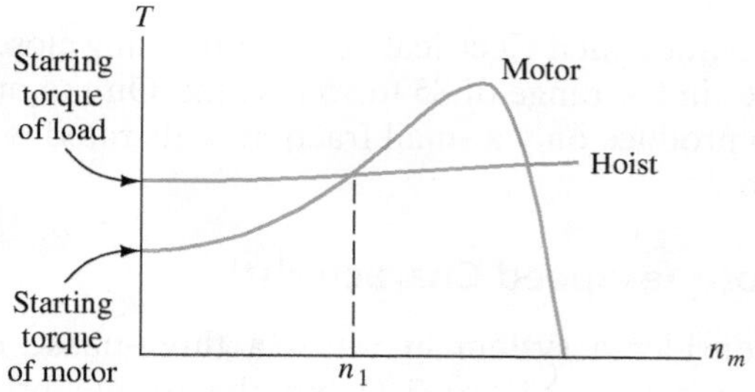

Figure 4 This system will not start from a standstill because the motor cannot supply the starting torque demanded by the load.

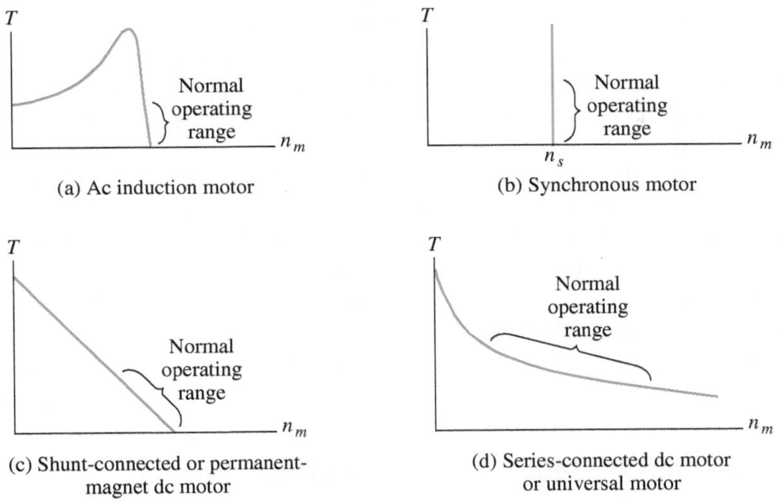

Figure 5 Torque versus speed characteristics for the most common types of electrical motors.

Synchronous-Motor Operating Characteristics

The torque–speed characteristic for ac synchronous motors is shown in Figure 5(b). The operating speed of a synchronous motor is constant and is given by

$$\omega_s = \frac{2\omega}{P} \tag{8}$$

in which ω is the angular frequency of the ac source and P is the number of magnetic poles possessed by the machine. In rpm, the synchronous speed is

$$n_s = \frac{120f}{P} \tag{9}$$

in which f is the frequency of the ac source in hertz.

We will see that the number of magnetic poles P is always an even integer. Substituting various values for P into Equation 9 and assuming 60-Hz operation, the available speeds are 3600 rpm, 1800 rpm, 1200 rpm, 900 rpm, and so on. If some other speed is required, a synchronous machine is usually not a good choice. (Electronic systems known as cycloconverters can be used to convert 60-Hz power into any desired frequency. Thus, this speed limitation can be circumvented at additional cost.)

Synchronous motors operate at $(60 \times f)$ rpm or one of its submultiples. If the frequency f is fixed and if none of the available speeds is suitable for the load, some other type of motor is needed.

As shown in Figure 5(b), the starting torque of a synchronous motor is zero. Therefore, special provisions must be made for starting. We will see that one approach is to operate the motor as an induction motor with reduced load until the speed approaches synchronous speed, and then to switch to synchronous operation.

The starting torque of a synchronous motor is zero.

Induction-Motor Operating Characteristics

Induction motors have starting torques that are comparable to their rated full-load torques.

The torque–speed characteristic typical of an induction motor is shown in Figure 5(a). The motor has good starting torque. In normal operation, the speed of an induction motor is only slightly less than synchronous speed, which is given by Equations 8 and 9. For example, at full load, a typical four-pole ($P = 4$) induction motor runs at 1750 rpm, and at no load, its speed approaches 1800 rpm. The comments given earlier about speed limitations of synchronous motors also apply to induction motors.

Induction motors operate in narrow ranges of speed that are slightly less than $(60 \times f)$ rpm or one of its submultiples. If the frequency is fixed, the speeds available may not be suitable for the load.

During startup, the current drawn by an induction motor can be many times larger than its rated full-load current. To avoid excessive currents, large induction motors are usually started with reduced voltage. As you might expect, the torque produced by a motor depends on the applied voltage. At a given speed, the torque of an induction motor is proportional to the square of the magnitude of the voltage applied to the armature. When starting a motor at, say, half of its rated voltage, its torque is one-fourth of its value at rated voltage.

Shunt-Connected DC Motor Operating Characteristics

Dc motors contain field windings on the stator and armature windings located on the rotor. Depending on whether the field windings are connected in shunt (i.e., parallel) or in series with the armature windings, the torque–speed characteristics are quite different. We examine why this is true later in this chapter.

The torque–speed characteristic of the shunt-connected dc motor is shown in Figure 5(c). The shunt-connected motor has very high starting torque and draws very large starting currents. Usually, resistance is inserted in series with the armature during starting to limit the current to reasonable levels.

Dc motors can be designed to operate over a wide range of speeds.

For fixed supply voltage and fixed field current, the shunt dc machine shows only a small variation in speed within its normal operating range. However, we will see that several methods can be used to shift the torque–speed characteristic of the shunt motor to achieve excellent speed control. Unlike ac induction and synchronous motors, the speeds of dc motors are not limited to specific values.

Series-Connected DC Motor Operating Characteristics

The torque–speed characteristic of the series dc motor is shown in Figure 5(d). The series-connected dc motor has moderate starting torque and starting current. Its speed automatically adjusts over a large range as the load torque varies. Because it slows down for heavier loads, its output power is more nearly constant than for other motor types. This is advantageous because the motor can operate within its maximum power rating for a wide range of load torque. The starter motor in automobiles is a series dc motor. When the engine is cold and stiff, the starter motor operates at a lower speed. On the other hand, when the engine is warm, the starter spins faster. In either case, the current drawn from the battery remains within acceptable limits. (On the other hand, without sophisticated controls, a shunt motor would attempt to turn the load at a constant speed and would draw too much current in starting a cold engine.)

In some cases, the no-load speed of a series dc motor can be excessive—to the point of being dangerous. A control system that disconnects the motor from the electrical source is needed if the possibility of losing the mechanical load exists. We will see that a very useful type of ac motor known as a universal motor is essentially identical to the series-connected dc motor.

Example 1 Motor Performance Calculations

A certain 5-hp three-phase induction motor operates from a 440-V-rms (line-to-line) three-phase source and draws a line current of 6.8 A rms at a power factor of 78 percent lagging [i.e., $\cos(\theta) = 0.78$] under rated full-load conditions. The full-load speed is 1150 rpm. Under no-load conditions, the speed is 1195 rpm, and the line current is 1.2 A rms at a power factor of 30 percent lagging. Find the power loss and efficiency with full load, the input power with no load, and the speed regulation.

Solution The rated output power is 5 hp. Converting to watts, we have

$$P_{\text{out}} = 5 \times 746 = 3730\ \text{W}$$

Substituting into Equation 1, we find the input power under full load:

$$\begin{aligned} P_{\text{in}} &= \sqrt{3} V_{\text{rms}} I_{\text{rms}} \cos(\theta) \\ &= \sqrt{3}(440)(6.8)(0.78) = 4042\ \text{W} \end{aligned}$$

The power loss is given by

$$P_{\text{loss}} = P_{\text{in}} - P_{\text{out}} = 4042 - 3730 = 312\ \text{W}$$

The full-load efficiency is

$$\eta = \frac{P_{\text{out}}}{P_{\text{in}}} \times 100\% = \frac{3730}{4042} \times 100\% = 92.28\%$$

Under no-load conditions, we have

$$\begin{aligned} P_{\text{in}} &= \sqrt{3}(440)(1.2)(0.30) = 274.4\ \text{W} \\ P_{\text{out}} &= 0 \\ P_{\text{loss}} &= P_{\text{in}} = 274.4\ \text{W} \end{aligned}$$

and the efficiency is

$$\eta = 0\%$$

Speed regulation for the motor is given by Equation 7. Substituting values, we get

$$\begin{aligned} \text{speed regulation} &= \frac{n_{\text{no-load}} - n_{\text{full-load}}}{n_{\text{full-load}}} \times 100\% \\ &= \frac{1195 - 1150}{1150} \times 100\% = 3.91\% \end{aligned}$$

■

Now that we have presented an overall view of electrical motors, we will make a more detailed examination of the most common and useful types. In the remainder of this chapter, we consider dc machines.

Exercise 1 A certain 50-hp dc motor operates from a 220-V dc source with losses of 3350 W under rated full-load conditions. The full-load speed is 1150 rpm. Under no-load conditions, the speed is 1200 rpm. Find the source current, the efficiency with full load, and the speed regulation.

Answer $I_{\text{source}} = 184.8$ A, $\eta = 91.76$ percent, speed regulation $= 4.35$ percent. □

Exercise 2 Consider the torque–speed characteristics shown in Figure 5. **a.** Which type of motor would have the most difficulty in starting a high-inertia load from a standing start? **b.** Which type of motor would have the poorest (i.e., largest) speed regulation in its normal operating range? **c.** Which would have the best (i.e., smallest) speed regulation? **d.** Which has the best combination of high starting torque and good speed regulation? **e.** Which should not be operated without a load?

Answer **a.** The synchronous motor, because its starting torque is zero; **b.** the series-connected dc motor; **c.** the synchronous motor; **d.** the ac induction motor; **e.** the series-connected dc motor because the speed can become excessive for zero load torque. □

2 PRINCIPLES OF DC MACHINES

Study of the idealized linear dc machine clearly demonstrates how the principles of electromagnetism apply to dc machines in general.

In this section, we introduce the basic principles of dc machines by considering the idealized linear machine shown in Figure 6. Later, we will see that the operation of rotating dc machines is very similar to that of this simple linear machine. In Figure 6, a dc voltage source V_T is connected through a resistance R_A and a switch that closes at $t = 0$ to a pair of conducting rails. A conducting bar slides without friction on the rails. We assume that the rails and the bar have zero resistance. A magnetic field is directed into the page, perpendicular to the plane of the rails and the bar.

Suppose that the bar is stationary when the switch is closed at $t = 0$. Then, just after the switch is closed, an initial current given by $i_A(0+) = V_T/R_A$ flows clockwise around the circuit. A force given by

$$\mathbf{f} = i_A \mathbf{l} \times \mathbf{B} \tag{10}$$

is exerted on the bar. The direction of the current (and $\mathbf{l}$) is toward the bottom of the page. Thus, the force is directed to the right. Because the current and the field are mutually perpendicular, the force magnitude is given by

$$f = i_A l B \tag{11}$$

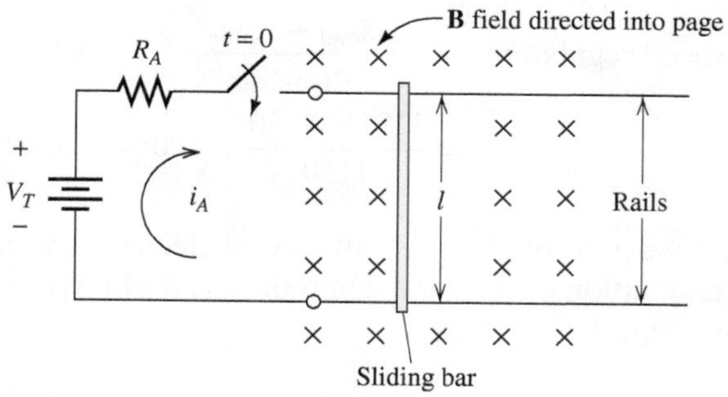

Figure 6 A simple dc machine consisting of a conducting bar sliding on conducting rails.

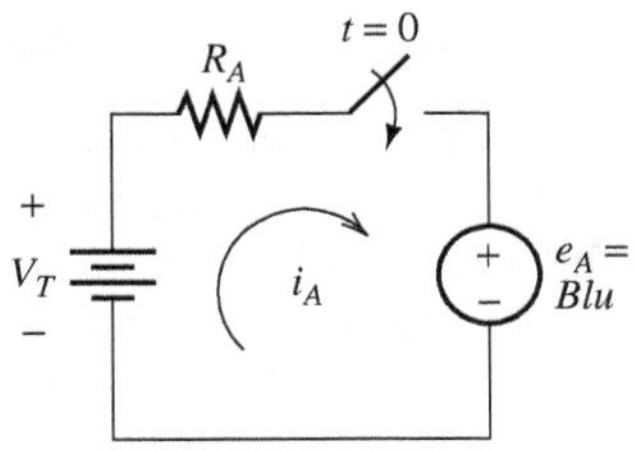

Figure 7 Equivalent circuit for the linear machine operating as a motor.

This force causes the bar to be accelerated toward the right. As the bar gains velocity u and cuts through the magnetic field lines, a voltage is induced across the bar. The voltage is positive at the top end of the bar (with a change in notation):

$$e_A = Blu \tag{12}$$

An equivalent circuit for the system is shown in Figure 7. Notice that the induced voltage e_A opposes the source V_T. The current is

$$i_A = \frac{V_T - e_A}{R_A} \tag{13}$$

As the velocity of the bar builds up, energy is absorbed by the induced voltage e_A, and this energy shows up as the kinetic energy of the bar. Eventually, the bar speed becomes high enough that $e_A = V_T$. Then, the current and the force become zero, and the bar coasts at constant velocity.

Operation as a Motor

Now, suppose that a mechanical load exerting a force to the left is connected to the moving bar. Then, the bar slows down slightly, resulting in a reduction in the induced voltage e_A. Current flows clockwise in the circuit, resulting in a magnetically induced force directed to the right. Eventually, the bar slows just enough so that the force created by the magnetic field ($f = i_A lB$) equals the load force. Then, the system moves at constant velocity.

In this situation, power delivered by the source V_T is converted partly to heat in the resistance R_A and partly to mechanical power. It is the power $p = e_A i_A$ delivered to the induced voltage that shows up as mechanical power $p = fu$.

Operation as a Generator

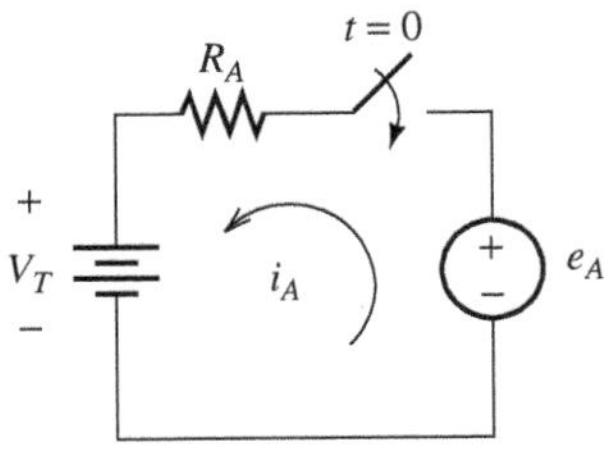

Figure 8 Equivalent circuit for the linear machine operating as a generator.

Again suppose that the bar is moving at constant velocity such that $e_A = V_T$ and the current is zero. Then, if a force is applied pulling the bar even faster toward the right, the bar speeds up, the induced voltage e_A exceeds the source voltage V_T, and current circulates counterclockwise as illustrated in Figure 8. Because the current has reversed direction, the force induced in the bar by the field also reverses and points to the left. Eventually, the bar speed stabilizes with the pulling force equal to the induced force. Then, the induced voltage delivers power $p = e_A i_A$, partly to the resistance ($p_R = R_A i_A^2$) and partly to the battery ($p_t = V_T i_A$). Thus, mechanical energy is converted into electrical energy that eventually shows up as loss (i.e., heat) in the resistance or as stored chemical energy in the battery.

Example 2 Idealized Linear Machine

Suppose that for the linear machine shown in Figure 6, we have $B = 1$ T, $l = 0.3$ m, $V_T = 2$ V, and $R = 0.05\ \Omega$. **a.** Assuming that the bar is stationary at $t = 0$, compute the initial current and the initial force on the bar. Also, determine the final (i.e., steady-state) speed assuming that no mechanical load is applied to the bar. **b.** Now, suppose that a mechanical load of 4 N directed to the left is applied to the moving bar. In steady state, determine the speed, the power delivered by V_T, the power delivered to the mechanical load, the power lost to heat in the resistance R_A, and the efficiency. **c.** Now, suppose that a mechanical pulling force of 2 N directed to the right is applied to the moving bar. In steady state, determine the speed, the power taken from the mechanical source, the power delivered to the battery, the power lost to heat in the resistance R_A, and the efficiency.

Solution

a. Initially, for $u = 0$, we have $e_A = 0$, and the initial current is given by

$$i_A(0+) = \frac{V_T}{R_A} = \frac{2}{0.05} = 40 \text{ A}$$

The resulting initial force on the bar is

$$f(0+) = Bli_A(0+) = 1(0.3)40 = 12 \text{ N}$$

In steady state with no load, the induced voltage equals the battery voltage. Thus, we have

$$e_A = Blu = V_T$$

Solving for the velocity and substituting values, we get

$$u = \frac{V_T}{Bl} = \frac{2}{1(0.3)} = 6.667 \text{ m/s}$$

b. Because the mechanical force opposes the motion of the bar, we have motor action. In steady state, the net force on the bar is zero—the force created by the magnetic field equals the load force. Thus, we obtain

$$f = Bli_A = f_{\text{load}}$$

Solving for the current and substituting values, we find that

$$i_A = \frac{f_{\text{load}}}{Bl} = \frac{4}{1(0.3)} = 13.33 \text{ A}$$

From the circuit shown in Figure 7, we have

$$e_A = V_T - R_A i_A = 2 - 0.05(13.33) = 1.333 \text{ V}$$

Now, we can find the steady-state speed:

$$u = \frac{e_A}{Bl} = \frac{1.333}{1(0.3)} = 4.444 \text{ m/s}$$

The mechanical power delivered to the load is

$$p_m = f_{\text{load}}u = 4(4.444) = 17.77 \text{ W}$$

The power taken from the battery is

$$p_t = V_T i_A = 2(13.33) = 26.67 \text{ W}$$

The power dissipated in the resistance is

$$p_R = i_A^2 R = (13.33)^2 \times 0.05 = 8.889 \text{ W}$$

As a check, we note that $p_t = p_m + p_R$ to within rounding error. Finally, the efficiency of converting electrical power from the battery into mechanical power is

$$\eta = \frac{p_m}{p_t} \times 100\% = \frac{17.77}{26.67} \times 100\% = 66.67\%$$

c. With a pulling force applied to the bar to the right, the bar speeds up, the induced voltage exceeds V_T, and current circulates counterclockwise, as illustrated in Figure 8. Thus, the machine operates as a generator. In steady state, the force induced by the field is directed to the left and equals the pulling force. Thus, we have

$$f = Bli_A = f_{\text{pull}}$$

Solving for i_A and substituting values, we find that

$$i_A = \frac{f_{\text{pull}}}{Bl} = \frac{2}{1(0.3)} = 6.667 \text{ A}$$

From the circuit shown in Figure 8, we obtain

$$e_A = V_T + R_A i_A = 2 + 0.05(6.67) = 2.333 \text{ V}$$

Now, we can find the steady-state speed:

$$u = \frac{e_A}{Bl} = \frac{2.333}{1(0.3)} = 7.778 \text{ m/s}$$

The mechanical power delivered by the pulling force is

$$p_m = f_{\text{pull}}u = 2(7.778) = 15.56 \text{ W}$$

The power absorbed by the battery is

$$p_t = V_T i_A = 2(6.667) = 13.33 \text{ W}$$

The power dissipated in the resistance is

$$p_R = i_A^2 R = (6.667)^2 \times 0.05 = 2.222 \text{ W}$$

As a check, we note that $p_m = p_t + p_R$ to within rounding error. Finally, the efficiency of converting mechanical power into electrical power charging the battery is

$$\eta = \frac{p_t}{p_m} \times 100\% = \frac{13.33}{15.56} \times 100\% = 85.67\%$$

■

In Example 2, we have seen that only modest forces (12 N) were produced on a conductor carrying a fairly large current (40 A). The force could be increased by using a longer conductor, but this increases the size of the machine. Another option would be to increase the field strength. However, because of the fact that magnetic materials used in motors saturate in the neighborhood of 1 T, it is not practical to increase the forces on conductors greatly by increasing the field.

On the other hand, a cylindrical rotor containing many conductors is a practical way to obtain large forces in a compact design. Furthermore, rotary motion is more useful than translation in many applications. Thus, most (but not all) practical motors are based on rotational motion. We study rotating dc machines in the remaining sections of this chapter.

Exercise 3 Repeat the calculations of Example 2 if the field strength is doubled to 2 T.

Answer **a.** $i_A(0+) = 40$ A, $f(0+) = 24$ N, $u = 3.333$ m/s; **b.** $i_A = 6.667$, $e_A = 1.667$, $u = 2.778$ m/s, $p_m = 11.11$ W, $p_t = 13.33$ W, $p_R = 2.22$ W, $\eta = 83.33\%$; **c.** $i_A = 3.333$ A, $e_A = 2.167$ V, $u = 3.612$ m/s, $p_m = 7.222$ W, $p_t = 6.667$ W, $p_R = 0.555$ W, $\eta = 92.3\%$. □

PRACTICAL APPLICATION 1

Magnetic Flowmeters, Faraday, and *The Hunt for Red October*

Flowmeters measure the flow rate of liquids through pipes and are very important sensors in chemical-process-control systems. A commonly used type is the magnetic flowmeter (also called a *magflow*), which operates on the same principles as the linear machine discussed in Section 2.

The basic operation of a magflow is illustrated in Figure PA1. Coils set up a vertical magnetic field in the fluid, and electrodes are located at opposite sides of the pipe, which is lined with an electrical insulating material such as ceramic or epoxy resin. Thus, the magnetic field, the direction of flow, and the line between the electrodes are mutually perpendicular. As the conductive fluid moves through the magnetic field, a voltage proportional to velocity is induced between the electrodes. The flow rate can be determined by multiplying the cross-sectional area of the pipe times the velocity. Hence, the meter measures the induced voltage, but can be calibrated in units of volumetric flow.

Faraday realized the potential for using his law of electromagnetic induction to measure water flow, and attempted to measure the flow rate of the Thames River with a device suspended from a bridge. However, lacking the advantages of modern electronics, he was not successful.

In modern meters, an electronic amplifier is used to amplify the induced voltage. In many units, this voltage is converted to digital form by an analog-to-digital converter and processed by a microcomputer that drives a display or sends data to a central plant-control computer.

If the fluid has low electrical conductivity, the Thévenin resistance seen looking into the electrode terminals is very high. Then, it is important for the amplifier input impedance to be very high; otherwise, the observed voltage would vary with changes in electrical conductivity of the fluid, leading to gross inaccuracies in flow rate. Of course, it is important for chemical engineers employing magflows to understand this limitation. Even with their limitations, well-designed meters are available for a wide range of applications.

As a meter, the magflow acts as a generator. However, it can also act as a motor if an electrical current is passed through the fluid between the electrodes. Then force is exerted directly on the fluid by the interaction of the magnetic field with the electrical current. Of course, if we wanted to build a pump based on this approach, we would want a fluid with high conductivity, such as seawater. We would also need a strong magnetic field and high current. By making these modifications, a powerful pump can be constructed. This is the operating principle of the ultraquiet submarine propulsion system mentioned by Tom Clancy in *The Hunt for Red October*. Such a system can be very quiet because force is applied smoothly and directly to the seawater without rotating parts or valves that could cause vibration.

Sources: Ian Robertson, "Magnetic flowmeters: the whole story," *The Chemical Engineer*, February 24, 1994, pp. 17–18; The Magmeter Flowmeter Homepage, `http://www.magmeter.com`.

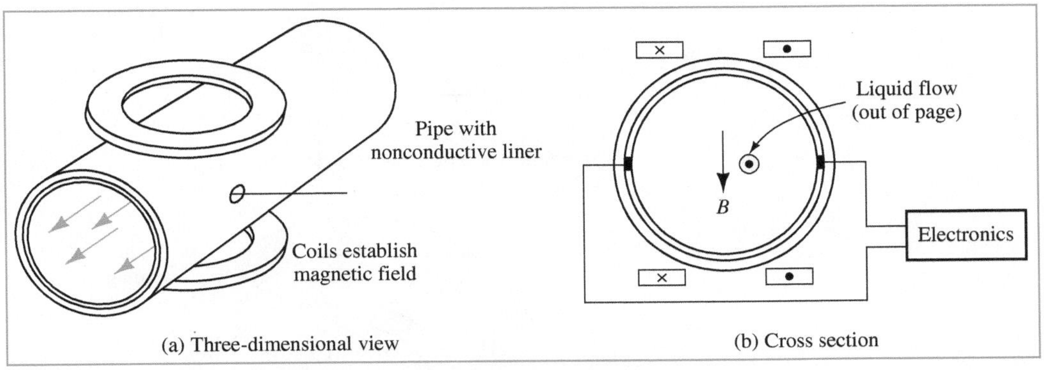

Figure PA1 A magnetic flowmeter.

3 ROTATING DC MACHINES

We have gained some familiarity with basic principles of dc machines from our analysis of the linear machine in the preceding section. In this section, we will see that the same principles apply to rotating dc machines.

The basic principles of rotating dc machines are the same as those of the linear dc machine.

Structure of the Rotor and Stator

The most common type of dc machine contains a cylindrical stator with an even number P of magnetic poles that are established by field windings or by permanent magnets. The poles alternate between north and south around the periphery of the stator.

Inside the stator is a rotor consisting of a laminated iron cylinder mounted on a shaft that is supported by bearings so that it can rotate. Slots cut lengthwise into the surface of the rotor contain the armature windings. A rotor with armature conductors (and other features to be discussed shortly) is illustrated in Figure 9.

The cross section of a two-pole machine showing the flux lines in the air gap is illustrated in Figure 10. Magnetic flux tends to take the path of least reluctance. Because the reluctance of air is much higher than that of iron, the flux takes the shortest path from the stator into the rotor. Thus, the flux in the air gap is perpendicular to the surface of the rotor and to the armature conductors. Furthermore, the flux density is nearly constant in magnitude over the surface of each pole face. Between poles, the gap flux density is small in magnitude.

In a motor, external electrical sources provide the currents in the field windings and in the armature conductors. The current directions shown in Figure 10 result

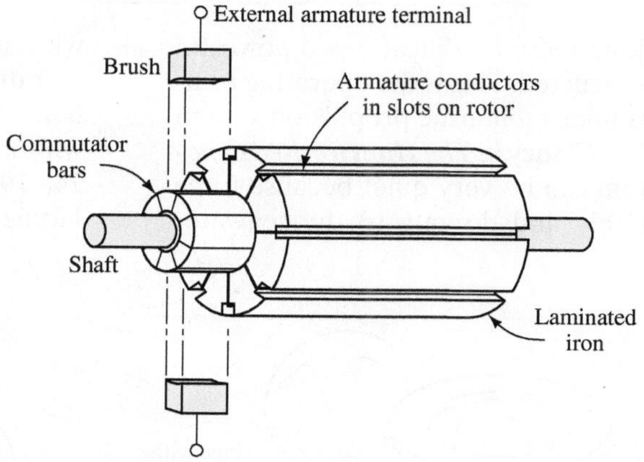

Figure 9 Rotor assembly of a dc machine.

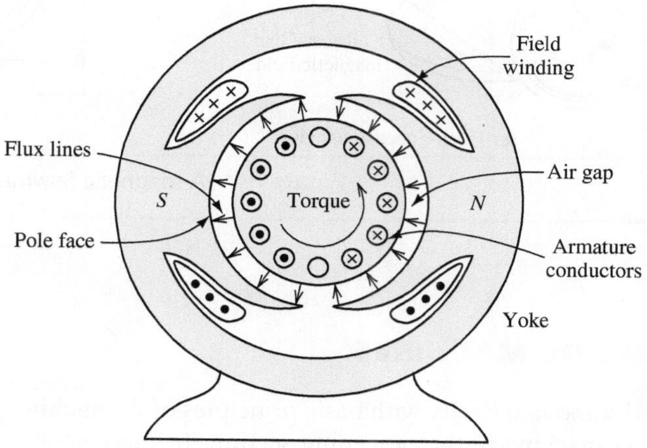

Figure 10 Cross section of a two-pole dc machine.

in a counterclockwise torque. This can be verified by applying the equation $\mathbf{f} = i\mathbf{l} \times \mathbf{B}$ that gives the force on a current-carrying conductor.

The cross section of a four-pole machine is shown in Figure 11. Notice that the directions of the currents in the armature must be reversed under south poles relative to the direction under the north poles to achieve aiding contributions to total torque.

Induced EMF and Commutation

As the rotor turns, the conductors move through the magnetic field produced by the stator. Under the pole faces, the conductors, the field, and the direction of motion are mutually perpendicular, just as in the linear machine discussed in Section 2. Thus, a nearly constant voltage is induced in each conductor as it moves under a pole. However, as the conductors move between poles, the field direction reverses. Therefore, the induced voltages fall to zero and build up with the opposite polarity. A mechanical switch known as a **commutator** reverses the connections to the conductors as they move between poles so that the polarity of the induced voltage seen from the external machine terminals is constant.

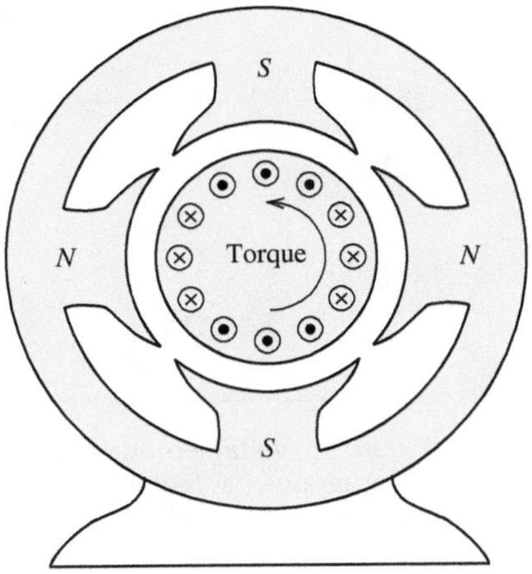

Figure 11 Cross section of a four-pole dc machine.

The commutator and brushes form a mechanical switch that reverses the external connections to conductors as they move from pole to pole.

Let us illustrate these points with a two-pole machine containing one armature coil, as shown in Figure 12. In this case, the ends of the coil are attached to a two-segment commutator mounted on the shaft. The segments are insulated from one another and from the shaft. Brushes mounted to the stator make electrical contact with the commutator segments. (For clarity, we have shown the brushes inside the commutator, but in a real machine, they ride on the outside surface of the commutator. A more realistic version of the commutator and brushes was shown in Figure 9.)

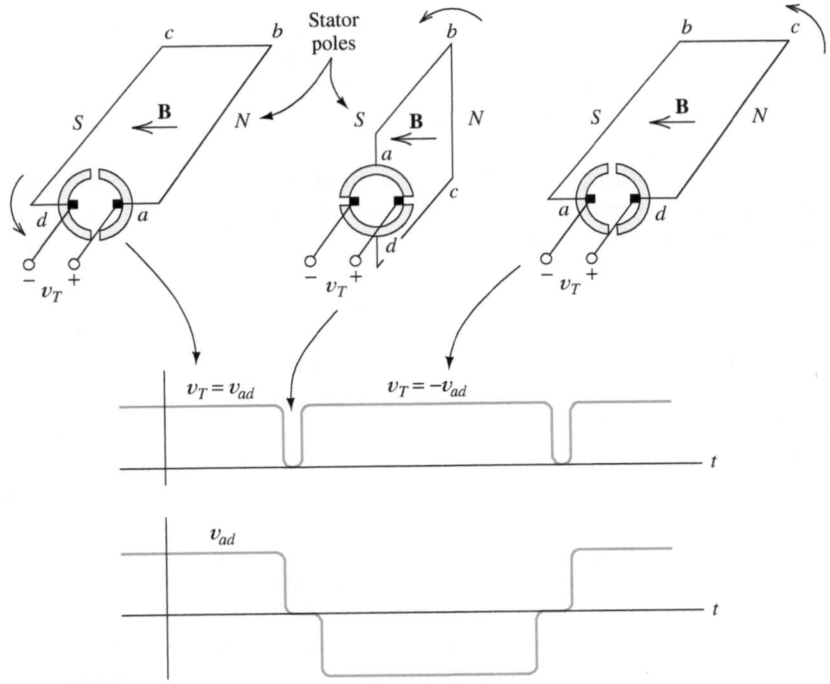

Figure 12 Commutation for a single armature winding.

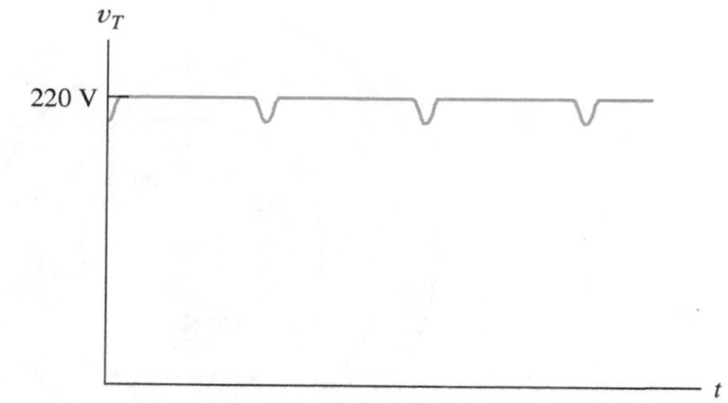

Figure 13 Voltage produced by a practical dc machine. Because only a few (out of many) conductors are commutated (switched) at a time, the voltage fluctuations are less pronounced than in the single-loop case illustrated in Figure 12.

Notice that as the rotor turns in Figure 12, the left-hand brush is connected to the conductor under the south stator pole, and the right-hand brush is connected to the conductor under the north stator pole.

The voltage v_{ad} induced across the terminals of the coil is an ac voltage, as shown in the figure. As mentioned earlier, this voltage passes through zero when the conductors are between poles where the flux density goes to zero. While the conductors are under the pole faces where the flux density is constant, the induced voltage has nearly constant magnitude. Because the commutator reverses the external connections to the coil as it rotates, the voltage v_T seen at the external terminals is of constant polarity.

Notice that the brushes short the armature winding briefly during the switching process. This occurs because the brushes are wider than the insulation between commutator segments. This shorting is not a problem, provided that the voltage is small when it occurs. (Actual machines have various provisions to ensure that the coil voltage is close to zero during commutation for all operating conditions.)

Commutators in typical machines contain 20 to 50 segments. Because only part of the coils are commutated at a time, the terminal voltage of a real machine shows relatively little fluctuation compared to the two-segment example that we used for the illustration of concepts. The terminal voltage of an actual dc machine is shown in Figure 13.

Generally, the commutator segments are copper bars insulated from one another and from the shaft. The brushes contain graphite that lubricates the sliding contact. Even so, a significant disadvantage of dc machines is the need to replace brushes and redress the commutator surface because of mechanical wear.

Actual armatures consist of a large number of conductors placed around the circumference of the rotor. To attain high terminal voltages, many conductors are placed in series, forming coils. Furthermore, there are usually several parallel current paths through the armature. The armature conductors and their connections to the commutator are configured so that the currents flow in the opposite direction under south stator poles than they do under north stator poles. As mentioned earlier, this is necessary so that the forces on the conductors produce aiding torques. The construction details needed to produce these conditions are beyond the scope of our discussion. As a user of electrical motors, you will find the external behavior of machines more helpful than the details of their internal design.

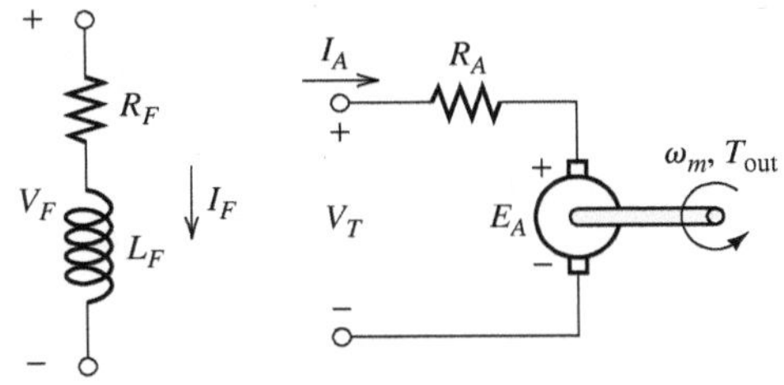

Figure 14 Equivalent circuit for the rotating dc machine.

Equivalent Circuit of the DC Motor

The equivalent circuit of the dc motor is shown in Figure 14. The field circuit is represented by a resistance R_F and an inductance L_F in series. We consider steady-state operation in which the currents are constant, and we can neglect the inductance because it behaves as a short circuit for dc currents. Thus, for dc field currents, we have

$$V_F = R_F I_F \tag{14}$$

The voltage E_A shown in the equivalent circuit represents the average voltage induced in the armature due to the motion of the conductors relative to the magnetic field. In a motor, E_A is sometimes called a **back emf** (electromotive force) because it opposes the applied external electrical source. The resistance R_A is the resistance of the armature windings plus the brush resistance. (Sometimes, the drop across the brushes is estimated as a constant voltage of about 2 V rather than as a resistance. However, in this text, we lump the brush drop with the armature resistance.)

The induced armature voltage is given by

$$E_A = K\phi\omega_m \tag{15}$$

in which K is a **machine constant** that depends on the design parameters of the machine, ϕ is the magnetic flux produced by each stator pole, and ω_m is the angular velocity of the rotor.

The torque developed in the machine is given by

$$T_{\text{dev}} = K\phi I_A \tag{16}$$

in which I_A is the armature current. (We will see that the *output* torque of a dc motor is less than the *developed* torque because of friction and other rotational losses.)

The **developed power** is the power converted to mechanical form, which is given by the product of developed torque and angular velocity:

$$P_{\text{dev}} = \omega_m T_{\text{dev}} \tag{17}$$

This is the power delivered to the induced armature voltage, and therefore, is also given by

$$P_{\text{dev}} = E_A I_A \tag{18}$$

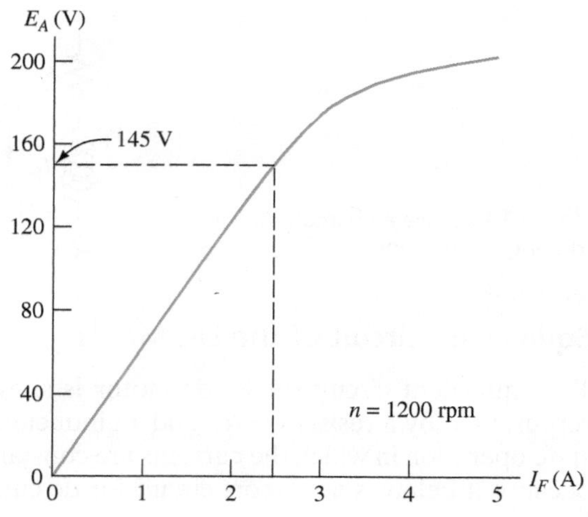

Figure 15 Magnetization curve for a 200-V 10-hp dc motor.

Magnetization Curve

The magnetization curve of a dc machine is a plot of E_A versus the field current I_F with the machine being driven at a constant speed.

The **magnetization curve** of a dc machine is a plot of E_A versus the field current I_F with the machine being driven at a constant speed. (E_A can be found by measuring the open-circuit voltage at the armature terminals.) A typical magnetization curve is shown in Figure 15.

Because E_A is proportional to the flux ϕ, the magnetization curve has the same shape as a ϕ versus I_F plot, which depends on the parameters of the magnetic circuit for the field. The magnetization curve flattens out for high field currents due to magnetic saturation of the iron. Of course, different machines usually have differently shaped magnetization curves.

The equivalent circuit, Equations 14 through 19, and the magnetization curve are the key elements needed to solve dc machine problems.

As Equation 15 shows, the induced armature voltage E_A is directly proportional to speed. If E_{A1} represents the voltage at speed n_1, and E_{A2} is the voltage at a second speed n_2, we have

$$\frac{E_{A1}}{E_{A2}} = \frac{n_1}{n_2} = \frac{\omega_1}{\omega_2} \tag{19}$$

Equations 14 through 19, in combination with the equivalent circuit shown in Figure 14 and the magnetization curve, provide the basis for analyzing a dc machine.

Example 3 DC Machine Performance Calculations

The machine having the magnetization curve shown in Figure 15 is operating as a motor at a speed of 800 rpm with $I_A = 30$ A and $I_F = 2.5$ A. The armature resistance is 0.3 Ω and the field resistance is $R_F = 50$ Ω. Find the voltage V_F applied to the field circuit, the voltage V_T applied to the armature, the developed torque, and the developed power.

Solution Equation 14 allows us to find the voltage for the field coil:

$$V_F = R_F I_F = 50 \times 2.5 = 125 \text{ V}$$

From the magnetization curve, we see that the induced voltage is $E_{A1} = 145$ V at $I_F = 2.5$ A and $n_1 = 1200$ rpm. Rearranging Equation 19, we can find the induced voltage E_{A2} for $n_2 = 800$ rpm:

$$E_{A2} = \frac{n_2}{n_1} \times E_{A1} = \frac{800}{1200} \times 145 = 96.67 \text{ V}$$

The machine speed in radians per second is

$$\omega_m = n_2 \times \frac{2\pi}{60} = 800 \times \frac{2\pi}{60} = 83.78 \text{ rad/s}$$

Rearranging Equation 15, we have

$$K\phi = \frac{E_A}{\omega_m} = \frac{96.67}{83.78} = 1.154$$

From Equation 16, the developed torque is

$$T_{\text{dev}} = K\phi I_A = 1.154 \times 30 = 34.62 \text{ Nm}$$

The developed power is

$$P_{\text{dev}} = \omega_m T_{\text{dev}} = 2900 \text{ W}$$

As a check, we can also compute the developed power by using Equation 18:

$$P_{\text{dev}} = I_A E_A = 30 \times 96.67 = 2900 \text{ W}$$

Applying Kirchhoff's voltage law to the armature circuit in Figure 14, we have

$$V_T = R_A I_A + E_A = 0.3(30) + 96.67 = 105.67$$

■

Exercise 4 Find the voltage E_A for the machine having the magnetization curve shown in Figure 15 for $I_F = 2$ A and a speed of 1500 rpm.

Answer $E_A \cong 156$ V. □

Exercise 5 The machine having the magnetization curve shown in Figure 15 is operating as a motor at a speed of 1500 rpm with a developed power of 10 hp and $I_F = 2.5$ A. The armature resistance is 0.3 Ω and the field resistance is $R_F = 50$ Ω. Find the developed torque, the armature current I_A, and the voltage V_T applied to the armature circuit.

Answer $T_{\text{dev}} = 47.49$ Nm, $I_A = 41.16$ A, $V_T = 193.6$ V. □

In the next several sections, we will see that different torque–speed characteristics can result, depending on how the field windings and the armature are connected to the dc source.

4 SHUNT-CONNECTED AND SEPARATELY EXCITED DC MOTORS

In a shunt-connected dc machine, the field circuit is in parallel with the armature, as shown in Figure 16. The field circuit consists of a rheostat having a variable resistance, denoted as R_{adj}, in series with the field coil. Later, we will see that the rheostat can be used to adjust the torque–speed characteristic of the machine.

By designing the field windings to be connected either in parallel or in series with the armature, we can obtain drastically different torque–speed characteristics.

We assume that the machine is supplied by a constant voltage source V_T. The resistance of the armature circuit is R_A, and the induced voltage is E_A. We denote the mechanical shaft speed as ω_m and the developed torque as T_{dev}.

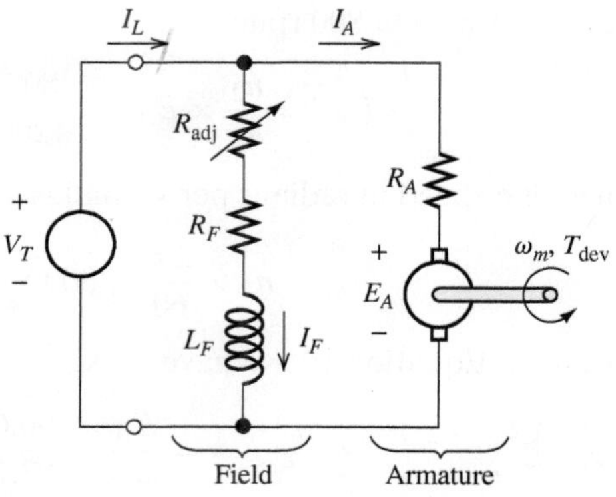

Figure 16 Equivalent circuit of a shunt-connected dc motor. R_{adj} is a rheostat that can be used to adjust motor speed.

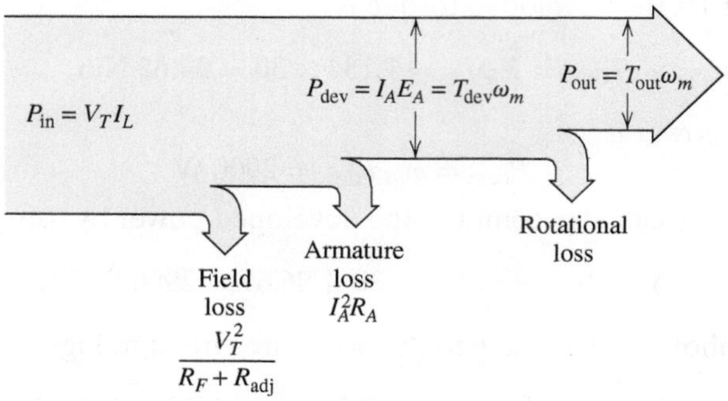

Figure 17 Power flow in a shunt-connected dc motor.

Power Flow

Figure 17 shows the flow of power in the shunt-connected dc machine. The electrical source supplies an input power given by the product of the supply voltage and the line current I_L:

$$P_{in} = V_T I_L \tag{20}$$

Some of this power is used to establish the field. The power absorbed by the field circuit is converted to heat. The **field loss** is given by

$$P_{field\text{-}loss} = \frac{V_T^2}{R_F + R_{adj}} = V_T I_F \tag{21}$$

Furthermore, **armature loss** occurs due to heating of the armature resistance:

$$P_{arm\text{-}loss} = I_A^2 R_A \tag{22}$$

Sometimes, the sum of the field loss and armature loss is called **copper loss.**

The power delivered to the induced armature voltage is converted to mechanical form and is called the **developed power**, given by

$$P_{dev} = I_A E_A = \omega_m T_{dev} \tag{23}$$

in which T_{dev} is the developed torque.

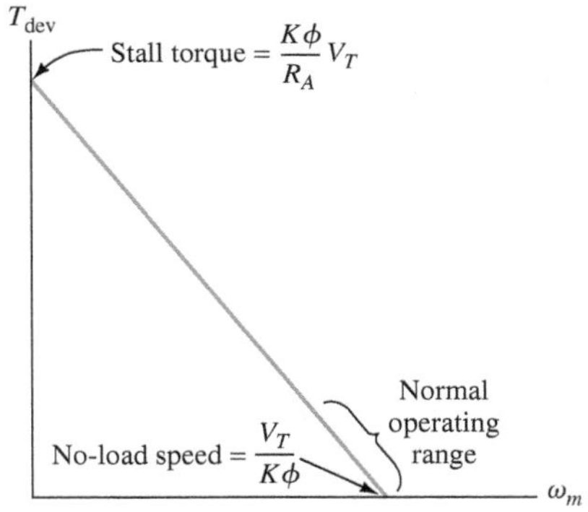

Figure 18 Torque–speed characteristic of the shunt dc motor.

The output power P_{out} and output torque T_{out} are less than the developed values because of **rotational losses**, which include friction, windage, eddy-current loss, and hysteresis loss. Rotational power loss is approximately proportional to speed.

Torque–Speed Characteristic

Next, we derive the torque–speed relationship for the shunt-connected machine. Applying Kirchhoff's voltage law to the equivalent circuit shown in Figure 16, we obtain

$$V_T = R_A I_A + E_A \tag{24}$$

Next, rearranging Equation 16 yields

$$I_A = \frac{T_{dev}}{K\phi} \tag{25}$$

Then, using Equation 15 to substitute for E_A and Equation 25 to substitute for I_A in Equation 24, we obtain

$$V_T = \frac{R_A T_{dev}}{K\phi} + K\phi\omega_m \tag{26}$$

Finally, solving for the developed torque, we get

$$T_{dev} = \frac{K\phi}{R_A}(V_T - K\phi\omega_m) \tag{27}$$

which is the torque–speed relationship that we desire. Notice that this torque–speed relationship plots as a straight line, as illustrated in Figure 18. The speed for no load (i.e., $T_{dev} = 0$) and the stall torque are labeled in the figure. The normal operating range for most motors is on the lower portion of the torque–speed characteristic, as illustrated in the figure.

The starting or stall torque of a shunt-connected machine is usually many times higher than the rated full-load torque.

Example 4 Shunt-Connected DC Motor

A 50-hp shunt-connected dc motor has the magnetization curve shown in Figure 19. The dc supply voltage is $V_T = 240$ V, the armature resistance is $R_A = 0.065\ \Omega$, the field resistance is $R_F = 10\ \Omega$, and the adjustable resistance is

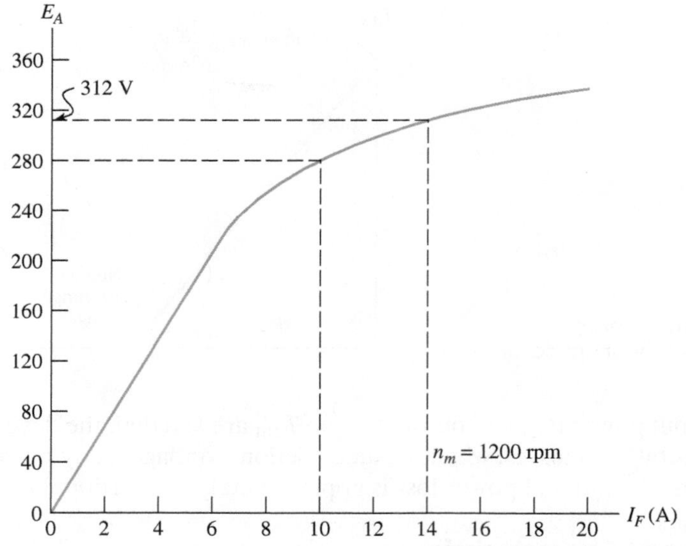

Figure 19 Magnetization curve for the motor of Example 4.

$R_{\text{adj}} = 14\ \Omega$. At a speed of 1200 rpm, the rotational loss is $P_{\text{rot}} = 1450$ W. If this motor drives a hoist that demands a torque of $T_{\text{out}} = 250$ Nm independent of speed, determine the motor speed and efficiency.

Solution The equivalent circuit is shown in Figure 20. The field current is given by

$$I_F = \frac{V_T}{R_F + R_{\text{adj}}} = \frac{240}{10 + 14} = 10 \text{ A}$$

Next, we use the magnetization curve to find the machine constant $K\phi$ for this value of field current. From the curve shown in Figure 19, we see that the induced armature voltage is $E_A = 280$ V at $I_F = 10$ A and $n_m = 1200$ rpm. Thus, rearranging Equation 15 and substituting values, we find that the machine constant is

$$K\phi = \frac{E_A}{\omega_m} = \frac{280}{1200(2\pi/60)} = 2.228$$

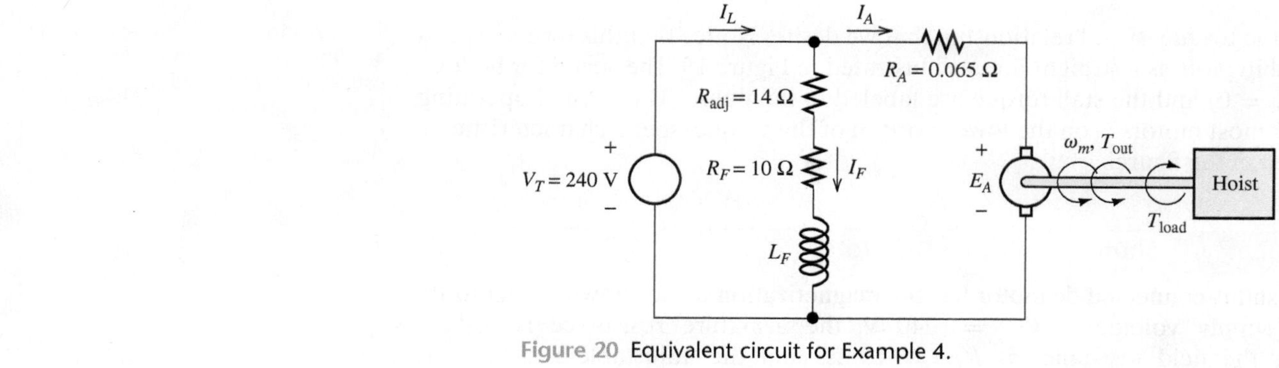

Figure 20 Equivalent circuit for Example 4.

We assume that the rotational power loss is proportional to speed. This is equivalent to assuming constant torque for the rotational loss. The rotational-loss torque is

$$T_{\text{rot}} = \frac{P_{\text{rot}}}{\omega_m} = \frac{1450}{1200(2\pi/60)} = 11.54 \text{ Nm}$$

Thus, the developed torque is

$$T_{\text{dev}} = T_{\text{out}} + T_{\text{rot}} = 250 + 11.54 = 261.5 \text{ Nm}$$

Now, we use Equation 16 to find the armature current:

$$I_A = \frac{T_{\text{dev}}}{K\phi} = \frac{261.5}{2.228} = 117.4 \text{ A}$$

Then, applying Kirchhoff's voltage law to the armature circuit, we have

$$E_A = V_T - R_A I_A = 240 - 0.065(117.4) = 232.4 \text{ V}$$

Solving Equation 15 for speed and substituting values, we get

$$\omega_m = \frac{E_A}{K\phi} = \frac{232.4}{2.228} = 104.3 \text{ rad/s}$$

or

$$n_m = \omega_m \left(\frac{60}{2\pi}\right) = 996.0 \text{ rpm}$$

To find efficiency, we first compute the output power and the input power, given by

$$P_{\text{out}} = T_{\text{out}}\omega_m = 250(104.3) = 26.08 \text{ kW}$$

$$P_{\text{in}} = V_T I_L = V_T(I_F + I_A) = 240(10 + 117.4) = 30.58 \text{ kW}$$

$$\eta = \frac{P_{\text{out}}}{P_{\text{in}}} \times 100\% = \frac{26.08}{30.58} \times 100\% = 85.3\%$$

■

Exercise 6 Repeat Example 4 with the supply voltage increased to 300 V while holding the field current constant by increasing R_{adj}. What is the new value of R_{adj}? What happens to the speed?

Answer $R_{\text{adj}} = 20\ \Omega$; the speed increases to $\omega_m = 131.2$ rad/s or $n_m = 1253$ rpm. □

Exercise 7 Repeat Example 4 if the adjustable resistance R_{adj} is increased in value to 30 Ω while holding V_T constant at 240 V. What happens to the speed?

Answer $I_F = 6$ A, $E_A = 229.3$ V, $I_A = 164.3$ A, $\omega_m = 144.0$, $\eta = 88.08$ percent, $n_m = 1376$ rpm; thus, speed increases as R_{adj} is increased. □

Separately Excited DC Motors

A separately excited dc motor is similar to a shunt-connected motor except that different sources are used for the armature and field circuits. The equivalent circuit for a separately excited dc machine is shown in Figure 21. Analysis of a separately excited machine is very similar to that of a shunt-connected machine. The chief reason for using two separate sources for the armature and field is to be able to control speed by varying one of the two sources.

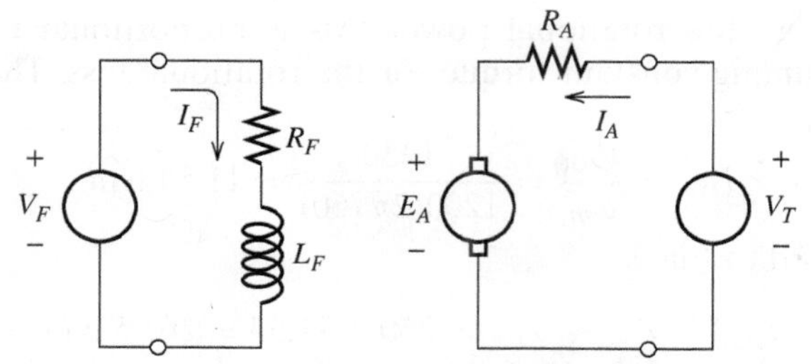

Figure 21 Equivalent circuit for a separately excited dc motor. Speed can be controlled by varying either source voltage (V_F or V_T).

Permanent-Magnet Motors

Separately excited and permanent-magnet motors have similar characteristics to those of shunt-connected motors.

In a permanent-magnet (PM) dc motor, the field is supplied by magnets mounted on the stator rather than by field coils. Its characteristics are similar to those of the separately excited machine except that the field cannot be adjusted. PM motors have several advantages compared to motors with field windings. First, no power is required to establish the field—leading to better efficiency. Second, PM motors can be smaller than equivalent machines with field windings. PM motors are common in applications calling for fractional- or subfractional-horsepower sizes. Typical applications include fan and power-window motors in automobiles.

PM motors also have some disadvantages. The magnets can become demagnetized by overheating or because of excessive armature currents. Also, the flux density magnitude is smaller in PM motors than in wound-field machines. Consequently, the torque produced per ampere of armature current is smaller in PM motors than in wound-field motors with equal power ratings. PM motors are confined to operation at lower torque and higher speed than wound-field motors with the same power rating.

5 SERIES-CONNECTED DC MOTORS

The equivalent circuit of a **series-connected dc motor** is shown in Figure 22. Notice that the field winding is in series with the armature. In this section, we will see that the series connection leads to a torque–speed characteristic that is useful in many applications.

Field windings are designed differently for series-connected machines than they are for shunt-connected machines.

In series dc motors, the field windings are made of larger diameter wire and the field resistances are much smaller than those of shunt machines of comparable size. This is necessary to avoid dropping too much of the source voltage across the field winding.

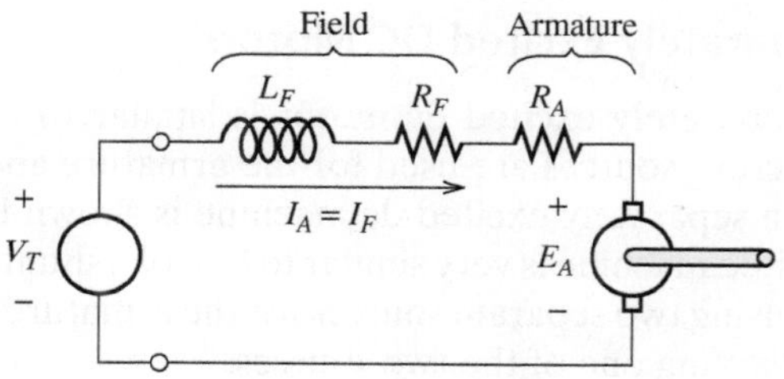

Figure 22 Equivalent circuit of the series-connected dc motor.

Next, we derive the relationship between torque and speed for the series motor. We use a linear equation to approximate the relationship between magnetic flux and field current. In equation form, we have

$$\phi = K_F I_F \tag{28}$$

in which K_F is a constant that depends on the number of field windings, the geometry of the magnetic circuit, and the B–H characteristics of the iron. Of course, the actual relationship between ϕ and I_F is nonlinear, due to magnetic saturation of the iron. (A plot of ϕ versus I_F has exactly the same shape as the magnetization curve of the machine.) However, Equation 28 will give us insight into the behavior of the series dc motor. Later, we consider saturation effects.

Because $I_A = I_F$ in the series machine, we have

$$\phi = K_F I_A \tag{29}$$

Using Equation 29 to substitute for ϕ in Equations 15 and 16, we obtain

$$E_A = KK_F \omega_m I_A \tag{30}$$

and

$$T_{\text{dev}} = KK_F I_A^2 \tag{31}$$

If we apply Kirchhoff's voltage law to the equivalent circuit shown in Figure 22, we get

$$V_T = R_F I_A + R_A I_A + E_A \tag{32}$$

As usual, we are assuming steady-state conditions so that the voltage across the inductance is zero.

Then using Equation 30 to substitute for E_A in Equation 32 and solving for I_A, we have

$$I_A = \frac{V_T}{R_A + R_F + KK_F \omega_m} \tag{33}$$

Finally, using Equation 33 to substitute for I_A in Equation 31, we obtain the desired relationship between torque and speed:

$$T_{\text{dev}} = \frac{KK_F V_T^2}{(R_A + R_F + KK_F \omega_m)^2} \tag{34}$$

Torque–speed relationship for series-connected dc machines.

A plot of torque versus speed for the series dc motor is shown in Figure 23. The figure shows a plot of Equation 34 as well as an actual curve of torque versus speed, illustrating the effects of rotational loss and magnetic saturation. Equation 34 predicts infinite no-load speed. (In other words, for $T_{\text{dev}} = 0$, the speed must be infinite.) Yet, at high speeds, rotational losses due to windage and eddy currents become large, and the motor speed is limited.

However, in some cases, *the no-load speed can become large enough to be dangerous. It is important to have protection devices that remove electrical power to a series machine when the load becomes disconnected.*

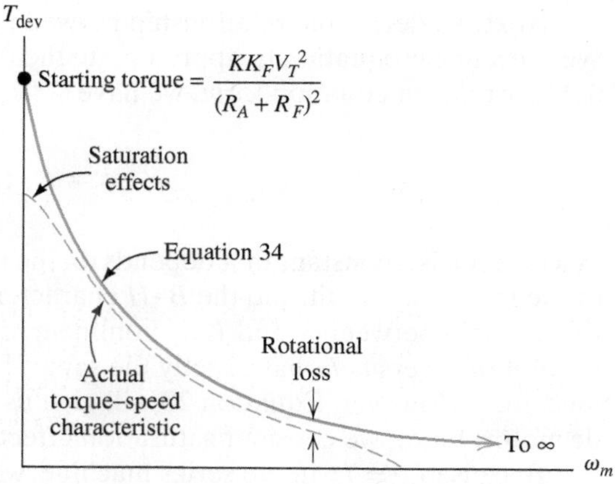

Figure 23 Torque–speed characteristic of the series-connected dc motor.

At very low speeds, Equation 33 shows that the current $I_F = I_A$ becomes large. Then, magnetic saturation occurs. Therefore, the starting torque is not as large as predicted by Equation 34.

Example 5 Series-Connected DC Motor

A series-connected dc motor runs at $n_{m1} = 1200$ rpm while driving a load that demands a torque of 12 Nm. Neglect the resistances, rotational loss, and saturation effects. Find the power output. Then, find the new speed and output power if the load torque increases to 24 Nm.

Solution Since we are neglecting losses, the output torque and power are equal to the developed torque and power, respectively. First, the angular speed is

$$\omega_{m1} = n_{m1} \times \frac{2\pi}{60} = 125.7 \text{ rad/s}$$

and the output power is

$$P_{\text{dev1}} = P_{\text{out1}} = \omega_{m1} T_{\text{out1}} = 1508 \text{ W}$$

Setting $R_A = R_F = 0$ in Equation 34 gives

$$T_{\text{dev}} = \frac{KK_F V_T^2}{(R_A + R_F + KK_F \omega_m)^2} = \frac{V_T^2}{KK_F \omega_m^2}$$

Thus, for a fixed supply voltage V_T, torque is inversely proportional to speed squared, and we can write

$$\frac{T_{\text{dev1}}}{T_{\text{dev2}}} = \frac{\omega_{m2}^2}{\omega_{m1}^2}$$

Solving for ω_{m2} and substituting values, we have

$$\omega_{m2} = \omega_{m1} \sqrt{\frac{T_{\text{dev1}}}{T_{\text{dev2}}}} = 125.7 \sqrt{\frac{12}{24}} = 88.88 \text{ rad/s}$$

which corresponds to

$$n_{m2} = 848.5 \text{ rpm}$$

Finally, the output power with the heavier load is

$$P_{\text{out2}} = T_{\text{dev2}}\omega_{m2} = 2133\text{ W}$$

■

Exercise 8 Find the speed and output power in Example 5 for a load torque of $T_{\text{dev3}} = 6$ Nm.

Answer $P_{\text{out3}} = 1066$ W, $\omega_{m3} = 177.8$ rad/s, $n_{m3} = 1697$ rpm. □

Exercise 9 Repeat Example 5 for a shunt-connected motor. (In an ideal shunt-connected motor, the field resistance would be very large rather than zero.)

Answer With $R_A = 0$ and fixed V_T, the shunt motor runs at constant speed, independent of load. Thus, $n_{m1} = n_{m2} = 1200$ rpm, $P_{\text{out1}} = 1508$ W, and $P_{\text{out2}} = 3016$ W. □

Notice that by comparing the results of Exercise 9 with those of Example 5 we find that the output power variation is larger for the shunt-connected motor than for the series-connected motor.

Universal Motors

The universal motor is an important type of ac motor.

Equation 34 shows that the torque produced by the series dc motor is proportional to the square of the source voltage. Thus, the direction of the torque is independent of the polarity of the applied voltage. The series-connected machine can be operated from a single-phase ac source, provided that the stator is laminated to avoid excessive losses due to eddy currents. Since the field and armature inductances have nonzero impedances for ac currents, the current is not as large for an ac source as it would be for a dc source of the same average magnitude.

Series motors that are intended for use with ac sources are called **universal motors** because in principle they can operate from either ac or dc. Any time that you examine an ac motor and find brushes and a commutator, you have a universal motor. Compared with other types of single-phase ac motors, the universal motor has several advantages:

1. For a given weight, universal motors produce more power than other types. This is a large advantage for hand-held tools and small appliances, such as drills, saws, mixers, and blenders.
2. The universal motor produces large starting torque without excessive current.
3. When load torque increases, the universal motor slows down. Hence, the power produced is relatively constant, and the current magnitude remains within reasonable bounds. (In contrast, shunt dc motors or ac induction motors tend to run at constant speed and are more prone to drawing excessive currents for high-torque loads.) Thus, the universal motor is more suitable for loads that demand a wide range of torque, such as drills and food mixers. (For the same reason, series dc motors are used as starter motors in automobiles.)
4. Universal motors can be designed to operate at very high speeds, whereas we will see that other types of ac motors are limited to 3600 rpm, assuming a 60-Hz source.

One disadvantage of universal motors (as well as dc machines in general) is that the brushes and commutators wear out relatively quickly. Thus, the service life is much less than for ac induction motors. Induction motors are better choices than universal motors in applications that need to run often over a long life, such as refrigerator compressors, water pumps, or furnace fans.

6 SPEED CONTROL OF DC MOTORS

Speed control is an important consideration in the design of many systems.

Several methods can be used to control the speed of dc motors:

1. Vary the voltage supplied to the armature circuit while holding the field constant.
2. Vary the field current while holding the armature supply voltage constant.
3. Insert resistance in series with the armature circuit.

In this section, we discuss briefly each of these approaches to speed control.

Variation of the Supply Voltage

This method is applicable to separately excited motors and PM motors. For the shunt motor, varying the supply voltage is not an appropriate method of speed control, because the field current and flux vary with V_T. The effects of increasing both armature supply voltage and the field current tend to offset one another, resulting in little change in speed.

In normal operation, the drop across the armature resistance is small compared to E_A, and we have

$$E_A \cong V_T$$

Since we also have

$$E_A = K\phi\omega_m$$

we can write

$$\omega_m \cong \frac{V_T}{K\phi} \tag{35}$$

Thus, the speed of a separately excited motor with constant field current or of a PM motor is approximately proportional to the source voltage.

Variation of the supply voltage is also appropriate for control of a series-connected dc motor; however, the flux does not remain constant in this case. Equation 34 shows that the torque of a series machine is proportional to the square of the source voltage at any given speed. Thus, depending on the torque–speed characteristic of the load, the speed varies with applied voltage. Generally, higher voltage produces higher speed.

Variable DC Voltage Sources

Historically, variable dc voltages were obtained from dc generators. For example, one popular approach was the **Ward Leonard system**, in which a three-phase induction motor drives a dc generator that in turn supplies a variable dc voltage to the motor to be controlled. The magnitude and polarity of the dc supply voltage are controlled by using a rheostat or switches to vary the field current of the dc generator. A disadvantage of this scheme is that three machines are needed to drive one load.

Since the advent of high-power electronics, a more economical approach is to use a rectifier to convert three-phase ac into dc, as illustrated in Figure 24. The resulting dc voltage v_L has some ripple, but a smoother voltage can be obtained with a full-wave version of the rectifier using six diodes. In any case, it is not necessary for the dc source supplying motors to be absolutely free of ripple, because the inductances and inertia tend to smooth the response.

Once a constant dc source has been created, an electronic switching circuit can be used to control the average voltage delivered to a load, as illustrated in Figure 25. (Electronic devices such as BJTs and FETs can be used as switches. In high-power

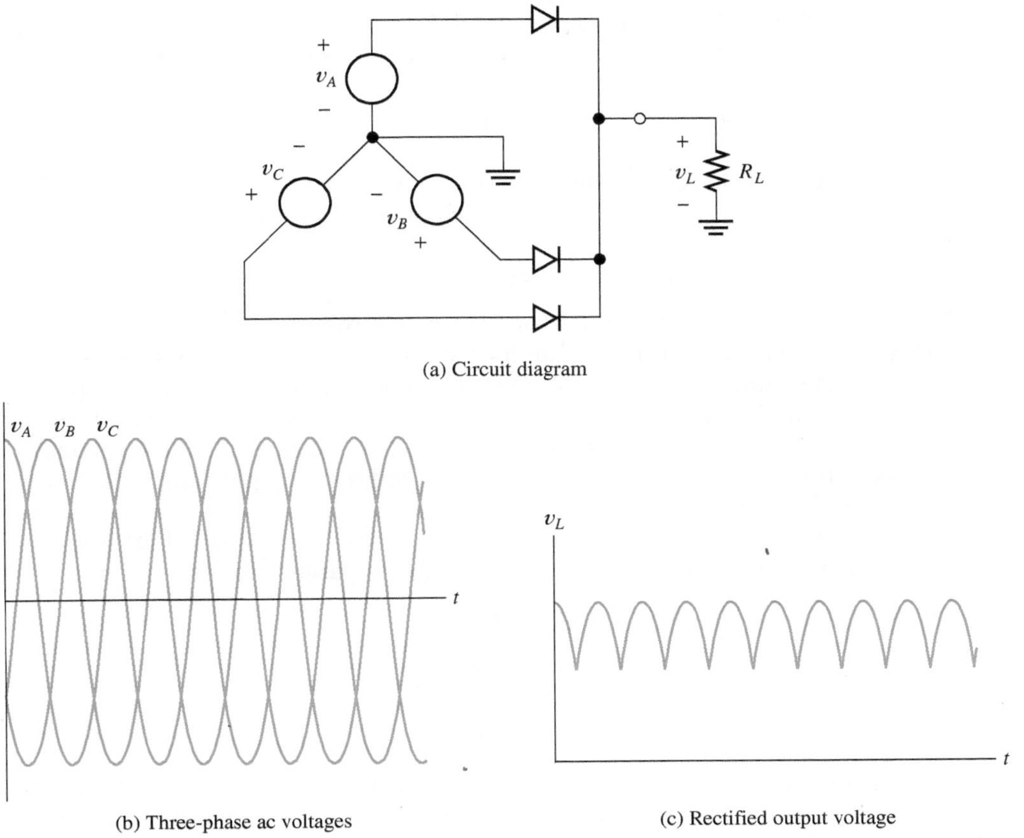

(b) Three-phase ac voltages

(c) Rectified output voltage

Figure 24 Three-phase half-wave rectifier circuit used to convert ac power to dc.

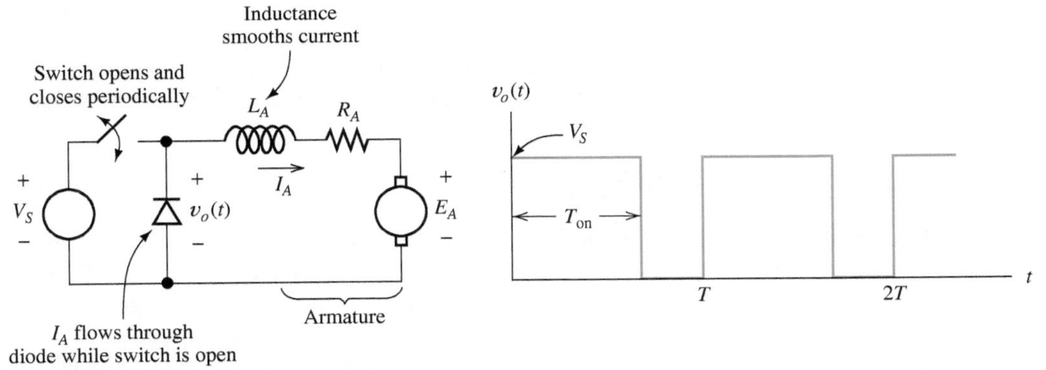

Figure 25 An electronic switch that opens and closes periodically can efficiently supply a variable dc voltage to a motor from a fixed dc supply voltage.

electronics, similar devices such as silicon-controlled rectifiers perform the switching function.)

The switch periodically opens and closes with period T, spending T_{on} in the closed state and the remainder of the period open. The inductance L_A tends to cause the armature current to continue flowing when the switch is open. Thus, the armature current I_A is nearly constant even though the voltage $v_o(t)$ switches rapidly between zero and V_s. The diode provides a path for the armature current while the switch is open. The average value of the voltage applied to the motor is given by

$$V_T = V_s \frac{T_{\text{on}}}{T} \tag{36}$$

Thus, the average voltage, and therefore the speed of the motor, can be controlled by varying the fraction of the period for which the switch is closed.

Speed Control by Varying the Field Current

The speed of either a shunt-connected or a separately excited motor can be controlled by varying the field current. The circuit for the shunt-connected machine was shown in Figure 16, in which the rheostat R_{adj} provides the means to control field current.

On the other hand, PM motors have constant flux. In series-connected motors, the field current is the same as the armature current and cannot be independently controlled. Thus, using field current to control speed is not appropriate for either of these types of motors.

To understand the effect of field current on motor torque and speed, let us review the following equations for the shunt-connected or separately excited motor:

$$E_A = K\phi\omega_m$$

$$I_A = \frac{V_T - E_A}{R_A}$$

$$T_{\text{dev}} = K\phi I_A$$

Now, consider what happens when I_F is reduced (by increasing R_{adj}). Reducing I_F reduces the flux ϕ. Immediately, the induced voltage E_A is reduced. This in turn causes I_A to increase. In fact, the percentage increase in I_A is much greater than the percentage reduction in ϕ, because V_T and E_A are nearly equal. Thus, $I_A = (V_T - E_A)/R_A$ increases rapidly when E_A is reduced. Two of the terms in the equation for torque $T_{\text{dev}} = K\phi I_A$ change in opposite directions; specifically, ϕ falls and I_A rises. However, the change in I_A is much greater and the torque rises rapidly when I_F falls. (You can verify this by comparing your solution to Exercise 7 to the values in Example 4.)

Danger of an Open Field Circuit

What happens in a shunt or separately excited motor if the field circuit becomes open circuited and ϕ falls to nearly zero? (Because of residual magnetization, the field is not zero for zero field current.) The answer is that I_A becomes very large and the machine speeds up very rapidly. In fact, it is possible for excessive speeds to cause the armature to fly apart. Then, in a matter of seconds, the machine is reduced to a pile of useless scrap consisting of loose windings and commutator bars. Thus, it is important to operate shunt machines with well-designed protection circuits that open the armature circuit automatically when the field current vanishes.

It is important to operate shunt machines with well-designed protection circuits that automatically open the armature circuit when the field current vanishes.

Speed Control by Inserting Resistance in Series with the Armature

Another method for controlling the speed of a dc motor is to insert additional resistance in series with the armature circuit. This approach can be applied to all types of dc motors: shunt, separately excited, series, or PM. For example, a shunt-connected motor with added armature resistance is illustrated in Figure 26(a). We denote the

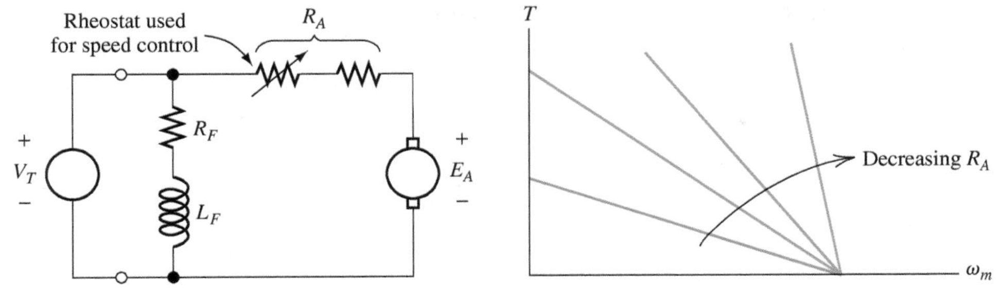

(a) Circuit diagram (b) Torque–speed characteristic

Figure 26 Speed can be adjusted by varying a rheostat that is in series with the armature.

total resistance as R_A, which consists of the control resistance plus the resistance of the armature winding. The torque–speed relationship for a shunt-connected motor is given by Equation 27, repeated here for convenience:

$$T_{\text{dev}} = \frac{K\phi}{R_A}(V_T - K\phi\omega_m)$$

Plots of the torque–speed characteristic for various resistances are shown in Figure 26(b). Similar results apply to separately excited and PM motors.

Look at Figures 26, 27, and 28 to see how the torque–speed characteristics of shunt-connected and separately excited dc motors can be changed by varying armature resistance, armature supply voltage, or field current to achieve speed control.

Starting controls for shunt or separately excited dc motors usually place resistance in series with the armature to limit armature current to reasonable values while the machine comes up to speed.

A disadvantage of inserting resistance in series with the armature to control speed is that it is wasteful of energy. When running at low speeds, much of the energy taken from the source is converted directly into heat in the series resistance.

Equation 34 gives the torque for series-connected machines. For convenience, the equation is repeated here:

$$T_{\text{dev}} = \frac{KK_F V_T^2}{(R_A + R_F + KK_F\omega_m)^2}$$

Notice that if R_A is made larger by adding resistance in series with the armature, the torque is reduced for any given speed.

Exercise 10 Why is variation of the supply voltage V_T in the shunt machine (see Figure 16) an ineffective way to control speed?

Answer Decreasing V_T decreases the field current, and therefore the flux. In the linear portion of the magnetization curve, the flux is proportional to the field current. Thus, reduction of V_T leads to reduction of ϕ, and according to Equation 35, the speed remains constant. (Actually, some variation of speed may occur due to saturation effects.) □

Exercise 11 Figure 26(b) shows a family of torque–speed curves for various values of R_A. Sketch a similar family of torque–speed characteristics for a separately excited machine (see Figure 21) with various values of V_T and constant field current.

Answer The torque–speed relationship is given by Equation 27. With constant field current, ϕ is constant. The family of characteristics is shown in Figure 27. □

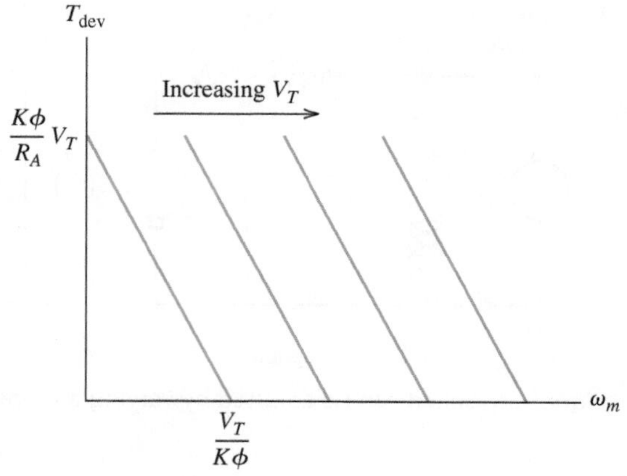

Figure 27 Torque versus speed for the separately excited dc motor for various values of armature supply voltage V_T.

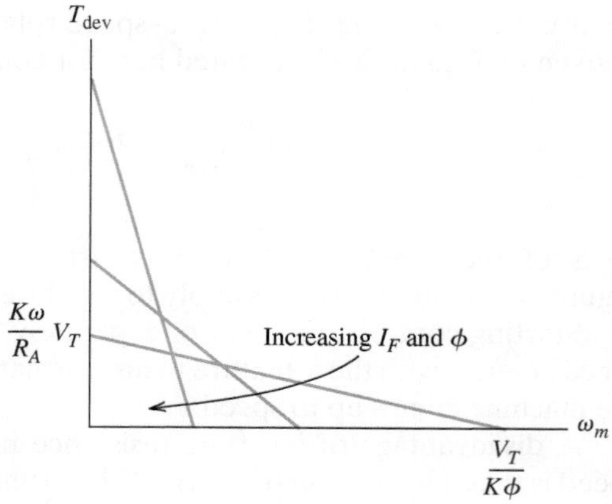

Figure 28 Effect of varying I_F on the torque–speed characteristics of the shunt-connected or separately excited dc motor.

Exercise 12 Sketch a family of torque–speed characteristics for a shunt-connected or separately excited machine with constant V_T and variable I_F.

Answer The torque–speed relationship is given in Equation 27. As field current is increased, the flux ϕ increases. The family of characteristics is shown in Figure 28. □

7 DC GENERATORS

Generators convert kinetic energy from a **prime mover**, such as a steam turbine or a diesel engine, into electrical energy. When dc power is needed, we can use a dc generator or an ac source combined with a rectifier. The trend is toward ac sources and rectifiers; however, many dc generators are in use, and for some applications they are still a good choice.

Several connections, illustrated in Figure 29, are useful for dc generators. We will discuss each type of connection briefly and conclude with an example illustrating performance calculations for the separately excited generator.

Separately Excited DC Generators

The equivalent circuit for a separately excited dc generator is shown in Figure 29(a). A prime mover drives the armature shaft at an angular speed ω_m, and

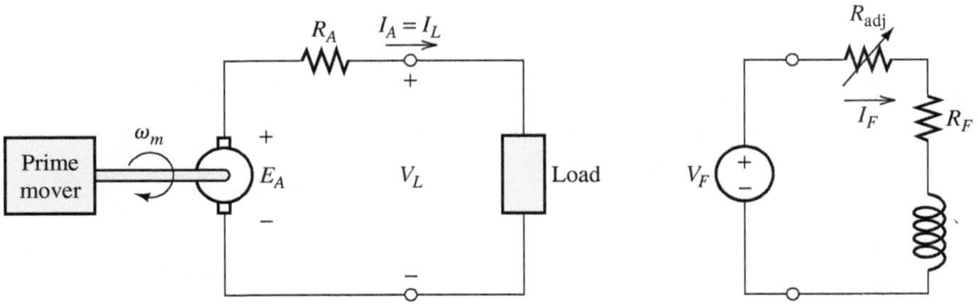

(a) Separately excited

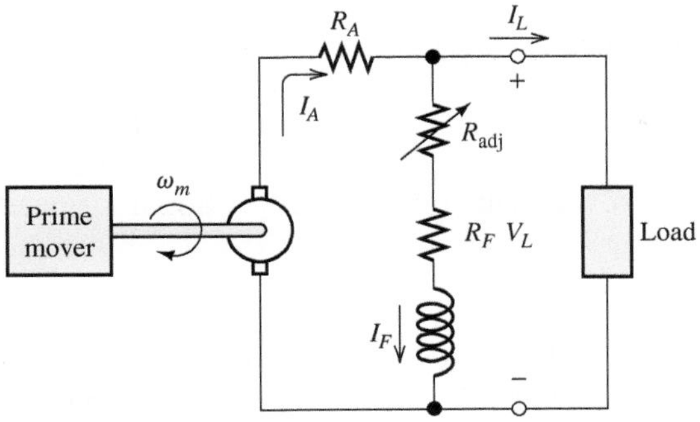

(b) Shunt connected

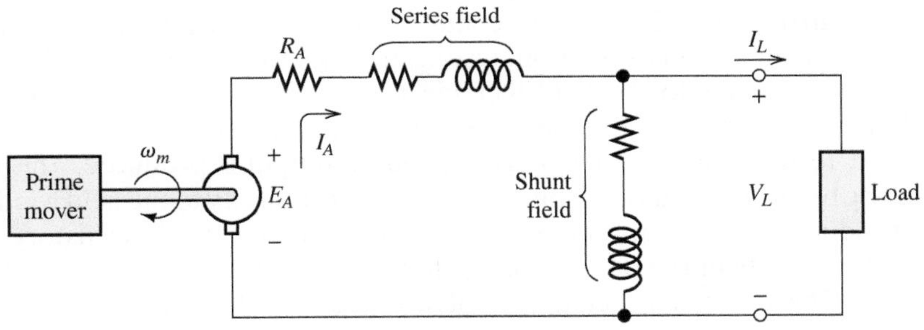

(c) Compound connected

Figure 29 DC generator equivalent circuits.

the external dc source V_F supplies current I_F to the field coils. The induced armature voltage causes current to flow through the load. Because of the drop across the armature resistance, the load voltage V_L decreases as the load current I_L increases, assuming constant speed and field current. This is illustrated in Figure 30(a).

For some applications, it is desirable for the load voltage to be nearly independent of the load current. A measure of the amount of decrease in load voltage with current is the percentage load voltage regulation given by

$$\text{voltage regulation} = \frac{V_{NL} - V_{FL}}{V_{FL}} \times 100\% \qquad (37)$$

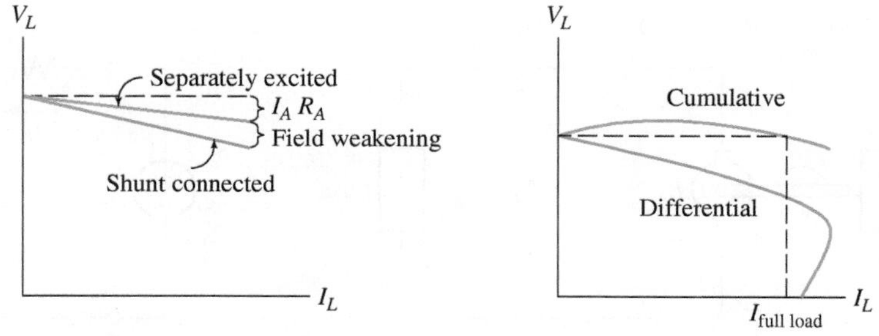

(a) Separately excited and shunt connected (b) Compound connected

Figure 30 Load voltage versus load current for various dc generators.

in which V_{NL} is the no-load voltage (i.e., $I_L = 0$) and V_{FL} is the full-load voltage (i.e., with full-rated load current).

One of the advantages of the separately excited dc generator is that the load voltage can be adjusted over a wide range by varying the field current either by changing V_F or by changing R_{adj}. Also, the load voltage is proportional to speed.

Shunt-Connected DC Generators

One of the disadvantages of the separately excited dc generator is the need for a separate dc source to supply the field windings. This disadvantage is overcome in the shunt-connected machine, for which the field circuit is in parallel with the armature and the load, as shown in Figure 29(b). The output voltage can be adjusted by changing the resistance R_{adj} that is in series with the field winding.

Initial buildup of voltage in the shunt-connected machine usually occurs because of the residual magnetic field of the iron. (Adjusting R_{adj} to its minimum value and reversing the connections to the field winding may be needed to ensure voltage buildup.) However, if the machine becomes demagnetized, the induced armature voltage is zero, resulting in zero field current, and no output is produced. This can be remedied by briefly applying a dc source of the correct polarity to the field winding to create a residual field in the machine. Also, depending on the machine history, it is possible for the polarity of the output voltage to build up with the opposite polarity to that desired. This can be corrected by applying an external source of the correct polarity to the field winding or by reversing the connections to the machine.

The load regulation of the shunt-connected generator is poorer (i.e., larger) than that of the separately excited machine because the field current falls as the load current increases due to the drop across the armature resistance. This increased drop due to field weakening is illustrated in Figure 30(a).

Compound-Connected DC Generators

It is possible to design a dc generator with both series and shunt windings. When both are connected, we have a compound-connected machine. Several variations of the connections are possible. Figure 29(c) illustrates a **long-shunt compound connection**. Another possibility is the **short-shunt compound connection**, in which the shunt field is directly in parallel with the armature and the series field is in series with the load. Furthermore, in either the short-shunt or the long-shunt, the field of the series field coil can either aid or oppose the field of the shunt field coil. If the fields aid, we have a **cumulative shunt connection**. On the other hand, if the fields oppose, we have a **differential shunt connection**. Thus, we have four types of connections in all.

It is possible to design a **fully compensated** cumulative-connected machine for which the full-load voltage is equal to the no-load voltage, as illustrated in Figure 30(b). Curvature of the voltage versus current characteristic is due to saturation effects. If the full-load voltage is less than the no-load voltage, the machine is said to be **undercompensated**. In an **overcompensated** machine, the full-load voltage is greater than the no-load voltage.

In a differential shunt connection, the output voltage falls rapidly with load current because the field of the series winding opposes that of the shunt winding. Considerable load current may flow even after the load voltage drops to zero. This is illustrated in Figure 30(b).

Performance Calculations

Next, we illustrate performance calculations for the separately excited generator. Analysis of the other connections is left for the problems.

As for dc motors, the following equations apply to dc generators:

$$E_A = K\phi\omega_m \tag{38}$$

$$T_{\text{dev}} = K\phi\omega_m \tag{39}$$

Referring to Figure 29(a), we can write:

$$E_A = R_A I_A + V_L \tag{40}$$

$$V_F = (R_F + R_{\text{adj}})I_F \tag{41}$$

Figure 31 illustrates the power flow of a dc generator. The efficiency is given by

$$\text{efficiency} = \frac{P_{\text{out}}}{P_{\text{in}}} \times 100\% \tag{42}$$

Equations 37 through 42, the magnetization curve of the machine, and Figure 31 are the tools for analysis of the separately excited dc generator. (Recall that the magnetization curve is a plot of E_A versus I_F for a given speed.)

Example 6 Separately Excited DC Generator

A separately excited dc generator has $V_F = 140$, $R_F = 10\ \Omega$, $R_{\text{adj}} = 4\ \Omega$, $R_A = 0.065\ \Omega$, the prime mover rotates the armature at a speed of 1000 rpm, and the magnetization curve is shown in Figure 19. Determine the field current, the no-load voltage, the full-load voltage, and the percentage voltage regulation for a full-load current of 200 A. Assuming that the overall efficiency (not including the power supplied to the field circuit) of the machine is 85 percent, determine the input torque, the developed torque, and the losses associated with friction, windage, eddy currents, and hysteresis.

Solution The field current is

$$I_F = \frac{V_F}{R_{\text{adj}} + R_F} = \frac{140}{4+10} = 10\ \text{A}$$

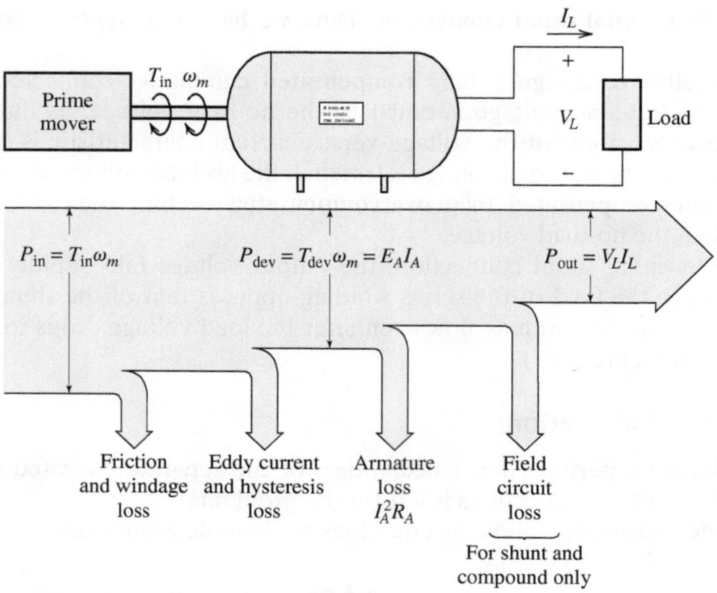

Figure 31 Power flow in dc generators.

Then, referring to the magnetization curve, we find that $E_A = 280$ V for a speed of 1200 rpm. Equation 38 shows that E_A is proportional to speed. So, for a speed of 1000 rpm, we have

$$E_A = 280\frac{1000}{1200} = 233.3 \text{ V}$$

which is also the no-load voltage of the machine. For a load current of 200 A, we get

$$V_{FL} = E_A - R_A I_A = 233.3 - 200 \times 0.065 = 220.3 \text{ V}$$

Finally, we obtain

$$\text{voltage regulation} = \frac{V_{NL} - V_{FL}}{V_{FL}} \times 100\% = \frac{233.3 - 220.3}{220.3} \times 100\% = 5.900\%$$

The output power is

$$P_{out} = I_L V_{FL} = 200 \times 220.3 = 44.06 \text{ kW}$$

The developed power is the sum of the output power and the armature loss:

$$P_{dev} = P_{out} + R_A I_A^2 = 44060 + 0.065(200)^2 = 46.66 \text{ kW}$$

The angular speed is

$$\omega_m = n_m \frac{2\pi}{60} = 104.7 \text{ rad/s}$$

The input power is

$$P_{in} = \frac{P_{out}}{0.85} = \frac{44.06}{0.85} = 51.84 \text{ kW}$$

The power losses associated with friction, windage, eddy currents, and hysteresis are

$$P_{\text{losses}} = P_{\text{in}} - P_{\text{dev}} = 51.84 - 46.66 = 5.18 \text{ kW}$$

The input and developed torques are

$$T_{\text{in}} = \frac{P_{\text{in}}}{\omega_m} = \frac{51{,}840}{104.7} = 495.1 \text{ N}\cdot\text{m}$$

$$T_{\text{dev}} = \frac{P_{\text{dev}}}{\omega_m} = \frac{46{,}660}{104.7} = 445.7 \text{ N}\cdot\text{m}$$

■

Exercise 13 Repeat Example 6 for $R_{\text{adj}} = 0$.
Answer $I_F = 14$ A, $V_{NL} = 260$, $V_{FL} = 247$, voltage regulation $= 5.263\%$, $P_{\text{losses}} = 6.1$ kW, $T_{\text{in}} = 555$ N·m, $T_{\text{dev}} = 497$ N·m. □

Summary

1. An electrical motor consists of a rotor and a stator, both of which may contain windings. A given winding may be classified as either an armature winding or as a field winding.
2. The electrical source for a motor can be dc, single-phase ac, or three-phase ac.
3. Factors to consider in selecting an electrical motor for a given application include the electrical sources available, the output power required, load torque versus speed, the service-life requirements, efficiency, speed regulation, starting current, the desired operating speed, ambient temperature, and the acceptable frequency of maintenance.
4. Dc motors in common use contain brushes and commutators that reverse the connections to the armature conductors with rotation. The need for frequent maintenance of these parts is a significant disadvantage of dc motors.
5. An advantage of dc motors is the ease with which their speed can be controlled. However, ac motors used with modern electronic systems that can change the frequencies of ac sources are taking over in many speed-control applications.
6. The speed of a motor–load combination self-adjusts to the point at which the output torque of the motor equals the torque demanded by the load. Thus, if the torque–speed characteristics of the motor and of the load are plotted on the same axes, the steady-state operating point is at the intersection of the characteristics.
7. The linear dc machine illustrates the basic principles of dc machines in an uncomplicated manner. However, it is not practical for the vast majority of applications.
8. Commonly used dc machines have field windings on the stator that establish an even number of magnetic poles. The armature windings on the rotor carry currents, resulting in forces induced by the field. To achieve aiding contributions to torque (and induced armature voltage), a commutator and a set of brushes reverse the connections to the armature conductors as they move between poles.
9. The magnetization curve of a dc machine is a plot of the induced armature voltage versus field current with the machine being driven at a constant speed. The equivalent circuit shown in Figure 14, the magnetization curve, and the following equations provide the basis for analyzing dc machines:

$$E_A = K\phi\omega_m$$

$$T_{\text{dev}} = K\phi I_A$$

$$P_{\text{dev}} = E_A I_A = \omega_m T_{\text{dev}}$$

10. The equivalent circuit of a shunt-connected dc motor is shown in Figure 16. The torque–speed characteristic is shown in Figure 18. Speed can be controlled either by using R_{adj} to vary the field current or by inserting a variable resistance in series with the armature. Variation of V_T is not an effective means of speed control.
11. The equivalent circuit of a separately excited dc motor is shown in Figure 21. The torque–speed characteristic is identical to that of the shunt-connected machine shown in Figure 18. Speed can be controlled by varying the field current, by varying the armature source voltage V_T, or by inserting additional resistance in series with the armature.
12. The characteristics of a permanent-magnet dc motor are similar to those of a separately excited motor, except that no means is available to vary the field. Speed control can be achieved by varying the armature supply voltage or by inserting additional resistance in series with the armature.
13. The equivalent circuit of the series-connected dc motor is shown in Figure 22. In the normal range of operation, its torque is almost inversely proportional to the square of its speed. The series-connected dc motor is suitable for starting heavy loads. It can reach dangerous speeds if the load is totally removed.
14. The universal motor is basically a series dc motor designed for operation from an ac source. It is to be found in applications where a large power-to-weight ratio is needed. However, due to commutator wear, its service life is limited. Its speed can be controlled by varying the applied voltage or by inserting series resistance.
15. Historically, variable dc voltages for speed control of dc motors were obtained by employing dc generators. Presently, the approach of choice is to use rectifiers that first convert ac into dc. Then, electronic chopper circuits with adjustable duty factors provide variable average voltages.
16. Figures 26, 27, and 28 show how the torque–speed characteristics of shunt-connected and separately excited dc motors can be changed by varying armature resistance, armature supply voltage, or field current to achieve speed control.
17. Dc generators can be separately excited, shunt connected, or compound connected. Analysis of dc generators is similar to that for dc motors.

Problems

Section 1: Overview of Motors

P1. What two types of windings are used in electrical machines? Which type is not used in permanent-magnet machines? Why not?

P2. In what application would dc motors be more advantageous than ac motors?

P3. What types of motors contain brushes and a commutator? What is the function of these parts?

P4. Name the principal parts of a rotating electrical machine.

P5. List the two principal types of three-phase ac motors. Which is in more common use?

***P6.** List two practical disadvantages of dc motors compared to single-phase ac induction motors for supplying power to a ventilation fan in a home or small business.

***P7.** A three-phase induction motor is rated at 5 hp, 1760 rpm, with a line-to-line voltage of 220 V rms. The no-load speed of the motor is 1800 rpm. Determine the percentage speed regulation.

P8. A three-phase induction motor is rated at 5 hp, 1760 rpm, with a line-to-line voltage of 220 V rms. The motor has a power factor of 80 percent lagging and an efficiency of 75 percent under full-load conditions. Find the electrical input power absorbed by the motor under full-load conditions. Also, find the rms line current.

P9. A three-phase induction motor is rated at 5 hp, 1760 rpm, with a line-to-line voltage

* Denotes that answers are contained in the Student Solutions files. See Appendix "On-Line Student Resources" for more information about accessing the Student Solutions.

of 220 V rms. Find the output torque and angular velocity of the motor under full-load conditions.

***P10.** A certain 25-hp three-phase induction motor operates from a 440-V-rms (line-to-line) three-phase source. The full-load speed is 1750 rpm. The motor has a starting torque equal to 200 percent of its full-load torque when started at rated voltage. For an engineering estimate, assume that the starting torque of an induction motor is proportional to the square of the applied voltage. To reduce the starting current of the motor, we decide to start it with a line-to-line voltage of 220 V. Estimate the starting torque with this reduced line voltage.

P11. We want a four-pole synchronous motor that operates at a speed of 1000 rpm. Determine the frequency of the ac source. List several other speeds that can be achieved by using synchronous motors operating from this ac source. What is the highest speed achievable?

P12. Consider a system consisting of a motor driving a load. The motor has the torque–speed characteristic shown in Figure P12. The load is a fan requiring a torque given by

$$T_{\text{load}} = K\omega_m^2$$

At a speed of $n = 1000$ rpm, the power absorbed by the load is 0.75 hp. Determine the speed of the system in radians per second and the power delivered to the fan in watts. Convert your answers to rpm and horsepower.

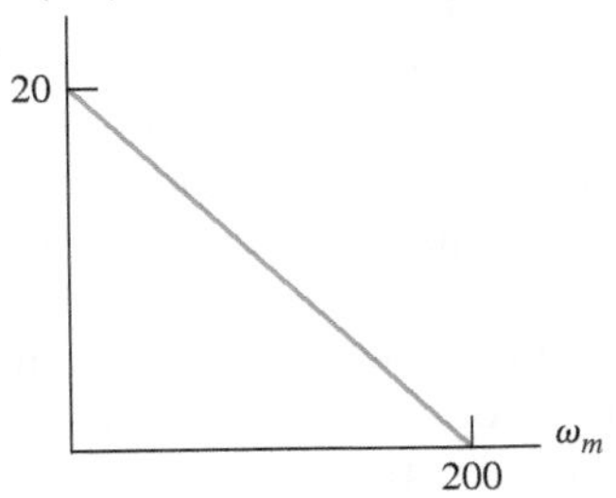

Figure P12

P13. A certain 25-hp three-phase induction motor operates from a 440-V-rms (line-to-line) three-phase source and draws a line current of 35 A rms at a power factor of 83 percent lagging under rated full-load conditions. The full-load speed is 1750 rpm. Under no-load conditions, the speed is 1797 rpm, and the line current is 6.5 A rms at a power factor of 30 percent lagging. Find the power loss and efficiency with full load, the input power with no load, and the speed regulation.

P14. Operating from a line-to-line voltage of 440 V rms with a line current of 14 A rms and a power factor of 85 percent, a three-phase induction motor produces an output power of 6.5 hp. Determine the losses in watts and the efficiency of the motor.

***P15.** A 440-V-rms (line-to-line voltage) three-phase induction motor runs at 1150 rpm driving a load requiring 15 Nm of torque. The line current is 3.4 A rms at a power factor of 80 percent lagging. Find the output power, the power loss, and the efficiency.

P16. A motor drives a load for which the torque required is given by

$$T_{\text{load}} = \frac{800}{20 + \omega_m} \text{ Nm}$$

The torque–speed characteristic of the motor is shown in Figure P12. **a.** Will this system start from zero speed? Why or why not? **b.** Suppose that the system is brought up to speed by an auxiliary driver, which is then disengaged. In principle, at what two constant speeds can the system rotate? **c.** If the system is operating at the lower of the two speeds and power to the motor is briefly interrupted so the system slows by a few radians per second, what will happen after power is restored? Why? **d.** Repeat (c) if the system is initially operating at the higher speed.

P17. A motor has output torque given by

$$T_{\text{out}} = 10^{-2}(60\pi - \omega_m)\omega_m$$

where ω_m is angular velocity in rad/s and T_{out} is the output torque in newton meters. **a.** Find the no-load speed of the motor. **b.** At what speed between zero and the no-load speed is the output torque maximum? What is the maximum output torque? **c.** At what speed between zero and the no-load speed is the output power maximum? What is the maximum output power? **d.** Find the starting torque of the motor. How could this motor be started?

P18. A 220-V-rms (line-to-line), 60-Hz, three-phase induction motor operates at 3500 rpm while delivering its rated full-load output power. Estimate the no-load speed and speed regulation for the motor.

P19. A 220-V-rms (line-to-line), 60-Hz, three-phase induction motor operates at 3500 rpm while delivering its rated output power of 3 hp. The line current is 8 A rms and the losses are 300 W. Find the input power, power factor, and efficiency.

Section 2: Principles of DC Machines

***P20.** Consider the linear dc machine shown in Figure 6 with no load force applied. What happens to the steady-state velocity of the bar if: **a.** the source voltage V_T is doubled in magnitude; **b.** the resistance R_A is doubled; **c.** the magnetic flux density B is doubled in magnitude?

***P21.** Consider the linear dc machine of Figure P21. When the switch closes, is the force on the bar toward the top of the page or toward the bottom? Determine the magnitude of the initial (starting) force. Also, determine the final velocity of the bar neglecting friction.

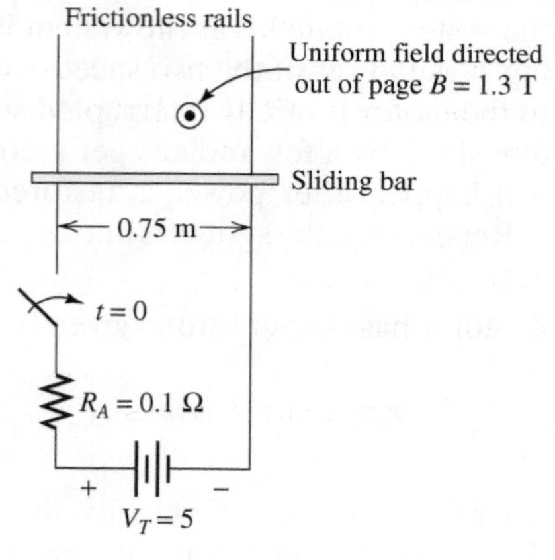

Figure P21

P22. Suppose that we wish to design a linear motor based on Figure 6 that can deliver 1 hp at a steady bar velocity of 20 m/s. The flux density is limited to 1 T by the magnetic properties of the materials to be used. The length of the bar is to be 0.5 m, and the resistance is 0.05 Ω. Find the current i_A, the source voltage V_T, and the efficiency of the machine. Assume that the only loss is due to the resistance R_A.

P23. Consider the linear dc machine shown in Figure 6. What happens to the initial force (i.e., starting force) induced in the bar if: **a.** the source voltage V_T is doubled in magnitude; **b.** the resistance R_A is doubled; **c.** the magnetic flux density B is doubled in magnitude?

P24. Suppose that an external force of 10 N directed toward the top of the page is applied to the bar as shown in Figure P24. In steady state, is the machine acting as a motor or as a generator? Find the power supplied by or absorbed by: **a.** the electrical voltage source V_T; **b.** R_A; **c.** the external force.

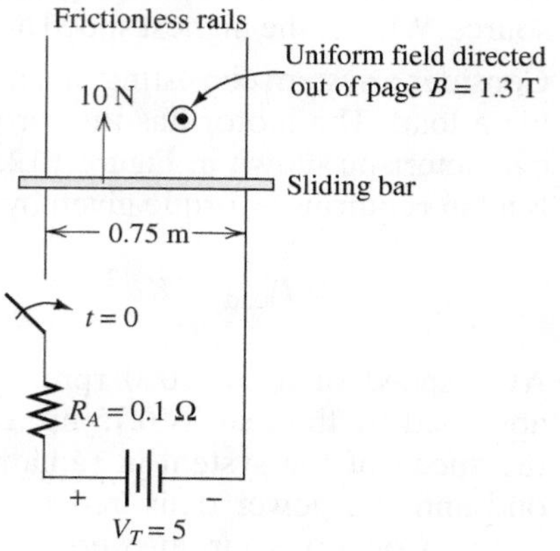

Figure P24

P25. We have presented the linear dc machine with an applied magnetic field, such as we might have in a dc motor. However, forces are exerted on the slider by the magnetic field produced by the currents in the rails. This is the principle of the **electromagnetic rail gun** for which you can find many references on the web including many practical construction tips. A version of such a rail gun is shown in Figure P25. **a.** When the switch closes, in which direction is force exerted on the projectile? Use physical principles discussed in this text to explain how you arrived at your answer. **b.** Suppose that the projectile mass is 3 g (which is about that of a penny). Assuming that all of the energy stored in the capacitor is transferred to kinetic energy in the slider, determine its final velocity. (*Note:* The highest velocity achievable by ordinary rifle bullets is about 1200 m/s.) **c.** List as many effects as you can that cause the velocity to be lower than the value calculated in part (b).

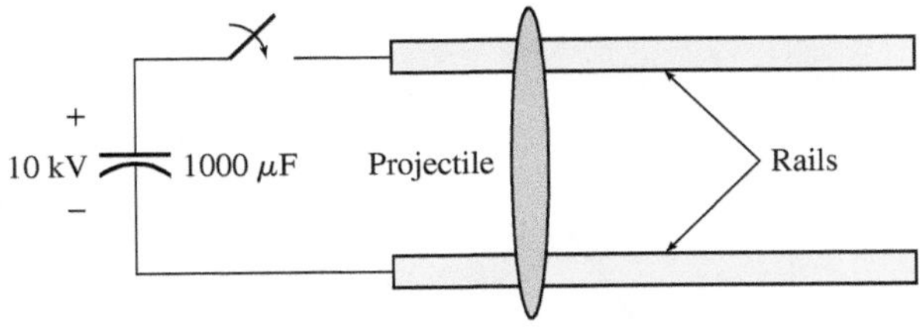

Figure P25

P26. Suppose that an external force of 10 N directed toward the bottom of the page is applied to the bar as shown in Figure P26. In steady state, is the machine acting as a motor or as a generator? Find the power supplied by or absorbed by: **a.** the electrical voltage source V_T; **b.** R_A; **c.** the external force.

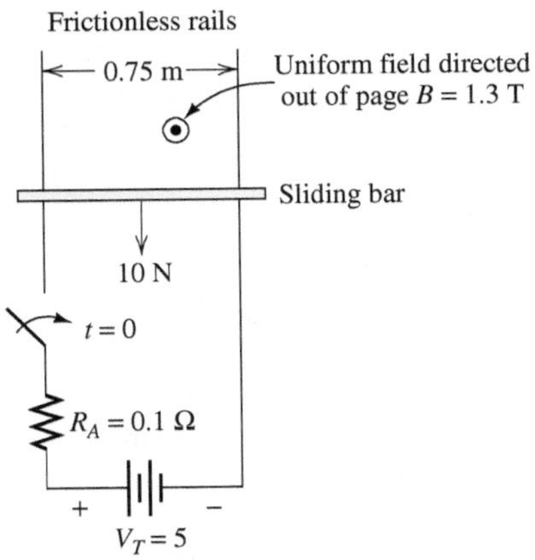

Figure P26

Section 3: Rotating DC Machines

***P27.** An alternative way to determine the direction of the torque produced by a dc machine is to consider the interaction of the magnetic poles produced by the armature current with the stator poles. Consider the cross section of a two-pole dc motor shown in Figure 10. The magnetic poles established on the stator by the field windings are shown. For the armature current directions shown in the figure, find the locations and label the rotor poles. Of course, the rotor poles try to align with unlike stator poles. Which direction is the resulting torque, clockwise or counterclockwise? Repeat for the four-pole machine shown in Figure 11.

***P28.** A certain dc motor has $R_A = 1.3\ \Omega$, $I_A = 10$ A, and produces a back emf $E_A = 240$ V, while operating at a speed of 1200 rpm. Determine the voltage applied to the armature, the developed torque, and the developed power.

***P29.** Suppose that we are designing a 1200-rpm dc motor to run from a 240-V source. We have determined that the flux density will be 1 T because smaller fluxes make inefficient use of the iron and larger fluxes result in saturation. The radius of the rotor (and thus, the torque arm for the armature conductors) is 0.1 m. The lengths of the armature conductors are 0.3 m. Approximately how many armature conductors must be placed in series in this machine?

***P30.** A dc motor operates with a load that demands constant developed torque. With $V_T = 200$ V, the motor operates at 1200 rpm and has $I_A = 10$ A. The armature resistance is 5 Ω and the field current remains constant. Determine the speed if V_T is increased to 250 V.

P31. A permanent-magnet dc motor has $R_A = 7\ \Omega$, $V_T = 240$ V, and operates under no-load conditions at a speed of 1500 rpm with $I_A = 1$ A. A load is connected and the speed drops to 1300 rpm. Determine the efficiency of the motor under loaded conditions. Assume that the losses consist solely of heating of R_A and frictional loss torque that is independent of speed.

P32. Consider a motor having the model shown in Figure 14. The motor runs at a speed of 1200 rpm and has $R_F = 150\ \Omega$, $V_F = V_T = 180$ V, $I_A = 10$ A, and $R_A = 1.2\ \Omega$. Find E_A, T_{dev},

P_{dev}, and the power converted to heat in the resistances.

P33. Consider the two-pole motor shown in Figure 10. The gap between the rotor and stator is 1.5 mm. Each of the two field coils has 250 turns and carries a current of 3 A. Assume that the permeability of the iron is infinite. **a.** Determine the flux density in the air gap. **b.** Each armature conductor carries a current of 30 A and has a length of 0.5 m. Find the force induced in each conductor.

P34. Under no-load conditions, a certain motor operates at 1200 rpm with an armature current of 0.5 A and a terminal voltage of 480 V. The armature resistance is 2 Ω. Determine the speed and speed regulation if a load demanding a torque of 50 Nm is connected to the motor. Assume that the losses consist solely of heating of R_A and frictional loss torque that is independent of speed.

P35. A certain motor has an induced armature voltage of 200 V at $n_{m1} = 1200$ rpm. Suppose that this motor is operating at a speed of $n_{m2} = 1500$ rpm with a developed power of 5 hp. Find the armature current and the developed torque.

P36. A certain dc motor produces a back emf of $E_A = 240$ V at a speed of 1200 rpm. Assume that the field current remains constant. Find the back emf for a speed of 600 rpm and for a speed of 1500 rpm.

P37. Sometimes the stator, particularly the yoke (shown in Figure 10), of a dc machine is not laminated. However, it is always necessary to laminate the rotor. Explain.

Section 4: Shunt-Connected and Separately Excited DC Motors

***P38.** A shunt dc motor has $R_A = 0.1$ Ω and $V_T = 440$ V. For an output power of 50 hp, we have $n_m = 1500$ rpm and $I_A = 103$ A. The field current remains constant for all parts of this problem. **a.** Find the developed power, power lost in R_A, and the rotational losses. **b.** Assuming that the rotational power loss is proportional to speed, find the no-load speed of the motor.

***P39.** A shunt-connected motor has the magnetization curve shown in Figure P39. Ignore rotational losses in this problem. The motor is supplied from a source of $V_T = 240$ V and has $R_A = 1.5$ Ω. The total field resistance is $R_F + R_{adj} = 240$ Ω. **a.** Find the no-load speed. **b.** A load is connected and the speed drops by 6 percent. Find the load torque, output power, armature current, field loss, and armature loss.

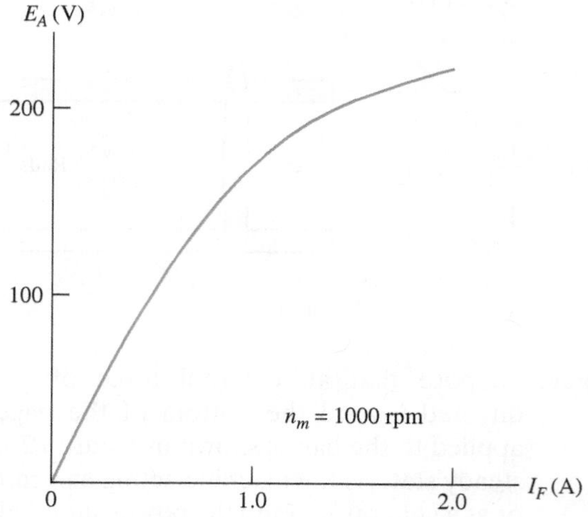

Figure P39

***P40.** A certain shunt-connected dc motor has $R_A = 1$ Ω, $R_F + R_{adj} = 200$ Ω, and $V_T = 200$ V. At a speed of 1200 rpm, the rotational losses are 50 W and $E_A = 175$ V. **a.** Find the no-load speed in rpm. **b.** Plot T_{dev}, I_A, and P_{dev} versus speed for speed ranging from zero to the no-load speed.

***P41.** A shunt-connected dc motor has $K\phi = 1$ V/(rad/s), $R_A = 1.2$ Ω, and $V_T = 200$ V. Find the two speeds for which the developed power is 5 hp. Neglect field loss and rotational loss. Find the value of I_A and efficiency for each speed. Which answer is most likely to be in the normal operating range of the machine?

***P42.** Is a magnetization curve needed for a permanent-magnet dc motor? Explain.

***P43.** A permanent-magnet dc motor has $R_A = 0.5$ Ω. With no load, it operates at 1070 rpm and draws 0.5 A from a 12.6-V source. Assume that rotational power loss is proportional to speed. Find the output power and efficiency for a load that drops the speed to 950 rpm.

P44. A permanent-magnet automotive fan motor draws 20 A from a 12-V source when the rotor is locked (i.e., held motionless). The motor has a speed of 800 rpm and draws 3.5 A when operating the fan with a terminal voltage of $V_T = 12$ V. Assume that the load (including the rotational losses) requires a developed torque that is proportional to the square of the speed. Find the speed for operation at 10 V. Repeat for 14 V.

P45. A shunt-connected 5-hp dc motor is rated for operation at $V_T = 200$ V, $I_L = 23.3$ A, and $n_m = 1500$ rpm. Furthermore, $I_F = 1.5$ A and $R_A = 0.4\ \Omega$. Under rated conditions find: **a.** the input power; **b.** the power supplied to the field circuit; **c.** the power lost in the armature resistance; **d.** the rotational loss; **e.** the efficiency.

P46. A separately excited dc motor (see the equivalent circuit shown in Figure 21) has $R_A = 1.3\ \Omega$ and $V_T = 220$ V. For an output power of 3 hp, $n_m = 950$ rpm and $I_A = 12.2$ A. The field current remains constant for all parts of this problem. **a.** Find the developed power, developed torque, power lost in R_A, and the rotational losses. **b.** Assuming that the rotational power loss is proportional to speed, find the no-load speed of the motor.

P47. A permanent-magnet automotive fan motor draws 20 A from a 12-V source when the rotor is locked (i.e., held motionless). **a.** Find the armature resistance. **b.** Find the maximum developed power that this motor can produce when operated from a 12-V source. **c.** Repeat part (b) for operation at 10 V (this represents a nearly dead battery) and at 14 V (this is the terminal voltage during charging of the battery after the engine is started).

P48. A shunt-connected motor delivers an output power of 24 hp at 1200 rpm while operating from a source voltage of 440 V and drawing $I_L = 50$ A. The resistances are $R_A = 0.05\ \Omega$ and $R_F + R_{adj} = 100\ \Omega$. Find the developed torque and efficiency of the motor.

P49. A shunt-connected dc motor has zero rotational losses and $R_A = 0$. Assume that $R_F + R_{adj}$ is constant [except in part (d)] and that ϕ is directly proportional to field current. For $V_T = 200$ V and $P_{out} = 2$ hp, the speed is 1200 rpm. What is the effect on I_A and speed if: **a.** the load torque doubles; **b.** the load power doubles; **c.** V_T is changed to 100 V and P_{out} remains constant; **d.** $R_F + R_{adj}$ is doubled in value and P_{out} remains constant?

P50. Consider a shunt-connected dc motor that has the magnetization curve shown in Figure 19. The dc supply voltage is $V_T = 200$ V, the armature resistance is $R_A = 0.085\ \Omega$, the field resistance is $R_F = 10\ \Omega$, and the adjustable resistance is $R_{adj} = 2.5\ \Omega$. At a speed of 1200 rpm, the rotational loss is $P_{rot} = 1000$ W. If this motor drives a load that demands a torque of $T_{out} = 200$ Nm independent of speed, determine the motor speed and efficiency.

P51. A shunt-connected dc motor has $R_A = 0.5\ \Omega$ and $R_F + R_{adj} = 400\ \Omega$. For $V_T = 200$ V and no load, the motor runs at 1150 rpm and the line current is $I_L = 1.2$ A. Find the rotational loss at this speed.

P52. A certain shunt-connected dc motor has $R_A = 4\ \Omega$ and $V_T = 240$ V. At a speed of 1000 rpm, the induced armature voltage is 120 V. Plot the torque–speed characteristic (T_{dev} versus n_m) to scale.

P53. Suppose that a dc machine is designed such that the voltage applied to the field V_F is equal to the voltage V_T applied to the armature. (Refer to Figure 14.) In a well-designed machine, which current, I_F or I_A, is larger under full-load operating conditions? Why? What do you estimate as an acceptable value for the ratio I_A/I_F under full load?

P54. A shunt-connected motor has the magnetization curve shown in Figure P54. Ignore rotational losses in this problem. The motor is supplied from a source of $V_T = 240$ V and has $R_A = 1.5\ \Omega$. The total field resistance is $R_F + R_{adj} = 160\ \Omega$. **a.** Find the no-load speed. **b.** A load is connected and the speed drops by 6 percent. Find the load torque, output power, armature current, field loss, and armature loss.

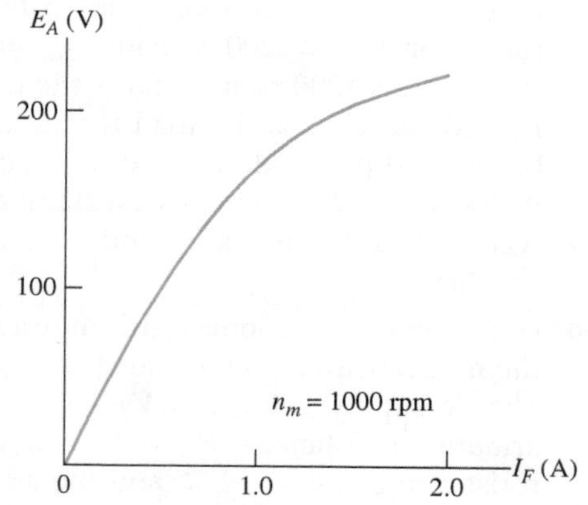

Figure P54

Section 5: Series-Connected DC Motors

***P55.** A series-connected dc motor has $R_F + R_A = 0.6\ \Omega$ and draws $I_A = 40$ A from the dc source voltage $V_T = 220$ V, while running at 900 rpm. What is the speed for $I_A = 20$ A? Assume a linear relationship between I_A and ϕ.

P56. Would a universal motor be a good choice for a clock? For a furnace fan motor? For a home coffee grinder? Give reasons for your answers.

P57. In examining a single-phase ac motor, what features could we look for to identify it as a universal motor?

P58. List four potential advantages of universal motors compared to other types of ac motors.

P59. Running at 1200 rpm from a 280-V source, a series-connected dc motor draws an armature current of 25 A. The field resistance is 0.2 Ω, and the armature resistance is 0.3 Ω. Rotational losses are 350 W and can be assumed to be proportional to speed. Determine the output power and developed torque. Determine the new armature current and speed if the load torque is increased by a factor of two.

P60. Running at 1200 rpm from a 280-V source, a series-connected dc motor draws an armature current of 25 A. The field resistance is 0.2 Ω, and the armature resistance is 0.3 Ω. Assuming that the flux is proportional to the field current, determine the speed at which the armature current is 10 A.

P61. A series-connected dc motor has $R_F + R_A = 0.6\ \Omega$ and draws $I_A = 40$ A from the dc source voltage $V_T = 220$ V, while running at 900 rpm. The rotational losses are 400 W. Find the output power and developed torque. Suppose that the load torque is reduced by a factor of two and that the rotational power loss is proportional to speed. Find the new values of I_A and speed.

P62. A series-connected dc motor is designed to operate with a variable load. The resistances R_A and R_F are negligible. To attain high efficiency, the motor has been designed to have very small rotational losses. For a load torque of 100 Nm, the machine runs at its maximum rated speed of 1200 rpm. **a.** Find the speed for a load torque of 300 Nm. **b.** What is the no-load speed? What are the potential consequences of having the load become disconnected from the motor without disconnecting the dc source?

P63. A series-connected dc motor has $R_A = 0.5\ \Omega$ and $R_F = 1.5\ \Omega$. In driving a certain load at 1200 rpm, the current is $I_A = 20$ A from a source voltage of $V_T = 220$ V. The rotational loss is 150 W. Find the output power and efficiency.

Section 6: Speed Control of DC Motors

***P64.** Sketch the family of torque–speed characteristics for a separately excited dc motor obtained by:

a. varying the field current;

b. varying the voltage applied to the armature;

c. varying the resistance in series with the armature.

***P65.** A series-connected motor drives a constant torque load from a 50-V source at a speed of 1500 rpm. The resistances $R_F = R_A = 0$. Neglect rotational losses. What average source voltage is needed to achieve a speed of 1000 rpm? If this is achieved by chopping the 50-V source as illustrated in Figure 25, find the duty ratio T_{on}/T.

***P66.** A series-connected dc motor operates at 1400 rpm from a source voltage of $V_T = 75$ V. The developed torque (load torque plus loss torque) is constant at 25 Nm. The resistance is $R_A + R_F = 0.1\ \Omega$. Determine the value of resistance that must be placed in series with the motor to reduce the speed to 1000 rpm.

P67. Consider a shunt-connected dc motor that has the magnetization curve shown in Figure 19. The dc supply voltage is $V_T = 200$ V, the armature resistance is $R_A = 0.085\ \Omega$, the field resistance is $R_F = 10\ \Omega$, and the adjustable resistance is $R_{adj} = 2.5\ \Omega$. At a speed of 1200 rpm, the rotational loss is $P_{rot} = 1000$ W. Assume that the rotational power loss is proportional to speed.

a. With a load that demands a torque of $T_{load} = 200$ Nm independent of speed, determine the steady-state armature current.

b. Suppose that in starting this machine, the field circuit has reached steady state and the motor is not moving when power is applied to the armature circuit. What is the initial value of I_A? Determine the starting value of the developed torque. Compare these values to the steady-state values from part (a).

c. What additional resistance must be inserted in series with the armature to limit the starting current to 200 A? Find the starting torque with this resistance in place.

P68. Suppose that a shunt-connected machine operates at 800 rpm on the linear portion of its magnetization characteristic. The motor drives a load that requires constant torque. Assume that $R_A = 0$. The resistances in the field circuit are $R_F = 50\ \Omega$ and $R_{adj} = 25\ \Omega$. Find a new value for R_{adj} so that the speed becomes 1200 rpm. What is the slowest speed that can be achieved by varying R_{adj}?

P69. Consider a PM motor that operates from a 12-V source with a no-load speed of 1700 rpm. Neglect rotational losses. What average source voltage is needed to achieve a no-load speed of 1000 rpm? If this is achieved by chopping the 12-V source as illustrated in Figure 25, find the duty ratio T_{on}/T.

P70. List three methods that can be used to control the speed of dc motors. Which of these apply to shunt-connected motors? To separately excited motors? To permanent-magnet motors? To series-connected motors?

P71. A series-connected motor drives a load from a 50-V source at a speed of 1500 rpm. The load torque is proportional to speed. The resistances $R_F = R_A = 0$. Neglect rotational losses. What average source voltage is needed to achieve a speed of 1000 rpm? If this is achieved by chopping the 50-V source as illustrated in Figure 25, find the duty ratio T_{on}/T.

Section 7: DC Generators

***P72.** A separately excited dc generator is rated for a load voltage of 150 V for a full load current of 20 A at 1500 rpm. With the load disconnected, the output voltage is 160 V. **a.** Determine the voltage regulation, the load resistance, the armature resistance, and the developed torque at full load. **b.** The speed of the generator is decreased to 1200 rpm, and the load resistance is unchanged. Determine the load current, the load voltage, and the developed power.

P73. What is the value of the voltage regulation for a fully compensated compound dc generator?

P74. What methods can be used to increase the load voltage of: **a.** a separately excited dc generator? **b.** a shunt-connected dc generator?

P75. Name the four types of compound connections for dc generators.

P76. Using Figure 30 as a guide, list the types of connections for dc generators considered in Section 7, in order of percentage voltage regulation from highest to lowest.

P77. A separately excited dc generator has the magnetization curve shown in Figure P77,

$V_F = 150$, $R_F = 40\ \Omega$, $R_{adj} = 60\ \Omega$, and $R_A = 1.5\ \Omega$. The prime mover rotates the armature at a speed of 1300 rpm. Determine the field current, the no-load voltage, the full-load voltage, and the percentage voltage regulation for a full-load current of 10 A. Assuming that the overall efficiency (not including the power supplied to the field circuit) of the machine is 80 percent, determine the input torque, the developed torque, and the losses associated with friction, windage, eddy currents, and hysteresis.

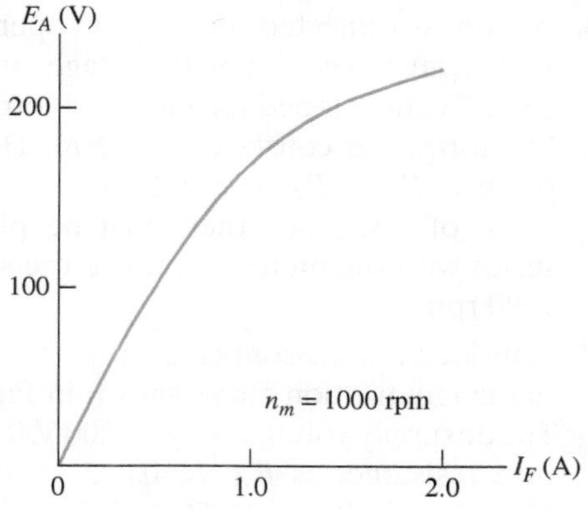

Figure P77

Practice Test

Here is a practice test you can use to check your comprehension of the most important concepts in this chapter. Answers can be found in Appendix "Answers for the Practice Tests" and complete solutions are included in the Student Solutions files. See Appendix "On-Line Student Resources" for more information about the Student Solutions.

T1. Consider a shunt-connected dc motor. What are the names of the two windings? Which is on the stator? On the rotor? For which does the current vary with mechanical load?

T2. Sketch the torque versus speed characteristic for a shunt-connected dc motor. What happens to the speed if the machine is lightly loaded and the field winding becomes disconnected?

T3. Sketch the torque versus speed characteristic for a series-connected dc motor.

T4. Give the definition of percentage speed regulation.

T5. Explain how the magnetization curve is measured for a dc machine.

T6. Name and briefly discuss the types of power loss in a shunt-connected dc motor.

T7. What is a universal motor? What are its advantages and disadvantages compared to other types of ac motors?

T8. List three methods for controlling the speed of a dc motor.

T9. Suppose we have a dc motor that produces a back emf of $E_A = 240$ V at a speed of 1500 rpm. **a.** If the field current remains constant, what is the back emf for a speed of 500 rpm? **b.** For a speed of 2000 rpm?

T10. We have a dc motor that has an induced armature voltage of 120 V at $n_{m1} = 1200$ rpm. If the field remains constant and this motor is operating at a speed of $n_{m2} = 900$ rpm with a developed power of 4 hp, what are the values for the armature current and the developed torque?

T11. Consider a separately excited dc motor (see the equivalent circuit shown in Figure 21) that has $R_A = 0.5\ \Omega$ and $V_T = 240$ V. For a full-load output power of 6 hp, we have $n_m = 1200$ rpm and $I_A = 20$ A. The field current remains constant for all parts of this problem. **a.** Find the developed power, developed torque, power lost in R_A, and the rotational losses. **b.** Assuming that the rotational power loss is proportional to speed, find the speed regulation of the motor.

T12. We have a series-connected dc motor that draws an armature current of 20 A while running at 1000 rpm from a 240-V source. The field resistance is 0.3 Ω, and the armature resistance is 0.4 Ω. Assuming that the flux is proportional to the field current, determine the speed at which the armature current is 10 A.

ANSWERS FOR THE PRACTICE TESTS

Complete solutions for the practice tests are included in the Student Solutions files. See Appendix "On-Line Student Resources" for information on how to access these files.

T1. The windings are the field winding, which is on the stator, and the armature winding, which is on the rotor. The armature current varies with mechanical load.

T2. See Figure 5(c). If the field becomes disconnected, the speed becomes very high, and the machine can be destroyed.

T3. See Figure 5(d).

T4. Speed regulation $= [(n_{\text{no-load}} - n_{\text{full-load}})/n_{\text{full-load}}] \times 100$ percent.

T5. To obtain the magnetization curve, we drive the machine at constant speed and plot the open-circuit armature voltage E_A versus field current I_F.

T6. Power losses in a shunt-connected dc motor are: 1. Field loss, which is the power consumed in the resistances of the field circuit. 2. Armature loss, which is the power converted to heat in the armature resistance. 3. Rotational losses, which include friction, windage, eddy-current loss, and hysteresis loss.

T7. A universal motor is an ac motor that is similar in construction to a series-connected dc motor. In principle, it can be operated from either ac or dc sources. The stator of a universal motor is usually laminated to reduce eddy-current loss. Compared to other single-phase ac motors, the universal motor has a higher power-to-weight ratio, produces a larger starting torque without excessive current, slows down under heavy loads so the power is more nearly constant, and can be designed to operate at higher speeds. A disadvantage of the universal motor is that it contains brushes and a commutator resulting in shorter service life.

T8. 1. Vary the voltage supplied to the armature circuit while holding the field constant. 2. Vary the field current while holding the armature supply voltage constant. 3. Insert resistance in series with the armature circuit.

T9. **a.** 80 V; **b.** 320 V.

T10. $I_A = 33.16$ A; $T_{\text{dev}} = 31.66$ Nm.

T11. **a.** $P_{\text{dev}} = 4600$ W; $T_{\text{dev}} = 36.60$ Nm; $P_{RA} = 200$ W; $P_{\text{rot}} = 124$ W. **b.** speed regulation = 4.25 percent.

T12. 2062 rpm.

ON-LINE STUDENT RESOURCES

Users of the text can access the Student Solutions Manual (and other folders mentioned below) in electronic form by following links starting from the website:

`www.pearsonhighered.com/hambley`

The MATLAB folder contains m-files. Except for the examples that use the Symbolic Toolbox, these files work equally well with MathScript, which is sometimes included with the LabVIEW program. The Hambley MathScript folder contains the m-files that work with MathScript.

The Virtual Instruments folder contains LabVIEW programs.

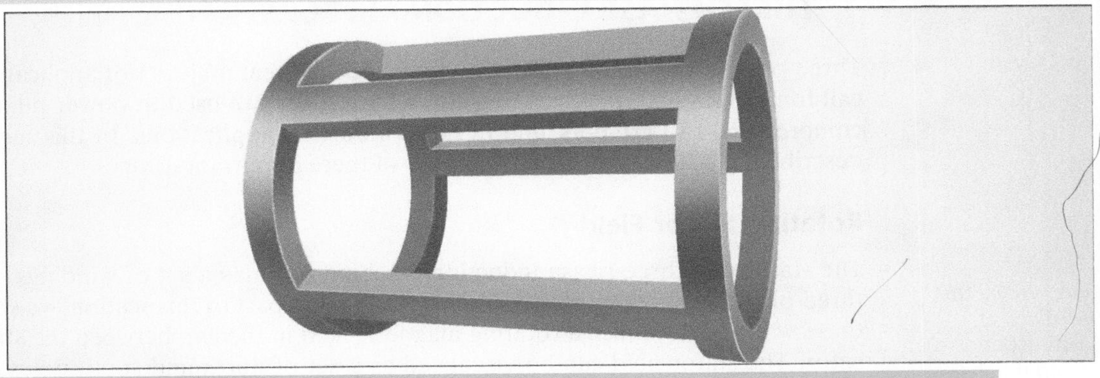

AC Machines

Study of this chapter will enable you to:

- Select the proper ac motor type for various applications.
- State how torque varies with speed for various ac motors.
- Compute electrical and mechanical quantities for ac motors.
- Use motor nameplate data.
- Understand the operation and characteristics of three-phase induction motors, three-phase synchronous machines, various types of single-phase ac motors, stepper motors, and brushless dc motors.

In this chapter, our discussion is of electrical machines. It would be good to be familiar with the general concepts related to electrical machines before starting this chapter.

1 THREE-PHASE INDUCTION MOTORS

Three-phase induction machines account for the great majority of applications that call for motors with power ratings over 5 hp. They are used to power pumps, fans, compressors, and grinders, and in other industrial applications. In this section, we describe the construction and principles of these important devices.

Rotating Stator Field

In this section, we see that the stator windings of three-phase induction machines set up magnetic poles that rotate around the circumference of the stator.

The stator of a three-phase induction machine contains a set of windings to which three-phase electrical power is applied. In the first part of this section, we show that these windings establish a rotating magnetic field in the gap between the stator and rotor. The stator field can be visualized as a set of north and south poles rotating around the circumference of the stator. (North stator poles are where magnetic flux lines leave the stator, and south stator poles are where magnetic flux lines enter the stator.) Because north and south poles occur in pairs, the total number of poles P is always even. The field is illustrated for two-pole and four-pole machines in Figure 1. Similarly, it is possible for a three-phase induction motor to have six, eight, or more poles.

Next, we examine the stator windings and how the rotating field is established in a two-pole machine. The stator of the two-pole machine contains three windings embedded in slots cut lengthwise on the inside of the stator. One of the three stator windings is illustrated in Figure 2.

For simplicity, we represent each winding by only two conductors on opposite sides of the stator. However, each winding actually consists of a large number of conductors distributed in various slots in such a manner that the resulting air-gap flux varies approximately sinusoidally with the angle θ (which is defined in Figure 2). Thus, the field in the air gap due to the current $i_a(t)$ in winding a is given by

$$B_a = Ki_a(t)\cos(\theta) \tag{1}$$

where K is a constant that depends on the geometry and materials of the stator and rotor as well as the number of turns in winding a. B_a is taken as positive when directed from the stator toward the rotor and negative when directed in the opposite direction.

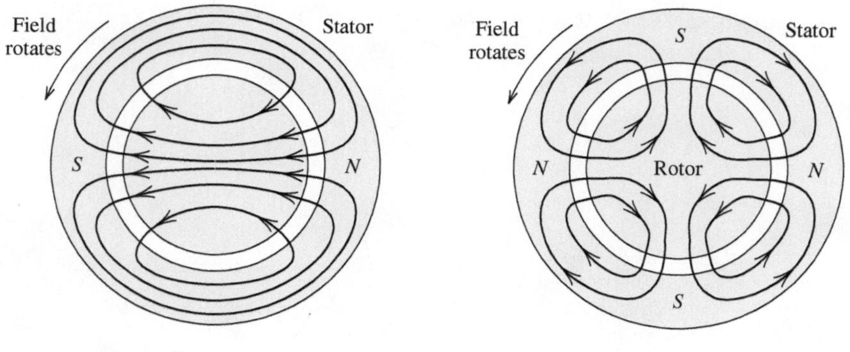

(a) Two-pole machine

(b) Four-pole machine

Figure 1 The field established by the stator windings of a three-phase induction machine consists of an even number of magnetic poles. The field rotates at a speed known as synchronous speed.

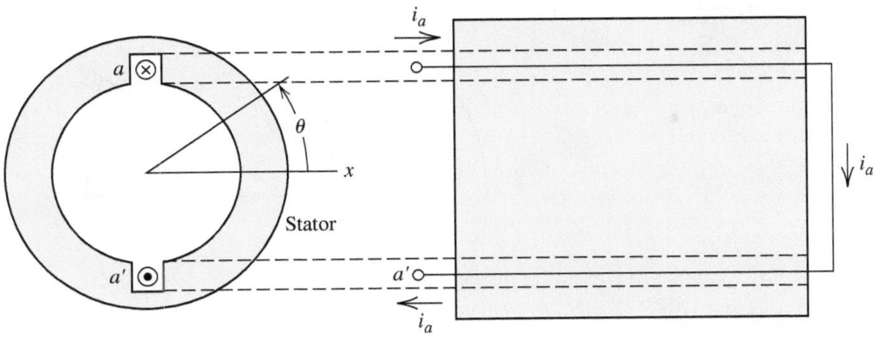

(a) End view (b) Lengthwise view

Figure 2 Two views of a two-pole stator showing one of the three windings. For simplicity, we represent the winding with a single turn, but in a real machine, each winding has many turns distributed around the circumference of the stator such that the air-gap flux varies sinusoidally with θ.

The field in the gap due to winding a is shown in Figure 3. Notice that the field is strongest at $\theta = 0$ and at $\theta = 180°$. Although it fluctuates in strength and polarity as the current changes with time, the field produced by winding a alone does not rotate. However, we are about to demonstrate that the combined field produced by all three windings does rotate.

The other two windings (b and c) are identical to winding a, except that they are rotated in space by 120° and 240°, respectively. This is illustrated in Figure 4. Thus, the fields in the air gap due to windings b and c are given by

Each winding sets up a field that varies sinusoidally around the circumference of the gap and varies sinusoidally with time. These fields are displaced from one another by 120° in both time and space.

$$B_b = Ki_b(t)\cos(\theta - 120°) \tag{2}$$

$$B_c = Ki_c(t)\cos(\theta - 240°) \tag{3}$$

The total field in the gap is the sum of the individual fields produced by the three coils. Thus, the total field is

$$B_{\text{gap}} = B_a + B_b + B_c \tag{4}$$

Using Equations 1 through 3 to substitute into Equation 4, we have

$$B_{\text{gap}} = Ki_a(t)\cos(\theta) + Ki_b(t)\cos(\theta - 120°) + Ki_c(t)\cos(\theta - 240°) \tag{5}$$

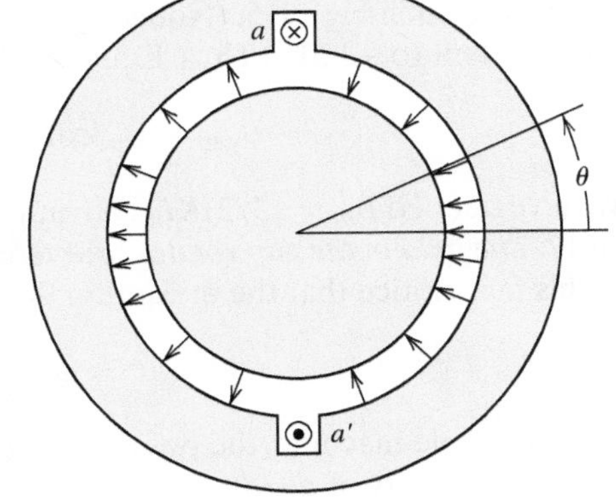

Figure 3 The field produced by the current in winding a varies sinusoidally in space around the circumference of the gap. The field is shown here for the positive maximum of the current $i_a(t)$. As illustrated, the field is strongest in magnitude at $\theta = 0$ and at $\theta = 180°$. Furthermore, the current and the field vary sinusoidally with time. Over time, the field dies to zero and then builds up in the opposite direction.

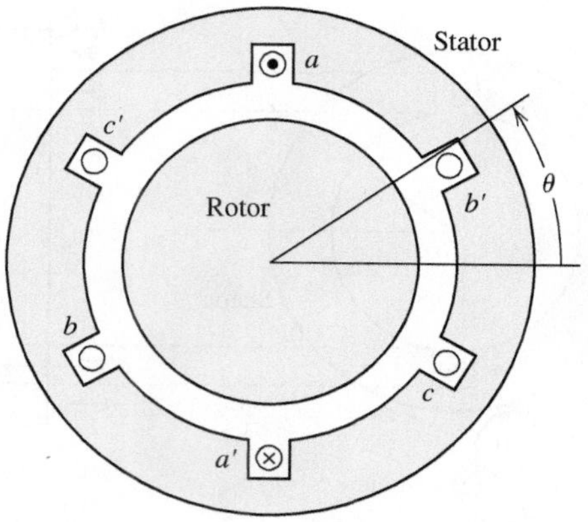

Figure 4 The stator of a two-pole machine contains three identical windings spaced 120° apart.

Application of a balanced three-phase source to the windings results in currents given by

$$i_a(t) = I_m \cos(\omega t) \tag{6}$$

$$i_b(t) = I_m \cos(\omega t - 120^\circ) \tag{7}$$

$$i_c(t) = I_m \cos(\omega t - 240^\circ) \tag{8}$$

Now, using Equations 6, 7, and 8 to substitute for the currents in Equation 5 yields

$$B_{\text{gap}} = KI_m \cos(\omega t)\cos(\theta) + KI_m \cos(\omega t - 120^\circ)\cos(\theta - 120^\circ) + KI_m \cos(\omega t - 240^\circ)\cos(\theta - 240^\circ) \tag{9}$$

The trigonometric identity $\cos(x)\cos(y) = (1/2)[\cos(x - y) + \cos(x + y)]$ can be used to write Equation 9 as

$$B_{\text{gap}} = \frac{3}{2}KI_m \cos(\omega t - \theta) + \frac{1}{2}KI_m[\cos(\omega t + \theta) + \cos(\omega t + \theta - 240^\circ) + \cos(\omega t + \theta - 480^\circ)] \tag{10}$$

Furthermore, we can write

$$[\cos(\omega t + \theta) + \cos(\omega t + \theta - 240^\circ) + \cos(\omega t + \theta - 480^\circ)] = 0 \tag{11}$$

because the three terms form a balanced three-phase set. A phasor diagram for these terms is shown in Figure 5. (Notice that -240° is equivalent to $+120^\circ$, and that -480° is equivalent to -120°.) Thus, Equation 10 reduces to

$$B_{\text{gap}} = B_m \cos(\omega t - \theta) \tag{12}$$

The field in the gap rotates counterclockwise with an angular speed ω.

where we have defined $B_m = (3/2)KI_m$. An important conclusion can be drawn from Equation 12: *The field in the gap rotates counterclockwise with an angular speed of* ω. To verify this fact, notice that the maximum flux density occurs for

$$\theta = \omega t$$

Thus, in the two-pole machine, the point of maximum flux rotates counterclockwise with an angular velocity of $d\theta/dt = \omega$.

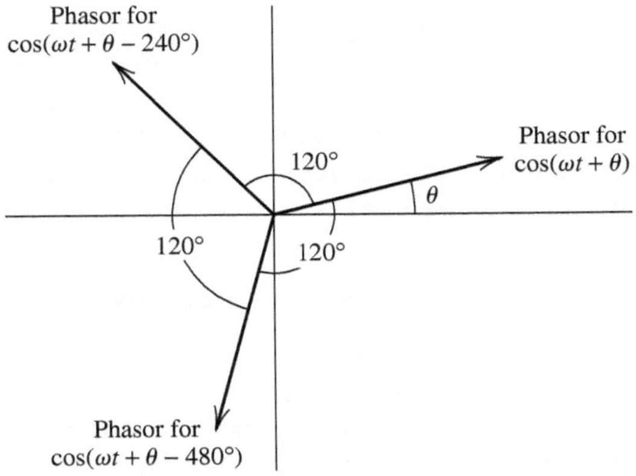

Figure 5 Phasor diagram for the three terms on the left-hand side of Equation 11. Regardless of the value of θ, the phasors add to zero.

Synchronous Speed

By a similar analysis, it can be shown that for a P-pole machine, the field rotates at an angular velocity of

In a P-pole machine, the field rotates at the synchronous speed ω_s.

$$\omega_s = \frac{\omega}{P/2} \tag{13}$$

which is called the **synchronous angular velocity**. In rpm, the synchronous speed is

$$n_s = \frac{120f}{P} \tag{14}$$

Table 1 gives synchronous speeds versus the number of poles assuming a frequency of 60 Hz.

In summary, we have shown that the field set up by the stator windings consists of a system of P magnetic poles that rotate at synchronous speed. These fields were illustrated in Figure 1 for two- and four-pole machines.

Exercise 1 If the connections of b and c to the three-phase source are interchanged, the currents become

The direction of rotation of a three-phase induction motor can be reversed by interchanging any two of the three line connections to the three-phase source.

$$i_a(t) = I_m \cos(\omega t)$$
$$i_b(t) = I_m \cos(\omega t - 240°)$$
$$i_c(t) = I_m \cos(\omega t - 120°)$$

Show that, in this case, the field rotates clockwise rather than counterclockwise. □

Table 1. Synchronous Speed versus Number of Poles for $f = 60$ Hz

P	n_s
2	3600
4	1800
6	1200
8	900
10	720
12	600

The result of Exercise 1 shows that the direction of rotation of the field in a three-phase induction machine can be reversed by interchanging any two of the line connections to the electrical source. We will see that this reverses the direction of mechanical rotation. You may find the fact that interchanging two of the electrical connections to the source reverses the direction of rotation to be useful in working with three-phase motors.

Squirrel-Cage Induction Machines

The rotor windings of a three-phase induction machine can take two forms. The simplest, least expensive, and most rugged is known as a **squirrel-cage rotor**. It consists simply of bars of aluminum with shorting rings at the ends, as illustrated in Figure 6. The squirrel cage is embedded in the laminated iron rotor by casting molten aluminum into slots cut into the rotor. In the squirrel-cage induction machine, there are no external electrical connections to the rotor. The other type of rotor construction, which we discuss later, is known as a **wound rotor**.

Next, we consider how torque is produced in squirrel-cage induction machines. We have seen earlier in this section that the stator sets up a system of P magnetic poles that rotate at synchronous speed. As this magnetic field moves past, voltages are induced in the squirrel-cage conductors. Since the field, the direction of relative motion, and the length of the conductors are mutually perpendicular, the induced voltage v_c is given by the equation $e{=}Blu$:

$$v_c = Blu \tag{15}$$

in which B is the flux density, l is the length of the conductor, and u is the relative velocity between the conductor and the field.

The rotating stator field induces voltages in the rotor conductors resulting in currents that produce magnetic poles on the rotor. The interaction of the rotor poles and stator poles produces torque.

This voltage causes currents to flow in the conductors as illustrated in Figure 7. Of course, the largest voltages are induced in the conductors that are directly under the stator poles because that is where the flux density B is largest in magnitude. Furthermore, for conductors under south poles, the voltage polarity and current direction are opposite to those for conductors under north poles. Currents flow through the bars under the north pole, around the shorting ring, and back in the opposite direction through the bars under the south pole.

The rotor currents establish magnetic poles on the rotor. It is the interaction of the rotor poles with the stator poles that produces torque. The north rotor pole N_r attempts to align itself with the south stator pole S_s.

If the impedances of the rotor conductors were purely resistive, the largest currents would occur directly under the stator poles S_s and N_s, as shown in Figure 7. Consequently, the rotor poles would be displaced by $\delta_{rs} = 90°$ with respect to the stator poles, as illustrated for a two-pole machine in Figure 7. This is exactly the

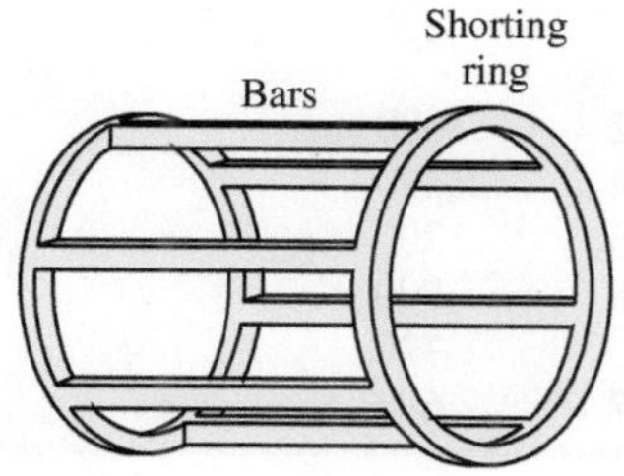

Figure 6 The rotor conductors of a squirrel-cage induction machine are aluminum bars connected to rings that short the ends together. These conductors are formed by casting molten aluminum into slots in the laminated iron rotor.

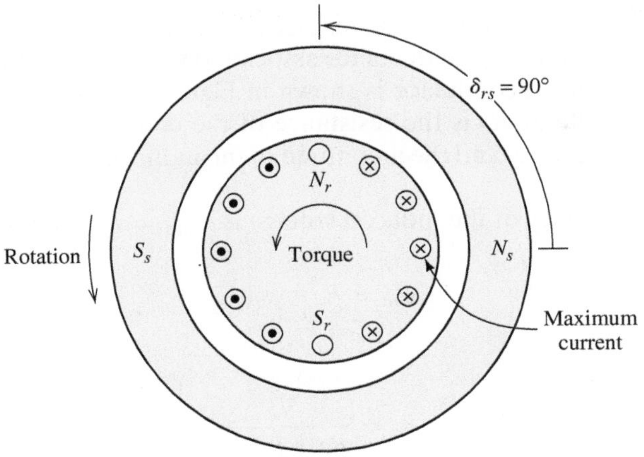

Figure 7 Cross section of a squirrel-cage induction motor. The rotating stator field induces currents in the conducting bars which in turn set up magnetic poles on the rotor. Torque is produced because the rotor poles are attracted to the stator poles.

angular displacement between the sets of magnetic poles that produces maximum torque.

Slip and Slip Frequency

The frequency of the voltages induced in the rotor conductors depends on the rotational speed of the stator field relative to the rotor and on the number of poles. We have seen that the stator field rotates at synchronous speed denoted as either ω_s or n_s. We denote the mechanical speed of the rotor as ω_m (or n_m). In an induction motor, the mechanical speed ω_m varies from zero to almost synchronous speed. Thus, the speed of the stator field relative to the rotor is $\omega_s - \omega_m$ (or $n_s - n_m$).

The **slip** s is defined to be the relative speed as a fraction of synchronous speed:

$$s = \frac{\omega_s - \omega_m}{\omega_s} = \frac{n_s - n_m}{n_s} \tag{16}$$

Slip s varies from 1 when the rotor is stationary to 0 when the rotor turns at synchronous speed.

The angular frequency of the voltages induced in the squirrel cage, called the **slip frequency**, is given by

The frequency of the rotor currents is called the slip frequency.

$$\omega_{\text{slip}} = s\omega \tag{17}$$

Notice that when the mechanical speed approaches the speed of the stator field (which is the synchronous speed), the frequency of the induced voltages approaches zero.

Effect of Rotor Inductance on Torque

In Figure 7, we saw how torque is produced in an induction motor assuming purely resistive impedances for the rotor conductors. However, the impedances of

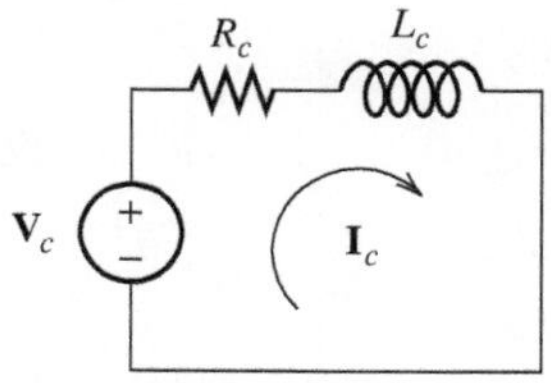

Figure 8 Equivalent circuit for a rotor conductor. $\mathbf{V}_c$ is the phasor for the induced voltage, R_c is the resistance of the conductor, and L_c is the inductance.

the conductors are not purely resistive. Because the conductors are embedded in iron, there is significant series inductance associated with each conductor. The equivalent circuit for a given conductor is shown in Figure 8, in which $\mathbf{V}_c$ is the phasor for the induced voltage, R_c is the resistance of the conductor, and L_c is its inductance. Both the frequency and the amplitude of the induced voltage are proportional to slip.

Since the frequency of the induced voltage is $\omega_{\text{slip}} = s\omega$, the impedance is

$$Z_c = R_c + js\omega L_c \tag{18}$$

The current is

$$\mathbf{I}_c = \frac{\mathbf{V}_c}{R_c + js\omega L_c} \tag{19}$$

Because of the inductances of the rotor conductors, the rotor currents lag the induced voltages.

Because of the inductance, the current lags the induced voltage. As the slip s increases, the amount of phase lag approaches 90°. Consequently, the peak current in a given rotor conductor occurs somewhat after the stator pole passes by. Furthermore, the rotor poles are displaced from the stator poles by less than 90°. This is illustrated in Figure 9. Because of this, the torque is reduced. (If the stator and rotor poles were aligned, no torque would be produced.)

Torque–Speed Characteristic

Now we are in a position to explain qualitatively the torque–speed characteristic shown in Figure 10 for the squirrel-cage induction motor. First, assume that the rotor speed n_m equals the synchronous speed n_s (i.e., the slip s equals zero). In this case, the relative velocity between the conductors and the field is zero (i.e., $u = 0$). Then according to Equation 15, the induced voltage v_c is zero. Consequently, the rotor currents are zero and the torque is zero.

As the rotor slows down from synchronous speed, the stator field moves past the rotor conductors. The magnitudes of the voltages induced in the rotor conductors increase linearly with slip. For small slips, the inductive reactances of the conductors, given by $s\omega L_c$, are negligible, and maximum rotor current is aligned with maximum stator field, which is the optimum situation for producing torque. Because the induced

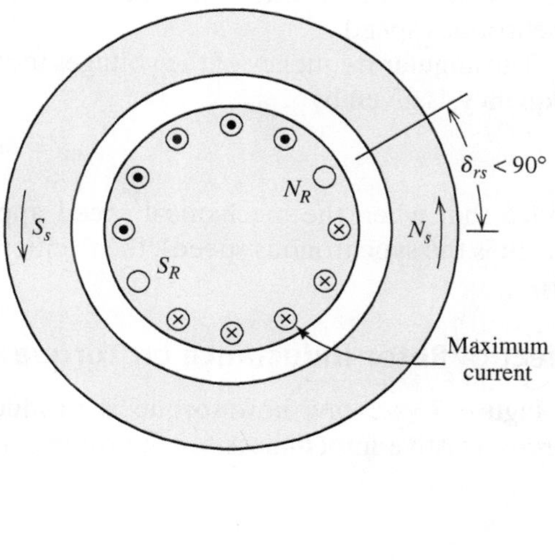

Figure 9 As slip s increases, the conductor currents lag the induced voltages. Consequently, the angular displacement δ_{rs} between the rotor poles and the stator poles approaches 0°.

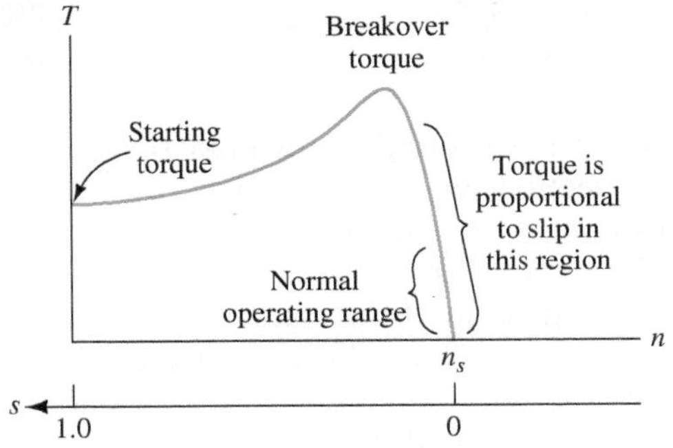

Figure 10 Torque-versus-speed characteristic for a typical three-phase induction motor.

voltage is proportional to slip and the impedance is independent of slip, the currents are proportional to slip. Torque is proportional to the product of the field and the current. Hence, we conclude that *torque is proportional to slip, assuming small slip.* This fact is illustrated in Figure 10.

For small values of slip, developed torque is proportional to slip.

As the motor slows further, the inductive reactance eventually dominates the denominator of Equation 19. Then, the magnitude of the current is nearly independent of slip. Thus, the torque tends to level out as the motor slows. Because the poles on the rotor tend to become aligned with the stator poles, the torque decreases as the motor slows to a stop. The torque for zero speed is called either the **starting torque** or the **stall torque**. The maximum torque is called either the **pull-out torque** or the **breakover torque**.

Our discussion has revealed the general characteristics of the three-phase induction motor. The motor designer can modify the shape of the torque–speed characteristic by variations in the dimensions and geometry of the motor and by materials selection. Some examples of torque–speed characteristics available in induction motors are shown in Figure 11. However, the details of motor design are beyond the scope of our discussion.

Motor designers can modify the shape of the torque–speed curve by changing various aspects of the machine design, such as the cross section and depth of the rotor conductors.

Exercise 2 A 5-hp four-pole 60-Hz three-phase induction motor runs at 1750 rpm under full-load conditions. Determine the slip and the frequency of the rotor currents at full load. Also, estimate the speed if the load torque drops in half.

Answer $s = 50/1800 = 0.02778, f_{\text{slip}} = 1.667$ Hz, $n = 1775$ rpm. □

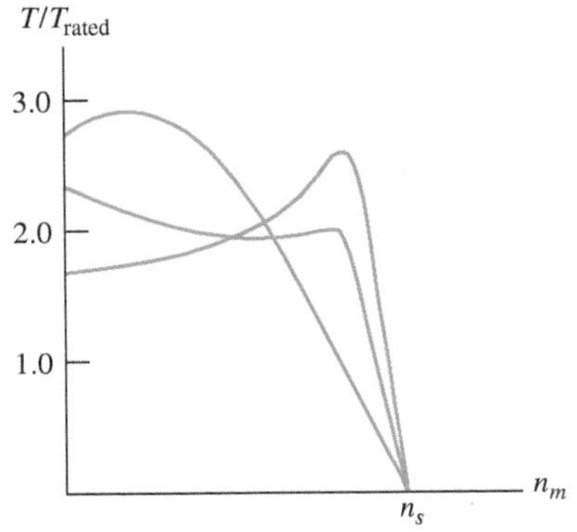

Figure 11 Depending on various design features, the torque–speed characteristic of the three-phase induction motor can be modified to better suit particular applications.

2 EQUIVALENT-CIRCUIT AND PERFORMANCE CALCULATIONS FOR INDUCTION MOTORS

In Section 1, we described the induction motor and its operation in qualitative terms. In this section, we develop an equivalent circuit and show how to calculate the performance of induction motors.

The equivalent circuit for each phase of an induction motor is similar to that of a transformer with the secondary winding shorted.

Consider the induction motor with the rotor locked so that it cannot turn. Then, the magnetic field of the stator links the rotor windings and causes current to flow in them. Basically, the locked-rotor induction motor is the same as a three-phase transformer with the stator windings acting as the primary. The rotor conductors act as short-circuited secondary windings. Thus, we can expect the equivalent circuit for each phase of the motor to be very similar to the transformer equivalent circuit. Of course, modifications to the transformer equivalent circuit are necessary before it can be applied to the induction motor because of rotation and the conversion of electrical energy into mechanical form.

Rotor Equivalent Circuit

An equivalent circuit for one phase of the rotor windings is shown in Figure 12(a). (Equivalent circuits for the other two phases are identical except for the phase angles of the current and voltage.) $\mathbf{E}_r$ represents the induced voltage in phase *a* of the rotor under locked conditions. As discussed in the preceding section, the voltage induced in the rotor is proportional to slip s. Thus, the induced voltage is represented by the voltage source $s\mathbf{E}_r$. (Recall that for a stationary rotor $s = 1$.)

We have seen that the frequency of the rotor currents is $s\omega$. The rotor inductance (per phase) is denoted by L_r and has a reactance of $js\omega L_r = jsX_r$, where $X_r = \omega L_r$ is the reactance under locked-rotor conditions. The resistance per phase is denoted by R_r, and the current in one phase of the rotor is $\mathbf{I}_r$, which is given by

$$\mathbf{I}_r = \frac{s\mathbf{E}_r}{R_r + jsX_r} \tag{20}$$

Dividing the numerator and denominator of the right-hand side of Equation 20 by s, we have

$$\mathbf{I}_r = \frac{\mathbf{E}_r}{R_r/s + jX_r} \tag{21}$$

This can be represented by the circuit shown in Figure 12(b).

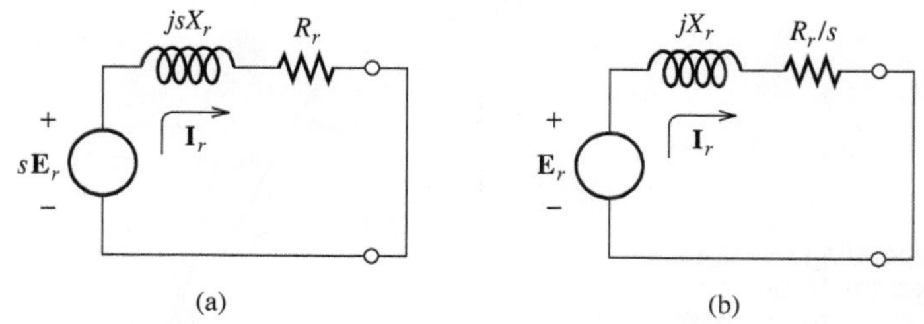

Figure 12 Two equivalent circuits for one phase of the rotor windings.

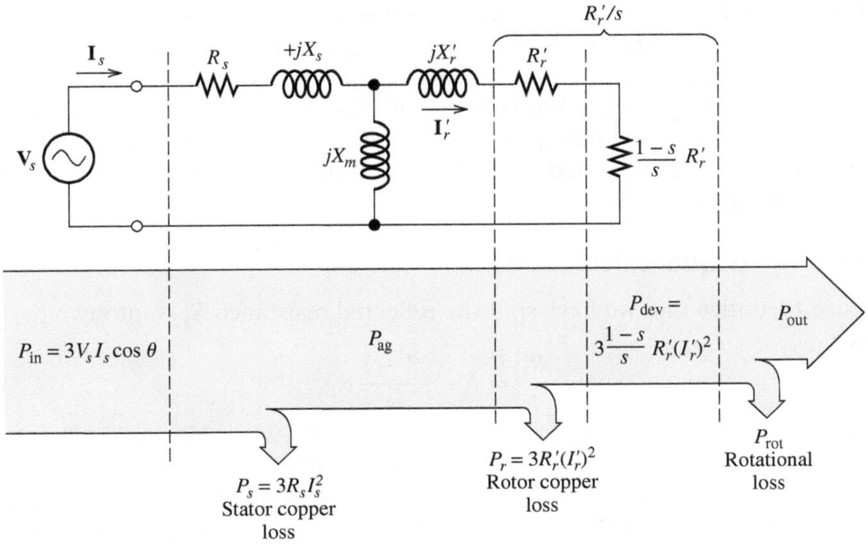

Figure 13 Equivalent circuit for one phase of an induction motor and the associated power-flow diagram. V_s is the rms phase voltage and I_s is the rms phase current.

Figure 13 provides a convenient reference for the information needed to analyze induction machines.

Complete Induction-Motor Equivalent Circuit

As in a transformer, the induced rotor voltage E_r under locked conditions is related to the stator voltage by the turns ratio. Thus, we can reflect the rotor impedances of Figure 12(b) to the primary (stator) side of the equivalent circuit. We denote the reflected values of X_r and R_r/s by X_r' and R_r'/s, respectively.

The completed (per phase) induction-motor equivalent circuit is shown in Figure 13. The resistance of the stator winding is R_s, and the stator leakage reactance is X_s. The magnetizing reactance X_m accounts for the current needed to set up the rotating stator field. Except for changes in notation, these parts of the equivalent circuit are the same as the transformer equivalent circuit.

Phase versus Line Quantities

The voltage V_s across each winding and current I_s through each winding shown in Figure 13 are called the **phase voltage** and **phase current**, respectively.

The windings of an induction motor may be connected in either a delta or a wye. In the case of a delta connection, the phase voltage V_s is the same as the line-to-line voltage V_{line}. The line current I_{line} is $\sqrt{3}$ times the phase current I_s. In equation form for the delta connection, we have

Relationships between line and phase quantities for a delta-connected motor.

$$V_s = V_{\text{line}}$$

$$I_{\text{line}} = I_s\sqrt{3}$$

On the other hand, for a wye connection, we get

Relationships between line and phase quantities for a wye-connected motor.

$$V_s = \frac{V_{\text{line}}}{\sqrt{3}}$$

$$I_{\text{line}} = I_s$$

The voltage rating stated for a machine is invariably the line-to-line voltage.

The voltage rating stated for a machine is invariably the line-to-line voltage. For a given three-phase source, the voltage across the windings is smaller by a factor of $\sqrt{3}$ for the wye connection.

We will see that the starting current for induction motors can be very large compared to the full-load running current. Sometimes, motors are started in the wye configuration and then switched to delta as the motor approaches its running speed to lessen starting currents.

Power and Torque Calculations

In Figure 13, notice that we have split the reflected resistance R_r'/s into two parts as follows:

$$\frac{R_r'}{s} = R_r' + \frac{1-s}{s}R_r' \tag{22}$$

A power-flow diagram for induction motors is also shown in Figure 13. The power delivered to the resistance $[(1-s)/s]R_r'$ is the part that is converted to mechanical form. This portion of the power, called the **developed power**, is denoted by P_{dev}. The equivalent circuit shown in Figure 13 represents one of three phases, so the total developed power is

$$P_{\text{dev}} = 3 \times \frac{1-s}{s}R_r'(I_r')^2 \tag{23}$$

On the other hand, the power delivered to the rotor resistance R_r' is converted to heat. Generally, we refer to I^2R losses as **copper losses** (even though the conductors are sometimes aluminum). The total copper loss in the rotor is

$$P_r = 3R_r'(I_r')^2 \tag{24}$$

and the stator copper loss is

$$P_s = 3R_sI_s^2 \tag{25}$$

The input power from the three-phase source is

$$P_{\text{in}} = 3I_sV_s\cos(\theta) \tag{26}$$

in which $\cos(\theta)$ is the power factor.

Part of the developed power is lost to friction and windage. Another loss is core loss due to hysteresis and eddy currents. Sometimes, a resistance is included in parallel with the magnetization reactance jX_m to account for core loss. However, we will include the core loss with the rotational losses. Unless stated otherwise, we assume that the rotational power loss is proportional to speed. The output power is the developed power minus the rotational loss:

$$P_{\text{out}} = P_{\text{dev}} - P_{\text{rot}} \tag{27}$$

As usual, the efficiency of the machine is given by

$$\eta = \frac{P_{\text{out}}}{P_{\text{in}}} \times 100\%$$

The developed torque is

$$T_{\text{dev}} = \frac{P_{\text{dev}}}{\omega_m} \tag{28}$$

The power P_{ag} that crosses the air gap into the rotor is delivered to the rotor resistances. Thus, we can find the air-gap power by adding the respective sides of Equations 23 and 24:

$$P_{\text{ag}} = P_r + P_{\text{dev}} \tag{29}$$

$$P_{\text{ag}} = 3R'_r(I'_r)^2 + 3 \times \frac{1-s}{s} R'_r(I'_r)^2 \tag{30}$$

$$P_{\text{ag}} = 3 \times \frac{1}{s} R'_r(I'_r)^2 \tag{31}$$

Comparing Equations 23 and 31, we have

$$P_{\text{dev}} = (1-s)P_{\text{ag}} \tag{32}$$

Using Equation 32 to substitute for P_{dev} in Equation 28, we get

$$T_{\text{dev}} = \frac{(1-s)P_{\text{ag}}}{\omega_m} \tag{33}$$

However, we also have $\omega_m = (1-s)\omega_s$. Using this to substitute into Equation 33, we obtain

$$T_{\text{dev}} = \frac{P_{\text{ag}}}{\omega_s} \tag{34}$$

For speed to increase from a standing start, the initial torque or starting torque produced by the motor must be larger than the torque required by the load. We can find starting torque as follows. Under starting conditions (i.e., $\omega_m = 0$), we have $s = 1$ and $P_{\text{ag}} = 3R'_r(I'_r)^2$. Then, the starting torque can be computed by using Equation 34.

Equation 34 can be used to compute starting torque.

Example 1 Induction-Motor Performance

A certain 30-hp four-pole 440-V-rms 60-Hz three-phase delta-connected induction motor has

$$R_s = 1.2\ \Omega \qquad R'_r = 0.6\ \Omega$$
$$X_s = 2.0\ \Omega \qquad X'_r = 0.8\ \Omega$$
$$X_m = 50\ \Omega$$

Under load, the machine operates at 1746 rpm and has rotational losses of 900 W. Find the power factor, the line current, the output power, copper losses, output torque, and efficiency.

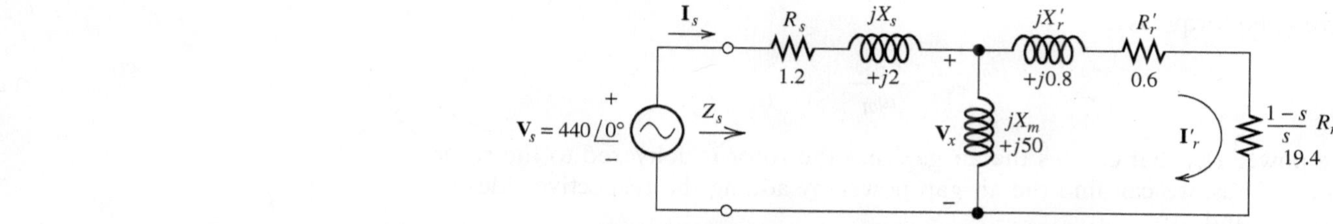

Figure 14 Equivalent circuit for one phase of the motor of Example 1.

Solution From Table 1, we find that synchronous speed for a four-pole motor is $n_s = 1800$ rpm. Then, we utilize Equation 16 to compute the slip:

$$s = \frac{n_s - n_m}{n_s} = \frac{1800 - 1746}{1800} = 0.03$$

We can use the data given to draw the equivalent circuit shown in Figure 14 for one phase of the motor. The impedance seen by the source is

$$\begin{aligned} Z_s &= 1.2 + j2 + \frac{j50(0.6 + 19.4 + j0.8)}{j50 + 0.6 + 19.4 + j0.8} \\ &= 1.2 + j2 + 16.77 + j7.392 \\ &= 17.97 + j9.392 \\ &= 20.28\angle 27.59° \ \Omega \end{aligned}$$

The power factor is the cosine of the impedance angle. Because the impedance is inductive, we know that the power factor is lagging:

$$\text{power factor} = \cos(27.59°) = 88.63\% \text{ lagging}$$

For a delta-connected machine, the phase voltage is equal to the line voltage, which is specified to be 440 V rms. The phase current is

$$\mathbf{I}_s = \frac{\mathbf{V}_s}{Z_s} = \frac{440\angle 0°}{20.28\angle 27.59°} = 21.70\angle -27.59° \text{ A rms}$$

Thus, the magnitude of the line current is

$$I_{\text{line}} = I_s\sqrt{3} = 21.70\sqrt{3} = 37.59 \text{ A rms}$$

In ac machine calculations, we take the rms values of currents and voltages for the phasor magnitudes (instead of peak values as we have done previously).

The input power is

$$\begin{aligned} P_{\text{in}} &= 3I_s V_s \cos\theta \\ &= 3(21.70)440 \cos(27.59°) \\ &= 25.38 \text{ kW} \end{aligned}$$

Next, we compute $\mathbf{V}_x$ and $\mathbf{I}'_r$:

$$\mathbf{V}_x = \mathbf{I}_s \frac{j50(0.6 + 19.4 + j0.8)}{j50 + 0.6 + 19.4 + j0.8}$$
$$= 21.70\angle{-27.59^\circ} \times 18.33\angle{23.78^\circ}$$
$$= 397.8\angle{-3.807^\circ} \text{ V rms}$$
$$\mathbf{I}'_r = \frac{\mathbf{V}_x}{j0.8 + 0.6 + 19.4}$$
$$= \frac{397.8\angle{-3.807^\circ}}{20.01\angle{1.718^\circ}}$$
$$= 19.88\angle{-5.52^\circ} \text{ A rms}$$

The copper losses in the stator and rotor are

$$P_s = 3R_s I_s^2$$
$$= 3(1.2)(21.70)^2$$
$$= 1695 \text{ W}$$

and

$$P_r = 3R'_r(I'_r)^2$$
$$= 3(0.6)(19.88)^2$$
$$= 711.4 \text{ W}$$

Finally, the developed power is

$$P_{\text{dev}} = 3 \times \frac{1-s}{s} R'_r(I'_r)^2$$
$$= 3(19.4)(19.88)^2$$
$$= 23.00 \text{ kW}$$

As a check, we note that

$$P_{\text{in}} = P_{\text{dev}} + P_s + P_r$$

to within rounding error.

The output power is the developed power minus the rotational loss, given by

$$P_{\text{out}} = P_{\text{dev}} - P_{\text{rot}}$$
$$= 23.00 - 0.900$$
$$= 22.1 \text{ kW}$$

This corresponds to 29.62 hp, so the motor is operating at nearly its rated load. The output torque is

$$T_{\text{out}} = \frac{P_{\text{out}}}{\omega_m}$$
$$= \frac{22{,}100}{1746(2\pi/60)}$$
$$= 120.9 \text{ Nm}$$

The efficiency is

$$\eta = \frac{P_{\text{out}}}{P_{\text{in}}} \times 100\%$$
$$= \frac{22{,}100}{25{,}380} \times 100\%$$
$$= 87.0\%$$

■

Example 2 Starting Current and Torque

Calculate the starting line current and torque for the motor of Example 1.

Solution For starting from a standstill, we have $s = 1$. The equivalent circuit is shown in Figure 15(a). Combining the impedances to the right of the dashed line, we have

$$Z_{\text{eq}} = R_{\text{eq}} + jX_{\text{eq}} = \frac{j50(0.6 + j0.8)}{j50 + 0.6 + j0.8} = 0.5812 + j0.7943\ \Omega$$

The circuit with the combined impedances is shown in Figure 15(b).

The impedance seen by the source is

$$Z_s = 1.2 + j2 + Z_{\text{eq}}$$
$$= 1.2 + j2 + 0.5812 + j0.7943$$
$$= 1.7812 + j2.7943$$
$$= 3.314\angle 57.48^\circ\ \Omega$$

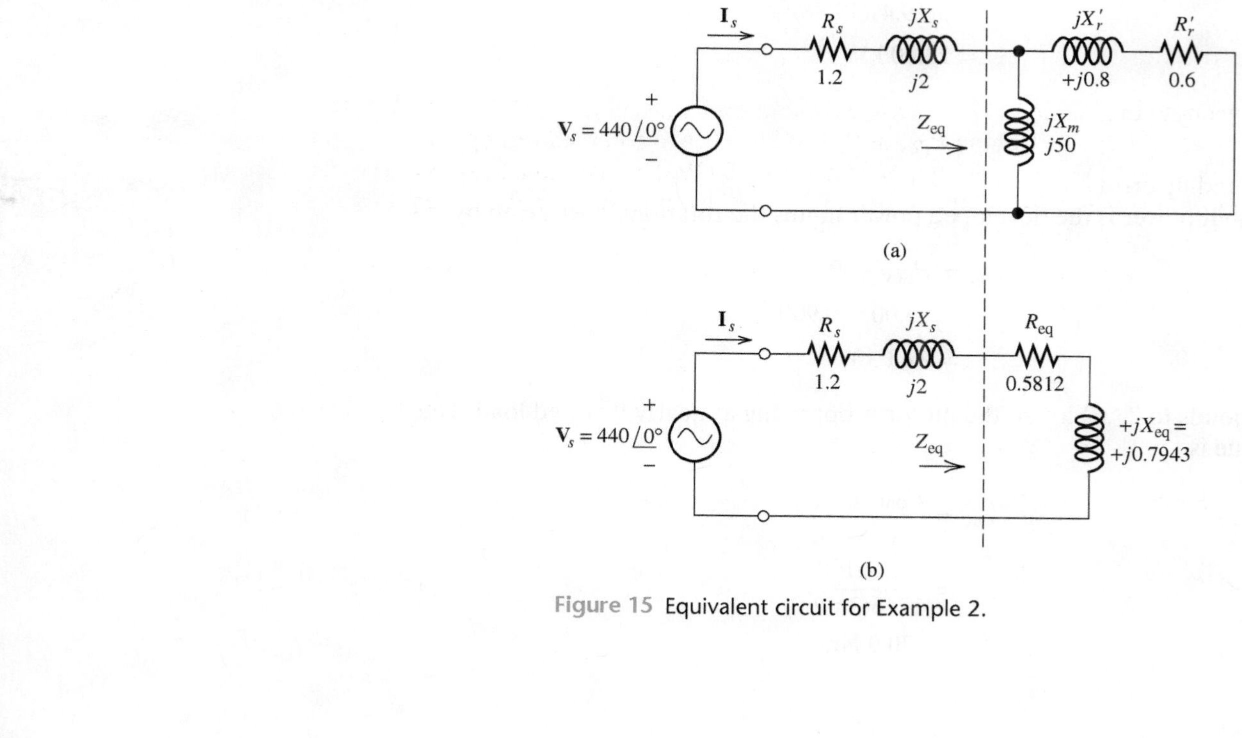

Figure 15 Equivalent circuit for Example 2.

Thus, the starting phase current is

$$\mathbf{I}_{s,\,\text{starting}} = \frac{\mathbf{V}_s}{Z_s} = \frac{440\angle 0^\circ}{3.314\angle 57.48^\circ}$$
$$= 132.8\angle -57.48^\circ \text{ A rms}$$

and, because the motor is delta connected, the starting-line-current magnitude is

$$I_{\text{line, starting}} = \sqrt{3} I_{s,\,\text{starting}} = 230.0 \text{ A rms}$$

In Example 1, with the motor running under nearly a full load, the line current is $I_{\text{line}} = 37.59$ A. Thus, the starting current is approximately six times larger than the full-load running current. This is typical of induction motors.

The power crossing the air gap is three times the power delivered to the right of the dashed line in Figure 15, given by

$$P_{\text{ag}} = 3R_{\text{eq}}(I_{s,\,\text{starting}})^2$$
$$= 30.75 \text{ kW}$$

Finally, Equation 34 gives us the starting torque:

$$T_{\text{dev, starting}} = \frac{P_{\text{ag}}}{\omega_s}$$
$$= \frac{30{,}750}{2\pi(60)/2}$$
$$= 163.1 \text{ Nm}$$

Notice that the starting torque is larger than the torque while running under full-load conditions. This is also typical of induction motors. ■

Example 3 Induction-Motor Performance

A 220-V-rms 60-Hz three-phase wye-connected induction motor draws 31.87 A at a power factor of 75 percent lagging. For all three phases, the total stator copper losses are 400 W, and the total rotor copper losses are 150 W. The rotational losses are 500 W. Find the power crossing the air gap P_{ag}, the developed power P_{dev}, the output power P_{out}, and the efficiency.

Solution The phase voltage is $V_s = V_{\text{line}}/\sqrt{3} = 127.0$ V rms. Next, we find the input power:

$$P_{\text{in}} = 3V_s I_s \cos(\theta)$$
$$= 3(127)(31.87)(0.75)$$
$$= 9107 \text{ W}$$

The air-gap power is the input power minus the stator copper loss:

$$P_{\text{ag}} = P_{\text{in}} - P_s$$
$$= 9107 - 400$$
$$= 8707 \text{ W}$$

The developed power is the input power minus the copper losses:

$$P_{\text{dev}} = 9107 - 400 - 150 = 8557 \text{ W}$$

Next, by subtracting the rotational losses we find that the output power is

$$\begin{aligned} P_{\text{out}} &= P_{\text{dev}} - P_{\text{rot}} \\ &= 8557 - 500 \\ &= 8057 \text{ W} \end{aligned}$$

Finally, the efficiency is

$$\begin{aligned} \eta &= \frac{P_{\text{out}}}{P_{\text{in}}} \times 100\% \\ &= 94.0\% \end{aligned}$$

■

Exercise 3 Repeat Example 1 for a running speed of 1764 rpm.
Answer $s = 0.02$; power factor $= 82.62\%$; $P_{\text{in}} = 17.43$ kW; $P_{\text{out}} = 15.27$ kW; $P_s = 919$ W; $P_r = 330$ W; $T_{\text{out}} = 82.66$ Nm; $\eta = 87.61\%$. □

Exercise 4 Repeat Example 2 if the rotor resistance is increased to 1.2 Ω. Compare the starting torque with the value found in the example.
Answer $\mathbf{I}_{s,\text{ starting}} = 119.7\angle{-50^\circ}$; $T_{\text{dev, starting}} = 265.0$ Nm. □

Wound-Rotor Induction Machine

A variation of the induction motor is the **wound-rotor machine**. The stator is identical to that of a squirrel-cage motor. Instead of a cast aluminum cage, the rotor contains a set of three-phase coils that are placed in slots. The windings are configured to produce the same number of poles on the rotor as on the stator. The windings are usually wye connected and the three terminals are brought out to external terminals through slip rings.

The results of Exercise 4 show that the starting torque of an induction motor can be increased by increasing the rotor resistance. By using a set of variable resistances connected to the rotor terminals, the torque–speed characteristic of the machine can be modified as illustrated in Figure 16. A degree of speed control can be achieved by varying the resistances. However, efficiency becomes poorer as the resistance is increased.

A disadvantage of the wound-rotor machine is that it is more expensive and less rugged than the cage machine.

Selection of Induction Motors

Some of the most important considerations in selecting an induction motor are

1. Efficiency
2. Starting torque
3. Pull-out torque
4. Power factor
5. Starting current

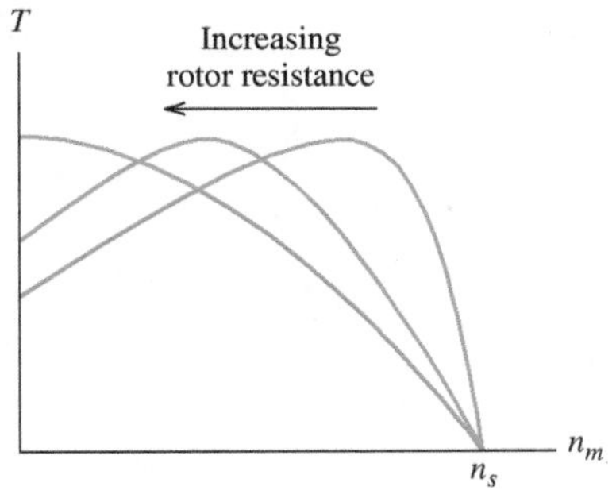

Figure 16 Variation of resistance in series with the rotor windings changes the torque–speed characteristic of the wound-rotor machine.

High values for the first four factors and low starting current are generally most desirable. Unfortunately, it is not possible to design a motor having the most desirable values for all of these criteria. It turns out that in the design of a motor, various trade-offs between these criteria must be made. For example, higher rotor resistance leads to lower efficiency and higher starting torque. Larger leakage reactance X_s leads to lower starting current but poorer power factor. The design engineer must consider the various motors available and select the one that best meets the needs of the application at hand.

3 SYNCHRONOUS MACHINES

In this section, we discuss synchronous ac machines. These machines are used for nearly all electrical-energy generation by utility companies. As motors, they tend to be used in higher-power, lower-speed applications than those for which induction motors are used. Unlike other types of ac and dc motors that we have studied to this point, the speed of a synchronous motor does not vary with mechanical load (assuming a constant-frequency ac source). Instead, we will see that they run at synchronous speed ω_s, which is given by Equation 13, repeated here for convenience:

Generation of electrical energy by utility companies is done almost exclusively with synchronous machines.

Assuming a constant frequency source, the speed of a synchronous motor does not vary with load.

$$\omega_s = \frac{\omega}{P/2}$$

(Recall that ω is the angular frequency of the ac source and P is the number of magnetic poles of the stator or rotor.) Unless stated otherwise, we assume that the rotor is turning at synchronous speed throughout our discussion of synchronous machines.

The stator of a synchronous machine has the same construction as the stator of a three-phase induction motor, which was described in Section 1. In review, the stator contains a set of three-phase windings that establish the stator field. This field consists of P magnetic poles, alternating between north and south around the circumference of the stator and rotating at synchronous speed. In a synchronous machine, the set of stator windings is called the **armature**.

The stator windings of a synchronous machine are basically the same as those of an induction machine.

The rotor of a synchronous machine is usually a P-pole electromagnet with **field windings** that carry dc currents. (In smaller machines, the rotor can be a permanent magnet, but we will concentrate on machines with field windings.) The field current can be supplied from an external dc source through stationary brushes to **slip rings** mounted on the shaft. The slip rings are insulated from one another and from the shaft. Another method is to place a small ac generator, known as an **exciter**, on the

The rotor of a synchronous machine is a P-pole electromagnet or (in low-power machines) a permanent magnet.

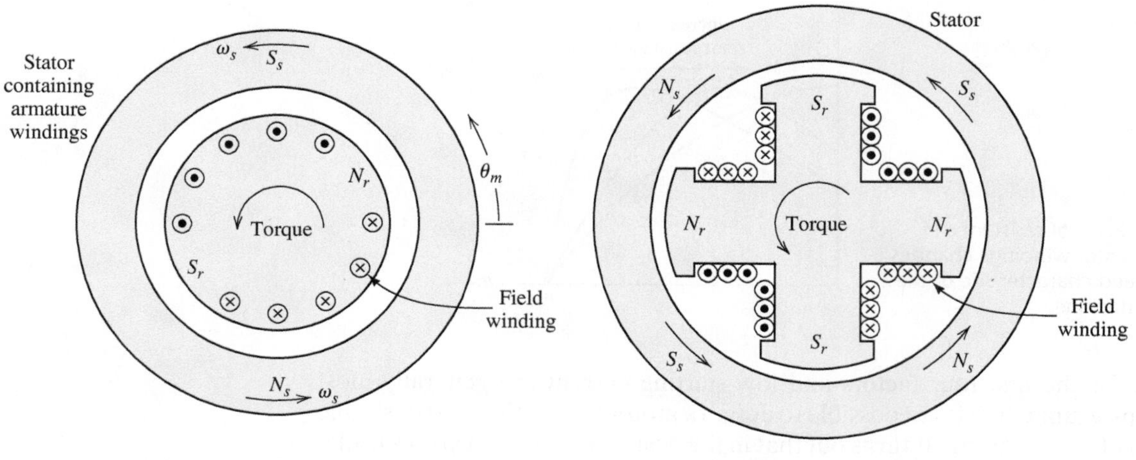

(a) Two-pole cylindrical rotor machine

(b) Four-pole salient rotor machine

Figure 17 Cross-sections of two synchronous machines. The relative positions of the stator and rotor poles are shown for motor action. Torque is developed in the direction of rotation because the rotor poles try to align themselves with the opposite stator poles.

same shaft and use diodes mounted on the shaft to rectify the ac. This avoids the maintenance associated with brushes and slip rings.

Two- and four-pole synchronous machines are illustrated in Figure 17. The rotor can either be **cylindrical**, as shown for the two-pole machine, or it can have **salient poles** as illustrated for the four-pole machine. Generally, salient-pole construction is less costly but is limited to low-speed machines having many poles. High-speed machines usually have cylindrical rotors. Salient-pole machines are common in hydroelectric power generation, whereas cylindrical-rotor machines are common in thermal (coal, nuclear, etc.) power plants.

Automobile Alternator

The alternators found in most automobiles are basically synchronous machines, except that the armature is not connected to an independent ac source. Therefore, the speed of the alternator is not fixed. As the rotor spins, the rotating field cuts the armature conductors, inducing a set of ac voltages. The ac armature voltages are rectified, and the resulting dc is used to power the headlights, charge the battery, and so on. The frequency and amplitude of the ac voltages increase with speed. The amplitude of the induced ac armature voltages is proportional to the flux density, which in turn depends on the field current. An electronic control circuit (or regulator) varies the field current to maintain approximately 14 V dc at the output of the rectifier.

Motor Action

In using the machine as a motor, the armature is connected to a three-phase ac source. We have seen that the resulting three-phase currents in the armature windings set up a rotating stator field. The rotor turns at synchronous speed with the rotor poles lagging behind the stator poles. Torque is produced because the rotor poles attempt to align with the stator poles. This is illustrated in Figure 17.

Electrical Angles

We denote the angular displacement around the air gap as θ_m, which is illustrated in Figure 17(a). Sometimes, it is convenient to measure angular displacements in **electrical degrees**, for which 180° corresponds to the angular distance from a north pole to the adjacent south pole. Thus, a four-pole machine has 720 electrical degrees around the circumference of its air gap, a two-pole machine has 360 electrical degrees, and a six-pole machine has 3 × 360 degrees. We denote displacement in electrical degrees as θ_e. Electrical and mechanical angular displacements are related by

Angles can be measured in electrical degrees for which the angle between adjacent north and south poles is 180°.

$$\theta_e = \theta_m \frac{P}{2} \tag{35}$$

Field Components

The total rotating field in the air gap is due partly to dc current in the field windings on the rotor and partly to ac currents flowing in the armature windings. The air-gap flux components are functions of both time and angular displacement. The field lines cross perpendicular to the gap, because that is the path of least reluctance. Thus, at any given point, the field is directed perpendicular to the armature conductors, which lie in slots cut lengthwise into the inside face of the stator.

The total field rotating in the air gap is partly due to the dc currents in the rotor windings and partly due to the ac currents in the stator (armature) windings.

Most synchronous machines are designed so that the flux density varies sinusoidally with θ_m. Because the field rotates at a uniform rate, the flux density at any point in the gap varies sinusoidally with time. Thus, we can represent the field components at $\theta_m = 0$ by phasors denoted by $\mathbf{B}_s$, $\mathbf{B}_r$, and $\mathbf{B}_{\text{total}}$, which correspond to the stator flux component, rotor flux component, and total flux, respectively. Then, we can write

Synchronous machines are designed so the flux varies sinusoidally around the air gap.

$$\mathbf{B}_{\text{total}} = \mathbf{B}_s + \mathbf{B}_r \tag{36}$$

The torque developed in the rotor is given by

$$T_{\text{dev}} = KB_rB_{\text{total}} \sin(\delta) \tag{37}$$

in which K is a constant that depends on the dimensions and other features of the machine. B_{total} and B_r are the magnitudes of the phasors $\mathbf{B}_{\text{total}}$ and $\mathbf{B}_r$, respectively. δ is the electrical angle, called the **torque angle**, by which the rotor field lags the total field.

Equivalent Circuit

The rotating field components induce corresponding voltage components in the armature windings. We concentrate on the a phase of the armature winding. The voltages and currents in the other two armature windings are identical except for phase shifts of ±120°.

The voltage component induced by the rotor flux can be represented as a phasor that is given by

$$\mathbf{E}_r = k\mathbf{B}_r \tag{38}$$

in which k is a constant that depends on the machine construction features.

A second voltage component is induced in each winding by the rotating stator field. This voltage component is given by

$$\mathbf{E}_s = k\mathbf{B}_s \tag{39}$$

As we have seen, the stator field is established by the armature currents. The stator is a mutually coupled three-phase inductor, and the voltage due to the stator field can be written as

$$\mathbf{E}_s = jX_s\mathbf{I}_a \tag{40}$$

where X_s is an inductive reactance known as the **synchronous reactance**, and $\mathbf{I}_a$ is the phasor for the armature current. [Actually, the stator windings also have resistance, and more precisely, we have $\mathbf{E}_s = (R_a + jX_s)\mathbf{I}_a$. However, the resistance R_a is usually very small compared to the synchronous reactance, so Equation 40 is sufficiently accurate.]

$\mathbf{V}_a$ and $\mathbf{I}_a$ represent the rms phase voltage and phase current, respectively. The relationship to line voltage and line current depends on whether the machine is wye or delta connected.

The voltage observed at the terminals of the armature winding is the sum of these two components. Thus, we can write

$$\mathbf{V}_a = \mathbf{E}_r + \mathbf{E}_s \tag{41}$$

where $\mathbf{V}_a$ is the phasor for the terminal voltage for the a-phase winding. Using Equation 40 to substitute for $\mathbf{E}_s$, we have

$$\mathbf{V}_a = \mathbf{E}_r + jX_s\mathbf{I}_a \tag{42}$$

Throughout our discussion, we assume that the phase angle of $\mathbf{V}_a$ is 0.

Also, we can write

$$\mathbf{V}_a = k\mathbf{B}_{\text{total}} \tag{43}$$

because the total voltage is proportional to the total flux.

The equivalent circuit of the synchronous motor is shown in Figure 18. Only the a phase of the armature is shown. The three-phase source $\mathbf{V}_a$ supplies current $\mathbf{I}_a$ to the armature. The ac voltage induced in the armature by the rotor field is represented by the voltage source $\mathbf{E}_r$. The dc voltage source V_f supplies the field current I_f to the rotor. An adjustable resistance R_{adj} is included in the field circuit so that the field current can be varied. This in turn adjusts the magnitudes of the rotor field $\mathbf{B}_r$ and the resulting induced voltage $\mathbf{E}_r$.

The armature windings can be connected either in a wye or in a delta configuration. In our discussion, we do not specify the way in which the windings are connected. For either connection, $\mathbf{V}_a$ represents the voltage across the a winding. In a wye connection, $\mathbf{V}_a$ corresponds to the line-to-neutral voltage, whereas in a delta connection, $\mathbf{V}_a$ corresponds to the line-to-line voltage. Similarly, $\mathbf{I}_a$ is the current through the a winding, which corresponds to the line current in a wye connection but not in a delta connection. The important things to remember are that $\mathbf{V}_a$ is the voltage across the a winding and that $\mathbf{I}_a$ is the current through the a winding, regardless of the manner in which the machine is connected.

The phasor diagram for the current and voltages is shown in Figure 19(a). The corresponding phasor diagram for the fields is shown in Figure 19(b). Because the

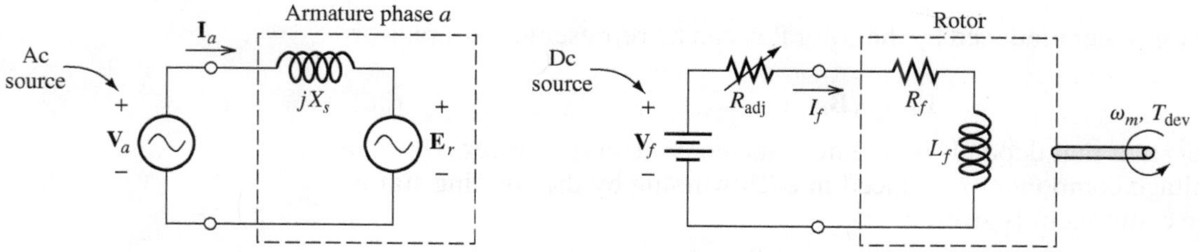

Figure 18 Equivalent circuit for the synchronous motor. The armature circuit is based on Equation 42.

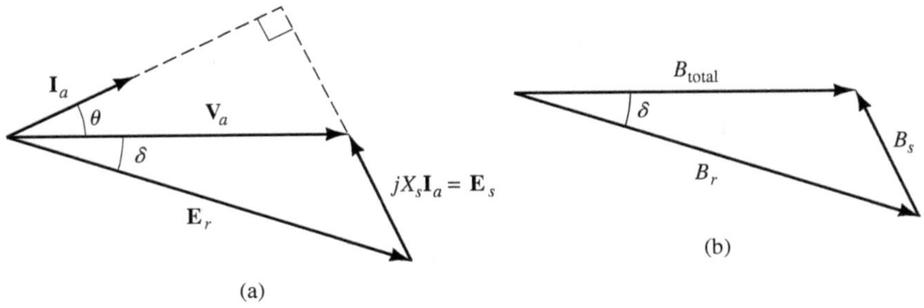

Figure 19 Phasor diagrams for the synchronous motor. Notice that the stator component of voltage $\mathbf{E}_s = jX_s\mathbf{I}_a$ is at right angles to the current $\mathbf{I}_a$. The developed torque is given by $T_{dev} = KB_rB_{total}\sin\delta$, and the power factor is $\cos(\theta)$.

rotor field is lagging the total field, positive torque (given by Equation 37) and output power are being developed. In other words, the machine is acting as a motor.

The input power taken from the three-phase ac source is given by

$$P_{dev} = P_{in} = 3V_aI_a\cos(\theta) \tag{44}$$

in which the factor of three accounts for the fact that there are three sets of windings. Since the equivalent circuit does not include any losses, the input power and the developed mechanical power are equal.

Potential for Power-Factor Correction

The total reactive power absorbed by the three windings is given by

$$Q = 3V_aI_a\sin(\theta) \tag{45}$$

in which θ is defined to be the angle by which the phase current $\mathbf{I}_a$ *lags* the phase voltage $\mathbf{V}_a$.

Notice in Figure 19(a) that θ takes a negative value because the phase current $\mathbf{I}_a$ *leads* the phase voltage $\mathbf{V}_a$. Therefore, the reactive power for the machine is negative, indicating that the synchronous motor can supply reactive power. This is a significant advantage because most industrial plants have an overall lagging power factor (due largely to the widespread employment of induction motors). Poor power factor leads to larger currents in the transmission lines and transformers supplying the plant. Thus, utility companies invariably charge their industrial customers more for energy supplied while the power factor is low. By using some synchronous motors in an industrial plant, part of the reactive power taken by inductive loads can be supplied locally, thereby lowering energy costs. Should you someday be employed as a plant engineer, you will need to have a good understanding of these issues.

The synchronous motor can act as a source of reactive power.

Unloaded synchronous machines have sometimes been installed solely for the purpose of power-factor correction. With zero load (and neglecting losses), the rotor field and the total field align so that the torque angle δ is zero, and according to Equation 37, the developed torque is zero. Phasor diagrams for unloaded synchronous machines are shown in Figure 20.

Proper use of synchronous motors can lower energy costs of an industrial plant by increasing the power factor.

If we have

$$V_a > E_r\cos(\delta) \tag{46}$$

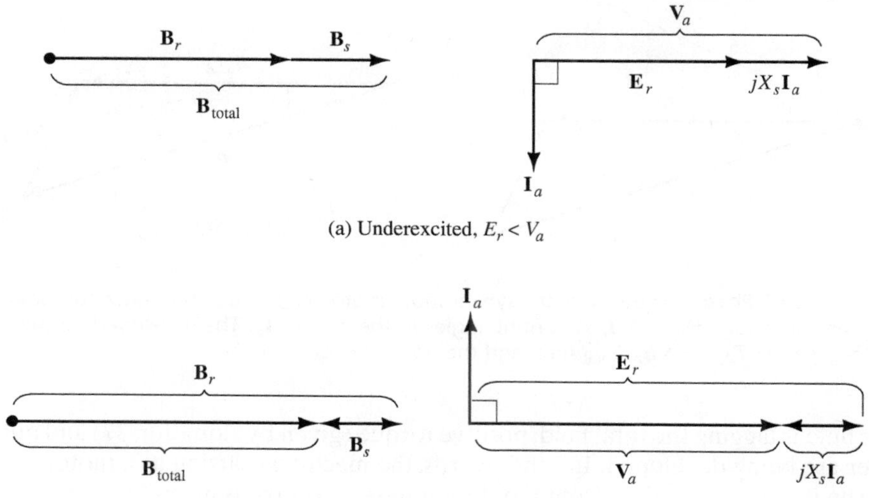

(a) Underexcited, $E_r < V_a$

(b) Overexcited, $E_r > V_a$

Figure 20 Phasor diagrams for unloaded synchronous machines. When a machine has $E_r > V_a$, the current $\mathbf{I}_a$ leads the applied voltage $\mathbf{V}_a$ by 90°, and each phase of the machine is electrically equivalent to a capacitor. Thus, the machine supplies reactive power.

we say that the machine is **underexcited**. For an unloaded machine with $\delta = 0$, the machine is underexcited if the magnitude of $\mathbf{E}_r$ is less than the magnitude of the applied phase voltage $\mathbf{V}_a$. Then, the current $\mathbf{I}_a$ lags $\mathbf{V}_a$ by $\theta = 90°$. Consequently, the real power supplied (which is given by Equation 44) is zero, as we expect for an unloaded machine (neglecting losses). The underexcited machine absorbs reactive power. This is the opposite of the desired result for most applications.

However, if the field current is increased such that

$$V_a < E_r \cos(\delta) \tag{47}$$

we say that the machine is **overexcited**. The phasor diagram is shown in Figure 20(b) for an unloaded overexcited machine. In this case, the current leads the voltage by 90°, and the machine supplies reactive power. In the overexcited state, an unloaded synchronous machine appears as a pure capacitive reactance to the ac source. Machines used in this manner are called **synchronous capacitors**.

Operation with Variable Load and Constant Field Current

Motors are usually operated from ac voltage sources of constant magnitude and phase. This fact in combination with Equation 43 shows that the total flux phasor $\mathbf{B}_{\text{total}}$ is constant in magnitude and phase. Because speed is constant in a synchronous machine, power is proportional to torque, which in turn is proportional to $B_r \sin(\delta)$, as shown by Equation 37. Thus, we can write

$$P_{\text{dev}} \propto B_r \sin(\delta) \tag{48}$$

This fact is illustrated in Figure 21(a).

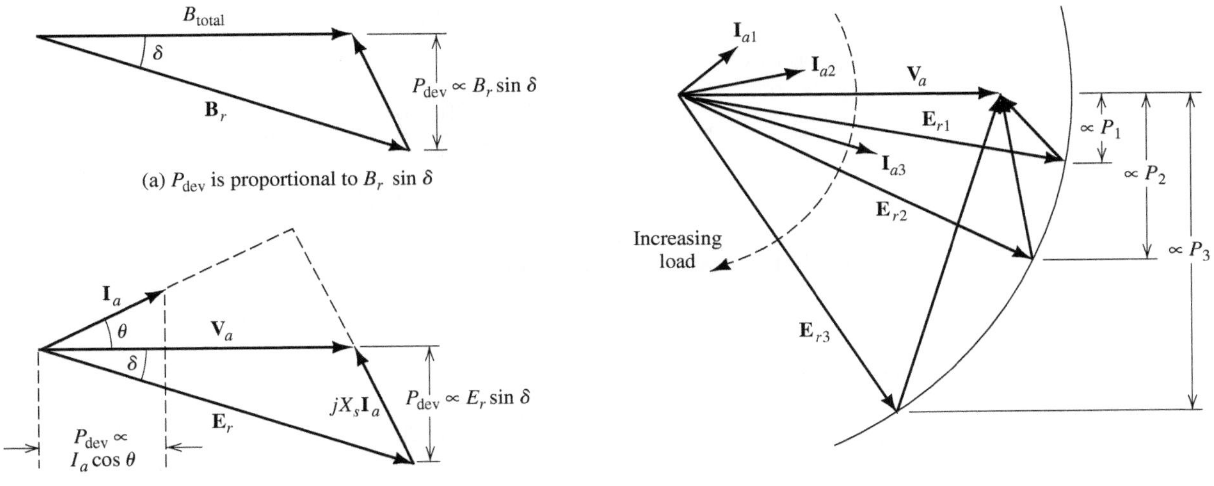

Figure 21 Phasor diagrams for a synchronous motor.

Furthermore, E_r is proportional to B_r. Hence, we have established that

$$P_{dev} \propto E_r \sin(\delta) \tag{49}$$

Since $P_{dev} = P_{in} = 3V_aI_a\cos(\theta)$ (neglecting stator copper loss) and since V_a is constant, we also have

$$P_{dev} \propto I_a \cos(\theta) \tag{50}$$

Equations 49 and 50 are illustrated in the phasor diagram shown in Figure 21(b).

Now suppose that we have a synchronous motor operating with a variable load and constant field current. Because the field current is constant, $\mathbf{E}_r$ is constant in magnitude. As the load changes, $\mathbf{E}_r$ can change in phase, but not in magnitude. Therefore, the locus formed by $\mathbf{E}_r$ is a circle. The phasor diagram for a machine with a variable load is shown in Figure 21(c). Notice that the power factor tends to become lagging as the load is increased.

As the load varies with constant field current, the locus of $\mathbf{E}_r$ is a circle. Notice that if $jX_s\mathbf{I}_a$ and $\mathbf{I}_a$ are extended, they meet at right angles.

Example 4 Synchronous-Motor Performance

A 480-V-rms 200-hp 60-Hz eight-pole delta-connected synchronous motor operates with a developed power (including losses) of 50 hp and a power factor of 90 percent leading. The synchronous reactance is $X_s = 1.4\ \Omega$. **a.** Find the speed and developed torque. **b.** Determine the values of $\mathbf{I}_a$, $\mathbf{E}_r$, and the torque angle. **c.** Suppose that the excitation remains constant and the load torque increases until the developed power is 100 hp. Determine the new values of $\mathbf{I}_a$, $\mathbf{E}_r$, the torque angle, and the power factor.

Solution

a. The speed of the machine is given by Equation 14:

$$n_s = \frac{120f}{P} = \frac{120(60)}{8} = 900 \text{ rpm}$$

$$\omega_s = n_s \frac{2\pi}{60} = 30\pi = 94.25 \text{ rad/s}$$

For the first operating condition, the developed power is

$$P_{\text{dev1}} = 50 \times 746 = 37.3 \text{ kW}$$

and the developed torque is

$$T_{\text{dev1}} = \frac{P_{\text{dev1}}}{\omega_s} = \frac{37{,}300}{94.25} = 396 \text{ Nm}$$

b. The voltage rating refers to the rms line-to-line voltage. Because the windings are delta connected, we have $V_a = V_{\text{line}} = 480$ V rms. Solving Equation 44 for I_a and substituting values, we have

$$I_{a1} = \frac{P_{\text{dev1}}}{3V_a \cos(\theta_1)} = \frac{37{,}300}{3(480)(0.9)} = 28.78 \text{ A rms}$$

Next, the power factor is $\cos(\theta_1) = 0.9$, which yields

$$\theta_1 = 25.84°$$

Because the power factor was given as leading, we know that the phase of $\mathbf{I}_{a1}$ is positive. Thus, we have

$$\mathbf{I}_{a1} = 28.78\angle 25.84° \text{ A rms}$$

Then from Equation 42, we have

$$\begin{aligned}\mathbf{E}_{r1} &= \mathbf{V}_{a1} - jX_s\mathbf{I}_a = 480 - j1.4(28.78\angle 25.84°) \\ &= 497.6 - j36.3 \\ &= 498.9\angle -4.168° \text{ V rms}\end{aligned}$$

Consequently, the torque angle is $\delta_1 = 4.168°$.

c. When the load torque is increased while holding excitation constant (i.e., the values of I_f, B_r, and E_r are constant), the torque angle must increase. In Figure 21(b), we see that the developed power is proportional to $\sin(\delta)$. Hence, we can write

$$\frac{\sin(\delta_2)}{\sin(\delta_1)} = \frac{P_2}{P_1}$$

Solving for $\sin(\delta_2)$ and substituting values, we find that

$$\sin(\delta_2) = \frac{P_2}{P_1}\sin(\delta_1) = \frac{100 \text{ hp}}{50 \text{ hp}}\sin(4.168°)$$

$$\delta_2 = 8.360°$$

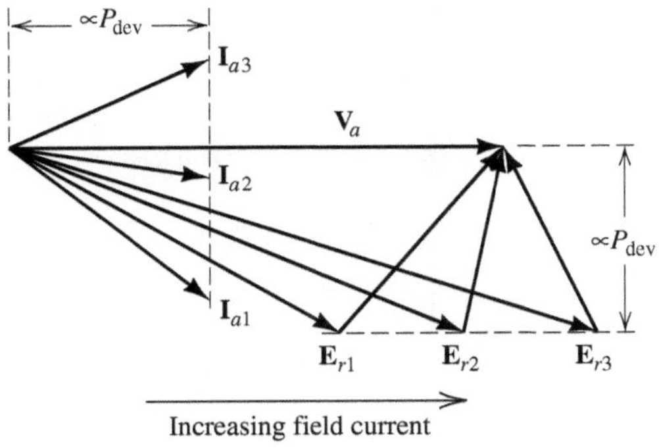

Figure 22 Phasor diagram for constant developed power and increasing field current.

Because E_r is constant in magnitude, we get

$$\mathbf{E}_{r2} = 498.9\angle{-8.360^\circ} \text{ V rms}$$

(We know that $\mathbf{E}_{r2}$ lags $\mathbf{V}_a = 480\angle{0^\circ}$ because the machine is acting as a motor.) Next, we can find the new current:

$$\mathbf{I}_{a2} = \frac{\mathbf{V}_a - \mathbf{E}_{r2}}{jX_s} = 52.70\angle{10.61^\circ} \text{ A rms}$$

Finally, the new power factor is

$$\cos(\theta_2) = \cos(10.61^\circ) = 98.3\% \text{ leading}$$

■

Exercise 5 For the motor of Example 4, suppose that the excitation remains constant and the load torque increases until the developed power is $P_{dev3} = 200$ hp. Determine the new values of $\mathbf{I}_a$, $\mathbf{E}_r$, the torque angle, and the power factor.

Answer $\mathbf{I}_{a3} = 103.6\angle{-1.05^\circ}$; $\mathbf{E}_{r3} = 498.9\angle{-16.90^\circ}$; $\delta_3 = 16.90^\circ$; power factor = 99.98% lagging. □

Operation with Constant Load and Variable Field Current

When operating with constant developed power P_{dev}, Figure 21(b) shows that the values of $I_a \cos(\theta)$ and $E_r \sin(\delta)$ are constant. Then, if the field current increases, the magnitude of E_r increases. The resulting phasor diagram for several values of field current is shown in Figure 22. Notice that as the field current increases, the armature current decreases in magnitude, reaching a minimum for $\theta = 0^\circ$ (or unity power factor) and then increases with a leading power factor. The current magnitude reaches a minimum when $\mathbf{I}_a$ is in phase with $\mathbf{V}_a$ (i.e., when $\theta = 0$ and the power factor is unity). Plots of I_a versus field current are shown in Figure 23. These plots are called **V curves** because of their shape.

Power factor tends to become leading as field current, and consequently, $\mathbf{E}_r$ increase in magnitude.

Example 5 Power-Factor Control

A 480-V-rms 200-hp 60-Hz eight-pole delta-connected synchronous motor operates with a developed power (including losses) of 200 hp and a power factor of 85 percent lagging. The synchronous reactance is $X_s = 1.4\ \Omega$. The field current is $I_f = 10$ A. What must the new field current be to produce 100 percent power factor? Assume that magnetic saturation does not occur, so that B_r is proportional to I_f.

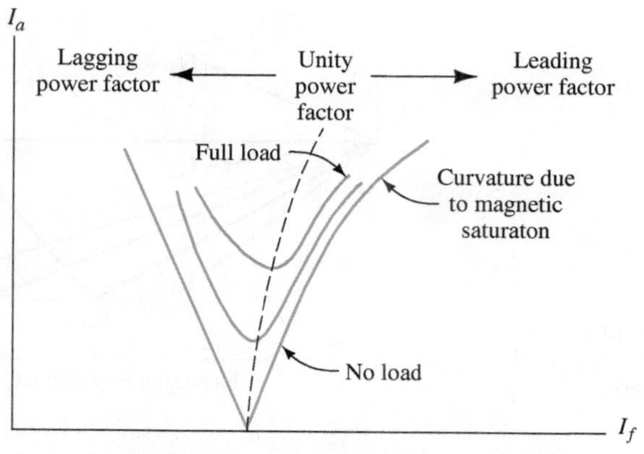

Figure 23 V curves for a synchronous motor with variable excitation.

Solution First, we determine the initial value of E_r. Because the initial power factor is $\cos(\theta_1) = 0.85$, we can determine that

$$\theta_1 = 31.79°$$

Then, the phase current is

$$I_{a1} = \frac{P_{\text{dev}}}{3V_a \cos(\theta_1)} = \frac{200(746)}{3(480)0.85} = 121.9 \text{ A rms}$$

Thus, the phasor current is

$$\mathbf{I}_{a1} = 121.9\angle{-31.79°} \text{ A rms}$$

The induced voltage is

$$\begin{aligned}\mathbf{E}_{r1} &= \mathbf{V}_{a1} - jX_s\mathbf{I}_{a1} = 480 - j1.4(121.9\angle{-31.79°}) \\ &= 390.1 - j145.0 \\ &= 416.2\angle{-20.39°} \text{ V rms}\end{aligned}$$

The phasor diagram for the initial excitation is shown in Figure 24(a).

To achieve 100 percent power factor, we need to increase the field current and the magnitude of $\mathbf{E}_r$ until $\mathbf{I}_a$ is in phase with $\mathbf{V}_a$, as shown in Figure 24(b). The new value of the phase current is

$$I_{a2} = \frac{P_{\text{dev}}}{3V_a \cos(\theta_2)} = \frac{200(746)}{3(480)} = 103.6 \text{ A rms}$$

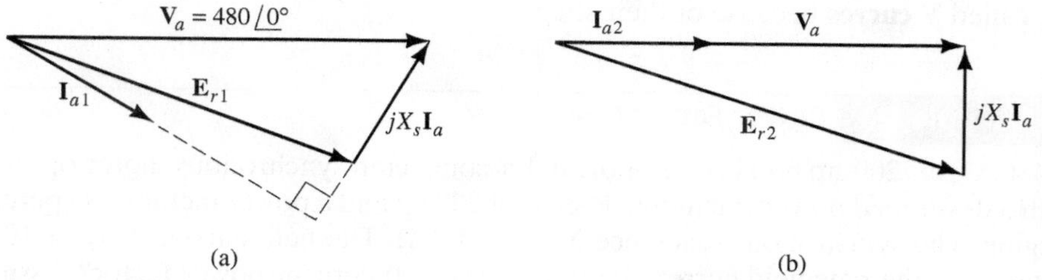

Figure 24 Phasor diagrams for Example 5.

Then, we have

$$\mathbf{E}_{r2} = \mathbf{V}_{a2} - jX_s\mathbf{I}_{a2} = 480 - j1.4(103.6)$$
$$= 480 - j145.0$$
$$= 501.4\angle{-16.81^\circ} \text{ V rms}$$

Now the magnitude of $\mathbf{E}_r$ is proportional to the field current, so we can write

$$I_{f2} = I_{f1}\frac{E_{r2}}{E_{r1}} = 10\frac{501.4}{416.2} = 12.05 \text{ A dc}$$ ■

Exercise 6 Find the field current needed to achieve a power factor of 90 percent leading for the motor of Example 5.
Answer $I_f = 13.67$ A. □

Pull-Out Torque

The developed torque of a synchronous motor is given by Equation 37, which states that

$$T_{\text{dev}} = KB_rB_{\text{total}}\sin(\delta)$$

This is plotted in Figure 25. The maximum or **pull-out torque** $T_{\max}$ occurs for a torque angle of $\delta = 90°$:

$$T_{\max} = KB_rB_{\text{total}} \tag{51}$$

The pull-out torque is the maximum torque that the synchronous motor can produce, which occurs for a torque angle of 90°.

Typically, the rated torque is about 30 percent of the maximum torque.

Suppose that a synchronous motor is initially unloaded. Then, it runs at synchronous speed with $\delta = 0$. As the load increases, the motor slows momentarily and δ increases just enough so that the developed torque meets the demands of the load plus losses. Then, the machine again runs at synchronous speed.

However, if the load on a synchronous machine was to exceed the pull-out torque, it would no longer be possible for the machine to drive the load at synchronous speed and δ would keep on increasing. Then, the machine would produce enormous surges in torque back and forth, resulting in great vibration. Once the rotor pulls out of synchronism with the rotating armature field, the average torque falls to zero, and the system slows to a stop.

The torque–speed characteristic of a synchronous motor is shown in Figure 26. Generally, it is desirable to operate synchronous motors in an overexcited state (i.e., large values of I_f, B_r, and E_r), for several reasons. First, the machine produces reactive power. Second, as shown by Equation 51, the pull-out torque is higher with higher B_r.

Generally, it is desirable to operate synchronous motors in the overexcited state to obtain large pull-out torque and to generate reactive power.

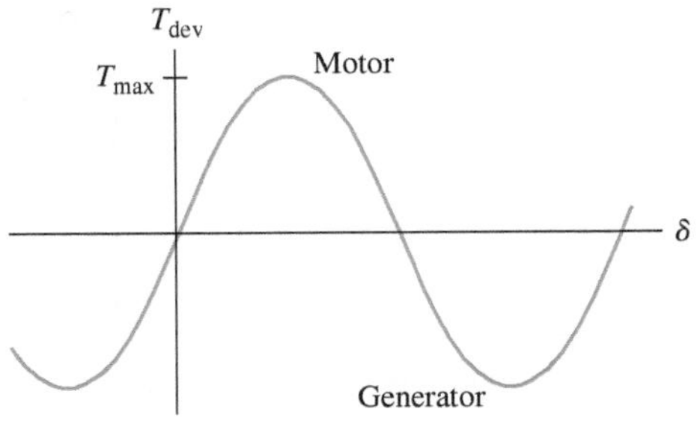

Figure 25 Torque versus torque angle. $T_{\max}$ is the maximum or pull-out torque.

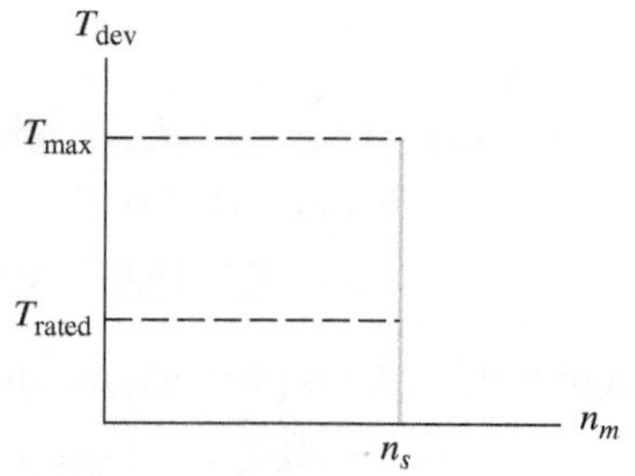

Figure 26 Torque–speed characteristic of synchronous motors.

Starting Methods

Because the starting torque of the synchronous motor is zero, special starting provisions are needed.

Because a synchronous motor develops zero starting torque, we need to make special provisions for starting. Several methods can be used:

1. Vary the frequency of the ac source starting very low (a fraction of a hertz) and gradually increasing to the operating speed desired. This can be accomplished with power electronic circuits known as *cycloconverters* that can convert 60-Hz ac power into three-phase power of any desired frequency. Such a system can also be used for very accurate speed control.
2. Use a prime mover to bring the synchronous motor up to speed. Then, the motor is connected to the ac source and the load is connected. Before the ac source is connected, it is important to wait until the phases of the voltages induced in the armature closely match those of the line voltages. In other words, we want the torque angle δ to be close to zero before closing the switches to the ac source. Otherwise, excessive currents and torques occur as the rotor tries to rapidly align itself with the stator field.
3. The rotors of many synchronous motors contain **amortisseur** or **damper conductors**, which are similar in structure to the squirrel-cage conductors used in induction motors. Then, the motor can be started as an induction motor with the field windings shorted and without load. After the motor has approached synchronous speed, the dc source is connected to the field and the motor pulls into synchronism. Then, the load is connected.

Damper conductors have another purpose besides use in starting. It is possible for the speed of a synchronous motor to oscillate above and below synchronous speed so that the torque angle δ swings back and forth. This action is similar to that of a pendulum. By including the damper bars, the oscillation is damped out. When running at synchronous speed, no voltage is induced in the damper bars and they have no effect.

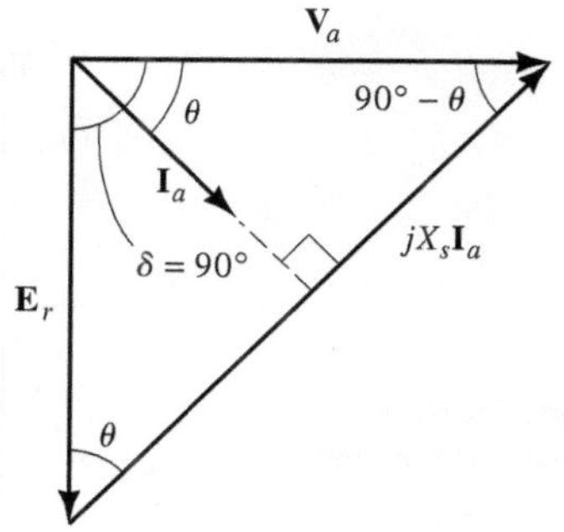

Figure 27 Phasor diagram for maximum developed torque and maximum power conditions. See Exercise 7.

Exercise 7 A synchronous motor produces maximum torque and maximum power for $\delta = 90°$. Draw the phasor diagram for this case and show that $P_{\max} = 3(V_a E_r / X_s)$ and $T_{\max} = 3(V_a E_r / \omega_m X_s)$.

Answer The phasor diagram is shown in Figure 27. □

4 SINGLE-PHASE MOTORS

In this section, we discuss briefly several additional types of single-phase ac motors. Single-phase motors are important because three-phase power is not available for homes, most offices, and many small businesses.

Compared with induction motors, universal motors have a higher power/weight ratio, but they do not have as long a service life, due to wear of the brushes. Assuming constant source frequency, induction motors are essentially constant-speed devices. On the other hand, the speed of a universal motor can be varied by changing the amplitude of the applied voltage.

Universal motors have relatively large power-to-weight ratios but short service lives.

Basic Single-Phase Induction Motor

Let us begin by considering the basic single-phase induction motor shown in Figure 28. The stator of this motor has a **main winding** that is connected to an ac source. (Later, we will see that an auxiliary winding is needed for starting.) It has a squirrel-cage rotor that is identical to the rotor of the three-phase induction motor shown in Figure 6.

Ideally, the air-gap flux varies sinusoidally in space around the circumference of the gap. Thus, the flux is given by

$$B = Ki(t)\cos(\theta) \tag{52}$$

which is the same, except for changes in notation, as Equation 1 for the flux due to winding a of a three-phase induction motor. The stator current is given by

$$i(t) = I_m \cos(\omega t) \tag{53}$$

Substituting this expression for the current into Equation 52, we have

$$B = KI_m \cos(\omega t)\cos(\theta) \tag{54}$$

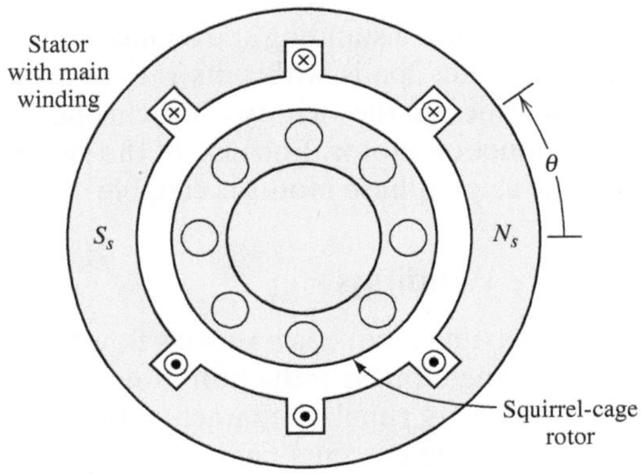

Figure 28 Cross-section of the basic single-phase induction motor.

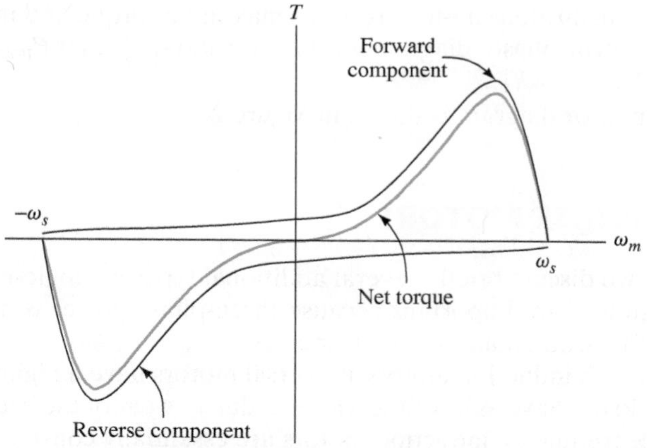

Figure 29 The main winding produces two counter-rotating flux components each of which induces torque in the rotor. The main winding alone induces no net starting torque.

Instead of rotating, this flux pulsates, switching direction twice per cycle.

However, by applying the trigonometric identity for the product of cosines, we can write Equation 54 as

$$B = \frac{1}{2}KI_m \cos(\omega t - \theta) + \frac{1}{2}KI_m \cos(\omega t + \theta) \tag{55}$$

The pulsating flux produced by the main winding can be resolved into two counter rotating components.

The first term on the right-hand side of Equation 55 represents a flux that rotates counterclockwise (i.e., in the positive θ direction), while the second term rotates clockwise. Thus, the pulsating flux in the basic single-phase induction motor can be resolved into two counter rotating components. On the other hand, the three-phase motor has flux rotating in one direction only.

We assume that the rotor spins counterclockwise with speed ω_m. The field component that rotates in the same direction as the rotor is called the **forward component**. The other component is called the **reverse component**. Each of these components produces torque, but in opposite directions. The torque versus speed characteristic for each component is similar to that of a three-phase induction motor. The torques produced by the forward component, the reverse component, and the total torque are shown in Figure 29.

Notice that the net starting torque is zero, and therefore the main winding will not start a load from a standing start. Once started, however, the motor develops torque and accelerates loads within its ratings to nearly synchronous speed. Its running characteristics (in the vicinity of synchronous speed) are similar to those of the three-phase induction motor. Because of the symmetry of its torque–speed characteristic, the basic single-phase motor is capable of running equally well in either direction.

Auxiliary Windings

Two windings that are 90° apart physically and carry currents 90° apart in phase produce a rotating magnetic field.

Lack of starting torque is a serious flaw for a motor in most applications. However, the basic single-phase induction motor can be modified to provide starting torque and improve its running characteristics. It can be shown (see Problem P11) that equal-amplitude currents having a 90° phase relationship and flowing in windings

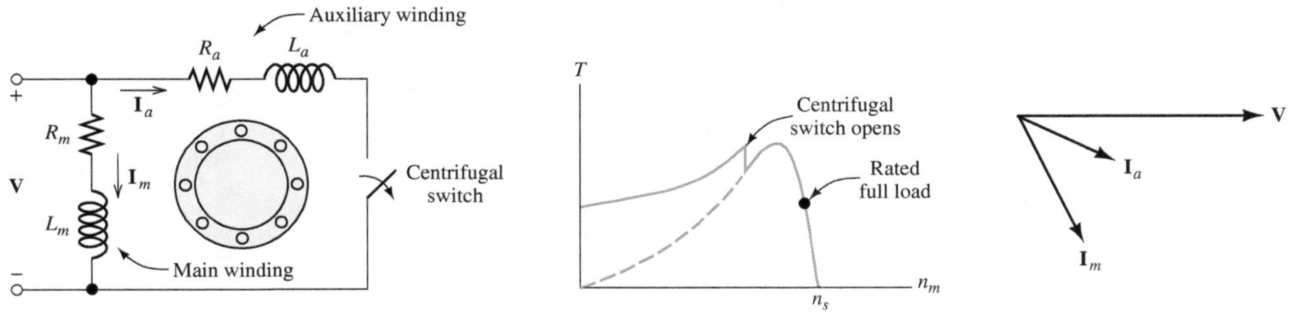

Figure 30 The split-phase induction motor.

that are at right angles produce only a forward rotating component of flux. (This is similar to the rotating flux produced by balanced three-phase currents flowing in windings displaced by 120° from one another.) If the two currents differ in phase by less than 90° (but by more than 0°), the forward flux component is larger than the reverse flux component and net starting torque results. Thus, nearly all single-phase induction motors have an **auxiliary winding** rotated in space by 90 electrical degrees from the main winding. Various provisions can be made to achieve the requisite phase shift between the current in the main winding and the current in the auxiliary winding.

Single-phase induction motors contain an auxiliary winding displaced by 90 electrical degrees from the main winding.

One possibility is to wind the auxiliary winding with smaller wire that has a higher ratio of resistance to inductive reactance than the main winding. Then, the current in the auxiliary winding has a different phase angle than that of the main current. Motors using this approach are called **split-phase motors** (Figure 30). Usually, the auxiliary winding is designed to be used only briefly during starting, and a centrifugal switch disconnects it when the motor approaches rated speed. (A common failure in this type of motor is for the switch to fail to open, and then the auxiliary winding overheats and burns out.)

When running on the main winding, the torque of a single-phase motor pulsates at twice the frequency of the ac source, because no torque is produced when the stator current passes through zero. On the other hand, torque is constant in a three-phase motor because the current is nonzero in at least two of the three windings at all instants. Thus, single-phase induction motors display more noise and vibration than do three-phase motors. Furthermore, single-phase induction motors are larger and heavier than three-phase motors of the same ratings.

Single-phase induction motors produce more noise and vibration and are larger than three-phase motors with equal power ratings.

In a **capacitor-start motor**, a capacitor is placed in series with the auxiliary winding, resulting in much higher starting torque than that of the split-phase motor, because the phase relationship between $\mathbf{I}_a$ and $\mathbf{I}_m$ is closer to 90°. In a **capacitor-run motor**, the auxiliary winding is a permanent part of the circuit, resulting in smoother torque and less vibration. Another variation is the **capacitor-start, capacitor-run motor** shown in Figure 31.

Shaded-Pole Motors

The least expensive approach to providing self-starting for single-phase induction motors is the **shaded-pole motor**, shown in Figure 32. A shorted copper band is placed around part of each pole face. As the field builds up, current is induced in this *shading ring*. The current retards changes in the field for that part of the pole face encircled by the ring. As the current in the ring decays, the center of the magnetic

Shaded-pole motors are used for inexpensive low-power applications.

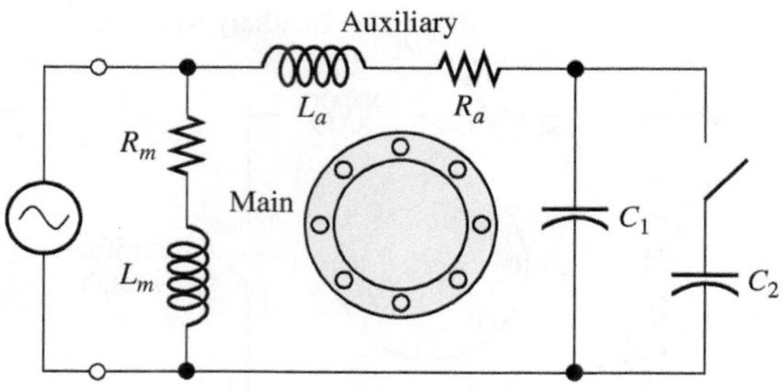

Figure 31 The capacitor-start, capacitor-run motor.

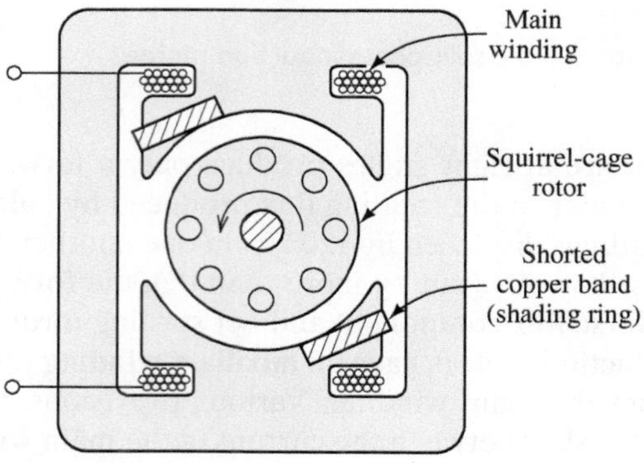

Figure 32 The shaded-pole motor.

pole moves in the direction of the ring. This favors rotation in one direction over the other, resulting in starting torque. This approach is used only for very small motors (1/20 hp or less).

5 STEPPER MOTORS AND BRUSHLESS DC MOTORS

Anytime you need accurate repeatable positioning, consider using a stepper motor.

Stepper motors are used for accurate, repeatable positioning such as machine tool applications or for moving the head in an ink-jet printer. By using an electronic controller that applies electrical pulses to the motor windings, the motor shaft can be rotated in either direction in multiples of the step angle, which can range from 0.72° (500 steps per revolution) to 15° (24 steps per revolution). Stepper motors are available with rotational accuracies on the order of 3 percent of a step, which is noncumulative as the motor is stepped back and forth. By controlling the rate at which pulses are applied to the windings of the stepper motor, speed can be varied continuously from a standing stop to a maximum that depends on the motor and load.

There are several types of stepper motors. Figure 33(a) shows the cross-section of the simplest, which is known as a **variable-reluctance stepper motor**. Notice that the stator has eight salient poles that are 45° apart. On the other hand, the rotor has six salient poles 60° apart. Thus, when 1 is aligned with A as shown, 2 is 15° counterclockwise from B, and 3 is 15° clockwise from D.

The stator contains four windings (which are not shown in the cross-section). A controller applies power to one of the coils at a time as shown in Figure 33(b). Coil A is wound partly around pole A and partly around A', such that, when current is applied, A becomes a north magnetic pole and A' becomes a south pole. Then, the rotor moves to shorten the air gaps between A (and A') and the rotor. As long as power is applied to coil A, the rotor is held in the position shown in the figure.

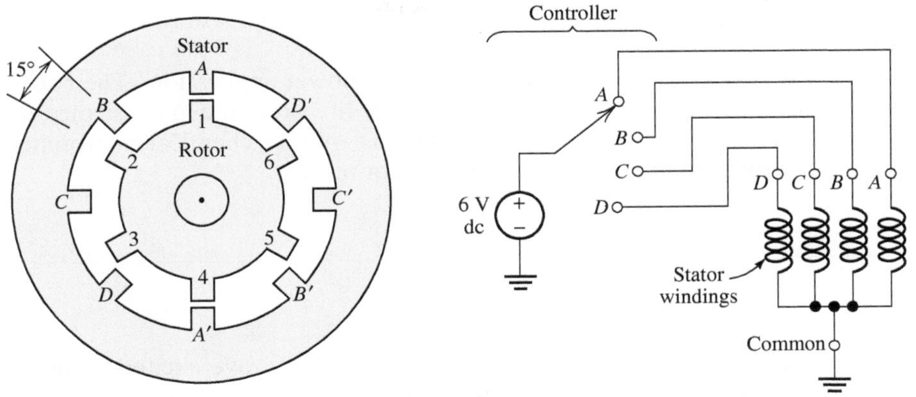

(a) Motor cross section (For simplicity, the windings on the stator poles are not shown)

(b) Circuit diagram

Figure 33 Variable-reluctance stepper motor.

However, if power is removed from A and applied to B by moving the controller switch, the rotor moves 15° clockwise so that 2 is aligned with B. Then if power is removed from B and applied to C, the shaft rotates another 15° clockwise. Thus, applying power to the coils in the sequence $ABCDABC\ldots$ results in clockwise rotation of the shaft in 15° increments. By changing the switching rate, the motor speed can be varied upward from a standing stop. Furthermore, by reversing the switching sequence to $ADCBADCB\ldots$, the direction of rotation can be reversed.

Another type is the **permanent-magnet stepper motor**, which has a cylindrical rotor (called a "tin-can rotor") that is permanently magnetized with north and south poles alternating around its circumference. The stator of the permanent magnet motor is similar to that of the reluctance motor. As in the reluctance type, the rotor position is stepped by applying a sequence of pulses to the stator windings. **Hybrid stepper motors** that combine variable reluctance with permanent magnets are also available. Of course, detailed specifications for stepper motors can be found from manufacturers' websites.

Brushless DC Motors

Conventional dc motors are particularly useful in applications that require high speeds and in those for which dc power is available, such as those in aircraft and automobiles. However, because they contain commutators and brushes, conventional dc motors have several disadvantages. These include relatively short service lives due to brush and commutator wear, particularly at very high speeds. Also, arcing as the brushes move between commutator segments can pose a hazard in explosive environments and can create severe radio interference. A relatively new development, the **brushless dc motor**, provides an excellent alternative when the disadvantages of conventional dc motors are prohibitive.

Brushless dc motors are essentially permanent-magnet stepping motors equipped with position sensors (either Hall effect or optical) and enhanced control units. As in the stepper motor, power is applied to one stator winding at a time. When the position sensor indicates that the rotor has approached alignment with the stator field, the controller electronically switches power to the next stator winding so that smooth motion continues. By varying the amplitude and duration of the pulses applied to the stator windings, speed can be readily controlled. The result is a motor that can operate from a dc source with characteristics similar to those of a conventional shunt dc motor.

Brushless dc motors are used primarily in low-power applications. Their advantages include relatively high efficiency, long service life with little maintenance, freedom from radio interference, ability to operate in explosive chemical environments, and capability for very high speeds (50,000 rpm or more).

Summary

1. Application of a three-phase source to the stator windings of an induction motor produces a magnetic field in the air gap that rotates at synchronous speed. Interchanging any two of the connections to the three-phase source reverses the direction of rotation.
2. A squirrel-cage rotor contains aluminum conductors embedded in the rotor. As the stator field moves past, currents are induced in the rotor resulting in torque. The torque–speed characteristic takes the form shown in Figure 10. In normal steady-state operation, typical motors operate with 0 to 5 percent slip, and the output power and torque are approximately proportional to slip.
3. The per-phase equivalent circuit shown in Figure 13 is useful in performance calculations for induction motors.
4. Some of the most important considerations in selecting an induction motor are efficiency, starting torque, pull-out torque, power factor, and starting current.
5. Typically, the starting torque of an induction motor is 150 percent or more of the rated full-load running torque. Thus, induction motors can start all constant-torque loads that are within their full-load ratings. Starting current with rated voltage is typically five to six times the full-load running current.
6. A three-phase synchronous machine has stator windings that produce a magnetic field consisting of P poles that rotate at synchronous speed. The rotor is an electromagnet. The machine runs at synchronous speed, and the torque–speed characteristic is shown in Figure 26.
7. When operated in the overexcited state, synchronous machines produce reactive power and can help to correct the power factor of industrial plants, saving on energy costs.
8. The equivalent circuit for three-phase synchronous machines shown in Figure 18 can be used in performance calculations.
9. Synchronous motors have zero starting torque, and special provisions must be made for starting.
10. Single-phase induction motors have a main winding and an auxiliary winding displaced by 90 electrical degrees. With power applied to only the main winding, the motor can run but has zero starting torque. Because of differences in the resistance/reactance ratio or because a capacitor is in the circuit, the currents in the two windings have different phases and this produces starting torque. Frequently, the starting winding is disconnected from the ac source when the motor approaches rated speed.
11. Single-phase induction motors are heavier and produce more vibration than do three-phase motors of the same power rating.
12. Stepper motors are useful in applications that require accurate repeatable positioning.
13. Brushless dc motors are a good alternative to conventional dc motors for low-power applications that require long life with little maintenance, operation in explosive environments, freedom from radio interference, or very high speed.

Problems

Section 1: Three-Phase Induction Motors

***P1.** A 60-Hz induction motor is needed to drive a load at approximately 850 rpm. How many poles should the motor have? What is the slip of this motor for a speed of 850 rpm?

***P2.** A four-pole induction motor drives a load at 2500 rpm. This is to be accomplished by using an electronic converter to convert a 400-V dc source into a set of three-phase ac voltages. Find the frequency required for the ac voltages assuming that the slip is 4 percent. The load requires 2 hp. If the dc-to-ac converter has a power efficiency of 88 percent and the motor has a power efficiency of 80 percent, estimate the current taken from the dc source.

***P3.** It is necessary to reduce the voltage applied to an induction motor as the frequency is reduced from the rated value. Explain why this is so.

***P4.** The air-gap flux density of a two-pole induction motor is given by

$$B = B_m \cos(\omega t - \theta)$$

where B_m is the peak flux density, θ is the angular displacement around the air gap, and we have assumed clockwise rotation. Give the corresponding expression for the flux density of a four-pole induction motor; of a six-pole induction motor.

P5. Explain why induction motors develop zero torque at synchronous speed.

P6. Prepare a table that shows synchronous speeds for three-phase induction motors operating at 50 Hz. Consider motors having eight or fewer poles. Repeat for 400-Hz motors.

P7. The magnetic field produced in the air gap of an induction motor by the stator windings is given by $B = B_m \cos(\omega t - 2\theta)$, in which θ is angular displacement in the counterclockwise direction as illustrated in Figure 4. How many poles does this machine have? Given that the frequency of the source is 50 Hz, determine the speed of rotation of the field. Does the field rotate clockwise or counterclockwise? Repeat for a field given by $B = B_m \cos(\omega t + 3\theta)$.

P8. Consider the induction motor shown in Figure 7. Redraw the figure showing the current directions in the rotor conductors, the magnetic rotor poles, and the direction of the developed torque if a prime mover drives the rotor at a speed higher than synchronous speed. In this case, does the machine operate as a motor or as a generator?

P9. A 10-hp six-pole 60-Hz three-phase induction motor runs at 1160 rpm under full-load conditions. Determine the slip and the frequency of the rotor currents at full load. Also estimate the speed if the load torque drops in half.

P10. In a proposed design for an electric automobile, the shaft of a four-pole three-phase induction motor is connected directly to the drive axle; in other words, there is no gear train. The outside diameter of the tires is 20 inches. Instead of a transmission, an electronic converter produces variable-frequency three-phase ac from a 48-V battery. Assuming negligible slip, find the range of frequencies needed for speeds ranging from 5 to 70 mph. The vehicle, including batteries and occupants, has a mass of 1000 kg. The power efficiency of the dc-to-ac converter is 85 percent, and the power efficiency of the motor is 89 percent. **a.** Find the current taken from the battery as a function of time while accelerating from 0 to 40 mph uniformly (i.e., acceleration is constant) in 10 seconds. Neglect wind load and road friction. **b.** Repeat assuming that the vehicle is accelerated with constant power.

P11. Consider the two-pole two-phase induction motor having two windings displaced 90° in space shown in Figure P11. The fields produced by the windings are given by $B_a = Ki_a(t)\cos(\theta)$ and $B_b = Ki_b(t)\cos(\theta - 90°)$.

* Denotes that answers are contained in the Student Solutions files. See Appendix "On-Line Student Resources" for more information about accessing the Student Solutions.

The two-phase source produces currents given by $i_a(t) = I_m \cos(\omega t)$ and $i_b(t) = I_m \cos(\omega t - 90°)$. Show that the total field rotates. Determine the speed and direction of rotation. Also find the maximum flux density of the rotating field in terms of K and I_m.

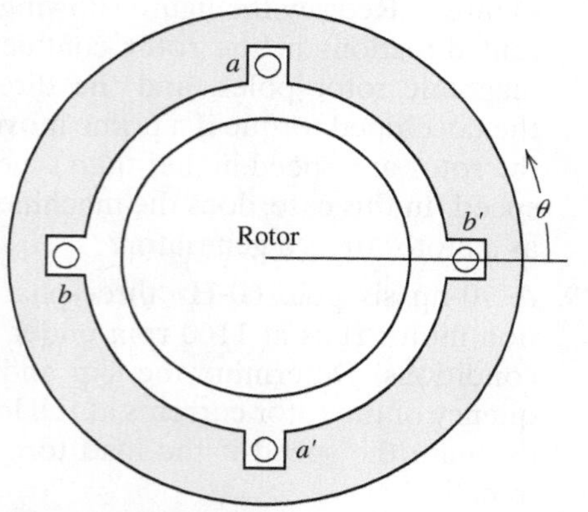

Figure P11 Two-phase induction motor.

P12. Suppose that we could use superconducting material for the rotor conductors (i.e., rotor conductors with inductance and zero resistance) of an induction motor. Would this improve the performance of the motor? Explain by considering the torque–speed characteristic.

P13. Consider the two-pole two-phase induction motor having two windings displaced 90° in space shown in Figure P11. The fields produced by the windings are given by $B_a = Ki_a(t)\cos(\theta)$ and $B_b = Ki_b(t)\cos(\theta - 90°)$. The two-phase source produces currents given by $i_a(t) = I_m \cos(2\omega t)$ and $i_b(t) = I_m \cos(2\omega t + 90°)$. Show that the total field rotates. Determine the speed and direction of rotation. Also find the maximum flux density of the rotating field in terms of K and I_m.

Section 2: Equivalent-Circuit and Performance Calculations for Induction Motors

***P14.** Sketch the torque–speed characteristic of a delta-connected 220-V-rms 5-hp four-pole 60-Hz three-phase induction motor. Estimate values and label key features for things such as the full-load running speed, the full-load torque, the pull-out torque, and the starting torque. Estimate the full-load line current and the starting line current.

***P15.** Sometimes, to reduce starting current to reasonable values, induction motors are started with reduced source voltage. When the motor approaches its operating speed, the voltage is increased to full rated value. Compute the starting line current and torque for the motor of Example 2 if it is started with a source voltage of 220 V. Compare results with the values found in the example, and comment.

***P16.** A certain four-pole 240-V-rms 60-Hz delta-connected three-phase induction motor has

$$R_s = 1\ \Omega \qquad R'_r = 0.5\ \Omega$$
$$X_s = 1.5\ \Omega \qquad X'_r = 0.8\ \Omega$$
$$X_m = 40\ \Omega$$

Under load, the machine operates at 1728 rpm and has rotational losses of 200 W. Neglecting the rotational losses, find the no-load speed, line current, and power factor for the motor.

***P17.** A certain six-pole 440-V-rms 60-Hz three-phase delta-connected induction motor has

$$R_s = 0.08\ \Omega \qquad R'_r = 0.06\ \Omega$$
$$X_s = 0.20\ \Omega \qquad X'_r = 0.15\ \Omega$$
$$X_m = 7.5\ \Omega$$

Neglecting the rotational losses, find the no-load speed, line current, and power factor for the motor.

***P18.** A 440-V-rms (line-to-line) 60-Hz three-phase wye-connected induction motor draws 16.8 A at a power factor of 80 percent lagging. The stator copper losses are 350 W, the rotor copper loss is 120 W, and the rotational losses are 400 W. Find the power crossing the air gap P_{ag}, the developed power P_{dev}, the output power P_{out}, and the efficiency.

***P19.** A two-pole 60-Hz induction motor produces an output power of 5 hp at a speed of 3500 rpm. With no load, the speed is 3598 rpm. Assume that the rotational torque loss is independent of speed. Find the rotational power loss at 3500 rpm.

P20. What are the two basic types of construction used for the rotors of induction motors? Which is the most rugged?

P21. List five important specifications to be considered (besides cost) in selecting induction motors. Indicate the optimum value or whether a high or low value is desirable for each specification.

P22. A 60-Hz wound-rotor induction motor operates at 40 percent slip with added rotor resistance to achieve speed control. The stator resistance is negligible compared with the rotor resistance. Neglect rotational losses. Find the efficiency of this motor.

P23. An eight-pole 60-Hz ac induction motor produces an output power of 2 hp and has rotational losses of 100 W at a speed of 850 rpm. Determine the slip, the frequency of the stator currents, the frequency of the rotor currents, and the rotor copper loss.

P24. A certain six-pole 440-V-rms 60-Hz three-phase delta-connected induction motor has

$$R_s = 0.08\ \Omega \qquad R'_r = 0.06\ \Omega$$
$$X_s = 0.20\ \Omega \qquad X'_r = 0.15\ \Omega$$
$$X_m = 7.5\ \Omega$$

Neglecting losses, find the starting torque and starting line current for the motor.

P25. Another method that is used to limit starting current is to place additional resistance in series with the stator windings during starting. The resistance is switched out of the circuit when the motor approaches full speed. Compute the resistance that must be placed in series with each phase of the motor of Examples 1 and 2 to limit the starting line current to $50\sqrt{3}$ A rms. Determine the starting torque with this resistance in place. Compare the starting torque with the value found in Example 2 and comment.

P26. A certain four-pole 240-V-rms 60-Hz delta-connected three-phase induction motor has

$$R_s = 1\ \Omega \qquad R'_r = 0.5\ \Omega$$
$$X_s = 1.5\ \Omega \qquad X'_r = 0.8\ \Omega$$
$$X_m = 40\ \Omega$$

Under load, the machine operates at 1728 rpm and has rotational losses of 200 W. Find the power factor, output power, copper losses, output torque, and efficiency.

P27. A certain four-pole 240-V-rms 60-Hz delta-connected three-phase induction motor has

$$R_s = 1\ \Omega \qquad R'_r = 0.5\ \Omega$$
$$X_s = 1.5\ \Omega \qquad X'_r = 0.8\ \Omega$$
$$X_m = 40\ \Omega$$

Neglecting losses, find the starting torque and starting line current for the motor.

P28. A certain six-pole 440-V-rms 60-Hz three-phase delta-connected induction motor has

$$R_s = 0.08\ \Omega \qquad R'_r = 0.06\ \Omega$$
$$X_s = 0.20\ \Omega \qquad X'_r = 0.15\ \Omega$$
$$X_m = 7.5\ \Omega$$

Under load, the machine operates with a slip of 4 percent and has rotational losses of 2 kW. Determine the power factor, output power, copper losses, output torque, and efficiency.

P29. A 2-hp six-pole 60-Hz delta-connected three-phase induction motor is rated for 1140 rpm, 220 V rms, and 5.72 A rms (line current) at an 80 percent lagging power factor. Find the full-load efficiency.

P30. The torque–speed characteristics of a 60-Hz induction motor and a load are shown in Figure P30. How many poles does the motor have? In steady-state operation, find the speed, the slip, the output power, and the rotor copper loss. Neglect rotational losses.

P31. The torque–speed characteristics of a 60-Hz induction motor and a load are shown in Figure P30. The rotational inertia of the motor and load is 5 kgm^2. Estimate the time required for the motor to accelerate the load from a standing start to 1000 rpm. (*Hint:* The difference between the motor output torque and the load torque is approximately 25 Nm in the range of speeds under consideration.)

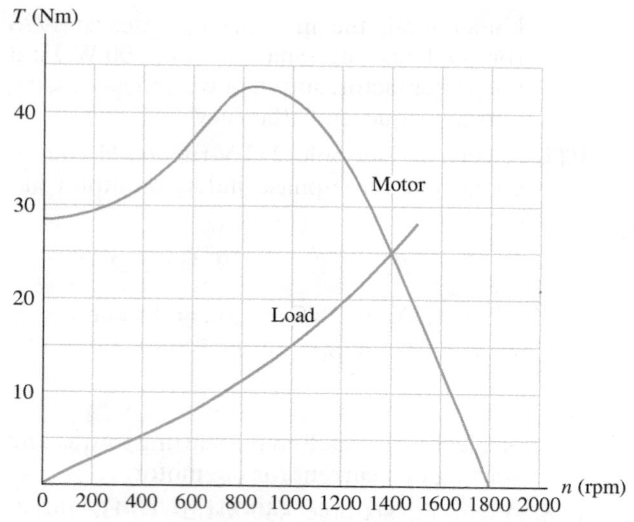

Figure P30

P32. A four-pole 60-Hz 240-V-rms induction motor operates at 1750 rpm and produces 2 hp of output power. The load is a hoist that requires constant torque versus speed. Assume that the motor is operating in the range for which torque is proportional to slip and write an equation for motor torque in terms of slip when operating at rated voltage. Then modify the equation for operation from a 220-V-rms source. Estimate the speed when operating the hoist from a 220-V-rms source.

Section 3: Synchronous Machines

***P33.** List several methods for starting synchronous motors.

***P34.** A synchronous motor is running at 75 percent of rated load with unity power factor. If the load increases to the rated output power, how do the following quantities change? **a.** field current; **b.** mechanical speed; **c.** output torque; **d.** armature current; **e.** power factor; **f.** torque angle.

***P35.** A 10-pole 60-Hz synchronous motor operates with a developed power of 100 hp, which is its rated full load. The torque angle is 20°. Plot the torque–speed characteristic to scale, showing the values for rated torque and for the pull-out torque.

***P36.** A certain 480-V-rms delta-connected synchronous motor operates with zero developed power and draws a phase current of 15 A rms, which lags the voltage. The synchronous reactance is 5 Ω. The field current is 5 A. Assuming that the rotor field magnitude is proportional to field current, what field current is needed to reduce the armature current to zero?

***P37.** **a.** A 12-pole 60-Hz synchronous motor drives a 10-pole synchronous machine that acts as a generator. What is the frequency of the voltages induced in the armature windings of the generator? **b.** Suppose that we need to drive a load at exactly 1000 rpm. The power available is 60-Hz three-phase. Diagram a system of synchronous machines to drive the load, specifying the number of poles and frequency of operation for each. (Multiple correct answers exist.)

P38. Sketch the V curve for a synchronous motor. Label the axes. Indicate where the power factor is lagging and where it is leading. Draw the phasor diagram corresponding to the minimum point on the V curve.

P39. What is a synchronous capacitor? What is the practical benefit of using one?

P40. Give two situations for which a synchronous motor would be a better choice than an induction motor in an industrial application.

P41. An eight-pole 240-V-rms 60-Hz delta-connected synchronous motor operates with a constant developed power of 50 hp, unity power factor, and a torque angle of 15°. Then, the field current is increased such that B_r increases in magnitude by 20 percent. Find the new torque angle and power factor. Is the new power factor leading or lagging?

P42. A six-pole 60-Hz synchronous motor is operating with a developed power of 5 hp and a torque angle of 5°. Find the speed and developed torque. Suppose that the load increases such that the developed torque doubles. Find the new torque angle. Find the pull-out torque and maximum developed power for this machine.

P43. A synchronous motor is running at 100 percent of rated load with unity power factor. If the field current is increased, how do the following quantities change? **a.** output power; **b.** mechanical speed; **c.** output torque; **d.** armature current; **e.** power factor; **f.** torque angle.

P44. A 240-V-rms 100-hp 60-Hz six-pole delta-connected synchronous motor operates with a developed power (including losses) of 100 hp and a power factor of 85 percent lagging. The synchronous reactance is $X_s = 0.5\ \Omega$. The field current is $I_f = 10$ A. What must the new field current be to produce 100 percent power factor? Assume that magnetic saturation does not occur so that B_r is proportional to I_f.

P45. A six-pole 240-V-rms 60-Hz delta-connected synchronous motor operates with a developed power of 50 hp, unity power factor, and a torque angle of 15°. Find the phase current. Suppose that the load is removed so that the developed power is zero. Find the new values of the current, power factor, and torque angle.

P46. A 240-V-rms delta-connected 100-hp 60-Hz six-pole synchronous motor operates with a developed power (including losses) of 50 hp and a power factor of 90 percent leading. The synchronous reactance is $X_s = 0.5\ \Omega$. **a.** Find the speed and developed torque. **b.** Determine the values of $\mathbf{I}_a$, $\mathbf{E}_r$, and the torque angle. **c.** Suppose that the excitation remains constant and the load torque increases until the developed power is 100 hp. Determine the new values of $\mathbf{I}_a$, $\mathbf{E}_r$, the torque angle, and the power factor.

P47. Suppose that a synchronous motor is instrumented to measure its armature current, armature voltage, and field current. The field circuit contains a rheostat so that the field current can be adjusted. Discuss how to adjust the field current to obtain unity power factor.

P48. A 60-Hz 480-V-rms 200-hp delta-connected synchronous motor runs under no-load conditions. The field current is adjusted for minimum line current, which turns out to be 16.45 A rms. The per-phase armature impedance is $R_s + jX_s = 0.05 + j1.4$. (Until now in this chapter, we have neglected R_s. However, it is significant in efficiency calculations.) Estimate the efficiency of the machine under full-load conditions operating with 90 percent leading power factor.

Section 4: Single-Phase Motors

***P49.** A 1-hp 120-V-rms 1740-rpm 60-Hz capacitor-start induction-run motor draws a current of 10.2 A rms at full load and has an efficiency of 80 percent. Find the values of **a.** the power factor and **b.** the impedance of the motor at full load. **c.** Determine the number of poles that the motor has.

***P50.** A farm house is located at the end of a country road in northern Michigan. The Thévenin impedance seen looking back into the power line from the electrical distribution panel is $0.2 + j0.2\ \Omega$. The Thévenin voltage is 240 V rms 60 Hz ac. A 2-hp 240-V-rms capacitor-start motor is used for pumping water. We want to estimate the voltage drop observed in the house when the motor starts. Typically, such a motor has a power factor of 75 percent and an efficiency of 80 percent at full load. Also, the starting current can be estimated as six times the full-load current. Estimate the worst-case percentage voltage drop observed when the motor starts.

P51. The winding impedances under starting conditions for a 60-Hz 0.5-hp motor are shown in Figure P51. Determine the capacitance C needed so that the phase angle between the currents $\mathbf{I}_a$ and $\mathbf{I}_m$ is 90°.

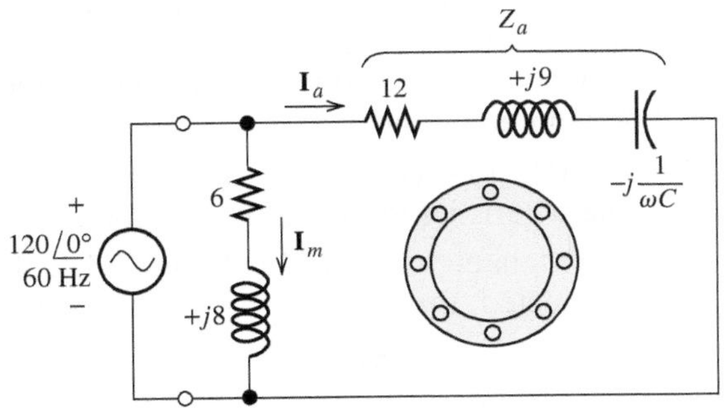

Figure P51

P52. Assuming small slip, the output power of a single-phase induction motor can be written as $P_{\text{out}} = K_1 s - K_2$, where K_1 and K_2 are constants and s is the slip. A 0.5-hp motor has a full-load speed of 3500 rpm and a no-load speed of 3595 rpm. Determine the speed for 0.2-hp output.

P53. How could the direction of rotation of a single-phase capacitor-start induction motor be reversed?

P54. Which would be more suitable for use in a portable vacuum cleaner, an induction motor or a universal motor? For the fan in a home heating system? For the compressor motor in a refrigerator? For a variable-speed hand-held drill? Give the reasons for your answer in each case.

Section 5: Stepper Motors and Brushless DC Motors

P55. Sketch the cross-section of a reluctance stepper motor that has six stator poles and eight rotor poles. Your sketch should be similar to Figure 33(a). Label the windings and specify the sequence of activation for clockwise rotation. What is the rotation angle per step?

P56. Use the Web to find two or more sources for stepper motors.

P57. List several advantages of brushless dc motors compared to conventional dc motors.

Practice Test

Here is a practice test you can use to check your comprehension of the most important concepts in this chapter. Answers can be found in Appendix "Answers for the Practice Tests" and complete solutions are included in the Student Solutions files. See Appendix "On-Line Student Resources" for more information about the Student Solutions.

T1. **a.** Qualitatively describe the magnetic field set up in the air gap of a four-pole three-phase induction motor by the currents in the stator windings. **b.** Give an equation for the field intensity as a function of angular position around the gap and time, defining the terms in your equation.

T2. Besides low cost, what are five desirable characteristics for an induction motor?

T3. A certain eight-pole, 240-V-rms, 60-Hz, wye-connected, three-phase induction motor has

$$R_s = 0.5\,\Omega \qquad R'_r = 0.5\,\Omega$$
$$X_s = 2\,\Omega \qquad X'_r = 0.8\,\Omega$$
$$X_m = 40\,\Omega$$

Under load, the machine operates at 864 rpm and has rotational losses of 150 W. Find the power factor, output power, line current, copper losses, output torque, and efficiency.

T4. We have a 20-hp, eight-pole, 60-Hz, three-phase induction motor that runs at 850 rpm under full-load conditions. What are the values of the slip and the frequency of the rotor currents at full load? Also, estimate the speed if the load torque drops by 20 percent.

T5. In one or two paragraphs, describe the construction and principles of operation for a six-pole 60-Hz three-phase synchronous motor.

T6. We have a six-pole, 440-V-rms, 60-Hz delta-connected synchronous motor operating with a constant developed power of 20 hp, unity power factor, and a torque angle of 10°. Then, the field current is reduced such that B_r is reduced in magnitude by 25 percent. Find the new torque angle and power factor. Is the new power factor leading or lagging?

ANSWERS FOR THE PRACTICE TESTS

Complete solutions for the practice tests are included in the Student Solutions files. See Appendix "On-Line Student Resources" for information on how to access these files.

T1. **a.** The magnetic field set up in the air gap of a four-pole three-phase induction motor consists of four magnetic poles spaced 90° from one another in alternating order (i.e., north-south-north-south). The field points from the stator toward the rotor under the north poles and in the opposite direction under the south poles. The poles rotate with time at synchronous speed around the axis of the motor. **b.** $B_{gap} = B_m \cos(\omega t - 2\theta)$ in which B_m is the peak field intensity, ω is the angular frequency of the three-phase source, and θ denotes angular position around the gap.

T2. Five of the most important characteristics for an induction motor are: **1.** nearly unity power factor; **2.** high starting torque; **3.** close to 100 percent efficiency; **4.** low starting current; **5.** high pull-out torque.

T3. power factor = 88.16 percent lagging; $P_{out} = 3.429$ kW; $I_{line} = 10.64$ A rms; $P_s = 169.7$ W; $P_r = 149.1$ W; $T_{out} = 37.90$ Nm; $\eta = 87.97$ percent.

T4. $s = 5.556$ percent; $f_{slip} = 3.333$ Hz; 860 rpm.

T5. The stator of a six-pole synchronous motor contains a set of windings (collectively known as the armature) that are energized by a three-phase ac source. These windings produce six magnetic poles spaced 60° from one another in alternating order (i.e., north-south-north-south-north-south). The field points from the stator toward the rotor under the north stator poles and in the opposite direction under the south stator poles. The poles rotate with time at synchronous speed (1200 rpm) around the axis of the motor.

The rotor contains windings that carry dc currents and set up six north and south magnetic poles evenly spaced around the rotor. When driving a load, the rotor spins at synchronous speed with the north poles of the rotor lagging slightly behind and attracted by the south poles of the stator. (In some cases, the rotor may be composed of permanent magnets.)

T6. $\delta_2 = 13.39°$; power factor = 56.25 percent lagging.

ON-LINE STUDENT RESOURCES

Users of the text can access the Student Solutions Manual (and other folders mentioned below) in electronic form by following links starting from the website:

`www.pearsonhighered.com/hambley`

The MATLAB folder contains m-files. Except for the examples that use the Symbolic Toolbox, these files work equally well with MathScript, which is sometimes included with the LabVIEW program. The Hambley MathScript folder contains the m-files that work with MathScript.

The Virtual Instruments folder contains LabVIEW programs.

APPENDIX

Complex Numbers

Any sinusoidal signal, like the one shown in Figure 1, can be represented by its amplitude and its phase. These signals can be expressed using complex numbers.

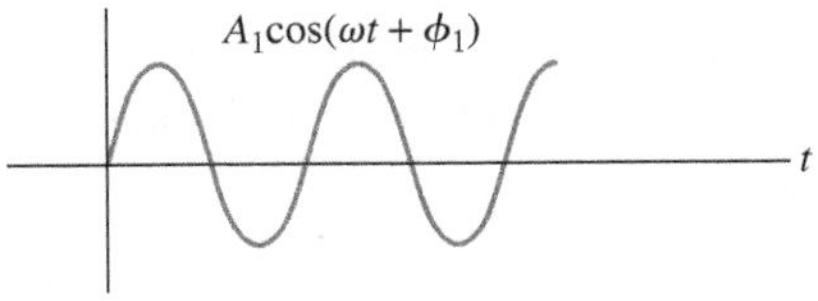

FIGURE 1 A sinusoidal signal.

The signal shown in Figure 1 can also be expressed in exponential form, that is, $A_1 \cos(\omega t + \phi_1) = \text{Re}\{A_1 e^{j\omega t} e^{j\phi_1}\}$. Here, $A_1 e^{j\phi_1}$ is the complex number in exponential form.

From the 13th century to the early 17th century, numbers were only used to represent real things, for example, ONE piece of cake or TWO cars, as seen below.

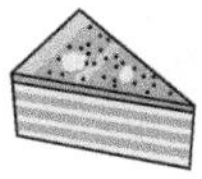

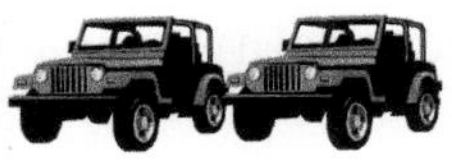

At that time, a mathematician solving $X^2 = 4$ would have arrived at a single solution, $X = 2$.

In the middle of the 17th century, negative numbers were added to the number system to represent things like debt, height below sea level, for example, −2\$, −30 m, and so on.

Once negative numbers appeared, solving $X^2 = 4$ results in the solutions $X_1 = 2$ and $X_2 = -2$.

By the end of 18th century, the notion of complex numbers had been developed in the mind of scientists. However, the scientists could not intuitively explain the concept using real identities.

Now that complex numbers were available, solving $X^2 = -4$ resulted in the solution $X = \pm j2$, that is, $(j2)^2 = -4$, $(-j2)^2 = -4$, where $j = \sqrt{-1}$.

DEFINITION OF A COMPLEX NUMBER

First, $j^2 = -1$; correspondingly $j = \sqrt{-1}$. Here, j represents the square root of −1. Sometimes, symbol i is used instead of j.

Second, an *imaginary number* is defined as the product of a real number and the imaginary operator j; for example, $j5$ is an imaginary number, or, a pure imaginary number.

A *complex number* is defined as the sum of a real number and an imaginary number, that is, $a + jb$, where a and b are real numbers. $2 + j3$ and $1.1 + j5.3$ are examples of complex numbers. A complex number, for example, $Z = a + jb$ is said to have a real part a and an imaginary part b.

Actually, a *real number* is simply a complex number with an imaginary part equal to zero, that is, $a + j0$. For example, $1.1 + j0 = 1.1$, $2.4 + j0 = 2.4$ . . . . A pure imaginary number is a complex number with a real part equal to zero.

A *complex number* can be expressed in rectangular form $a + bj$, in exponential form $re^{j\theta}$, or in polar form $r\angle\theta$.

The addition, subtraction, multiplication, and division of complex numbers in rectangular form can be accomplished in a way similar to algebraic arithmetic.

From Appendix C of *Electrical Engineering: Concepts and Applications,* First Edition. S. A. Reza Zekavat.

OPERATIONS OF COMPLEX NUMBERS IN RECTANGULAR FORM

Assume: $Z_1 = a + jb$ and $Z_2 = c + jd$.

- The conjugate of the complex number, Z_1, is (changing the sign of the imaginary part):

$$Z_1{}^* = a - jb, \text{ where * represents the conjugate.}$$

- If $Z_1 = Z_2$, then $a = c$ and $b = d$.

If two complex numbers are equal, then each number's real part and imaginary part must be equal to the real part and imaginary part of the other number, respectively.

- Addition: $Z_1 + Z_2 = (a + c) + j(b + d)$.

To add two complex numbers, add the real and the imaginary parts of them, respectively.

- Subtraction: $Z_1 - Z_2 = (a - c) + j(b - d)$.

To subtract two complex numbers, subtract the real part of Z_2 from the real part of Z_1, and subtract the imaginary part of Z_2 from the imaginary part of Z_1.

- Multiplication: $Z_1 \times Z_2 = (ac - bd) + j(bc + ad)$.

To multiply two complex numbers, use the same rules as in the algebraic arithmetic.

$$Z_1 \times Z_2 = (a + jb)(c + jd) = ac + jad + jbc - bd = (ac - bd) + j(bc + ad).$$

- Division:

$$\frac{Z_1}{Z_2} = \frac{a + jb}{c + jd} = \frac{(a + jb)(c - jd)}{(c + jd)(c - jd)} = \frac{(ac + bd) + j(bc - ad)}{c^2 + d^2}$$

To divide two complex numbers, multiply the numerator and the denominator by the complex conjugate of the denominator.

EXAMPLE 1 Operations of Complex Numbers

For the given complex numbers: $Z_1 = 3 + j4$; $Z_2 = 9 + j12$.

- Addition: $Z_1 + Z_2 = (3 + 9) + j(4 + 12) = 12 + j16$
- Subtraction: $Z_1 - Z_2 = (3 - 9) + j(4 - 12) = -6 - j8$
- Multiplication: $Z_1 \times Z_2 = 27 + j36 + j36 - 48 = -21 + j72$
- Division: $\frac{Z_1}{Z_2} = \frac{(3 + j4)(9 - j12)}{(9 + j12)(9 - j12)} = \frac{75}{81 + 144} = \frac{75}{225} = \frac{1}{3}$
- Conjugate of Z_1: $Z_1^* = 3 - j4$

COMPLEX PLANE

A complex number can be represented in a *complex plane*, like the one shown in Figure 2 (*x*-axis: real part; *y*-axis: imaginary part).

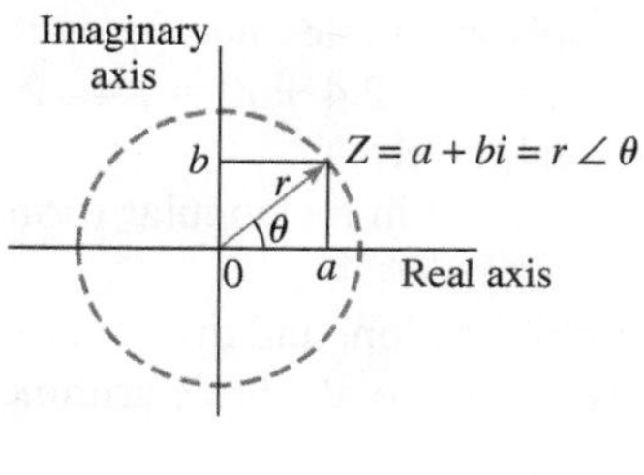

FIGURE 2 A Complex Plane.

A complex number has three forms:

Rectangular Form: $Z_1 = a + jb$

Exponential Form: $Z_1 = re^{j\theta}$

$$\begin{cases} r = \sqrt{a^2 + b^2} \\ \theta = \tan^{-1}\dfrac{b}{a} \end{cases} \qquad (1)$$
$$\begin{cases} a = r \cdot \cos\theta \\ b = r \cdot \sin\theta \end{cases}$$

Polar Form: $Z_1 = r\angle\theta$

In the complex plane, the length, r, of the arrow represents the magnitude of the complex number, and θ is the angle between the arrow and the positive real axis.

Using Equation (1), a complex number can be converted from rectangular form to exponential form, or vice versa. It is easy to convert the exponential form to polar form, because both forms use magnitude and angle to express the complex number.

EXAMPLE 2 Rectangular Form to Exponential and Polar Form Conversion

Convert the complex number $Z_1 = 4 + j3$ from rectangular form to exponential and polar forms.

SOLUTION

Using Equation (1):

$$r = \sqrt{3^2 + 4^2} = 5, \quad \text{and}$$

$$\tan\theta = \frac{3}{4} = 0.75, \quad \theta = \tan^{-1}0.75 = 36.87°$$

Therefore:

$$Z_1 = 5e^{j36.87°}$$

The corresponding polar form is:

$$Z_1 = 5\angle 36.87°$$

EXAMPLE 3 Exponential to Rectangular and Polar Form Conversion

Convert the complex number $Z_1 = 2.828e^{j45°}$ from exponential form to rectangular form and polar forms.

SOLUTION

The polar form for $Z_1 = 2.828e^{j45°}$ is:

$$Z_1 = 2.828\angle 45°$$

Using Equation (1):

$$a = r\cos\theta = 2.828 \times \cos(45°) = 2$$
$$b = r\sin\theta = 2.828 \times \sin(45°) = 2$$

Therefore, the rectangular form is:

$$Z_1 = a + jb = 2 + j2$$

EXAMPLE 4 Polar to Exponential and Rectangular Form Conversion

Convert the complex number $Z_1 = 10\angle 60°$ from polar form to exponential and rectangular forms.

SOLUTION

The exponential form for $Z_1 = 10\angle 60°$ is:

$$Z_1 = 10e^{j60°}$$

Using Equation (1):

$$a = r\cos\theta = 10 \times \cos(60°) = 5$$

$$b = r\sin\theta = 10 \times \sin(60°) = 8.66$$

Therefore, the rectangular form is:

$$Z_1 = a + jb = 5 + j8.66$$

OPERATIONS IN EXPONENTIAL AND POLAR FORMS

Assume that complex numbers Z_1 and Z_2 are expressed in exponential form: $Z_1 = r_1e^{j\theta}$, $Z_2 = r_2e^{j\phi}$.

- Complex conjugates are:

$$Z_1^* = r_1e^{-j\theta} = r_1\angle(-\theta) \quad \text{and} \quad Z_2^* = r_2e^{-j\phi} = r_2\angle(-\phi)$$

- Addition and subtraction:

  If the complex numbers are expressed in exponential or polar form, they need to be converted into rectangular form for addition and subtraction.

- Multiplication:

$$Z_1 \times Z_2 = r_1e^{j\theta} \cdot r_2e^{j\phi} = r_1r_2e^{j(\theta+\phi)} = r_1r_2\angle(\theta + \phi)$$

  To multiply two complex numbers in exponential or polar form, multiply the magnitude of them and add the angles.

- Division:

$$\frac{Z_1}{Z_2} = \frac{r_1e^{j\theta}}{r_2e^{j\phi}} = \frac{r_1\angle\theta}{r_2\angle\phi} = \frac{r_1}{r_2}\angle(\theta - \phi)$$

  To divide two complex numbers in exponential or polar form, divide the magnitude of them and subtract the angle of the divisor from the angle of the dividend.

- Power, n, of a complex number:

$$Z_1^n = (r_1e^{j\theta})^n = r_1^n e^{jn\theta} = r_1^n\angle n\theta,$$

  The magnitude is powered to n and the n of the angles are added together.

- n root of a complex number:

$$Z_1^{\frac{1}{n}} = (r_1e^{j\theta})^{\frac{1}{n}} = r_1^{\frac{1}{n}} e^{j\theta\cdot\frac{1}{n}} = r_1^{\frac{1}{n}}\angle\left(\frac{\theta + 2k\pi}{n}\right), \quad k = 0, \pm 1, \pm 2, \ldots$$

EXAMPLE 5 Multiplicaton and Division in Polar Form

Assume $Z_1 = 2.828\angle 45°$ and $Z_2 = 3\angle 30°$, calculate Z_1Z_2 and Z_1/Z_2.

SOLUTION

$$Z_1 \times Z_2 = (2.828 \times 3)\angle(45° + 30°) = 8.484\angle 75°$$

$$\frac{Z_1}{Z_2} = \frac{2.828}{3}\angle(45° - 30°) = \frac{2.828}{3}\angle 15° = 0.9427\angle 15°$$

EXAMPLE 6 Complex Operations

Assume $Z_1 = 3\angle 45°$, $Z_2 = 4\angle 45°$, calculate $Z_1 + Z_2$, Z_1Z_2, and Z_1/Z_2.

SOLUTION

First, convert Z_1 and Z_2 to rectangular form, then add them.

Using Equation (B.1):

The real part a of the Z_1 is:

$$a = 3 \times \cos(45°) = 2.1213$$

The imaginary part b of the Z_1 is:

$$b = 3 \times \sin(45°) = 2.1213$$

The real part c of the Z_2 is:

$$c = 4 \times \cos(45°) = 2.8284$$

The imaginary part d of the Z_2 is:

$$d = 4 \times \sin(45°) = 2.8284$$

Therefore:

$$Z_1 + Z_2 = 2.1213 + j2.1213 + 2.8284 + j2.8284 = 4.9497 + j4.9497$$

Convert the result to polar form:

$$Z_1 + Z_2 = 7\angle 45°$$

$$Z_1 \times Z_2 = (3 \times 4)\angle(45° + 45°) = 12\angle 90°$$

$$\frac{Z_1}{Z_2} = \frac{3}{4}\angle(45° - 45°) = 0.75\angle 0°$$

EULER'S IDENTITY

Euler's identities state that:

$$e^{j\theta} = \cos\theta + j\sin\theta \quad \textbf{(2)}$$

$$e^{-j\theta} = \cos\theta - j\sin\theta \quad \textbf{(3)}$$

$$\cos\theta = \frac{e^{j\theta} + e^{-j\theta}}{2} \quad \textbf{(4)}$$

$$\sin\theta = \frac{e^{j\theta} - e^{-j\theta}}{j2} \quad \textbf{(5)}$$

Using the Euler's identities, the cosine and sinusoidal functions can be expressed as complex numbers, and the calculation can be simplified.

EXAMPLE 7 Application of Euler's Identity

Calculate e^{1-j1}.

SOLUTION

Method 1: Angle in radians:

$$e^{1-j1} = e^1 \cdot e^{-j1} = e^1(\cos 1 - j\sin 1) = 2.71828(0.5403 - j0.8415) = 1.469 - j2.29$$

Method 2: Angle in degrees:

$$e^{1-j1} = e^1 \cdot e^{-j1} = e^1(\cos 1 - j\sin 1) = e^1(\cos 57.3° - j\sin 57.3°) = 2.71828(0.5403 - j0.8415)$$
$$= 1.469 - j2.29$$

Here, "1" is the angle in radians. To convert radians into degrees or vice versa, use the following equation:

$$\frac{\theta_{\text{rad}}}{\theta_{\text{deg}}} = \frac{\pi}{180}$$

where, $\pi = 3.1415926$.

SUMMARY

A complex number can be expressed as:

$$Z_1 = a + jb = \text{Re}[Z_1] + j\text{Im}[Z_1] = re^{j\theta} = \sqrt{a^2+b^2}e^{j\tan^{-1}(b/a)} = \sqrt{a^2+b^2}\angle\tan^{-1}(b/a).$$

Appendix

Complex Numbers

Complex numbers were invented to permit the extraction of the square roots of negative numbers. Complex numbers simplify the solution of problems that would otherwise be very difficult. The equation $x^2 + 8x + 41 = 0$, for example, has no solution in a number system that excludes complex numbers. These numbers, and the ability to manipulate them algebraically, are extremely useful in circuit analysis.

1 Notation

There are two ways to designate a complex number: with the cartesian, or rectangular, form or with the polar, or trigonometric, form. In the **rectangular form**, a complex number is written in terms of its real and imaginary components; hence

$$n = a + jb, \tag{1}$$

where a is the real component, b is the imaginary component, and j is by definition $\sqrt{-1}$.[1]

In the **polar form**, a complex number is written in terms of its magnitude (or modulus) and angle (or argument); hence

$$n = ce^{j\theta} \tag{2}$$

where c is the magnitude, θ is the angle, e is the base of the natural logarithm, and, as before, $j = \sqrt{-1}$. In the literature, the symbol $\underline{/\theta^\circ}$ is frequently used in place of $e^{j\theta}$; that is, the polar form is written

$$n = c\underline{/\theta^\circ}. \tag{3}$$

Although Eq. 3 is more convenient in printing text material, Eq. 2 is of primary importance in mathematical operations because the rules for manipulating an exponential quantity are well known. For example, because $(y^x)^n = y^{xn}$, then $(e^{j\theta})^n = e^{jn\theta}$; because $y^{-x} = 1/y^x$, then $e^{-j\theta} = 1/e^{j\theta}$; and so forth.

Because there are two ways of expressing the same complex number, we need to relate one form to the other. The transition from the polar to the rectangular form makes use of Euler's identity:

$$e^{\pm j\theta} = \cos\theta \pm j\sin\theta. \tag{4}$$

[1] You may be more familiar with the notation $i = \sqrt{-1}$. In electrical engineering, i is used as the symbol for current, and hence in electrical engineering literature, j is used to denote $\sqrt{-1}$.

A complex number in polar form can be put in rectangular form by writing

$$\begin{aligned} ce^{j\theta} &= c(\cos\theta + j\sin\theta) \\ &= c\cos\theta + jc\sin\theta) \\ &= a + jb. \end{aligned} \tag{5}$$

The transition from rectangular to polar form makes use of the geometry of the right triangle, namely,

$$\begin{aligned} a + jb &= \left(\sqrt{a^2 + b^2}\right)e^{j\theta} \\ &= ce^{j\theta}, \end{aligned} \tag{6}$$

where

$$\tan\theta = b/a. \tag{7}$$

It is not obvious from Eq. 7 in which quadrant the angle θ lies. The ambiguity can be resolved by a graphical representation of the complex number.

2 The Graphical Representation of a Complex Number

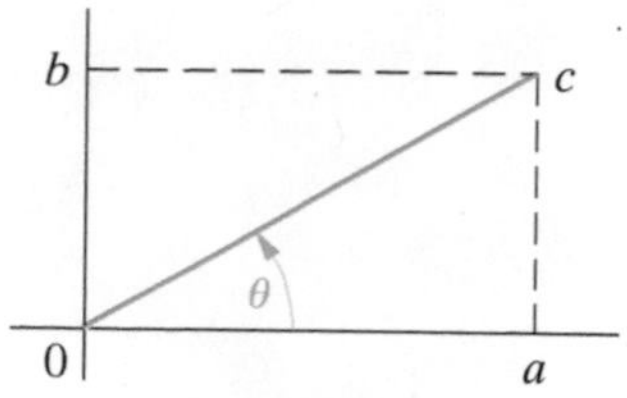

Figure 1 ▲ The graphical representation of $a + jb$ when a and b are both positive.

A complex number is represented graphically on a complex-number plane, which uses the horizontal axis for plotting the real component and the vertical axis for plotting the imaginary component. The angle of the complex number is measured counterclockwise from the positive real axis. The graphical plot of the complex number $n = a + jb = c\ \underline{/\theta°}$, if we assume that a and b are both positive, is shown in Fig. 1.

This plot makes very clear the relationship between the rectangular and polar forms. Any point in the complex-number plane is uniquely defined by giving either its distance from each axis (that is, a and b) or its radial distance from the origin (c) and the angle of the radial measurement θ.

It follows from Fig. 1 that θ is in the first quadrant when a and b are both positive, in the second quadrant when a is negative and b is positive, in the third quadrant when a and b are both negative, and in the fourth quadrant when a is positive and b is negative. These observations are illustrated in Fig. 2, where we have plotted $4 + j3$, $-4 + j3$, $-4 - j3$, and $4 - j3$.

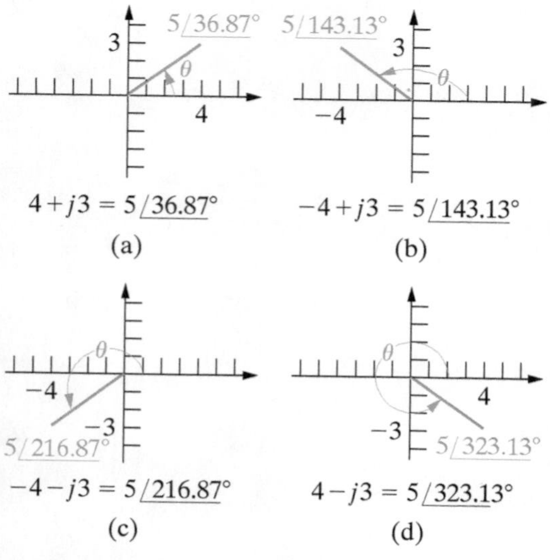

Figure 2 ▲ The graphical representation of four complex numbers.

Note that we can also specify θ as a clockwise angle from the positive real axis. Thus in Fig. 2(c) we could also designate $-4 - j3$ as $5\underline{/-143.13°}$. In Fig. 2(d) we observe that $5\underline{/323.13°} = 5\underline{/-36.87°}$. It is customary to express θ in terms of negative values when θ lies in the third or fourth quadrant.

The graphical interpretation of a complex number also shows the relationship between a complex number and its conjugate. The **conjugate of a complex number** is formed by reversing the sign of its imaginary component. Thus the conjugate of $a + jb$ is $a - jb$, and the conjugate of $-a + jb$ is $-a - jb$. When we write a complex number in polar form, we form its conjugate simply by reversing the sign of the angle θ. Therefore the conjugate of $c\underline{/\theta°}$ is $c\underline{/-\theta°}$. The conjugate of a complex number is designated with an asterisk. In other words, n^* is understood to be the conjugate of n. Figure 3 shows two complex numbers and their conjugates plotted on the complex-number plane.

Note that conjugation simply reflects the complex numbers about the real axis.

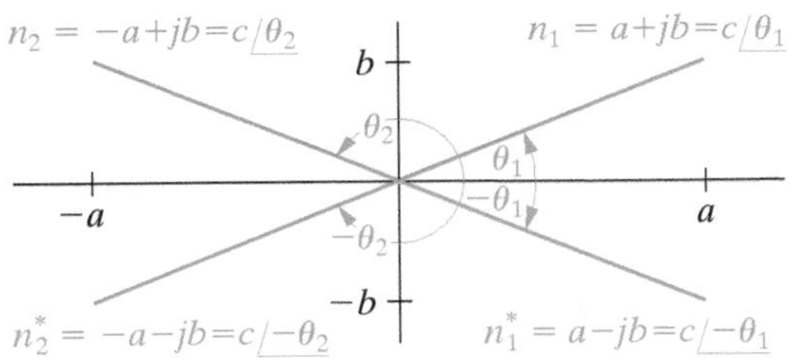

Figure 3 ▲ The complex numbers n_1 and n_2 amd their conjugates n_1^* and n_2^*.

3 Arithmetic Operations

Addition (Subtraction)

To add or subtract complex numbers, we must express the numbers in rectangular form. Addition involves adding the real parts of the complex numbers to form the real part of the sum, and the imaginary parts to form the imaginary part of the sum. Thus, if we are given

$$n_1 = 8 + j16$$

and

$$n_2 = 12 - j3,$$

then

$$n_1 + n_2 = (8 + 12) + j(16 - 3) = 20 + j13.$$

Subtraction follows the same rule. Thus

$$n_2 - n_1 = (12 - 8) + j(-3 - 16) = 4 - j19.$$

If the numbers to be added or subtracted are given in polar form, they are first converted to rectangular form. For example, if

$$n_1 = 10\angle 53.13^\circ$$

and

$$n_2 = 5\angle -135^\circ,$$

then

$$\begin{aligned} n_1 + n_2 &= 6 + j8 - 3.535 - j3.535 \\ &= (6 - 3.535) + j(8 - 3.535) \\ &= 2.465 + j4.465 = 5.10\angle 61.10^\circ, \end{aligned}$$

and

$$\begin{aligned} n_1 - n_2 &= 6 + j8 - (-3.535 - j3.535) \\ &= 9.535 + j11.535 \\ &= 14.966\angle 50.42^\circ. \end{aligned}$$

Multiplication (Division)

Multiplication or division of complex numbers can be carried out with the numbers written in either rectangular or polar form. However, in most cases, the polar form is more convenient. As an example, let's find the product n_1n_2 when $n_1 = 8 + j10$ and $n_2 = 5 - j4$. Using the rectangular form, we have

$$\begin{aligned} n_1n_2 &= (8 + j10)(5 - j4) = 40 - j32 + j50 + 40 \\ &= 80 + j18 \\ &= 82\underline{/12.68^\circ}. \end{aligned}$$

If we use the polar form, the multiplication n_1n_2 becomes

$$\begin{aligned} n_1n_2 &= (12.81\ \underline{/51.34^\circ})(6.40\ \underline{/-38.66^\circ}) \\ &= 82\ \underline{/12.68^\circ} \\ &= 80 + j18. \end{aligned}$$

The first step in dividing two complex numbers in rectangular form is to multiply the numerator and denominator by the conjugate of the denominator. This reduces the denominator to a real number. We then divide the real number into the new numerator. As an example, let's find the value of n_1/n_2, where $n_1 = 6 + j3$ and $n_2 = 3 - j1$. We have

$$\begin{aligned} \frac{n_1}{n_2} &= \frac{6 + j3}{3 - j1} = \frac{(6 + j3)(3 + j1)}{(3 - j1)(3 + j1)} \\ &= \frac{18 + j6 + j9 - 3}{9 + 1} \\ &= \frac{15 + j15}{10} = 1.5 + j1.5 \\ &= 2.12\ \underline{/45^\circ}. \end{aligned}$$

In polar form, the division of n_1 by n_2 is

$$\begin{aligned} \frac{n_1}{n_2} &= \frac{6.71\ \underline{/26.57^\circ}}{3.16\ \underline{/-18.43^\circ}} = 2.12\ \underline{/45^\circ} \\ &= 1.5 + j1.5. \end{aligned}$$

4 Useful Identities

In working with complex numbers and quantities, the following identities are very useful:

$$\pm j^2 = \mp 1, \tag{8}$$

$$(-j)(j) = 1, \tag{9}$$

$$j = \frac{1}{-j}, \tag{10}$$

$$e^{\pm j\pi} = -1, \tag{11}$$

$$e^{\pm j\pi/2} = \pm j. \tag{12}$$

Given that $n = a + jb = c\angle\theta°$, it follows that

$$nn^* = a^2 + b^2 = c^2, \tag{13}$$

$$n + n^* = 2a, \tag{14}$$

$$n - n^* = j2b, \tag{15}$$

$$n/n^* = 1\angle 2\theta°. \tag{16}$$

5 The Integer Power of a Complex Number

To raise a complex number to an integer power k, it is easier to first write the complex number in polar form. Thus

$$\begin{aligned} n^k &= (a + jb)^k \\ &= (ce^{j\theta})^k = c^k e^{jk\theta} \\ &= c^k(\cos k\theta + j\sin k\theta). \end{aligned}$$

For example,

$$\begin{aligned} (2e^{j12°})^5 &= 2^5 e^{j60°} = 32e^{j60°} \\ &= 16 + j27.71, \end{aligned}$$

and

$$\begin{aligned} (3 + j4)^4 &= (5e^{j53.13°})^4 = 5^4 e^{j212.52°} \\ &= 625e^{j212.52°} \\ &= -527 - j336. \end{aligned}$$

6 The Roots of a Complex Number

To find the kth root of a complex number, we must recognize that we are solving the equation

$$x^k - ce^{j\theta} = 0, \tag{17}$$

which is an equation of the kth degree and therefore has k roots.

To find the k roots, we first note that

$$ce^{j\theta} = ce^{j(\theta+2\pi)} = ce^{j(\theta+4\pi)} = \cdots. \tag{18}$$

It follows from Eqs. 17 and 18 that

$$x_1 = (ce^{j\theta})^{1/k} = c^{1/k}e^{j\theta/k}, \tag{19}$$
$$x_2 = [ce^{j(\theta+2\pi)}]^{1/k} = c^{1/k}e^{j(\theta+2\pi)/k}, \tag{20}$$
$$x_3 = [ce^{j(\theta+4\pi)}]^{1/k} = c^{1/k}e^{j(\theta+4\pi)/k}, \tag{21}$$
$$\vdots$$

We continue the process outlined by Eqs. 19, 20, and 21 until the roots start repeating. This will happen when the multiple of π is equal to $2k$. For example, let's find the four roots of $81e^{j60°}$. We have

$$x_1 = 81^{1/4}e^{j60/4} = 3e^{j15°},$$
$$x_2 = 81^{1/4}e^{j(60+360)/4} = 3e^{j105°},$$
$$x_3 = 81^{1/4}e^{j(60+720)/4} = 3e^{j195°},$$
$$x_4 = 81^{1/4}e^{j(60+1080)/4} = 3e^{j285°},$$
$$x_5 = 81^{1/4}e^{j(60+1440)/4} = 3e^{j375°} = 3e^{j15°}.$$

Here, x_5 is the same as x_1, so the roots have started to repeat. Therefore we know the four roots of $81e^{j60°}$ are the values given by x_1, x_2, x_3, and x_4.

It is worth noting that the roots of a complex number lie on a circle in the complex-number plane. The radius of the circle is $c^{1/k}$. The roots are uniformly distributed around the circle, the angle between adjacent roots being equal to $2\pi/k$ radians, or $360/k$ degrees. The four roots of $81e^{j60°}$ are shown plotted in Fig. 4.

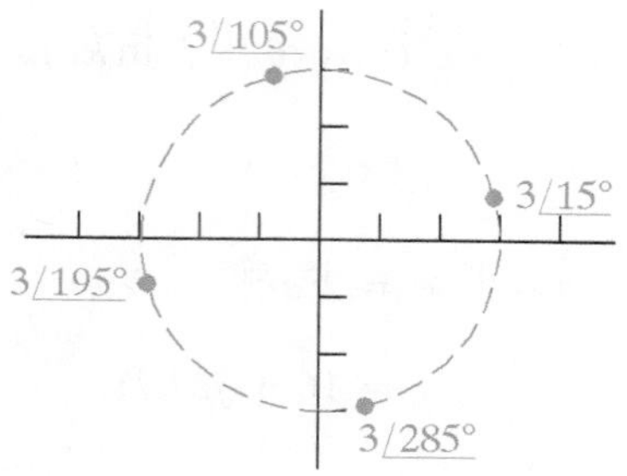

Figure 4 ▲ The four roots of $81e^{j60°}$.

APPENDIX

The Arithmetic of Complex Numbers

To understand digital signal processing, we have to get comfortable using complex numbers. The first step toward this goal is learning to manipulate complex numbers arithmetically. Fortunately, we can take advantage of our knowledge of real numbers to make this job easier. The following discussion provides the arithmetic rules governing complex numbers.

1 GRAPHICAL REPRESENTATION OF REAL AND COMPLEX NUMBERS

To get started, real numbers are those positive or negative numbers we're used to thinking about in our daily lives. Examples of real numbers are 0.3, –2.2, 5.1, etc. Keeping this in mind, we see how a real number can be represented by a point on a one-dimensional axis, called the *real* axis, as shown in Figure 1.

We can, in fact, consider that all real numbers correspond to all of the points on the real axis line on a one-to-one basis.

A complex number, unlike a real number, has two parts: a real part and an imaginary part. Just as a real number can be considered to be a point on

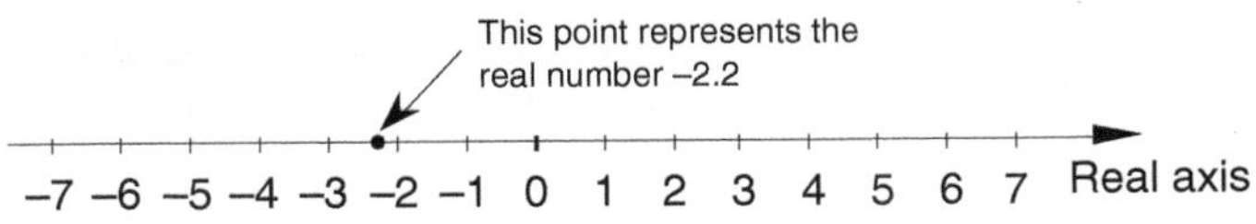

Figure 1 The representation of a real number as a point on the one-dimensional real axis.

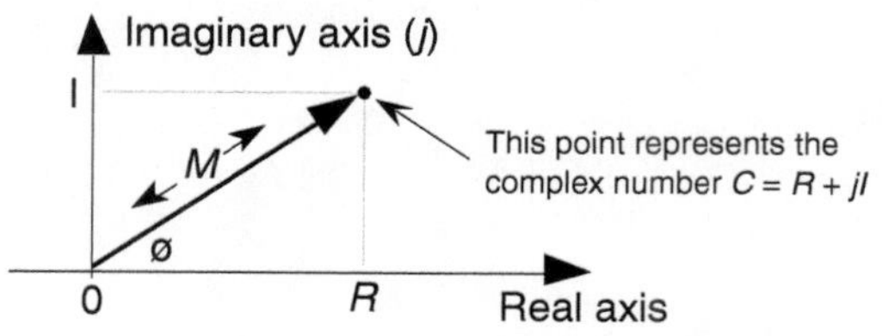

Figure 2 The phasor representation of the complex number $C = R + jI$ on the complex plane.

the one-dimensional real axis, a complex number can be treated as a point on a complex plane as shown in Figure 2. We'll use this geometrical concept to help us understand the arithmetic of complex numbers.†

2 ARITHMETIC REPRESENTATION OF COMPLEX NUMBERS

A complex number C is represented in a number of different ways in the literature, such as

Rectangular form: →
$$C = R + jI, \tag{1}$$

Trigonometric form: →
$$C = M[\cos(ø) + j\sin(ø)], \tag{1'}$$

Exponential form: →
$$C = M e^{jø}, \tag{1''}$$

Magnitude and angle form: →
$$C = M \angle ø. \tag{1'''}$$

Equations (1″) and (1‴) remind us that the complex number C can also be considered the tip of a phasor on the complex plane, with magnitude M, in the direction of ø degrees relative to the positive real axis as shown in Figure 2. (We'll avoid calling phasor M a vector because the term *vector* means different things in different contexts. In linear algebra, *vector* is the term used to signify a one-dimensional matrix. On the other hand, in mechanical engineering and field theory, vectors are used to signify magnitudes and directions, but there are vector operations (*scalar* or *dot product*, and *vector* or *cross-product*) that don't apply to our definition of a phasor. The relationships between the variables in this figure follow the standard trigonometry of right triangles. Keep in mind that C is a complex number, and the variables R, I, M, and ø are all real numbers. The magnitude of C, sometimes called the *modulus* of C, is

† The complex plane representation of a complex number is sometimes called an *Argand diagram*—named after the French mathematician Jean Robert Argand (1768–1825).

$$M = |C| = \sqrt{R^2 + I^2}, \tag{2}$$

and, by definition, the phase angle, or *argument*, of C is the arctangent of I/R, or

$$\o = \tan^{-1}\left(\frac{I}{R}\right). \tag{3}$$

The variable $\o$ in Eq. (3) is a general angle term. It can have dimensions of degrees or radians. Of course, we can convert back and forth between degrees and radians using π radians = 180°. So, if $\o_r$ is in radians and $\o_d$ is in degrees, then we can convert $\o_r$ to degrees by the expression

$$\o_d = \frac{180\o_r}{\pi}. \tag{4}$$

Likewise, we can convert $\o_d$ to radians by the expression

$$-_r = \frac{\pi\o_d}{180}. \tag{5}$$

The exponential form of a complex number has an interesting characteristic that we need to keep in mind. Whereas only a single expression in rectangular form can describe a single complex number, an infinite number of exponential expressions can describe a single complex number; that is, while, in the exponential form, a complex number C can be represented by $C = Me^{j\o}$, it can also be represented by

$$C = Me^{j\o} = Me^{j(\o + 2\pi n)}, \tag{6}$$

where $n = \pm 1, \pm 2, \pm 3, \ldots$ and $\o$ is in radians. When $\o$ is in degrees, Eq. (6) is in the form

$$C = Me^{j\o} = Me^{j(\o + n360°)}. \tag{7}$$

Equations (6) and (7) are *almost* self-explanatory. They indicate that the point on the complex plane represented by the tip of the phasor C remains unchanged if we rotate the phasor some integral multiple of 2π radians or an integral multiple of 360°. So, for example, if $C = Me^{j(20°)}$, then

$$C = Me^{j(20°)} = Me^{j(380°)} = Me^{j(740°)}. \tag{8}$$

The variable $\o$, the angle of the phasor in Figure 2, need not be constant. We'll often encounter expressions containing a complex sinusoid that takes the form

$$C = Me^{j\omega t}. \tag{9}$$

Equation (9) represents a phasor of magnitude M whose angle in Figure 2 is increasing linearly with time at a rate of ω radians each second. If $\omega = 2\pi$, the phasor described by Eq. (9) is rotating counterclockwise at a rate of 2π radians per second—one revolution per second—and that's why ω is called the radian frequency. In terms of frequency, Eq. (9)'s phasor is rotating counterclockwise at $\omega = 2\pi f$ radians per second, where f is the cyclic frequency in cycles per second (Hz). If the cyclic frequency is $f = 10$ Hz, the phasor is rotating at 20π radians per second. Likewise, the expression

$$C = Me^{-j\omega t} \tag{9'}$$

represents a phasor of magnitude M that rotates in a clockwise direction about the origin of the complex plane at a negative radian frequency of $-\omega$ radians per second.

3 ARITHMETIC OPERATIONS OF COMPLEX NUMBERS

3.1 Addition and Subtraction of Complex Numbers

Which of the above forms for C in Eq. (1) is the best to use? It depends on the arithmetic operation we want to perform. For example, if we're adding two complex numbers, the rectangular form in Eq. (1) is the easiest to use. The addition of two complex numbers, $C_1 = R_1 + jI_1$ and $C_2 = R_2 + jI_2$, is merely the sum of the real parts plus j times the sum of the imaginary parts as

$$C_1 + C_2 = R_1 + jI_1 + R_2 + jI_2 = R_1 + R_2 + j(I_1 + I_2). \tag{10}$$

Figure 3 is a graphical depiction of the sum of two complex numbers using the concept of phasors. Here the sum phasor $C_1 + C_2$ in Figure 3(a) is the new phasor from the beginning of phasor C_1 to the end of phasor C_2 in Figure 3(b). Remember, the Rs and the Is can be either positive or negative numbers. Subtracting one complex number from the other is straightforward as long as we find the differences between the two real parts and the two imaginary parts separately. Thus

$$C_1 - C_2 = (R_1 + jI_1) - (R_2 + jI_2) = R_1 - R_2 + j(I_1 - I_2). \tag{11}$$

3.2 Multiplication of Complex Numbers

We can use the rectangular form to multiply two complex numbers as

$$C_1C_2 = (R_1 + jI_1)\,(R_2 + jI_2) = (R_1R_2 - I_1\,I_2) + j(R_1I_2 + R_2\,I_1). \tag{12}$$

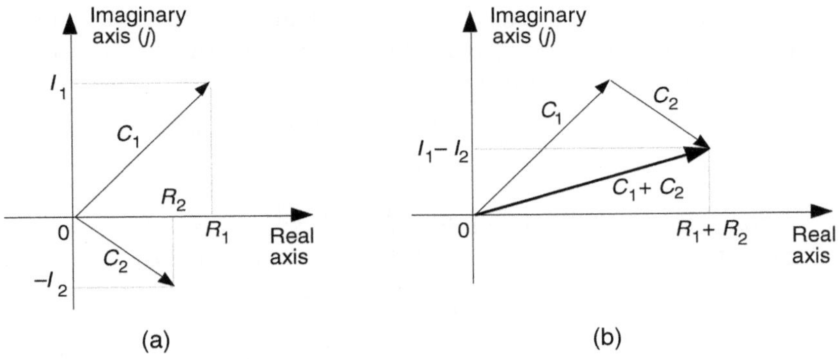

Figure 3 Geometrical representation of the sum of two complex numbers.

However, if we represent the two complex numbers in exponential form, their product takes the simpler form

$$C_1C_2 = M_1e^{j\o_1}M_2e^{j\o_2} = M_1M_2e^{j(\o_1+\o_2)} \tag{13}$$

because multiplication results in the addition of the exponents. Of some interest is the fact that the product of the magnitudes of two complex numbers is equal to the magnitude of their product. That is,

$$|C_1|\cdot|C_2| = |C_1C_2|. \tag{13'}$$

As a special case of multiplication of two complex numbers, *scaling* is multiplying a complex number by another complex number whose imaginary part is zero. We can use the rectangular or exponential forms with equal ease as follows:

$$kC = k(R + jI) = kR + jkI, \tag{14}$$

or in exponential form,

$$kC = k(Me^{j\o}) = kMe^{j\o}. \tag{15}$$

3.3 Conjugation of a Complex Number

The complex conjugate of a complex number is obtained merely by changing the sign of the number's imaginary part. So, if we denote C^* as the complex conjugate of the number $C = R + jI = Me^{j\o}$, then C^* is expressed as

$$C^* = R - jI = Me^{-j\o}. \tag{16}$$

There are three characteristics of conjugates that occasionally come in handy. First, the conjugate of a product is equal to the product of the conjugates. That is, if $C = C_1C_2$, then from Eq. (13)

$$C^* = (C_1C_2)^* = (M_1M_2e^{j(\text{ø}_1+\text{ø}_2)})^* = M_1M_2e^{-j(\text{ø}_1+\text{ø}_2)}$$
$$= M_1e^{-j\text{ø}_1}M_2e^{-j\text{ø}_2} = C_1^*C_2^*. \quad (17)$$

Second, the sum of conjugates of two complex numbers is equal to the conjugate of the sum. We can show this in rectangular form as

$$(R_1 + jI_1)^* + (R_2 + jI_2)^* = (R_1 - jI_1) + (R_2 - jI_2)$$
$$= R_1 + R_2 - j(I_1 + I_2) = [R_1 + R_2 + j(I_1 + I_2)]^*. \quad (17')$$

Third, the product of a complex number and its conjugate is the complex number's magnitude squared. It's easy to prove this in exponential form as

$$CC^* = Me^{j\text{ø}}Me^{-j\text{ø}} = M^2e^{j0} = M^2. \quad (18)$$

(This property is often used in digital signal processing to determine the relative power of a complex sinusoidal phasor represented by $Me^{j\omega t}$.)

3.4 Division of Complex Numbers

The division of two complex numbers is also convenient using the exponential and magnitude and angle forms, such as

$$\frac{C_1}{C_2} = \frac{M_1e^{j\text{ø}_1}}{M_2e^{j\text{ø}_2}} = \frac{M_1}{M_2}e^{j(\text{ø}_1-\text{ø}_2)} \quad (19)$$

and

$$\frac{C_1}{C_2} = \frac{M_1}{M_2}\angle(\text{ø}_1 - \text{ø}_2). \quad (19')$$

Although not nearly so handy, we can perform complex division in rectangular notation by multiplying the numerator and the denominator by the complex conjugate of the denominator as

$$\frac{C_1}{C_2} = \frac{R_1 + jI_1}{R_2 + jI_2}$$
$$= \frac{R_1 + jI_1}{R_2 + jI_2} \cdot \frac{R_2 - jI_2}{R_2 - jI_2} \quad (20)$$
$$= \frac{(R_1R_2 + I_1I_2) + j(R_2I_1 - R_1I_2)}{R_2^2 + I_2^2}.$$